D1319883

FAN ENGINEERING

An Engineer's Handbook

On Air, Its Movement and Distribution
in
Air Conditioning, Industrial Ventilation,
Mechanical Draft, Conveying
and
Other Applications Employing Fans

Edited by
ROBERT JORGENSEN

Seventh Edition
Total Issue 104,250

Published by
BUFFALO FORGE COMPANY
BUFFALO, NEW YORK

Obtainable in the U.S.A. from the
BUFFALO FORGE COMPANY
Buffalo, New York

Obtainable in Canada from the
CANADIAN BLOWER AND FORGE COMPANY, LTD.
Kitchener, Ontario

Twelve and One-Half Dollars per Copy

Printed in U.S.A.—Wm. J. Keller Inc., Buffalo, N. Y. 10-70-20M

PREFACE

This, the seventh edition of Fan Engineering, is organized in substantially the same manner as the sixth edition which was published in 1961. All material from the earlier edition has been critically reviewed and modified where necessary to reflect the present state of the art. Important changes include new data on plane and conical diffuser performance, duct construction, octave band standards, damage risk levels, duct and elbow attenuation, specific size, T-frame motors, WK^2 limits, and outdoor design temperatures. New equations have been included for density in terms of absolute humidity, coefficient of friction for smooth pipes, compressible flow horsepower, and impaction parameter. All equations and data involving sound power level have been revised to incorporate the new standard reference power of 10^{-12} watts. Among the discussions given new treatment are those on the equation of state, specific gravity, density, flow regimes and boundary layers, diffusers, compressibility, fan test codes, fan pressure requirements, erosion-resistant construction, equilibrium and the height of a transfer unit, gas absorption, atmospheric air cleaners, and stack gas cleaners.

Although this work has been designed primarily as a handbook, experience indicates that it has often served as a textbook. For this reason, many physical phenomena have been explained in more detail than is customary for a handbook, both in this and in previous editions. Some of the 571 equations, 150 tables and 190 charts are given for their explanatory value, but most can be used for problem solving. Footnote references are given for each of the tables and charts unless they were designed specifically for this or previous editions of Fan Engineering.

The major works which were consulted in the preparation of this handbook are listed in the Appendix or as footnote references. A considerable portion of the material in this edition can be traced back through previous editions. The first edition was edited by Dr. Willis H. Carrier and published in 1914. The next four editions were written by Richard D. Madison and published in 1925, 1933, 1938, and 1948.

The writer gratefully acknowledges the technical suggestions and other assistance contributed by many Buffalo Forge Company personnel. Special thanks are due to Theodor Ranov, Dr. Ing., Consultant to the Buffalo Forge Company on fluid mechanics and stress analysis, and to Melvin W. First, Sc. D., Consultant on air cleaning, both of whom provided valuable technical assistance.

ROBERT JORGENSEN

Buffalo, New York
April, 1970

OUTLINE OF CONTENTS

PART I—PHYSICS OF AIR

PART I—PHYSICS OF AIR (cont.)

PART II—FANS

PART II—FANS (cont.)

PART III—FAN APPLICATIONS

PART III—FAN APPLICATIONS (cont.)

PART III—FAN APPLICATIONS (cont.)

PART IV—APPENDICES

PART I
PHYSICS OF AIR

CHAPTER 1

PROPERTIES OF AIR AND AIR-VAPOR MIXTURES

For most fan applications, atmospheric air may be considered to be a mixture of dry air, water vapor, and impurities. Dry air is a mechanical mixture of gases. The relative amounts of the various dry constituents are listed in Table 1. The table values may be considered representative of the composition of normal, outdoor air throughout the troposphere. The composition of the air in a confined space will depend on the activities taking place and the ventilation provided.

TABLE 1—NORMAL COMPOSITION OF DRY, OUTDOOR AIR

Component	Fraction by Volume	Fraction by Weight
Nitrogen	0.7809	0.7552
Oxygen	0.2095	0.2315
Argon	0.0093	0.0128
Carbon Dioxide	0.0003	0.0004
Also, slight traces of neon, hydrogen, helium, krypton, ozone, and others.		

Adapted from the data of J. A. Goff, Standardization of Thermodynamic Properties of Moist Air, *Trans. ASHVE*, vol. 55, pp. 459-484, 1949, pp. 462-464.

Although the dry gas composition of air remains essentially constant, the amount of water vapor varies considerably. The properties of moist air, therefore, must be expressed in such a way that the relative amounts of water vapor and dry air are indicated. In the various formulas, tables, and charts which follow, specific properties of moist air are generally referred to a unit weight of the dry gas. However, in many cases reference to a unit weight of the mixture is considered equally desirable so this is also given.

The nature and amount of impurities in the air depend on the forces at work in producing or dispersing contaminants. Atmospheric impurities may be particulate (solids or liquids) or molecular (gases or vapors). They may be heavier or lighter than air. Settling rates vary with particle size and air motion. Particle behavior and removal are discussed under "Air Cleaning."

Contaminants may be of mineral, vegetable, or animal origin. Industrial, urban, rural, seaside, and other areas have characteristic atmospheres due to differences in impurities. The physiological effects of dusts, pollens, microorganisms, odors, ions, and other impurities are discussed under "Ventilation."

Standard Air

Standard air is air with a density of 0.075 lb per cu ft and an absolute viscosity of 1.225 x 10^{-5} lbm* per ft-sec. This is substantially equivalent to dry air of the composition shown in Table 1 at a temperature of 70°F and a barometric pressure of 29.92″ Hg.

The temperature and barometric pressure of atmospheric air vary widely with weather conditions and geographical location, notably altitude. If 59°F and 29.92″ Hg are assumed at sea level, the corresponding physical properties of air at various altitudes are as shown in Table 2. The temperature is assumed to bear a linear relation to altitude throughout the troposphere and to be constant in the lower reaches of the stratosphere. The data given in Table 2 are the barometric pressure (b), the density (δ), the absolute viscosity (μ), the kinematic viscosity (ν), and the speed of sound (c), as well as temperature (t) and altitude (Z).

Molecular Weight

Because air is a mechanical mixture of gases, it does not have a true molecular weight. However, its apparent molecular weight, like that of any mixture of gases, may be computed from either a volumetric or weight analysis in the manner indicated in Examples 1 and 2.

EXAMPLE 1. Apparent Molecular Weight of Dry Air from Volumetric Analysis

Component	*Vol., Mol, or Press. Fract.*		*Mol. Wt.*		*lb/(lb)mol*
Nitrogen	0.7809	×	28.016	=	21.878
Oxygen	0.2095	×	32.000	=	6.704
Argon	0.0093	×	39.944	=	.371
Carbon Dioxide	0.0003	×	44.010	=	.013
	1.0000				28.966

$$\text{Apparent molecular weight} = \frac{28.966}{1.0000} = 28.966 \text{ lb/(lb)mol}$$

EXAMPLE 2. Apparent Molecular Weight of Dry Air from Weight Analysis

Component	*Wt. Fract.*		*Mol. Wt.*		*(lb)mol/lb*
Nitrogen	0.7552	÷	28.016	=	0.02696
Oxygen	0.2315	÷	32.000	=	0.00723
Argon	0.0128	÷	39.944	=	0.00032
Carbon Dioxide	0.0004	÷	44.010	=	0.00001
	0.9999				0.03452

$$\text{Apparent molecular weight} = \frac{0.9999}{.03452} = 28.966 \text{ lb/(lb)mol}$$

*Refer to Appendix 1 for discussion of units and Appendix 2 for definitions of symbols and abbreviations.

The value of the apparent molecular weight of dry air is given as 28.966 lb/(lb)mol in the references for both Table 1 and Table 2. A mol is the weight or mass of a substance equal numerically to its molecular weight. A (lb)mol is the weight in lb equal to the molecular weight. A (kg)mol is the mass in kg equal to the molecular weight. For a gas constituent, volume fraction, mol fraction, and pressure fraction are equal.

TABLE 2—STANDARD ATMOSPHERIC DATA VERSUS ALTITUDE

Z	t	b	δ	$\mu \times 10^5$	$\nu \times 10^4$	c
ft	°F	″Hg	$\frac{\text{lb}}{\text{ft}^3}$	$\frac{\text{lbm}}{\text{ft-sec}}$	$\frac{\text{ft}^2}{\text{sec}}$	$\frac{\text{ft}}{\text{sec}}$
−1000	62.6	31.02	.0787	1.212	1.539	1120.7
−500	60.8	30.47	.0776	1.208	1.557	1118.8
0	59.0	29.92	.0765	1.205	1.576	1116.9
500	57.2	29.38	.0754	1.202	1.595	1115.0
1000	55.4	28.86	.0743	1.198	1.614	1113.1
1500	53.7	28.33	.0732	1.195	1.633	1111.1
2000	51.9	27.82	.0721	1.192	1.653	1109.2
2500	50.1	27.32	.0710	1.189	1.673	1107.3
3000	48.3	26.82	.0700	1.185	1.694	1105.3
3500	46.5	26.33	.0689	1.182	1.714	1103.4
4000	44.7	25.84	.0679	1.179	1.735	1101.4
4500	43.0	25.37	.0669	1.175	1.757	1099.5
5000	41.2	24.90	.0659	1.172	1.778	1097.5
5500	39.4	24.43	.0649	1.169	1.800	1095.6
6000	37.6	23.98	.0639	1.165	1.823	1093.6
6500	35.8	23.53	.0630	1.162	1.846	1091.7
7000	34.0	23.09	.0620	1.158	1.869	1089.7
7500	32.3	22.65	.0610	1.155	1.892	1087.7
8000	30.5	22.22	.0601	1.152	1.916	1085.7
8500	28.7	21.80	.0592	1.148	1.940	1083.8
9000	26.9	21.39	.0583	1.145	1.965	1081.8
9500	25.1	20.98	.0574	1.142	1.990	1079.8
10000	23.3	20.58	.0565	1.138	2.015	1077.8
11000	19.8	19.79	.0547	1.131	2.067	1073.8
12000	16.2	19.03	.0530	1.125	2.121	1069.8
13000	12.6	18.29	.0513	1.118	2.177	1065.8
14000	9.1	17.58	.0497	1.111	2.234	1061.8
15000	5.5	16.89	.0481	1.104	2.294	1057.7
20000	−12.3	13.75	.0407	1.069	2.624	1037.3
25000	−30.2	11.10	.0343	1.034	3.016	1016.4
30000	−48.0	8.89	.0286	0.997	3.486	995.1
35000	−65.8	7.04	.0237	0.961	4.053	973.3
40000	−69.7	5.54	.0188	0.952	5.059	968.5
45000	−69.7	4.35	.0148	0.952	6.434	968.5
50000	−69.7	3.42	.0116	0.952	8.181	968.5
55000	−69.7	2.69	.0092	0.952	10.404	968.5
60000	−69.7	2.12	.0072	0.952	13.230	968.5
65000	−69.7	1.67	.0057	0.952	16.824	968.5

Adapted from the data of Standard Atmosphere—Tables and Data for Altitudes to 65,800 Feet, NACA Report 1235, Washington, D.C., 1955, pp. 66-81.

Equation of State

Boyle's and Charles' laws* may be combined to give an equation of state. For perfect gases†

$$PQ = WRT. \qquad (1)$$

Any consistent set of units may be used. In U.S. Customary Units, pressure (P) is in lb/ft^2, volume (Q) is in ft^3, weight (W) is in lb, gas constant (R) is in ft/°R, and absolute temperature (T) is in °R. In S. I. (Système International) units, pressure (P) is in N/m^2, volume (Q) is in m^3, weight (W) is in N, gas constant (R) is in m/°K, and absolute temperature (T) is in °K. Mass[⊙] may be substituted for weight in which case the U.S. units would be lbm for (W) and ft-lb/lbm-°R for (R) and the S.I. units would be kg for (W) and m-N/kg-°K or J/kg-°K for (R). The equation of state may also be written:

$$pQ = WRT/144, \text{ or} \qquad (2)$$

$$bQ = WRT/70.73. \qquad (3)$$

where the above U.S. units are employed, except that pressures (p) and (b) are in lb/in^2 and ″Hg respectively.

The value of the gas constant (R) may be determined approximately from the molecular weight of the gas (MW) in lb/(lb)mol and the universal gas constant (*1545*) in ft-lb/(lb)mol-°R using

$$R = 1545/MW. \qquad (4)$$

If S. I. units are employed, a value of 8314 J/(kg)mol-°K must be substituted for the universal gas constant.

The U. S. Weather Bureau reports barometric pressure in ″Hg and it is customary in fan engineering to use the equation of state based on pressure (b) in ″Hg as expressed in Equation 3. That practice is followed in this handbook. Tables of conversion factors are given in Appendix 3.

Specific Gravity and Relative Density

Since air is the gas most frequently involved in fan engineering, it is convenient to have equations and data based on the properties of air. One of the properties of air which is used as a common reference is its density. The ratio of the density of any gas to the density of dry air at the same temperature and pressure is called the specific gravity (SG) of the gas. For perfect gases, specific gravity may be obtained by dividing molecular weight by 28.966, the molecular weight of air.

Water vapor does not behave like a perfect gas. For this reason, and to

---

*Boyle's and Charles' laws state that the volume of a perfect gas varies inversely with absolute pressure and directly with absolute temperature respectively.

†The equation of state for real gases can be stated as:

$$PQ = WRT\,(1 + B_pP + C_pP^2 + D_pP^3 + \ldots),$$

where the empirical coefficients (B_p, C_p, D_p, ..) are temperature-dependent. For most fan applications, the air or gas can be treated as a perfect gas but water vapor cannot be so treated without sacrificing appreciable accuracy.

⊙Refer to Appendix 1 for discussion of mass and weight. Actually, there is no S.I. unit for weight but the newton (N) being the force unit is equivalent to a weight unit.

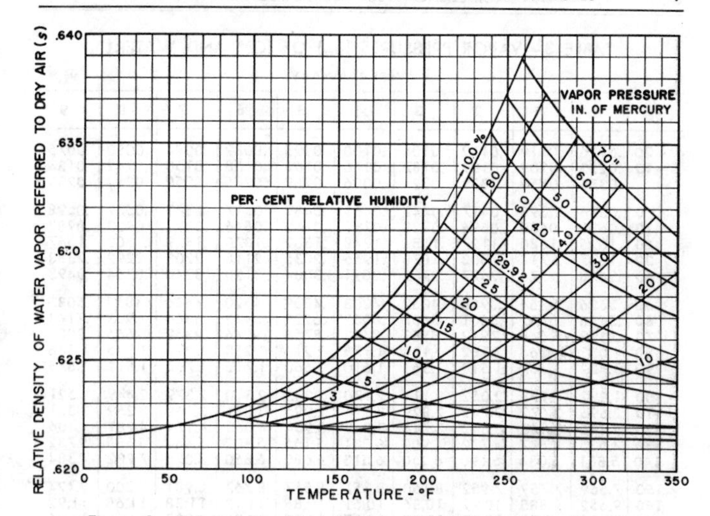

Figure 1—Relative Densities of Water Vapor Referred to Dry Air

Calculated from the data of J. H. Keenan and F. G. Keyes, "Thermodynamic Properties of Steam," John Wiley & Sons, Inc., New York, 1936.

---

avoid confusion, the ratio of the density of vapor to the density of air at the same dry-bulb temperature and pressure is called the relative density (s) of the water vapor, not its specific gravity. Figure 1 can be used to determine relative density over a range of temperatures if the relative humidity (h) or the vapor pressure is known. The following formula which is accurate to 0.1%, in the range of temperatures from 32°F to 400°F, can also be used:

$$s = 0.6214 + \frac{h\,(e_w)^{1/1.42}}{1130}. \tag{5}$$

The vapor pressure of pure water (e_w) may be determined from Table 3 opposite the dry-bulb temperature (t) of the gas. The ratio of molecular weights, (18.016/28.966) would indicate a value of s equal to 0.622, so that Figure 1 and Equation 5 illustrate that water vapor behaves differently from a perfect gas, but only slightly.

The density of water vapor (s_g) relative to that of a gas other than air can be determined from the molecular weight (MW) of the dry gas and

$$s_g = s\,\frac{28.966}{MW}. \tag{6}$$

However, Equations 8 to 18 are so arranged that the values of (s) from Figure 1 apply directly even when the gas is not air.

TABLE 3—VAPOR PRESSURES (e_w) OF ICE* AND WATER‡

In Inches of Mercury

t °F	0	1	2	3	4	5	6	7	8	9
−20	.0126	.0119	.0112	.0106	.0100	.0095	.0089	.0084	.0080	.0075
−10	.0222	.0209	.0199	.0187	.0176	.0168	.0158	.0150	.0142	.0134
—	.0376	.0359	.0339	.0324	.0306	.0289	.0275	.0259	.0247	.0233
0	.0376	.0398	.0417	.0441	.0463	.0489	.0517	.0541	.0571	.0598
10	.0631	.0660	.0696	.0728	.0768	.0810	.0846	.0892	.0932	.0982
20	.1025	.1080	.1127	.1186	.1248	.1302	.1370	.1429	.1502	.1567
30	.1647	.1716	.1803	.1878	.1955	.2035	.2118	.2203	.2292	.2383
40	.2478	.2576	.2677	.2782	.2891	.3004	.3120	.3240	.3364	.3493
50	.3626	.3764	.3906	.4052	.4203	.4359	.4520	.4686	.4858	.5035
60	.5218	.5407	.5601	.5802	.6009	.6222	.6442	.6669	.6903	.7144
70	.7392	.7648	.7912	.8183	.8462	.8750	.9046	.9352	.9666	.9989
80	1.032	1.066	1.102	1.138	1.175	1.213	1.253	1.293	1.335	1.378
90	1.422	1.467	1.513	1.561	1.610	1.660	1.712	1.765	1.819	1.875
100	1.932	1.992	2.052	2.114	2.178	2.243	2.310	2.379	2.449	2.521
110	2.596	2.672	2.749	2.829	2.911	2.995	3.081	3.169	3.259	3.351
120	3.446	3.543	3.642	3.744	3.848	3.954	4.063	4.174	4.289	4.406
130	4.525	4.647	4.772	4.900	5.031	5.165	5.302	5.442	5.585	5.732
140	5.881	6.034	6.190	6.350	6.513	6.680	6.850	7.024	7.202	7.384
150	7.569	7.759	7.952	8.150	8.351	8.557	8.767	8.981	9.200	9.424
160	9.652	9.885	10.12	10.36	10.61	10.86	11.12	11.38	11.65	11.92
170	12.20	12.48	12.77	13.07	13.37	13.67	13.98	14.30	14.62	14.96
180	15.29	15.63	15.98	16.34	16.70	17.07	17.44	17.82	18.21	18.61
190	19.01	19.42	19.84	20.27	20.70	21.14	21.59	22.05	22.52	22.99
200	23.47	23.96	24.46	24.97	25.48	26.00	26.53	27.07	27.62	28.18
210	28.75	29.33	29.92	30.52	31.13	31.75	32.38	33.02	33.67	34.33
220	35.00	35.68	36.37	37.07	37.78	38.50	39.24	39.99	40.75	41.52
230	42.31	43.11	43.92	44.74	45.57	46.41	47.27	48.14	49.03	49.93
240	50.84	51.76	52.70	53.65	54.62	55.60	56.60	57.61	58.63	59.67
250	60.72	61.79	62.88	63.98	65.10	66.23	67.38	68.54	69.72	70.92
260	72.13	74.36	74.61	75.88	77.16	78.46	79.78	81.11	82.46	83.83
270	85.22	86.63	88.06	89.51	90.97	92.45	93.96	95.49	97.03	98.61
280	100.2	101.8	103.4	105.0	106.7	108.4	110.1	111.8	113.6	115.4
290	117.2	119.0	120.8	122.7	124.6	126.5	128.4	130.4	132.4	134.4
300	136.4	138.5	140.6	142.7	144.8	147.0	149.2	151.4	153.6	155.9
310	158.2	160.5	162.8	165.2	167.6	170.0	172.5	175.0	177.5	180.0
320	182.6	185.2	187.8	190.4	193.1	195.8	198.5	201.3	204.1	206.9
330	209.8	212.7	215.6	218.6	221.6	224.6	227.7	230.8	233.9	237.1
340	240.3	243.5	246.8	250.1	253.4	256.7	260.1	263.6	267.1	270.6
350	274.1	277.7	281.3	284.9	288.6	292.3	296.1	299.9	303.8	307.7
360	311.6	315.5	319.5	323.5	327.6	331.7	335.9	340.1	344.4	348.7
370	353.0	357.4	361.8	366.2	370.7	375.2	379.8	384.4	389.1	393.8
380	398.6	403.4	408.2	413.1	418.1	423.1	428.1	433.1	438.2	443.4
390	448.6	453.9	459.2	464.6	470.0	475.5	481.0	486.6	492.2	497.9
400	503.6	509.3	515.1	521.0	526.9	532.9	538.9	545.0	551.1	557.3

*Adapted from data of International Critical Tables, vol. 3, National Research Council by McGraw-Hill Book Co., Inc., New York, 1928, p. 210.

‡Adapted from data of J. H. Keenan and F. G. Keyes, "Thermodynamic Properties of Steam," John Wiley & Sons, Inc., New York, 1936. These data differ but slightly from the data of J. A. Goff and S. Gratch, "Thermodynamic Properties of Moist Air," *Trans. ASHVE*, vol. 51, pp. 125-164, 1945, and corrections thereto by J. A. Goff, "Saturation Pressure of Water on the New Kelvin Temperature Scale," *Trans. ASHVE*, vol. 63, pp. 347-354, 1957.

Relative and Absolute Humidity

The state of an air-water vapor mixture is completely defined by specifying the pressure, temperature, and humidity.

The Gibbs-Dalton rule§ concerning the partial pressures of the components of a mixture of perfect gases may be applied to air-water vapor mixtures. With no water vapor present, the partial pressure of the air must equal the barometric pressure. When present, water vapor exerts a certain pressure, regardless of whether air is present or not. A "saturated" condition is said to exist when the actual vapor pressure (e_a) is equal to the vapor pressure of pure liquid (e_w) at the same temperature. Partially saturated air contains vapor that is superheated, i.e., the temperature of the mixture, and therefore that of the vapor, is higher than the saturation temperature for the existing vapor pressure. As indicated in Table 3 the vapor pressures of pure water vary only with temperature. Below the freezing point the magnitude of the pressure is generally higher over sub-cooled water than it is over ice.

The relative humidity (h) of an air-water vapor mixture is defined as the ratio of the vapor pressure existing (e_a), compared to that at saturation (e_w) for the same dry-bulb temperature.

$$h = \frac{e_a}{e_w}. \tag{7}$$

This is also equal to the ratio of the mole fractions under the same conditions. Since the relative density of water vapor compared to air is not constant, as indicated in Figure 1, the weight ratio of water vapor existing to that at saturation at the same temperature or percentage absolute humidity is only a very close approximation to the relative humidity.

Absolute humidity (H) is the actual weight of water vapor existing per unit weight of dry air or gas. It may be expressed in pounds of water vapor per pound of dry air, grains of water vapor per pound of dry air, or grains of water vapor per cubic foot of mixture. The absolute humidity, in lb per lb of dry air, can be determined from

$$H = \frac{W_v}{W_g} = \frac{e_w h s}{(b - e_w h)(SG)}. \tag{8}$$

Similarly, the vapor content (H_m), in lb per lb of mixture, can be calculated from

$$H_m = \frac{W_v}{W_m} = \frac{e_w h s}{(b - e_w h)(SG) + e_w h s}. \tag{9}$$

The total pressure (b) and the vapor pressure of pure water (e_w), must be in consistent units. The relative density (s) of the water vapor, the specific gravity of the dry gas (SG), and the relative humidity of the mixture are all dimensionless. Values of (H) and (H_m) are tabulated in Table 5 for saturated air at standard barometer.

§The Gibbs-Dalton rule states that each component of a gas mixture exerts a pressure which is determined by the volume and temperature of the mixture regardless of the other components involved.

Dry-Bulb, Wet-Bulb, and Dew-Point Temperatures

Unless otherwise specified, the temperature of an air-water vapor mixture is that temperature which is indicated by an ordinary or dry-bulb thermometer. This dry-bulb temperature (t) is the temperature of both the air and water vapor in the mixture.

A wet-bulb temperature (t') may be determined by submerging a water covered bulb in the air-water vapor mixture until equilibrium is obtained. The wet-bulb temperature will be lower than the dry-bulb temperature as long as evaporation continues. At saturation, no evaporation can take place; hence the wet- and dry-bulb temperatures for this condition will be identical.

The temperature of adiabatic saturation (t''') of an air-water vapor mixture, for most purposes, is equal to the wet-bulb temperature. Appreciable deviations occur with other gas-vapor mixtures. The temperature of adiabatic saturation is that temperature which a gas-water vapor mixture would attain in a perfect "saturator" with no loss or gain of heat to surroundings. A wet-bulb thermometer, unshielded from radiation, will read a temperature equal to that of adiabatic saturation of air with water vapor, if the velocity of air past the bulb is between 500 and 1000 feet per minute. The basic difference between a wet-bulb thermometer reading and the temperature of adiabatic saturation results from a difference in mass and thermal diffusivity. Compensating effects result from thermal radiation and velocity over the wet-bulb. The same degree of compensation is not obtained with other gas-vapor mixtures.

The dew-point temperature (t'') of an air-water vapor mixture is the saturation temperature corresponding to the absolute humidity of the mixture. The vapor pressure (e''_w) corresponding to the dew-point temperature is equal to the vapor pressure (e_w) corresponding to the dry-bulb temperature multiplied by the relative humidity (h). As indicated by Equation 10, a rearrangement of Equation 8, the dew-point vapor pressure and therefore the dew-point temperature are constant as long as the absolute humidity (H), barometer (b), specific gravity (SG) and relative density of water vapor (s) are constant regardless of the wet-and dry-bulb temperatures.

$$e''_w = e_w h = \frac{b(SG)H}{(SG)H + s}. \tag{10}$$

The dew-point temperature of a mixture may also be considered as that temperature at which condensation begins when the mixture is gradually cooled.

Density and Specific Volume

Density may be based on weight or mass. Following common practice, density (δ) will be used to indicate weight per unit volume. Mass density (ρ) should be substituted whenever mass per unit volume would be more appropriate, e.g., when gravitational acceleration is not standard. Specific volume is the reciprocal of density ($1/\delta$).

The density of a dry gas can be determined from its molecular weight

(MW), absolute temperature (T) in °R, and pressure (b) in ″Hg using

$$\delta = \frac{MW}{386.7} \frac{529.7}{T} \frac{b}{29.92}, \tag{11}$$

which is a mathematical expression of Avogadro's hypothesis.† This equation was derived from Equations 3 and 4 using the standard conditions of 529.7°R and 29.92″ Hg. It indicates that at standard conditions a (lb)mol of gas will occupy 386.7 ft³. Similar equations can be derived for other units and conditions. Using S. I. units, mass density would be in kg/m³ and a value of 22.414 would have to be substituted for the 386.7 if standard conditions were taken as 273.2°K and 760 mm Hg indicating that a (kg)mol of gas at those conditions will occupy 22.414 m³.

The density of an air-water vapor mixture cannot be calculated quite so simply because water vapor does not obey the gas laws. The density of a gas-vapor mixture can be determined if either the relative or absolute humidity is known as well as the pressure and temperature. The Gibbs-Dalton rule of partial pressures§ or Amagat's law of partial volumes# may be used with Equation 3 to calculate the density of the mixture or the partial densities of the dry gas and vapor components.

If the relative humidity (h) is known, the partial pressure of the water vapor ($e_w h$) can be determined. The vapor pressure of pure water (e_w) may be found opposite the dry-bulb temperature (t) in Table 3. The partial pressure of the dry air or gas ($b - e_w h$) is the total pressure less the partial pressure of the vapor.

The partial density of the gas component (δ_g), i.e., the weight of dry gas per unit volume of mixture, is

$$\delta_g = \frac{(b - e_w h)\, SG}{.7538\,(t + 459.7)}. \tag{12}$$

The partial density of the vapor component (δ_v), i.e., the weight of water vapor per unit volume of mixture, is

$$\delta_v = \frac{e_w h s}{.7538\,(t + 459.7)}. \tag{13}$$

The density of the mixture (δ), the sum of the partial densities, is

$$\delta = \frac{(b - e_w h)\, SG + e_w h s}{.7538\,(t + 459.7)}. \tag{14}$$

The partial densities of the dry gas and water vapor vary with specific gravity (SG) and relative density (s) as well as partial pressure and dry-bulb temperature (t).

---

†Avogadro's hypothesis is that the number of gas molecules in any given volume at any given pressure and temperature is a constant regardless of the gas or gases involved.

§The Gibbs-Dalton rule states that each component of a gas mixture exerts a pressure which is determined by the volume and temperature of the mixture regardless of the other components involved.

#Amagat's law states that each component of a gas mixture occupies a volume which is determined by the pressure and temperature of the mixture regardless of the other components involved.

If the absolute humidity (H) is known, the partial volume of the dry gas will be $1/SG(1 + H)$ and the partial volume of the water vapor will be $H/s(1 + H)$, both expressed as fractions of the total volume. Similarly, if the vapor content (H_m) is known, the partial volume of the dry gas will be $(1 - H_m)/SG$ and the partial volume of the water vapor will be H_m/s when expressed as fractions of the total volume. Accordingly, the specific volume ($1/\delta$), in cu ft per lb of mixture, will be

$$\frac{1}{\delta} = \frac{.7538\ (t + 459.7)}{b}\left(\frac{1}{SG(1 + H)} + \frac{H}{s(1 + H)}\right), \text{ or} \tag{15}$$

$$\frac{1}{\delta} = \frac{.7538\ (t + 459.7)}{b}\left(\frac{1 - H_m}{SG} + \frac{H_m}{s}\right). \tag{16}$$

The specific volume of the gas component ($1/\delta_g$), i.e., the volume per unit weight of dry gas is a useful quantity which can be determined from

$$\frac{1}{\delta_g} = \frac{.7538\ (t + 459.7)}{b}\left(\frac{1}{SG} + \frac{H}{s}\right), \text{ or} \tag{17}$$

$$\frac{1}{\delta_g} = \frac{.7538\ (t + 459.7)}{b}\left(\frac{1}{SG} + \frac{H_m}{s(1 - H_m)}\right). \tag{18}$$

Densities and partial densities can be obtained by taking the reciprocals of the appropriate specific volumes.

The densities and specific volumes of dry air are tabulated for various temperatures with standard barometer in Table 4. The densities, specific volumes, and absolute humidities of air-water vapor mixtures at saturation for various temperatures and standard barometer are listed in Table 5.

Tables 4 and 5 were checked against the data of Boehnlein* and only minor differences of the order of .05 percent were found. However, this reference contains air density data for a range of barometric pressures from 26.0 to 31.1 inches of mercury by increments of 0.1 inches. The temperature range extends from 60°F to 100°F in steps of 1 degree, and the wet-bulb depression data range from 0 to the maximum integral degree variation for dry air.

Moist air is less dense than dry air at any particular temperature, because in a cubic foot of mixture some of the air molecules are displaced by lighter water vapor molecules. The erroneous belief than an air-water vapor mixture is heavier than dry air, because moisture is added, does not take into account Avogadro's hypothesis.

*C. T. Boehnlein, Air Density Tables, University of Minnesota Institute of Technology, *Technical Paper No. 17.*

TABLE 4—PROPERTIES OF DRY AIR

Barometric Pressure 29.92 Inches of Mercury

t °F	$\delta = \frac{W}{Q}$ lb/ft³	$\frac{1}{\delta} = \frac{Q}{W}$ ft³/lb	$c_p\delta$ Btu/ft³-°F	$\frac{1}{c_p\delta}$ ft³-°F/Btu	t °F	$\delta = \frac{W}{Q}$ lb/ft³	$\frac{1}{\delta} = \frac{Q}{W}$ ft³/lb	$c_p\delta$ Btu/ft³-°F	$\frac{1}{c_p\delta}$ ft³-°F/Btu
−25	.09134	10.95	.02189	45.68	56	.07698	12.99	.01848	54.13
−20	.09028	11.08	.02164	46.21	57	.07683	13.02	.01844	54.24
−15	.08926	11.20	.02139	46.74	58	.07668	13.04	.01840	54.35
−10	.08827	11.33	.02116	47.27	59	.07653	13.07	.01837	54.44
−5	.08732	11.45	.02093	47.80	60	.07640	13.09	.01834	54.54
0	.08635	11.58	.02070	48.31	61	.07624	13.12	.01830	54.64
5	.08542	11.71	.02048	48.82	62	.07610	13.14	.01826	54.76
10	.08452	11.83	.02026	49.35	63	.07595	13.17	.01823	54.85
15	.08363	11.96	.02005	49.87	64	.07580	13.19	.01819	54.97
20	.08275	12.09	.01984	50.40	65	.07566	13.22	.01816	55.06
21	.08260	12.11	.01980	50.50	66	.07552	13.24	.01812	55.18
22	.08241	12.13	.01976	50.60	67	.07538	13.27	.01809	55.27
23	.08226	12.16	.01972	50.70	68	.07524	13.29	.01806	55.37
24	.08207	12.19	.01968	50.81	69	.07509	13.32	.01802	55.48
25	.08192	12.21	.01964	50.91	70	.07495	13.34	.01799	55.58
26	.08173	12.24	.01959	51.04	71	.07481	13.37	.01795	55.69
27	.08155	12.26	.01955	51.14	72	.07468	13.39	.01792	55.79
28	.08140	12.28	.01951	51.24	73	.07454	13.42	.01789	55.88
29	.08125	12.31	.01948	51.34	74	.07440	13.44	.01786	55.97
30	.08107	12.34	.01944	51.44	75	.07424	13.47	.01783	56.09
31	.08089	12.36	.01940	51.54	76	.07412	13.49	.01780	56.19
32	.08074	12.38	.01937	51.64	77	.07398	13.52	.01776	56.30
33	.08056	12.41	.01933	51.75	78	.07384	13.54	.01773	56.40
34	.08042	12.44	.01929	51.86	79	.07370	13.57	.01770	56.49
35	.08025	12.46	.01925	51.96	80	.07357	13.59	.01767	56.59
36	.08009	12.49	.01921	52.07	81	.07343	13.62	.01764	56.70
37	.07992	12.51	.01917	52.19	82	.07330	13.64	.01761	56.80
38	.07978	12.54	.01913	52.30	83	.07316	13.67	.01758	56.90
39	.07960	12.56	.01909	52.41	84	.07302	13.70	.01755	57.01
40	.07945	12.59	.01906	52.51	85	.07290	13.72	.01752	57.11
41	.07928	12.61	.01902	52.61	86	.07275	13.74	.01748	57.22
42	.07914	12.64	.01898	52.72	87	.07261	13.77	.01744	57.35
43	.07897	12.66	.01894	52.83	88	.07248	13.80	.01741	57.44
44	.07880	12.69	.01890	52.94	89	.07234	13.82	.01738	57.54
45	.07866	12.71	.01886	53.04	90	.07223	13.85	.01735	57.63
46	.07850	12.74	.01882	53.14	91	.07209	13.87	.01732	57.73
47	.07835	12.76	.01878	53.25	92	.07196	13.90	.01729	57.83
48	.07819	12.79	.01874	53.36	93	.07182	13.92	.01726	57.92
49	.07804	12.81	.01871	53.46	94	.07170	13.95	.01723	58.02
50	.07788	12.84	.01867	53.56	95	.07156	13.97	.01720	58.15
51	.07773	12.86	.01864	53.64	96	.07144	14.00	.01717	58.25
52	.07758	12.89	.01860	53.73	97	.07131	14.02	.01714	58.35
53	.07743	12.92	.01857	53.84	98	.07120	14.05	.01711	58.45
54	.07728	12.94	.01855	53.94	99	.07106	14.07	.01708	58.55
55	.07713	12.97	.01851	54.05	100	.07093	14.10	.01705	58.65

TABLE 4 (Concluded)—PROPERTIES OF DRY AIR

Barometric Pressure 29.92 Inches of Mercury

t °F	$\delta = \frac{W}{Q}$ lb/ft³	$\frac{1}{\delta} = \frac{Q}{W}$ ft³/lb	$c_p\delta$ Btu/ft³-°F	$\frac{1}{c_p\delta}$ ft³-°F/Btu	t °F	$\delta = \frac{W}{Q}$ lb/ft³	$\frac{1}{\delta} = \frac{Q}{W}$ ft³/lb	$c_p\delta$ Btu/ft³-°F	$\frac{1}{c_p\delta}$ ft³-°F/Btu
101	.07080	14.12	.01702	58.74	**230**	.05756	17.37	.01392	71.89
102	.07067	14.15	.01699	58.84	**235**	.05716	17.49	.01380	72.44
103	.07056	14.17	.01696	58.93	**240**	.05674	17.62	.01373	72.88
104	.07042	14.20	.01693	59.03	**245**	.05635	17.75	.01362	73.44
105	.07031	14.22	.01690	59.12	**250**	.05594	17.88	.01355	73.87
106	.07017	14.25	.01687	59.20	**260**	.05517	18.13	.01339	74.84
107	.07006	14.27	.01684	59.30	**270**	.05442	18.38	.01320	75.76
108	.06993	14.30	.01681	59.40	**280**	.05367	18.63	.01302	76.79
109	.06982	14.32	.01678	59.49	**290**	.05296	18.88	.01285	77.81
110	.06968	14.35	.01675	59.58	**300**	.05226	19.13	.01269	78.80
111	.06957	14.37	.01672	59.69	**310**	.05158	19.39	.01253	79.81
112	.06944	14.40	.01669	59.85	**320**	.05092	19.64	.01238	80.77
113	.06933	14.42	.01666	60.02	**330**	.05028	19.89	.01225	81.63
114	.06920	14.45	.01663	60.13	**340**	.04965	20.14	.01210	82.62
115	.06908	14.48	.01660	60.24	**350**	.04904	20.39	.01196	83.61
116	.06896	14.50	.01657	60.35	**360**	.04844	20.64	.01182	84.60
117	.06884	14.53	.01654	60.46	**370**	.04785	20.90	.01169	85.55
118	.06872	14.55	.01651	60.57	**380**	.04728	21.15	.01156	86.51
119	.06860	14.58	.01648	60.67	**390**	.04672	21.40	.01144	87.41
120	.06849	14.60	.01646	60.75	**400**	.04618	21.65	.01131	88.42
121	.06837	14.63	.01643	60.87	**420**	.04513	22.16	.01107	90.33
122	.06826	14.65	.01640	60.98	**440**	.04413	22.66	.01084	92.25
123	.06814	14.68	.01637	61.08	**460**	.04317	23.16	.01066	93.62
124	.06802	14.70	.01635	61.18	**480**	.04225	23.67	.01044	95.78
125	.06790	14.72	.01632	61.28	**500**	.04138	24.17	.01025	97.56
130	.06732	14.86	.01619	61.76	**520**	.04053	24.68	.01006	99.40
135	.06676	14.98	.01604	62.34	**540**	.03974	25.18	.00988	101.2
140	.06614	15.11	.01591	62.85	**560**	.03894	25.68	.00972	102.8
145	.06565	15.23	.01580	63.29	**580**	.03819	26.19	.00954	104.8
150	.06512	15.36	.01568	63.77	**600**	.03751	26.69	.00940	106.4
155	.06459	15.48	.01555	64.31	**650**	.03578	27.95	.00903	110.7
160	.06406	15.61	.01543	64.81	**700**	.03424	29.21	.00868	115.2
165	.06356	15.74	.01531	65.31	**750**	.03282	30.47	.00836	119.6
170	.06304	15.86	.01519	65.83	**800**	.03152	31.73	.00809	123.6
175	.06256	15.99	.01507	66.35	**850**	.03032	32.99	.00779	128.3
180	.06207	16.11	.01496	66.81	**900**	.02920	34.24	.00754	132.6
185	.06158	16.24	.01484	67.33	**950**	.02816	35.51	.00739	135.3
190	.06111	16.37	.01473	67.85	**1000**	.02720	36.76	.00716	139.6
195	.06065	16.49	.01462	68.25	**1050**	.02630	38.02	.00689	145.1
200	.06018	16.62	.01452	68.85	**1100**	.02546	39.28	.00674	148.3
205	.05973	16.74	.01442	69.34	**1150**	.02467	40.54	.00659	151.8
210	.05928	16.87	.01432	69.83	**1200**	.02392	41.80	.00643	155.5
215	.05884	17.00	.01421	70.34	**1500**	.02026	49.36	.00560	178.5
220	.05840	17.12	.01411	70.87	**1800**	.01757	56.91	.00496	201.4
225	.05799	17.24	.01400	71.45	**2100**	.01551	64.47	.00447	223.5

TABLE 5—PROPERTIES OF SATURATED AIR

Barometric Pressure 29.92 Inches of Mercury

t °F	$\delta_g = \frac{W_g}{Q_m}$ lb/ft³	$\delta_v = \frac{W_v}{Q_m}$ lb/ft³	$\delta = \frac{W_m}{Q_m}$ lb/ft³	$\frac{1}{\delta_g} = \frac{Q_m}{W_g}$ ft³/lb	$H = \frac{W_v}{W_g}$ lb/lb	$H_m = \frac{W_v}{W_m}$ lb/lb	$(c_p)_m$ Btu/lb-°F	$(c_p)_m\delta$ Btu/ft³-°F	$\frac{1}{(c_p)_m\delta}$ ft³-°F/Btu
−25	.09134	.000018	.09136	10.95	.00020	.00020	.2400	.02192	45.60
−20	.09025	.000024	.09027	11.07	.00027	.00027	.2400	.02167	46.15
−15	.08922	.000031	.08925	11.21	.00035	.00035	.2400	.02142	46.69
−10	.08820	.000041	.08824	11.34	.00046	.00046	.2401	.02119	47.20
− 5	.08723	.000053	.08728	11.46	.00061	.00061	.2401	.02096	47.69
0	.08625	.000068	.08632	11.59	.00080	.00080	.2402	.02073	48.24
5	.08529	.000087	.08538	11.72	.00102	.00102	.2402	.02051	48.62
10	.08434	.000110	.08445	11.85	.00130	.00130	.2403	.02029	49.29
15	.08340	.000140	.08354	11.99	.00168	.00168	.2404	.02008	49.80
20	.08247	.000176	.08264	12.12	.00213	.00213	.2404	.01987	50.33
21	.08230	.000185	.08248	12.15	.00225	.00224	.2404	.01983	50.43
22	.08210	.000193	.08229	12.18	.00235	.00234	.2405	.01979	50.54
23	.08193	.000202	.08213	12.20	.00246	.00245	.2405	.01975	50.64
24	.08173	.000213	.08194	12.23	.00260	.00259	.2405	.01971	50.74
25	.08156	.000222	.08178	12.26	.00272	.00271	.2405	.01967	50.84
26	.08136	.000233	.08159	12.29	.00285	.00284	.2406	.01963	50.95
27	.08117	.000243	.08141	12.32	.00300	.00299	.2406	.01959	51.05
28	.08099	.000254	.08124	12.34	.00314	.00313	.2406	.01955	51.16
29	.08083	.000264	.08109	12.37	.00328	.00327	.2407	.01952	51.26
30	.08063	.000277	.08090	12.40	.00345	.00344	.2407	.01947	51.36
31	.08043	.000290	.08072	12.43	.00362	.00361	.2407	.01943	51.47
32	.08025	.000303	.08055	12.46	.00378	.00376	.2408	.01940	51.57
33	.08006	.000315	.08038	12.49	.00393	.00392	.2408	.01935	51.68
34	.07989	.000327	.08022	12.51	.00409	.00408	.2408	.01932	51.76
35	.07970	.000339	.08004	12.54	.00426	.00425	.2409	.01928	51.87
36	.07952	.000353	.07987	12.57	.00444	.00442	.2409	.01924	51.98
37	.07933	.000364	.07969	12.60	.00460	.00458	.2409	.01920	52.09
38	.07916	.000380	.07954	12.63	.00480	.00478	.2410	.01917	52.17
39	.07897	.000394	.07936	12.66	.00499	.00496	.2410	.01913	52.28
40	.07880	.000409	.07921	12.69	.00519	.00516	.2410	.01909	52.39
41	.07860	.000425	.07902	12.72	.00541	.00538	.2411	.01905	52.50
42	.07843	.000440	.07887	12.75	.00561	.00558	.2411	.01902	52.58
43	.07825	.000456	.07871	12.78	.00583	.00579	.2412	.01898	52.69
44	.07805	.000473	.07852	12.81	.00606	.00602	.2412	.01894	52.80
45	.07788	.000491	.07837	12.84	.00630	.00626	.2413	.01891	52.89
46	.07768	.000509	.07819	12.87	.00655	.00651	.2413	.01887	53.00
47	.07750	.000527	.07803	12.90	.00680	.00675	.2414	.01884	53.08
48	.07731	.000545	.07785	12.93	.00705	.00700	.2415	.01880	53.19
49	.07714	.000567	.07771	12.96	.00734	.00728	.2415	.01877	53.31
50	.07694	.000587	.07753	12.99	.00762	.00756	.2416	.01873	53.42
51	.07676	.000608	.07737	13.02	.00792	.00786	.2416	.01869	53.51
52	.07657	.000632	.07720	13.06	.00823	.00819	.2417	.01866	53.60
53	.07637	.000651	.07702	13.09	.00854	.00845	.2418	.01862	53.71
54	.07620	.000675	.07687	13.12	.00884	.00877	.2419	.01859	53.80
55	.07600	.000700	.07670	13.15	.00921	.00913	.2420	.01856	53.88

TABLE 5 (Cont.)—PROPERTIES OF SATURATED AIR

Barometric Pressure 29.92 Inches of Mercury

t	$\delta_g = \frac{W_g}{Q_m}$	$\delta_v = \frac{W_v}{Q_m}$	$\delta = \frac{W_m}{Q_m}$	$\frac{1}{\delta_g} = \frac{Q_m}{W_g}$	$H = \frac{W_v}{W_g}$	$H_m = \frac{W_v}{W_m}$	$(c_p)_m$	$(c_p)_m\delta$	$\frac{1}{(c_p)_m\delta}$
°F	lb/ft³	lb/ft³	lb/ft³	ft³/lb	lb/lb	lb/lb	Btu/lb-°F	Btu/ft³-°F	ft³-°F/Btu
56	.07582	.000723	.07654	13.19	.00952	.00943	.2421	.01853	53.97
57	.07562	.000749	.07637	13.22	.00989	.00980	.2421	.01849	54.09
58	.07544	.000775	.07622	13.25	.01026	.01016	.2421	.01845	54.20
59	.07524	.000801	.07604	13.29	.01063	.01052	.2422	.01842	54.30
60	.07506	.000829	.07589	13.32	.01103	.01091	.2423	.01839	54.38
61	.07486	.000857	.07572	13.35	.01143	.01130	.2425	.01836	54.47
62	.07468	.000886	.07557	13.39	.01185	.01171	.2426	.01833	54.56
63	.07447	.000916	.07539	13.42	.01229	.01214	.2427	.01830	54.65
64	.07429	.000947	.07524	13.46	.01273	.01257	.2427	.01826	54.77
65	.07408	.000979	.07506	13.49	.01320	.01303	.2428	.01822	54.89
66	.07390	.001012	.07491	13.53	.01368	.01349	.2429	.01819	54.98
67	.07369	.001045	.07473	13.57	.01417	.01397	.2430	.01816	55.07
68	.07350	.001080	.07458	13.60	.01468	.01447	.2431	.01813	55.16
69	.07330	.001115	.07441	13.64	.01520	.01497	.2432	.01810	55.25
70	.07310	.001152	.07425	13.68	.01576	.01551	.2434	.01807	55.34
71	.07290	.001189	.07409	13.71	.01630	.01604	.2435	.01804	55.44
72	.07270	.001229	.07393	13.75	.01691	.01662	.2436	.01801	55.53
73	.07250	.001268	.07377	13.79	.01748	.01717	.2437	.01798	55.62
74	.07229	.001310	.07360	13.83	.01812	.01780	.2439	.01795	55.71
75	.07208	.001352	.07343	13.87	.01876	.01841	.2440	.01792	55.80
76	.07188	.001395	.07328	13.91	.01941	.01904	.2442	.01789	55.90
77	.07166	.001439	.07310	13.95	.02008	.01968	.2443	.01786	56.00
78	.07144	.001485	.07293	13.99	.02079	.02036	.2445	.01783	56.09
79	.07124	.001532	.07277	14.03	.02150	.02106	.2446	.01780	56.18
80	.07104	.001579	.07262	14.08	.02223	.02174	.2447	.01777	56.28
81	.07081	.001629	.07244	14.12	.02301	.02249	.2448	.01773	56.40
82	.07059	.001680	.07227	14.16	.02380	.02325	.2449	.01770	56.50
83	.07038	.001733	.07211	14.21	.02462	.02403	.2452	.01768	56.57
84	.07015	.001785	.07193	14.26	.02545	.02482	.2454	.01765	56.66
85	.06993	.001840	.07177	14.30	.02631	.02566	.2455	.01762	56.76
86	.06970	.001898	.07160	14.34	.02723	.02651	.2457	.01759	56.85
87	.06947	.001954	.07142	14.39	.02813	.02736	.2459	.01756	56.95
88	.06925	.002014	.07126	14.44	.02908	.02826	.2461	.01754	57.02
89	.06902	.002072	.07109	14.48	.03002	.02915	.2463	.01751	57.12
90	.06880	.002139	.07094	14.53	.03109	.03015	.2464	.01748	57.21
91	.06855	.002201	.07075	14.58	.03211	.03111	.2466	.01745	57.31
92	.06832	.002267	.07058	14.63	.03318	.03212	.2469	.01743	57.38
93	.06809	.002334	.07042	14.69	.03428	.03314	.2471	.01740	57.48
94	.06785	.002404	.07025	14.73	.03543	.03422	.2474	.01738	57.54
95	.06760	.002474	.07007	14.79	.03660	.03531	.2476	.01735	57.64
96	.06736	.002546	.06991	14.84	.03780	.03642	.2478	.01732	57.74
97	.06711	.002620	.06973	14.90	.03904	.03757	.2481	.01730	57.81
98	.06688	.002692	.06957	14.95	.04025	.03870	.2484	.01728	57.88
99	.06660	.002770	.06931	15.01	.04159	.03993	.2487	.01725	57.98
100	.06634	.002853	.06919	15.07	.04300	.04124	.2489	.01723	58.04

TABLE 5 (Concluded)—PROPERTIES OF SATURATED AIR

Barometric Pressure 29.92 Inches of Mercury

t	$\delta_g = \frac{W_g}{Q_m}$	$\delta_v = \frac{W_v}{Q_m}$	$\delta = \frac{W_m}{Q_m}$	$\frac{1}{\delta_g} = \frac{Q_m}{W_g}$	$H = \frac{W_v}{W_g}$	$H_m = \frac{W_v}{W_m}$	$(c_p)_m$	$(c_p)_m\delta$	$\frac{1}{(c_p)_m\delta}$
°F	$\frac{lb}{ft^3}$	$\frac{lb}{ft^3}$	$\frac{lb}{ft^3}$	$\frac{ft^3}{lb}$	$\frac{lb}{lb}$	$\frac{lb}{lb}$	$\frac{Btu}{lb\text{-}°F}$	$\frac{Btu}{ft^3\text{-}°F}$	$\frac{ft^3\text{-}°F}{Btu}$
101	.06610	.002937	.06904	15.12	.04443	.04255	.2491	.01720	58.14
102	.06583	.003019	.06885	15.18	.04586	.04385	.2494	.01717	58.24
103	.06557	.003106	.06868	15.25	.04737	.04523	.2497	.01715	58.31
104	.06530	.003193	.06849	15.31	.04890	.04662	.2501	.01713	58.38
105	.06504	.003283	.06832	15.37	.05048	.04806	.2504	.01711	58.45
106	.06477	.003375	.06814	15.44	.05212	.04953	.2508	.01709	58.52
107	.06451	.003470	.06798	15.50	.05379	.05105	.2511	.01707	58.58
108	.06421	.003568	.06778	15.57	.05556	.05264	.2515	.01705	58.65
109	.06394	.003666	.06761	15.64	.05734	.05422	.2519	.01703	58.72
110	.06364	.003766	.06741	15.71	.05917	.05587	.2522	.01700	58.83
111	.06336	.003872	.06723	15.78	.06111	.05760	.2526	.01698	58.90
112	.06306	.003978	.06704	15.85	.06308	.05934	.2530	.01696	58.96
113	.06278	.004085	.06686	15.93	.06507	.06110	.2534	.01694	59.03
114	.06247	.004199	.06667	16.00	.06722	.06299	.2538	.01692	59.10
115	.06216	.004311	.06647	16.08	.06935	.06486	.2542	.01690	59.18
116	.06186	.004427	.06629	16.16	.07157	.06678	.2547	.01688	59.25
117	.06154	.004548	.06609	16.24	.07390	.06882	.2552	.01686	59.32
118	.06124	.004669	.06591	16.32	.07625	.07084	.2557	.01685	59.35
119	.06092	.004794	.06571	16.41	.07869	.07296	.2561	.01683	59.42
120	.06060	.004921	.06552	16.50	.08121	.07511	.2566	.01681	59.49
121	.06027	.005049	.06532	16.58	.08376	.07729	.2571	.01679	59.56
122	.05995	.005183	.06513	16.68	.08646	.07958	.2576	.01678	59.60
123	.05960	.005319	.06492	16.77	.08925	.08194	.2582	.01676	59.67
124	.05927	.005456	.06473	16.87	.09204	.08428	.2587	.01674	59.74
125	.05892	.005598	.06452	16.96	.09502	.08677	.2593	.01673	59.78
130	.05713	.006355	.06349	17.49	.11125	.10010	.2625	.01666	60.03
135	.05524	.007195	.06244	18.10	.13026	.11523	.2659	.01660	60.24
140	.05319	.008128	.06132	18.79	.15280	.13255	.2701	.01656	60.39
145	.05100	.009162	.06016	19.60	.17966	.15230	.2748	.01653	60.54
150	.04865	.010303	.05895	20.55	.21178	.17478	.2802	.01652	60.64
155	.04612	.011547	.05767	21.67	.25038	.20022	.2865	.01652	60.68
160	.04340	.012937	.05634	23.03	.29810	.22962	.2934	.01653	60.61
165	.04048	.014436	.05492	24.69	.35660	.26285	.3017	.01657	60.54
170	.03734	.016118	.05346	26.77	.43168	.30150	.3115	.01665	60.32
175	.03398	.017926	.05191	29.43	.52750	.34530	.3223	.01673	59.99
180	.03035	.019905	.05036	32.94	.65580	.39525	.3346	.01685	59.70
185	.02645	.022062	.04851	37.78	.83410	.45425	.3501	.01703	59.28
190	.02228	.024393	.04667	44.85	1.0948	.52270	.3684	.01719	58.72
195	.01779	.026957	.04475	56.20	1.5153	.60240	.3898	.01744	58.04
200	.01297	.029730	.04270	77.11	2.2923	.69660	.4145	.01770	57.21
205	.00782	.032715	.04064	127.9	4.1838	.80500	.4425	.01798	56.47
210	.00232	.035942	.03836	431.0	15.493	.93700	.4787	.01836	55.47
212	.00000	.037298	.03730	——	Inf.	1.0000	.4960	.01850	55.07

TABLE 6—SPECIFIC HEATS OF VARIOUS GASES

In Btu per lb-°F

Temperature °R	°F	Air 28.966	N_2 28.016	O_2 32.000	CO_2 44.010	CO 28.010	H_2 2.016	H_2O 18.016	Monatomic Gases
100	−359.7	.2392	—	—	—	—	—	—	—
200	−259.7	.2392	.2480	.2173	.1589	.2481	2.7599	.4411	5.454/MW
300	−159.7	.2392	.2480	.2173	.1674	.2481	3.0957	.4415	5.162/MW
400	−59.7	.2393	.2481	.2174	.1815	.2482	3.2961	.4421	5.072/MW
500	40.3	.2396	.2481	.2184	.1964	.2483	3.3948	.4439	5.032/MW
600	140.3	.2403	.2485	.2206	.2100	.2487	3.4355	.4473	5.013/MW
700	240.3	.2416	.2491	.2239	.2221	.2498	3.4509	.4527	4.998/MW
800	340.3	.2434	.2503	.2278	.2326	.2517	3.4598	.4592	4.989/MW
900	440.3	.2458	.2521	.2321	.2421	.2541	3.4648	.4667	4.984/MW
1000	540.3	.2486	.2546	.2363	.2507	.2570	3.4692	.4748	4.981/MW
1100	640.3	.2516	.2573	.2404	.2584	.2603	3.4742	.4833	4.979/MW
1200	740.3	.2547	.2603	.2442	.2654	.2638	3.4811	.4919	4.978/MW
1300	840.3	.2579	.2635	.2476	.2716	.2673	3.4906	.5008	4.977/MW
1400	940.3	.2611	.2668	.2507	.2773	.2707	3.5025	.5099	4.975/MW
1500	1040.3	.2642	.2700	.2534	.2824	.2741	3.5169	.5191	4.974/MW
1600	1140.3	.2671	.2731	.2560	.2870	.2773	3.5352	.5285	4.973/MW
1700	1240.3	.2698	.2760	.2583	.2913	.2803	3.5560	.5380	4.972/MW
1800	1340.3	.2725	.2789	.2604	.2951	.2830	3.5789	.5476	4.972/MW
1900	1440.3	.2750	.2816	.2622	.2986	.2856	3.6032	.5570	4.971/MW
2000	1540.3	.2773	.2842	.2638	.3017	.2881	3.6290	.5663	4.971/MW
2100	1640.3	.2794	.2865	.2654	.3046	.2903	3.6553	.5754	4.970/MW
2200	1740.3	.2813	.2886	.2668	.3072	.2924	3.6825	.5843	4.970/MW
2300	1840.3	.2831	.2905	.2682	.3097	.2942	3.7098	.5929	4.969/MW
2400	1940.3	.2848	.2924	.2694	.3119	.2959	3.7376	.6013	4.969/MW
2500	2040.3	.2863	.2942	.2705	.3140	.2976	3.7659	.6093	4.968/MW

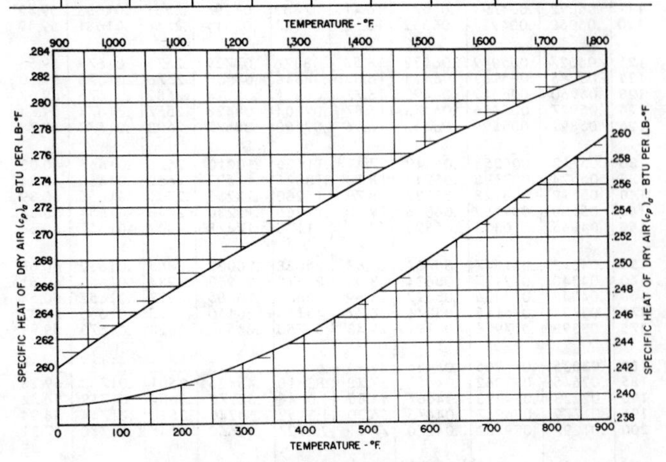

Figure 2—Specific Heats of Dry Air

Adapted from the data of J. H. Keenan and J. Kaye, "Gas Tables," John Wiley & Sons Inc., 1948, pp. 34, 102, 107, 112, 117, 122, 127 and 128.

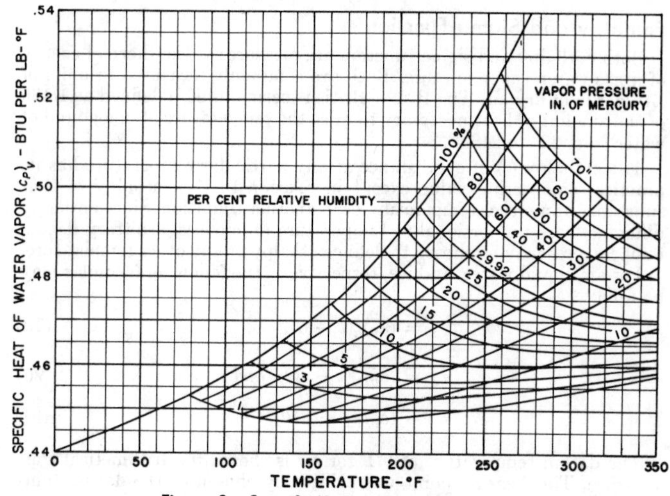

Figure 3—Specific Heats of Water Vapor

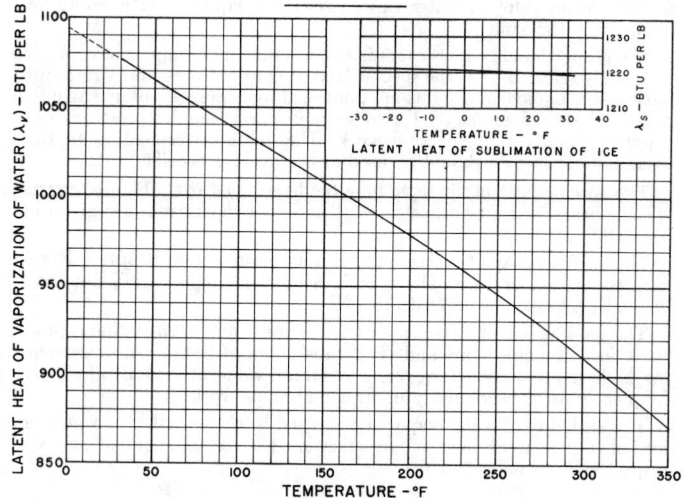

Figure 4—Latent Heats of Water and Ice

Adapted from the data of J. H. Keenan and F. G. Keyes, "Thermodynamic Properties of Steam," John Wiley & Sons, Inc., New York, 1936.

Enthalpy and Sigma Function

Both enthalpy and sigma function are measures of the thermal energy of a gas-water vapor mixture. Both are commonly measured in units of Btu per lb of dry air. The Btu or British thermal unit is defined as 1/180 of the amount of heat necessary to raise the temperature of one pound of water from 32° to 212°F.

The enthalpy (i) of a substance at any particular temperature has no practical engineering value except in relation to the enthalpy of that substance at another temperature or in another condition. Since enthalpy differences are proportional to temperature differences, arbitrary datum temperatures may be chosen to define enthalpy at any other temperature.

For air, liquid water, and ice, respectively, the following formulas may be used:

$$i_a = (c_p)_a(t - 0), \tag{19}$$

$$i_w = (c_p)_w(t - 32), \text{ and} \tag{20}$$

$$i_i = (c_p)_i(t - 340). \tag{21}$$

The datum temperature of 0°F for air is chosen for arithmetical convenience. The freezing point was arbitrarily chosen as the datum temperature for water, and the 340° datum temperature for ice was selected so that the enthalpy of water vapor over ice or liquid at 32°F would be numerically the same.

The proportionality factor (c_p) is also a function of temperature and is commonly referred to as the specific heat at constant pressure. Values for most gases, liquids, and solids are published for a pressure of one atmosphere. These values may be used without correction for pressures encountered in most engineering work. The value corresponding to the average temperature should be used as the average specific heat.

The specific heat of air $(c_p)_a$ may be determined from Figure 2. The specific heats for a few other gases at various temperatures are given in Table 6.

The specific heat of water $(c_p)_w$ is very close to 1.00 Btu/lb - °F, regardless of temperature. The specific heat of ice $(c_p)_i$ varies, but may generally be taken as 0.47 Btu/lb - °F.

The specific heat of water vapor $(c_p)_v$ is given in Figure 3. As shown, the variations in temperature and vapor pressure must be taken into account for highest accuracy. However, a constant value of 0.45 Btu/lb-°F is frequently used, particularly in air conditioning work.

The enthalpy of water vapor (i_v) is equal to the enthalpy of water or ice, plus the latent heat of vaporization (λ_v) or of sublimation (λ_s) respectively, as indicated by

$$i_v = i_w + \lambda_v, \text{ and} \tag{22}$$

$$i_v = i_i + \lambda_s. \tag{23}$$

The latent heat of vaporization or of sublimation may be determined from Figure 4 or approximately from

$$\lambda_v = 1092 - .55t, \text{ or} \tag{24}$$

$$\lambda_s = 1220 - .02t. \tag{25}$$

Combining Equations 20, 24, and 22, or 21, 25, and 23 yields

$$i_v = 1060 + .45t, \tag{26}$$

which corresponds very closely with the data of Keenan and Keyes*.

The enthalpy of an air-water vapor mixture may be determined from

$$i_m = i_a + Hi_v. \tag{27}$$

Similarly, the specific heat of an air-water vapor mixture $(c_p)_m$ may be calculated from

$$(c_p)_m = (c_p)_a + H(c_p)_v. \tag{28}$$

This last expression has meaning only when used over a range of temperatures where no condensation or evaporation occurs.

The sigma function (Σ) of a mixture of air and water vapor differs from the enthalpy of a mixture by an amount equal to the enthalpy of liquid water at the temperature of adiabatic saturation:

$$\Sigma = i_m - H\, i'''_w. \tag{29}$$

Equations 19 and 26 may be combined into Equation 27, yielding:

$$i_m = (c_p)_a t + H(1060 + .45t). \tag{30}$$

The equation for sigma function therefore becomes:

$$\Sigma = (c_p)_a t + H[1060 + .45t - (t''' - 32)]. \tag{31}$$

The sigma function for air-water vapor mixtures at any temperature of adiabatic saturation is constant, regardless of dry-bulb temperature. The difference between using sigma function or enthalpy for any air-water vapor mixture is usually negligible for most engineering applications. The use of sigma function was preferred in past years. There is a modern trend to the use of enthalpy. The use of a single enthalpy value for each wet-bulb temperature is no more accurate than the use of sigma function. Sigma function values are listed for various wet-bulb temperatures in Tables 7 and 8. Enthalpy values at saturation are tabulated in Table 9. One must be careful to use the same table for both temperatures when making computations. Performance tables for some equipment are evaluated from test data based on one or the other of these tables. In such cases the appropriate tables should be used for selection purposes.

*J. H. Keenan and F. G. Keyes, "Thermodynamic Properties of Steam," John Wiley & Sons, Inc., New York, 1936.

TABLE 7—SIGMA FUNCTIONS OF AIR-WATER VAPOR MIXTURES

In Btu per lb of dry air

t' °F	0	.1	.2	.3	.4	.5	.6	.7	.8	.9
32	11.75	11.79	11.83	11.87	11.91	11.95	11.99	12.03	12.07	12.11
33	12.15	12.19	12.23	12.27	12.31	12.36	12.40	12.44	12.48	12.52
34	12.56	12.60	12.64	12.69	12.73	12.77	12.81	12.85	12.90	12.94
35	12.98	13.02	13.06	13.11	13.15	13.19	13.23	13.27	13.32	13.36
36	13.40	13.44	13.49	13.53	13.57	13.62	13.66	13.70	13.74	13.79
37	13.83	13.87	13.92	13.96	14.01	14.05	14.09	14.14	14.18	14.23
38	14.27	14.31	14.36	14.40	14.45	14.49	14.53	14.58	14.62	14.67
39	14.71	14.76	14.80	14.85	14.89	14.94	14.98	15.03	15.07	15.12
40	15.16	15.21	15.25	15.30	15.34	15.39	15.44	15.48	15.53	15.57
41	15.62	15.67	15.71	15.76	15.81	15.86	15.90	15.95	16.00	16.04
42	16.09	16.14	16.18	16.23	16.28	16.33	16.37	16.42	16.47	16.51
43	16.56	16.61	16.66	16.70	16.75	16.80	16.85	16.90	16.94	16.99
44	17.04	17.09	17.14	17.19	17.24	17.29	17.33	17.38	17.43	17.48
45	17.53	17.58	17.63	17.68	17.73	17.78	17.83	17.88	17.93	17.98
46	18.03	18.08	18.13	18.18	18.23	18.29	18.34	18.39	18.44	18.49
47	18.54	18.59	18.64	18.70	18.75	18.80	18.85	18.90	18.96	19.01
48	19.06	19.11	19.17	19.22	19.27	19.33	19.38	19.43	19.48	19.54
49	19.59	19.64	19.70	19.75	19.81	19.86	19.91	19.97	20.02	20.08
50	20.13	20.19	20.24	20.30	20.35	20.41	20.46	20.52	20.57	20.63
51	20.68	20.74	20.79	20.85	20.90	20.96	21.02	21.07	21.13	21.18
52	21.24	21.30	21.35	21.41	21.47	21.53	21.58	21.64	21.70	21.75
53	21.81	21.87	21.93	21.98	22.04	22.10	22.16	22.22	22.27	22.33
54	22.39	22.45	22.51	22.57	22.63	22.69	22.74	22.80	22.86	22.92
55	22.98	23.04	23.10	23.16	23.22	23.28	23.34	23.40	23.46	23.52
56	23.58	23.64	23.70	23.76	23.82	23.89	23.95	24.01	24.07	24.13
57	24.19	24.25	24.31	24.38	24.44	24.50	24.56	24.62	24.69	24.75
58	24.81	24.87	24.94	25.00	25.06	25.13	25.19	25.25	25.31	25.38
59	25.44	25.50	25.57	25.63	25.70	25.76	25.82	25.89	25.95	26.02
60	26.08	26.15	26.21	26.28	26.34	26.41	26.48	26.54	26.61	26.67
61	26.74	26.81	26.88	26.94	27.01	27.08	27.15	27.22	27.28	27.35
62	27.42	27.49	27.56	27.63	27.70	27.77	27.84	27.91	27.98	28.05
63	28.12	28.19	28.26	28.33	28.40	28.48	28.55	28.62	28.69	28.76
64	28.83	28.90	28.97	29.05	29.12	29.19	29.26	29.33	29.41	29.48
65	29.55	29.62	29.70	29.77	29.85	29.92	29.99	30.07	30.14	30.22
66	30.29	30.37	30.44	30.52	30.59	30.67	30.75	30.82	30.90	30.97
67	31.05	31.13	31.20	31.28	31.36	31.44	31.51	31.59	31.67	31.74
68	31.82	31.90	31.98	32.06	32.14	32.22	32.29	32.37	32.45	32.53
69	32.61	32.69	32.77	32.85	32.93	33.02	33.10	33.18	33.26	33.34
70	33.42	33.50	33.59	33.67	33.75	33.84	33.92	34.00	34.08	34.17
71	34.25	34.33	34.42	34.50	34.59	34.67	34.75	34.84	34.92	35.01
72	35.09	35.18	35.26	35.35	35.43	35.52	35.61	35.69	35.78	35.86
73	35.95	36.04	36.12	36.21	36.30	36.39	36.47	36.56	36.65	36.73
74	36.82	36.91	37.00	37.09	37.18	37.27	37.36	37.45	37.54	37.63
75	37.72	37.81	37.90	38.00	38.09	38.18	38.27	38.36	38.46	38.55
76	38.64	38.73	38.83	38.92	39.02	39.11	39.20	39.30	39.39	39.49
77	39.58	39.68	39.77	39.87	39.96	40.06	40.16	40.25	40.35	40.44
78	40.54	40.64	40.74	40.83	40.93	41.03	41.13	41.23	41.32	41.42
79	41.52	41.62	41.72	41.82	41.92	42.02	42.12	42.22	42.32	42.42

TABLE 9 (Continued)

ENTHALPIES OF AIR-WATER VAPOR MIXTURES AT SATURATION

In Btu per lb of dry air

t' °F	0	.1	.2	.3	.4	.5	.6	.7	.8	.9
56	23.84	23.90	23.96	24.03	24.09	24.15	24.21	24.28	24.34	24.40
57	24.48	24.53	24.59	24.66	24.72	24.79	24.85	24.92	24.99	25.05
58	25.12	25.18	25.25	25.32	25.38	25.45	25.51	25.58	25.65	25.71
59	25.78	25.85	25.91	25.99	26.06	26.12	26.19	26.26	26.33	26.39
60	26.46	26.53	26.60	26.67	26.74	26.81	26.88	26.94	27.01	27.08
61	27.15	27.21	27.28	27.35	27.42	27.48	27.55	27.62	27.69	27.76
62	27.85	27.92	28.00	28.07	28.14	28.21	28.29	28.36	28.43	28.50
63	28.57	28.65	28.72	28.79	28.86	28.94	29.01	29.08	29.16	29.23
64	29.31	29.38	29.45	29.53	29.60	29.68	29.76	29.83	29.91	29.98
65	30.06	30.13	30.21	30.29	30.37	30.45	30.52	30.60	30.68	30.76
66	30.83	30.92	31.00	31.07	31.15	31.23	31.31	31.39	31.47	31.54
67	31.62	31.70	31.77	31.85	31.93	32.01	32.09	32.17	32.25	32.33
68	32.42	32.51	32.59	32.67	32.76	32.84	32.92	33.01	33.09	33.17
69	33.25	33.34	33.42	33.50	33.59	33.67	33.75	33.84	33.92	34.01
70	34.09	34.17	34.26	34.34	34.43	34.51	34.60	34.69	34.77	34.86
71	34.95	35.04	35.13	35.22	35.31	35.40	35.48	35.57	35.66	35.74
72	35.83	35.92	36.01	36.10	36.19	36.27	36.37	36.46	36.55	36.65
73	36.74	36.83	36.92	37.02	37.11	37.21	37.30	37.39	37.48	37.57
74	37.66	37.76	37.85	37.94	38.04	38.14	38.23	38.33	38.43	38.52
75	38.61	38.71	38.80	38.90	38.99	39.09	39.18	39.28	39.37	39.47
76	39.57	39.67	39.77	39.87	39.97	40.07	40.17	40.27	40.38	40.48
77	40.57	40.68	40.78	40.88	40.98	41.08	41.18	41.28	41.38	41.48
78	41.58	41.69	41.79	41.89	42.00	42.10	42.20	42.31	42.41	42.52
79	42.62	42.73	42.83	42.94	43.05	43.15	43.26	43.37	43.48	43.59
80	43.69	43.81	43.91	44.02	44.13	44.24	44.36	44.46	44.57	44.68
81	44.78	44.89	45.00	45.11	45.23	45.34	45.45	45.57	45.68	45.80
82	45.90	46.02	46.13	46.24	46.35	46.47	46.58	46.69	46.71	46.82
83	47.04	47.16	47.28	47.40	47.52	47.63	47.75	47.87	47.99	48.10
84	48.22	48.34	48.46	48.58	48.70	48.82	48.94	49.06	49.19	49.31
85	49.43	49.56	49.68	49.70	49.92	50.05	50.17	50.29	50.41	50.54
86	50.66	50.79	50.91	51.04	51.16	51.29	51.42	51.55	51.67	51.80
87	51.93	52.06	52.19	52.32	52.45	52.58	52.71	52.84	52.97	53.09
88	53.23	53.35	53.48	53.62	53.75	53.89	54.02	54.15	54.29	54.42
89	54.56	54.70	54.83	54.97	55.10	55.24	55.38	55.52	55.66	55.80
90	55.93	56.07	56.20	56.34	56.48	56.62	56.76	56.91	57.05	57.19
91	57.33	57.47	57.62	57.76	57.90	58.05	58.19	58.34	58.48	58.63
92	58.78	58.94	59.08	59.23	59.37	59.52	59.66	59.81	59.95	60.10
93	60.25	60.40	60.55	60.70	60.85	61.00	61.15	61.31	61.46	61.61
94	61.77	61.93	62.08	62.23	62.39	62.54	62.69	62.85	63.01	63.17
95	63.32	63.48	63.65	63.80	63.97	64.12	64.28	64.44	64.60	64.76
96	64.92	65.09	65.25	65.42	65.58	65.74	65.90	66.06	66.22	66.38
97	66.55	66.71	66.87	67.04	67.21	67.38	67.55	67.72	67.89	68.06
98	68.23	68.41	68.59	68.76	68.93	69.10	69.27	69.44	69.61	69.78
99	69.96	70.13	70.31	70.48	70.66	70.84	71.02	71.20	71.38	71.56

Calculated from the data of J. A. Goff and S. Gratch, Thermodynamic Properties of Moist Air, *Trans. ASHVE*, vol. 51, pp. 125-164, 1945.

TABLE 8—SIGMA FUNCTIONS OF AIR-WATER VAPOR MIXT

In Btu per lb of dry air

t′ °F	0	1	2	3	4	5	6	7	8
−20	−4.49	−4.75	−5.00	−5.25	−5.51	−5.76	−6.01	−6.27	−6.5
−10	−1.84	−2.11	−2.38	−2.65	−2.91	−3.17	−3.44	−3.70	−3.96
−	.96	.67	.38	.09	− .20	− .48	− .75	−1.02	−1.29
0	.96	1.25	1.54	1.84	2.14	2.45	2.75	3.06	3.37
10	3.99	4.31	4.64	4.97	5.31	5.65	5.99	6.34	6.69
20	7.40	7.77	8.15	8.54	8.93	9.33	9.73	10.14	10.55
30	11.41	11.85	†11.75	12.15	12.56	12.98	13.40	13.83	14.27
40	15.16	15.62	16.09	16.56	17.04	17.53	18.03	18.54	19.06
50	20.13	20.68	21.24	21.81	22.39	22.98	23.58	24.19	24.81
60	26.08	26.74	27.42	28.12	28.83	29.55	30.29	31.05	31.82
70	33.42	34.25	35.09	35.95	36.82	37.72	38.64	39.58	40.54
80	42.52	43.55	44.61	45.69	46.79	47.92	49.08	50.27	51.48
90	53.99	55.30	56.64	58.02	59.43	60.87	62.34	63.85	65.40
100	68.62	70.29	72.00	73.75	75.55	77.40	79.30	81.25	83.26
110	87.47	89.67	91.92	94.23	96.60	99.04	101.6	104.10	106.7
120	112.2	115.0	117.9	120.9	124.0	127.2	130.5	133.9	137.4
130	144.7	148.5	152.4	156.4	160.5	164.8	169.3	173.9	178.7
140	188.6	193.8	199.2	204.8	210.6	216.6	222.8	229.2	235.8

†Sigma function over ice is 12.29 Btu per lb of dry air.

TABLE 9
ENTHALPIES OF AIR-WATER VAPOR MIXTURES AT SATURATION

In Btu per lb of dry air

t′ °F	0	.1	.2	.3	.4	.5	.6	.7	.8	.9
33	12.17	12.21	12.25	12.30	12.34	12.38	12.42	12.46	12.50	12.
34	12.59	12.61	12.66	12.71	12.75	12.79	12.84	12.88	12.92	12
35	13.01	13.05	13.09	13.14	13.18	13.22	13.26	13.31	13.35	13
36	13.44	13.48	13.52	13.56	13.61	13.65	13.69	13.74	13.78	13
37	13.87	13.92	13.96	14.01	14.05	14.09	14.14	14.18	14.23	14
38	14.32	14.36	14.41	14.45	14.50	14.54	14.59	14.63	14.68	14
39	14.77	14.82	14.86	14.91	14.95	15.00	15.05	15.09	15.14	1
40	15.23	15.27	15.32	15.36	15.41	15.46	15.50	15.55	15.60	1
41	15.70	15.75	15.80	15.84	15.89	15.94	15.99	16.03	16.08	1
42	16.17	16.22	16.26	16.31	16.36	16.42	16.47	16.52	16.56	1
43	16.66	16.71	16.76	16.80	16.85	16.90	16.95	17.00	17.05	1
44	17.15	17.20	17.25	17.29	17.34	17.40	17.44	17.50	17.55	1
45	17.65	17.70	17.75	17.80	17.85	17.90	17.95	18.01	18.06	1
46	18.16	18.21	18.26	18.32	18.37	18.42	18.47	18.52	18.58	1
47	18.68	18.73	18.78	18.84	18.89	18.94	19.00	19.05	19.11	1
48	19.21	19.27	19.32	19.37	19.43	19.48	19.53	19.58	19.64	1
49	19.75	19.80	19.86	19.91	19.97	20.02	20.08	20.14	20.20	
50	20.30	20.36	20.42	20.47	20.53	20.58	20.64	20.70	20.75	
51	20.86	20.92	20.98	21.04	21.09	21.15	21.21	21.26	21.32	
52	21.44	21.49	21.55	21.60	21.66	21.72	21.78	21.83	21.89	
53	22.02	22.06	22.12	22.19	22.24	22.30	22.36	22.43	22.49	
54	22.62	22.68	22.74	22.80	22.86	22.92	22.98	23.04	23.11	
55	23.22	23.28	23.34	23.40	23.46	23.52	23.58	23.64	23.71	

Psychrometric Charts

Psychrometric charts can be made to express graphically the relations between pressure, temperature, humidity, density, and heat content for any gas-vapor mixture. Psychrometric charts are usually drawn for constant barometric pressure, using dry-bulb temperature for abscissa and absolute humidity for ordinate. (Barometric corrections are discussed in subsequent paragraphs.) In most cases, uniform scales are chosen for both dry-bulb temperature and absolute humidity so that curved wet-bulb temperature and relative humidity lines result. Various units of measurement may be employed. The most common are the Fahrenheit scale for temperature and either grains or pounds of moisture per pound of dry air for humidity.

Relative humidity is usually graphed as a series of percentile curves. However, in some types of charts, a series of percentage absolute humidity curves are shown instead. The two are not the same, as indicated in the discussion on page **9**, so that caution is necessary.

With air-water vapor mixtures the lines of constant wet-bulb and lines of constant temperature of adiabatic saturation practically coincide, so that only one is shown. With other gas-vapor mixtures an appreciable difference may exist, and both may be shown.

In the construction of a psychrometric chart, points on the various percentile relative humidity curves, including that for 100% or saturation, may be located by means of Equation 8. To determine the H coordinate for any given t coordinate and value of h, obtain the vapor pressure of pure water (e_w) corresponding to the dry-bulb temperature (t) from Table **3**, the relative weight of water vapor (s) at t and h from Figure 1, and calculate the corresponding absolute humidity (H).

In order to construct lines of constant wet-bulb temperature, Carrier's formula* may be used in simplified form:

$$e_a = e'_w - \frac{(c_p)_a (b - e'_w)(t - t')}{(s')_{sat}\, \lambda'}. \tag{32}$$

This expression gives the partial pressure of the vapor in air (e_a) in terms of: the barometric pressure (b), the dry-bulb temperature (t), the wet-bulb temperature (t'), the vapor pressure of water (e'_w) at t', the latent heat of vaporization or sublimation (λ') at t', the relative density of water vapor $(s')_{sat}$ at saturation at t', and the specific heat of dry air $(c_p)_a$ at $\frac{1}{2}(t + t')$. This expression does not include the H coordinate but a relationship between e_a and H can be obtained. Equation **7** may be rearranged so:

$$e_a = e_w h. \tag{33}$$

---

*W. H. Carrier, Rational Psychrometric Formulae, *Trans. ASME*, vol. 33, pp. 1309-1350, 1911.

A more elaborate version, like the following, must be used whenever the denominator differs appreciably from unity:

$$e_a = \frac{e'_w - \dfrac{(c_p)_a (b - e'_w)(t - t')}{s'\, \lambda'}}{\left(\dfrac{s}{s'}\right)\left(\dfrac{b - e'_w}{b - e_w}\right) + \dfrac{(c_p)_v (b - e'_w)(t - t')}{\lambda' (b - e_w)}}.$$

By comparing Equations 10 and 33, it will be noted that $e_a = e''_w$, i.e., the partial pressure of the vapor in air is equal to the dew-point vapor pressure. It follows that the absolute humidity corresponding to the partial pressure of the vapor in the air (e_a) must equal the absolute humidity corresponding to the dew-point vapor pressure (e''_w). Therefore, the H coordinate can be determined by solving Equation 32 for e_a. This can be accomplished by substituting: the values of s' as read from Figure 1 at t' and 100% h, the value of $(c_p)_a$ as read from Figure 2 at $\frac{1}{2}(t + t')$, the value of λ' as read from Figure 4 at t', and the value of e'_w as read from Table 3 opposite t'. Note the temperature in Table 3 corresponding to e_a. This is the dew-point temperature which defines the missing coordinate.

Curves of constant specific volume ($1/\delta_g$) may be drawn after sufficient calculations are made using Equation 17.

A sigma function (Σ) scale can be constructed after sufficient calculations are made using Equation 31.

An enthalpy at saturation $(i_m)_{sat}$ scale can be constructed after sufficient calculations are made using Equation 30. Enthalpy deviations in the partially saturated region may also be computed with the aid of Equation 30.

Various psychrometric charts are given in this section. Figure 5 is a low temperature psychrometric chart covering a range of dry-bulb temperatures from −20 to +40°F. Figure 6 is the standard psychrometric chart covering a range of dry-bulb temperatures from 30 to 125°F. Figure 7 is a high temperature psychrometric chart with a temperature range of 20-330°F. Figure 8 is a very high temperature psychrometric chart with a temperature range of 0-1500°F. Finally, a special psychrometric chart, drawn to show absolute humidity in grains of moisture per cubic foot of air or mixture, is shown in Figure 9. All five charts are drawn to uniform dry-bulb temperature and humidity scales. However, in Figures 5 and 6, the horizontal division lines correspond exactly to integral dew-point temperatures, giving each chart the appearance of having a non-uniform vertical scale. Relative humidity, which has very little significance at very high temperatures, has been omitted from Figure 8. Specific volume lines, which would be nearly vertical, have been omitted from Figure 5. All of the charts have been drawn for a standard barometric pressure of 29.92 inches of mercury. Unless one of the quantities has been intentionally omitted, the dry-bulb, wet-bulb, dew-point, absolute humidity, relative humidity, enthalpy, sigma function, and specific volume for air-water vapor mixtures may be determined if any two of the quantities are known. The dry-bulb, wet-bulb, relative humidity, and absolute humidity may all be determined by direct, graphical interpolation. The dew-point temperature of partially saturated air is the temperature indicated at the intersection of the saturation curve with a horizontal line drawn through the actual air condition or state. The sigma function or enthalpy at saturation can be determined for any wet-bulb condition from the appropriate scale opposite the wet-bulb temperature at saturation. This requires a vertical alignment in Figures 5 and 6 and a horizontal alignment in Figures 7 and 8.

Vapor pressures are not shown on any of the charts. If desired, values

For saturated air at a given temperature the value of e_w is constant regardless of barometer. At saturation the dry-bulb equals the wet-bulb and $e_w = e'_w$. The value of absolute humidity at saturation at the wet bulb temperature for standard barometer $(H'_{29.92})_{sat}$ and that for any other barometer $(H'_b)_{sat}$ may be calculated from Equation **8**. Assuming s and SG constant:

$$(H'_b)_{sat} = (H'_{29.92})_{sat} \left(\frac{29.92 - e'_w}{b - e'_w}\right). \tag{34}$$

Subtracting $(H'_{29.92})_{sat}$ from each side leaves:

$$(H'_b - H'_{29.92})_{sat} = (H'_{29.92})_{sat} \left(\frac{29.92 - b}{b - e'_w}\right). \tag{35}$$

The left side, $(H'_b - H'_{29.92})_{sat}$, may be called the difference in absolute humidity at saturation at the wet-bulb temperature for the difference in barometer $(29.92 - b)$. This difference may be used directly as a close approximation of the difference in absolute humidity of partially saturated air $(H_b - H_{29.92})$ for the same difference in barometer. A more accurate determination may be obtained from:

$$H_b - H_{29.92} = \frac{(H'_b - H'_{29.92})_{sat}}{1 + \dfrac{(c_p)_v\,(t - t')}{\lambda'}}. \tag{36}$$

The correction for the increased sensible heat of the vapor of partially saturated air given in the denominator is quite small and may frequently be omitted. Figure 10 is a graphical representation of Equation **35** and therefore of the numerator of Equation **36**.

If the difference in absolute humidity at saturation at the wet-bulb temperature for the difference in barometer $(29.92 - b)$ is multiplied by the latent heat of vaporization (λ') at t', the product equals the difference in sigma function $(\Sigma_b - \Sigma_{29.92})$ for the same difference in barometer as indicated by

$$\Sigma_b - \Sigma_{29.92} = \lambda'\,(H'_b - H'_{29.92})_{sat}. \tag{37}$$

Figure 11 is a graphical representation of Equation **37**.

Figures 10 and 11 may be used to obtain barometric corrections for any psychrometric chart which is drawn for **29.92″** Hg barometer.

Often only the density of air-water vapor mixtures is required. The psychrometric density chart in Figure **12** may be used to determine the density whenever the dry-bulb, wet-bulb, and barometer readings are known. After calculating the wet-bulb depression, i.e., the difference between wet-bulb and dry-bulb temperatures, enter the chart at lower right, proceed horizontally to the appropriate dry-bulb temperature, thence vertically to the appropriate barometer, and read the density directly at the right.

Tables 11 and **12** can be used to determine the relative specific gravity of air at various altitudes and temperatures, respectively.

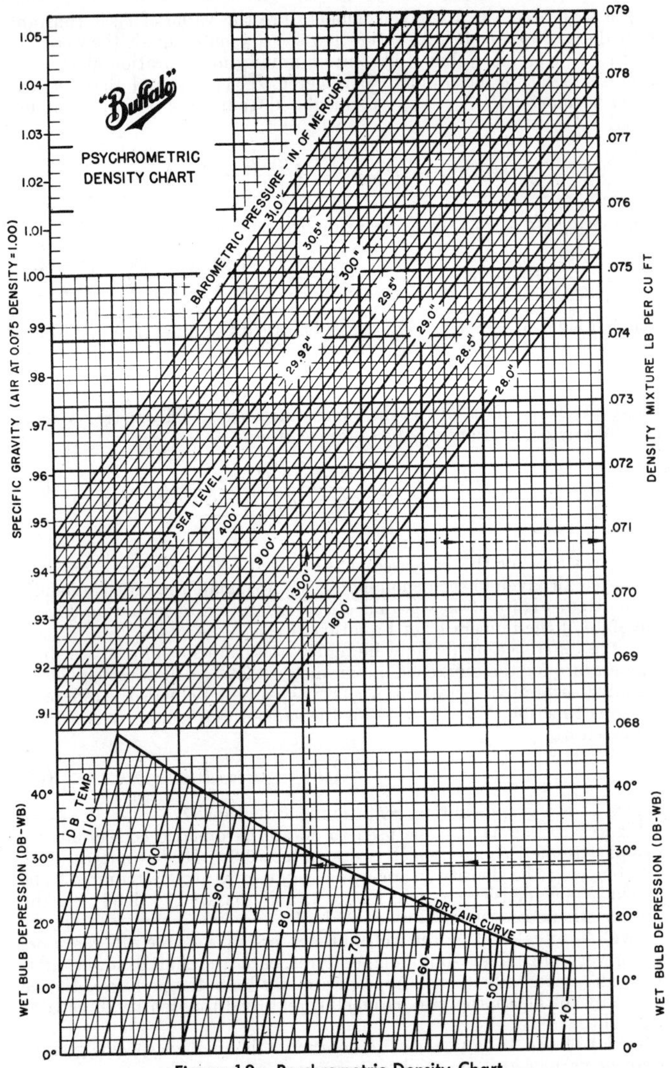

Figure 12—Psychrometric Density Chart

TABLE 10—RELATIVE SPECIFIC GRAVITY OF AIR AT VARIOUS ALTITUDES

Specific Gravity of Standard
Air at Sea Level and 29.92″ Hg = 1.00

Z-ft	$\overline{SG}$	b-″Hg	Z-ft	$\overline{SG}$	b-″Hg	Z-ft	$\overline{SG}$	b-″Hg	Z-ft	$\overline{SG}$	b-″Hg
0	1.000	29.92	**1500**	0.947	28.33	**3000**	0.896	26.82	**6000**	0.801	23.98
100	0.996	29.81	**1600**	0.944	28.23	**3200**	0.890	26.62	**6500**	0.786	23.53
200	0.993	29.70	**1700**	0.940	28.13	**3400**	0.883	26.42	**7000**	0.772	23.09
300	0.989	29.60	**1800**	0.937	28.02	**3600**	0.877	26.23	**7500**	0.757	22.65
400	0.986	29.49	**1900**	0.933	27.92	**3800**	0.870	26.03	**8000**	0.743	22.22
500	0.982	29.38	**2000**	0.930	27.82	**4000**	0.864	25.84	**8500**	0.729	21.80
600	0.979	29.28	**2100**	0.926	27.72	**4200**	0.857	25.65	**9000**	0.715	21.39
700	0.975	29.17	**2200**	0.923	27.62	**4400**	0.851	25.46	**9500**	0.701	20.98
800	0.971	29.07	**2300**	0.920	27.52	**4600**	0.845	25.27	**10000**	0.688	20.58
900	0.968	28.96	**2400**	0.916	27.42	**4800**	0.838	25.08	**15000**	0.564	16.89
1000	0.964	28.86	**2500**	0.913	27.32	**5000**	0.832	24.90	**20000**	0.460	13.75
1100	0.961	28.75	**2600**	0.909	27.21	**5200**	0.826	24.71	**25000**	0.371	11.10
1200	0.957	28.65	**2700**	0.906	27.11	**5400**	0.820	24.52	**30000**	0.297	8.89
1300	0.954	28.54	**2800**	0.903	27.01	**5600**	0.814	24.34	**35000**	0.235	7.04
1400	0.950	28.44	**2900**	0.899	26.91	**5800**	0.807	24.16	**40000**	0.185	5.54

Calculated from the data of Standard Atmosphere—Tables and Data for Altitudes to 65,800 Feet, NACA Report 1235, Washington, D. C., 1955, pp. 66-81.

TABLE 11—RELATIVE SPECIFIC GRAVITY OF AIR AT VARIOUS TEMPERATURES

Specific Gravity of Standard Air at 70°F = 1.00

t-°F	$\overline{SG}$	t-°F	$\overline{SG}$	t-°F	$\overline{SG}$	t-°F	$\overline{SG}$	t-°F	$\overline{SG}$
−10	1.178	**60**	1.019	**100**	.946	**200**	.803	**400**	.616
−5	1.165	**62**	1.015	**105**	.938	**210**	.791	**425**	.599
0	1.152	**64**	1.011	**110**	.930	**220**	.779	**450**	.582
5	1.140	**66**	1.008	**115**	.922	**230**	.768	**475**	.567
10	1.128	**68**	1.004	**120**	.914	**240**	.757	**500**	.552
15	1.116	**70**	1.000	**125**	.906	**250**	.747	**525**	.538
20	1.104	**72**	.996	**130**	.898	**260**	.736	**550**	.525
25	1.093	**74**	.992	**135**	.891	**270**	.726	**575**	.512
30	1.082	**76**	.989	**140**	.883	**280**	.716	**600**	.500
35	1.071	**78**	.985	**145**	.876	**290**	.707	**625**	.488
40	1.060	**80**	.982	**150**	.869	**300**	.697	**650**	.477
42	1.056	**82**	.978	**155**	.862	**310**	.688	**675**	.467
44	1.052	**84**	.974	**160**	.855	**320**	.680	**700**	.457
46	1.047	**86**	.971	**165**	.848	**330**	.671	**725**	.447
48	1.043	**88**	.967	**170**	.841	**340**	.662	**750**	.438
50	1.039	**90**	.964	**175**	.835	**350**	.654	**775**	.429
52	1.035	**92**	.960	**180**	.828	**360**	.646	**800**	.421
54	1.031	**94**	.957	**185**	.822	**370**	.638	**825**	.412
56	1.027	**96**	.953	**190**	.815	**380**	.631	**850**	.404
58	1.023	**98**	.950	**195**	.809	**390**	.624	**875**	.397

Psychrometric Measurements

With the aid of the appropriate psychrometric formulas or charts, the properties of an air-water vapor mixture may be completely defined from the dry-bulb temperature, wet-bulb temperature, and barometric pressure.

Barometers are of two types, mercurial and aneroid. An individual gage calibration must be used with aneroid barometers. Mercurial barometers give direct readings in inches of mercury. However, because of thermal expansion, the reading at any given pressure will vary with temperature to a slight degree. Corrections to the standard temperature of reference (32°F) may be made from Table 12. Theoretically, a latitude correction should be made to account for the difference in gravitational acceleration from the standard value of 32.174 ft/sec^2. Such a correction is negligibly small, as far as engineering calculations are concerned.

The U. S. Weather Bureau reports barometric pressures corrected to sea level conditions at 45° latitude. For calibration of personal data against Weather Bureau data, the same corrections must be applied to both sets of data. These corrections are tabulated in Tables 13 and 14.

TABLE 12—TEMPERATURE CORRECTIONS FOR BAROMETERS

(Use in all engineering calculations assuming brass scale is true at 62° F)

Temp. of Column	Observed reading of column in inches of mercury								
	16	18	20	22	24	26	28	30	32
°F	Add ("Hg)								
−20	0.07	0.08	0.09	0.10	0.11	0.11	0.12	0.13	0.14
−10	0.06	0.06	0.07	0.08	0.08	0.09	0.10	0.11	0.11
0	0.04	0.05	0.05	0.06	0.06	0.07	0.07	0.08	0.08
10	0.03	0.03	0.03	0.04	0.04	0.04	0.05	0.05	0.05
20	0.01	0.01	0.02	0.02	0.02	0.02	0.02	0.02	0.02
30	0.00	0.00	0.00	0.00	0.00	0.00	0.00	0.00	0.00
°F	Subtract ("Hg)								
35	0.01	0.01	0.01	0.01	0.01	0.01	0.02	0.02	0.02
40	0.02	0.02	0.02	0.02	0.02	0.03	0.03	0.03	0.03
45	0.02	0.03	0.03	0.03	0.04	0.04	0.04	0.04	0.05
50	0.03	0.03	0.04	0.04	0.05	0.05	0.05	0.06	0.06
55	0.04	0.04	0.05	0.05	0.06	0.06	0.07	0.07	0.08
60	0.05	0.05	0.06	0.06	0.07	0.07	0.08	0.08	0.09
65	0.05	0.06	0.07	0.07	0.08	0.09	0.09	0.10	0.10
70	0.06	0.07	0.07	0.08	0.09	0.10	0.10	0.11	0.12
75	0.07	0.07	0.08	0.09	0.10	0.11	0.12	0.13	0.13
80	0.07	0.08	0.09	0.10	0.11	0.12	0.13	0.14	0.15
85	0.08	0.09	0.10	0.11	0.12	0.13	0.14	0.15	0.16
90	0.09	0.10	0.11	0.12	0.13	0.14	0.15	0.17	0.18
95	0.10	0.11	0.12	0.13	0.14	0.16	0.17	0.18	0.19
100	0.10	0.12	0.13	0.14	0.15	0.17	0.18	0.19	0.20

Adapted from the data of Instruments and Apparatus, Part 2, Pressure Measurement, ASME Power Test Codes, PTC 19.2-1964, pp. 25-26.

TABLE 13—ELEVATION CORRECTIONS FOR BAROMETERS

(Use only for comparison of personal data with Weather Bureau data.)

Mean Altitude Ft.	Mean Atmospheric Temperature, °F						
	−20	0	20	40	60	80	100
	Subtract ("Hg/100')						
0	0.13	0.12	0.12	0.11	0.11	0.10	0.10
1000	0.12	0.12	0.11	0.11	0.10	0.10	0.10
2000	0.12	0.11	0.11	0.10	0.10	0.10	0.09
3000	0.11	0.11	0.10	0.10	0.10	0.09	0.09
4000	0.11	0.10	0.10	0.10	0.09	0.08	0.08
5000	0.10	0.10	0.10	0.09	0.09	0.08	0.08
6000	0.10	0.10	0.09	0.09	0.08	0.08	0.08
7000	0.10	0.09	0.09	0.09	0.08	0.08	0.08

Adapted from the data of Instruments and Apparatus, Part 2, Pressure Measurement, ASME Power Test Codes, PTC 19.2; 1, 6—1941, pp. 15-16.

TABLE 14—GRAVITY CORRECTIONS FOR BAROMETERS

(Negligible in engineering calculations)

North Latitude Degrees	Elevation, ft					
	0	2000	4000	6000	8000	10,000
	Add or subtract as indicated ("Hg)					
25	−0.05	−0.05	−0.05	−0.06	−0.06	−0.05
30	−0.04	−0.04	−0.05	−0.05	−0.05	−0.05
35	−0.03	−0.03	−0.03	−0.04	−0.04	−0.04
40	−0.02	−0.02	−0.02	−0.03	−0.03	−0.03
45	−0.00	−0.01	−0.01	−0.01	−0.02	−0.02
50	+0.01	+0.01	−0.00	−0.00	−0.01	−0.01

Adapted from the data of Instruments and Apparatus, Part 2, Pressure Measurement, ASME Power Test Codes, PTC 19.2; 1, 6—1941, pp. 15-16.

Temperatures may be measured with a variety of instruments. The most common, liquid-in-glass thermometers, may employ various liquids depending on the working range:

Material	*Working Range in °F*
Mercury	− 30 to 925
Alcohol	−100 to 250
Toluol	−150 to 200
Pentane	−300 to 70

Calibrated instruments may be read directly with sufficient accuracy for most engineering work. When only partially immersed, precautions must be taken to insure that heat conduction due to emergent stem is negligible or is accounted for. Figure 13 may be used to determine the necessary correction. In making average temperature determinations, make sure that the sample or samples are representative. Such determinations in a moving gas stream should be weighted according to mass flow. If a gas

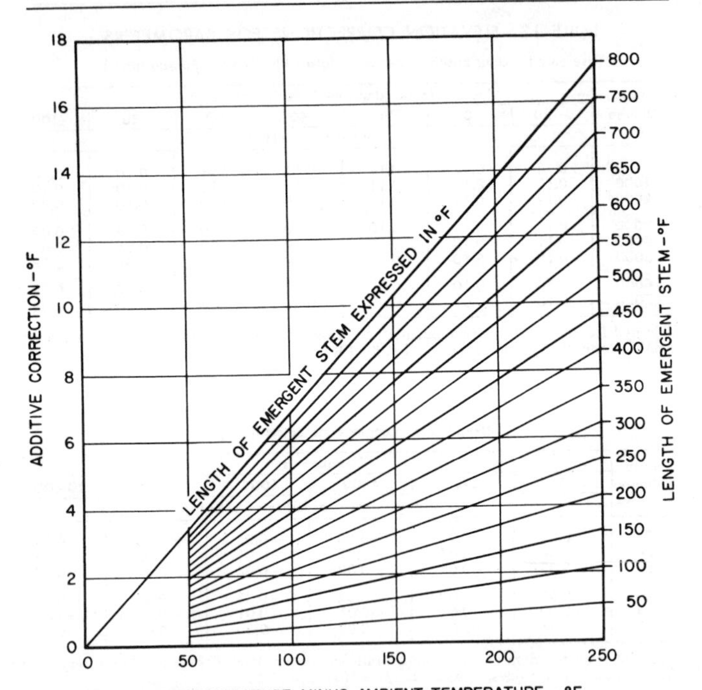

Figure 13—Emergent Stem Corrections for Mercury in Glass Thermometers

Adapted from the data of Instruments and Apparatus, Part 3, Temperature Measurement, ASME Power Test Codes, PTC 19.3-1961, p. 49.

stream and its retaining walls are at different temperatures, the thermometer should be shielded to eliminate radiation effects.

Resistance thermometers which determine temperature by measuring the change in resistance of a calibrated wire can be extremely accurate and suitable for temperatures from −400 to 1800°F.

When two dissimilar metal wires are joined together as in a thermocouple, the difference in temperature between the junction and the opposite ends produces an emf, the magnitude of which is a function of temperature difference. Combinations of metals which give nearly straight line relationships between emf and temperature are iron-constantan, copper-constantan, chromel-alumel, and platinum-platinum (87%) rhodium (13%). Very good accuracy is obtained by measuring the emf with a potentiometer and reading the corresponding temperature from calibration tables.

For measuring very high temperatures, pyrometers of either the radiation or optical types give reasonably accurate readings.

Wet-bulb temperatures may be obtained in the same manner as dry-bulb temperatures except that the bulb must be kept wet. As indicated in the discussion on the temperature of adiabatic saturation, both gas velocity and radiation from surroundings affect wet-bulb readings. The reading from an unshielded wet-bulb thermometer in an air stream at 800 or 900 feet per minute is accurate to within about 0.5% according to Carrier and Mackey*. A sling psychrometer can easily be whirled at speeds sufficient to produce this velocity past the bulb. Aspiration psychrometers which utilize tiny fans to produce a uniform circulation of air over the thermometer bulbs are available. Whenever the wet-bulb is shielded, it will yield a temperature slightly lower than the temperature of adiabatic saturation. In most cases this can be disregarded, but for accuracy a correction should be made, the value of which depends upon the velocity of air over the bulbs. There may be a 5% error in the wet-bulb depression if the velocity is 800 or 900 fpm. That is, up to 5% of the wet-bulb depression may have to be added to the observed wet-bulb reading to obtain the true temperature of adiabatic saturation.

If a thermometer is dipped in water and used to record wet-bulb temperatures below 32°, it will first indicate the wet-bulb temperature over sub-cooled water. When freezing begins, the temperature will return to and remain at 32° until freezing is completed. The thermometer will then ultimately register the wet-bulb temperature over ice after equilibrium is obtained and until the ice is all evaporated.

Psychrometric Processes

The various psychrometric processes include heating, cooling, humidifying, dehumidifying, and various combinations of these heat and moisture exchanges. All of these processes may be depicted on a psychrometric chart. As illustrated in Figure 14, the most common are:

1—Sensible heating by contact with a warm surface.

2—Heating and humidifying with warm sprays.

3—Evaporative cooling and humidifying with recirculated sprays.

4—Cooling and dehumidifying by contact with a cold surface (1st portion of curve—surface above dew point, 2nd portion of curve—surface below dew point).

5—Cooling and dehumidifying with cold sprays.

6—Dehumidifying (and heating) by absorption.

7—Dehumidifying (and heating) by adsorption.

*W. H. Carrier and C. O. Mackey, A Review of Existing Psychrometric Data in Relation to Practical Engineering Problems, *Trans. ASME*, vol. 59, paper PRO-59-1, pp. 33-47, 1937.

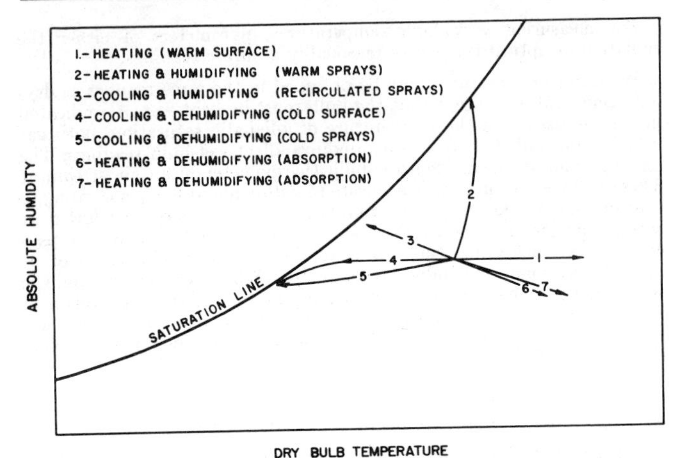

Figure 14—Psychrometric Processes

Another important psychrometric process is that of mixing two quantities $(w_1 + w_2)$ of air. If the specific heats of both vapor and dry air are assumed to be constant, a heat balance gives the dry-bulb temperature of any mixture (t_3) where there is no condensation, as:

$$t_3 = \frac{w_1 t_1 + w_2 t_2 + \frac{(c_p)_v}{(c_p)_a}(w_1 H_1 t_1 + w_2 H_2 t_2)}{w_1 + w_2 + \frac{(c_p)_v}{(c_p)_a}(w_1 H_1 + w_2 H_2)} \tag{38}$$

In most engineering work, a further simplification is justified. If the combined specific heats for all air-water vapor combinations are assumed to be equal,

$$t_3 = \frac{w_1 t_1 + w_2 t_2}{w_1 + w_2} \text{ (very closely).} \tag{39}$$

The humidity of the mixture (H_3) may be determined exactly from:

$$H_3 = \frac{w_1 H_1 + w_2 H_2}{w_1 + w_2} \text{ (exactly).} \tag{40}$$

These last two equations indicate that if the original state points (t_1,H_1) and (t_2,H_2) were spotted on the usual psychrometric chart and connected by a straight line, the combined state (t_3,H_3) would fall on that line.

Some obvious conclusions which may be drawn concerning combinations are: (1) when states 1 and 2 are dry, the mixture will be dry, (2) when states 1 and 2 have the same dew point, the mixture will have the same dew point, (3) when states 1 and 2 have the same dry-bulb, the mixture will have the same dry-bulb, (4) when states 1 and 2 have the same wet-bulb temperature, the mixture will have approximately the same wet-bulb temperature and the sigma functions for all three will be approximately the same, (5) when states 1 and 2 have the same relative humidity, the mixture will have a higher relative humidity, (6) when states 1 and 2 both lie on the saturation curve, the mixture will theoretically lie in the supersaturated zone to the left of the saturation curve. This is an unstable condition which will eventually lead to condensation of moisture. The resultant mixture will then consist of saturated air and liquid water. For this case the weight of condensate (H_c) must be subtracted in Equation 40, thus:

$$H_4 = \frac{w_1 H_1 + w_2 H_2}{w_1 + w_2} - H_c. \tag{41}$$

A heat balance indicates that:

$$\frac{w_1 (c_p)_{m1} t_1 + w_2 (c_p)_{m2} t_2}{w_1 + w_2} = (c_p)_{m4} t_4 + H_c \lambda \tag{42}$$

There is only one temperature of the mixture (t_4) that will satisfy both Equation 41 and 42, but it can be found only by trial.

CHAPTER 2

HEAT TRANSMISSION

Heat may be transferred from one region to another by conduction, convection, radiation, or various combinations of these three mechanisms. The direction of heat flow will be from the region which has the higher temperature to that which has the lower temperature. The region which emits the energy is called a heat source while the receiving region is called a heat sink. Whether one or another of the three mechanisms will predominate in a situation will depend on the space relations and the temperature difference between source and sink.

Radiation involves the net transfer of radiant energy between separated bodies. Such transfer does not require a connecting medium. Radiant energy is propagated as a wave motion from all bodies in all directions. Although there is energy transfer in both directions between a hot and a cold body, the heat source emits more energy than it absorbs, and the sink absorbs more than it emits.

Conduction involves the net transfer of molecular energy within a body by physical contact. Such transfer may also be achieved by bringing together two distinctly separate bodies. The bodies may both be solids or fluids, or one of each. Conduction within a single fluid is accompanied by convection.

Convection involves the net transfer of thermal energy within a fluid by mixing action. Convection or mixing may occur naturally due to buoyancy, or it may be forced as with a fan or pump.

In practical applications heat transfer always occurs as some combination of radiation, convection, and conduction, but it is convenient for both study and computations to separate these effects.

Thermal Conductivity

All solids, liquids, and gases resist the conduction of heat through them. In general, gases are the poorest conductors, and some solids the best. The thermal conductivity (k) is a measure of the ease with which heat will pass through a material by conduction. This quantity varies with temperature, but only little with pressure. Its variation over a limited temperature range is generally linear; therefore, in most engineering applications the average value should be taken as that at the average temperature. If the thermal conductivity (k) is divided by the actual thickness (x) of a material, the result (k/x) is known as the thermal conductance of that thickness of material. The reciprocal of the conductance is known as the resistance (r or x/k) of that thickness of material. Most of the good heat conductors are metals. Thermal conductivities and other properties for a variety of metals and alloys are given in Table 15.

TABLE 15—THERMAL PROPERTIES OF METALS AND ALLOYS

Metal or Alloy	t °F	δ $\frac{lb}{in^3}$	k $\frac{Btu\text{-}in.}{hr\text{-}ft^2\text{-}°F}$	c_p $\frac{Btu}{lb\text{-}°F}$
Aluminum Alloys				
1100-H18	77	.098	1510	.23
2024-T3	77	.100	840	.23
3003-H38	77	.099	1070	.23
5052-H38	77	.097	960	.23
5086-H34	77	.096	870	.23
6061-T6	77	.098	1070	.23
7075-T6	77	.101	840	.23
Copper Alloys				
pure Copper	68	.324	2730	.092
deoxidized Copper	68	.323	2350	.092
commercial Bronze	68	.318	1310	.09
red Brass	68	.316	1100	.09
Muntz Metal	68	.303	843	.09
Naval Brass	68	.304	803	.09
Admiralty Metal	68	.308	768	.09
Silicon Bronze	68	.308	252	.09
Nickel Alloys				
pure Nickel	77	.322	637	.112
Monel	32-212	.319	173	.127
"K" Monel	32-212	.306	130	.127
Inconel 600	70	.304	103	.106
Inconel X750	70	.298	83	.103
Hastelloy B	77	.334	78	.091
Hastelloy C	77	.323	87	.092
Hastelloy D	77	.282	145	.109
Miscellaneous Metals				
pure Lead	68-212	.41	240	.031
lead Babbitt	68	.36	168	.036
pure Magnesium	64	.063	1100	.25
pure Tin	32	.208	465	.05
Titanium	77	.163	105	.13
pure Zinc	77	.258	785	.091
Iron				
wrought	212	.28	410	.12
cast	212	.28	332	.12
pure	212	.284	440	.12
Steel				
1006	32	.284	410	.115
1006	932		284	.158
1040	32	.284	360	.116
1040	932		263	.155
Stainless Steel				
301, 302, 303, 304, 316, 317	212	.29	113	.12
	932		149	
309, 310	212	.29	96	.12
	932		130	
321, 349	212	.29	112	.12
	932		154	
403, 410, 414, 416, 420	212	.28	173	.11
	932		199	
430	212	.28	181	.11
501, 502	212	.28	255	.11
Non-Metals:				
Insulators, Refer Table 16				
Building Materials, Refer Chapter 15				
Miscellaneous, Refer Appendix				

Adapted from the data of S. L. Hoyt, "Metals Properties," *ASME Handbook*, McGraw-Hill Book Co., Inc., New York, 1954.

TABLE 16—THERMAL PROPERTIES OF INSULATING MATERIALS

Material	Description	δ lb/ft³	k Btu-in./hr-ft²-°F	t °F
RIGID				
Aerocor	Glass fiber material	4-26	.21-.56	50°-300°
Air Cell[1]	Corrugated asbestos paper	8.8	.50	
Armaglas Block	Glass fiber block	9.0	.23	75°
Armatemp Block	Mineral wool fiber block	21	.46-.57	400°-600°
Armstrong Corkboard	Baked granulated cork	.6 lb/ft²	.22-.28	(−80°)-160°
Asbestolux Board	Asbestos fiber and silica	42-44	.75	——
Asbestos, laminated[5]	....	22	.45	100°
Asbestos sheet[2]	....	48.3	.29	——
Balsa Wood[1]	Across grain, very light to medium	7.1-8.8	.31-.38	——
Banroc Board	Blended mineral fiber with moisture resisting binder	15	.34-.37	50°-150°
Careycell[8]	Asbestos board	15.72	.33-.53	50°-300°
Celotex[1]	Cane fiber boards	13.2	.34	——
Crete, all-weather	Volcanic glass	15-24	.42-.46	——
Featherweight Pipe Insulation	85% Magnesia, 10% asbestos fibers	13.3	.36-.42	100°-300°
Ferro-Therm[3]	Sheet iron, space ½"	——	.23	——
Fiberboards, glass[5]	Fiberglas PF	2	.248	50°
Fiberfrax	Ceramic fiber	6	.20-1.4	100°-1300°
Fiberglas[5]	With asphalt coating	11	.22	0°
Fiberglas XB-PF[5]	....	0.5	.245	50°
Fibrocel Pipe Insulation	Molded silica	9	.34-.41	50°-200°
Foamglas	Glass with sponge-like interstices	9	.35-.55	0°-300°
Frigiboard	Bonded mineral wool fibers	——	.262-.35	10°-100°
Impervo[8]	Laminated felt	17.45	.27-.37	50°-200°
Insulite, Graylite Group	Pressed wood pulp sheathing	19.5	.37	——
Insulite, Ins-Lite Group	Pressed wood pulp, boards and planks	17	.35	——
Jointite	Corkboard	8	.27-.29	30°-60°
K&M Bestfelt Lamino Sponge Pipe Insulation	Crimped asbestos felt, bonded with adhesive	30	.34-.54	100°-500°
K&M Simplex Super Shrunk Pipe Insulation	Bonded layers of corrugated and flat asbestos felt	——	.511-.607	100°-200°
Koldboard[11]	Felted, bonded spun mineral wool fibers	15	.262-.322	0°-100°
Maftex[3]	Pressed licorice root	16.1	.34	——
Maizewood	Rigid insulation of cornstalk	15.0	.33	——
Marinite 23 (sheets)	Asbestos fiber, diatomaceous silica and inorganic binder	21-25	.55-.63	100°-600°
Masonite[3]	Rigid insulation of wood fiber	19.8	.33	——
Masonite, Quarterboard	Rigid insulation of wood fiber	35.6	.53	——
Mineral Wool Blocks and Boards	Low temperature: asphalt or resin bonded	6-18	.28-.31	40°-100°
Mineral Wool Blocks and Boards	High temperature: with organic binder	14-24	.34-.64	100°-700°

TABLE 16 (Cont.)—THERMAL PROPERTIES OF INSULATING MATERIALS

Material	Description	δ lb/ft³	k Btu-in./hr-ft²-°F	t °F
Nu-Wood[3]	Rigid insulation of wood fibers	15.0	.32	—
Perfecto[8]	Organic felt, asbestos and canvas	16.7	.27-.35	50°-200°
Phenolic Resin Foam	....	2.0	.24	—
Protecto[8]	Hair felt and wool felt	14.9	.26-.32	50°-200°
Rock Cork	Mineral wool block with asphaltic binder	15	.27-.35	(−40°)-150°
Rubatex Insulation Hardboard	Expanded synthetic rubber	4.5	.21	70°
Sonoairduct[7]	Laminated fiberboard with aluminum foil	38.7	.47-.54	80°-180°
Styrofoam	Multicellular expanded polystyrene	1.3-2.3	.25-.28	room temp.
Superex	Calcined diatomaceous silica and asbestos fiber	10-12	.33-.63	100°-700°
Tectum[4]	Wood fiber with hydraulic cement binder	19.1	.474-.532	0°-100°
Teflon-coated glass fabric	....	—	.12-.27	—
Temlok[3]	Rigid insulation of wood fiber	15.0	.33	—
Thermalite	Magnesium carbonate plus asbestos fibers	11	.36-.60	100°-300°
Thermax[3]	Shredded wood and cement	24.2	.46	—
Thermobestos Blocks	Hydrous calcium silicate with asbestos fiber	10-12	.33-.60	100°-700°
Thermotex[3]	Rigid insulation of wood fiber	8.5	.30	—
Tricalite	Hydrous calcium silicate with asbestos fibers	12	.415-.690	200°-900°
Ultralite	....	.75-3.0	.22-.25	—
Unibestos[3, 6]	Asbestos fiber	15-18	.35-.75	100°-850°
Wallboard[1]	Stiff pasteboard	43.3	.50	—
Zerolite	Mineral wool block with thermoset resin binder	15	.27-.33	(−90°)-150°
SEMI-RIGID				
Eagle-Picher LTG Mineral Wool Felt[6, 9]	Mineral wool in felted form with binder	6	.22-.27	20°-120°
Fibrofelt[1]	Flax and rye fiber	13.6	.32	—
Flaxlinum[1]	Flax fiber	13.0	.31	—
Hair felt	Felted cattle hair	13.0	.26	—
Mono-Block	Felted spun mineral wool	15	.35-.90	200°-1200°
Spintex	Mineral wool air conditioning duct	6.5	.24-.28	50°-120°
FLEXIBLE				
Alfol	Multiple aluminum foil sheets	—	.221	—
Armaflex	Foamed plastic pipe insulation	—	.28	75°
Armatemp Blanket	Felted layers of mineral wool	10.0	.50-.66	400°-600°
Balsam Wool[1]	Wool fiber between paper	2.2	.27	—
B-H Spun Felt	Felted and bonded spun mineral wool	3	.25-.53	100°-450°
Cabot's Quilt[1]	Eel grass between Kraft paper	3.4	.25	—

TABLE 16 (Cont.)—THERMAL PROPERTIES OF INSULATING MATERIALS

Material	Description	δ $\frac{lb}{ft^3}$	k $\frac{Btu\text{-}in.}{hr\text{-}ft^2\text{-}°F}$	t °F
Cardinal	Felt of cattle hair and jute fiber	7.5	.24	——
Cellulose sponge[5]	....	2.2	.40	86°
Fine-Fyber Felt	Mineral fibers with resin binder	1	.22-.34	60°-240°
Flextite	Spun Felt (Mundet)	4	.24-.27	45°-95°
Flotofoam[5]	Rubber block	1.6	.20	92°
Kapok[1]	Hollow vegetable fiber loosely packed	.9	.24	——
Kimsul	Impregnated wood fibers	1.4	.27	——
Lo-"K"	Cotton Blankets (or Batt)	7-8	.24	——
Mineral Wool Blanket	Mineral wool reinforced with confining media	6-15	.29-.63	100°-600°
Mineral Wool Felt	Mineral wool with binder added and felted into flexible rolls	.5-3	.22-.45	10°-300°
Mono-Kover Pipe Insulation	Mineral wool fibers bonded with phenolic resin	3.5	.23-.31	100°-300°
Ozite Standard	Cattle hair felt	7.5	.24	——
Palco Wool	Redwood fiber	5.0	.17-.28	(−120°)-85°
Spongex Molded Cell-Tite	Sponge rubber	15-20	.28	75°
Tufflex	Felted, bonded cellulose fibers	2-4	.24	——
LOOSE FILL, BATT, OR SPRAY				
Amosite	Loose asbestos fiber	1	.21	75°
Armaglas TW-F Wood	....	3.0	.25	75°
Asbestos Wool	....	5.16	.317	——
Banroc	Spun mineral fiber	9	.28-.64	100°-600°
Calicel[3]	Silicate of lime and alumina	4.2	.24	——
Eagle-Picher Loose Wool	Loose mineral wool	7-8	.3-.96	100°-800°
Glass Wool[3]	Fibrous, 25 to 30 microns diameter	1.5	.27	——
Gypsum	Flaked, dry and fluffy	24.0	.48	——
Mineral Wool[3]	Loosely packed	19.0	.27	——
Poly-Cell	Isocyanate resin, foamed-in-place insulation	3-5 appr.	.21	75°
Regranulated Cork[1]	About 3/16 inch particles	8.1	.31	——
Rock Wool[1]	Fibrous material made from rock	14.0	.28	——
Santocel	Silica aerogel	8-8.5	.10-.30	(−115°)-500°
Sawdust or Shavings	....	12.5/8.7	.41	——
Silica[5]	Finely ground	50	.54	600°
Silica[5]	Gel	32.5	.59	131°
Sloss[10]	Mineral wool batts	3.1-5.3	.23-.26	79°-76°
Sprayo Flake[1]	Shredded paper with silica binder	4.2	.28	——

TABLE 16 (Concluded)—THERMAL PROPERTIES OF INSULATING MATERIALS

Material	Description	δ lb/ft³	k Btu-in./hr-ft²-°F	t °F
Vermiculite	Expanded magnesium-aluminum-iron silicate	6.2	.32	—
Wool, pure[1]	...	5.0	.26	—

REFERENCES FOR TABLE OF HEAT INSULATING MATERIALS

1. U. S. Bureau of Standards
2. A. C. Willard, University of Illinois
3. J. C. Peebles, Armour Research Foundation
4. F. B. Rowley, University of Minnesota
5. G. B. Wilkes, "Heat Insulation," John Wiley & Sons, Inc., New York, 1950
6. Purdue University
7. J. F. Sutton, Clemson College
8. Mellon Institute of Industrial Research
9. G. B. Wilkes, Massachusetts Institute of Technology
10. Southern Research Institute
11. Pittsburgh Testing Laboratory

Note: The data for all other brand name materials in this table were obtained from their manufacturers.

TABLE 17

CONDUCTANCE OF AIR SPACES AT VARIOUS MEAN TEMPERATURES

In Btu per hr-ft²-°F

Mean Temp. °F	Width of Air Space in Inches						
	.128	.250	.364	.493	.713	1.00	1.50
20	2.300	1.370	1.180	1.100	1.040	1.030	1.022
30	2.385	1.425	1.234	1.148	1.080	1.070	1.065
40	2.470	1.480	1.288	1.193	1.125	1.112	1.105
50	2.560	1.535	1.340	1.242	1.168	1.152	1.149
60	2.650	1.590	1.390	1.295	1.210	1.195	1.188
70	2.730	1.648	1.440	1.340	1.250	1.240	1.228
80	2.819	1.702	1.492	1.390	1.295	1.280	1.270
90	2.908	1.757	1.547	1.433	1.340	1.320	1.310
100	2.990	1.813	1.600	1.486	1.380	1.362	1.350
110	3.078	1.870	1.650	1.534	1.425	1.402	1.392
120	3.167	1.928	1.700	1.580	1.467	1.445	1.435
130	3.250	1.980	1.750	1.630	1.510	1.485	1.475
140	3.340	2.035	1.800	1.680	1.550	1.530	1.519
150	3.425	2.090	1.852	1.728	1.592	1.569	1.559

Adapted from the data of F. B. Rowley and A. B. Algren, "Thermal Resistances of Air Spaces," *Trans. ASHVE*, vol. 35, pp. 165-181, 1929.

Poor conductors or materials with high thermal resistance are known as insulators. Thermal conductivity values for a variety of insulation materials are given in Table 16. It will be noticed that the apparent densities are quite low. These materials are all fibrous or cellular with a high percentage of voids. The listed values are for air-filled voids, and such values can be decreased by using a higher molecular weight gas.*

Additional thermal conductivity values may be found in the heat exchanger chapter where tables are given for both liquids and gases, and in the Appendix for miscellaneous materials. Conductances for building materials and built-up walls, etc., are listed in various tables of the air conditioning chapter.

The conductances of various air spaces are given in Table 17. The values are listed for various mean temperatures and widths. The reference temperature is the mean temperature of the air between surfaces, not the mean wall temperature. Increases in the width over 1″ have very little effect. The effects of surface emissivity and direction of heat flow are not shown.

Steady Conduction

The rate of total heat exchange (TH) across a thickness of material (x) may be determined from

$$TH = kA\Delta t/x. \tag{43}$$

The proportionality factor (k) may be recognized as the thermal conductivity of the material and the fraction (k/x) as the thermal conductance for thickness (x). The area (A) is that which is normal to the flow of heat. This area depends on the relative shapes and amounts of inside (A_i) or outside surface area (A_o) as indicated by:

$$A = A_i = A_o \quad \textit{for parallel flat surfaces,} \tag{44}$$

$$A = (A_i - A_o)/ln(A_i/A_o) \quad \textit{for concentric cylindrical surfaces, and} \tag{45}$$

$$A = \sqrt{A_iA_o} \quad \textit{for concentric spherical surfaces.} \tag{46}$$

Approximate results may be obtained for any other shape by using the average area.

The temperature difference (Δt) must be constant for steady conduction. It is the difference in temperature between points separated by the thickness (x). Where x is the total thickness of the wall, the temperature difference is that between the two surface temperatures.

Film Coefficients

When heat is transferred to a fluid from a solid or vice versa, the process is one of conduction plus convection. The total heat transfer rate may be expressed in an equation similar to that for steady conduction:

$$TH = hA\Delta t. \tag{47}$$

The proportionality factor (h) is known as the local film coefficient of heat transfer. This factor varies with certain physical properties of both the fluid and the heat transfer system. The area (A) is that of contact

*R. M. Lander, Gas is an Important Factor in the Thermal Conductivity of Most Insulating Materials, *Trans. ASHVE*, vol. 61, pp. 151-168, 1955.

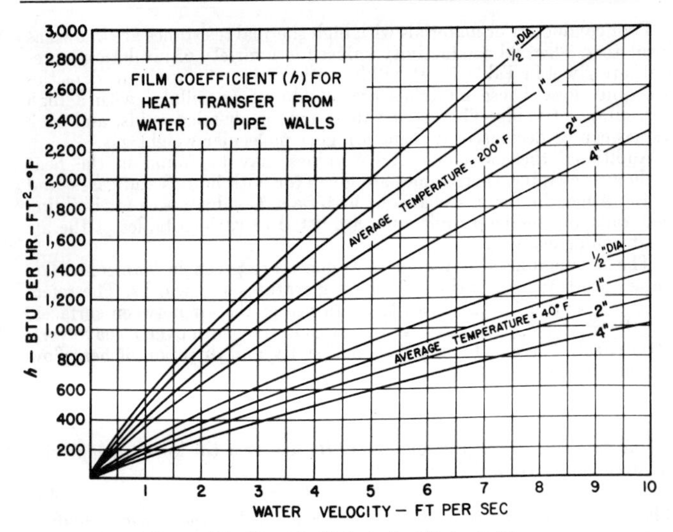

Figure 15—Film Coefficients for Water in Pipes

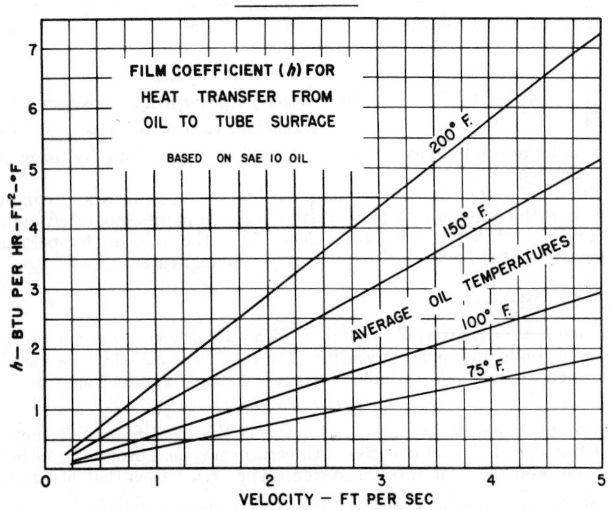

Figure 16—Film Coefficients for Oil in Pipes

between the fluid and solid, and the temperature difference (Δt) that across the film. This temperature difference is the same as the difference between the surface temperature and the bulk fluid temperature. Dimensional analysis* of any heating or cooling process involving a fluid flowing at a mass velocity (G) without a change of phase indicates that the Nusselt number is a function of Reynolds number and of Prandtl number as indicated by:

$$\frac{hD}{k} = \varphi \left(\frac{DG}{\mu}\right)^n \left(\frac{c_p\mu}{k}\right)^m \quad (48)$$

The characteristic dimension (D) of the system is usually a diameter. The coefficient (φ) and the exponents (n) and (m) depend on the temperature at which the physical properties (k), (μ), and (c_p) are evaluated and the geometry of the system as indicated in the following paragraphs. When the local temperature varies, the local film coefficient also varies. Average values are determined for the average condition.

Any consistent set of units may be used in most of the equations which follow. Specific units are listed for the dimensional equations except Equations 50, 54, and 55 which are based on h in Btu/hr-ft^2-°F, c_p in Btu/lb-°F, G in lb/hr-ft^2, and d in inches.

Heating and Cooling Fluids Inside Tubes

If the various physical properties of the fluid are evaluated at the bulk temperature (t)

$$\frac{h_iD_i}{k} = .023 \left(\frac{D_iG_i}{\mu}\right)^{.8} \left(\frac{c_p\mu}{k}\right)^{.4} \quad (49)$$

for turbulent flow inside (Subscript i) clean tubes. This expression can be simplified by utilizing the average properties of most gases:

$$h_i = .024\ c_pG_i^{.8}/d_i^{.2}. \quad (50)$$

The method outlined in Chapter 19 for evaluating film coefficients for liquids is recommended. The variation of film coefficient with velocity is shown for water in Figure 15 and for a viscous oil in Figure 16. A comparison of these two figures illustrates the effect of physical properties.

Heating and Cooling Fluids Outside Tubes

If the various physical properties of the fluid are evaluated at the film temperature (t_f), Equation 48 becomes

$$\frac{h_oD_o}{k_f} = .33 \left(\frac{D_oG_{max}}{\mu_f}\right)^{.6} \left(\frac{c_p\mu}{k}\right)_f^{.33} \quad (51)$$

for turbulent flow outside (Subscript o) tubes.

The film temperature (t_f) may be assumed to be the average of the bulk fluid temperature (t) and the surface temperature of the tube wall (t_w) as calculated by

$$t_f = \frac{t + t_w}{2}. \quad (52)$$

In the case of fluids in turbulent flow over single tubes, Equation 51 may be simplified to

$$\frac{h_oD_o}{k_f} = .24 \left(\frac{D_oG}{\mu_f}\right)^{.6} \quad (53)$$

---

*Refer to Appendix 1 for discussion of dimensional analysis.

Further simplification yields

$$h_o = .30\ c_p G^{.6}/d_o^{.4} \tag{54}$$

for gases over single tubes. Similarly, the film coefficient for gases over a bank of tubes may be obtained from

$$h_o = .36\ c_p G_{max}^{.6}/d_o^{.4}. \tag{55}$$

Natural Convection

Whenever a temperature difference (Δt) in °F exists between a surface and its surrounding atmosphere, natural convection currents are induced and heat transfer occurs by conduction and convection, as well as by radiation. The film coefficient (h_N) in Btu/hr-ft²-°F for air over horizontal pipes or long vertical pipes of diameter (d) in in. may be obtained from

$$h_N = .5\ [\Delta t/d]^{.25}. \tag{56}$$

The film coefficient for natural convection in air over flat plates varies with orientation and heated length (l) in in. For heated horizontal plates facing upward or cooled horizontal plates facing downward,

$$h_N = .5\ [\Delta t/l]^{.25}. \tag{57}$$

For heated horizontal plates facing downward or cooled horizontal plates facing upward,

$$h_N = .22\ [\Delta t/l]^{.25}. \tag{58}$$

For vertical plates more than approximately one foot high,

$$h_N = .19\ \Delta t^{.33}. \tag{59}$$

For heating coils submerged in water,

$$h_N = 28\ [\Delta t/d]^{.25}. \tag{60}$$

All equations are based on a laminar boundary layer except Equation 59.

Condensing Vapors

There are two major kinds of heat transfer involving condensation of vapors: (1) where only latent heat is transferred on the vapor side, as in heaters and condensers, and (2) where both sensible and latent heat are transferred on the vapor side, as in dehumidifiers discussed below. In both cases latent heat transfer takes place only at the surface unless there is fogging. The only resistance is that offered by the film of liquid condensate. Equation 47 may be rewritten to express the rate of transfer (LH) as

$$LH = h_L A \Delta t_L, \tag{61}$$

in which (Δt_L) is the mean difference between the saturation temperature (t_{sat}) and the surface temperature (t_w) of the tube. High liquid film coefficient (h_L) values may be obtained with so-called dropwise condensation, where most of the latent heat is transferred directly to the surface. Somewhat lower values are obtained with film-type condensation, where all of the latent heat must be transferred through the liquid film. Even with promoters, dropwise condensation is unstable so that designs are usually based on film-type condensation data. Whether the tubes are oriented horizontally or vertically makes a difference, as indicated by

$$\frac{h_L D}{k} = .76\ [D^3 \rho^2 g/\mu_f \Gamma_H]^{.33} \text{ and} \tag{62}$$

$$\frac{h_L L}{k} = .93\ [L^3 \rho^2 g/\mu_f \Gamma_V]^{.33}, \tag{63}$$

which are for horizontal and vertical arrangements respectively. The tube loading (Γ) may be determined from the mass rate (m_c) of vapor condensed per tube and the diameter (D) or length (L):

$$\Gamma_H = m_c/2L, \text{ or} \tag{64}$$

$$\Gamma_V = m_c/\pi D. \tag{65}$$

Typical values of liquid film coefficients are listed in Chapter 19, where a design method based on the above formulas is also presented.

Dehumidifying and Cooling Air-Vapor Mixtures

Although the transfer of the latent heat of condensation is not resisted by any air film on the vapor side of the tube wall, it is resisted, however slightly, by the condensate film. Any simultaneous sensible heat transfer is resisted by both the liquid and air films. Since gas film resistance is so much greater, the liquid film resistance to sensible heat transfer is completely ignored. The assertion in Chapter 15 that there is no resistance to condensation at a surface is true only if the surface is continuously condensate-free, but it yields completely satisfactory results in most air conditioning problems. For the usual dehumidifying coil, the steady state film coefficient (h) may be increased by the ratio of total to sensible heat (TH/SH). Rewriting Equation 47 gives

$$TH \approx \left(\frac{TH}{SH} h\right) A\Delta t, \tag{66}$$

in which the film coefficient (h), neglecting the liquid film, may be determined from Equation 55, and the temperature difference (Δt) is the mean difference between the temperature of the wall (t_w) and that of the bulk fluid (t).

Evaporating Liquids

As observed in Chapter 1, vapors form over their liquids or solids until equilibrium is obtained. The rate of evaporation from a water surface (w_v) in lb per hr, as indicated by Figure 17 and the following equations, varies with the latent heat of vaporization (λ_v) in Btu per lb, the nature and velocity (V) in fpm of air flow, and with the degree of saturation as represented by the difference in vapor pressures ($e_w - e_a$) in "Hg, as well as with the amount of exposed water surface (S) in sq ft:

$$w_v = S\,\frac{95 + .425V}{\lambda_v}\,(e_w - e_a) \text{ for parallel flow, and} \tag{67}$$

$$w_v = S\,\frac{201 + .88V}{\lambda_v}\,(e_w - e_a) \text{ for transverse flow.} \tag{68}$$

To obtain λ_v and e_w read the appropriate values opposite the dry-bulb temperature in Figure 4 and the water temperature in Table 3 respectively. To obtain e_a read Table 3 value opposite the dry-bulb temperature and multiply by relative humidity as indicated in Equation 33.

Water in contact with air tends to assume the wet-bulb temperature of the air. Equilibrium at this temperature is achieved quite rapidly in

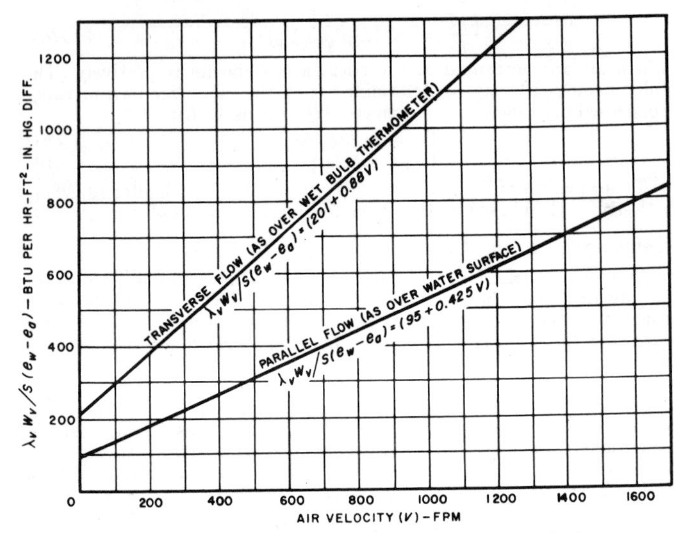

Figure 17—Heat Rates for Evaporation From a Water Surface

Adapted from the data of W. H. Carrier, The Temperature of Evaporation, *Trans. ASHVE*, vol. 24, pp. 25-50, 1918, p. 38.

---

an air washer or similar device where the water is continually mixed and large amounts of surface are exposed to the air. Under such conditions the rate of evaporation is substantially proportional to the wet-bulb depression, since the vapor pressure difference $(e_w - e_a)$ is practically proportional to the difference in wet- and dry-bulb temperatures of the air.

A container of water will assume a temperature somewhere between the wet- and dry-bulb temperatures, the exact value depending upon the amount of free surface relative to the amount of containing surface. Equilibrium at the wet-bulb temperature is not achieved because sensible heat is transferred through the container walls, neutralizing some of the sensible cooling which accompanies evaporation. The rate of evaporation will be approximately proportional to the difference in temperatures of the water and the air in contact with the water surface.

Boiling Liquids

Boiling heat transfer may be accomplished with or without a net generation of vapor depending on specific conditions. When there is no net generation of vapor because of recondensation in the cold surrounding liquid, the process is known as "local boiling" or "surface boiling." Very high heat transfer rates can be produced with submerged heater surface if local boiling can be achieved. Both "nucleate" and "film

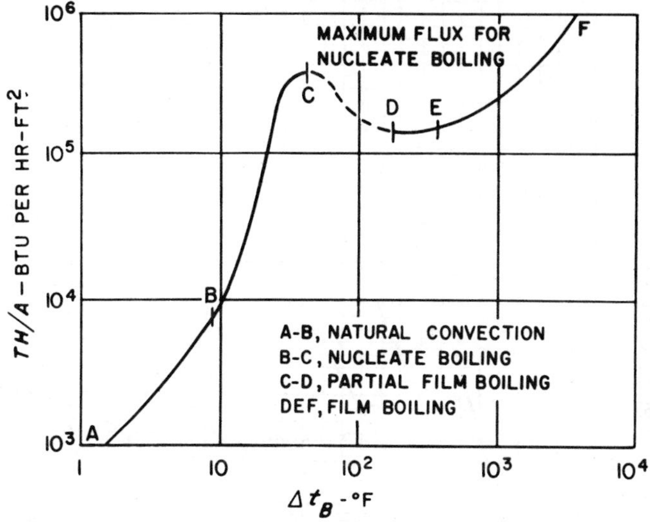

Figure 18—Boiling Flux for Water at 212°F

Adapted from the data of W. H. McAdams, "Heat Transmission, "McGraw-Hill Book Co., Inc., New York, 1954, p. 370.

boiling" take place with the liquid at the saturation temperature and therefore produce a net generation of vapor. For these cases Equation 47 can be rewritten as

$$TH = h_B A \Delta t_B, \tag{69}$$

in which (Δt_B) is the mean temperature difference between the temperature of saturation and that of the wall. This temperature difference is usually combined with the boiling coefficient and designated as "heat flux," expressed by rewriting Equation 69 as

$$h_B \Delta t_B = TH/A. \tag{70}$$

Figure 18 gives the boiling heat flux for water versus temperature difference.

Over-all Coefficients

Rewriting Equation 47 for the over-all heat transfer between two fluids separated by a wall of area (A) produces

$$TH = UA\Delta t_m = U_o A_o \Delta t_m = U_i A_i \Delta t_m. \tag{71}$$

The over-all coefficient of heat transfer (U) may be expressed in terms of outside area (U_o for A_o) or inside area (U_i for A_i) as indicated. The temperature difference (Δt_m) is the mean difference between the two fluids. The over-all coefficient (U) is the conductance of a wall; hence its reciprocal is the resistance of that wall. The over-all resistance of any wall

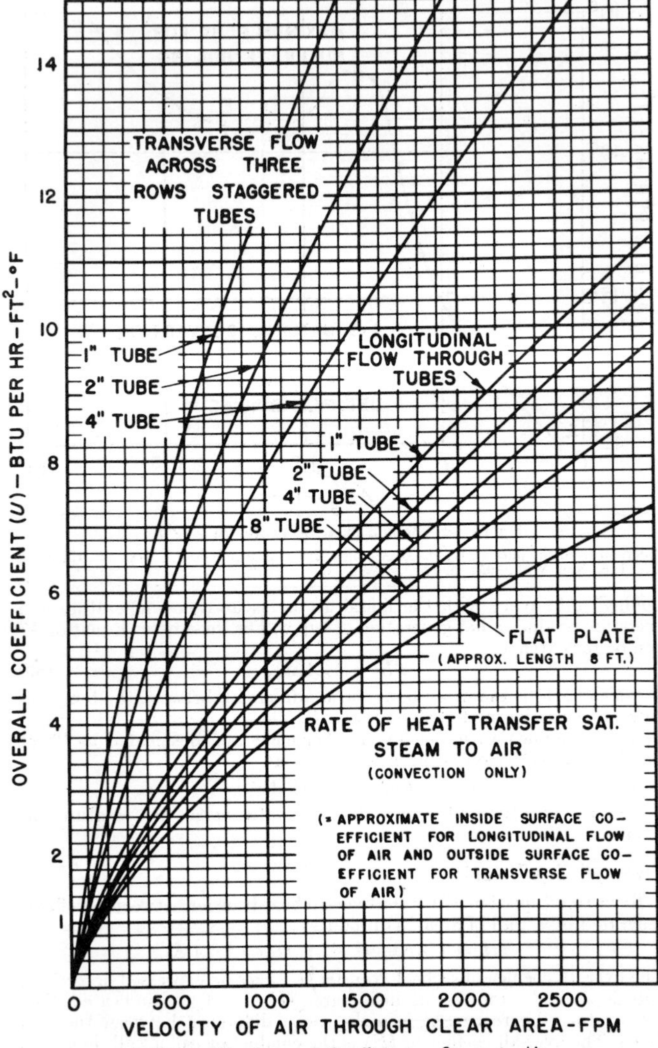

Figure 19—Over-all Coefficients—Steam to Air

TABLE 18

CALCULATED VALUES OF OVER-ALL HEAT TRANSFER COEFFICIENT FOR VARIOUS TYPES OF HEAT EXCHANGERS

Btu per hr-ft²-°F

Type of Exchanger		Convection	
Heat Source	Heat Sink	Natural	Forced
Water..........	Water.....	100	1000
Water..........	Oil........	22	222
Water..........	Gas.......	2	20
Water..........	Boiling Liquid	167	667
Oil............	Water.....	22	222
Oil............	Oil........	12	125
Oil............	Gas.......	2	18
Oil............	Boiling Liquid	24	200
Gas............	Water.....	2	20
Gas............	Oil........	2	18
Gas............	Gas.......	1	10
Gas............	Boiling Liquid	2	20
Condensing Vapor	Water.....	190	1330
Condensing Vapor	Oil........	25	236
Condensing Vapor	Gas.......	2	20
Condensing Vapor	Boiling Liquid	800	800

Based on zero metal resistance and the following values for h in free and forced convection respectively: 200 and 2000 for water, 50 and 500 for oil, 2 and 20 for gas, 4000 for condensing vapor, and 1000 for boiling liquid.

---

is equal to the sum of the individual resistances. For flat, parallel surfaces the over-all resistance of a composite wall may be determined from

$$\frac{1}{U} = \frac{1}{h_o} + \frac{1}{h_i} + \frac{x_1}{k_1} + \frac{x_2}{k_2} + \cdots + \frac{x_n}{k_n}. \tag{72}$$

For concentric, cylindrical surfaces such as pipes the over-all resistance based on outside surface may be determined from

$$\frac{1}{U_o} = \frac{1}{h_o} + \frac{1}{h_i}\left(\frac{A_o}{A_i}\right) + r_o + r_i\left(\frac{A_o}{A_i}\right). \tag{73}$$

For the usual dehumidifying coil where condensation takes place on the outside surface, the over-all resistance relative to outside area may be determined from

$$\frac{1}{U_o} = \frac{1}{h_o}\left(\frac{SH}{TH}\right) + \frac{1}{h_i}\left(\frac{A_o}{A_i}\right) + r_o + r_i\left(\frac{A_o}{A_i}\right). \tag{74}$$

In Equations 72-74 h_o and h_i are the outside and inside film coefficients based on the outside and inside areas respectively, r_o and r_i are the outside and inside fouling factors or resistances based on the outside and inside areas respectively, A_o/A_i is the ratio of outside to inside surface area, and SH/TH is the ratio of sensible heat to total heat transferred through the pipe or tube. Equations 73 and 74 may be used when extended surface is employed.

Occasionally, after the over-all coefficient (U) has been computed for a wall, the effect of an element added to that wall may be desired, for which case the new coefficient (U') may be determined from the added resistance (x/k) and

$$U' = \frac{1}{\frac{1}{U} + \frac{x}{k}}. \qquad (75)$$

Calculated values of the over-all coefficient (U) for various types of heat exchangers are listed in Table 18. For the specific case of heat transfer between steam and air, the variation of over-all coefficient with surface shape and air velocity is given in Figure 19.

Mean Effective Temperature Difference

Whenever either one or both of the reference temperatures in a difference varies, it is necessary to evaluate a mean temperature difference. For cases where the over-all coefficient (U) is substantially constant, as when a gas side resistance is controlling, the logarithmic-mean over-all temperature difference (Δt_m) as determined from

$$\Delta t_m = \frac{\Delta t_1 - \Delta t_2}{ln\ (\Delta t_1/\Delta t_2)} \qquad (76)$$

may be used. The terminal temperature differences (Δt_1 and Δt_2) are

$$\Delta t_1 = t_{i1} - t_{o1} \ and \qquad (77)$$

$$\Delta t_2 = t_{i2} - t_{o2}. \qquad (78)$$

For ease of computation the difference at terminal 1 should be the greater number and that at terminal 2 the smaller. Equation 76 is applicable for either parallel flow or counterflow of the two fluid streams. The difference in Δt_m for the two types of flow is best illustrated by an example.

EXAMPLE 3. Parallel Flow MED ($\Delta t_m \rightrightarrows$) and Counterflow MED ($\Delta t_m \rightleftarrows$)

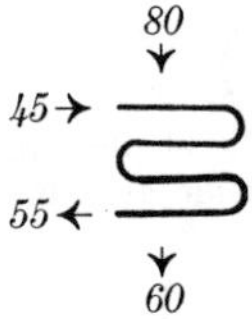

Parallel flow: hot fluid 80 in, 60 out; cold fluid 45 in, 55 out.

80	→ 60
45	→ 55
35	5

Counterflow: hot fluid 80 in, 60 out; cold fluid 45 in, 55 out.

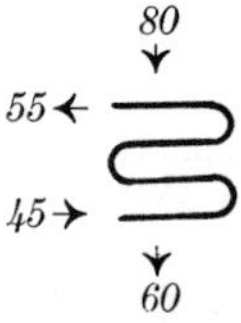

80	→ 60
55 ←	45
25	15

$$\frac{35 - 5}{ln\frac{35}{5}} = \frac{30}{1.95} = 15.4 = \Delta t_m \rightrightarrows \qquad \frac{25 - 15}{ln\frac{25}{15}} = \frac{10}{.51} = 19.6 = \Delta t_m \rightleftarrows$$

Slide rule computations may be eliminated by using Figure 20. Additional data on MED for multi-pass and crossflow arrangements are given in Chapter 19.

The mean temperature difference when there is no change of temperature in either fluid under steady state conditions is

$$\Delta t_m = t_i - t_o. \qquad (79)$$

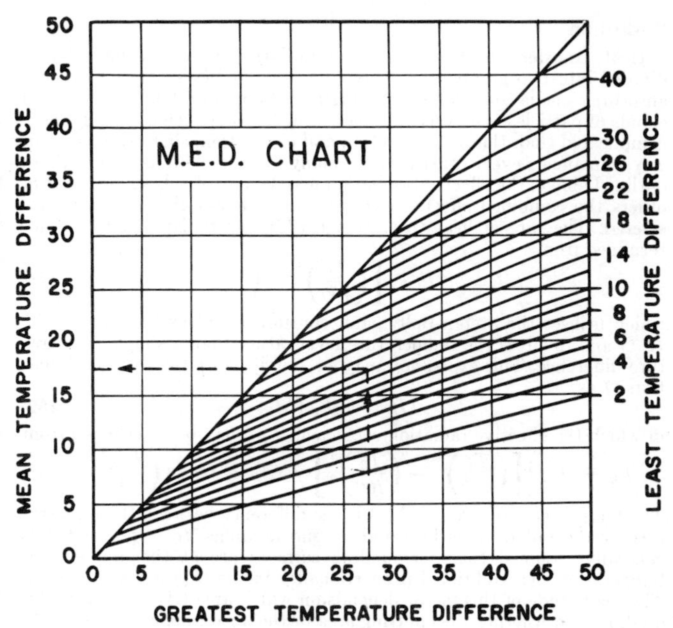

Figure 20—Logarithmic Mean Temperature Differences

Adapted from the data of Water Coils for Cooling, Aerofin Corporation, Bul. C-58, 1958.

Extended Surface

The over-all resistance to heat transmission based on inside area may be determined from

$$\frac{1}{U_i} = \frac{1}{h_o}\left(\frac{A_i}{A_o}\right) + \frac{1}{h_i} + r_o\left(\frac{A_i}{A_o}\right) + r_i. \tag{80}$$

As may be seen from this expression, the effect of extending the outside surface (A_o) depends on the magnitude of the outside resistances ($1/h_o$, r_o) relative to the inside resistances ($1/h_i$, r_i). The effect of increasing external surface is to reduce outside resistance (increase outside film coefficients). The effectiveness of any additional surface in promoting heat transfer is dependent on the bond between primary and secondary surface. In air conditioning coils the major resistance is usually on the air side which is the outside of the coil; hence external fins are the rule.

Radiation

Heat transfer problems involving radiation may be conveniently divided into two groups, those involving two bodies separated by non-absorbing media and those involving radiation from flames, gases, and clouds of particles. Analysis of radiant heat transfer is considerably more complicated than that of conduction and convection, since every part of a system affects every other part. In many cases, including most of those outlined above, the effects of radiation may be completely ignored but in others the combined effects of convection and radiation must be considered. The rate of heat transmission (TH) by radiation may be determined from

$$TH = .1713\, F_{\epsilon}\left[\left(\frac{T_1}{100}\right)^4 - \left(\frac{T_2}{100}\right)^4\right] A, \tag{81}$$

which utilizes the Stefan-Boltzmann constant for black bodies ($.1713 \times 10^{-8}$) and involves the temperature level rather than a simple temperature difference. This expression may be rewritten in the form of Equation 47 as

$$TH = h_R F_{\epsilon} A \Delta t_R, \tag{82}$$

in which the effective radiation coefficient (h_R) may be determined from

$$h_R = .1713\left[\left(\frac{T_1}{100}\right)^4 - \left(\frac{T_2}{100}\right)^4\right] \Big/ \Delta t_R \approx .00684\left(\frac{T_{avg}}{100}\right)^3. \tag{83}$$

The temperature difference (Δt_R) is the difference between the temperature of the radiating surface and its surroundings ($t_1 - t_2$), and it is generally assumed that surrounding surfaces are at the ambient air temperature. An additional proportionality factor (F_{ϵ}) is also involved. The magnitude of this factor depends on which area (A) is being evaluated, i.e., on whether the emitting area or the absorbing area is used. As indicated in Table 19, this factor is also dependent on the emissivity of the two surfaces involved. The emissivities (ϵ) of various common materials are listed in Table 20.

TABLE 19—EMISSIVITY FACTOR FORMULAS

Surface Sizes	Shapes	F_{ϵ}
Surface 1 small compared to Surface 2	any	ϵ_1
Surface 1 almost as large as Surface 2	any	$\dfrac{1}{\frac{1}{\epsilon_1} + \frac{1}{\epsilon_2} - 1}$
Surface 1 and Surface 2 both infinite	parallel planes	$\dfrac{1}{\frac{1}{\epsilon_1} + \frac{1}{\epsilon_2} - 1}$
Surface 1 smaller than Surface 2	concentric cylinders	$\dfrac{1}{\frac{1}{\epsilon_1} + \frac{r_1}{r_2}\left(\frac{1}{\epsilon_2} - 1\right)}$
Surface 1 smaller than Surface 2	concentric spheres	$\dfrac{1}{\frac{1}{\epsilon_1} + \left(\frac{r_1}{r_2}\right)^2\left(\frac{1}{\epsilon_2} - 1\right)}$

Adapted from the data of H. J. Stoever, "Applied Heat Transmission," McGraw-Hill Book Co., Inc., New York, 1941, p. 26.

TABLE 20 — EMISSIVITIES OF VARIOUS SURFACES

Material	Surface	t-°F	ϵ
Aluminum	Oxide	530-1520	.63-.26
	Cleaned	450-930	.22-.16
	Polished	212	.10
	High Polish	440-1070	.04-.06
Brass	Dull	120-660	.61-.59
	High Polish	490-710	.03-.04
Chromium	Polished	100-2000	.08-.36
Cast Iron	Oxidized	390-1100	.64-.78
	Polished	390	.21
Steel	Oxidized	390-1110	.79
	Cleaned	450-1950	.20-.32
Magnesium	Oxide	530-1520	.55-.20
Nickel	Polished	440-710	.07-.09
Stainless	Cleaned	450-1600	.57-.66
	Polished	450-1920	.26-.31
	Polished	212	.07
Zinc	Galvanized	212	.21
Brick	Rough	70	.93
Glass	Smooth	70	.94
Oil	Thick layer	70	.82
Lacquer	Black or White	100-200	.80-.95
	Aluminum	70	.39
Radiator Paint	White	212	.79
	Bronze	212	.51
Water		32-212	.95-.96

Adapted from the data of W. H. McAdams, "Heat Transmission," McGraw-Hill Book Co., Inc., New York, 1954, p. 107.

NOTE: Values are for normal (perpendicular) radiation. They decrease with increasing angularity between surfaces. They are approximately equal to the hemispherical emissivity, except those for highly polished metal surfaces which are 15-20% lower than hemispherical emissivity.

TABLE 21—RADIATION AND CONVECTION COEFFICIENTS

(For horizontal bare or insulated standard steel pipe of various sizes and for flat plates in a room at 80°F)

In Btu per hr-ft^2-°F

Nom. Pipe Diam., In.	Temperature difference, deg F, from surface to room												
	50	**100**	**200**	**300**	**400**	**500**	**600**	**700**	**800**	**900**	**1000**	**1100**	**1200**
½	2.12	2.48	3.10	3.75	4.47	5.30	6.21	7.25	8.40	9.73	11.20	12.81	14.65
1	2.03	2.38	2.98	3.62	4.33	5.16	6.07	7.11	8.25	9.57	11.04	12.65	14.48
2	1.93	2.27	2.85	3.47	4.18	4.99	5.89	6.92	8.07	9.38	10.85	12.46	14.28
4	1.84	2.16	2.72	3.33	4.02	4.83	5.72	6.75	7.89	9.21	10.66	12.27	14.09
8	1.76	2.06	2.60	3.20	3.88	4.68	5.57	6.60	7.73	9.05	10.50	12.10	13.93
12	1.71	2.01	2.54	3.13	3.83	4.61	5.50	6.52	7.65	8.96	10.42	12.03	13.84
24	1.64	1.93	2.45	3.03	3.70	4.48	5.37	6.39	7.52	8.83	10.28	11.90	13.70
Flat Plates													
Vertical	1.82	2.13	2.70	3.30	4.00	4.79	5.70	6.72	7.86	9.18	10.64	12.25	14.06
Horiz. Face up	2.00	2.35	2.97	3.59	4.31	5.12	6.04	7.07	8.21	9.54	11.01	12.63	14.45
Horiz. Face down	1.58	1.85	2.36	2.93	3.61	4.38	5.27	6.27	7.40	8.71	10.16	11.76	13.57

Adapted from the data of T. Baumeister, "Mechanical Engineers' Handbook," McGraw-Hill Book Co., Inc., New York, 1967, p. 4-106.

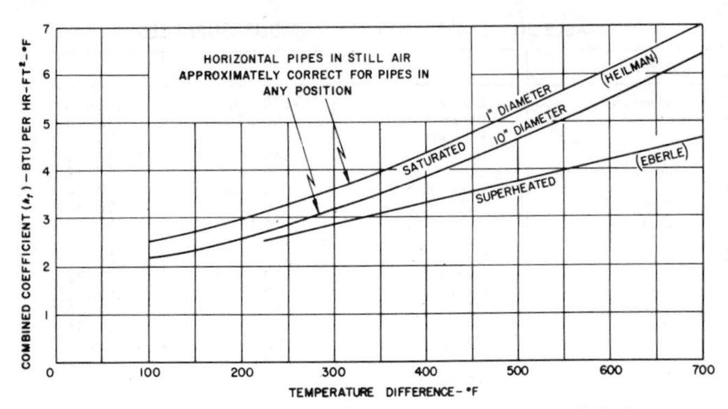

Figure 21—Combined Coefficients for Steam Pipes in Still Air

Adapted from the data of R. H. Heilman, Heat Losses from Bare and Covered Wrought Iron Pipe at Temperatures up to 800 Deg. Fahr., *Trans. ASME*, vol. 44, pp. 299-323, 1922 and that of B. N. Broido, High-Temperature and High-Pressure Steam Lines, *Trans. ASME*, vol. 44, pp. 1199-1242, 1922.

Combined Convection and Radiation

In some cases it is necessary to determine the effects of both convection and radiation on the heat transfer rate. Based on the difference in temperature between the surface and its surroundings (Δt_R), the expression for rate of heat transfer may be written

$$TH = h_T A \Delta t_R. \tag{84}$$

The combined coefficient (h_T) should be determined from

$$h_T = h_N + F_\epsilon h_R. \tag{85}$$

The combined coefficient for steam pipes in still air and its variation with temperature difference is illustrated in Figure 21. Additional data on combined coefficients are tabulated in Table 21.

Unsteady Heat Flow

In all of the above cases, steady heat flow conditions were assumed to exist. Such conditions usually prevail in any heat exchanger a short time after start-up. The most notable examples of transient or unsteady heat flow are examined in Chapters 15 and 21. In air conditioning, solar radiation often contributes the major portion of the cooling load. The relation between time of maximum solar intensity and time of maximum cooling load varies considerably for different materials. It is necessary therefore to take this time lag into account in determining both maximum cooling load and equipment size. In cases of heavy wall construction the time lag may be such that the time of maximum cooling load due to solar radiation occurs after the period of occupancy. An approximate method for calculating the length of time necessary to cool a hot body is given in Chapter 21 under "Air-Blast Cooling."

CHAPTER 3

FLUID FLOW

The flow of any real fluid is resisted by friction forces which arise due to the viscosity of the fluid. These forces are generated within the fluid wherever there are velocity gradients. They are transmitted between the fluid and any solid boundary by a layer of fluid which becomes attached to the boundary. Forces are transmitted between the fluid and any other fluid by a mixing layer of entrained fluid. The acceleration of a fluid is resisted by inertia forces. Work must be done to overcome these resistances if flow is to take place. The energy required may be transferred to the fluid by a fan or by other means. In a fan system, this energy is delivered to the air by the fan or fans and that portion which overcomes friction is gradually converted into heat as the resistance is encountered throughout the system.

Flow Regimes and Boundary Layers

Fluid flow may be laminar, turbulent, or in a transition state between these two regimes. Laminar flow, as the name implies, may be considered to proceed in layers, between which there is, in general, relative sliding motion. It is characterized by the absence of local macroscopic velocity fluctuations. Shearing stresses are transmitted essentially by intermolecular forces. Turbulent flow exhibits relatively large-scale local velocity fluctuations. This results in eddying, mixing, and transport of momentum which becomes the main shearing-force-transmission mechanism between adjacent portions of the flowing fluid.

The presence of a boundary surface in a flowing fluid produces various phenomena. As the fluid attaches itself to the boundary, gradually increasing amounts are retarded, forming a boundary layer whose thickness increases in the direction of flow. The flow in the layer may be laminar or turbulent, depending on the Reynolds number of the main flow and on the disturbances present. If the boundaries form a closed, uniform conduit of sufficient length, the flow will eventually become "established," i.e., the velocity profile will be uniform for all succeeding sections. This condition may not obtain if the conduit is non-uniform or strongly curved. Similarly, with external flow around immersed blunt bodies, the boundary layer may not have sufficient kinetic energy to overcome the resulting pressure gradients and other resistances. In this case, the flow will "separate," causing return flow and eddies which form and reform and are swept out into the main stream.

Unestablished flow may persist for 50 diameters of straight conduit after a disturbance. With a smooth entrance, flow may be established in 20 diameters or less depending on Reynolds number.

Separation does not occur in accelerated flow. Decelerated flow tends to promote separation. Since separation leads to eddy formation and, ultimately, energy dissipation, accelerated flow is usually less troublesome and more efficient than decelerated flow.

Another phenomenon due to the presence of boundaries is secondary flow. This may occur in either unestablished or established flow. It is the flow within a flow that occurs, for example, at bends or discontinuities.

Viscosity

The property of fluids known as viscosity may be determined for various temperatures from Figure 22 for common gases, Figure 23 for refrigerant vapors, and Figure 24 for various liquids.

The absolute viscosity (μ) of a fluid is that property which resists the movement of one layer over another. For gases this is conveniently measured by determining the pressure drop through a capillary (or series of capillaries in parallel) through which steady laminar flow is maintained. The equations regarding laminar flow given on page 108 may be used to correlate pressure drop and absolute viscosity. Needless to say, any viscosimeter incorporating this principle requires careful calibration to account for end effects and geometric imperfections.

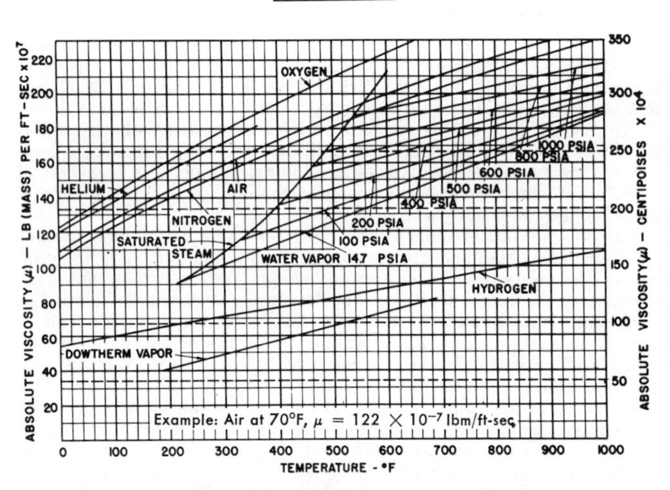

Figure 22—Absolute Viscosities of Common Gases

Adapted from the data of G. A. Hawkins, H. L. Solberg, and A. A. Potter, The Viscosity of Superheated Steam, *Trans. ASME*, vol. 62, pp. 677-688, 1940, and that of Aeronautical Information Report No. 24, SAE, 1952.

Absolute viscosity or coefficient of viscosity is the proportionality factor relating shearing stress (force per unit area) and velocity gradient (incremental velocity per incremental distance). Absolute viscosity is most frequently expressed in centipoises, the units of which are grams per sec-cm divided by 100. To obtain the English equivalent in lbm per ft-sec, the number of centipoises must be multiplied by .000672.

Kinematic viscosity (ν) is absolute viscosity divided by mass density (ρ):

$$\nu = \mu/\rho. \tag{86}$$

Kinematic viscosity is expressed in centistokes, the units of which are sq cm per sec divided by 100. The English equivalent in sq ft per sec may be obtained by multiplying centistokes by 1.076×10^{-5}. The kinematic viscosity for various fluids may be determined from Figure 25.

Liquid viscosity measurements are most easily obtained with one of the various efflux viscosimeters which include the Saybolt Universal, Saybolt Furol, Redwood No. 1 and No. 2, and Engler. With all these instruments the time required for a given volume of liquid to flow through a small bore tube is measured and converted to kinematic viscosity directly by means of a calibration such as those shown in Figure 26. Absolute viscosity in centipoises may be determined from kinematic viscosity in centistokes by multiplying the centistokes by the specific gravity of the fluid referred to water. For precision, capillary viscosimeters of the Ostwald-Cannon-Fenske type may be used.

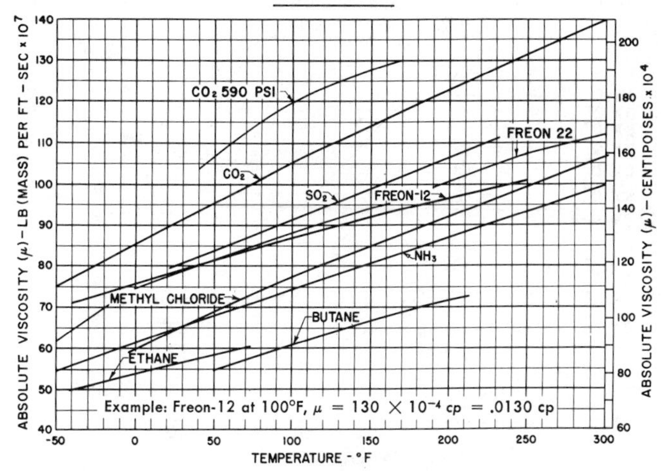

Figure 23—Absolute Viscosities of Refrigerant Vapors

Adapted from the data of J. C. Reed and E. E. Ambrosius, Viscosity of Refrigerants, *Heating, Piping and Air Conditioning*, pp. 455-461, June, 1930, and that of A. F. Benning and W. H. Markwood, Jr., The Viscosities of "Freon Refrigerants," *Journal of the ASRE* in *Refrigerating Engineering*, pp. 243-247, April, 1939.

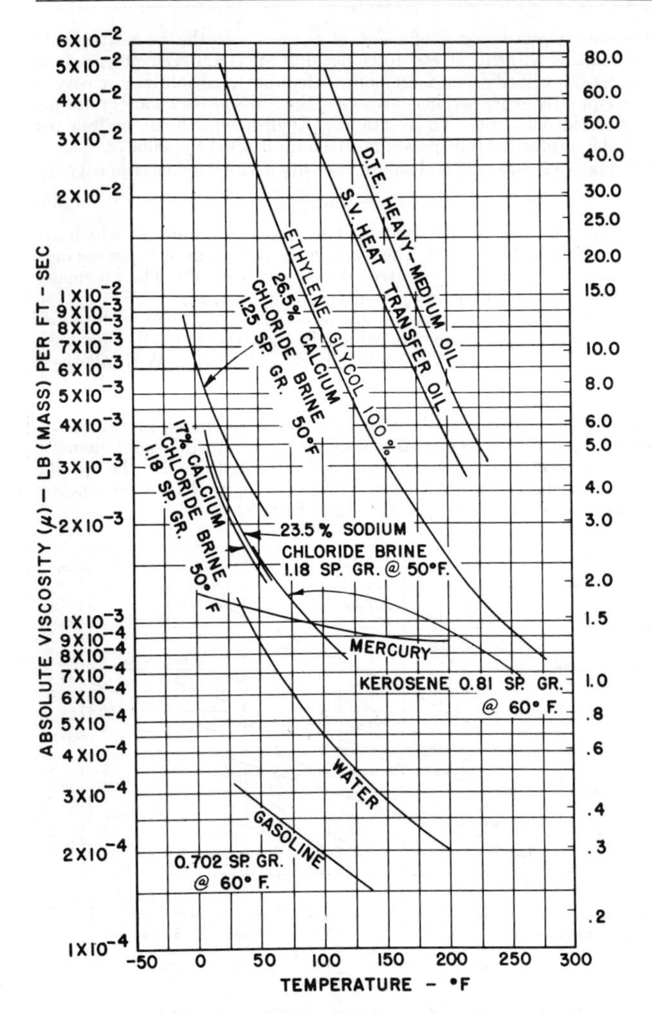

Figure 24—Absolute Viscosities of Liquids

Adapted from the data of Aeronautical Information Report No. 24, SAE, 1952.

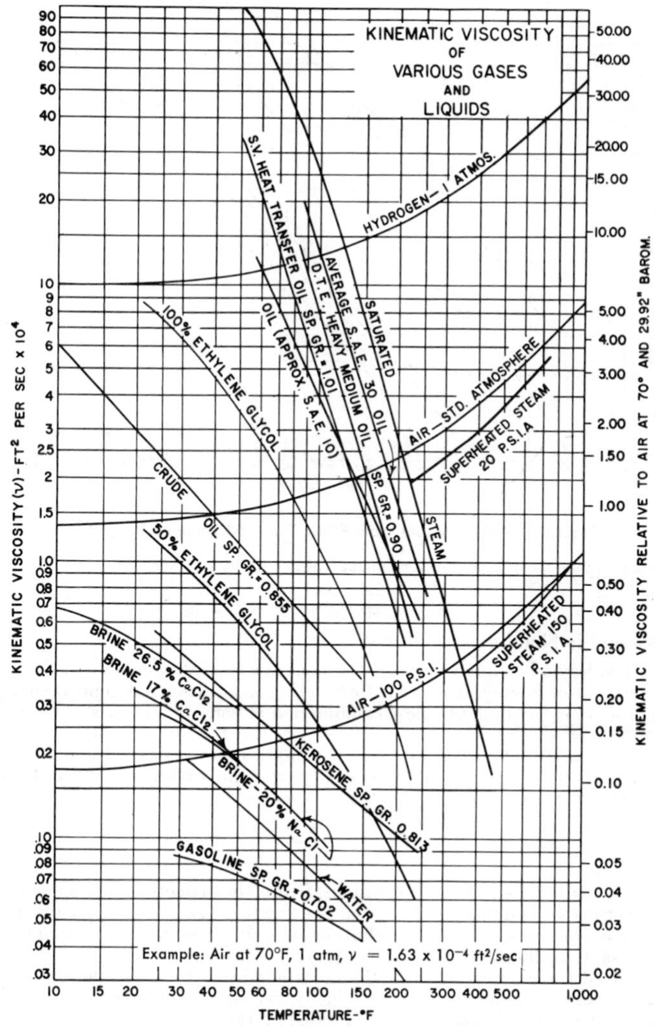

Figure 25—Kinematic Viscosities of Gases and Liquids

Adapted from the data of Aeronautical Information Report No. 24, SAE, 1952.

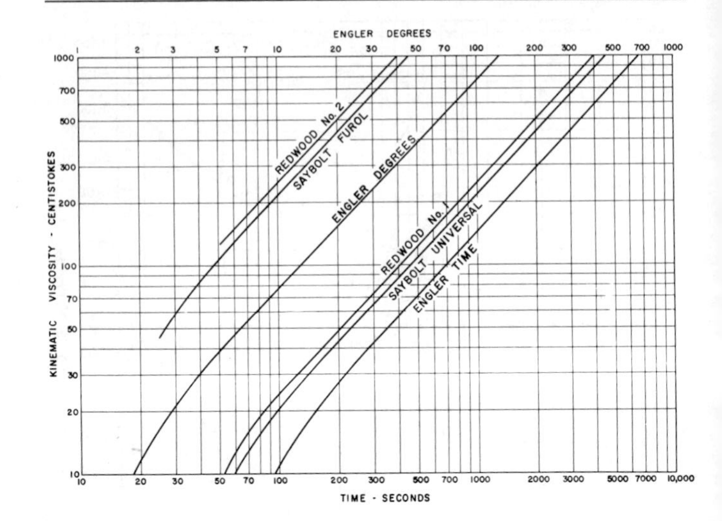

Figure 26—Conversions from Efflux Time to Kinematic Viscosity

Adapted from the data of Standards of the Tubular Exchanger Manufacturers Association, TEMA, 1959.

Reynolds Number

The Reynolds number (N_{Re}) at a point in a fluid stream is the ratio of inertia force to viscous shearing force acting on an element of fluid at that point. It is the dimensionless combination of some characteristic linear dimension of the boundary surface (D), the relative velocity of the element and that surface (V), and the physical properties of the fluid as represented by the absolute viscosity (μ) and the mass density (ρ) or the kinematic viscosity (ν):

$$N_{Re} = \frac{DV\rho}{\mu} = \frac{DV}{\nu}. \tag{87}$$

Some characteristic linear dimensions (D) are: the diameter of the opening for orifices, the diameter of the exit opening for nozzles, the inside diameter in the case of a round conduit, or the equivalent diameter based on the same hydraulic radius in the case of a rectangular duct.

In all these cases the local Reynolds number across a section varies from point to point due to the velocity variation. Therefore, it is convenient to use a Reynolds number based on the mean velocity (V_m).

Dimensional analyses* indicate and experimental data demonstrate

*Refer to Appendix 1 for a discussion of dimensional analysis.

that Reynolds number is an important natural physical variable in various flow situations. Refer to the chapter on fan laws for a discussion of dynamic similarity and Reynolds number effects on fan law predictions. Refer also to the air cleaning chapter for information on the effects of Reynolds numbers on particle behavior in an aerosol. The discussions which immediately follow are concerned directly with flow in conduits but the principles apply to various flow situations.

Absolute and Relative Roughness

Any surface, no matter how polished, has peaks and valleys. The mean distance between these high and low points is the absolute roughness (ϵ). Table 22 lists several roughness conditions with typical surfaces and corresponding absolute roughnesses in feet.

The relative roughness (ϵ/D) of the surface in a conduit is the absolute roughness divided by the effective diameter. Any consistent set of units may be used.

Hydraulically, any value of relative roughness may represent either a smooth or a rough condition depending on Reynolds number. A brief analysis of various flow phenomena may explain this.

It has been established that, for all but the most rarefied flow, there is a molecular layer of fluid firmly anchored to the boundary surfaces. In laminar flow there is a velocity gradient all the way across the stream. In turbulent flow there are velocity fluctuations but in the main stream the average velocity profile in a pipe is almost flat. However, there is a turbulent boundary layer across which there is a definite velocity gradient. There may also be a very thin laminar sublayer if the absolute roughness is small compared with the boundary layer thickness. If such a sublayer submerges the high points of the surface sufficiently, i.e., if sublayer thickness exceeds absolute roughness by a factor of 4, the pipe surface may be described as hydraulically smooth.

In the wholly rough zone of turbulent flow the condition of the surface may be described as hydraulically rough. The laminar sublayer is reduced to about 1/6 of the absolute roughness or less and may be prevented from forming at all as the roughness increases in comparison with the boundary layer thickness.

TABLE 22—ROUGHNESS INFORMATION FOR VARIOUS CONDITIONS

Condition	Typical Surface	Average ϵ	Range ϵ	n‡	c‡
Very smooth	Drawn tubing	.000005′	—	.20	0.1036
Medium smooth	Aluminum duct†°	.00015′	.00010′-.00020′	.18	0.0870
Average	Galvanized iron duct⊕	.0005′	.00045′-.00065′	.16	0.0746
Medium rough	Concrete pipe	.003′	.001′ -.01′	.14	0.0642
Very rough	Riveted steel pipe	.01′	.003′ -.03′	.12	0.0560

†Crimped slip joint every 3′
⊕Crimped slip joint every 2½′
°New steel pipe also typical
‡n and c are for use in Equation 146 and may be used with any units for P, L, V, δ, μ, g, and D provided they are consistent dimensionally.

Adapted from the data of F. W. Hutchinson, Friction Losses in Round Aluminum Ducts, *Trans. ASHVE*, vol. 59, pp. 127-138, 1953.

Coefficient of Friction

The coefficient of friction for flow in pipes (f) or Darcy friction factor is a dimensionless group which relates two other dimensionless groups: the ratio of the loss of total head between two points (H_L) to the velocity head (H_V), and the ratio of the distance between those two points (L) and some characteristic dimension (D) which determines velocity.

$$\frac{H_L}{H_V} = f\frac{L}{D}. \tag{88}$$

(Refer to page 69 for a discussion of head.)

In the laminar zone

$$f = 64/N_{Re}. \tag{89}$$

This appears as a straight sloping line on the Moody Chart in Figure 27. There is a critical value of N_{Re} above which laminar flow can exist only if the flow remains essentially undisturbed. This condition is quite easily upset; hence a dotted line is shown for Reynolds numbers greater than 2100. This critical Reynolds number is for conduit flow. Critical values vary with geometry. For example, for flow between parallel plates the critical Reynolds number, based on the distance between plates, is approximately 900.

In the wholly rough zone

$$f = \frac{1}{\left(2\log_{10}\frac{3.7}{\epsilon/D}\right)^2}. \tag{90}$$

This produces a series of straight horizontal lines in Figure 27. There is a value of N_{Re} for each value of relative roughness below which the flow cannot be considered independent of Reynolds number. These values are indicated by the dotted, curved line in Figure 27.

In the transition zone

$$\frac{1}{\sqrt{f}} = -2\log_{10}\left(\frac{\epsilon/D}{3.7} + \frac{2.51}{N_{Re}\sqrt{f}}\right). \tag{91}$$

This is the Colebrook* equation which is based on the research of Nikuradse, von Kármán, and others.

For hydraulically smooth pipes

$$f = 0.3164/N_{Re}^{0.25}. \tag{92}$$

This is the Blasius formula which may be used for Reynolds numbers between 3000 and 10^5.

Also for smooth pipes

$$\frac{1}{\sqrt{f}} = -2\log_{10}\left(\frac{2.51}{N_{Re}\sqrt{f}}\right). \tag{93}$$

This is the Prandtl universal resistance law which may be used for Reynolds numbers between 5×10^4 and 3.5×10^6.

---

*C. F. Colebrook, Turbulent Flow in Pipes with Particular Reference to the Transition Points between Smooth and Rough Laws, ICE Journal, vol. 11, pp. 133-156, 1938.

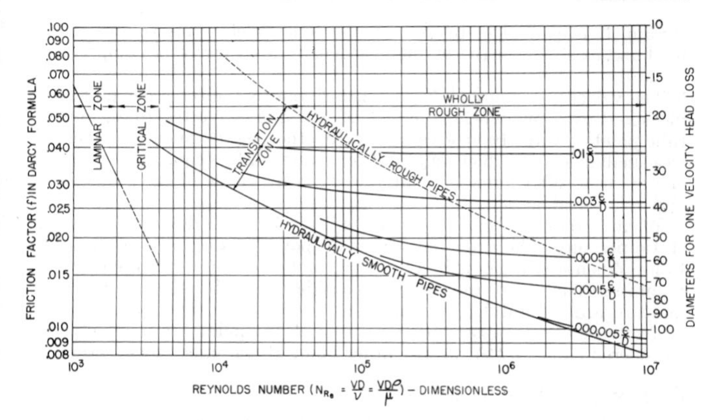

Figure 27—Moody Chart for Darcy Friction Factor

Adapted from the data of L. F. Moody, Friction Factors for Pipe Flow, *Trans. ASME*, vol. 66, pp. 671-684, 1944.

Head and Pressure

Fluids flow naturally from regions of relatively high total head to regions of relatively low total head. The term head is used in fluid mechanics to denote energy per unit weight of fluid. When energy is measured in ft-lb and weight is measured in lb, the corresponding unit of measurement for head is the ft-lb per lb of fluid flowing. This is usually abbreviated to ft of fluid flowing. The total head of a fluid is the sum of the potential and kinetic energies per unit weight.

In fan engineering it is usually more convenient to use the height of an equivalent column of water rather than the height of a column of air or gas for head measurements. The reason for this is that heads are usually measured with a water column gage.

The term pressure is used in fluid mechanics to denote energy per unit volume of fluid but is frequently reported in the same units as head or equivalent head particularly when incompressible fluids are involved. In fan engineering it is necessary to distinguish various pressures or heads according to the method by which they can be measured or the kind of energy with which they are associated.

The total pressure (TP) of a gas stream is the force per unit area measured by a manometer connected to an impact tube which points directly upstream. It is equivalent to the total kinetic and potential energy of a unit volume of the fluid and exists by virtue of the gas density, velocity, and degree of compression.

The static pressure (SP) of a gas stream is the force per unit area measured by a manometer connected to a small hole in the duct wall or other boundary, the surface of which must be parallel to the path of the stream. It is equivalent to the potential energy of a unit volume of the fluid and exists by virtue of the gas density and degree of compression alone.

The velocity pressure (VP) of a gas stream is the force per unit area measured by a manometer, one leg of which is connected to an impact tube pointing directly upstream and the other leg of which is connected to a small hole in the duct wall (or its equivalent). It is equal to the kinetic energy of a unit volume of fluid and exists by virtue of the gas density and velocity alone.

What is commonly called pressure is that which was described above as static pressure. The static pressure at a point acts equally in all directions. When a still gas is involved, the static pressure measured at any point in its container can usually be considered equal to that at any other point regardless of differences in elevation. Similarly, when a gas stream is involved, the static pressure measured at any point can frequently be considered equal to that at any other point at the same cross section.

Energy and Mass Balances

Fluid flow may be steady or unsteady, uniform or non-uniform. Flow is steady when the conditions at any cross section do not change with time, whereas unsteady flow proceeds in waves or pulsations. Uniform flow exists between two points when the velocity profile of the stream at all intermediate points is substantially constant.

The Bernoulli equation for steady flow, modified to include the effects of energy additions or losses, is a statement of the required mechanical energy balance in uniform or non-uniform flow:

$$\frac{P_1}{\delta_1} + \frac{V_1^2}{2g} + Z_1 = \frac{P_2}{\delta_2} + \frac{V_2^2}{2g} + Z_2 + losses_{1-2}. \quad (94)$$

In the above P_1/δ_1 is the pressure (static) head at Station 1, $V_1^2/2g$ is the velocity head* at Station 1, Z_1 is the elevation head at Station 1, etc. If the various heads, including losses, are to be in ft of fluid flowing, the absolute pressure (P) must be in lb per sq ft when the density (δ) is in lb per cu ft; the acceleration due to gravity (g) must be in ft per min^2 when the velocity (V) is in fpm; and the elevation (Z) must also be in ft. To convert to equivalent head in inches water gage ("WG), it is necessary to multiply each head by the ratio of air density to water density and by *12*, the number of inches per foot. To get equivalent heads in inches water gage at 70°F, the conversion factor becomes *12/62.302* times the density of the gas, or $\delta/5.192$. After applying this conversion factor to each term of Equation **94** and indicating the equivalent pressure heads in two parts: one, ambient barometer (BP) in "WG; the other, gage pressure above or below ambient (SP) in "WG, the mechanical energy balance becomes

*The average velocity head at any station if defined as the average velocity squared divided by 2g is not equal to the average kinetic energy per unit weight. The ratio of the latter to the former is usually called the α factor. It can be shown that $\alpha = (\int V^3\, dA) \div (V_m^3\, A)$ and that numerically this factor always exceeds unity unless V is constant and $V_m = V$. The α factor is close to unity for highly turbulent flow and is therefore ignored in most engineering applications.

$$(BP_1 + SP_1) + VP_1 + \frac{Z_1\delta_1}{5.192} = (BP_2 + SP_2) + VP_2 + \frac{Z_2\delta_2}{5.192} + \Delta TP_{1-2}. \tag{95}$$

It can be shown that, if the density of the flowing fluid equals the ambient fluid density, the change in barometer due to elevation equals the change in elevation head, or

$$BP_1 + \frac{Z_1\delta_1}{5.192} = BP_2 + \frac{Z_2\delta_2}{5.192}. \tag{96}$$

Subtracting Equation 96 from Equation 95 leaves

$$SP_1 + VP_1 = SP_2 + VP_2 + \Delta TP_{1-2}. \tag{97}$$

This expression involving gage pressures is a simplification applicable only when there is no substantial difference in density between the fluid flowing and ambient fluid or when there is no substantial difference in elevation between Stations 1 and 2.

Multiplying the velocity head in ft of fluid by the appropriate conversion factor produces the velocity head (VP) in ″WG, as indicated in

$$VP = \left(\frac{V^2}{2g}\right)\left(\frac{\delta}{5.192}\right) = \left(\frac{V}{1096.7}\right)^2 \delta. \tag{98}$$

This expression is also useful when solved for velocity (V) in fpm as indicated in

$$V = 1096.7\sqrt{\frac{VP}{\delta}}. \tag{99}$$

Substituting .075 lb per cu ft for the density of standard air produces

$$V = 4005\sqrt{VP}, \tag{100}$$

which indicates that 1″WG velocity pressure corresponds to a velocity of 4005 fpm. Numerous other solutions of this equation are given in Table 23. Similar solutions of Equation 99 are given in Table 24.

From Equations 98 and 99 it can be observed that a decrease in density decreases velocity pressure if the velocity is constant. Similarly, when the velocity pressure is constant, a decrease in density increases velocity. Since decreases in barometric pressure, increases in temperature, or increases in humidity all decrease density, such changes produce similar effects. When Equation 14 is incorporated into Equation 99.

$$V = 1096.7\sqrt{VP}\sqrt{\frac{.7538\,(t + 459.7)}{(b - e_w h)\,(SG) + e_w hs}}. \tag{101}$$

The equation of continuity is a statement of the required mass balance for steady uniform or non-uniform flow. Based on average local velocities and densities:

$$\delta_1 A_1 V_1 = \delta_2 A_2 V_2. \tag{102}$$

For incompressible flow the densities (δ) at Stations 1 and 2 are equal, and the volume rate of flow (q) is constant:

$$A_1 V_1 = A_2 V_2 = q. \tag{103}$$

TABLE 23—VELOCITIES OF DRY AIR FOR VARIOUS VELOCITY PRESSURES

At 70°F and 29.92 in. Hg Barometer
In fpm

VP "WG	0	.1	.2	.3	.4	.5	.6	.7	.8	.9
0		1266	1791	2194	2533	2832	3102	3351	3582	3800
1	4005	4200	4387	4566	4739	4905	5066	5222	5373	5521
2	5664	5804	5940	6074	6204	6332	6458	6581	6702	6820
3	6937	7052	7164	7275	7385	7493	7599	7704	7807	7909
4	8010	8110	8208	8305	8401	8496	8590	8683	8775	8865
5	8955	9045	9133	9220	9307	9393	9478	9562	9645	9728
6	9810	9892	9972	10052	10132	10211	10289	10367	10444	10520
7	10596	10672	10747	10821	10895	10968	11041	11113	11185	11257
8	11328	11398	11469	11538	11608	11676	11745	11813	11881	11948
9	12015	12082	12148	12214	12279	12344	12409	12474	12538	12601
	0	**1**	**2**	**3**	**4**	**5**	**6**	**7**	**8**	**9**
10	12665	13283	13874	14440	14985	15511	16020	16513	16992	17457
20	17911	18353	18785	19207	19620	20025	20422	20811	21192	21568
30	21936	22299	22656	23007	23353	23694	24030	24361	24688	25011
40	25330	25644	25956	26263	26566	26866	27163	27457	27747	28035

TABLE 24—VELOCITIES OF DRY AIR FOR VARIOUS VELOCITY PRESSURES

At Various Temperatures and 29.92 in. Hg Barometer
In fpm

VP "WG	Temperature °F									
	50°	60°	70°	80°	100°	150°	200°	300°	500°	650°
.1	1242	1254	1266	1278	1302	1359	1414	1517	1705	1833
.2	1757	1774	1791	1808	1841	1922	1999	2145	2411	2592
.3	2152	2173	2194	2214	2255	2354	2448	2627	2953	3175
.4	2485	2509	2533	2557	2604	2718	2827	3033	3410	3666
.5	2778	2805	2832	2859	2911	3038	3161	3391	3812	4099
.6	3043	3073	3102	3131	3189	3328	3462	3715	4176	4490
.7	3287	3319	3351	3382	3444	3595	3740	4013	4510	4850
.8	3514	3548	3582	3616	3682	3843	3998	4290	4822	5185
.9	3727	3763	3800	3835	3905	4076	4241	4550	5114	5500
1.00	3929	3967	4005	4043	4117	4297	4470	4796	5391	5797
1.25	4392	4435	4478	4520	4603	4804	4998	5362	6027	6481
1.50	4812	4859	4905	4951	5042	5263	5475	5874	6602	7100
1.75	5197	5248	5298	5348	5446	5684	5913	6345	7132	7669
2.00	5556	5609	5664	5717	5822	6077	6322	6783	7624	8198
2.25	5893	5951	6007	6064	6175	6446	6705	7194	8087	8696
2.50	6212	6272	6332	6392	6509	6794	7068	7583	8524	9166
2.75	6515	6577	6642	6704	6827	7126	7413	7953	8940	9613
3.00	6805	6871	6937	7002	7130	7443	7742	8307	9338	10040
4.00	7858	7934	8010	8085	8233	8594	8940	9592	10780	11590
5.00	8785	8870	8955	9040	9205	9608	9995	10720	12050	12960
6.00	9623	9715	9810	9902	10080	10520	10950	11750	13210	14200

Although all gases are compressible, it is convenient to treat them as incompressible fluids in most parts of this chapter. The error resulting from this simplification is negligible for the degree of compression involved in most fan applications. Indeed, engineering societies in their Fan Test Codes recognize and approve of this practice.

MEASUREMENT OF PRESSURE AND FLOW

There are several methods by which flow rates may be determined from pressure measurements. These include the use of the pitot tube traverse and the use of orifices, nozzles, or Venturi meters. In the first case, sufficient velocity pressures are measured to accurately determine the average velocity. In the other cases, a suitable pressure difference is measured and flow rate determined from an appropriate calibration of the meter. Discussions on these three meters can be found under separate headings below. In addition to these devices, any geometrically fixed resistance may be calibrated so that its pressure drop can be used to measure flow. Various calibrated instruments utilizing the kinetic energy of a moving stream to ultimately deflect an indicating needle can also be used to measure flow, at least approximately.

Pressure Taps and Probes

The measurement of static pressure in a fluid at rest is quite simply accomplished by connecting one leg of a manometer to a small opening in the fluid container and exposing the other leg to atmosphere. In the case of a moving stream, precautions are necessary to avoid any eddy, impact, or aspirating effects. Static pressure tap holes in the wall of a duct must be free from burrs, and the connectors should not project into the duct. It is equally important that such holes be sufficiently removed from disturbances such as elbows, dampers, etc. As a rough guide, static taps should be at least two diameters from any upstream disturbance, no matter how minor; at least five diameters from a major symmetrical disturbance; and ten diameters or more from a non-symmetrical disturbance. A side tap only allows measurement of the pressure at the area of the hole. Its location should therefore be chosen on the basis of known flow conditions to obtain the most representative reading possible. An average pressure at a cross section may be determined by connecting several side taps to a common manometer. Such an arrangement involving three or more static taps is usually referred to as a piezometer ring. Such an arrangement only permits measurement of the average of the static pressures at the wall areas near the taps.

Static pressure probes must be used to measure the static pressure in the body of a moving fluid. Such probes may consist of bent tubes with several static taps located on the portion pointing upstream. The holes must be sufficiently removed from the rounded upstream end to nullify any velocity disturbance. Calibration of such a static tube may be obtained by inserting it in the stream of a good flow nozzle discharging to atmosphere. The pressure in such a stream should be zero.

A Fechheimer tube* can sometimes be used to determine total pressure, static pressure, and direction of flow. It consists of a tube with two holes spaced 78½ degrees apart in one plane at right angles to the tube axis. These holes are small and are not intercommunicating, but lead to outside connections through separate passageways. In practice the tube is held so that both holes face into the air flow, and the tube is rotated until the gage which is differentially connected to the two pressure holes shows zero reading. In this position the radial line midway between the holes points in the direction of airflow, or at least in one component of it. If one or the other of the holes is attached to another gage, this should read the static pressure since the air stream impinging on a cylinder separates at 78½ degrees. For total pressure measurement, one hole may be pointed upstream.

Impact probes are used to measure the total pressure at any point in a fluid stream. One may be constructed using a bent tube with a central hole in the rounded, upstream end.

Pitot tubes are combination static pressure and impact probes. The most convenient arrangement is to use the tube-within-a-tube construction. The standard Pitot tube dimensions as recommended by Merriam & Spaulding† and adopted by the A.M.C.A., A.S.H.R.A.E., and A.S.M.E. are indicated in Figure 28.

By suitable connections between Pitot tube and manometers, any combination of static, velocity, and total pressure may be measured. The connection of one leg of a manometer to either the static pressure or total pressure connection produces the corresponding pressure on that leg of the manometer. The differential pressure or velocity pressure can be obtained by connecting the static pressure connection to one side and the total pressure connection to the other side of a single manometer. Simultaneous measurement of both static pressure and velocity pressure or total pressure and velocity pressure can be obtained on a second gage by inserting a T-connection in the appropriate line. The relation between the pressure being measured and atmospheric pressure should be considered, particularly to avoid blowing the fluid out of the manometer. In this regard the difference between total and static pressures, which is the velocity pressure, is always positive, but total pressure may be either negative or positive, depending on the location of the fan relative to the measuring station and static pressure may be either negative or positive depending on the values of the velocity and total pressures.

The reduction in cross sectional area occasioned by the insertion of a 5/16″ diameter tube in even a 6″ diameter pipe is less than 3/10ths of 1% and hence may be neglected in almost all cases.

There is no area reduction at the point of measurement when an impact tube is inserted into a stream.

The error produced by the insertion of a stem increases static pressure and decreases velocity pressure slightly. Additional errors may result if the flow is not parallel to the direction in which the Pitot tube is pointed.

---

*C. J. Fechheimer, Measurement of Static Pressure, *Trans. ASME*, vol. 48, pp. 965-977, 1926.

†K. G. Merriam and E. R. Spaulding, "Comparative Tests of Pitot-Static Tubes," *NACA TN* 546, 1935.

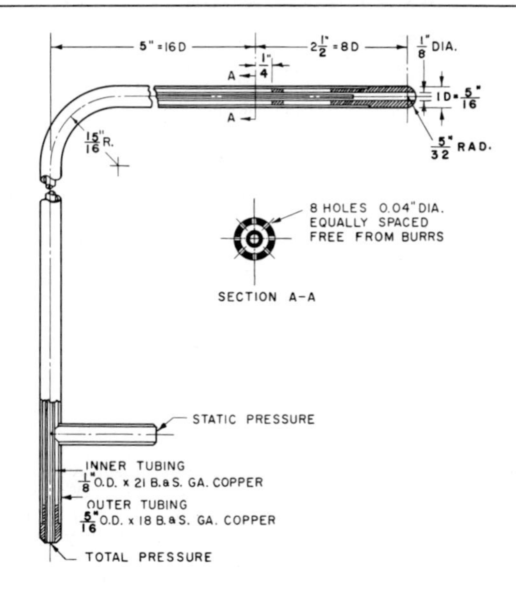

Figure 28—Standard Pitot Tube Construction

Adapted from the data of Standard Test Code for Air Moving Devices, AMCA, Standard 210-67, 1967, p. 20.

For this reason, it is desirable to utilize a straightener upstream of the Pitot tube.

In Europe the Prandtl-Pitot tube rather than the American standard Pitot tube is used. The essential difference is that a narrow, circular slot is used in place of the eight small static pressure holes.

The standard size Pitot tube is suitable for most laboratory work. Larger, stronger tubes are frequently needed for measurement in large ducts. In such cases it is recommended that complete proportionality be maintained for all dimensions. Calibration of Pitot tubes of both larger and smaller sizes than standard have been made in the laboratory of the Buffalo Forge Company and have indicated satisfactory agreement.

Various special Pitot tubes have been used for reasons of ease of insertion or magnification of gage reading. All such special designs require careful individual calibration. One of the easiest ways to magnify an impact reading is to combine a normal impact tube and a reverse impact tube and read the differential pressure. Miniature Venturis and similar devices have been incorporated to magnify gage readings.

Pressure Traverses

Because the velocity and pressure in a duct vary from point to point at any cross section, a single reading with an impact, static, or Pitot tube will not be accurate unless the quantity measured just happens to equal the average for the total cross section. Calibrations are sometimes feasible. The magnitude of any such single reading depends on its location and the velocity profile in the duct. The velocity profile in turn depends on the Reynolds number (i.e., velocity, hydraulic diameter, and kinematic viscosity) and the roughness of the duct. The velocity profile is also greatly affected by any disturbance. For Reynolds numbers greater than 5000 the approximate mean velocity (V_m) may be determined from the velocity (V_C) corresponding to the velocity pressure at the center of the duct and the friction factor (f) from:

$$V_m = V_C \frac{1}{1+1.439\sqrt{f}}. \tag{104}$$

Equation 104 will produce approximately correct results when the flow is turbulent and the test section is at least 40 diameters downstream from any disturbance. Somewhat higher mean velocities have been observed with shorter duct lengths.

A more accurate average velocity can be determined by measuring the velocity pressure at numerous locations across the duct. With round ducts the usual procedure in making a traverse is to divide the cross section into a number of equal area concentric rings and measure the pressure at four points in each ring. The formula giving the radius (r_x) of any Pitot tube marking for any number of readings (n) across a diameter (d) is

$$r_x = d\sqrt{\frac{2n_x - 1}{4n}} \tag{105}$$

in which n_x is the number of the reading point, counting from the center. The radii of the reading points for traverses with various n are given in Table 25. Figure 29 illustrates the standard marking for a 10 point Pitot tube traverse. The variation from 0.474 to 0.480 in the location of the outside reading point as adopted in this standard marking is a correction for the velocity gradient in close proximity to the wall.

With square or rectangular ducts, the procedure is to divide the cross section into a number of equal rectangular areas and measure the pressure at the center of each. The number of readings should not be fewer than 16 and need not be more than 64. Whenever fewer than 64 readings are taken, the greatest distance between centers should not exceed approximately six inches.

TABLE 25—PITOT TUBE MARKINGS

Number of points in traverse	Number of points in determination	Radii of reading points for $d=1.0$ where n_x is number of points from center					
n	$2n$	$n_x=1$	$n_x=2$	$n_x=3$	$n_x=4$	$n_x=5$	$n_x=6$
6	12	.204	.353	.457	—	—	—
8	16	.177	.306	.395	.468	—	—
10	20	.158	.274	.354	.418	.474	—
12	24	.144	.250	.323	.382	.433	.479

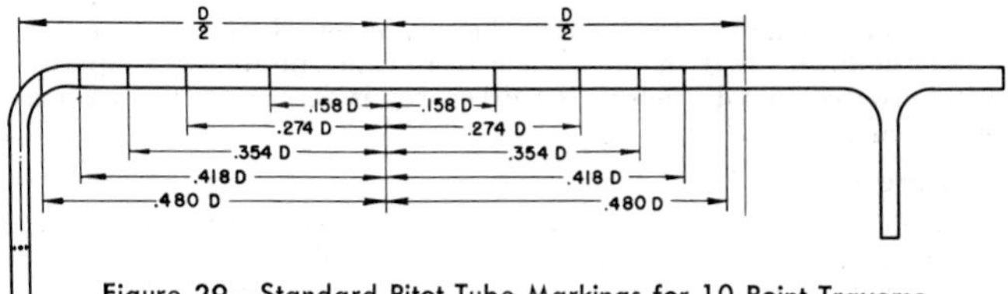

Figure 29—Standard Pitot Tube Markings for 10 Point Traverse

Adapted from the data of Standard Test Code for Air Moving Devices, AMCA, Standard 210-67, 1967, p. 20.

The method of averaging velocity pressures is to take the individual square roots, average them, and square the average. This in effect amounts to averaging the velocities rather than the velocity pressures.

The velocity pattern across a duct section can frequently be made more uni-directional by using straighteners. Low resistance straighteners will not produce uniform velocity, but they will partially or completely nullify spiral flows which would otherwise make measurement more difficult. Spiral flow may occur in a duct because of an upstream disturbance such as a fan or elbow or other non-symmetrical flow condition. The low velocity spirals produced by room air motion can frequently be nullified by a single division plate or simple crisscross (two plates at right angles). The resistance of the latter, if one and one half duct diameters long, is equal to that of four plain duct diameters. Test codes specify honeycomb type straighteners to nullify spirals caused by fan outlet conditions. Figure 30 illustrates the recommended proportions of such a honeycomb device. The length is somewhat less than a crisscross. The friction loss has

---

Straighteners shall be positioned so that sides of the cells are located approximately 45° from the traverse diameters.

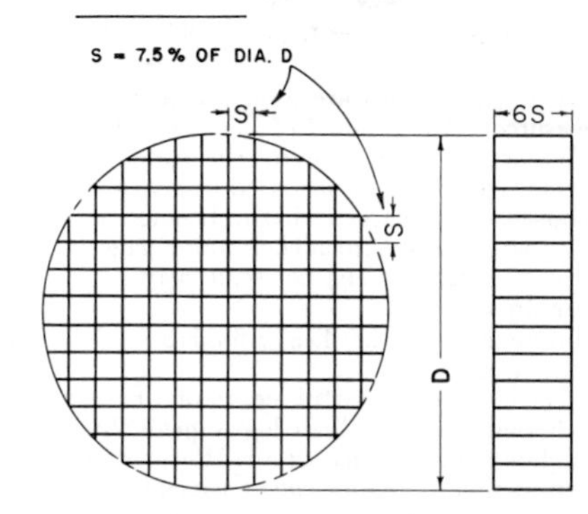

Figure 30—Air Straighteners for Round Ducts

Adapted from the data of Standard Test Code for Air Moving Devices, AMCA, Standard 210-67, 1967, p. 21.

been given as equal to that of four duct diameters. However, recent research* indicates that the loss, when there is no spiral flow, is approximately twelve duct diameters. If swirl energy is dissipated, the loss may be several times higher.

Pressure Gages

The measurement of pressure may be accomplished with various liquid column gages, or with Bourdon, bellows, or diaphragm gages. Only the former will be discussed here since they are the most suitable for the pressures encountered in fan engineering.

A simple, vertical U-tube manometer made of glass tubing with 3/16″ to 1/4″ bore when water filled gives direct readings of equivalent head in inches water gage. The smallest convenient reading is 0.02 to 0.03 inches. Scale lengths range from 2″ up. Gage pressures are determined by connecting one leg to the appropriate pressure probe and exposing the other leg to atmosphere. Differential pressures may be obtained by connecting each leg to an appropriate probe.

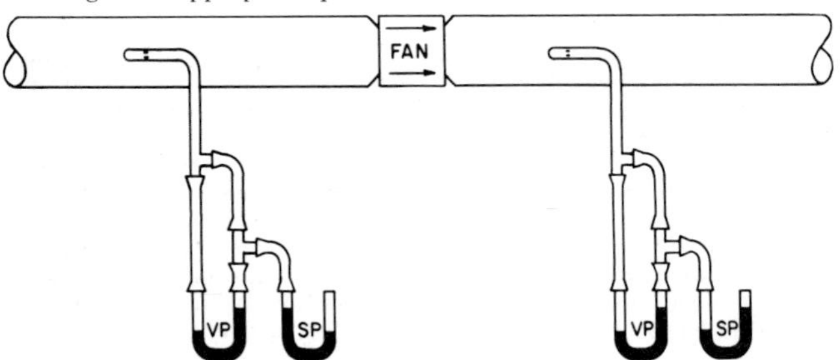

Figure 31—Pitot Tube—Vertical U-Tube Manometer Readings

Inclined U-tubes are used for greater accuracy. The actual pressure measured is the product of the sine of the angle of incline and the linear difference in reading along the tube. Special gage oils, kerosene, and various colored fluids are used to give a longer column or a more definite meniscus than water or both. The actual reading in inches of gage fluid may be converted to inches water gage by multiplying by the specific gravity. Alternatively, the scale may be graduated to read inches water gage directly.

Mercury and other heavy fluids are used to give a shorter column than a water gage.

The effect of the extra length of air column over the low leg compared with that over the high leg is negligible since the density of water is roughly 800 times that of air. However, when measuring water pressures with mercury columns the density ratio is 1 to 13.6 and should be taken into account.

*J. Whitaker, P. G. Bean and E. Hay, Measurement of Losses Across Flow Straighteners, Fluid Mechanics Memo No. 329, National Engineering Laboratory, East Kilbride, Scotland, 1969.

Single reading manometers of both the vertical and inclined types are available. The second leg may be an invisible reservoir, in which case diminished scales or the appropriate correction must be used to compensate for the fall in the reservoir. Readings should be multiplied by the sum of one plus the ratio of the area of the tube to the area of the reservoir. When the second leg is visible, its height may be manually adjusted to the zero point either by relocating the scale for each reading or relocating the reservoir level. The smallest convenient readings are the same as for U-tubes, that is, 0.02-0.03″ for vertical tubes and 0.003-0.005″ for inclined tubes, depending upon the length of the gage.

Manometers, particularly inclined types utilizing fluids other than water, require frequent calibration. Either hook gages or micromanometers, both of which are liquid column gages, may be used for calibration purposes. Micromanometers with accuracies of 0.001 to 0.0001″ are available in several types. All utilize a precision micrometer screw for measurement. Instruments with large ranges are frequently motorized. So long as the accuracy of the micrometer screw and the specific gravity of the gage fluid are known, no calibration is required.

Hook gages with accuracies of 0.001″ are also available in several types. Whereas in all of the previously described manometers some sort of meniscus was read, the method of reading a hook gage is different. In operation the pressure is equalized over the two legs, and zero difference is established between two reference points. This is accomplished with a micrometer (or double micrometer) whose position (or positions) in space is fixed in relation to the reference points. The heights of the two water surfaces are established by means of two hooks whose points all but break through the water surface. When a pressure difference is applied, the hooks must be reset to all but break through the water surface, and the distance between reference marks established by means of the micrometer (or micrometers). Hook points should be sharpened to a 60° or 90° angle. Viewing is best from below, using reflected light.

Gages will give different indications at different gage temperatures due to thermal expansion or contraction of the liquid column and the scale. The standard temperature for a mercury column is 32°F, and a convenient reference temperature for water columns is 70°F. The appropriate temperature correction for mercury columns may be obtained from Table 12 in Chapter 1, and temperature corrections for water columns may be obtained from Table 26. The mercury column corrections include a slight scale correction, but those for water columns do not.

The multiplier type corrections shown for water column were determined from

$$\frac{\textit{corrected reading}}{\textit{actual reading}} = \frac{\textit{actual density of gage fluid}}{\textit{standard fluid density for gage}}. \tag{106}$$

The density of water at 70°F was taken as standard. This formula is applicable regardless of gage fluid, providing, of course, that the proper standard density is used. The specific gravity of any gage fluid can be determined by means of a gage calibration.

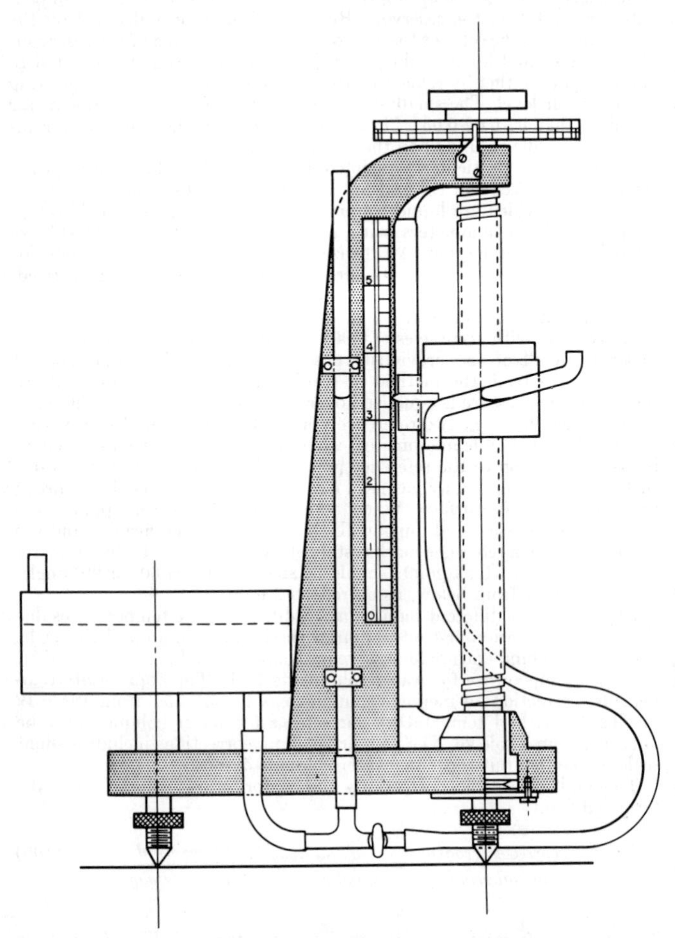

Figure 32—Micromanometer

Adapted from the data of E. Ower, "The Measurement of Air Flow," Chapman and Hall, Ltd., 1927, p. 157.

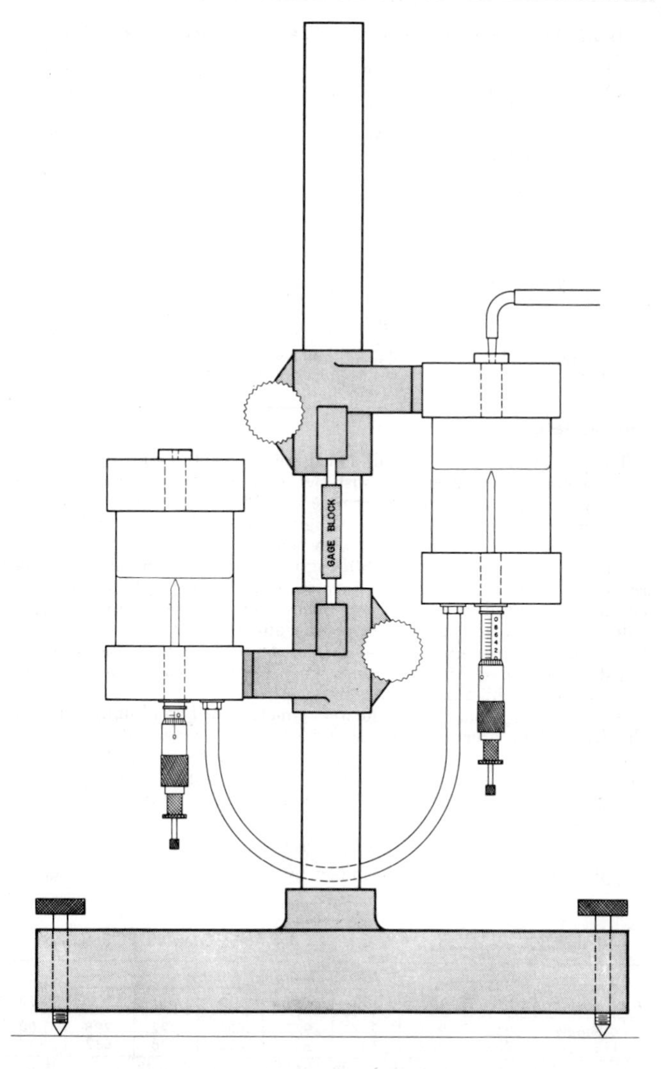

Figure 33—Hook Gage

TABLE 26—WATER DENSITY AND WATER COLUMN CORRECTIONS

°F	lb/ft³	WG corr.	°C	kg/m³	WG corr.
32	62.418	1.00186	0	.999841	1.00187
35	62.424	1.00196	2	.999941	1.00198
39.2	62.426	1.00199	4	.999973	1.00201
40	62.426	1.00199	6	.999941	1.00198
45	62.421	1.00191	8	.999849	1.00188
50	62.409	1.00172	10	.999700	1.00173
55	62.391	1.00143	12	.999498	1.00153
60	62.366	1.00103	14	.999244	1.00128
65	62.337	1.00056	16	.998943	1.00097
70	62.302	1.00000	18	.990595	1.00063
75	62.261	.99934	20	.998203	1.00023
80	62.215	.99860	21.1	.997970	1.00000
85	62.167	.99783	24	.997296	.99932
90	62.113	.99697	26	.996783	.99881
95	62.055	.99604	28	.996232	.99826
100	61.994	.99506	30	.995646	.99767

Adapted from the data of R. C. Weast, "Handbook of Chemistry and Physics," 49th Edition, 1968-1969, The Chemical Rubber Co., p. F-4.

Anemometers

The probes and gages just discussed are only suitable for indirect flow measurement, i.e., velocities must be computed from measured pressures. Velocities can also be determined in other ways. These include the rotating vane anemometer, the swinging vane velometer, and various devices which correlate heat loss with velocity.

The vane anemometer is a rotating vane type instrument which may register velocity or which may give a reading over a timed interval which can be converted into velocity. Such anemometers require frequent calibration because readings are greatly affected by the condition of the bearings. This instrument is useful in measuring low velocities at supply register and exhaust grill openings when in-duct measurements are not convenient and high accuracy is not required.

The operator should move the anemometer slowly and uniformly over the whole flow area in order to arrive at an average determination. Exhaust capacities (CFM) can be calculated by using the average velocity (V) obtained with the dial of the anemometer facing the grill, the gross area of the grill (A_g), and a correction factor (K, which may be determined from Table 27) in

$$CFM = KVA_g. \tag{107}$$

Supply capacities can be determined by using the average velocity (V)

TABLE 27—VALUES OF C AND K IN ANEMOMETER FORMULAS

Grilles	Average Indicated Velocity, fpm							
	150	200	300	400	500	600	700	800
C-Supply	.952	.957	.967	.977	.985	.992	.998	1.00
K-Exhaust	.762	.772	.789	.806	.820	.828	.832	—

Adapted from the data of L. E. Davies, The Measurement of the Flow of Air through Registers and Grilles, *Trans. ASHVE*, vol. 36, pp. 201-224, 1930.

obtained with the dial facing the operator, the gross area (A_g) plus the net free area (A_f), and a correction factor (C, determined from Table 27) in

$$CFM = .5\ CV\ (A_g + A_f). \tag{108}$$

The velometer is a direct reading air velocity meter which is operated by the impact of the flowing air against a swinging vane. By suitably designing the inlet and outlet jets, the instrument may be adapted to read either high or low velocities. The velocity may be taken at any point or an averaging jet used to obtain the average velocity over an area. These instruments have the advantages that they are direct reading, easy to use, and require no additional equipment. Occasionally the meter itself is placed in the air flow being investigated. If the flow is appreciably different at the two ends of the meter, such as in front of exhaust hoods, a material error may result.

Hot-wire anemometers consist of a resistance wire placed in the air stream and heated by an electric current. The temperature of a current-carrying wire in an air stream depends on the current and the rate of heat loss to the air. Since this heat loss varies with velocity, air flow can be established by the relation between the current and the temperature of the wire or between the current and the temperature rise of the air over the wire. Wire temperature can be established in terms of its resistance.

The time required for the reading of a heated Kata-thermometer to fall through a specified interval, usually 100° to 95°, is a measure of the non-directional air velocity. Heated thermocouple and heated thermometer anemometers each employ a pair of temperature sensitive devices, one heated and the other not. The difference in reading for a given heating rate is a measure of the air velocity over the elements. All of the above devices (when properly calibrated) may be used to measure low velocities with good accuracy.

FLOW COEFFICIENTS

If a pressure difference is maintained between the two sides of a plate having a hole in it, fluid will flow from all directions on the higher pressure side and issue as a jet on the lower pressure side. The jet becomes substantially uni-directional at a point somewhat downstream from the opening. At this point, called the *vena contracta*, the contraction of the jet (which occurs due to the multi-directional approach and corresponding directional momentum on the high pressure side) becomes a maximum. That is, the area at the *vena contracta* is the minimum that can be achieved with such a free jet. When the edge of the opening is perfectly square, the area of the stream at the *vena contracta* will be very close to 60% of the area of the opening. The location of the *vena contracta* will be one half of an opening diameter downstream of the face of the opening. Considerable potential energy is converted to kinetic energy in producing acceleration by means of an orifice such as this. The efficiency of this conversion is quite high, and the loss or amount of energy dissipated as heat is amazingly low. The opposite conversion from kinetic to potential requires careful design in order to obtain high efficiencies or avoid high losses. The loss of energy across an orifice or nozzle, or that dissipated as heat between the upstream face and the *vena contracta*, affects the velocity profile at the *vena contracta*.

The flow coefficients as defined below may be used to determine flow rates (*q or CFM*) and pressure losses for any orifice or nozzle. The subscript 1 will be used to denote the upstream location, whether it be pipe or plenum, and the subscript 3 to denote the plane of the *vena contracta*.

Based on Equation 97 the energy balance for incompressible flow for any orifice or nozzle may be written

$$SP_1 + VP_1 = SP_3 + VP_3 + \Delta TP_{1-3} \tag{109}$$

in which the energy converted into heat is denoted by ΔTP_{1-3}. The subscript 2 will be used to denote the plane of area A_2. For an orifice, A_2 is the area of the opening at entrance. For a nozzle, A_2 is the area of the opening at exit.

The coefficient of contraction, which may be defined as the ratio of the area of the *vena contracta* to that of the area at entrance to an orifice or at exit from a nozzle, may be written

$$C_C = \frac{A_3}{A_2}. \tag{110}$$

The coefficient of velocity, which may be defined as the ratio of the actual average velocity at the *vena contracta* to the velocity that would be obtained if there were no loss, may be expressed by

$$C_V = \frac{\sqrt{VP_3}}{\sqrt{\Delta TP_{1-3} + VP_3}}. \tag{111}$$

The coefficient of resistance, which may be defined as the ratio of the loss of total pressure to the velocity pressure at the *vena contracta*, may be written

$$C_R = \frac{\Delta TP_{1-3}}{VP_3} = \frac{1}{C_V^2} - 1. \tag{112}$$

The coefficient of discharge of an orifice or nozzle may be defined as the product of the coefficients of contraction and velocity, or

$$C_D = C_C \times C_V. \tag{113}$$

Equation 103, which is for incompressible flow, may be rewritten

$$CFM = A_3\, V_3 = A_2\, V_2 = A_1\, V_1 \tag{114}$$

where volume flow rate (*CFM*) is in cfm, areas (*A*) are in ft², and velocities (*V*) are in fpm. Combining this with Equation 99 produces

$$CFM = 1096.7\, A_3 \sqrt{\frac{VP_3}{\delta}} \tag{115}$$

where velocity pressures (*VP*) are in "*WG* and densities (δ) are in lb/ft³. Incorporating the definition of coefficient of contraction yields

$$CFM = 1096.7\, C_C\, A_2 \sqrt{\frac{VP_3}{\delta}}. \tag{116}$$

Similarly, employing the definition of coefficient of velocity results in

$$CFM = 1096.7\ C_C\ C_V\ A_2 \sqrt{\frac{VP_3 + \Delta TP_{1-3}}{\delta}}. \tag{117}$$

Substituting the coefficient of discharge for its equivalent produces

$$CFM = 1096.7\ C_D\ A_2 \sqrt{\frac{VP_3 + \Delta TP_{1-3}}{\delta}}. \tag{118}$$

Manipulating Equation 109 and making the appropriate substitution in Equation 118 yields

$$CFM = 1096.7\ C_D\ A_2 \sqrt{\frac{TP_1 - SP_3}{\delta}}, \qquad \text{or} \tag{119}$$

$$CFM = 1096.7\ C_D\ A_2 \sqrt{\frac{VP_1 + SP_1 - SP_3}{\delta}}. \tag{120}$$

After removing the approach velocity pressure (VP_1) from under the radical,

$$CFM = 1096.7\ C_D\ A_2\ \phi_i \sqrt{\frac{SP_1 - SP_3}{\delta}}. \tag{121}$$

The true velocity of approach factor for incompressible flow (ϕ_i) may be determined by equating Equations 120 and 121 or 119 and 121

$$\phi_i = \sqrt{\frac{VP_1 + SP_1 - SP_3}{SP_1 - SP_3}} = \sqrt{\frac{TP_1 - SP_3}{SP_1 - SP_3}}. \tag{122}$$

Utilizing the relationships embodied in Equations 109 and 111

$$\phi_i = \sqrt{\frac{1}{1 - VP_1/(VP_3 + \Delta TP_{1-3})}} = \sqrt{\frac{1}{1 - C_V^2(VP_1/VP_3)}}. \tag{123}$$

The true velocity of approach factor may also be written as a function of area ratio and coefficient of velocity or discharge:

$$\phi_i = \sqrt{\frac{1}{1 - C_V^2\ (A_3/A_1)^2}} = \sqrt{\frac{1}{1 - C_D^2\ (A_2/A_1)^2}}. \tag{124}$$

A pseudo velocity of approach factor, i.e., $\phi_i' = \sqrt{1/[1 - (A_2/A_1)^2]}$ or one based only on area ratio, is frequently used. In such cases a pseudo coefficient of discharge, i.e., $C_D' \neq C_C \times C_V$ or one different than that defined, must be used in Equation 121 (and in Equation 130 which is given in the section on nozzles). It should be noted that $\phi_i'\ C_D' = \phi_i\ C_D$.

For the special case of a nozzle or orifice discharging to atmosphere, the static pressure at the *vena contracta* (SP_3) is equal to zero. Thus it can be seen that it is necessary only to measure either the average total pressure or the average static pressure ahead of the nozzle or orifice in order to determine the flow rate. It is usually much more convenient to measure the average static pressure rather than the average total pressure; hence Equation 121 is used even though it does involve the velocity of approach factor. It may also be noted that for a plenum approach the velocity pressure (VP_1) equals zero, and therefore the velocity of approach factor (ϕ_i) equals 1.0.

Numerous values for the various flow coefficients have been established empirically. Where similar flow and measuring conditions exist, these data can be used to predict flow rates from pressure readings. However, if there is any doubt whatsoever about the uniformity of the upstream flow, or the conditions of measurement, or both, an in-place calibration against a Pitot tube should be made.

There are numerous devices which can be used to measure flow. The flow coefficients for these devices, together with the method of pressure measurement and brief details of construction, are given in the paragraphs below.

The Square-Edged Orifice

The square-edged orifice is a flat plate with a hole in it. The hole may be of any shape. In the extreme it may even be a slot with very large aspect ratio. The coefficient of discharge with a plenum approach is about 0.6 regardless of shape. Orifice plates should be perfectly flat and the holes accurately made for accurate area determinations. All burrs must be removed from the inlet edge so that the air flows over a sharp 90° corner. The thickness of the edge should not exceed 1/50 of the orifice diameter. Recommended thicknesses are 1/16″ up to 6″ diameter hole, 3/32″ up to 12″ diameter, 1/8″ up to 24″ diameter, and 3/16″ up to 48″ diameter. Thicker plates, when required for rigidity (as in high pressure work) should be beveled away on the downstream side of the orifice. Table 28 lists flow coefficients for square-edged orifices with various ratios of hole diameter to pipe diameter. The combined velocity of approach factors and coefficients of discharge ($\phi_i C_D$) represent the averages for pipe sizes ranging from 1½″ to 16″. This data is based on *vena contracta* taps and pipe Reynolds numbers of 1,000,000, and will give reasonably accurate results whether flange, radius, or *vena contracta* taps are used. Figure 34 shows the location of the various types of pressure taps. Of the remaining coefficients of flow listed in Table 28, the coefficient of velocity (C_V) for orifices in pipes was assumed to be 0.975 which is the average for values generally listed for orifices discharging from plenums. The coefficient of contraction (C_C) was calculated using the listed values of $\phi_i C_D$, the appropriate definitions, and the assumed value for C_V. The coefficient of discharge (C_D) was then calculated using the coefficients of velocity and contraction, and the velocity of approach factor determined accordingly.

The pseudo velocity of approach factor (ϕ_i') and the pseudo coefficient of discharge (C_D') are also given. All data are based on the difference in pressure from the upstream location to the *vena contracta* location. The static pressure at the *vena contracta* will be zero only when discharge is to atmosphere. In all other cases, the discharge pressure must be measured.

An average coefficient of resistance is shown. This value is calculated from the assumed coefficient of velocity. It is about equal to the average usually shown for orifices discharging from plenums. The contraction loss (ΔTP_{1-3}) may be determined from the coefficient of resistance (C_R) and the velocity pressure at the *vena contracta* (VP_3) using:

$$\Delta TP_{1-3} = C_R VP_3. \quad (125)$$

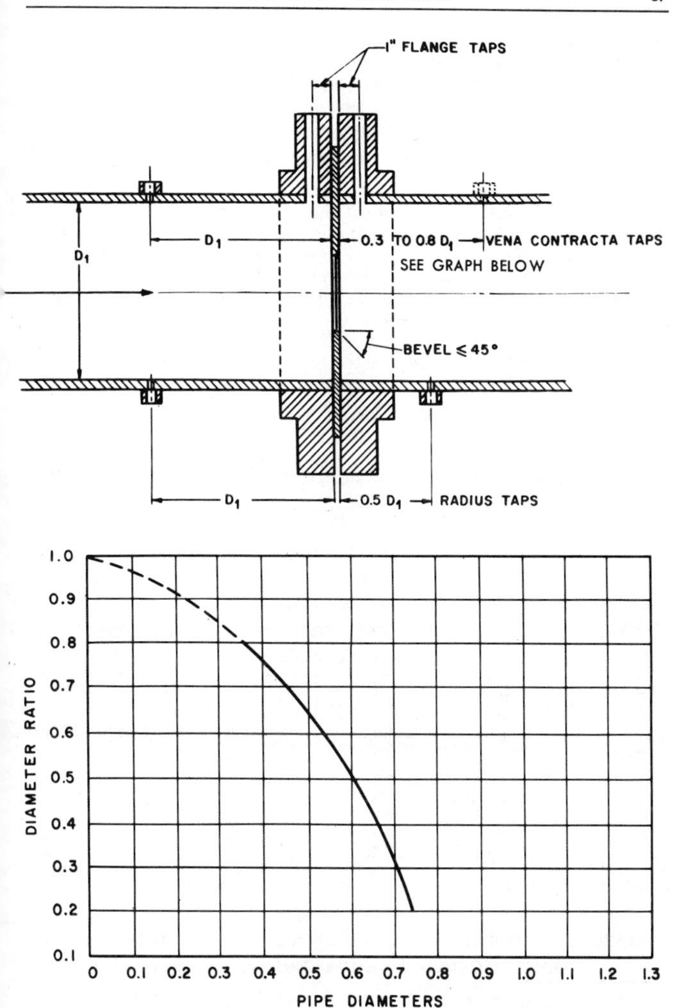

Figure 34—Square-Edged Orifice and Pressure Tap Locations

Adapted from the data of Instruments and Apparatus, Part 5, Measurement of Quantity of Materials, ASME Power Test Codes, PTC 19.5; 4-1959, p. 9.

When discharge is to atmosphere, the pressure corresponding to the velocity at the *vena contracta* represents an additional loss.

When the orifice is in a uniform pipe, the over-all contraction and re-expansion loss ($\Delta\ TP_{1-4}$) may be determined from the meter differential ($SP_1 - SP_3$) and the data of Figure 35 using:

$$\Delta TP_{1-4} = K\ (SP_1 - SP_3). \tag{126}$$

When the square-edged orifice is formed by a uniform downstream pipe, some of the velocity pressure at the *vena contracta* is converted to or regained as static pressure, provided the discharge pipe is long enough for complete expansion to take place. The minimum length of pipe usually necessary for this to occur is three opening diameters. When such a configuration is used, the coefficients listed in Table 28 still apply provided the pressure at the *vena contracta* is used as indicated. Alternatively, the equivalent coefficients of discharge ($Eq.\ C_D$) and resistance ($Eq.\ C_R$) given in Table 29 may be used in the following equations:

$$CFM = 1096.7\ (Eq.\ C_D)\ A_2 \sqrt{\frac{TP_1 - SP_4}{\delta}}, \tag{127}$$

$$CFM = 1096.7\ (\phi_i\ Eq.\ C_D)\ A_2 \sqrt{\frac{SP_1 - SP_4}{\delta}}, \text{ and} \tag{128}$$

$$\Delta TP_{1-4} = (Eq.\ C_R)\ VP_4 \tag{129}$$

where the subscript 4 indicates the location where full flow is established in the downstream pipe. With a short pipe SP_4 will be zero.

TABLE 28—FLOW COEFFICIENTS FOR SQUARE-EDGED ORIFICES

(Also Abrupt Contractions)

D_2/D_1 A_2/A_1	.7 .490	.65 .422	.6 .360	.55 .302	.5 .250	.45 .202	.4 .160	.35 .122	.3 .090	From Plenum
$\phi_i C_D$	.699	.670	.650	.635	.623	.614	.608	.603	.600	.60-.61
C_V	.975	.975	.975	.975	.975	.975	.975	.975	.975	.97-.98
C_C	.673	.660	.648	.638	.631	.625	.621	.617	.615	.62
C_D	.660	.644	.632	.623	.615	.609	.605	.601	.599	.60-.61
C_R	.052	.052	.052	.052	.052	.052	.052	.052	.052	.06-.04
ϕ_i	1.059	1.041	1.028	1.018	1.012	1.007	1.005	1.003	1.001	1.00
ϕ_i'	1.147	1.104	1.072	1.049	1.033	1.022	1.013	1.007	1.004	1.00
C_D'	.609	.607	.606	.605	.604	.602	.600	.598	.597	.60-.61

Adapted from the data of Instruments and Apparatus, Part 5, Measurement of Quantity of Materials, ASME Power Test Codes, PTC 19.5; 4-1959, pp. 20-39.

TABLE 29—EQUIVALENT FLOW COEFFICIENTS FOR SQUARE-EDGED ORIFICES FORMED BY A UNIFORM DOWNSTREAM PIPE

D_2/D_1 A_2/A_1	.7 .490	.65 .422	.6 .360	.55 .302	.5 .250	.45 .202	.4 .160	.35 .122	.3 .090	From Plenum
$Eq.\ C_D$	.861	.850	.839	.831	.823	.818	.813	.811	.81	.81-.83
$\phi_i Eq.\ C_D$	.912	.885	.863	.849	.835	.824	.817	.813	.81	.81-.83
$Eq.\ C_R$	.35	.39	.42	.45	.47	.49	.51	.52	.53	.53-.48

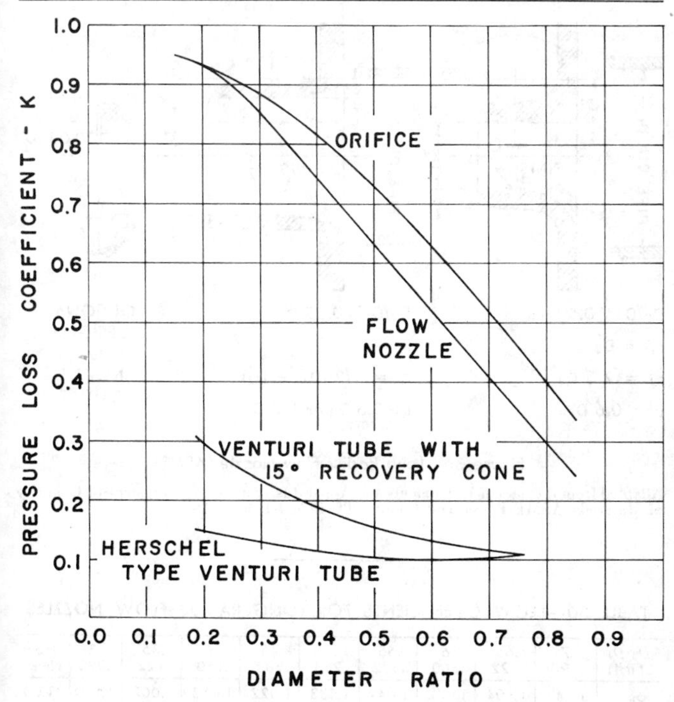

Figure 35—Pressure Loss Coefficients for Flow Meters

Adapted from the data of Instruments and Apparatus, Part 5, Measurement of Quantity of Materials, ASME Power Test Codes, PTC 19.5; 4-1959, p. 12.

Rounded Entry Nozzles

If the edge of an orifice opening is rounded rather than square, the coefficient of contraction is increased. In the extreme, when the opening is rounded to the degree indicated in Figure 36, the coefficient of contraction reaches unity. There is no contraction beyond the nozzle, and the stream issues from the nozzle full bore.

In all real nozzles there is some small loss of energy due to fluid friction. For accurately made contours, this loss will be less than the corresponding loss in a free jet issuing from a square-edged orifice. This loss increases with roughness, but decreases with Reynolds number. The *ASME Power Test Code* PTC 19.5; 4-1959 shows a coefficient of discharge of 0.994 for long radius, low ratio nozzles handling air when the Reynolds number is

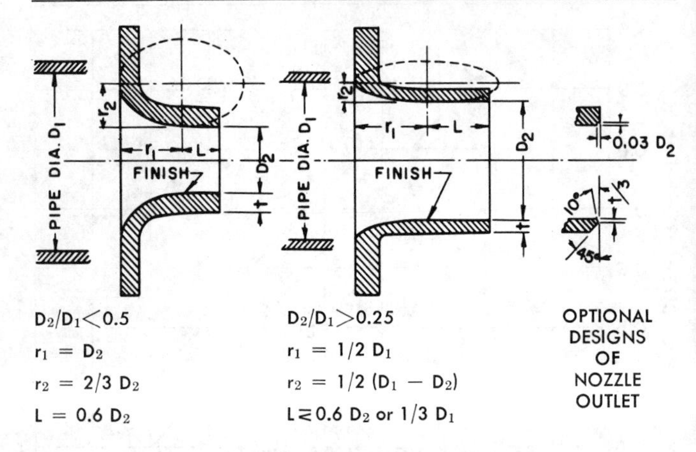

Figure 36—Long Radius Flow Nozzle (ASME)

Adapted from the data of Instruments and Apparatus, Part 5, Measurement of Quantity of Materials, ASME Power Test Codes, PTC 19.5; 4-1959, p. 13.

TABLE 30—FLOW COEFFICIENTS FOR LONG RADIUS FLOW NOZZLES

D_3/D_1 A_3/A_1	.7 .490	.65 .422	.6 .360	.55 .302	.5 .250	.45 .202	.4 .160	.35 .122	.3 .090	From Plenum
ϕ_i	1.147	1.104	1.072	1.049	1.033	1.022	1.013	1.007	1.004	1.00
$.99\phi_i$	1.136	1.093	1.061	1.039	1.023	1.012	1.003	.997	.994	.99
$.98\phi_i$	1.124	1.082	1.051	1.028	1.012	1.002	.993	.987	.984	.98

above 500,000. The coefficient of discharge drops to a value of 0.942 at a Reynolds number of 10,000 for long radius, high ratio nozzles.

As distinguished from the reference area of an orifice, which is the opening area or entrance area, the reference area for a nozzle is the discharge or exit area. When the coefficient of contraction is 1.0, A_2 is equal to A_3. Accordingly, the capacity equations are often rewritten using the area of the *vena contracta* (A_3):

$$CFM = 1096.7\, C_D\, A_3\, \phi_i \sqrt{\frac{SP_1 - SP_3}{\delta}} \quad \text{and} \tag{130}$$

$$CFM = 1096.7\, C_D\, A_3 \sqrt{\frac{TP_1 - SP_3}{\delta}}. \tag{131}$$

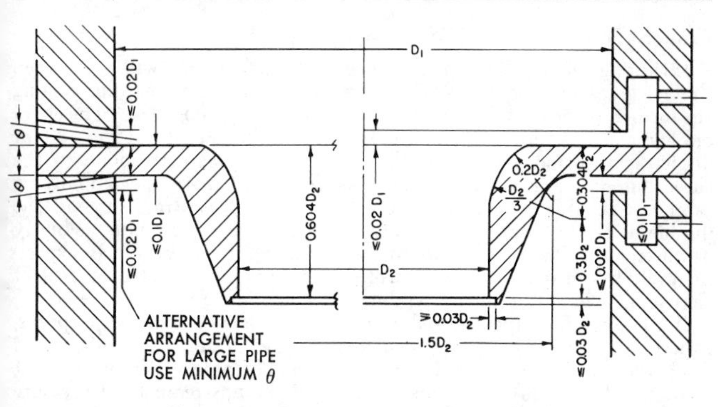

Figure 37—Short Radius Flow Nozzle (ISA)

Adapted from the data of Instruments and Apparatus, Part 5, Measurement of Quantity of Materials, ASME Power Test Codes, PTC 19.5; 4-1940, p. 26.

TABLE 31—FLOW COEFFICIENTS FOR ISA FLOW NOZZLES

A_3/A_1	.5	.45	.4	.35	.3	.25	.2	.15	.1	.05
$\phi_i C_D$	1.081	1.059	1.041	1.028	1.016	1.006	.999	.993	.989	.987

Adapted from the data of Instruments and Apparatus, Part 5, Measurement of Quantity of Materials, ASME Power Test Codes, PTC 19.5; 4-1940, p. 26.

Velocity of approach factors, together with combined coefficients utilizing a coefficient of discharge of either 0.99 or 0.98, are listed in Table 30 for various ratios of nozzle discharge area (A_3) to upstream pipe area (A_1). The coefficient of velocity may be taken as equal to the coefficient of discharge whenever full bore flow is assumed, i.e., whenever the coefficient of contraction equals 1.0. Accordingly, the coefficient of resistance may be taken as 0.02 for coefficients of discharge of 0.99 and as 0.04 for coefficients of discharge of 0.98. The loss may be calculated from either Equation 125 or 126 using C_R as listed above or K from Figure 35.

A short radius nozzle known as the I.S.A. (International Standards Association) nozzle is illustrated in Figure 37. According to *ASME Power Test Code* PTC 19.5; 4-1940, the combined coefficient of discharge —velocity of approach factor is as listed for various areas in Table 31 for Reynolds numbers above 100,000 approximately. Data on the I.S.A. nozzle was omitted from PTC 19.5; 4-1959 presumably because results obtained therewith are not always accurate.

Conical Entry Nozzles (Converging Tapers)

If the edge of an orifice opening is beveled, performance will be between that of a square-edged orifice and a rounded entry nozzle, approaching the former as the included angle between sides approaches 180°. The effect of degree of taper on coefficient of discharge is illustrated in Figure 38 for discharge to atmosphere. The three different curves correspond to the three different approach conditions as illustrated in the accompanying sketches. In all instances the jet will continue to contract beyond the discharge of the nozzle, producing a *vena contracta* at a point slightly downstream. The *vena contracta* location may be determined experimentally by means of an impact tube in the center of the stream. It is at that point where the impact reading is a maximum.

If a converging taper is used as a nozzle for flow measuring purposes, Equation 119 may be used to calculate flow rate (CFM). The coefficient of discharge may be obtained from Figure 38. The area of the nozzle exit (A_2), the density (δ) of the air or gas, and the upstream total pressure (TP_1) can all be measured. The static pressure at the *vena contracta* is zero.

Re-entrant Pipes

The flow nozzle or rounded entry orifice represents one extreme in orifice construction. The opposite extreme is the re-entrant pipe. For a perfect re-entrant pipe, which would have an infinitely thin pipe wall and would be just long enough to insure completely reverse flow along the outer surface but not so long that the flow re-attaches to the inner surface, the theoretical coefficient of contraction would be 0.50. Table 32 gives flow coefficients for two flow situations, one where the flow remains separated and the other where it re-attaches to the pipe wall. Re-attachment is generally assumed to occur between three and four diameters downstream from the opening. Table values are all approximate since they are based on assumed values for C_C and C_V. Flow rates may be determined from measurements of the upstream plenum total pressure (TP_1) and static pressure at the *vena contracta* (SP_3) using Equation 119 and C_D. Alternately, Equation 127 and Eq. C_D may be used with measurements of the static pressure at the point where the flow re-attaches (SP_4). Both cases involve the area of the pipe opening (A_2). Similarly, total pressure losses may be determined from either Equation 125 or 129 and the appropriate coefficients and velocity pressures.

TABLE 32—FLOW COEFFICIENTS FOR RE-ENTRANT PIPES

Flow	C_C	C_V	C_D	C_R	Eq. C_D	Eq. C_R
Separated	.545	.975	.531	.052	—	—
Re-attached	.545	.975	.531	.052	.799	.872

Abrupt Enlargement

In an abrupt enlargement the fluid flows into a conduit without contraction but at less than full bore and subsequently expands to full bore. Not every sudden enlargement of duct section fulfills these conditions.

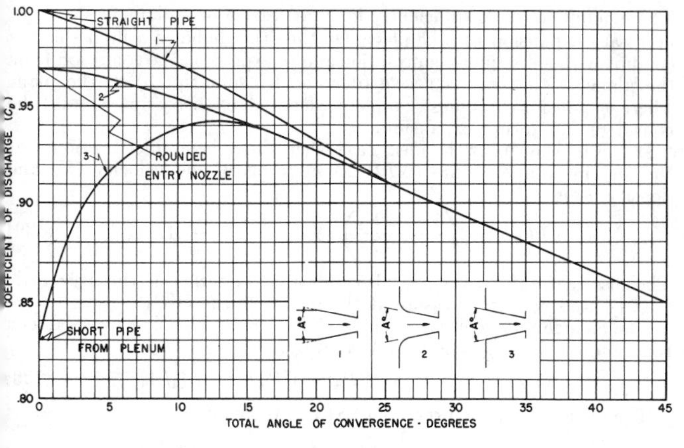

Figure 38—Discharge Coefficients for Converging Tapers Discharging to Atmosphere

---

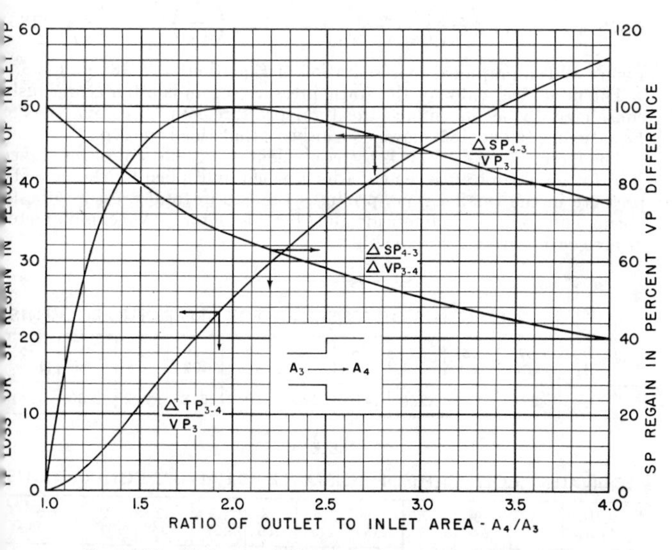

Figure 39—TP Loss and SP Regain for Abrupt Enlargements

The conduit must be sufficiently long (at least 3 or 4 diameters) for the necessary expansion to take place. On the other hand, if a fluid enters a conduit with subsequent contraction and re-expansion the condition from the plane of the *vena contracta* (denoted by subscript 3) to the plane where expansion becomes complete (denoted by subscript 4) may be considered an abrupt expansion.

It can be shown for the ideal case where there is no duct friction that the loss in total pressure (ΔTP_{3-4}) in terms of the velocity (V) and density (δ) is

$$\Delta TP_{3-4} = \left(\frac{V_3 - V_4}{1096.7}\right)^2 \delta = VP_3 \, (1 - A_3/A_4)^2. \qquad (132)$$

The loss in total pressure is also indicated in terms of the area ratio (A_3/A_4) and velocity pressure at the *vena contracta* (VP_3).

The change in velocity pressure (ΔVP_{3-4}) may also be expressed as a function of this area ratio as indicated by:

$$\Delta VP_{3-4} = VP_3 - VP_4 = VP_3 \, (1 - [A_3/A_4]^2). \qquad (133)$$

The change in static pressure (ΔSP_{3-4}) is therefore:

$$\Delta SP_{3-4} = \Delta TP_{3-4} - \Delta VP_{3-4} = 2 \, VP_3 \left(\frac{A_3}{A_4}\right)\left(\frac{A_3}{A_4} - 1\right). \qquad (134)$$

The "regain" or increase in static pressure (ΔSP_{4-3}) is:

$$\Delta SP_{4-3} = 2 \, VP_3 \left(\frac{A_3}{A_4}\right)\left(1 - \frac{A_3}{A_4}\right) = 2 \, VP_3 \left(\frac{V_4}{V_3}\right)\left(1 - \frac{V_4}{V_3}\right). \qquad (135)$$

Figure 39 is a graphical representation of Equations 132, 133 and 135.

The numerical value of the static pressure regain is often erroneously considered to be one minus the total pressure loss. A comparison of Equations 132 and 135 shows conclusively that this is not so.

The factor $(1 - A_3/A_4)^2$ is the equivalent of a coefficient of resistance (C_R) for an abrupt enlargement which, when multiplied by the velocity pressure in the smaller pipe, produces the loss in total pressure due to abrupt enlargement. Numerical values for this factor for various diameter or area ratios are given in Table 33.

TABLE 33—COEFFICIENTS OF RESISTANCE FOR ABRUPT ENLARGEMENTS

D_3/D_4 A_3/A_4	.9 .81	.8 .64	.7 .49	.6 .36	.5 .25	.4 .16	.3 .09	.2 .04	.1 .01	To Plenum
C_R	.036	.130	.260	.410	.562	.706	.828	.922	.980	1.00

TABLE 34

EQUIVALENT COEFFICIENT OF RESISTANCE FOR ABRUPT CONTRACTIONS

D_2/D_1 A_2/A_1	.9 .81	.8 .64	.7 .49	.6 .36	.5 .25	.4 .16	.3 .09	.2 .04	.1 .01	From Plenum
Eq. C_R	.18	.26	.35	.42	.48	.50	.52	.52	.52	.55-.46

Abrupt Contraction

In an abrupt contraction the fluid flows into a conduit at full bore but immediately contracts and subsequently re-expands to full bore. Not every sudden reduction of duct section fulfills these conditions. The conduit must be sufficiently long for the necessary contraction and re-expansion to take place. The conditions up to the *vena contracta* are the same as for a square-edged orifice with an opening equal to the cross section of the conduit. The conditions beyond the *vena contracta* are the same as for an abrupt expansion.

For the ideal case where there is no duct friction the loss in total pressure (ΔTP_{1-4}) may be determined from Equation **112** and **132** as indicated by:

$$\Delta TP_{1-4} = \Delta TP_{1-3} + \Delta TP_{3-4} = VP_3\left[\left(\frac{1}{C_V^2} - 1\right) + \left(1 - A_3/A_2\right)^2\right]. \quad (136)$$

By suitable algebraic manipulation this loss can be expressed in terms of the velocity pressure (VP_2) at the opening and the flow coefficients (C_D & C_C), if the opening is assumed to be a square-edged orifice. The velocity pressure (VP_4) in the downstream or smaller duct is equal to that at the opening (VP_2):

$$\Delta TP_{1-4} = VP_2\left(\frac{A_2}{A_3}\right)^2\left[\frac{1}{C_V^2} - 1 + 1 - 2C_C + C_C^2\right] = VP_2\left[\frac{1}{C_D^2} - \frac{2}{C_C} + 1\right]. \quad (137)$$

The bracketed term may be considered an equivalent coefficient of resistance based on the average velocity corresponding to the small pipe size. Values for this equivalent coefficient of resistance for use in Equation **129** are listed in Table **34** for various diameter and area ratios. The values shown are based on data taken from Table **28** except for the bold figures which are based on extrapolated data. The wide range of values shown for discharge from a plenum through an abrupt contraction illustrates the effect of a change in coefficient of discharge from 0.60 to 0.61.

Diffusers and Evasés (Diverging Tapers)

A diffuser is a flow passage in which kinetic energy is converted into pressure. For subsonic flow the passage must diverge in the direction of flow. Gradual divergence distinguishes the diffuser from an abrupt enlargement. When a diffuser is located at the exit end of a duct it is known as an *evasé*. Sometimes a diffuser on the outlet of a fan is called an *evasé* even if there is additional ductwork. Frequently the fan is said to be "coned" even if the cross sections of the diffuser are not circular. A conical diffuser, however, has circular cross sections. Two-dimensional, or plane diffusers have rectangular cross sections and two parallel sides. Any other diverging passage with rectangular sections is called a three-dimensional diffuser.

The performance of a diffuser, like that of an abrupt enlargement, will

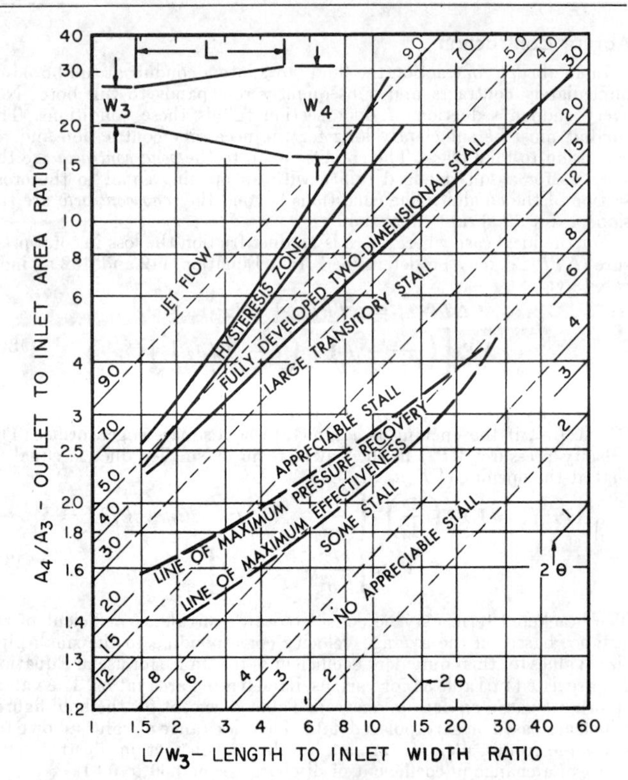

Figure 40—Flow Regimes in Plane Diffusers

Adapted from the data of L. R. Reneau, J. P. Johnston and S. J. Kline, Performance and Design of Straight Two-Dimensional Diffusers, ASME Paper No. 66-FE-10, 1966.

---

vary with inlet velocity pressure (VP_3) and the ratio of outlet to inlet area (A_4/A_3). In addition, performance will vary with the centerline length (L) and the total included angle of divergence (2θ).

In an ideal diffuser the "regain" (ΔSP_{4-3}) would equal the change in velocity pressure (ΔVP_{3-4}) and the loss in total pressure (ΔTP_{3-4}) would be zero. In a real diffuser there will always be a loss in total pressure and the effectiveness (η) which is equal to ($\Delta SP_{4-3}/\Delta VP_{3-4}$), will be less than unity. Regain is frequently given in percent of inlet velocity pressure. The dimensionless fraction ($\Delta SP_{4-3}/VP_3$) is also known as the coefficient of pressure recovery (C_p).

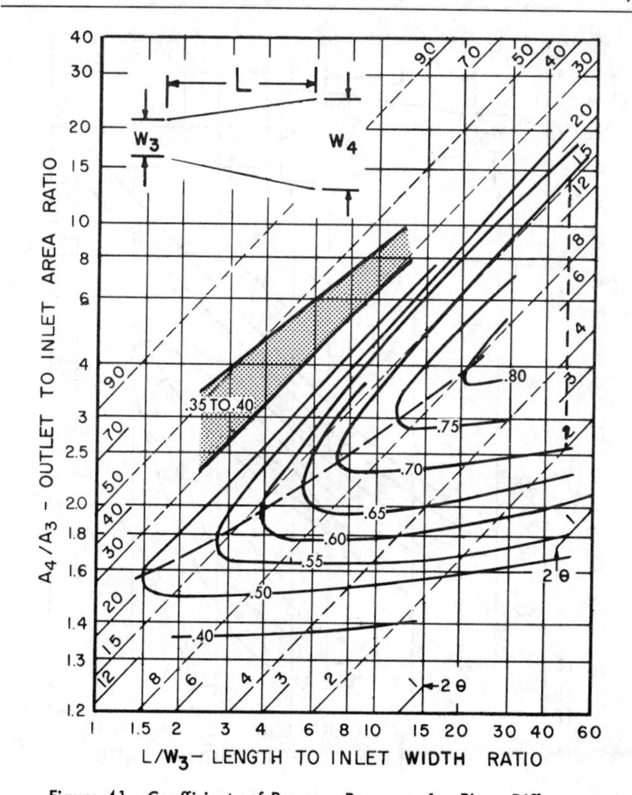

Figure 41—Coefficients of Pressure Recovery for Plane Diffusers

Adapted from the data of L. R. Reneau, J. P. Johnston and S. J. Kline, Performance and Design of Straight Two-Dimensional Diffusers, ASME Paper No. 66-FE-10, 1966.

The flow in diffusers may follow the walls of the passage or it may stall and be deflected away from the walls by reverse flow. Figure 40 shows the various flow regimes that may be encountered. The chart is drawn for plane diffusers with straight walls. It is generally applicable for entrance Reynolds numbers greater than 5 x 10^4 and Mach numbers less than 0.2. The coordinates are area ratio (A_4/A_3) and the ratio of length to inlet width (L/W_1) but the angle of divergence is also shown. The flow in each regime is described in detail in the reference cited but brief explanations follow.

In jet flow, separation from both walls begins near the throat and covers

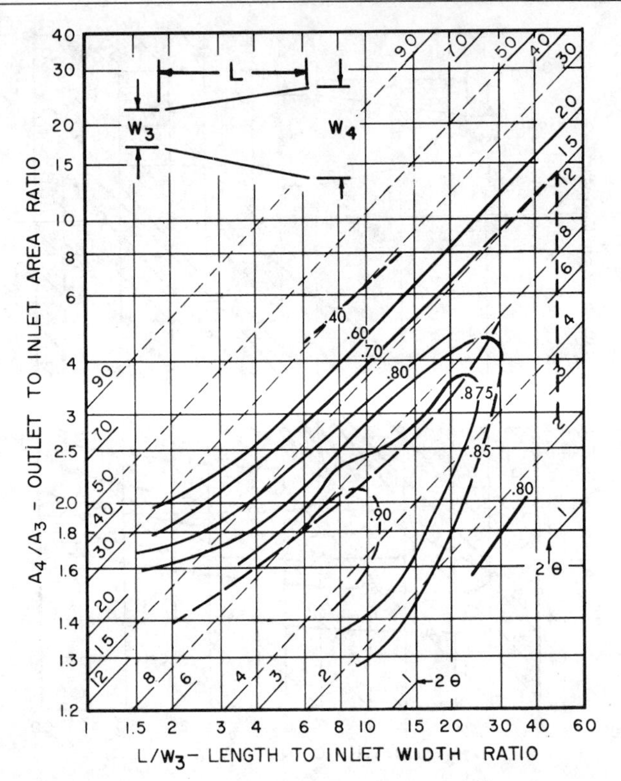

Figure 42—Effectiveness Values for Plane Diffusers

Adapted from the data of L. R. Reneau, J. P. Johnston and S. J. Kline, Performance and Design of Straight Two-Dimensional Diffusers, ASME Paper No. 66-FE-10, 1966.

---

both walls. In two-dimensional stall, separation begins near the throat and covers one wall. This fixed stall will remain on that wall but may be switched to the other wall by a large disturbance at the inlet or outlet. There is a region between the two zones where either jet flow or two-dimensional stall can exist. Transitory stall varies with diffuser geometry but generally begins in the corners, builds up, and is swept away repeatedly.

Figures 41 and 42 are also drawn for plane diffusers. They show the coefficients of pressure recovery and the effectiveness values, respectively, for the various geometries. These charts are drawn for only one inlet

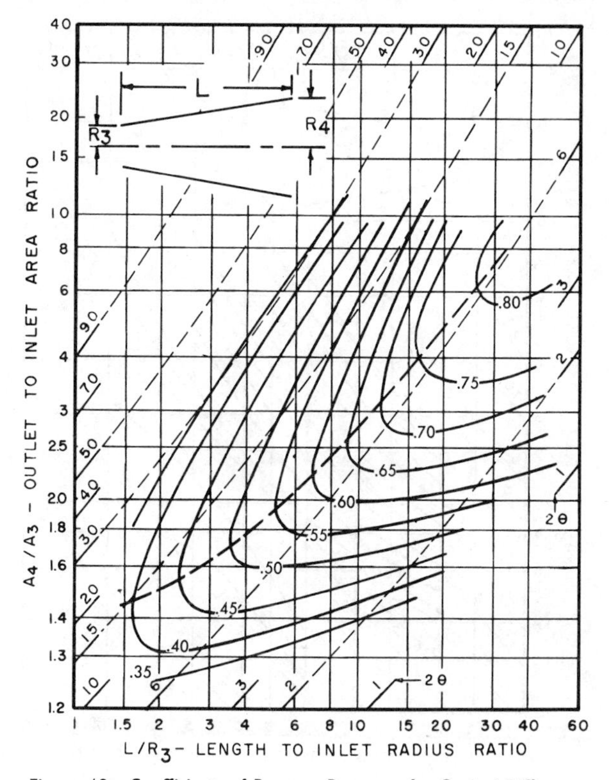

Figure 43—Coefficients of Pressure Recovery for Conical Diffusers
Adapted from the data of A. T. McDonald and R. W. Fox, An Experimental Investigation of Incompressible Flow in Conical Diffusers, ASME Paper No. 65-FE-25, 1965.

---

boundary layer condition. Plots for other conditions are given in the reference. The condition for Figures 41 and 42 is for turbulent inlet boundary layer such as might be generated if the diffuser is preceded by several diameters of straight duct and flow is uniform. Chart values should be reduced as much as 25% when used for cases involving non-uniform inlet flow or thicker boundary layers.

To determine static pressure regain use either

$$\Delta SP_{4-3} = C_p VP_3 \quad \text{or} \tag{138}$$

$$\Delta SP_{4-3} = \eta\,(\Delta VP_{3-4}). \tag{139}$$

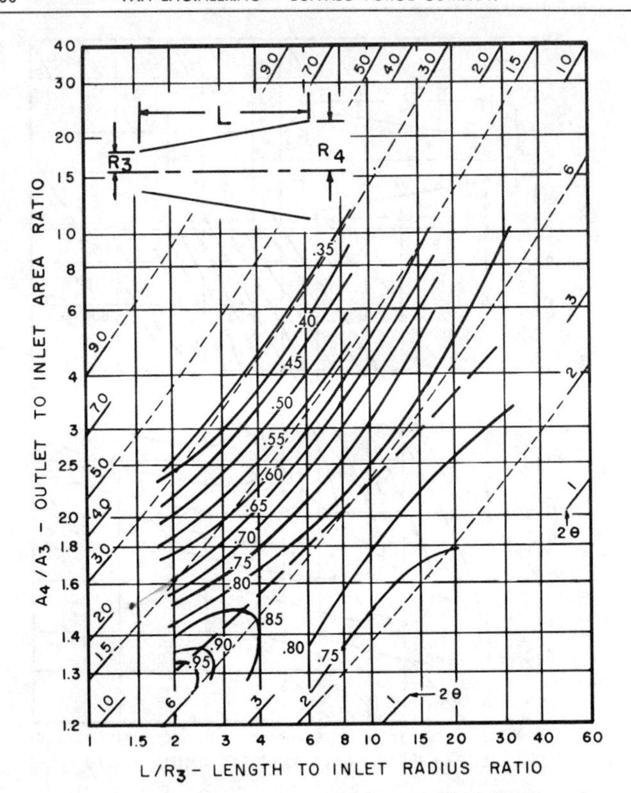

Figure 44—Effectiveness Values for Conical Diffusers

Adapted from the data of A. T. McDonald and R. W. Fox, An Experimental Investigation of Incompressible Flow in Conical Diffusers, ASME Paper No. 65-FE-25, 1965.

To determine total pressure loss use

$$\Delta TP_{3-4} = (1 - \eta)\,(\Delta VP_{3-4}). \tag{140}$$

Figure 41 can be used to determine peak pressure recovery for a given length or a given area ratio by inspection. Lines connecting all such points are drawn on the chart. They are also drawn on Figure 40 to illustrate that peak recovery occurs in the zone of transitory stall. On the other hand, maximum effectiveness generally occurs in the unstalled flow zone. An inspection of Figure 42 shows that maximum effectiveness at constant area ratio will be produced with a plane diffuser angle of approximately 7°.

Figures 43 and 44 are drawn for conical diffusers using area ratio (A_4/A_3) and length to inlet radius ratio (L/R_1) as coordinates. They can be used to determine performance for any geometry or to optimize performance in the same manner as Figures 41 and 42. The conical diffuser data are for free jet exit conditions so that some improvement could be expected if a discharge duct were used at least for large angles of divergence. Contrary to the situation for plane diffusers, conical diffusers attain peak recovery for a given length or area ratio before the onset of stall, probably due to the absence of side wall corners.

The performance of any diffuser will benefit from fairing of the entrance corners. There is some evidence* that the presence of a resistance at the exit of a diffuser allows the use of greater angles of divergence for a given total pressure loss and may prevent the onset of stall. Wide-angle diffusers can be improved by the use of splitter vanes†. Diffusers with curved centerlines have lower performance than straight-walled diffusers.⊙

The coefficients of pressure recovery for conical diffusers with low angles of divergence increase as inlet Mach number is increased to about 0.9 according to Fox#. Effectiveness appears to decrease rapidly as Mach number is increased to about 0.2 or 0.3. Effectiveness is relatively constant over the range of Mach numbers from 0.3 to 0.9. At Mach numbers above 0.9 both effectiveness and coefficient of pressure recovery fall off rapidly.

Venturi Meter

The Venturi meter provides a very convenient method for producing a pressure difference suitable for measurement and convertible to flow rate. As indicated in Figure 45 the Venturi meter consists of a combination of converging and diverging tapers, usually connected by a short, straight pipe known as the throat. For minimum loss the included angle in the convergent section should be 30° or less and the included angle in the divergent section should be 7° to 8°. Suitable pressure differences are obtained with diameter ratios of ½ to ⅓ or area ratios of ¼ to ⅑. For accurate work the meter should be calibrated in place; however, for the proportions listed, a coefficient of discharge equal to about 0.98 may be used in Equation 130 where Subscript 1 refers to the upstream pipe and Subscript 3 refers to the throat. The pressure loss may be estimated from Figure 35 and Equation 126.

Two datum lines are shown in Figure 45. The lower datum line yields positive gage pressures for SP_3. The higher datum line illustrates the case where a negative gage pressure is developed in the throat as shown for SP_3'.

---

*C. H. McLellan and M. R. Nichols, An Investigation of Diffuser-Resistance Combinations in Duct Systems, NACA Wartime Report L-329, 1942.

†O. G. Fail, Vane Systems for Very-Wide-Angle Subsonic Diffusers, ASME Paper No. 64-FE-4, 1964.

⊙C. J. Sagi and J. P. Johnston, The Design and Performance of Two-Dimensional Curved Diffusers, ASME Paper No. 67-FE-6, 1967.

#R. W. Fox, Subsonic Flow in Conical Diffusers, Technical Report FMTR-67-1, Purdue Research Foundation, Lafayette, Ind., 1967.

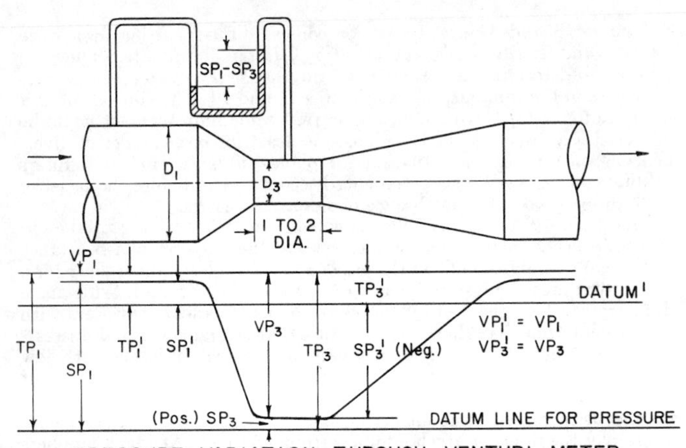

Figure 45—Venturi Meter and Pressure Graph

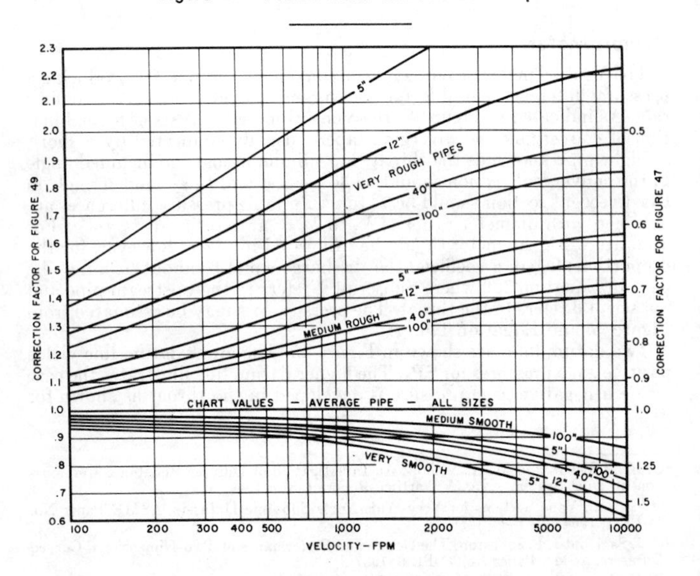

Figure 46—Roughness Corrections for Ducts

RESISTANCE TO FLOW THROUGH DUCTS

The resistance to flow through a straight duct, expressed as an equivalent head loss in inches water gage (ΔTP), may be determined from the equivalent velocity head (VP), the length (L), and the equivalent diameter (D).

For any straight round duct

$$\Delta TP = f \frac{L}{D} VP. \tag{141}$$

The proportionality factor (f) is known as the Darcy friction factor. This is the previously discussed coefficient of friction which may be determined from Figure 27. As noted there it is a function of Reynolds number and relative roughness. Since there are so many significant factors that influence duct resistance, it is common practice to draw duct friction charts for an average relative roughness and apply roughness corrections if necessary. A roughness correction chart is drawn in Figure 46. The correction as read at the right or left should be applied as a multiplying factor to the values from the appropriate chart.

For any straight rectangular duct

$$\Delta TP = f' \frac{L}{M} VP = 4f' \frac{L}{D} VP. \tag{142}$$

The proportionality factor (f') is known as the Fanning friction factor. It is equal to the Darcy friction factor divided by 4.

The equivalent diameter (D) for the same mean hydraulic radius (M) is $4M$. Since the mean hydraulic radius is the cross sectional area divided by the wetted perimeter, the equivalent diameter in terms of duct dimensions (x) and (y) is

$$D = 4M = 4xy/2(x + y) = 2xy/(x + y). \tag{143}$$

The coefficient of friction (f) may be considered to be the number of velocity heads lost divided by the number of diameters. Its reciprocal (N) is the number of diameters for a loss of one velocity head. After rewriting, Equation 91 becomes

$$\sqrt{N} = -2 \log_{10} \left(\frac{\epsilon/D}{3.7} + \frac{2.51\sqrt{N}}{N_{Re}} \right). \tag{144}$$

Figure 47 is a graphical representation of Equation 144 for standard air and average roughness. Corrections for other degrees of roughness may be made by using the appropriate factor from Figure 46 based on the descriptions in Table 22. Corrections can also be made for kinematic viscosity, if different from that of standard air. Since kinematic viscosity appears in the Reynolds number in the denominator and velocity appears in the numerator, an equivalent velocity equal to the actual velocity multiplied by the ratio of standard kinematic viscosity to actual kinematic viscosity may be used with Figure 47.

The total pressure losses in terms of N for round and rectangular ducts are

$$\Delta TP = \frac{1}{N} \frac{L}{D} VP = \frac{L}{N} \frac{x + y}{2xy} VP. \tag{145}$$

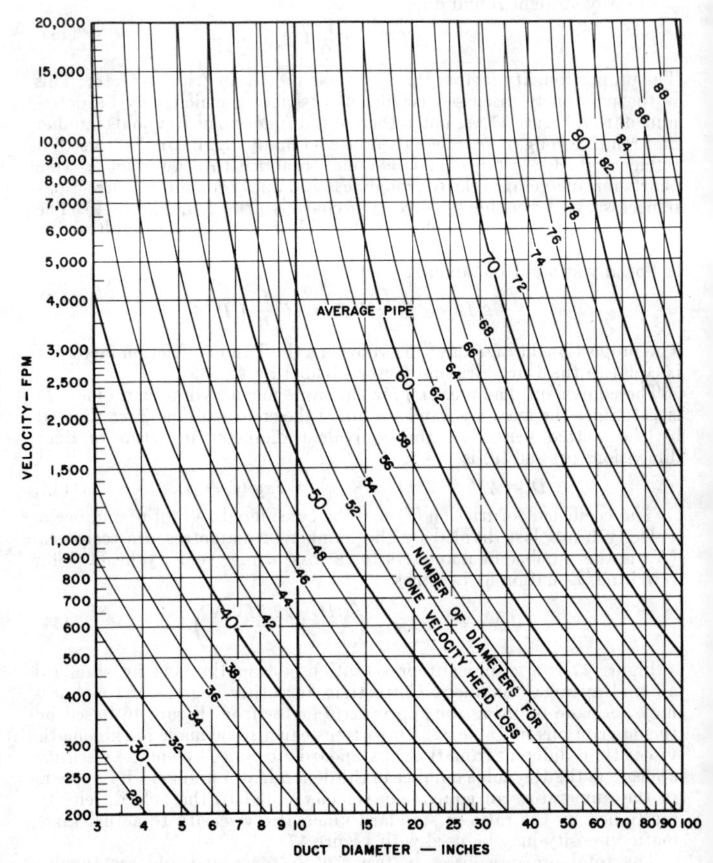

Figure 47—Duct Friction Chart in Diameters per Velocity Head

Adapted from the data of R. D. Madison and W. R. Elliot, Friction Charts for Gases Including Correction for Temperature, Viscosity and Pipe Roughness, *ASHVE Journal Section* of *Heating, Piping and Air Conditioning*, pp. 107-112, October, 1946.

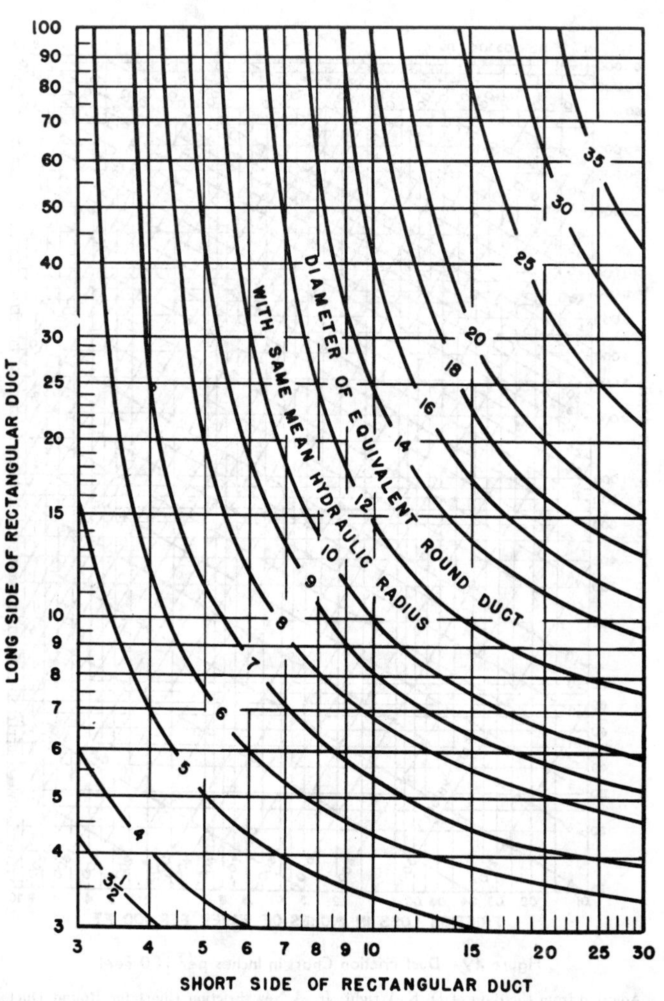

Figure 48—Equivalent Diameters for Use With Constant Velocity

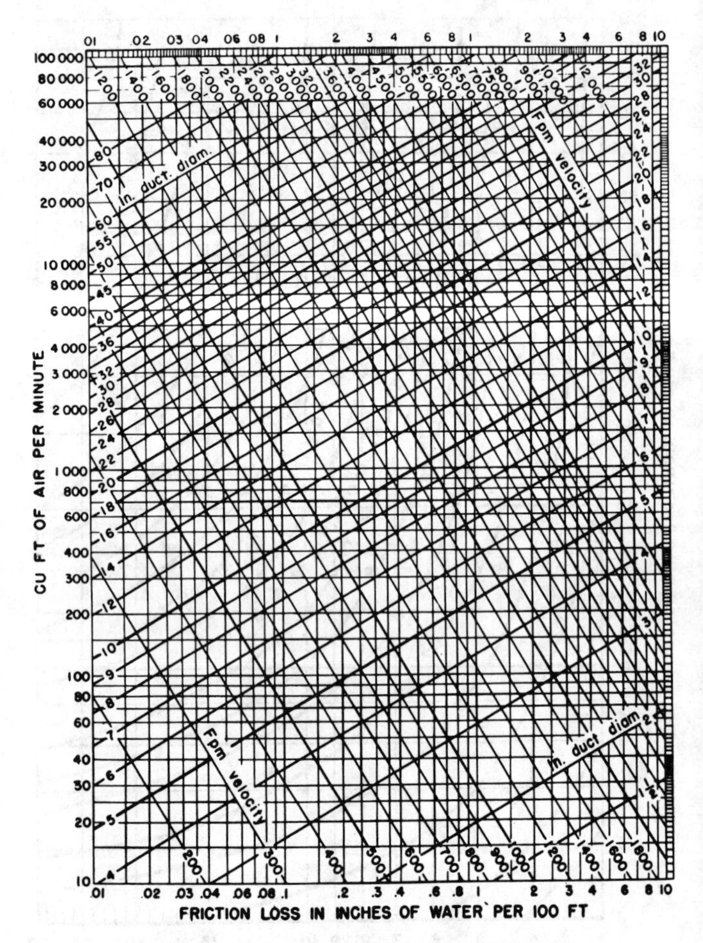

Figure 49—Duct Friction Chart in Inches per 100 Feet

Adapted from the data of D. K. Wright, Jr., A New Friction Chart for Round Ducts, *Trans. ASHVE*, vol. 51, pp. 303-316, 1945.

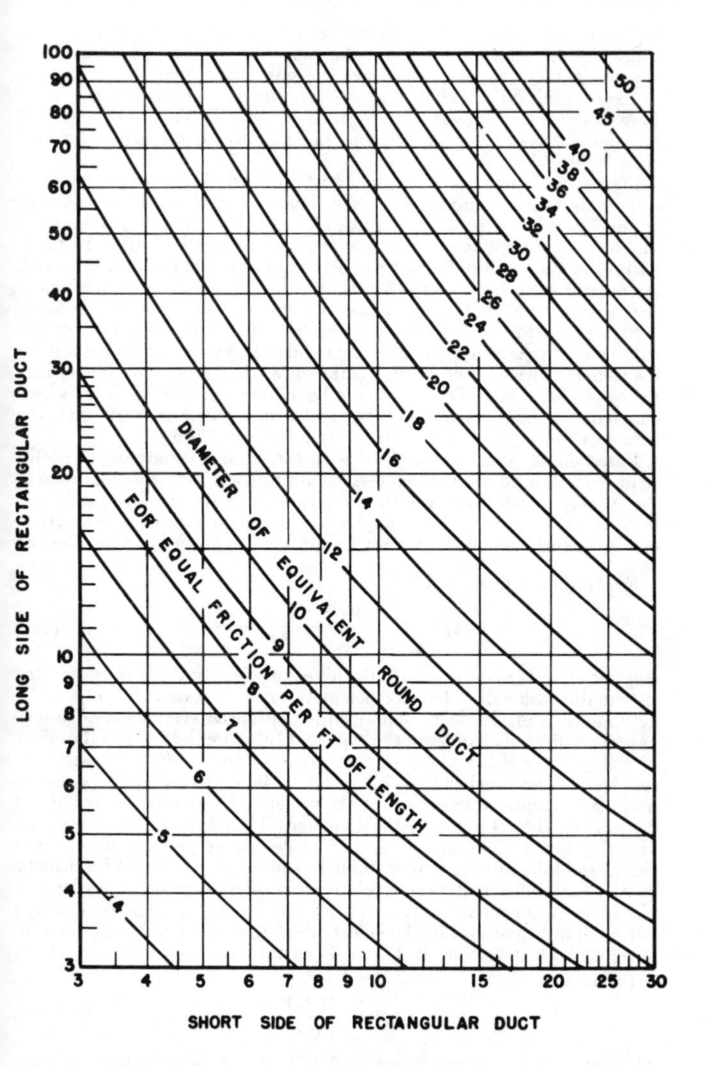

Figure 50—Equivalent Diameters for Use With Constant Capacity

Figure 48 can be used to determine the equivalent diameter (for use with constant velocity) for any rectangular dimensions. This chart gives the round duct diameter which has the same mean hydraulic radius as the rectangular duct. The two do not have the same cross sectional areas. This equivalent diameter may be used directly in Figure 47 with the actual duct velocity to determine the number of diameters for one velocity head loss.

Figure 49 is another type of duct friction chart also based on standard air and average roughness. The appropriate factor from Figure 46 may be used to correct for other degrees of roughness. However, there is no simple way of applying a viscosity correction. This limitation is unimportant in air conditioning but can be a source of significant error at high temperatures or for gases other than air. This chart possesses many desirable features including a capacity-velocity-diameter conversion.

Figure 50 can be used to determine the equivalent diameter (for use with constant capacity) for any rectangular dimensions. This chart gives the round duct diameter which has the same friction per foot of length as the rectangular duct. The two do not have the same cross sectional areas. This equivalent diameter may be used directly in Figure 49 with the actual capacity to determine the friction loss per 100 feet.

Equation 141 can be combined with the various equations for coefficient of friction to produce expressions for pressure drop for each zone of the Moody chart. The resulting expressions in the wholly rough and transition zones are rather complex. A compromise expression is given below for turbulent flow. An exact expression is given later for laminar flow.

For turbulent flow

$$\Delta P = \frac{c\,L\,V^{2.0-n}\,\delta^{\,1.0-n}\,\mu^{n}}{g\quad D^{1.4-n}}. \tag{146}$$

Any set of units may be used with this expression provided they are consistent dimensionally. The coefficient (c) and the exponent (n) can be determined from Table 22 opposite the appropriate condition of roughness. The effect of changes in the exponent (n) more than offsets the effect of changes in coefficient (c) so that pressure drop (ΔP) increases with roughness. The rougher the pipe or duct, the more nearly the pressure drop (ΔP) varies as the square of the velocity (V), the first power of the density (δ), the 1.4 power of the diameter (D), and the zero power of the viscosity (μ). It is common practice to determine pressure drops from charts and tables drawn up for standard conditions, to correct for density on the basis of a first power relationship, and to ignore the effect of viscosity. A somewhat better approach is to utilize the relationships indicated in Equation 146. The most accurate results can be obtained by using equivalent velocity in Figure 47 as outlined above.

For laminar flow

$$\Delta P = \frac{32\,L\,V\,\mu}{g\,D^2}. \tag{147}$$

This expression is correct when used with any set of units that are consistent dimensionally. The differences between the losses in turbulent and laminar flow are easily detected by comparing Equations 146 and 147. In laminar flow the loss (ΔP) is independent of fluid density (δ). The actual value of roughness has no effect on loss. As in any kind of flow, the loss is proportional to length (L), but the relationships with velocity (V) and diameter (D) for laminar flow are different from those for turbulent flow.

The resistance to flow through any duct element or fitting may be considered to be the sum of a friction loss and a shock loss. Friction losses are those which correspond to the losses in a uniform straight conduit. As such, they vary directly with the length of the fitting. Shock losses result whenever there is a change in area or direction of the conduit. When there is an abrupt change in the conduit, shock losses predominate over friction losses. For gradual changes friction losses become relatively more significant. As can be seen from Equation 146, friction losses in turbulent flow vary as something less than the square of the velocity, depending on roughness. Shock losses vary as the square of the velocity and are independent of roughness. Methods of estimating the losses for various duct elements are given below.

Elbows

Elbows, bends, and miters are used to guide a fluid through a change in direction of flow. Both shock losses and friction losses are occasioned by such devices. The relative amounts of each as well as the total resistance will depend on the abruptness of the change in direction, the Reynolds number, and the roughness.

Elbow losses may be expressed as a percentage of the entering velocity head, as an equivalent length of straight duct, or as an extra equivalent length of straight duct.

If the first method of expressing the loss is used, the size of the elbow will have very little effect compared with certain other geometrical considerations. The most significant factors are: the shape of the elbow, i.e., whether round, square, or rectangular; the aspect ratio, if rectangular; the angle of bend; and the radius ratio or curve ratio.

The curve ratio (CR) of an elbow is its inside radius (R_a) divided by its outside radius (R_b), assuming concentricity as indicated in Figure 51. The radius ratio (RR) of an elbow is its centerline radius (R) divided by its width (W) in the plane of the bend, also assuming concentricity as indicated in Figure 51. The aspect ratio (AR) of an elbow is its depth (D) along the axis of the bend divided by the width (W) in the plane of the bend as indicated.

For square elbows the depth equals the width (W). For round elbows both depth and width equal diameter (D). In either of these special cases $AR = 1.0$ and CR and RR are related according to:

$$CR = \frac{RR - .5}{RR + .5} \quad \textit{and} \tag{148}$$

$$RR = .5\left(\frac{1 + CR}{1 - CR}\right). \tag{149}$$

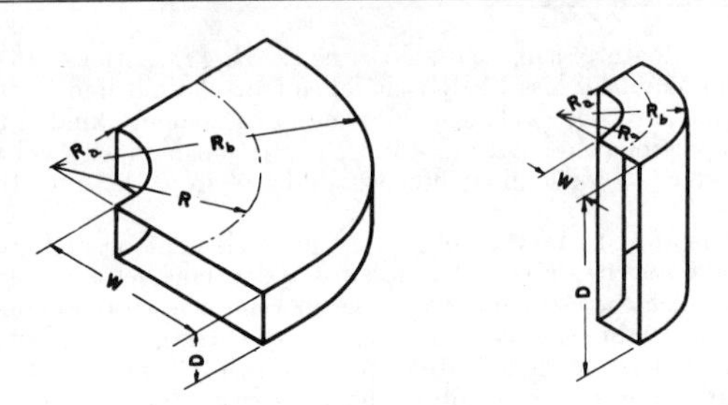

Figure 51—Hard and Easy Bends

Figure 52 may be used to predict the losses for 90° round elbows, bends, or miters of various curve or radius ratios. This figure is based on averages similar to those of Locklin. Both shock and friction losses are included.

The amount of the loss is not exactly proportional to the angle of bend, as is indicated by Figure 53. This chart presents the correction for any elbow angle as a multiplying factor to be applied to the loss for the corresponding 90° elbow.

Figure 54 may be used to determine the losses for 90° square elbows and miters of various curve or radius ratios. This is based on tests conducted in the Buffalo Forge Co. laboratory. (There is remarkable agreement between this data and the average of data by several investigators as given by Locklin.)* It is apparent that size effect is negligible except at high curve ratios where shock losses decrease to the point of insignificance compared with friction losses.

Figure 55 gives aspect ratio corrections for rectangular elbows which should be applied as a multiplication factor to the loss for a square elbow with the same curve or radius ratio. Note that there is a broad range of aspect ratios for which essentially no correction is necessary.

The loss in an elbow located at the end of a duct is much higher than that for a similar elbow followed by a short run of straight pipe. This is quite similar to the phenomenon observed with orifices in that there is a contraction of the stream, and, unless expansion is allowed to take place before exit, a considerable amount of kinetic energy is wasted. The curves of Figure 56 illustrate the effect of both aspect ratio and curve or radius ratio on the pressure loss in a 90° elbow discharging directly into atmosphere.

The combined loss of a compound elbow may be quite different from the sum of the individual losses, as is indicated by Figures 57 and 58. The columns marked "actual" are the losses in per cent of velocity head as measured. The columns marked "estimated sum" are the sums of the individual losses, estimating the loss for the upstream elbow as if followed by a duct and estimating the loss for the downstream elbow according to

*D. W. Locklin, Energy Losses in 90 Degree Duct Elbows, *Trans. ASHVE*, vol. 56, pp. 479-502, 1950.

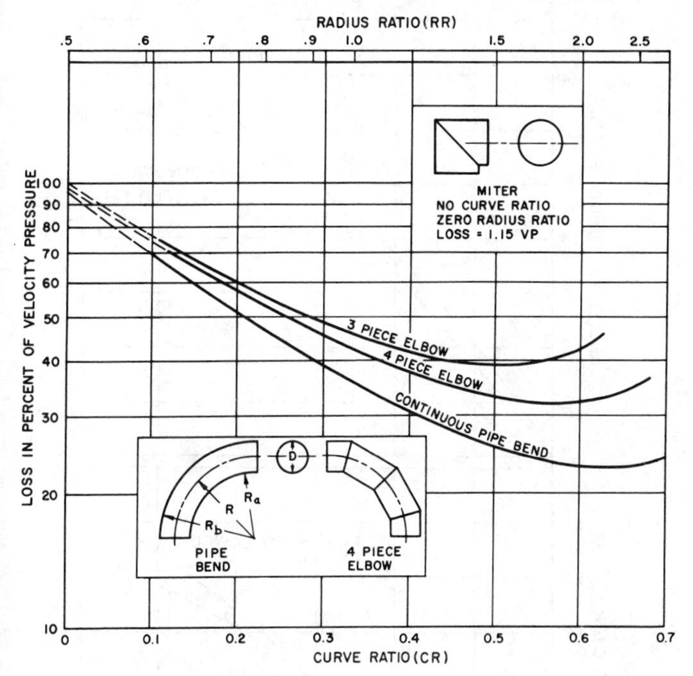

Figure 52—Pressure Losses for 90° Round Elbows and Miters

Adapted from the data of D. W. Locklin, Energy Losses in 90 Degree Duct Elbows, *Trans. ASHVE*, vol. 56, pp. 479-502, 1950.

---

conditions as marked. The ratio of actual to estimated loss is given as "% of est." The estimated combined loss with splitters is usually quite close to the actual loss.

Conventional elbows are those having concentric inner and outer radii and constant area of cross section throughout the bend. Various special elbows incorporating either a change in area or a change in the shape of that area throughout the bend have been proposed from time to time. For comparable curve and aspect ratios, conventional elbows are superior to special elbows. For the lowest possible loss, conventional elbows with splitters or miters with turning vanes should be used.

Splitters are curved vanes placed in an elbow concentric with both the inside and outside radii and extending the full angle of bend from face to face. Splitters, in effect, divide the flow into parallel channels, each having a larger curve ratio and a larger aspect ratio than that of the original elbow. In most cases the change in aspect ratio has much less effect upon

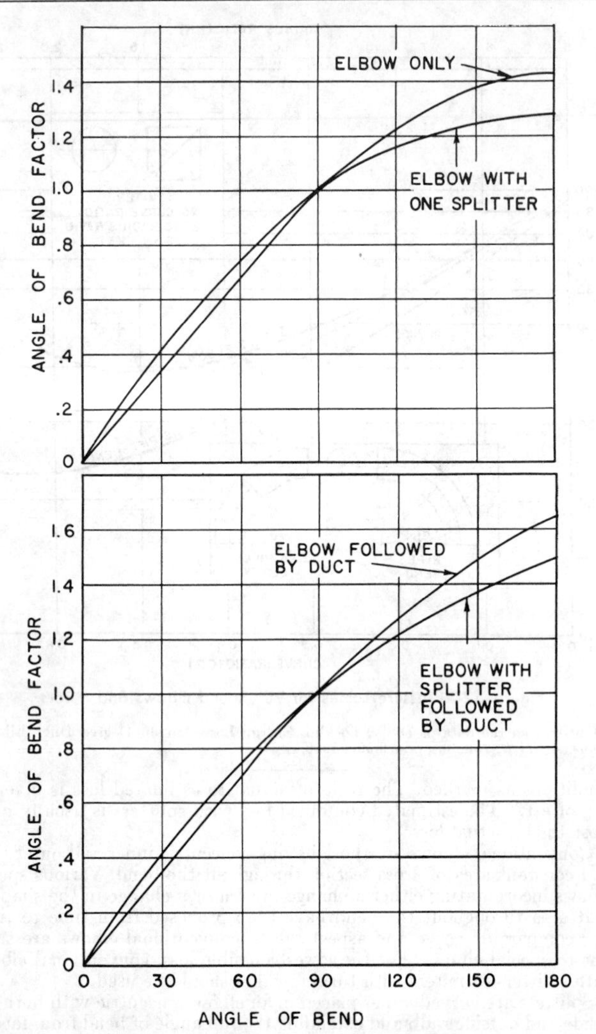

Figure 53—Angle of Bend Factors for Elbows

Adapted from the data of R. D. Madison and J. R. Parker, Pressure Losses in Rectangular Elbows, *Trans. ASME*, vol. 58, pp. 167-176, 1936.

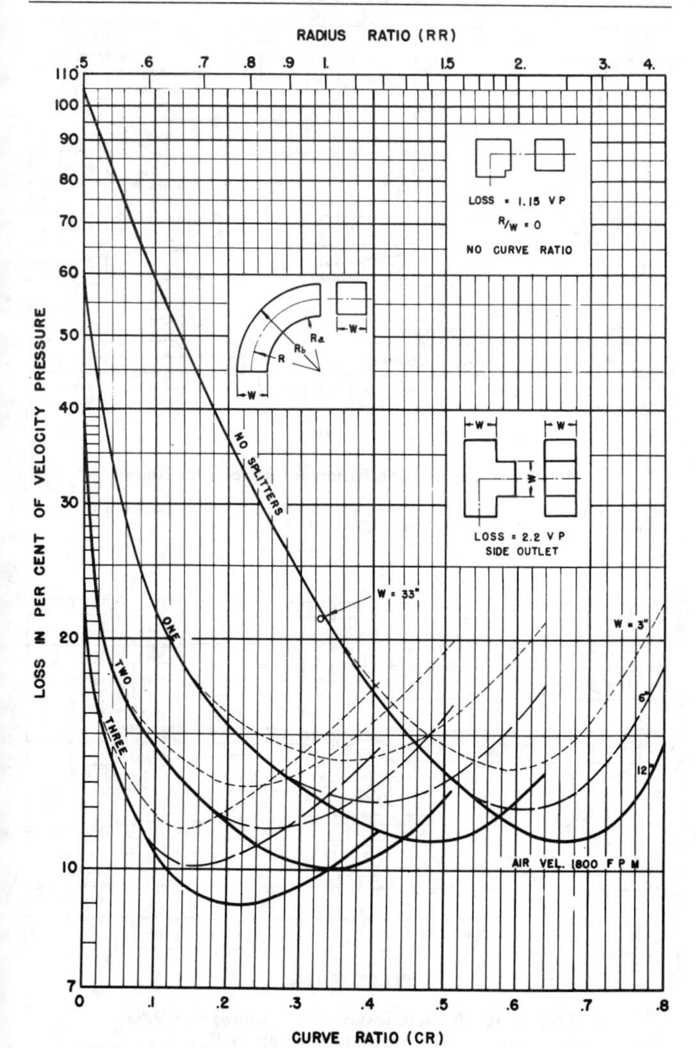

Figure 54—Pressure Losses for 90° Square Elbows and Miters

Adapted from the data of R. D. Madison and J. R. Parker, Pressure Losses in Rectangular Elbows, *Trans. ASME*, vol. 58, pp. 167-176, 1936.

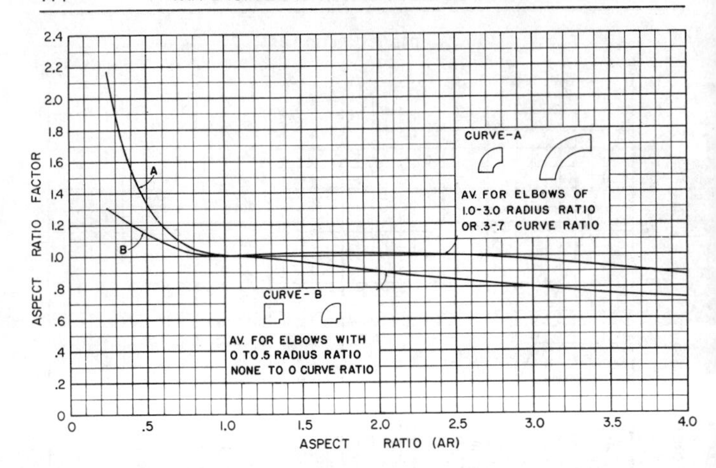

Figure 55—Aspect Ratio Factors for Rectangular Elbows

Adapted from the data of R. D. Madison and J. R. Parker, Pressure Losses in Rectangular Elbows, *Trans. ASME*, vol. 58, pp. 167-176, 1936.

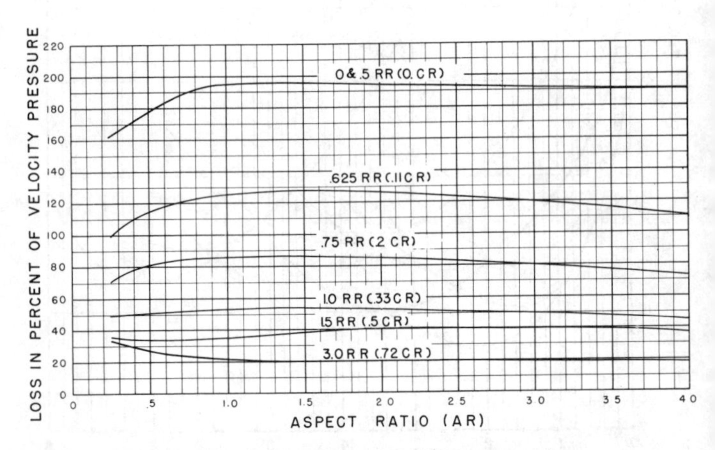

Figure 56—Pressure Losses for 90° Elbows and Miters Discharging to Atmosphere

Adapted from the data of R. D. Madison and J. R. Parker, Pressure Losses in Rectangular Elbows, *Trans. ASME*, vol. 58, pp. 167-176, 1936.

CASE NO.	FIRST ELBOW		SECOND ELBOW		ELBOWS ONLY			ELS. FOLLOWED BY DUCT		
	RR	AR	RR	AR	ACT.	EST. SUM	% OF EST.	ACT.	EST. SUM	% OF EST.
(1) 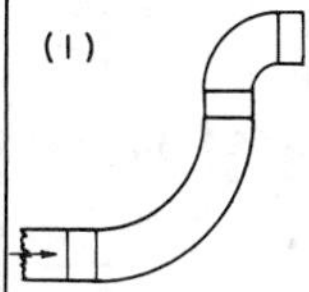	3	4	1.5	4	37.2	48.5	77	27.6	21.5	128
(2) 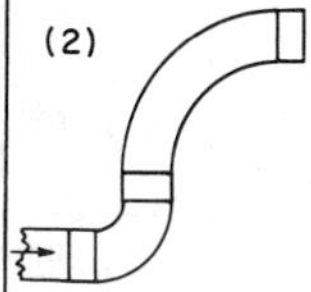	1.5	4	3	4	24.2	30	81	26.4	21.5	123
(3) 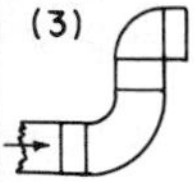	1.5	4	0.5	4	245	202	121	115	85	135
(4) 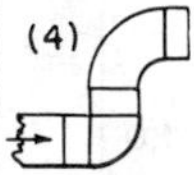	0.5	4	1.5	4	162	112	145	103	85	121
(5) 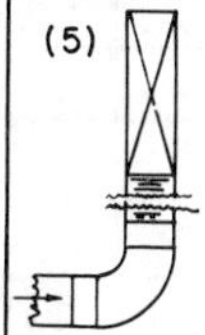	1.5	4	1.5	0.25	45.5	48	95	34.6	38	91
(6) 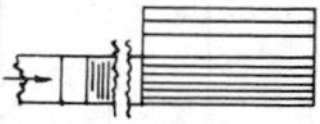	1.5	0.25	1.5	4	55	65	85	38.5	38	101

Figure 57—Actual and Estimated Losses for Compound Elbows (3″ x 12″)

Adapted from the data of R. D. Madison and J. R. Parker, Pressure Losses in Rectangular Elbows, *Trans. ASME*, vol. 58, pp. 167-176, 1936.

CASE NO.	PLAIN ELBOWS			ONE DIAMETER BTW. ELBOWS			SPLITTER IN EACH ELBOW		
	ACT.	EST. SUM	% OF EST.	ACT.	EST. SUM	% OF EST.	ACT.	EST. SUM	% OF EST.
(1) 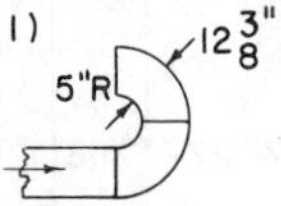 5"R, $12\frac{3}{8}$"	104.2	100	104	54.9	100	55	26	30	87
(2) 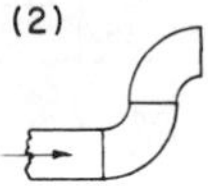	93.7	100	94	106	100	106	22	30	73
(3) 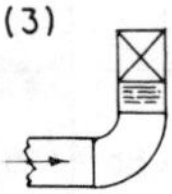	65.5	100	66	75.1	100	75	27.4	30	94
(4) 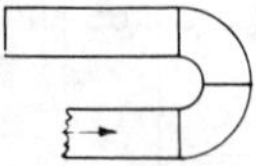	43	52	83	31.4	52	60	15	20	75
(5) 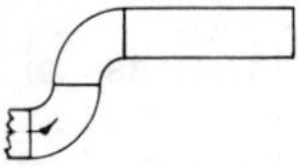	66.2	52	120	68.3	52	131	18.8	20	94
(6) 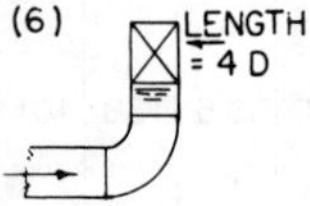 LENGTH = 4 D	41.8	52	81	45.7	52	88	20.5	20	102

Figure 58—Actual and Estimated Losses for Compound Elbows (12" x 12")

Adapted from the data of R. D. Madison and J. R. Parker, Pressure Losses in Rectangular Elbows, *Trans. ASME*, vol. 58, pp. 167-176, 1936.

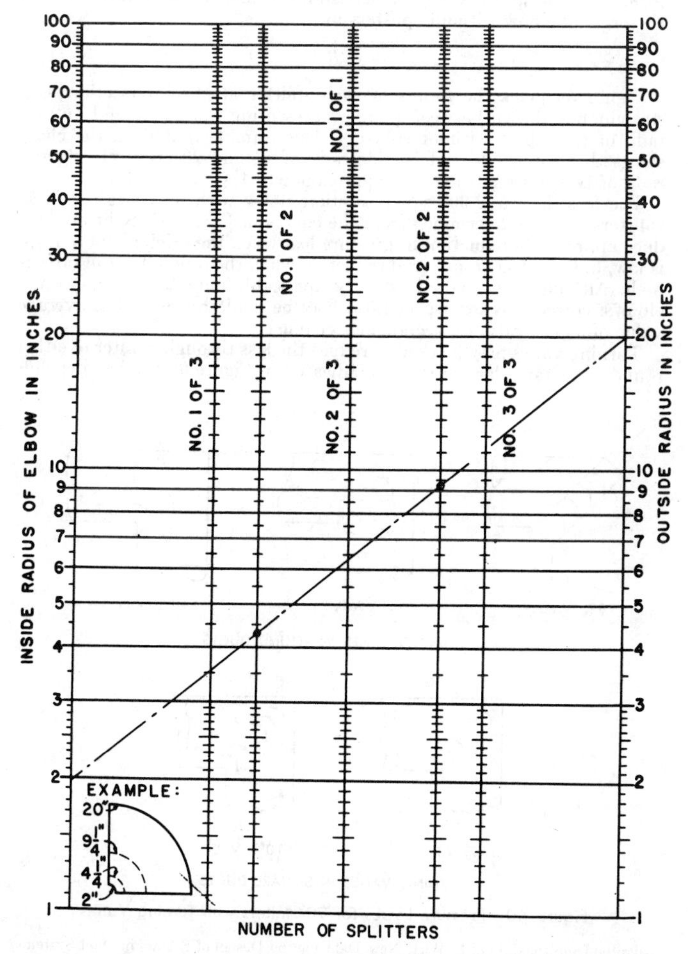

Figure 59—Locations of Splitters in Rectangular Elbows

elbow loss than the change in curve ratio. Neglecting the change in aspect ratio, the ideal locations for splitters are those that divide the elbow into components, each with the same curve ratio. For any number of splitters (n) the new curve ratio (CR') of each component elbow formed by the splitters may be determined using the curve ratio (CR) of the original elbow without splitters in

$$CR' = (CR)^{1/(n+1)}. \tag{150}$$

Figure 59 gives the radius of each splitter at the intersection of a straight line drawn between points representing the inside and outside radii of the elbow without splitters. The example drawn on the chart shows that for inside and outside radii of 2″ and 20″ respectively the radii of two splitters should be approximately 4¼″ and 9¼″.

The loss due to a 90° square section elbow with one, two, or three splitters may be determined from the curves in Figure 54. Splitters produce appreciable reduction in pressure loss when the original curve ratio is low, but there is no material reduction when the original curve ratio is high. Although this data is strictly applicable only to square section elbows, corrections for aspect ratio may be made by using the average value of aspect ratio for rectangular channels.

Turning vanes may be used to reduce the loss through a miter of either round or rectangular section. As indicated in Figure 60 the loss depends

---

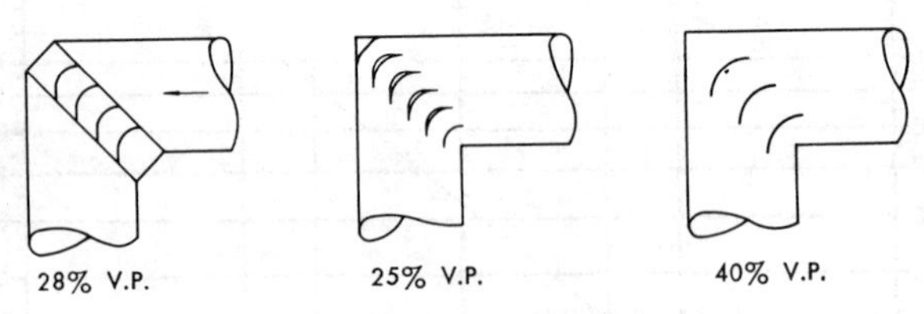

TURNING VANES IN ROUND DUCTS

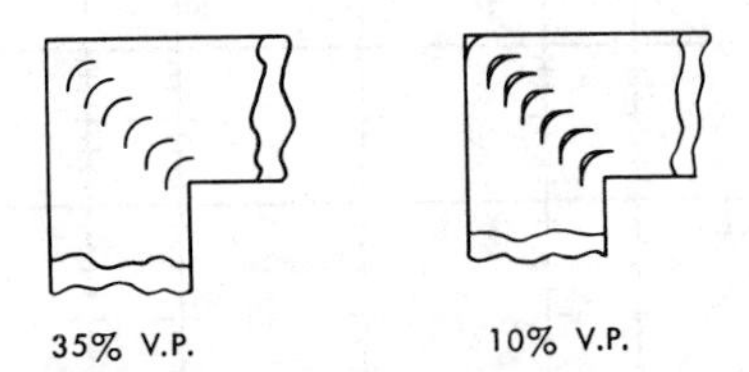

TURNING VANES IN SQUARE DUCTS

Figure 60—Pressure Losses for 90° Miters with Turning Vanes

Adapted from the data of L. Wirt, New Data for the Design of Elbows in Duct Systems, *General Electric Review*, pp. 286-296, June, 1927.

upon the type of miter and the type of turning vane. The estimated values shown are based on a vane depth of approximately six times the spacing and, where thickened vanes are indicated, a value of 0.5 curve ratio between the back of one and the front of the next. The very considerable reduction in loss from a value of 115% of a velocity head to the approximate values indicated in Figure 60 results from the conversion of the miter into a series of high aspect ratio or easy-bend elbows.

As a rule of thumb, in the region of 0.5 curve ratio the equivalent length of straight duct for a 90° round elbow is about 9 to 10 diameters. Similarly the equivalent length of a 90° rectangular elbow is about 6 to 8 equivalent diameters.

When estimating duct friction it is often convenient to measure straight lengths as if all elbows were miters. To compensate, elbow losses are figured on the extra equivalent length basis. Values are reported on this basis in the Guide.*

Entrance Conditions

The data given below on losses for various entrance conditions are based on the information given under the heading of flow coefficients. It should be borne in mind that losses always represent the drop in total pressure that can be measured with a pair of impact tubes, one located upstream and the other downstream of the device. Since an entrance condition involves the acceleration of air from zero velocity in the atmosphere to the pipe velocity, there must be a conversion of potential energy to kinetic energy. The upstream static, total, and velocity pressures will all be zero, but since velocity pressure is always positive and since flow proceeds from a region of high total pressure to one of relatively low total pressure, the downstream total pressure will be negative and the downstream static pressure will be even more negative by an amount equal to the velocity pressure. Negative pressures are, of course, gage pressures since all pressures are positive on the absolute scale.

A plain open-end pipe which produces a re-entrant condition (refer to page 92) has a total pressure loss of from 0.85 to 0.95 velocity heads. The static pressure downstream will be negative in an amount 1.85 times to 1.95 times or almost twice the velocity pressure.

If an open-end pipe is flanged, producing a square-edged entry condition, the loss in total pressure will be equal to about 0.5 velocity heads. The downstream static pressure will be 1.5 times the velocity pressure and negative.

For a nozzle approach or bell-mouthed entry, the loss in total pressure will be of the order of 0.05 velocity heads. Therefore, the downstream static pressure will be 1.05 times or just slightly greater than one velocity pressure, and negative in sign.

A converging taper may be used to approximate a bell-mouthed entry. The loss in total pressure in such cases varies both with the area ratio and the included angle. Figure 61 gives the coefficient of entry and the entry loss for both round and rectangular hoods employing converging tapers.

* ASHRAE Guide and Data Book, Equipment, ASHRAE, New York, 1969, p. 32.

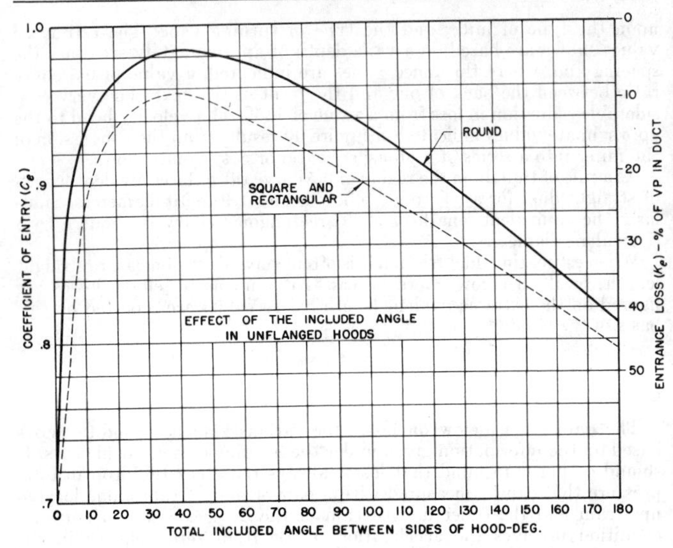

Figure 61—Flow Coefficients for Hoods

Adapted from data of A. D. Brandt, Energy Losses at Suction Hoods, *Trans. ASHVE*, vol. 52, pp. 205-236, 1946.

The coefficient of entry (C_e) for a hood may be used with the hood suction to determine the flow rate or vice versa. The hood suction (SP) is the negative static pressure measured in the pipe just upstream of the hood (and bell or taper, if any). The hood entry loss factor (K_e) may be used with the velocity pressure in the pipe (VP) to determine the loss (ΔTP) through the hood:

$$CFM = 1096.7\ C_e\ A \sqrt{\frac{SP}{\delta}} \qquad and \qquad (151)$$

$$\Delta TP = K_e\ VP. \qquad (152)$$

The coefficient of entry and hood entry loss factors are used for hoods in the same way as coefficient of discharge and coefficient of resistance are used for orifices and nozzles. Note that hood suction measurements are meaningful only when the area of the pipe (A) is specified.

The curves shown here are based on an area ratio of 5 to 1. The peak values need not be reduced more than 4 or 5%, even for an area ratio of 2 to 1. For area ratios in these ranges the loss around the outer edge of the hood is quite small compared with that due to contraction in the pipe, so that the addition of a flange will not materially change the loss. Nevertheless, flanges may serve to control the pattern of air flow and thereby perform a very useful function.

Changes in Duct Section

Various in-line, full-flow fittings can be used to connect two ducts of different size. Total pressure losses (ΔTP) may be calculated as follows: (1)—for conical nozzles use Equation 141 and mean values for D and f, (2)—for plane or conical diffusers use Equation 140 and data from Figures 42 or 44 as appropriate, (3)—for abrupt contractions use Equation 129 and data from Table 34, and (4)—for abrupt enlargements use Equation 125 and data from Table 33 or use Figure 39.

Transformations are used to achieve a gradual change in shape or a change in shape and area. On occasion they are used to produce an offset as well. The simplest transformation between two equal area rectangles is one having four straight sides. Such a device involves an expansion and subsequent contraction since the area in the middle is greater than at

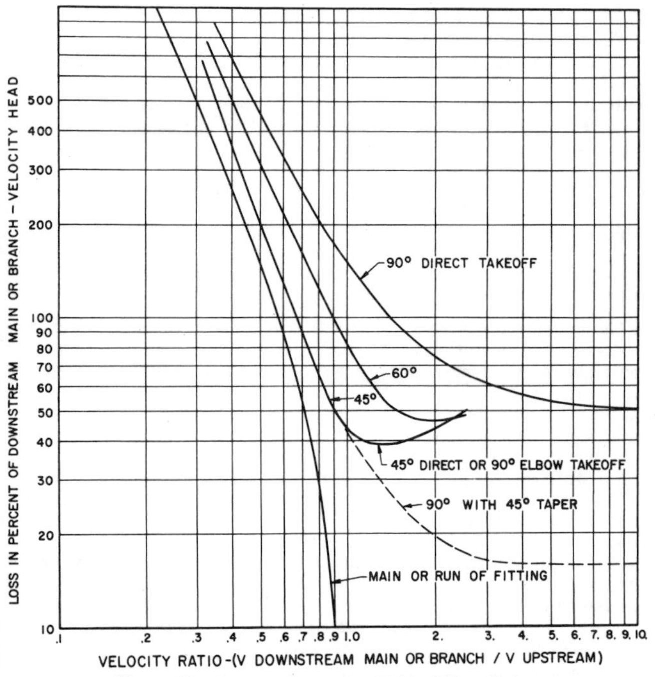

Figure 62—Pressure Losses for Divided Flow Fittings

Adapted from the data of S. F. Gilman, Pressure Losses of Divided-Flow Fittings, *Trans. ASHAE*, vol. 61, pp. 281-296, 1955.

either end. The total amount of area change can be reduced by using multiple straight-sided transformations instead of single straight-sided transformations. The loss in total pressure in either case may be estimated by adding the average duct friction to the shock loss for a divergent-convergent section. This usually amounts to 5 to 10% of a velocity head when the flow is along a single axis. When the axis is offset, an elbow effect is introduced and the loss should be determined from the data on elbows and miters.

The total pressure losses of take-offs and junctions are influenced by the ratio of downstream to upstream velocity, by the branching angle, and by other geometrical relations. Figure 62 shows the average loss for a divided-flow fitting of round cross section for both the run-of-the-main and the take-off. Three different branching angles are shown for the latter. The loss in the take-off can be reduced considerably by utilizing a converging taper between the main and the branch pipe. The dotted curve shows the approximate influence of a generous taper, one side of which makes a branching angle of approximately 45°.

The above data apply only to take-offs where one stream is divided into two. Similar fittings are used at junctions where two streams are combined into one. The recommended procedure is to join the upstream main with the downstream main by means of a taper at least two upstream diameters long and to join the branch to the taper at an angle of 30° with the upstream main. For the case where the velocity in both the downstream main and the branch are identical, the loss in total pressure across the junction from either upstream point is frequently assumed to equal 0.18 and 0.28 velocity heads for 30° and 45° included angles respectively.

Immersed Bodies

The pressure drop occasioned by the obstruction to flow due to tube banks or other immersed bodies can be approximated by analysis of the contractions and enlargements caused by the object. Indeed, lacking any other information this is the only method available for computation. Fortunately, considerable data are published on the aerodynamic characteristics of many shapes as well as on the pressure loss of various common duct elements.

The drag coefficient in aerodynamics may be interpreted as the proportionality factor relating stagnation pressure with the force per unit area on the body. The coefficient of drag, like the friction factor, is a function of the properties of the fluid and the body (as expressed in the Reynolds number) and the shape and relation of the body to the air stream. Table 35 lists drag coefficients (f_D) for various sharp-edged and rounded objects. These data may be used with Equation 153 to determine the force (F_D) on the object if the density (δ), the projected area (A_D) perpendicular to the wind, and the velocity (V) or velocity pressure (VP) are known:

$$F_D = f_D\, A_D\, \delta\, \frac{V^2}{2g} = f_D\, A_D\, VP \times 5.192\,. \tag{153}$$

TABLE 35—DRAG COEFFICIENTS FOR VARIOUS OBJECTS

Sharp-edged objects—independent of N_{Re}

Rectangular Plate with sides a and b

a:b	1:1	4:1	8:1	25:1	50:1	∞
f_D	1.16	1.17	1.23	1.57	1.76	2.00

Cylinder with length l and diameter d

l:d	1	2	4	7
f_D	0.91	0.85	0.87	0.99

Circular Disk: $f_D = 1.11$

Hemispherical Cup: $f_D = 0.41$ (open back)
$f_D = 1.35$ (open front)

Cone, Apex Front, Base Closed $f_D = 0.51$ (60°)
$f_D = 0.34$ (30°)

Rounded Objects—vary with N_{Re} See Figure 183

N_{Re}	10	10^2	10^3	10^4	10^5	10^6
f_D (Sphere)	4.0	1.0	0.42	0.40	0.45	0.15
f_D (Cylinder)	2.7	1.4	1.0	1.1	1.2	0.33

Adapted from the data of T. Baumeister, "Mechanical Engineers Handbook," McGraw-Hill Book Co., Inc., New York, 1958, pp. *11*-82 and *11*-84. See Figure 183.

The best way to determine the resistance due to an obstruction in a duct is by experiment. Fairly accurate estimates may be made by calculating the loss due to contraction and subsequent re-expansion. In the case of square-edged obstructions, a coefficient of contraction of approximately 0.62 may be used. This must be modified for velocity of approach where necessary. When the edges of the obstruction are rounded the data for square-edged orifices and that for nozzles may be averaged according to the degree to which either one is approached. The total shock loss will equal the velocity pressure at the *vena contracta* multiplied by the sum of the coefficient of resistance due to contraction and the effective coefficient of resistance due to expansion. If the obstruction is rather large relative to the duct size, the duct friction in the vicinity of the obstruction will be greatly increased.

Exit Conditions

The energy content of a stream of air issuing from a duct into the atmosphere is primarily a function of the exit velocity. The pressure head at the exit plane must be zero. The change in elevation head from entrance to exit for unheated air is exactly offset by the change in barometer. The velocity head at exit represents a corresponding amount of kinetic energy. It may or may not be desirable to have a high kinetic energy content. Sometimes the stream must be projected a great distance from the exit, in which case a high exit velocity will be required. The corresponding energy must be supplied by the fan. If a nozzle or other device is used at the exit to increase velocity, the fan must not only supply the higher kinetic energy but the additional energy corresponding to the resistance of the device as well.

When there is no need for a high exit velocity an *evasé* should be used if possible. The small amount of energy loss due to resistance is more than compensated by the reduction in kinetic energy of the exit stream.

OTHER FLOW SITUATIONS

There are several interesting flow situations which may be classified as radial flow or as vortex flow. The various cases of radial and vortex flow have practical applications in fan design and other areas of fluid flow.

In the radial flow of air through a device such as indicated in Figure 63, the radial velocity (V), assuming uniform flow, ideally varies inversely as the radius (R), as indicated by

$$\frac{V_2}{V_1} = \frac{R_1}{R_2}. \tag{154}$$

The conversion of velocity pressure into static pressure in a radial diffuser of this type, neglecting friction, may be determined from

$$\Delta SP_{2-1} = VP_1 \left[1 - \left(\frac{R_1}{R_2}\right)^2\right]. \tag{155}$$

This is equal to the difference in velocity pressures. The flow at AA must be essentially radial to prevent separation from the guiding surfaces. Equations 154 and 155 apply only to frictionless flow without separation. The latter condition will only exist if the dimensions are approximately as shown on Figure 63. When the discharge is to atmosphere the average pressure within the radial diffuser will be less than atmospheric, so that the confining walls will tend to approach each other in spite of the impingement of the jet.

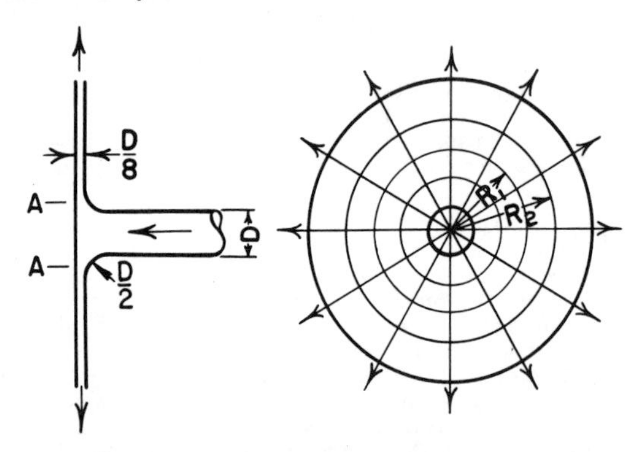

Figure 63—Confined Radial Flow

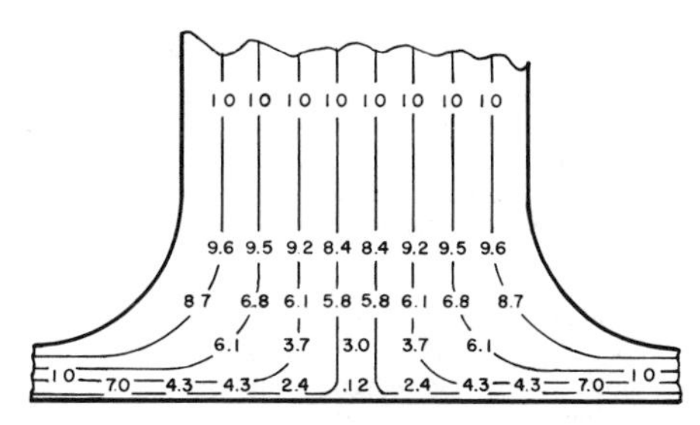

Figure 64—Impingement of Free Jet on a Flat Plate

A free jet impinging against a flat plate has the velocity pattern indicated in Figure 64. The central portion slows up as it approaches the plate, producing a corresponding increase in static pressure. This is followed by a reconversion of static pressure to velocity pressure which in the frictionless case would reaccelerate the flow to the original velocity. This type of flow, when bounded by walls approximating the natural flow boundaries, is an efficient means of turning an air stream in a very short distance.

The term "vortex flow" is used to describe the motion of a fluid whenever a "whirl" exists. Circular and spiral vortices are distinguished by the lack of or presence of a radial component respectively. The radial component of a spiral vortex may be directed inwardly or outwardly.

In a free circular vortex the velocity varies inversely as the radius according to Equation 154, just as for radial flow. In the absence of friction the velocity at the center would become infinitely great. In a free spiral vortex both the radial and tangential components of the velocity vary inversely with the radius. Various types of vortex flow occur in nature and in various fan applications. Free spiral vortex conditions are approached in the scroll-shaped housing of centrifugal fans as well as in cyclone collectors. The velocity-radius relation as expressed in Equation 154 may be greatly modified by friction and other forces. The extent of this modification can be appreciated by noting that in a frictionless straight blade centrifugal fan which produces one kind of forced vortex the tangential velocity varies directly with the radius as indicated by

$$\frac{V_2}{V_1} = \frac{R_2}{R_1}. \tag{156}$$

The change in static pressure due to such a change in tangential velocity may be determined from

$$\Delta SP_{2-1} = VP_1 \left[1 - \left(\frac{R_2}{R_1}\right)^2\right]. \tag{157}$$

The analysis of radial and vortex flow, together with an analysis of friction and shock losses based on the data given in this section, will define certain limiting conditions for the designer.

Air Horsepower

Another useful limiting quantity is that of air horsepower (AHP). The minimum horsepower, based on theoretically perfect efficiency, required to move any amount of air against any resistance may be determined either by multiplying the product of capacity in cubic feet per minute and the total system resistance pressure in inches of water by the constant *.0001573* or by dividing the product by the constant *6356*. Because this constant in either form is based on the equivalent head in inches water gage rather than on the actual head in feet of fluid flowing, the actual density (δ) of the gas is immaterial. The actual value of the constant may be derived by multiplying the weight in pounds corresponding to one cubic foot by the head in feet of fluid flowing corresponding to one inch water gage to obtain foot pounds per minute and dividing by 33,000, the number of foot pounds per minute per horsepower, as indicated by

$$AHP \, for \, 1 \, CFM \, @ \, 1''WG = \frac{(1 \times \delta)}{33000}\left(\frac{1 \times 62.3}{12\,\delta}\right) = .0001573 = \frac{1}{6356}. \tag{158}$$

Models

The use of models in experimental work provides many advantages in both cost and convenience. In order to accurately predict the performance of the full scale prototype from the small scale model complete similarity of the flow pattern is required. This requires both kinematic and dynamic similarity, as well as geometric similarity. Kinematic similarity requires that velocities and velocity gradients be exactly proportional, and dynamic similarity requires that the various force ratios be equal in each case. It is usually impossible to obtain complete similarity, but fortunately this is not always required for satisfactory results. For instance, for a reduced geometric scale factor it is necessary either to increase the velocity or decrease the kinematic viscosity in order to obtain the same Reynolds number. In either case the Mach number will vary, and the effect of this variation may or may not be important. At relatively low velocities the Reynolds number is of governing importance and the Mach number relatively insignificant. This situation changes rapidly at high velocities. The fan laws given later are quite useful for predicting the performance of a fan from a model test. It will be recognized that complete dynamic similarity is not preserved and that therefore the fan laws, strictly speaking, are not exact. Dynamic dissimilarity arises principally in the boundary layer flow conditions. These are of secondary importance, since the predominant losses occurring in a fan are those due to shock. For this reason, the performance of low pressure fans can be predicted more accurately than that of high pressure fans.

Liquid Flow

The data for the incompressible flow of air and gases may be applied to the flow of liquids in most cases. Since water at ordinary temperatures weighs approximately 800 times more than air, elevation differences assume more significance than they have with air flow. In addition,

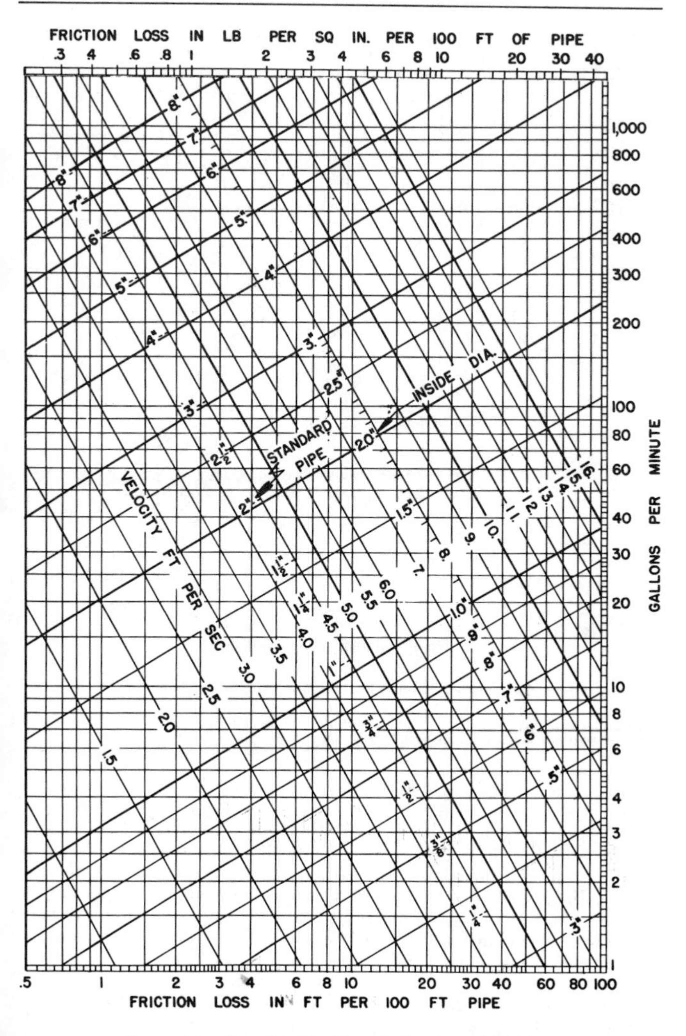

Figure 65—Pipe Friction Chart in Feet per 100 Feet

Adapted from the data of R. D. Madison and W. R. Elliot, Pressure Losses for Liquid Flow in Pipes, *Chemical Engineering Progress*, vol. 44, pp. 703-706, September 1948.

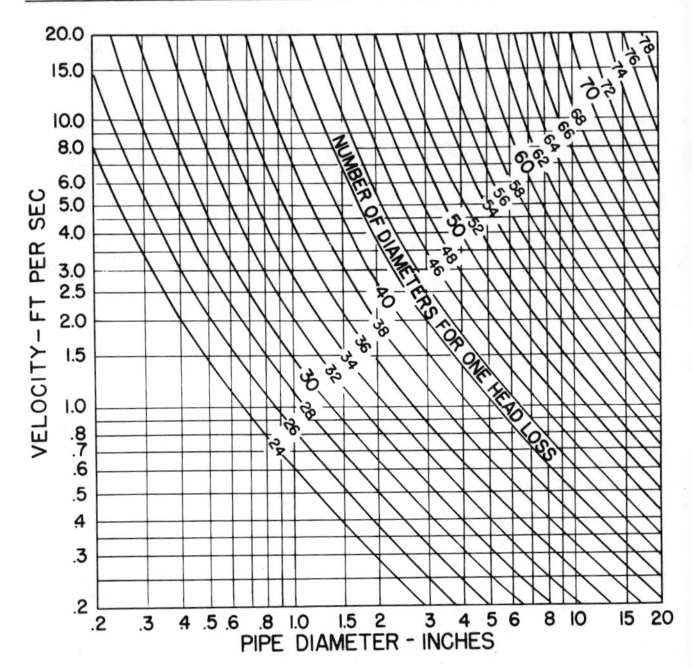

Figure 66—Pipe Friction Chart in Diameters per Velocity Head

Adapted from the data of R. D. Madison and W. R. Elliot, Pressure Losses for Liquid Flow in Pipes, *Chemical Engineering Progress*, vol. 44, pp. 703-706, September 1948.

---

under certain conditions of reduced pressure or increased temperature the vapor pressure of the liquid may approach the pressure of the liquid. When it does, both the vapor and liquid phases may exist. Cavitation results from the alternate formation and collapse of vapor bubbles in the liquid, producing noise, wear on parts, and pressure surges. The friction charts, Figures 47 and 49, for the flow of air through conduits may be used for the flow of water provided the appropriate corrections are made for differences in kinematic viscosity and roughness. For convenience, two similar charts, Figures 65 and 66, have been drawn for 70° water flowing through clean steel or wrought iron pipes. Figure 67 may be used to correct for very rough pipe. Figure 66 like Figure 47 is particularly suitable when differences in kinematic viscosity must be taken into account. The method, as previously described, is simply one of maintaining the same Reynolds number by calculating an equivalent velocity corresponding to the new kinematic viscosity.

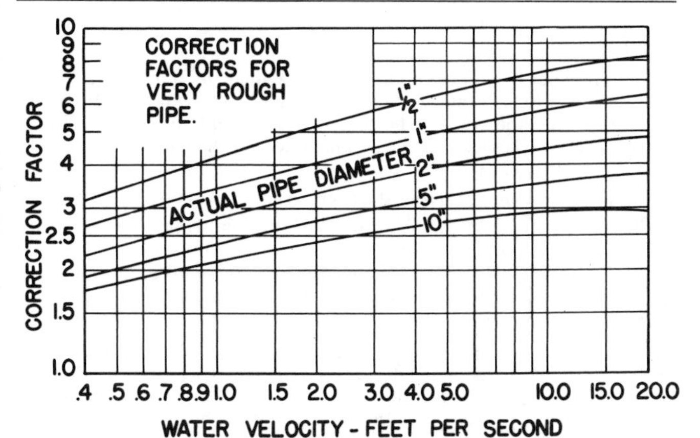

Figure 67 — Roughness Corrections for Pipes

Adapted from the data of R. D. Madison and W. R. Elliot, Pressure Losses for Liquid Flow in Pipes, *Chemical Engineering Progress*, vol. 44, pp. 703-706, September 1948.

Much of the data on elbows and other fittings given for air and gases was actually determined from tests with water and other liquids. Additional data on the resistance, in equivalent length, of certain standard pipe fittings are given in Table 36. The second column in this table gives a factor for converting the loss in equivalent length to the loss in velocity heads. For instance, the equivalent length of a standard 3″ diameter 90° elbow is 7.8 feet, and the corresponding number of velocity heads loss is equal to 7.8 × 0.067 or 0.52 velocity heads.

TABLE 36
RESISTANCES OF STANDARD PIPE FITTINGS TO FLOW OF LIQUIDS
Equivalent Lengths in Feet

Size	Velocity Head Factor	Elbow			Close Return	90° Pipe Miter	Valves (open)			
		Std 90°	Std 45°	Long 90°			Globe	Angle	Gate	Check
½″	.490	1.6	.86	1.1	2.7	3.1	18.0	7.0	.70	7.0
¾″	.340	2.1	1.1	1.4	3.7	4.0	24.0	8.5	.90	9.0
1″	.270	2.6	1.4	1.8	4.2	5.0	30.0	13.0	1.10	11.0
1¼″	.180	3.6	1.9	2.4	5.8	7.0	40.0	16.0	1.50	15.0
1½″	.145	4.1	2.2	2.8	6.8	8.0	46.0	18.0	1.80	18.0
2″	.110	5.3	2.9	3.5	8.5	10.0	60.0	25.0	2.30	23.0
2½″	.090	6.2	3.5	4.1	11.0	13.0	70.0	29.0	2.60	26.0
3″	.067	7.8	4.0	5.3	13.0	15.0	90.0	35.0	3.50	33.0
4″	.049	10.2	5.6	7.0	16.0	20.0	120.0	48.0	4.40	44.0
5″	.036	13.0	7.0	9.0	21.0	25.0	145.0	60.0	5.50	55.0
6″	.029	16.0	8.0	11.0	25.0	30.0	170.0	73.0	6.50	65.0
8″	.021	20.0	11.0	14.0	34.0	41.0	220.0	98.0	9.00	85.0

Adapted from the data of "Flow of Fluids Through Valves, Fittings, and Pipe," Crane Co., Tech. Paper No. 110, 1957, p. A-31.

Compressible Flow

Compressible flow is characterized by changes in the volume (Q) or volume flow rate (q) along the flow path, when the weight rate of flow (w) is constant. As indicated by the characteristic equation for gases (Equations 1-3) such changes must be accompanied by changes in pressure (P) or temperature (T).

The pressure-volume relationships for various processes may be written:

PQ^{∞} = constant for isometric or constant volume processes,
PQ^{0} = constant for isobaric or constant pressure processes,
PQ = constant for isothermal or constant temperature processes,
PQ^{γ} = constant for isentropic or constant entropy processes, and
PQ^{n} = constant for polytropic processes.

Another name for an isentropic process is "reversible adiabatic." Reversibility implies the complete absence of fluid friction and adiabatic implies that no heat is transferred to or from the working substance. The isentropic exponent (γ) is the ratio of specific heats (c_p/c_v).

The flow in a uniform duct or pipe may range from isothermal to isentropic. The first case is approached when the duct is short and uninsulated. The second case is approximated when the duct is well insulated and there is relatively little frictional heat generated. Formulas for the pressure drops may be obtained from standard fluid mechanics textbooks.

Most cases of compression or expansion may be described as polytropic. If there is no attempt made to transfer heat to or from the working substance, the process will be more or less adiabatic depending on the amount of insulation and on ambient conditions. Since friction is inevitable, real processes cannot be completely reversible and the polytropic exponent (n) can only approach the isentropic exponent (γ) even for well insulated processes at high efficiencies.

The flow through a well designed nozzle may be considered isentropic for all practical purposes. The subscript 1 will be used to denote the inlet or admission plane, the subscript 2 to denote the plane of the throat, and subscript 3 to denote the plane just beyond discharge or the area into which the nozzle discharges. The weight rate of flow (w) may be determined from the absolute static pressures (P_1) and (P_2) using any consistent set of units in

$$w = \phi_c \, C_D \, A_2 \sqrt{2g\left(\frac{\gamma}{\gamma - 1}\right) P_1 \delta_1 \left[\left(\frac{P_2}{P_1}\right)^{\frac{2}{\gamma}} - \left(\frac{P_2}{P_1}\right)^{\frac{\gamma+1}{\gamma}}\right]}. \quad (159)$$

The volume rate of flow at inlet conditions (CFM_1) may be determined from the gage pressures (SP_1) and (SP_2) in inches water gage, area (A) in sq ft, and density (δ) in lb per cu ft using

$$CFM_1 = 1096.7 \, \phi_c \, C_D \, A_2 \, \psi \sqrt{\frac{SP_1 - SP_2}{\delta}}. \quad (160)$$

The velocity of approach factor (ϕ_c) for compressible flow may be determined from Figure 68 which is based on

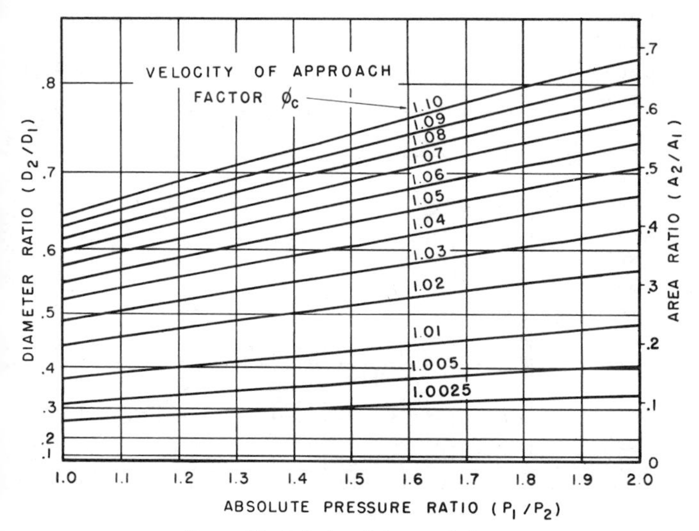

Figure 68—Velocity of Approach Factors

$$\phi_c = \sqrt{\frac{1}{1 - \left(\frac{A_2}{A_1}\right)^2 \left(\frac{P_2}{P_1}\right)^{\frac{2}{\gamma}}}}. \tag{161}$$

The expansion or compression factor (ψ) may be determined from Figure 69 which is based on

$$\psi = \sqrt{\frac{\gamma}{\gamma - 1} \left(\frac{P_2}{P_1}\right)^{\frac{2}{\gamma}} \left[\frac{1 - \left(\frac{P_2}{P_1}\right)^{\frac{\gamma-1}{\gamma}}}{1 - \frac{P_2}{P_1}}\right]}. \tag{162}$$

The coordinate scales of Figure 69 were chosen so that data could be read directly for expansion processes in which the absolute static pressure ratios (P_1/P_2) exceed unity. For compression processes in which the reciprocal pressure ratios (P_2/P_1) exceed unity, the compression factor (ψ_c) is the reciprocal of the expansion factor (ψ_e) indicated on the chart. Similarly the temperature at the downstream location(T_2) will be higher than the upstream temperature (T_1) after compression, whereas the reverse is true after expansion. The indicated temperature ratio is for expansion, so that its reciprocal should be used for compression. The product of ϕ_c and ψ is usually called Y in compressor test codes.

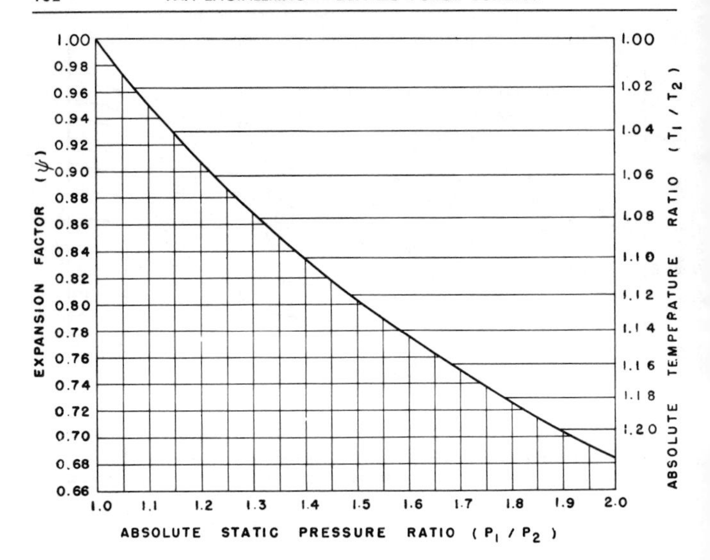

Figure 69—Expansion Factors

Because pressure variations cannot be transmitted through a fluid at a velocity greater than that of sound through the fluid, a limiting condition develops when the fluid velocity reaches the acoustic velocity.

In the equations presented above it cannot be assumed that the pressure at the throat (P_2) (even with a steadily converging shape) is always equal to the back pressure (P_3) into which the nozzle discharges. There is a critical pressure ratio $(P_2/P_1)_{cr}$ which defines the lowest throat pressure that can exist for any admission pressure (P_1). The numerical value of this critical pressure ratio is about 0.53 for normal air, 0.55 for highly superheated steam, and about 0.58 for saturated steam. It may be determined from the ratio of specific heats (γ) using

$$\left(\frac{P_2}{P_1}\right)_{cr} = \left(\frac{2}{\gamma + 1}\right)^{\gamma/(\gamma - 1)} . \tag{163}$$

The critical or acoustical velocity (c_2) may be determined from

$$c_2 = \sqrt{\frac{g_c \gamma \, P_2}{\rho_2}} = \sqrt{g_c \gamma \, RT_2} \tag{164}$$

using the mass density (ρ) and the absolute pressure (P) or the gas constant (R) and the absolute temperature (T).

The critical value of the throat pressure, $(P_2)_{cr}$, is the lowest value that can exist for any given admission pressure (P_1). P_2 will equal P_3 whenever

P_3 is equal to or greater than $(P_2)_{cr}$. For lower P_3 values, P_2 will equal $(P_2)_{cr}$ and therefore will be higher than P_3. In the first case the maximum possible velocity can be achieved with a purely converging nozzle. In the second case an increase in velocity can be achieved beyond the throat by adding a diverging section. In fact, this is the only type of nozzle which will produce supersonic velocities.

Adiabatic Horsepower and Heat of Compression

The flow of air or gas through a compressor must be considered a polytropic process. Comparisons with the ideal or isentropic process are often valuable.

The rate at which work would be performed if compression were isentropic is frequently called adiabatic horsepower (HP') and the ratio of this to actual horsepower (BHP) is referred to as adiabatic efficiency (η_c):

$$HP' = \frac{P_1\ CFM_1}{33000}\left(\frac{\gamma}{\gamma - 1}\right)\left[\left(\frac{P_2}{P_1}\right)^{\frac{\gamma-1}{\gamma}} - 1\right] \qquad (165)$$

where P_1 is in lb/ft^2.

$$\eta_c = \frac{HP'}{BHP} = \frac{T'_2 - T_1}{T_2 - T_1} = \frac{\left(\frac{P_2}{P_1}\right)^{\frac{\gamma-1}{\gamma}} - 1}{\left(\frac{T_2}{T_1}\right) - 1}. \qquad (166)$$

The subscripts 1 and 2 refer to inlet and outlet planes respectively. The prime mark is used to indicate that the reference quantity is the theoretical result of an isentropic process.

The temperature rise (ΔT) across a compressor may be considered the result of two processes: friction, and isentropic compression. The "total" temperature rise due to isentropic compression ($\Delta T'$) is

$$\Delta T' = T_1\left[\left(\frac{P_2}{P_1}\right)^{\frac{\gamma-1}{\gamma}} - 1\right]. \qquad (167)$$

The "total" temperature is the temperature which would be measured at the stagnation point if a gas stream were brought to rest and its kinetic energy converted by an isentropic compression from the flow condition to its stagnation pressure equivalent. The temperature measured by a thermometer inserted in a moving gas stream is very nearly equal to the "total" temperature.

It is possible to write an approximation of Equation 167 in terms of total pressure (TP) in "WG, the specific heat (c_p) in Btu/lb-°F, and density (δ) of the gas in lb/ft^3. Equating the energy per unit weight corresponding to the "total" temperature difference, i.e., $778.2\ c_p\Delta T'$, and the energy per unit weight corresponding to the difference in "total" head, i.e., $5.192(TP_2/\delta_2 - TP_1/\delta_1)$ produces

$$\Delta T' \approx \frac{5.192(TP_2 - TP_1)}{778.2\ c_p\ \delta_1}. \qquad (168)$$

The "total" temperature rise across a fan handling air near standard conditions with perfect efficiency and no heat loss should be approximately 0.37°F/″TP.

No fan has perfect efficiency, i.e., $\eta_T \neq 1$. If the energy loss due to friction is dissipated as heat which must be stored in the air, the additional temperature rise ($\Delta T''$) will be

$$\Delta T'' \approx \frac{5.192(TP_2 - TP_1)(1 - \eta_T)}{778.2\, c_p\, \delta_1\, \eta_T}. \tag{169}$$

The over-all rise in "total" temperature (ΔT) that can be measured by inserting thermometers in the streams at inlet and outlet can be predicted approximately from

$$\Delta T \approx \frac{5.192(TP_2 - TP_1)}{778.2\, c_p\, \delta_1\, \eta_T}. \tag{170}$$

Gas properties, heat transfer rates, etc. should be based on "static" temperature or that which would be measured in still air or gas. The temperature rise corresponding to its kinetic energy does not occur in a gas until the gas is brought to rest.

Temperature rise can also be calculated from the power (BHP) in hp delivered to the air and the capacity (CFM) in cfm using

$$\Delta T \approx \frac{42.42\, BHP}{c_p \delta_1\, CFM}. \tag{171}$$

The power delivered to the air includes the air horsepower, the horsepower corresponding to the inefficiency of the fan, and the horsepower corresponding to the inefficiency of the drive, if the drive is located in the air stream. Either Equation 170 or 171 can be used to calculate temperature rise over the range of ratings from design to free delivery. The rise at free delivery is usually slightly less than that at design. Neither Equation 170 or 171 can be used to predict the temperature rise at the no-flow or shut-off condition. Experience shows that the temperature within the casing gradually rises after the fan is brought up to speed and eventually levels off at some finite value even though the net fan efficiency is zero. The temperature rise will vary depending upon the method of achieving the shut-off condition. For instance, a much higher rise is obtained if both the inlet and outlet are blocked than if only the outlet is blocked. With inlet and outlet blocked the impeller continues to deliver energy to the air and the temperature rises until the energy lost by radiation and convection from the casing equals the input energy. With the inlet open puffing occurs which allows some relatively cool ambient air to enter the system.

The effect of altitude changes on temperature rise should be considered. For instance, in the ventilation of deep mines, assuming no loss or gain of heat from the walls of the shaft, etc., the temperature rise for each 1000 ft increase of depth is approximately 5°F. There is of course a corresponding decrease in temperature as the air rises to the surface.

CHAPTER 4

TRANSMISSION AND DISTRIBUTION OF AIR

A fan may be employed to deliver air to one or more points in space, to remove air from one or more areas, or both. Delivery to or removal from any number of areas can be achieved by connecting the necessary number of branch ducts to a main duct. In this chapter the principles of fluid flow are applied to the problem of proportioning the system so that the required flow will be transmitted through the various duct branches and to the equally important problem of achieving the necessary distribution in the rooms or spaces being served. Considerable details are given on specific applications, particularly that of ventilation. Additional details on various types of systems are given in Chapters 14 through 23. Fan-system relations are also discussed in Chapter 10.

PRINCIPLES OF DUCT DESIGN

As in any engineering problem, the best duct design is the one which produces the desired results most economically. More specifically, in the design of transmission and distribution systems, the flow must be proportioned as desired, the combined cost of materials and operation must be a minimum, and no undesirable features should develop during operation.

The location of the fan in any system will be dictated by the direction of flow and the desired pressure relations. That is, a supply fan may be used to pump air into a space or an exhaust fan may be used to draw air out of the space. The same through flow conditions will be obtained but the pressure relations will be different. In the first case there will be a buildup of pressure in the space and in the second a reduction in the space pressure will occur. Both supply and exhaust fans may be used, in which case the space pressure will depend on the relative amounts of air handled by each fan, i.e., space pressure will be positive if there is an excess of supply over exhaust, or negative with an excess of exhaust over supply. Assuming the same capacities and end pressures for all cases, the total energy delivered by the fan or fans to the air passing through a given system must be a certain value, whether a supply fan, an exhaust fan, or both are used.

Obviously, if one fan is to supply air to several spaces it must be located upstream relative to each space. A downstream location relative to each space is required if a fan is to exhaust air from several spaces.

When there must be several branches the fan should be as centrally located as possible so that each particle of air will require approximately the same amount of energy for transport as all others. Only one pressure can exist at a single point in space or in a duct system. This applies at the junction of any two branches regardless of any differences in branch size, length, or configuration. Accordingly, the pressure drop along one branch must equal that along the other. If the branches are not designed to provide equal pressure drops at the required flow rates the flow rates will differ from design. When the available pressure exceeds that required, the flow through a branch can be reduced to the design value by dampering. This is a waste of energy which sometimes cannot be avoided. In many cases the size of the duct can be reduced to balance the pressure drops.

It is often stated that the fan must be selected for a pressure sufficient to overcome the total losses based on the flow through the longest run. This is simply another way of saying that the same pressure must be dissipated by each portion of the air flowing, regardless of the lengths of the runs. Balanced design may be accomplished by using balancing dampers or by the use of appropriate duct sizes in all branches.

It can be demonstrated that there is an optimum duct size which will produce the most economical balance between owning and operating costs. If owning costs are proportional to duct weight and operating costs proportional to pressure loss, each can be related to velocity. For a given metal thickness, duct weight is proportional to diameter which in turn is proportional to the square root of velocity ($V^{1/2}$), and pressure drop is closely proportional to the square of the velocity (V^2). If these two costs are totaled at various velocities a minimum cost will result at the optimum velocity. The optimum velocity (V_{opt}) or that velocity which will produce the minimum total of operating and owning costs for a system as just described may be determined from

$$\left(\frac{V_{opt}}{1000}\right) = \left(\frac{440\ x_m''\ \delta_m'' \left(\frac{1st\ \$}{\#\ m}\right)\left(\frac{ann\ \$}{1st\ \$}\right)}{f\ \delta_a\ (ann\ hrs)\ (\$/HP\text{-}hr)}\right)^{1/3}. \quad (172)$$

As indicated, the optimum velocity is a function of the metal thickness (x_m'') in inches, the density of the metal (δ_m'') in lb per cu in., the first cost per pound of metal (*1st $/# m*), the annual owning cost as a fraction of the first cost figured from average interest and depreciation rates (*ann $/1st $*), the Darcy friction factor (f), the density of air (δ_a) in lb per cu ft, the operating hours each year (*ann hrs*), and the cost of power (*$/HP-hr*). The expression as given assumes negligible exit loss and perfect fan efficiency so that it yields only approximate results even for simple straight run systems. For the more complex systems it is customary to use different design velocities in the different branches as required to equalize friction. The inclusion of fittings and other duct elements such as heaters, etc., which reduce the fraction of the total system pressure loss due to straight duct friction, reduce the accuracy of the results of Equation 172.

In most cases the mains and branches will transmit a constant volume of air at all times. Whenever a system is expected to handle a variable volume, the duct sizes should reflect the anticipated operation. The fan in such cases must be capable of delivering the maximum amount even if ducts are sized for some lesser amount.

Another special situation where the optimum duct sizes may be based on reduced volume is that of a double duct system. Even though each space served may receive a constant volume of conditioned air (hot plus cold) the amounts handled by the hot and cold mains individually may fluctuate. As the number of spaces increases, there is a decrease in the probability that either main will be required to deliver the maximum amount of conditioned air at any particular time. The probability may be even further reduced by employing controls to reset the temperature of the air in one or both mains. According to Wilson* some designers take this into account by arbitrarily sizing the hot mains for 75% of the total possible capacity. The cold mains are generally sized to handle 100% of demand in the extreme downstream section. Successive upstream sections, each with several branches, may be sized for a progressively smaller percentage of demand. Typical values may be 90%, 80%, and 70% for the third, second, and first quarter sections. The total pressure requirement must be calculated on the basis of maximum demand through all sections. The fan and the volume controls must be so designed that operation under both full and partial load is satisfactory. Refer to Chapter 16 for further discussion of design and operating problems.

The optimum velocity based on owning and operating costs of the ducts alone is not always the controlling factor in determining duct sizes. In the so-called conventional systems which do not employ elaborate sound treatment, duct velocities may be limited to rather low values by noise considerations. On the other hand very high velocities may be justified in cases where the savings in building costs, etc., due to reduction in duct size more than offset the increase in power requirements to move the air through the system.

In the design of high-velocity systems it is important to limit the use of high velocities to those sections where the saving in space justifies the increase in power requirements. Progressively lower velocities will probably be indicated after each successive take-off. The static-regain method is particularly suitable for sizing the main risers in multi-story building systems. The equal-friction method or the static-regain method may be indicated for the horizontal mains on each floor depending on the particular layouts.

Ranges of design velocities for conventional and high-velocity systems are given in Table 37.

Although considerable discussion has been devoted to determining duct velocities and duct sizes, the importance of reducing the pressure losses due to elbows and other fittings cannot be overemphasized. For maximum economy it is extremely important that the most direct routes be used in laying out the duct system. Naturally, where exposed duct work cannot be tolerated, there must be some compromise on directness. In any case, when elbows or other fittings are necessary, easy bends, splitters, or turning vanes should be used.

Duct Design Methods

The common design methods for sizing ducts may be listed as: (1) constant-velocity, (2) velocity-reduction, (3) equal-friction, and (4) static-regain.

*C. M. Wilson, "Handbook" on High Velocity Air Distribution Design, *Heating, Piping and Air Conditioning*, pp. 94-108, November, 1954.

TABLE 37

DESIGN VELOCITIES FOR CONVENTIONAL AND HIGH-VELOCITY SYSTEMS

Duct Element	CONVENTIONAL						HIGH-VELOCITY	
	Residences		Public Bldgs.		Industrial Bldgs.		Commercial Bldgs.	
	Normal	Max.	Normal	Max.	Normal	Max.	Normal	Max.
Main Ducts........	700	1200	1000	1600	1500	2200	2500	6000
Branch Ducts.......	600	1000	800	1300	1000	1800	2000	4500
Outside Air Intakes..	500	800	500	900	500	1200	600	1000
Filters............	250	300	300	350	350	350	350	350
Heating Coils......	450	500	500	600	600	700	600	700
Air Washers.......	500	500	500	500	500	500	500	500
Cooling Coils.......	450	450	500	500	500	600	500	500

Adapted from the data of ASHRAE Guide and Data Book, Equipment, 1969, p. 38.

The constant-velocity method is applied in simple systems without branches and in those exhaust systems in which the material transported might settle if the velocity were reduced. This method may also be used in combination with other methods. For instance, in high-velocity design a constant velocity is often employed in the mains up to the point where the friction equals 1″ per 100′ or so.

An approximate optimum velocity as determined from Equation 172 may be used. Alternatively, the velocity may be chosen from Table 37 or several trial values may be selected and evaluated if the design effort can be justified. Duct sizes are determined from the appropriate capacity and the design velocity using the equation of continuity or Figure 49. Friction losses may be determined from the data in Chapter 3.

The velocity-reduction method may be employed in designing supply or exhaust systems having numerous branches. For designing supply systems this method consists of selecting an appropriate velocity as indicated in Table 37 for the first section of main and progressively decreasing the velocity at each take-off. For designing return or exhaust systems an appropriate velocity is selected for the duct at the grill or hood and progressively higher velocities are used at each junction. Subsequently all main and branch sizes are determined from the appropriate velocity and capacity, using the equation of continuity or Figure 49. Friction losses may be determined from the data in Chapter 3.

Since in this method the branch velocity is arbitrarily chosen as a certain fraction of that in the main, it is necessary to check whether the available pressure is equal to or greater than the loss for the design flow. Dampers may be used for balancing when the loss is less than the available pressure. In the event that the available pressure at any take-off or junction is not sufficient to produce the desired flow in the branch, either the available pressure must be increased by selecting a fan for a greater pressure requirement or the loss in the branch must be decreased accordingly by increasing duct sizes.

The equal-friction method is also employed in designing a variety of supply and exhaust systems. It is most effective for symmetrical systems or for systems where the lengths of all the various runs are approximately equal. For such systems balancing is automatically achieved by designing for equal friction per foot of length. Velocity reduction in the direction of flow on supply systems is also achieved automatically. Figures 70 and 71 may be used to size the remainder of the system after the first section of main is sized. For systems with some unequal branches, the mains and symmetrical branches may be designed according to the equal-friction-per-foot-of-length method. The remaining branches may then be sized in accordance with the pressure available at the take-off.

The static-regain method may be employed for designing supply or exhaust systems having numerous branches each connected to a single relatively long main. This method utilizes the increase in static pressure (which accompanies any velocity reduction) to provide equal static pressures at each take-off or junction. If the length of main between branches is either very long or very short, this method may not be practical.

The static-regain method of proportioning duct systems involves equating the static pressure regain occasioned by a change in velocity pressure at a take-off to the friction loss occasioned by the subsequent length of main up to the succeeding take-off. Assuming a constant coefficient of friction and a constant coefficient of regain,

$$f\frac{L_2}{D_2}VP_2 = C(VP_1 - VP_2). \tag{173}$$

Figure 72 is based on this equation using a value of .02 for the coefficient of friction (f) and a value of 0.5 for the coefficient of regain (C). The value of 0.5 for the recovery coefficient is reasonable for most applications but the actual value may be as high as 0.7 or 0.8 under best conditions. The friction coefficient is also subject to considerable variation but results obtained by using this chart are sufficiently accurate in most cases. When elbows are encountered in any length of main the appropriate equivalent length of straight duct may be added to the actual length of straight duct.

Round Ducts

In all methods of design the equation of continuity may be used to determine the duct size from the capacity and velocity. Accordingly, the ratio of duct sizes (d_a/d_b) is related to the capacity ratio (q_a/q_b) and velocity ratio (V_a/V_b) by

$$\frac{d_a}{d_b} = \left(\frac{q_a}{q_b}\right)^{1/2}\left(\frac{V_b}{V_a}\right)^{1/2} \tag{174}$$

in which subscripts a and b are used to denote two different sections of a duct system. In the constant velocity method of system design the velocity ratio is of course equal to unity and therefore the diameter ratio is equal to the square root of the capacity ratio. In the velocity-reduction method the ratio of velocities is a constant with a value less than unity when subscript b denotes a location farther from the fan than that denoted by subscript a.

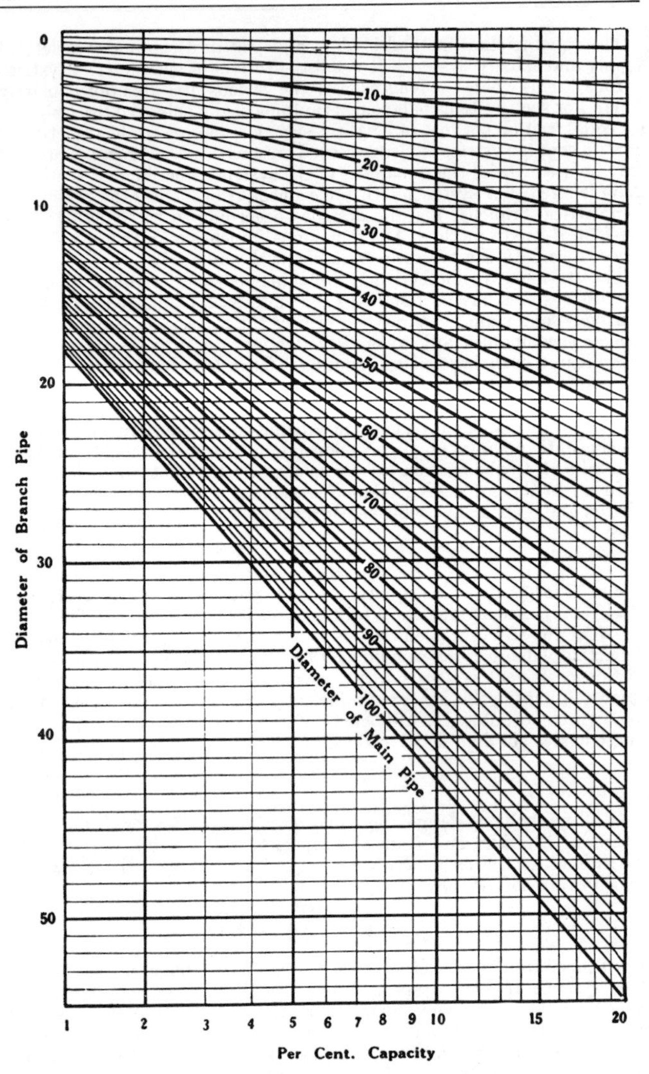

Figure 70—Round Pipe Sizes for Equal-Friction-per-Foot-of-Length

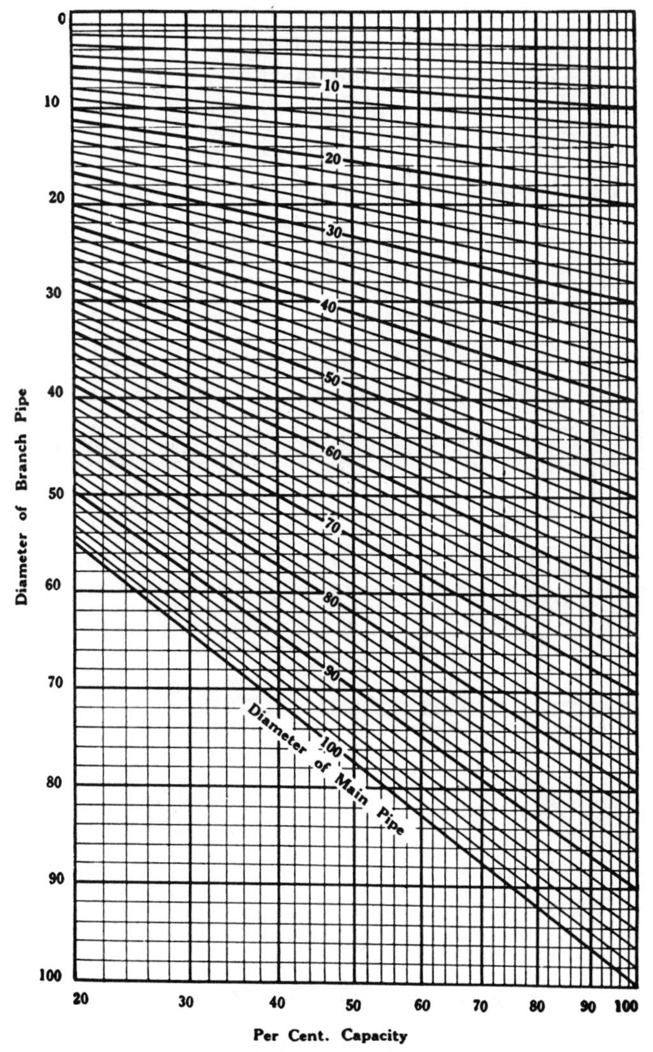

Figure 71—Round Pipe Sizes for Equal-Friction-per-Foot-of-Length

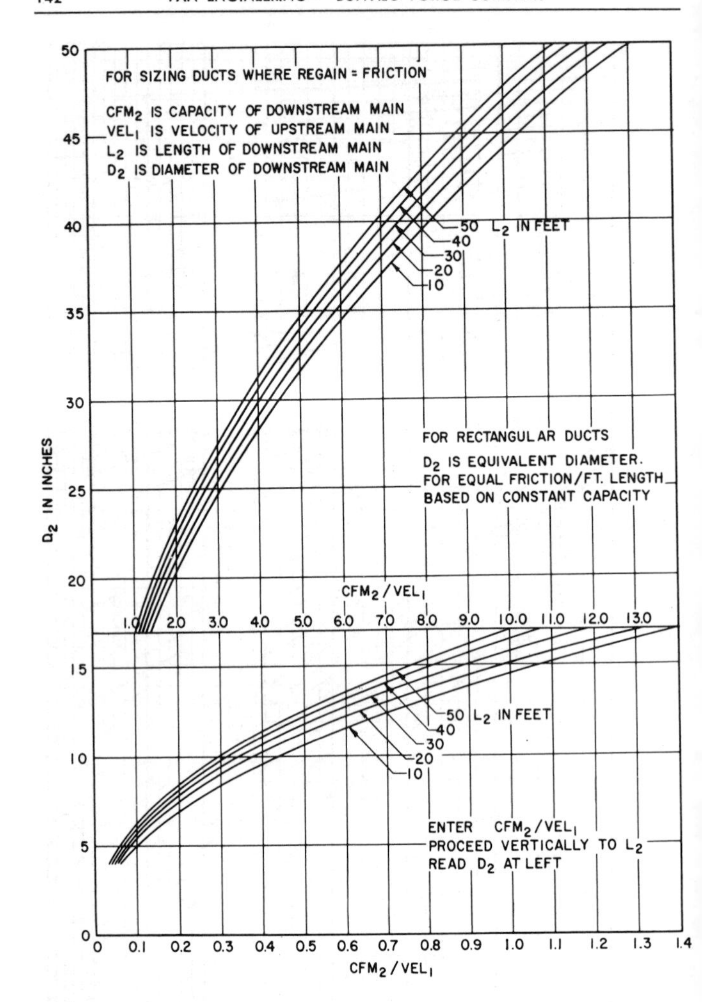

Figure 72—Static Regain Method of Sizing Pipes

Adapted from the data of R. Jorgensen, New Chart Sizes Ducts Directly by Static Regain Method, *Heating, Piping and Air Conditioning*, pp. 107-108, October 1958.

For turbulent flow through the straight pipe sections the ratio of the loss in section a (ΔTP_a) to that in section b (ΔTP_b) may be determined from

$$\left(\frac{\Delta TP_a}{\Delta TP_b}\right) = \left(\frac{l_a}{l_b}\right)^{1.0} \left(\frac{V_a}{V_b}\right)^{2.0-n} \left(\frac{d_b}{d_a}\right)^{1.4-n} \left(\frac{\delta_a}{\delta_b}\right)^{1.0-n} \left(\frac{\mu_a}{\mu_b}\right)^{n} \left(\frac{c_a}{c_b}\right). \tag{175}$$

The various symbols have their usual meanings and the values of n and c for various roughness conditions may be determined from Table 22 in Chapter 3. This expression yields approximately the same results as the Colebrook equation and is considerably easier to manipulate. Equation 175 is equivalent to Equation 146 and further states that the coefficient of friction (f) is inversely proportional to a constant times the Reynolds number raised to the (n) power and the roughness ratio raised to the ($0.4 - 2n$) power. The velocity pressure is of course proportional to the velocity squared as indicated by

$$\frac{VP_a}{VP_b} = \left(\frac{V_a}{V_b}\right)^2. \tag{176}$$

For equal friction per foot of length the expression ($\Delta TP/l$) is a constant. For the same gas conditions in branches a and b, density (δ) and viscosity (μ) are both constant. The necessary diameter ratio for equal friction per foot of length in terms of either the velocity ratio or the capacity ratio may be determined from Equation 175 and written

$$\left(\frac{d_a}{d_b}\right) = \left(\frac{V_a}{V_b}\right)^{\frac{2.0-n}{1.4-n}} = \left(\frac{q_a}{q_b}\right)^{\frac{(2.0-n)/(1.4-n)}{1.0 + 2.0\,(2.0-n)/(1.4-n)}}. \tag{177}$$

The graphical solution of this equation for average roughness conditions (i.e., $n = .16$) is given in Figures 70 and 71. Similar charts can be drawn for other values of n. However, suitable engineering accuracy is obtained by using these charts in most instances. Reasonably accurate results can also be obtained by reading duct sizes directly from Figure 49 along the appropriate vertical line.

Another convenient relation can be derived from Equation 175 for the case of uniform gas composition and equal friction for unequal lengths (l) of duct:

$$\left(\frac{l_a}{l_b}\right) = \left(\frac{d_a}{d_b}\right)^{1.4-n} \left(\frac{V_b}{V_a}\right)^{2.0-n} = \left(\frac{d_a}{d_b}\right)^{5.4-3n}. \tag{178}$$

Therefore, the appropriate diameter ratio in terms of length ratio is

$$\left(\frac{d_a}{d_b}\right) = \left(\frac{l_a}{l_b}\right)^{1/(5.4-3n)} \approx \left(\frac{l_a}{l_b}\right)^{1/5}. \tag{179}$$

This equation of course is only applicable for turbulent flow. The approximation involving the *1/5* power yields reasonably accurate results in most instances.

An expression giving the diameter ratio in terms of the ratio of pressure loss ($\Delta TP_b/\Delta TP_a$) for constant capacity and uniform gas composition is

$$\left(\frac{d_a}{d_b}\right) = \left(\frac{\Delta TP_b}{\Delta TP_a}\right)^{1/(5.4-3n)} \approx \left(\frac{\Delta TP_b}{\Delta TP_a}\right)^{1/5}. \tag{180}$$

This too is only appropriate for turbulent flow and the final approximation gives reasonably accurate results in most cases.

The ratio of pressure losses for any two capacities may also be determined from the appropriate velocity ratios and diameter ratios as indicated by

$$\left(\frac{\Delta TP_a}{\Delta TP_b}\right) = \left(\frac{V_a}{V_b}\right)^{2.0-n} \left(\frac{d_b}{d_a}\right)^{1.4-n}. \tag{181}$$

Pressure losses may also be expressed as a certain number of velocity heads ($\Delta TP/VP$). Substituting the velocity pressure ratio from Equation 176 into Equation 181 produces

$$\left(\frac{\Delta TP_a/VP_a}{\Delta TP_b/VP_b}\right) = \left(\frac{V_a}{V_b}\right)^{-n} \left(\frac{d_b}{d_a}\right)^{1.4-n} \approx \left(\frac{d_b}{d_a}\right)^{1.4-n}. \tag{182}$$

The final approximation should only be used when the velocities are nearly constant.

Total pressure losses may also be expressed as per cent or fraction of a velocity head ($VP/\Delta TP$). This is the reciprocal of the number of velocity heads and accordingly

$$\left(\frac{VP_a/\Delta TP_a}{VP_b/\Delta TP_b}\right) = \left(\frac{V_b}{V_a}\right)^{-n} \left(\frac{d_a}{d_b}\right)^{1.4-n} \approx \left(\frac{d_a}{d_b}\right)^{1.4-n}. \tag{183}$$

For laminar flow

$$\left(\frac{\Delta TP_a}{\Delta TP_b}\right) = \left(\frac{l_a}{l_b}\right) \left(\frac{V_a}{V_b}\right) \left(\frac{d_b}{d_a}\right)^2 \left(\frac{\mu_a}{\mu_b}\right) \text{(Laminar flow)}. \tag{184}$$

In laminar flow the friction factor or coefficient of friction varies inversely with the Reynolds numbers and is independent of roughness so that Equation 184 is considerably simpler than Equation 175. The expressions corresponding to Equations 177 through 183 are also simpler for laminar flow. For equal friction per foot of length with uniform gas composition the diameter ratio in terms of either velocity or capacity ratios is expressed by

$$\left(\frac{d_a}{d_b}\right) = \left(\frac{V_a}{V_b}\right)^{1/2} = \left(\frac{q_a}{q_b}\right)^{1/4} \text{(Laminar flow)}. \tag{185}$$

For unequal lengths and equal friction, the length and diameter ratios are related as indicated in

$$\left(\frac{l_a}{l_b}\right) = \left(\frac{d_a}{d_b}\right)^2 \left(\frac{V_b}{V_a}\right) = \left(\frac{d_a}{d_b}\right)^4 \text{(Laminar flow), and} \tag{186}$$

$$\left(\frac{d_a}{d_b}\right) = \left(\frac{l_a}{l_b}\right)^{1/4} \text{(Laminar flow)}. \tag{187}$$

For constant capacity and uniform gas composition, diameters and total pressure losses are related as indicated by

$$\left(\frac{d_a}{d_b}\right) = \left(\frac{\Delta TP_b}{\Delta TP_a}\right)^{1/4} \text{(Laminar flow)}. \tag{188}$$

For equal lengths and uniform gas composition the total pressure loss ratio may be determined from velocity and diameter or from capacity ratios as indicated by

$$\left(\frac{\Delta TP_a}{\Delta TP_b}\right) = \left(\frac{V_a}{V_b}\right)\left(\frac{d_b}{d_a}\right)^2 = \left(\frac{V_a}{V_b}\right)^2\left(\frac{q_b}{q_a}\right) \text{ (Laminar flow).} \quad (189)$$

The same loss in velocity heads is expressed by

$$\left(\frac{\Delta TP_a/VP_a}{\Delta TP_b/VP_b}\right) = \left(\frac{q_b}{q_a}\right) \text{ (Laminar flow),} \quad (190)$$

and the loss as a per cent of velocity pressure is expressed by

$$\left(\frac{VP_a/\Delta TP_a}{VP_b/\Delta TP_b}\right) = \left(\frac{q_a}{q_b}\right) \text{ (Laminar flow).} \quad (191)$$

Equations 184 through 191 are all for laminar flow and consequently quite limited in application.

Although Equations 175 through 191 are based on the flow of air through straight ducts, certain of them can be used to proportion systems involving elbows. For easy bends, where it is safe to assume that the loss is equal to a certain number of diameters regardless of size, the ratio of losses for any two such bends may be determined from Equation 181. It is usually even more convenient to add the equivalent length of straight duct for each elbow to the actual length of straight duct in each case and proportion the system as if it consisted entirely of straight duct. When abrupt turns are involved, for which the equivalent lengths of straight pipe vary appreciably with size, greater accuracy is obtained by calculating the losses for these turns separately from the straight sections to which they join. If the loss for one such turn is determined in velocity heads or per cent velocity pressure, Equations 182 and 183 respectively may be used to determine the loss for any similar turn regardless of size.

Rectangular Ducts

All of the preceding equations and charts are for round ducts. When rectangular ducts are to be employed, it is necessary to determine the diameter of an equivalent round duct. Two charts, Figures 48 and 50, were given in Chapter 3. Figure 48 is based on equal velocities and equal mean hydraulic radii for the rectangular duct and its equivalent round duct. It is a graphical solution of the equation

$$Equiv.\ d_{const.\ v} = \frac{2\,x\,y}{x + y} \quad (192)$$

which may be derived by equating the mean hydraulic radii for equivalent round and rectangular sections.

Figure 50 is based on equal capacities and equal friction per foot of length for the rectangular duct and its equivalent round duct. It is a graphical solution of the equation

$$Equiv.\ d_{const.\ q} = \left(\frac{4}{\pi}\right)^{\frac{2.0-n}{5.4-3n}}\left(xy\right)^{\frac{3.4-2n}{5.4-3n}}\left(\frac{2}{x+y}\right)^{\frac{1.4-n}{5.4-3n}} \quad (193)$$

which may be derived from Equations 177 and 192. Figure 50 is drawn for average roughness (i.e., $n = .16$). Similar charts can be drawn for other conditions of roughness. Equation 193 is for turbulent flow. For laminar flow

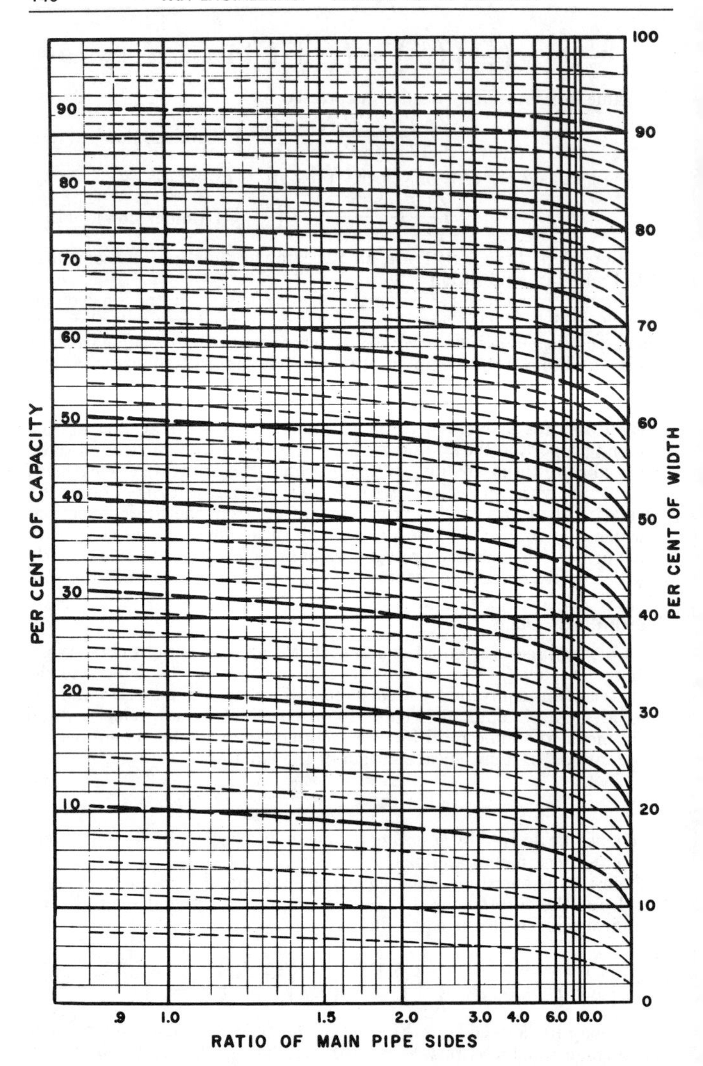

Figure 73 — Rectangular Pipe Sizes for Equal Friction per Foot of Length

$$Equiv.\ d_{const.\ q} = \left(\frac{4}{\pi}\right)^{1/4} \left(xy\right)^{3/4} \left(\frac{2}{x+y}\right)^{1/2}. \qquad (194)$$

Figure 73 may be used to proportion the width of constant-depth rectangular ducts for equal friction per foot of length. This figure is a graphical solution of the expression

$$\left(\frac{q_a}{q_b}\right)^{2.0-n} = \left(\frac{x_a\, y_a}{x_b\, y_b}\right)^{3.4-2n} \left(\frac{x_b + y_b}{x_a + y_a}\right)^{1.4-n}, \qquad (195)$$

using average roughness (i.e., $n = .16$) and setting $y_a = y_b$.

To proportion rectangular ducts by the equal-friction method, Figures 70 and 71 may be used with the appropriate equivalent diameters (based on constant capacity as obtained from Figure 50) for any case. For the special case of one side constant, Figure 73 may be used directly.

To proportion rectangular ducts by the static-regain method, Figure 72 may be used with the appropriate equivalent diameters (as determined from Figure 50) and the actual areas.

The following examples illustrate many principles of the various methods of sizing ducts.

EXAMPLE 4. Round Duct Design for Exhaust System

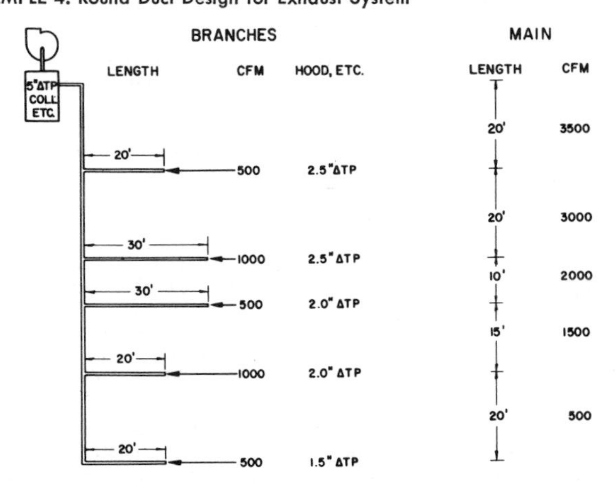

Given the system sketched above with the problem of determining duct sizes and fan requirements we may calculate the theoretical optimum velocity from Equation 172 at least approximately by using the appropriate rates and other factors indicated. For this problem let us assume that we use 20 ga (.036″) steel (.283 lb/cu in.) duct work costing $1.00 per lb installed, that the system operates 8000 hours a year handling standard air (.075 lb/cu ft), and that the power rate is 6 mils per kilowatt hour.

If we further assume that 20% of the first cost represents the annual owning cost the optimum velocity for an average friction factor of .02 is 2550 fpm as indicated by

$$V_{opt} = 1000 \left(\frac{440 \times .036 \times .283 \times 1.00 \times .20}{.02 \times .075 \times 8000 \times .006 \times .746} \right)^{1/3} =$$
$$1000\,(16.7)^{1/3} = 2550\,fpm.$$

It is not necessary in this case to check the validity of the .02 friction factor since we will assume that the material being handled with the air requires approximately 4000 fpm transport velocity. The duct sizes may be determined directly from the capacity and the velocity, but as indicated in the table below this procedure yields odd duct sizes. Practical duct sizes giving velocities within 10% of the required transport velocity will generally prove satisfactory. The duct friction per 100′ of length ($\Delta TP/100'$) may be determined from Figure 49.

CFM	500	1000	1500	2000	3000	3500
d for 4000	4.8	6.8	8.4	9.7	11.6	13.0
d practical	5.0	7.0	8.0	10.0	12.0	12.0
V actual	3700	3800	4300	3700	3800	4400
ΔTP/100′	4.4	3.1	3.4	1.8	1.6	2.2

The over-all pressure drop in ″WG for each of the alternate air paths may be determined by summing the appropriate individual drops as indicated in the following table:

Hoods, els, etc.	1.50	2.00	2.00	2.50	2.50	—
Branch duct	.88	.62	1.32	.93	.88	—
Main ducts	.88	—	—	—	—	—
Main ducts	.51	.51	—	—	—	—
Main ducts	.18	.18	.18	—	—	—
Main ducts	.32	.32	.32	.32	—	—
Main ducts	.44	.44	.44	.44	.44	—
Collector, etc.	5.00	5.00	5.00	5.00	5.00	—
Over-all	9.71	9.07	9.26	9.19	8.82	—
CFM	500	1000	500	1000	500	3500

The calculations for this example have been simplified a great deal since the losses through hoods, elbows, etc., have been predetermined. The losses through the various ducts are based on average friction but for most exhaust systems smooth or medium smooth duct friction corrections should be made depending upon the material and the number of joints used. As is usually the case, the longest run has the highest pressure drop. With enough experience a designer can determine by inspection which run will have the highest pressure drop. However, when there is doubt, all pressure drops should be calculated as in this example.

The fan requirements may be stated as 3500 cfm and 9.71″ SP if blast gates can be used to balance the friction loss in the runs which do not have a loss as great as 9.71″ WG. If blast gates are not used and the fan is selected for 3500 cfm at 9.71″SP the actual capacities through the various branches will be different from design values. The run with the greatest pressure drop will suffer a loss in capacity while the shortest run will handle more air than required. The exact values for all runs could be calculated by a trial and error procedure but the differences will generally be negligibly small. The conservative designer might add 5%-10% to the fan capacity to insure that the longest run would not suffer too big a drop in the amount of air handled.

It is also possible to balance the total pressure losses by reducing the duct size in those branches with less than maximum pressure drop. In this problem for the branch nearest the fan the over-all pressure drop is 9.71″ − 8.82″ or 0.89″ less than the maximum. The branch loss could theoretically be 0.89″ + 0.88″ or 1.77″WG. With Equation 180 the diameter required to produce this higher pressure drop can be calculated to be 4.34″ as indicated below

$$d = 5.0\left(\frac{.88}{1.77}\right)^{1/5} = 4.34''.$$

If the ducts could be sized exactly to the required fractions of an inch the fan could be selected for 3500 cfm @ 9.71″ SP and theoretically no blast gates would be required. Except where blast gates might create great hazards they are frequently used, even if the system is theoretically balanced according to the design, so that the inevitable discrepancies between actual and theoretical requirements may be balanced out.

EXAMPLE 5. Round and Rectangular Duct Design for Supply Systems

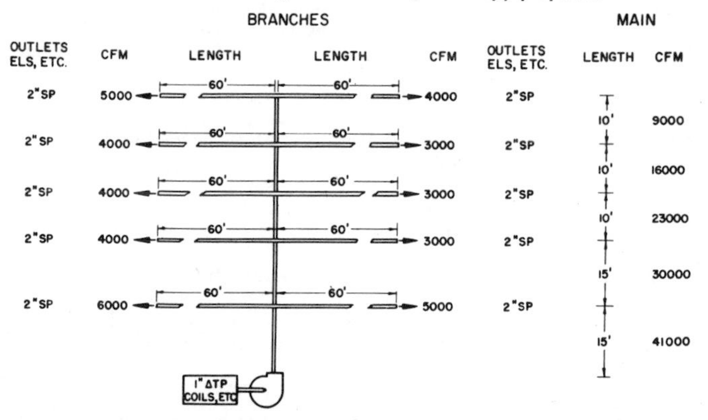

The optimum velocity for round duct costing $1.00 per lb installed when the power rate is 6 mils per kilowatt hour assuming 20 ga (.036″) steel (.283 lb/cu in.) and 3000 hours annual operation may be determined by means of Equation 172.

$$V_{opt} = 1000\left(\frac{440 \times .036 \times .283 \times 1.00 \times .10}{.02 \times .075 \times 3000 \times .006 \times .746}\right)^{1/3} =$$
$$1000\,(22.2)^{1/3} = 2810\ fpm.$$

A velocity of 2810 fpm is obtained for a .02 friction factor and an annual operating charge equal to 10% of the initial installed cost. The validity of the assumed .02 friction factor may be determined by calculating Reynolds number and referring to Figure 27 for the appropriate roughness condition.

Because the horizontal branches are of equal length, a well-balanced system will result if we design them for equal friction per foot of length and if we design the main risers by the static-regain method so that the static pressures at each take-off will be equal. It is impossible to utilize either of these methods with constant velocity, so some compromise on the optimum velocity is required. The procedure followed below utilizes the optimum velocity for the 4000 cfm branches. This establishes the size and friction loss per 100 ft according to Figure 49. The other branches are then sized for the same friction loss per 100 ft by noting the corresponding diameters and velocities at the appropriate capacity on the friction chart.

CFM	4000	CFM	6000	5000	3000
V	2800	ΔTP/100′	.62	.62	.62
d	17	d	19	18.5	14.5
ΔTP/100′	.62	V	3100	2930	2650

The first section of main riser may be sized for any reasonable velocity. The static-regain method produces a considerable reduction in main riser velocity, so that for an average riser velocity approaching the optimum the velocity in the first section must exceed the optimum. A value of 3500 fpm requires an area of 11.72 sq ft which roughly corresponds to 46″ diameter and a 0.27″WG pressure loss or friction per 100′.

The remaining main riser sizes may be obtained directly from Figure 72. The most convenient method of utilizing this chart is to tabulate the information indicated below using the subscript *2* to indicate the portion of main riser under consideration and the subscript *1* to indicate the preceding or upstream portion of main riser. For the second portion of main riser which must handle 30,000 cfm we have already established that the velocity in the upstream portion will be 3500 fpm. From 30,000 divided by 3500 a figure of 8.57 is obtained and at the intersection of this value of CFM_2/VEL_1 with the appropriate length L_2 of 15′ a diameter of 42″ can be read directly from the chart. The velocity in a 42″ pipe carrying 30,000 cfm is 3120 fpm. Similar calculations are required for the remaining sections of main riser.

CFM_2	VEL_1	CFM_2/VEL_1	L_2	D_2	VEL_2
30,000	3500	8.57	15	42	3120
23,000	3120	7.37	10	38	2920
16,000	2920	5.48	10	33	2690
9,000	2690	3.48	10	26	2260

At this point the design of the transmission system is essentially completed. For this example the calculations were simplified somewhat by using pre-determined values for the losses in elbows, outlets, etc. The static pressure required of the fan may be determined as indicated by the following tabulation and calculations.

	2.00″WG	Terminal Requirement
$60/100 \times .62 =$	*0.37*	Horizontal Branches
$(3100/4000)^2 \times .52 =$	*.31*	Take-off (worst 3500 to 3100)
$15/100 \times .27 =$	*.04*	Main Riser
	1.00	Coils, etc.
	3.72″WG	Over-all

The procedure for sizing rectangular ducts is basically the same. The installed cost of rectangular duct is slightly higher than that of round duct so that, assuming all other conditions to be the same, the optimum velocity for the case of rectangular duct costing $1.10 per lb installed would be 2900 fpm as indicated by

$$V_{opt} = 2810 \left(\frac{1.10}{1.00}\right)^{1/3} = 2900\ fpm$$

Once again sizing the 4000 cfm branch for the optimum velocity, the required area is 1.38 sq ft which can be satisfied with rectangular dimensions of 16″ × 12.4″. The equivalent diameter based on constant friction per foot of length as determined from Figure 50 is 15″ and the corresponding friction per 100′ is 0.92″WG. The remaining branches are easily sized by noting the appropriate equivalent diameter opposite the necessary CFM for the same friction per 100′ on Figure 49. The corresponding rectangular dimensions can be determined from Figure 50 and the actual velocity calculated as indicated.

CFM	4000	CFM	6000	5000	3000
V	2900	ΔTP/100′	.92	.92	.92
x × y	16 × 12.4	Eq. d	17.5	16.5	13.5
Eq. d	15	x × y	16 × 16.7	16 × 14.4	16 × 9.8
ΔTP/100′	.92	V	3240	3120	2750

Sizing the first section of main for 3800 fpm means that 10.79 sq ft are required. This requirement is matched by a 24″ × 65″ rectangular cross section. The equivalent diameter based on constant capacity is approximately 42″ and the corresponding friction is 0.32″WG per 100′ of length. Using 3800 fpm in the first section of main and 30,000 cfm in the second, the CFM_2/VEL_1 equals 7.90 and for a 15′ L_2 the equivalent diameter D_2 is 39.8″. From Figure 50 this corresponds to a rectangular section 24″ × 59″ and the actual velocity here is 3050 fpm. Similar calculations must be made for the remaining sections of main as indicated below.

CFM_2	VEL_1	CFM_2/VEL_1	L_2	D_2	x × y	VEL_2
30,000	3800	7.90	15	39.8	24 × 59	3050
23,000	3050	7.54	10	38.3	24 × 54	2650
16,000	2650	6.03	10	34.5	24 × 44	2180
9,000	2180	4.13	10	28.7	14 × 7	1860

The fan should be selected for a capacity of 41,000 cfm and a static pressure of at least 3.97″WG as indicated by the following tabulation.

	2.00″WG	Terminal Requirement
$60/100 \times .92$	$= 0.55$	Horizontal Branches
$(3120/4000)^2 \times .61$	$= 0.37$	90° Elbow Take-off (Worst 3800-3120)
$15/100 \times .32$	$= 0.05$	Main Riser
	1.00	Coils, Etc.
	3.97″WG	Over-all

In both the round and rectangular duct examples the velocities in some of the horizontal mains exceeded the velocity in the main riser immediately upstream. This condition is no worse than that caused by balancing dampers which would otherwise be required. It should also be noted that the design velocities are in the high velocity range of Table 37 so some sort of sound treatment will be required.

Examples 4 and 5 both led to the determination of fan static pressure even though total pressure losses were calculated. This is so because the fan velocity pressure was ignored in Example 4 and because static pressures were given in Example 5. Refer to Chapter 13.

Construction Details

The Sheet Metal and Air Conditioning Contractors National Association has established standards for duct construction based on experience and tests. Table 38 lists sheet metal thicknesses and some of the joint and reinforcing details found in those standards. The joint details for low-velocity ducts are keyed to the sketches given in Figure 74. The joints indicated provide sufficient rigidity except that additional transverse stiffening is required when the length of a duct section exceeds the centers listed. No special provisions for air tightness are required if joints are made in a workmanlike manner. Round duct is generally less expensive but more space consuming than rectangular duct. A round duct requires the least metal for a given cross sectional area and the least reinforcing to prevent vibration. Flat oval ducts are frequently used in high-velocity systems because they can be more economical than rectangular duct and will fit into tighter spaces than round duct. No details are given in Table 38 because the combination of sheet metal thickness and reinforcing will vary with manufacturer.

The joints in high-velocity systems must be sealed to provide adequate air-tightness. Welded or gasketed flanged joints may be used and liquid or mastic sealants may be applied to slip joints and standing seams. Tapes are not recommended. Tie rods may be used at joints as well as at intermediate locations. Complete details are given by SMACNA.

Ducts for industrial exhaust systems should be made from thicker sheets if abrasive action is expected. A rule-of-thumb guide is to use two gauges heavier for slight abrasive action and four gauges heavier for greater abrasive action. Round ducts are commonly used.

TABLE 38—CONSTRUCTION DETAILS FOR DUCTS

LOW VELOCITY—2000 fpm max. LOW PRESSURE—2″ WG max.

Rect. Longest Side	Sheet Metal Thickness			Transverse Joints		Longitudinal	Transverse Reinforcing	
	Galv.	Alum.	Copper	Types	H-dim.	Joint Types	Angle	Centers
3″-12″	26 ga	.020″	16 oz	A,B,K	1″	N,O,Z	—	—
13″-18″	24 ga	.025″	24 oz	A,B,K	1″	B,O,Z	—	—
19″-30″	24 ga	.025″	24 oz	C,E,K	1″	N,O,Z	1″x1″x⅛″	5′
31″-42″	22 ga	.032″	32 oz	E,G,K	1″	N,I,Z	1″x1″x⅛″	5′
43″-54″	22 ga	.032″	32 oz	E,G,K	1 ½″	N,I,Z	1 ½″x1 ½″x⅛″	5′
55″-60″	20 ga	.040″	36 oz	E,G,K	1 ½″	N,I,Z	1 ½″x1 ½″x⅛″	5′
61″-84″	20 ga	.040″	36 oz	F,G,H,J,L	1 ½″	N,I,Z	1 ½″x1 ½″x⅛″	2′6″
85″-96″	18 ga	.051″	48 oz	H,J,L,M	1 ½″	N,I	1 ½″x1 ½″x3/16″	2′6″
over 96″	18 ga	.051″	48 oz	H,J,L,M	2″	N,I	2″x2″x¼″	2′6″

Round Duct Diameter	Galvanized Sheet Metal Thickness		
	Spiral Lock Seam Duct	Longitudinal Seam Duct	Round Duct Fittings
3″-12″	28 ga	26 ga	26 ga
13″-18″	26 ga	24 ga	24 ga
19″-28″	24 ga	22 ga	22 ga
29″-36″	22 ga	20 ga	20 ga
37″-52″	20 ga	18 ga	18 ga

HIGH VELOCITY—over 2000 fpm

Rectangular Duct Longest Side	MEDIUM PRESSURE—to 6″ WG				HIGH PRESSURE—to 10″ WG			
		Transverse Reinforcing				Transverse Reinforcing		
	Galv. Sheet	Tie Rods	Angle	Centers	Galv. Sheet	Tie Rods	Angle	Centers
3″-12″	24 ga	—	—	—	22 ga	—	—	—
13″-18″	24 ga	1	—	48″	22 ga	1	—	40″
		—	1″x1″x16 ga	48″		—	1″x1″x16 ga	48″
19″-24″	22 ga	1	—	48″	22 ga	2	—	40″
		—	1″x1″x⅛″	48″		—	1″x1″x⅛″	48″
25″-36″	22 ga	—	1″x1″x⅛″	32″	22 ga	—	1 ¼″x1 ¼″x⅛″	32″
37″-48″	22 ga	—	1 ½″x1 ½″x⅛″	30″	22 ga	—	2″x2″x⅛″	30″
49″-60″	20 ga	1	1 ½″x1 ½″x⅛″	24″	20 ga	1	1 ½″x1 ½″x⅛″	24″
		—	2″x2″x⅛″	24″		—	2″x2″x3/16″	24″
61″-72″	20 ga	1	1 ½″x1 ½″x⅛″	24″	20 ga	1	1 ½″x1 ½″x⅛″	24″
		—	2 ½″x2 ½″x3/16″	24″		—	2 ½″x2 ½″x3/16″	24″
73″-84″	18 ga	1	1 ½″x1 ½″x⅛″	24″	18 ga	1	1 ½″x1 ½″x⅛″	24″
		—	2 ½″x2 ½″x3/16″	24″				
85″-96″	18 ga	1	1 ½″x1 ½″x⅛″	24″	18 ga	1	1 ½″x1 ½″x⅛″	24″
over 96″	18 ga	2	2″x2″x⅛″	24″	16 ga	2	2″x2″x⅛″	24″

Round Duct Diameter	Galvanized Sheet Thickness			Girth Reinforcing	
	Spiral Lock Seam Duct	Longitudinal Seam Duct	Round Duct Fittings	Angle	Centers
3″-8″	26 ga	24 ga	22 ga	—	—
9″-22″	24 ga	22 ga	20 ga	—	—
23″-36″	22 ga	20 ga	20 ga	—	—
37″-50″	20 ga	20 ga	18 ga	1 ¼″x1 ¼″x⅛″	72″
51″-60″		18 ga	18 ga	1 ¼″x1 ¼″x⅛″	72″
61″-84″		16 ga	16 ga	1 ½″x1 ½″x⅛″	48″

Adapted from the data of Low Velocity Duct Construction Standards, SMACNA, April, 1969, pp. 11-39, and High Velocity Duct Construction Standards, SMACNA, January, 1969, pp. 6, 14-17. Copper data added.

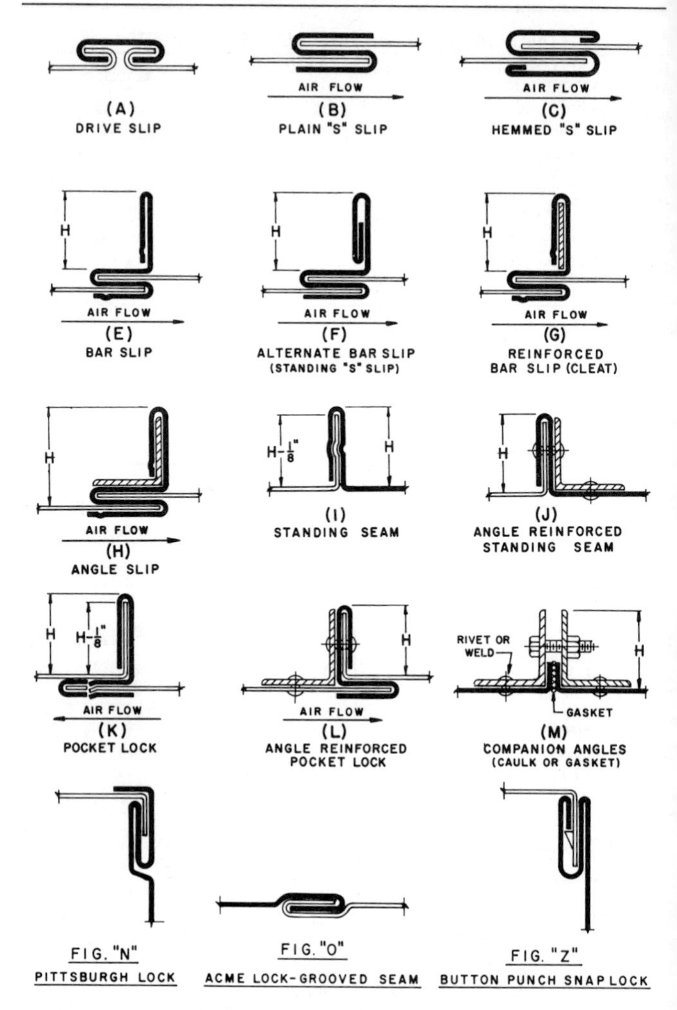

Figure 74—Low Velocity Duct Joints

Adapted from the data of Low Velocity Duct Construction Standards, SMACNA, April 1969, pp. 13 and 15.

The usual material in a heating, air conditioning, or ventilation system is galvanized steel. Aluminum or copper can be justified in certain cases. Various materials or protective coatings may be used on industrial exhaust systems as indicated by the nature of the gas or material being handled. The weight per linear foot of galvanized steel rectangular ducts including an allowance for the recommended standing seams may be determined from Table 40. Additions must be made for any extra reinforcing. Similar tables for round galvanized and black steel ducts are given in Tables 39 and 41 respectively.

TABLE 39—WEIGHTS OF GALVANIZED STEEL ROUND DUCTS

In pounds per lineal foot

Diam of Duct	Sq Ft per Running Ft	U.S.S. Gauge					
		26	24	22	20	18	16
4	1.13	1.13	1.47	1.69	1.97	2.56	3.10
5	1.39	1.39	1.80	2.08	2.43	3.19	3.82
6	1.65	1.65	2.14	2.47	2.89	3.79	4.54
7	1.91	1.91	2.48	2.86	3.34	4.39	5.25
8	2.18	2.18	2.83	3.27	3.81	5.01	6.00
9	2.44	2.44	3.17	3.66	4.27	5.61	6.71
10	2.70	2.70	3.51	4.05	4.72	6.21	7.42
11	2.96	2.96	3.85	4.44	5.18	6.80	8.14
12	3.22	3.22	4.18	4.83	5.63	7.40	8.85
13	3.48	3.48	4.52	5.22	6.09	8.00	9.57
14	3.74	3.74	4.86	5.61	6.54	8.60	10.28
15	4.01	4.01	5.21	6.01	7.01	9.22	10.86
16	4.27	4.27	5.55	6.40	7.47	9.82	11.74
17	4.53	4.53	5.85	6.79	7.92	10.42	12.45
18	4.87	4.87	6.33	7.30	8.51	11.18	13.36
19	5.14	5.14	6.68	7.71	9.00	11.80	14.11
20	5.40	5.40	7.02	8.10	9.45	12.42	14.85
21	5.59	5.59	7.26	8.39	9.78	12.85	15.36
22	5.92	5.92	7.70	8.88	10.35	13.60	16.25
23	6.18	6.18	8.04	9.27	10.81	14.40	17.00
24	6.45	6.45	8.38	9.67	11.30	14.84	17.71
25	6.71	6.71	8.72	10.06	11.74	15.41	18.41
26	6.97	6.97	9.05	10.45	12.20	16.00	19.15
27	7.33	7.33	9.40	10.85	12.67	16.62	19.87
28	7.50	7.50	9.75	11.27	13.13	17.26	20.60
29	7.75	7.75	10.07	11.63	13.58	17.81	21.30
30	8.10	8.10	10.54	12.17	14.20	18.62	22.25
31	8.36	8.36	10.87	12.54	14.63	19.20	23.00
32	8.62	8.62	11.20	12.93	15.10	19.84	23.70
33	8.88	8.88	11.56	13.34	15.56	20.42	24.40
34	9.15	9.15	11.90	13.73	16.00	21.08	25.18
35	9.41	9.41	12.23	14.10	16.48	21.65	25.85
36	9.67	9.67	12.57	14.50	16.91	22.22	26.60
37	9.93	9.93	12.91	14.90	17.40	22.84	27.30
38	10.19	10.19	13.25	15.29	17.81	23.40	28.00
39	10.46	10.46	13.60	15.60	18.31	24.02	28.70

TABLE 40—WEIGHTS OF GALVANIZED STEEL RECTANGULAR DUCTS

In pounds per lineal foot

Size of Duct	26 U.S.S. Gauge						
	6	7	8	9	10	11	12
6	2.00	2.17	2.34	2.50	2.67	2.84	3.0
7	2.17	2.34	2.50	2.67	2.84	3.0	3.17
8	2.34	2.50	2.67	2.84	3.0	3.17	3.34
9	2.50	2.67	2.84	3.0	3.17	3.34	3.50
10	2.67	2.84	3.0	3.17	3.34	3.50	3.67
11	2.84	3.0	3.17	3.34	3.50	3.67	3.84
12	3.0	3.17	3.34	3.50	3.67	3.84	4.0
14	3.34	3.50	3.67	3.84	4.0	4.17	4.34
16	3.67	3.84	4.0	4.17	4.34	4.5	4.67
18	4.0	4.17	4.34	4.5	4.67	4.84	5.0

Size of Duct	24 U.S.S. Gauge						
	18	20	22	24	26	28	30
6	5.22	5.64	6.07	6.5	6.94	7.37	7.8
7	5.43	5.85	6.29	6.72	7.15	7.59	8.02
8	5.65	6.07	6.5	6.94	7.37	7.8	8.24
9	5.87	6.29	6.72	7.15	7.59	8.02	8.45
10	6.08	6.5	6.94	7.37	7.8	8.24	8.67
11	6.30	6.72	7.15	7.59	8.02	8.45	8.89
12	6.52	6.94	7.37	7.8	8.24	8.67	9.10
14	6.95	7.37	7.8	8.24	8.67	9.10	9.54
16	7.38	7.8	8.24	8.67	9.10	9.54	9.97
18	7.82	8.24	8.67	9.10	9.54	9.97	10.42
20	8.25	8.67	9.10	9.54	9.97	10.42	10.85
22	8.68	9.10	9.54	9.97	10.42	10.85	11.29
24	9.12	9.54	9.97	10.42	10.85	11.29	11.72
26	9.55	9.97	10.42	10.85	11.29	11.72	12.13
28	10.00	10.42	10.85	11.29	11.72	12.13	12.56
30	10.43	10.85	11.29	11.72	12.13	12.56	13.0

Size of Duct	22 U.S.S. Gauge					
	32	34	36	38	40	42
6	9.5	10.0	10.5	11.0	11.5	12.0
7	9.75	10.25	10.75	11.25	11.75	12.25
8	10.0	10.5	11.0	11.5	12.0	12.5
9	10.25	10.75	11.25	11.75	12.25	12.75
10	10.5	11.0	11.5	12.0	12.5	13.0
11	10.75	11.25	11.75	12.25	12.75	13.25
12	11.0	11.5	12.0	12.5	13.0	13.5
13	11.25	11.75	12.25	12.75	13.25	13.75
14	11.5	12.0	12.5	13.0	13.5	14.0
15	11.75	12.25	12.75	13.25	13.75	14.25
16	12.0	12.5	13.0	13.5	14.0	14.5
17	12.25	12.75	13.25	13.75	14.25	14.75
18	12.5	13.0	13.5	14.0	14.5	15.0
19	12.75	13.25	13.75	14.25	14.75	15.25
20	13.0	13.5	14.0	14.5	15.0	15.5
21	13.25	13.75	14.25	14.75	15.25	15.75
22	13.5	14.0	14.5	15.0	15.5	16.0
23	13.75	14.25	14.75	15.25	15.75	16.25
24	14.0	14.5	15.0	15.5	16.0	16.5
26	14.5	15.0	15.5	16.0	16.5	17.0
28	15.0	15.5	16.0	16.5	17.0	17.5
30	15.5	16.0	16.5	17.0	17.5	18.0
32	16.0	16.5	17.0	17.5	18.0	18.5
34	16.5	17.0	17.5	18.0	18.5	19.0
36	17.0	17.5	18.0	18.5	19.0	19.5

TABLE 40 (Concluded)—WEIGHTS OF RECTANGULAR DUCTS

In pounds per lineal foot

Size of Duct	22 U.S.S. Gauge					
	44	**46**	**48**	**50**	**52**	**54**
6	12.5	13.0	13.5	14.0	14.5	15.0
7	12.75	13.25	13.75	14.25	14.75	15.25
8	13.0	13.5	14.0	14.5	15.0	15.5
9	13.25	13.75	14.25	14.75	15.25	15.75
10	13.5	14.0	14.5	15.0	15.5	16.0
11	13.75	14.25	14.75	15.25	15.75	16.25
12	14.0	14.5	15.0	15.5	16.0	16.5
14	14.5	15.0	15.5	16.0	16.5	17.0
16	15.0	15.5	16.0	16.5	17.0	17.5
18	15.5	16.0	16.5	17.0	17.5	18.0
20	16.0	16.5	17.0	17.5	18.0	18.5
22	16.5	17.0	17.5	18.0	18.5	19.0
24	17.0	17.5	18.0	18.5	19.0	19.5
26	17.5	18.0	18.5	19.0	19.5	20.0
28	18.0	18.5	19.0	19.5	20.0	20.5
30	18.5	19.0	19.5	20.0	20.5	21.0
32	19.0	19.5	20.0	20.5	21.0	21.5
34	19.5	20.0	20.5	21.0	21.5	22.0
36	20.0	20.5	21.0	21.5	22.0	22.5
38	20.5	21.0	21.5	22.0	22.5	23.0
40	21.0	21.5	22.0	22.5	23.0	23.5
42	21.5	22.0	22.5	23.0	23.5	24.0
44	22.0	22.5	23.0	23.5	24.0	24.5
46	22.5	23.0	23.5	24.0	24.5	25.0
48	23.0	23.5	24.0	24.5	25.0	25.5

Size of Duct	20 U.S.S. Gauge						
	64	**68**	**72**	**76**	**80**	**84**	**88**
6	20.4	21.6	22.8	23.9	25.1	26.3	27.4
8	21.0	22.1	23.4	24.5	25.7	26.7	28.0
10	21.6	22.8	23.9	25.1	26.3	27.4	28.6
12	22.1	23.4	24.5	25.7	26.7	28.0	29.2
14	22.8	23.9	25.1	26.3	27.4	28.6	29.8
16	23.4	24.5	25.7	26.7	28.0	29.2	30.4
18	23.9	25.1	26.3	27.4	28.6	29.8	30.9
20	24.5	25.7	26.7	28.0	29.2	30.4	31.5
22	25.1	26.3	27.4	28.6	29.8	30.9	32.1
24	25.7	26.7	28.0	29.2	30.4	31.5	32.7
26	26.3	27.4	28.6	29.8	30.9	32.1	33.3
28	26.7	28.0	29.2	30.4	31.5	32.7	33.9
30	27.4	28.6	29.8	30.9	32.1	33.3	34.4
32	28.0	29.2	30.4	31.5	32.7	33.9	35.0
34	28.6	29.8	30.9	32.1	33.3	34.4	35.6
36	29.2	30.4	31.5	32.7	33.9	35.0	36.2
38	29.8	30.9	32.1	33.3	34.4	35.6	36.8
40	30.4	31.5	32.7	33.9	35.0	36.2	37.3
42	30.9	32.1	33.3	34.4	35.6	36.8	37.9
44	31.5	32.7	33.9	35.0	36.2	37.3	38.5
46	32.1	33.3	34.4	35.6	36.8	37.9	39.0
48	32.7	33.9	35.0	36.2	37.3	38.5	39.6
50	33.3	34.4	35.6	36.8	37.9	39.0	40.2
52	33.9	35.0	36.2	37.3	38.5	39.6	40.8
54	34.4	35.6	36.8	37.9	39.0	40.2	41.4

TABLE 41—WEIGHTS OF BLACK STEEL ROUND DUCTS

In pounds per lineal foot

Diam of Duct	Sq Ft per Running Ft	U.S.S. Gauge						
		24	22	20	18	16	14	12
4	1.13	1.30	1.58	1.86	2.43	2.99	3.62	5.08
5	1.39	1.60	1.95	2.29	2.99	3.68	4.45	6.25
6	1.65	1.90	2.31	2.72	3.54	4.36	5.28	7.42
7	1.91	2.20	2.67	3.15	4.10	5.05	6.11	8.58
8	2.18	2.50	3.05	3.60	4.68	5.77	6.97	9.80
9	2.44	2.80	3.42	4.03	5.25	6.47	7.80	10.98
10	2.70	3.10	3.78	4.45	5.80	7.15	8.64	12.15
11	2.96	3.40	4.15	4.88	6.36	7.85	9.47	13.31
12	3.22	3.70	4.50	5.31	6.91	8.52	10.30	14.48
13	3.48	4.00	4.88	5.74	7.48	9.21	11.15	15.66
14	3.74	4.30	5.23	6.17	8.03	9.90	11.97	16.84
15	4.01	4.61	5.61	6.61	8.61	10.61	12.83	18.03
16	4.27	4.91	5.97	7.04	9.16	11.29	13.65	19.17
17	4.53	5.21	6.35	7.48	9.74	12.00	14.49	20.40
18	4.87	5.60	6.81	8.03	10.45	12.89	15.55	21.90
19	5.14	5.91	7.20	8.48	11.04	13.60	16.42	23.10
20	5.40	6.21	7.56	8.90	11.60	14.30	17.26	24.30
21	5.59	6.43	7.83	9.22	12.00	14.80	17.87	25.10
22	5.92	6.80	8.28	9.75	12.70	15.65	18.90	26.60
23	6.18	7.11	8.66	10.20	13.29	16.38	19.80	27.80
24	6.45	7.41	9.04	10.63	13.85	17.08	20.65	29.00
25	6.71	7.71	9.40	11.06	14.40	17.75	21.50	30.20
26	6.97	8.01	9.75	11.48	14.96	18.41	22.30	31.30
27	7.23	8.31	10.11	11.93	15.51	19.12	23.10	32.50
28	7.50	8.62	10.50	12.38	16.10	19.87	24.00	33.75
29	7.75	8.91	10.85	12.78	16.67	20.50	24.80	34.90
30	8.10	9.32	11.34	13.37	17.40	21.45	25.90	36.40
31	8.36	9.61	11.70	13.80	18.00	22.15	26.75	37.60
32	8.62	9.92	12.07	14.25	18.52	22.83	27.60	38.80
33	8.88	10.21	12.45	14.66	19.10	23.50	28.40	40.00
34	9.15	10.53	12.81	15.10	19.68	24.43	29.30	41.20
35	9.41	10.82	13.18	15.51	20.20	24.90	30.10	42.30
36	9.67	11.11	13.54	15.95	20.78	25.60	30.90	43.50
37	9.93	11.42	13.90	16.40	21.38	26.30	31.80	44.70
38	10.19	11.71	14.28	16.80	21.90	27.00	32.60	45.80
39	10.46	12.03	14.65	17.27	22.50	27.74	33.50	47.10
40	10.72	12.33	15.00	17.70	23.01	28.40	34.30	48.25
41	10.98	12.62	15.38	18.11	23.60	29.10	35.10	49.40
42	11.24	12.93	15.75	18.55	24.20	29.80	36.00	50.60
43	11.59	13.32	16.21	19.10	24.90	30.70	37.05	52.10
44	11.85	13.64	16.60	19.55	25.50	31.40	37.90	53.30
45	12.11	13.93	16.97	20.00	26.00	32.10	38.75	54.50
46	12.37	14.23	17.31	20.40	26.60	32.80	39.60	55.70
47	12.63	14.52	17.70	20.85	27.20	33.45	40.40	56.80
48	12.90	14.83	18.07	21.30	27.75	34.20	41.30	58.00
49	13.15	15.11	18.40	21.70	28.25	34.80	42.10	59.20
50	13.41	15.42	18.80	22.15	28.80	35.55	42.90	60.40
51	13.66	15.71	19.13	22.55	29.40	36.20	43.75	61.50
52	13.94	16.01	19.50	23.00	30.00	36.90	44.60	62.65
54	14.46	16.62	20.25	23.85	31.10	38.30	46.30	65.00
56	15.07	17.32	21.10	24.85	32.40	39.90	48.20	67.80
58	15.58	17.91	21.80	25.70	33.50	41.30	49.80	70.20
60	16.12	18.53	22.60	26.65	34.70	42.75	51.60	72.60
62	16.65	19.16	23.30	27.50	35.80	44.10	53.30	75.00
64	17.16	19.72	24.00	28.30	36.90	45.50	54.90	77.20
66	17.66	20.30	24.70	29.15	38.00	46.80	56.50	79.40
68	18.21	20.95	25.50	30.00	39.15	48.25	58.30	81.80
70	18.75	21.55	26.25	30.90	40.30	49.70	60.00	84.30
72	19.25	22.15	27.00	31.80	41.40	51.00	61.60	86.60
74	19.79	22.75	27.70	32.65	42.60	52.40	63.30	89.00

The surface area (S) of the material in a 90° elbow of either round or rectangular cross section may be determined from the cross section dimensions (d or x and y) and the centerline radius (r) as indicated by

$$S = \tfrac{1}{2}\,\pi^2\, r\, d = \pi\, r\,(x + y). \qquad (196)$$

For the same centerline radius it is immaterial whether the aspect ratio is x/y or y/x. Table 42 may be used in conjunction with Tables 39 through 41 to determine the weight of a galvanized or black steel elbow of either rectangular or round cross section. The thickness of the material in an elbow or other fitting should be equal to or greater than that of the connecting straight pipe or duct. Under highly abrasive conditions rectangular section elbows are generally used since replacement of the wearing surface can be accomplished more easily.

TABLE 42—WEIGHTS OF ELBOWS

Multiply value from Table 39-41 by factor below

Center Line Radius Inches	0	1	2	3	4	5	6	7	8	9
0		.14	.28	.43	.57	.71	.85	.99	1.13	1.27
10	1.42	1.56	1.70	1.84	1.98	2.12	2.27	2.41	2.55	2.69
20	2.83	2.98	3.12	3.26	3.40	3.54	3.68	3.82	3.97	4.11
30	4.25	4.39	4.54	4.67	4.81	4.96	5.10	5.24	5.38	5.52
40	5.66	5.81	5.95	6.09	6.24	6.37	6.52	6.66	6.80	6.94
50	7.08	7.22	7.36	7.51	7.65	7.79	7.94	8.07	8.22	8.35
60	8.50	8.64	8.78	8.92	9.06	9.21	9.35	9.49	9.63	9.77
70	9.92	10.1	10.2	10.3	10.5	10.6	10.8	10.9	11.1	11.2
80	11.3	11.5	11.6	11.8	11.9	12.0	12.2	12.3	12.5	12.6
90	12.7	12.9	13.0	13.2	13.3	13.5	13.6	13.7	13.9	14.0
100	14.2	14.3	14.4	14.6	14.7	14.9	15.0	15.2	15.3	15.4

PRINCIPLES OF DISTRIBUTION

Distribution requirements vary considerably from one application to another. On some systems a concentrated supply of air at high velocity may be required but on others uniform distribution without objectionable drafts over a broad area may be the objective.

The circulation and distribution of air within a space can be accomplished by utilizing the kinetic energy of one or more streams of air issuing into the space. The energy must be supplied directly or indirectly by a fan.

As mentioned under "Principles of Duct Design," supply and exhaust can be accomplished with a single fan in either position. A supply fan must develop the necessary total pressure to produce the kinetic energy required at the duct opening into a room, plus that necessary to overcome the losses due to friction, etc., in the duct system, plus that necessary to produce a static pressure in the space sufficient to force air through the available exhaust openings. An exhaust fan must develop the necessary total pressure to overcome the losses due to friction, etc., in the duct system plus that necessary to create a negative static pressure in the space sufficient to produce the required kinetic energy at the duct opening into the room.

Both supply and exhaust openings are required for through-circulation. Air discharging from an opening, like any moving object, tends to continue at its exit velocity along a straight line path. Various effects tend to slow down and deflect the stream. The effects of entrainment and temperature difference are discussed below. The mutual effect of supply and exhaust openings may also be important.

Air entering an exhaust opening tends to approach equally from all possible directions. For an opening located in the plane of the wall, the velocity at one diameter distance from the opening will be approximately 10% of that at the opening itself. The velocity decreases rapidly with distance so that the effect of an exhaust opening in producing air motion is limited to the immediate area of the opening.

"Short circuits" do develop to the detriment of room circulation when supply and exhaust openings are directly in line at relatively short distances. The seriousness of short circuiting can be greatly reduced by changing the "in line" relationship or by increasing the distance. The mutual influence of supply and exhaust openings on each other is usually of far less importance than, for example, the effect of cold window panes in producing drafts by convection. The effect of opening a door may also be more severe than short circuiting. Frequently the supply and exhaust openings can be located to counteract these effects. Devices combining both supply and exhaust in a single unit have been successfully employed.

Architectural and functional requirements of spaces frequently limit the location of supply and exhaust openings. Whenever uniform distribution is required in a large space the use of multiple openings should be considered for both supply and exhaust.

Throw of Isothermal Air Jets

The kinetic energy of a jet may be utilized to provide air motion at a considerable distance from the point where the jet originates, to promote mixing of the jet of supply air with the room air, or both. Neither effect can be achieved to the exclusion of the other.

The centerline velocity of a jet issuing from a plain round opening will persist for the first four diameters of throw. This maximum velocity will decrease as the square root of the distance over the next four diameters or so, after which the velocity will be inversely proportional to the distance from the outlet. When the residual velocity falls below about 500 fpm the decrease in velocity is more than proportional to the total throw or distance from the outlet. Room air will be entrained in gradually increasing amounts.

Similar effects will occur with openings of different shapes. A rectangular opening will produce a jet, the maximum velocity of which will not change for a throw of about four times the short dimension. Thereafter the maximum velocity will decrease as the square root of the total throw for a distance of about 4 times the aspect ratio times the short dimension. Even with an aspect ratio of 40 or 50 this stream eventually becomes an expanding cone with a solid angle of 20° to 24°. The point beyond which the maximum velocity decreases directly with the increase in total throw is about 20 effective diameters regardless of the opening shape. Closely spaced multiple openings produce streams similar to that of a single opening of the same total area.

The effective area (A_e) of any outlet is the total area at the *vena contracta* or the net free area if there is no contraction. The corresponding effective diameter (D_e) is

$$D_e = 1.13\sqrt{A_e}. \tag{197}$$

The effective diameter of any square-edged orifice, whether round, square, or rectangular in shape, can be determined from its basic dimensions using Figure 75.

This chart is based on a ratio of free area to gross area (R_A) of 1.00, a coefficient of discharge (C_D) of 0.6, and a velocity of approach factor (ϕ_i) of 1.00. For any other conditions the chart value $(D_e)_{Fig.\ 75}$ must be modified according to

$$D_e = (D_e)_{Fig.\ 75}\sqrt{R_A\ \phi_i\ C_D/0.6.} \tag{198}$$

Values of R_A and $\phi_i C_D$ for several typical outlets are given in Table 43.

The effective velocity of the jet issuing from the outlet (V_0) is that at the *vena contracta*. This may be determined from the capacity (q) and the effective area (A_e) using the equation of continuity or from the gross area (A_g) of the outlet using

$$V_o = \frac{q}{A_g\ R_A\ \phi_i\ C_D} = \frac{q}{A_e}. \tag{199}$$

The average residual velocity at any distance from the outlet, beyond approximately 10 effective diameters, is about ⅓ of the maximum residual velocity. The maximum or centerline residual velocity (V_r) relative to the effective velocity at the outlet (V_0) is a function of the throw (X) and the effective diameter (D_e). Conversely, the throw in diameters (X/D_e) is proportional to the velocity ratio (V_r/V_0) as indicated by

$$\frac{X}{D_e} = K\frac{V_0}{V_r}. \tag{200}$$

The proportionality constant (K) for orifices and nozzles can be determined directly from Table 44. These values should be modified as indicated in Table 43 for other types of outlets.

The entrainment ratio (R_q) or the ratio of the total moving quantity (q_t) to the primary or jet quantity (q_i) is also a function of the velocity ratio (V_r/V_0) as indicated by

$$R_q = \frac{q_t}{q_i} = 0.314\,\frac{V_r}{V_0}\left(1.12 + 0.395\,K\,\frac{V_0}{V_r}\right)^2 - 1. \tag{201}$$

Various solutions of Equations 200 and 201 are presented graphically in Figure 76.

This chart may be used to determine the entrainment ratio and maximum residual velocity at any distance from a given outlet. It may also be used to determine the necessary combination of effective diameter and original velocity for a given throw and a specified residual velocity. Example 6 illustrates a typical use of this chart.

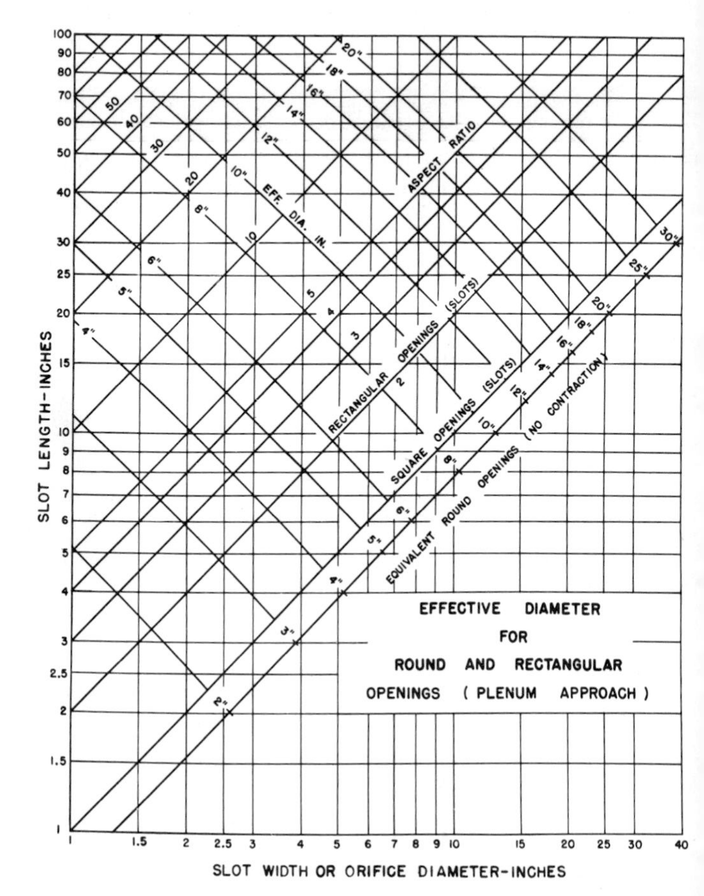

Figure 75—Effective Diameters of Round and Rectangular Square Edged Openings

Adapted from the data of R. D. Madison and W. R. Elliot, Throw of Air from Slots and Jets, *ASHVE Journal Section* of *Heating, Piping and Air Conditioning*, pp. 108-109, November, 1946.

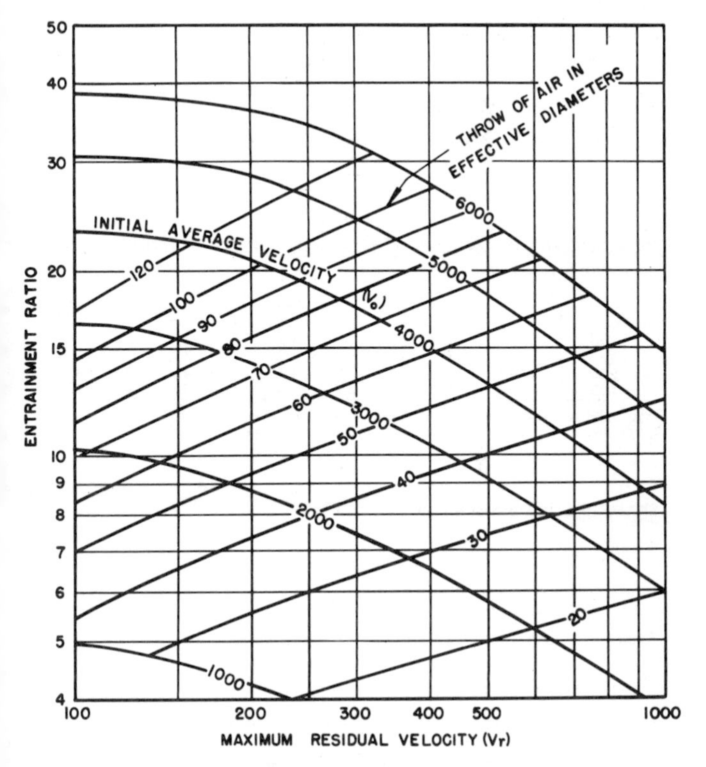

Figure 76—Throw of Air from Openings

Adapted from the data of R. D. Madison and W. R. Elliot, Throw of Air from Slots and Jets, *ASHVE Journal Section* of *Heating, Piping and Air Conditioning*, pp. 108-109, November, 1946.

TABLE 43—DISTRIBUTION FACTORS FOR VARIOUS OUTLETS

Outlet	R_A	Approx. $\phi_i C_D$*	Approx.‡ K
Rounded entrance nozzles	1.00	.99	Use Table 44 Values Directly
Square-edged orifices	1.00	.60	Use Table 44 Values Directly
Plain straight duct openings	1.00	1.00	Multi Table 44 Values by 1.05
Bar grilles	.84	.66	Multi Table 44 Values by .86
Bar grilles	.74	.78	Multi Table 44 Values by .72
Bar grilles	.72	.78	Multi Table 44 Values by .69
Perforated panels	.40	.83	Multi Table 44 Values by .89
Perforated panels	.09	.75	Multi Table 44 Values by .64
Perforated panels	.03	.79	Multi Table 44 Values by .39
Effect of high aspect ratios	—	—	Multi Table 44 Values by .86
Effect of adjacent wall parallel to axis of flow	—	—	Multi Table 44 Values by 1.42

Adapted from the data of A. Koestel, P. Hermann, and G. L. Tuve, Comparative Study of Ventilating Jets from Various Types of Outlets, *Trans. ASHVE*, vol. 56, pp. 459-478, 1950.
*Velocity of approach factors corresponding to 1400 fpm ahead of bar grilles are included in table.
‡Value of K increases for throw calculations but decreases for entrainment calculations.

TABLE 44
PROPORTIONALITY FACTORS (K) FOR THROW FROM NOZZLES & ORIFICES

V_r—fpm	V_o—fpm				
	1000	2000	3000	4000	5000
500 up	—	5.3	5.5	5.7	6.0
400	—	5.0	5.2	5.5	5.8
300	4.4	4.6	4.8	5.0	5.3
200	4.1	4.2	4.4	4.6	4.8
100	3.3	3.3	3.4	3.5	3.5

Adapted from the data of G. L. Tuve and G. B. Priester, Control of Air Streams in Large Spaces, *Trans. ASHVE*, vol. 50, pp. 153-172, 1944.

EXAMPLE 6. Isothermal Air Jet

Given: $q_j = 2000$ *cfm*
$A_g = 42'' \times 6'' = 1.75$ *sq ft*
$R_A = .74$ *(bar grill)*
$X = 30$ *ft*

Find: V_r *avg.*
q *total*

From Table 43: $\phi_i C_D = .78$

From Eq. 199: $V_o = \dfrac{2000}{1.75 \times .74 \times .78} = \dfrac{2000}{1.01} = 1980\ fpm$

From Eq. 197: $D_e = 1.13\sqrt{1.01} = 1.14\ ft$

From Fig. 75: $(D_e)_{Fig.\ 75} = 14'' = 1.17\ ft$

From Eq. 198 $D_e = 1.17\sqrt{.74 \times .78/.6} = 1.14\ ft$

From Fig. 76: *at* $V = 1980$
and $X/D_e = 30/1.14 = 26.3$

1st approx. for $V_r = 430$

From Table 43: $K = .72 \times$ *Table 44*

2nd approx. for $V_r = 430 \times .72 = 310$

From Table 44: $K = 4.6 \times .72 = 3.3$

From Eq. 200: $V_r = 3.3 \times 1980/26.3 = 249 =$ *final approx.*

$$\frac{V_o}{V_r} = 7.96$$

From Eq. 201:
$$R_a = \frac{0.314}{7.96}(1.12 + 0.395 \times 3.3 \times 7.96)^2 - 1 =$$
$$R_a = 5.21 - 1.00 = 4.21$$

Average residual velocity $= \frac{1}{3} \times 249 = 83$ *fpm*

Total air in motion $= 4.21 \times 2000 = 8420$ *cfm*

NOTE: The successive approximations of V_r are required since Figure 76 is based on Table 44 values of K. Wherever Table 44 can be used directly, Figure 76 may also be used directly.

Throw of Heated or Cooled Air Jets

If the primary air in a jet is heated above the temperature of the air in the room, there will be a tendency for the stream to rise as it proceeds away from the outlet.

The vertical rise (Y) of the centerline of a horizontally projected stream is a function of the throw (X/D_e), the original velocity (V_o), and temperature (T_o), the ambient temperature (T_a), and the effective diameter (D_e) as indicated by

$$\frac{Y}{D_e} = 0.065\left(\frac{X}{D_e}\right)^3\left(\frac{T_o - T_a}{T_a}\right)\left(\frac{gD_e}{V_o^2}\right). \tag{202}$$

Similarly, if the primary air is cooled below the ambient temperature, the stream will fall.

The maximum possible vertical downward projection (X_{max}) of a heated stream or the maximum upward projection of a cooled stream can be determined from

$$\frac{X_{max}}{D_e} = \sqrt{3.4\left(\frac{T_a}{T_o - T_a}\right)\left(\frac{V_o^2}{gD_e}\right)} - 2.85. \tag{203}$$

Equations 202 and 203 are adapted from the data of Koestel* which also gives the results of temperature distribution studies.

*A. Koestel, Paths of Horizontally Projected Heated and Chilled Air Jets, *Trans. ASHAE*, vol. 61, pp. 213-232, 1955.

*A. Koestel, Computing Temperatures and Velocities in Vertical Jets of Hot or Cold Air, *Trans. ASHVE*, vol. 60, pp. 385-410, 1954.

EXAMPLE 7. Heated Air Jet

Given: $q_i = 3000\ cfm$
$A_g = 12'' \times 12'' = 1.0\ sq\ ft$
$R_A = 1.00$ *square-edged orifice with plenum approach*
$T_a = 530°\ R$
$T_o = 640°\ R$

Find: X_{max} *for downward projection*
Y *at* $X = X_{max}$ *for horizontal projection*

From Table 43: $\phi_i C_D = 0.60$
From Eq. 199: $V_o = 3000/1.0 \times .60 = 5000\ fpm$
From Eq. 197: $D_e = 1.13\sqrt{.60} = 0.875\ ft$
From Fig. 75: $(D_e)_{Fig.\ 75} = 10\tfrac{1}{2}'' = 0.875\ ft$
From Eq. 198: $D_e = 0.875\sqrt{1.0} = 0.875\ ft$
From Eq. 203: $X_{max} =$

$$0.875\left(\sqrt{3.4\left(\frac{530}{640 - 530}\right)\left(\frac{5000^2}{32.2 \times 3600 \times .875}\right)} - 2.85\right)$$

$$X_{max} = 0.875\ (\sqrt{3.4\ (4.81)\ (247)} - 2.85)$$

$$X_{max} = 53\ ft$$

From Eq. 202: $Y = 0.875 \times .065\left(\frac{53}{.875}\right)^3\left(\frac{1}{4.81}\right)\left(\frac{1}{247}\right) = 10.6\ ft$

CHAPTER 5

SOUND

Certain characteristics distinguish one sound from another. Sounds are commonly described according to loudness and pitch. Loudness is a measure of the quantity of sound which reaches a listener's ear. Pitch is a measure of the quality of a pure tone. Some sounds are pure tones, others are a combination of several tones but most sounds are neither. Instead they are best described as "broad band" sounds. Even without distinctive tones these sounds may have a characteristic quality which identifies the source for the average listener.

Sounds have different characteristics under different environmental conditions. Rooms may be described as live or dead, hard or soft. A very dead room comes close to duplicating outdoor conditions. Increases in the distance between source and listener decrease loudness in such a "free field." In a very live room loudness does not change with distance except very near the source. The sound at any point in a hard room consists of both direct and reflected sound. In the "near field" direct sound predominates while in the "reverberant field" reflected sound prevails.

Some sources radiate more sound in one direction than another, and some obstructions in the path between source and listener are more effective in keeping out noise than are others.

Noise is unwanted or disturbing sound. Noise control can be accomplished: (1) by reducing the amount of noise generated, (2) by altering the characteristics of the acoustical path, or (3) by otherwise protecting the receiver. Both the quantity and quality are important factors in determining the undesirability of the sound. An understanding of these physical properties and how they are measured is necessary before numerical values can be assigned to: (1) generated noises, (2) acceptable noises, and (3) the required reduction in a particular situation.

Physical Properties

Sound travels in waves through any elastic medium. In air, sound waves take the form of alternating condensations and rarefactions. These changes in density result from particle displacement. They may be described and measured in terms of pressure change. Even though the pressure fluctuations are small compared to normal atmospheric pressure the difference in sound pressure for two sounds may be quite large. The effective sound pressure at a point is the root mean square value of the instantaneous sound pressure over a time interval at that point. The sound pressure of audible sound may range from .0002 to 200 microbar. The one millionth part of normal atmospheric pressure is called a microbar and is nearly equal to one dyne per square centimeter. Both the ear and the sound level meter respond to the effective sound pressure rather than the instantaneous sound pressure. Loudness is largely determined by sound pressure (see page 182).

The condensations and rarefactions which produce a pure tone occur at regular intervals. The time required for one complete cycle is called the period. The number of complete cycles occurring in a unit time is called the frequency. The usual units for period and frequency are the second and the hertz (cycle per second). Pitch is primarily determined by frequency (see page 183.)

Few sounds are pure tones. Most musical sounds are a combination of tones and overtones. Most noises are broad band sounds. Each tone or each portion of the band in the case of a broad band sound exerts its own sound pressure. The square root of the sum of the squares of the individual RMS pressures is the over-all RMS pressure (at least for sinusoidal waves). It is usually far more useful to know the individual sound pressures for each tone or partial band width than the over-all sound pressure. Such a statement of individual pressures and frequencies is called a sound spectrum.

Various band widths may be used in describing spectrums. An octave is a band ranging from one frequency to twice that frequency. Standard octave bands have been established as indicated in Table 45. In most fan engineering, octave band spectrums may be used with satisfactory results.

Full-octave band spectrums may not reveal the presence of significant pure tone components. Third-octave band spectrums are much more revealing and are recommended for fan noise studies where pure tones may be produced.

TABLE 45—OCTAVE BAND STANDARDS

Band Number	Octave	1	2	3	4	5	6	7	8
	⅓ oct.	18	21	24	27	30	33	36	39
STANDARD	FREQUENCIES FOR OCTAVE BANDS—Hz								
NEW S1.11—1966	Low	45	88	177	354	707	1414	2828	5657
	Mean	***63***	***125***	***250***	***500***	***1000***	***2000***	***4000***	***8000***
	High	88	177	354	707	1414	2828	5657	11314
OLD Z24.10—1953	Low	37.5	75	150	300	600	1200	2400	4800
	Mean	53	106	212	424	849	1697	3394	6788
	High	75	150	300	600	1200	2400	4800	9600

Mean frequency is geometric mean of low and high. To convert levels for old standard (L_z) to levels for new standard (L_s) add 0.237 times the difference between the corresponding band level (L_z) and the level in the next higher band (L_{z+1}), i.e.,

$$L_s = L_z + 0.237\,(L_z - L_{z+1}).$$

Adapted from the data of American Standard Specification for Octave, Half-Octave, and Third-Octave Band Filter Sets, ASA, S1.11-1966, pp.11, 12, and 20.

The distance that a sound wave travels in one period is called the wave length of the sound (Λ). This may be determined from the frequency (f) and the speed of sound (c) according to

$$\Lambda = c/f. \tag{204}$$

The speed of sound in air may be determined from Table 2 opposite the appropriate temperature or calculated from the temperature (T), gas constant (R), and ratio of specific heats (γ) of the medium as indicated by

$$c = \sqrt{g_c \gamma RT}. \tag{205}$$

The product of the mass density (ρ) and the speed of sound (c) is called the characteristic impedance (ρc) of the medium. It can be shown that the impedance and the RMS sound pressure (p) are related to the amount of sound power transmitted per unit area or the intensity (I) as expressed by

$$I = \frac{p^2}{\rho c}. \tag{206}$$

The intensity of a sound at any point in space depends upon the distance to the source, the power and directivity of the source, and the nature of the sound field.

For the particular case of a non-directional point source of sound radiating in a free field (i.e., one without obstructions) the sound will radiate equally in all directions diverging as it goes. Due to this divergence the wave front will be spherical. The intensity at any distance (x) may be determined from the sound power (W) of the source using

$$I = \frac{W}{4\pi x^2}. \tag{207}$$

The relation between sound power and the effective sound pressure in a free field may be written

$$W = \frac{4\pi x^2 \bar{p}^2}{\rho c}. \tag{208}$$

In other words when there is spherical divergence the sound pressure varies inversely with distance. However, this relation does not hold for any other wave front shapes.

At a distance of several diameters from the source any wave front in a free field becomes nearly spherical in shape. Equation 208 is therefore applicable for any source in a free field provided the distance is great enough. Most sources are directional, i.e., they radiate more sound in certain directions than in others. The relation expressed in Equation 208 is only applicable if the average effective sound pressure ($\bar{p}$) is used. The actual effective sound pressure in any particular direction may be expressed as the average effective sound pressure multiplied by a directivity factor (Q), so that

$$Q = \frac{p^2}{\bar{p}^2}. \tag{209}$$

Sound waves may be reflected by rigid surfaces, refracted by any difference in the medium which might change the velocity of sound, or absorbed by either the medium or the surface materials. No real surface is a perfect reflector of sound. Either the material will be set in motion by the sound pressure or a portion of the sound will be allowed to penetrate the surface or both. Transmission or absorption results and the reflected energy is thereby reduced.

When a sound is generated in a live room the waves radiate as in a free field until they strike an obstruction. They are then reflected from one obstruction to another, each reflection taking place at reduced strength. Eventually the total energy of the wave is dissipated as heat. With a continuously generated sound the noise will gradually build up in a live room until equilibrium results, i.e., until the rate of absorption equals the rate of generation.

The sound at any point in a live room is a combination of direct and reverberated sound. The average effective sound pressure due to reverberated sound ($\bar{p}_r$) may be determined from the sound power (W) of the source, the characteristic impedance of the medium (ρc), and the characteristics of the room:

$$\bar{p}_r^2 = W\rho c\left(\frac{4}{\mathcal{R}}\right). \tag{210}$$

The room constant ($\mathcal{R}$) varies with the amount of surface (S) and volume (V) of the room, the average sound absorption coefficient ($\bar{\alpha}$) of the boundary materials, and the energy attenuation constant (ζ) for the air:

$$\mathcal{R} = \frac{S\ [\bar{\alpha} + 4\zeta\ V/S]}{1 - [\bar{\alpha} + 4\zeta\ V/S]}. \tag{211}$$

This equation is only valid for rooms where the mean free path between reflections is 4 V/S, a condition met in most irregularly shaped rooms. The values of absorption coefficient ($\bar{\alpha}$) may be determined by averaging the individual coefficients ($\bar{\alpha}$) from Table 46 according to the amount of surface for each. The value of the energy attenuation constant (ζ) may be determined from Figure 77.

The reverberation time (θ_{60}) in sec of a room is defined as the time required for the intensity of an interrupted sound to decay to the one millionth part of its original value (60dB). It is related to the characteristics of the room (V) in ft^3, etc., as indicated by

$$\theta_{60} = \frac{0.049\ V}{S\ [\bar{\alpha} + 4\zeta\ V/S]}. \tag{212}$$

The average effective sound pressure due to direct sound ($\bar{p}_d$) for a point source may be determined from

$$\bar{p}_d^2 = W\rho c\left(\frac{1}{4\pi\ x^2}\right). \tag{213}$$

The sound power of the source (W) is related to the average effective sound pressure, both direct and reverberated ($\bar{p}$), according to

$$W = \frac{\bar{p}^2}{\rho c}\left[\frac{1}{\frac{1}{4\pi\ x^2} + \frac{4}{\mathcal{R}}}\right]. \tag{214}$$

In any large reverberant room there is a distance (x) beyond which the average RMS sound pressure ($\bar{p}$) is constant. In other words at a sufficient distance from the source the direct sound is negligible compared to the reverberant sound. The pressure at any point in this reverberant field will be the same as at any other such point unless there are standing wave effects. Each narrow band of frequencies may have numerous standing waves. The closer these standing waves are to each other the more uniform will be the sound pressure in the reverberant field. Generally speaking the sound pressure is most uniform in large irregular rooms.

TABLE 46

SOUND ABSORPTION COEFFICIENTS OF GENERAL BUILDING MATERIALS

Material	Thickness in.	Coefficients (α) for various frequencies					
		125	250	500	1000	2000	4000
Brick wall, unpainted	18	0.02	0.02	0.03	0.04	0.05	0.05
Brick wall, painted	18	0.01	0.01	0.02	0.02	0.02	0.02
Plaster, gypsum, on hollow tile, plain or painted	—	0.02	0.02	0.02	0.03	0.04	0.04
Plaster, gypsum, scratch and brown coats on metal lath, on wood studs	—	0.04	0.04	0.04	0.06	0.06	0.03
Plaster, lime, sand finish on metal lath	¾	0.04	0.05	0.06	0.08	0.04	0.06
Plaster, on wood wool	—	0.40	0.30	0.20	0.15	0.10	0.10
Plaster, fibrous	2	0.35	0.30	0.20	0.55	0.10	0.04
Poured concrete, unpainted	—	0.01	0.01	0.02	0.02	0.02	0.03
Poured concrete, painted	—	0.01	0.01	0.01	0.02	0.02	0.02
Wood, solid and polished	2	0.1	—	0.05	—	0.04	0.04
Wood, paneling, 2 to 4 in. air space behind	⅜-½	0.30	0.25	0.20	0.17	0.15	0.10
Wood platform with large space beneath	—	0.4	0.3	0.2	0.17	0.15	0.1
Glass	—	0.04	0.04	0.03	0.03	0.02	0.02
Floors:							
Slate on solid	—	0.01	0.01	0.01	0.02	0.02	0.02
Wood on solid	—	0.04	0.04	0.03	0.03	0.03	0.02
Cork, linoleum, gypsum, or rubber tile on solid	3/16	0.04	0.03	0.04	0.04	0.03	0.02
Wood block, pitch pine	—	0.05	0.03	0.06	0.09	0.10	0.22
Carpets:							
Wool pile, with underpad	⅝	0.20	0.25	0.35	0.40	0.50	0.75
Wool pile, on concrete	⅜	0.09	0.08	0.21	0.26	0.27	0.37
Draperies and fabrics:							
Velour, hung straight							
10 oz/yd²	—	0.04	0.05	0.11	0.18	0.30	0.35
14 oz/yd²	—	0.05	0.07	0.13	0.22	0.32	0.35
18 oz/yd²	—	0.05	0.12	0.35	0.48	0.38	0.36
Velour, draped to half area							
14 oz/yd²	—	0.07	0.31	0.49	0.75	0.70	0.60
18 oz/yd²	—	0.14	0.35	0.55	0.75	0.70	0.60
Seats and people	Coefficients x area (α S)—sq ft per person or seat						
Seats							
Chair: upholstered back, leather seats	—	2.0	2.5	3.0	3.0	3.0	2.5
Chair: theater, heavily upholstered	—	3.5	3.5	3.5	3.5	3.5	3.5
Orchestra chairs, wood	—	0.1	0.15	0.2	0.35	0.5	0.6
Cushions for pews, per person	1.5	1.0	1.5	1.7	1.7	1.6	1.4
People							
In upholstered seats (add to leather-seat chair absorption)	—	0.7	0.6	0.5	1.3	1.6	2.0
In heavily upholstered seats	—	0.7	0.6	0.6	1.0	1.0	1.0
In orchestra seats with instruments (add to wood-seat absorption)	—	4.0	7.5	11.0	13.0	13.5	11.0
Child in high school, seated, including seat	—	2.2	3.0	3.3	4.0	4.4	4.5
Child in elementary school, seated, including seat	—	1.8	2.3	2.8	3.2	3.5	4.0
Standing	—	2.0	3.5	4.7	4.5	5.0	4.0
In church pew (no seat cushion)	—	2.5	2.7	3.3	3.8	4.0	3.8

Adapted from the data of L. L. Beranek, "Acoustics," McGraw-Hill Book Co., Inc., New York, 1954, pp. 300-301.

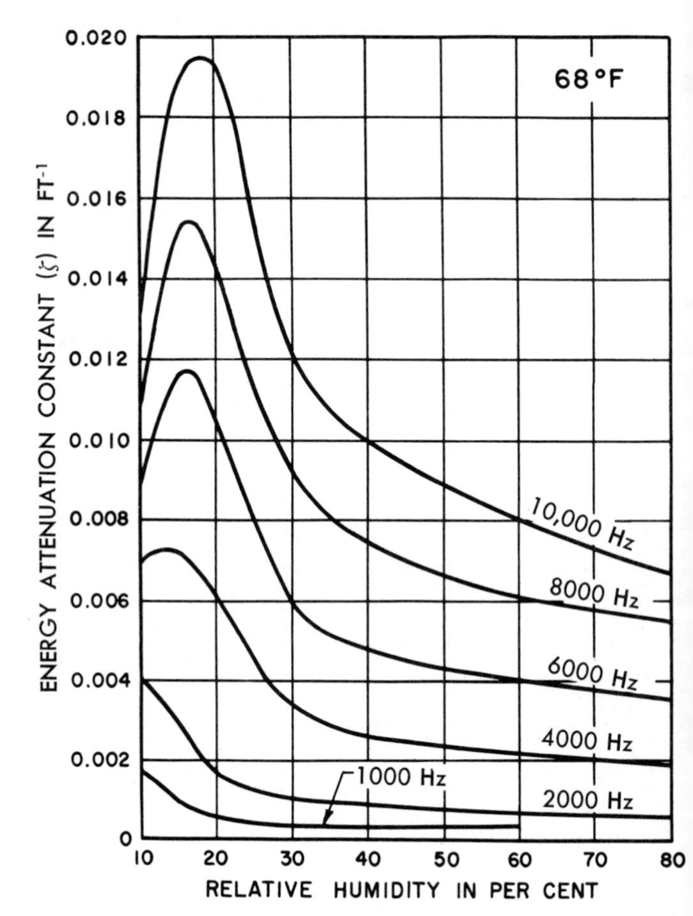

Figure 77—Energy Attenuation Constants for Air

Adapted from the data of V. O. Knudsen and C. M. Harris, "Acoustical Designing in Architecture," John Wiley & Sons, Inc., 1950, p. 160.

If more sound is radiated in one direction than another, the directivity factor (Q) should be applied, but only to the direct portion as indicated by

$$W = \frac{\overline{p}^2}{\rho c}\left[\frac{1}{\frac{Q}{4\pi\, x^2} + \frac{4}{R}}\right]. \tag{215}$$

If a sound is perfectly directional and prevented from diverging as is the case for a plane wave traveling down a straight duct or tube, the pressure will not vary with distance except for absorption. Neglecting absorption and reflection,

$$W = \frac{\overline{p}^2}{\rho c}(A) \tag{216}$$

gives a relation between the sound pressure in a plane wave, with an area (A), to the sound power of the source (W) and the characteristic impedance of the medium (ρc).

Measurement of Sound Properties

The properties of a sound are usually measured with a sound level meter and an octave band analyzer. Other electronic instruments including narrow band analyzers, oscillographs, and tape recorders are useful.

The sound pressure level of a noise is measured with the sound level meter. The sound pressure generates an electrical signal in the microphone which is then amplified and transmitted through an adjustable attenuator to an indicating meter. The sum of the attenuator setting and meter reading is the sound pressure level in decibels when the frequency weighting network is selected for "flat" response. This network is usually designated "C" and readings reported in dB(C).

The spectrum of a noise is determined with an octave band analyzer usually used in conjunction with a sound level meter. A series of filters is used to greatly attenuate components of the signal above and below certain frequencies. When the output of a sound level meter is fed into an analyzer the sum of the attenuator settings and analyzer meter reading is the sound pressure level in the band of frequencies indicated by the octave selector. The sound level meter should be set for flat response when used with an analyzer.

The accuracy of any sound measurement depends on the acoustical response of the microphone and the electrical response of the meters. Meters should be calibrated frequently. Microphones are usually nondirectional at low frequencies. When the wave length is comparable to the size of the "mike" a variation of response with both frequency and incidence occurs. For highest accuracy these effects should be determined by calibration.

The "A and B" networks of the sound level meter attenuate certain frequency components of sound so that the readings on these two scales are not sound pressure levels. To distinguish them, "A and B" network readings are called sound levels and designated in units of dB(A) and dB(B) respectively. More will be said about this under "Hearing."

It should be noted that the measurements made with a sound level meter are all called levels. The units of these levels are called decibels and are dimensionless. In each case a reference level of .0002 microbar is implied. The reason for using decibels is basically numerical convenience as is pointed out below.

Decibels

Decibels are convenient dimensionless units for measuring power, or some other property which is proportional to power, whenever the range of values is very large. For instance, the sound power of a whisper may be 0.000,000,001 watts and that of a jet airplane 100,000 watts. With a reference power of 10^{-12} watts the sound power levels can be given as 30 dB and 170 dB respectively. Although more convenient for numerical expression, the decibel does make it more difficult to visualize the difference between any two sound power levels. Table 47 shows the sound power and sound power level for several typical sources.

For most broad band noises the square of the sound pressure at any listener location varies directly with the sound power. Sound pressures in the audible range vary from .0002 to 200 microbar. The corresponding range of sound pressure levels with a reference pressure of .0002 microbar is 0 dB to 120 dB. Table 48 lists the sound pressure and sound pressure level for several typical noise situations. Note that distances are specified where applicable. In the near or free field of a localized source, sound pressure varies with distance. Sound pressure may be relatively constant throughout an area having multiple sources of sound or in areas having highly reflective surfaces.

The reason that both power levels and pressure levels can be expressed in decibels is simply that they are both levels. Both are logarithmic expressions of the ratio of the quantity in question to a particular reference quantity.

By definition the level of a quantity in decibels is 10 times the logarithm (to the base 10) of the ratio of that quantity (in dimensional units) to some reference quantity (in the same dimensional units). The only other qualification is that the quantity must be proportional to power.

The reference power (W) for sound power level (PWL) measurements is 10^{-12} watts so that

$$PWL = 10 \log_{10} \frac{W \text{ in watts}}{10^{-12} \text{ watts}}. \tag{217}$$

The reference pressure (p) for sound pressure level (SPL) measurements is .0002 microbar so that

TABLE 47—TYPICAL SOUND POWER AND SOUND POWER LEVELS

Power (watts)	Power Level (dB re 10^{-12} watts)	Source (long time average)
100,000	170	
10,000	160	Jet Airplane
1,000	150	
100	140	
10	130	Large Orchestra
1	120	
0.1	110	Blaring Radio
0.01	100	
0.001	90	Shouting
0.000,1	80	
0.000,01	70	Conversational speech
0.000,001	60	
0.000,000,1	50	Small Electric Clock
0.000,000,01	40	
0.000,000,001	30	Soft Whisper

Adapted from the data of C. M. Harris, "Handbook of Noise Control," McGraw-Hill Book Co., Inc., New York, 1957, p. 2-8.

$$SPL = 20 \log_{10} \frac{p \text{ in microbar}}{.0002 \text{ microbar}}. \tag{218}$$

This equation yields sound pressure levels in dB re .0002 microbar which is sometimes abbreviated dB(C). Actually this result is a sound pressure squared level as indicated by the substitution of 20 for 10. The ratio of sound pressures squared is proportional to the sound power ratio for broad band noises.

The reference intensity (I) for sound intensity level (IL) measurements is 10^{-16} watts per square centimeters so that

$$IL = 10 \log_{10} \frac{I \text{ in watts/sq cm}}{10^{-16} \text{ watts/sq cm}}. \tag{219}$$

This equation yields sound intensity levels in dB re 10^{-16} watts per square centimeter which is sometimes abbreviated dB(I).

TABLE 48

TYPICAL OVER-ALL SOUND PRESSURES AND SOUND PRESSURE LEVELS

Pressure (microbar)	Pressure Level (db re .0002 microbar)	Source (long time average)	Distance (if applicable)
2000	140	Threshold of Pain	—
	130		
200	120	Threshold of Discomfort	—
	110		
		Automobile Horn	20′
20	100		
	90		
		Automobile at 40 mph	Inside
2	80		
	70		
		Conversational speech	3′
0.2	60		
	50		
		Quiet Residence	Inside
0.02	40		
	30		
		Whisper	5′
0.002	20		
	10		
0.0002	0	Threshold of Hearing	—

Adapted from the data of C. M. Harris, "Handbook of Noise Control," McGraw-Hill Book Co., Inc., New York, 1957, p. 2-10.

It is frequently necessary to add the effect of one sound to another or to subtract the effect of one sound from a combination of sounds. The effects on both sound power and sound pressure are important.

The total sound power ($W_{1+2+..+n}$) of a combination of sounds is simply equal to the sum of the individual sound powers ($W_1 + W_2 + .. + W_n$). Due to the logarithmic character of sound power levels the total sound power level ($PWL_{1+2+..+n}$) is not equal to the sum of the individual sound power levels ($PWL_1 + PWL_2 + .. + PWL_n$). Rather,

$$PWL_{1+2+..+n} = 10 \log_{10}\left[\left(10\right)^{\frac{PWL_1}{10}} + \left(10\right)^{\frac{PWL_2}{10}} + .. + \left(10\right)^{\frac{PWL_n}{10}}\right]. \tag{220}$$

Both the ear and the sound level meter respond to the root mean square value of sound pressure rather than to the instantaneous value. Because response is proportional to the RMS value, the total sound pressure at a point ($p_{1+2+\cdots+n}$) is equal to the square root of the sum of the squares of the individual sound pressures ($\sqrt{p_1^2 + p_2^2 + \ldots + p_n^2}$) at that point. For most engineering applications Equation 218 might better be written

$$SPL = 10 \log_{10} \left(\frac{p \text{ in microbar}}{.0002 \text{ microbar}} \right)^2.$$

Due to the logarithmic character of sound pressure levels the total sound pressure level ($SPL_{1+2+\ldots+n}$) is not equal to the sum of the individual sound pressure levels ($SPL_1 + SPL_2 + \ldots + SPL_n$). As with sound power levels,

$$SPL_{1+2+\ldots+n} = 10 \log_{10} \left[(10)^{\frac{SPL_1}{10}} + (10)^{\frac{SPL_2}{10}} + \ldots + (10)^{\frac{SPL_n}{10}} \right]. \quad (221)$$

Equations 220 and 221 are cumbersome, to say the least. Figure 78 may be used to advantage in place of either of these formulas. The lower curve is for use in adding two sound power levels or in adding two sound pressure levels. If the two levels being combined have the same value the combined value will be 3 dB higher than either. This is easily verified. Multiplication of any two numbers is accomplished by adding their logarithms. Adding two equal values (sound powers or sound pressures squared) is the same as multiplying one value by a factor of 2. Ten times the logarithm (to the base 10) of the number 2 is equal to 3.0.

The upper curve in Figure 78 is for use in subtracting a component of the sound power level from the total or in subtracting a component of the sound pressure level from the total. In using either curve the difference between the two known values establishes the difference between the unknown value and one of the known values.

Examples 8 through 11 illustrate the use of both Figure 78 and Equations 220 and 221.

EXAMPLE 8. Combining Sound Power Levels

Given: $PWL_1 = 90\ dB$
$PWL_2 = 100\ dB$

Find: PWL_{1+2}

Using Eq. 220: $PWL_{1+2} = \log_{10} (10^9 + 10^{10})$
$PWL_{1+2} = 10 \log_{10} (1 \times 10^9 + 10 \times 10^9)$
$PWL_{1+2} = 10 \log_{10} 11 + 10 \log_{10} 10^9$
$PWL_{1+2} = 10.41 + 90 = 100.41\ dB$

Using Fig. 78: $PWL_2 - PWL_1 = 100 - 90 = 10$
$PWL_{1+2} - PWL_2 = .41$
$PWL_{1+2} = 100 + .41 = 100.41\ dB$

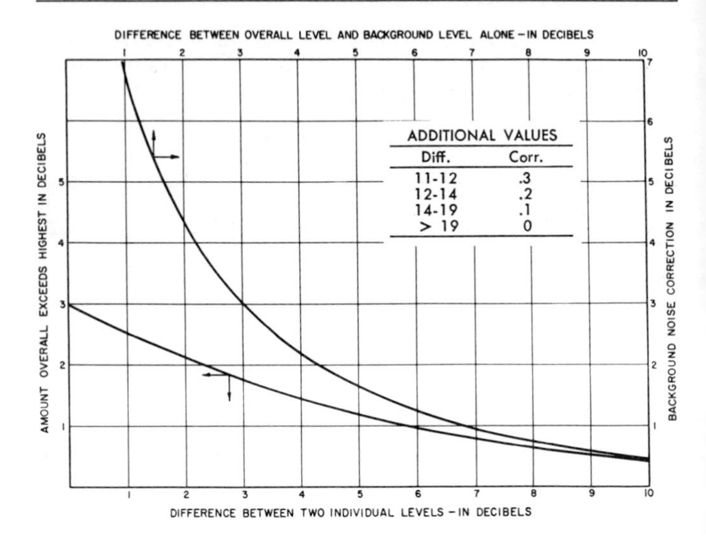

Figure 78—Corrections for Combined Levels

EXAMPLE 9. Combining Sound Pressure Levels

Given: $SPL_1 = 75\ dB(C)$
$SPL_2 = 74\ dB(C)$

Find: SPL_{1+2}

Using Eq. 221:
$$SPL_{1+2} = 10 \log_{10} (10^{7.5} + 10^{7.4})$$
$$SPL_{1+2} = 10 \log_{10} (10^{.5} \times 10^{7.0} + 10^{.4} \times 10^{7.0})$$
$$SPL_{1+2} = 10 \log_{10} [(3.16 + 2.50)(10^7)]$$
$$SPL_{1+2} = 10 (.75 + 7.0) = 77.5\ dB(C)$$

Using Fig. 78:
$$SPL_1 - SPL_2 = 75 - 74 = 1$$
$$SPL_{1+2} - SPL_1 = 2.5$$
$$SPL_{1+2} = 75 + 2.5 = 77.5\ dB(C)$$

EXAMPLE 10. Effect of Background Level

Given: $SPL_{1+2} = 60\ dB(C)$ *(over-all including background)*
$SPL_2 = 55\ dB(C)$ *(background)*

Find: SPL_1

Using Eq. 221:
$$SPL_1 = 10 \log_{10} (10^6 - 10^{5.5})$$
$$SPL_1 = 10 \log_{10} [(10^5)(10^{1.0} - 10^{0.5})]$$
$$SPL_1 = 50 + 10 \log_{10} (10 - 3.16) = 50 + 8.3 = 58.3\ dB(C)$$

Using Fig. 78: $SPL_{1+2} - SPL_2 = 60 - 55 = 5$
$SPL_{1+2} - SPL_1 = 1.7$
$SPL_1 = 60 - 1.7 = 58.3\ dB(C)$

EXAMPLE 11. Combining Band Pressure Levels

Given: BPL's of 80, 85, 90, 85, 80, 75, 70, 65 dB(C)

Find: SPL over-all

Using Eq. 221:

$$SPL = 10 \log_{10} (10^{9.0} + 10^{8.5} + 10^{8.5} + 10^{8.0} + 10^{8.0} + 10^{7.5} + 10^{7.0} + 10^{6.5})$$

$$SPL = 10 \log_{10} (10^{9.0}) (1 + 2 \times 10^{-0.5} + 2 \times 10^{-1.0} + 10^{-1.5} + 10^{-2.0} + 10^{-2.5})$$

$$SPL = 90 + 10 \log_{10} \left(1 + \frac{2}{3.16} + \frac{2}{10} + \frac{1}{33} + \frac{1}{100} + \frac{1}{330}\right)$$

$$SPL = 90 + 10 \log_{10} (1 + .63 + .20 + .03 + .01 + .003$$

$$SPL = 90 + 10 \log_{10} (1.87) = 90 + 2.71 = 92.7\ dB(C)$$

Using Fig. 78:

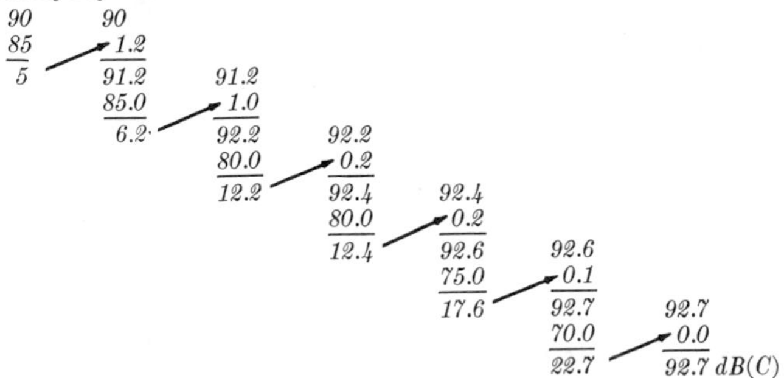

Measurement of Sound Power Levels

Under ideal conditions it is possible to determine the sound power level of a source from a single measurement of sound pressure level. Such ideal conditions may exist in either a free field or reverberant field. In either case the source of noise should be non-directional in all frequencies. For free field tests, measurements should be made at a sufficient distance to insure a spherical wave front. A distance of several times the largest dimension of the source is usually sufficient for this purpose. For a spherical free field with distance (x) in feet

$$PWL = SPL + 20 \log_{10} x + 0.5 - \Delta. \qquad (222)$$

The correction (Δ) for temperature and barometer if different from standard may be obtained from Figure 79. A minus 3 dB correction should also be applied to the above for cases of hemispherical radiation.

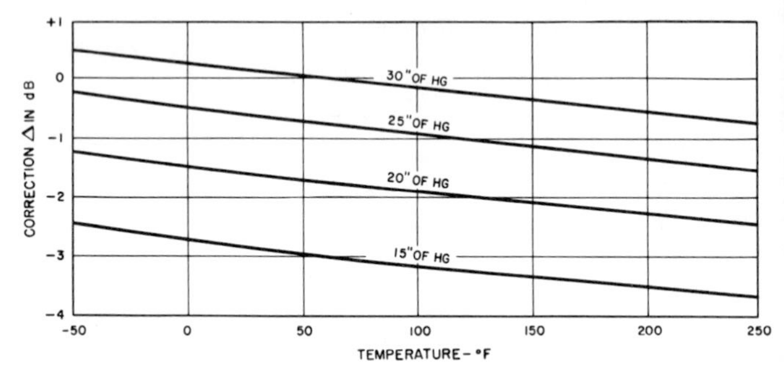

Figure 79—Corrections for Non-Standard Air

Adapted from the data of A. P. G. Peterson and E. E. Gross, Jr., "Handbook of Noise Measurement," General Radio Co., West Concord, Mass., 1967, p. 17.

Even if there is some directional effect, Equation 222 can be used by substituting the average sound pressure level $(\overline{SPL})$ in many cases. An arithmetic average of several measurements of sound pressure level is always low. If the spread between readings is less than 5 dB, the error in using this arithmetic average will be less than 1 dB. If the spread is around 10 dB, the error can be limited to plus or minus 1 dB by adding 1 dB to the calculated arithmetic average. For best accuracy several readings should be taken at the center points of equal area portions of the spherical or hemispherical surface. The coordinates of such points on a sphere divided into 8 or 12 equal areas are listed in Table 49.

TABLE 49—MICROPHONE LOCATIONS FOR FREE FIELD TESTS

Coordinates of the Center Points of Equal Area Surfaces on a Sphere of Unit Radius

SPHERICAL SURFACE DIVIDED INTO 8 EQUAL AREAS

Points	X	Y	Z
1 and 5	0	0.82	±0.58
2 and 6	0.82	0	±0.58
3 and 7	0	−0.82	±0.58
4 and 8	−0.82	0	±0.58

Note: For a 4-point Hemispherical traverse, use only the + values of Z.

SPHERICAL SURFACE DIVIDED INTO 12 EQUAL AREAS

Points	X	Y	Z
1 and 7	0	0	±1.0
2 and 8	0	±0.89	±0.45
3 and 9	0.53	±0.72	±0.45
4 and 10	−0.53	±0.72	±0.45
5 and 11	0.85	±0.28	±0.45
6 and 12	−0.85	±0.28	±0.45

Adapted from the data of A. P. G. Peterson and E. E. Gross, Jr., "Handbook of Noise Measurement," General Radio Co., West Concord, Mass., 1967, p. 25.

TABLE 50—DIRECTIVITY FACTORS

Non-Directional Sources with Reflective Surroundings

Position	Q
Near center of room..................	1
In center of one wall..................	2
In corner at center of two walls........	4
In corner formed by three walls........	8

Directional sources will have directivity factors larger than 1 in some directions and smaller than 1 in other directions.

The directivity factor to be used for positions in the near field of a duct opening are the same as for non-directional sources when the opening dimensions are about equal to the wave length of the band being considered. For wave lengths considerably shorter than the opening dimensions, the directivity factor approaches 8 for a position directly opposite the opening and 4 for a position at 45° to the plane of the opening.

Adapted from the data of L. L. Beranek, "Acoustics," McGraw-Hill Book Co., Inc., New York, 1954, p. 319.

The directivity factor correction in any particular direction ($10 \log_{10} Q$) may be determined from the average sound pressure level ($\overline{SPL}$) and the sound pressure level (SPL) at the reading point located in the direction of interest from

$$10 \log_{10} Q = SPL - \overline{SPL}. \tag{223}$$

Directivity factors may be estimated from the data of Table 50. Combining Equations **222** and **223** yields the sound power level in terms of the average sound pressure level in a particular direction, the directivity in that direction, and distance in a free field for a point source of sound:

$$PWL = \overline{SPL} + 10 \log_{10} Q + 20 \log_{10} x + 0.5 - \Delta. \tag{224}$$

In reverberant field tests, measurements should be made while moving the microphone continuously over about a wave length in space so that standing wave effects are averaged out. The distance x should be great enough so that the factor ($1/4 \pi x^2$) is negligible compared to factor ($4/\mathcal{R}$).

$$PWL = \overline{SPL} - 10 \log_{10} \left(\frac{1}{4 \pi x^2} + \frac{4}{\mathcal{R}} \right) - 10.5 - \Delta. \tag{225}$$

The correction (Δ) for differences in temperature and barometer can be obtained from Figure 79. The room constant ($\mathcal{R}$) can be calculated from Equation **211**. It is usually much more accurate to determine ($\mathcal{R}$) by either of two other means. The reverberation time (θ_{60}) may be measured or a calibrated sound source may be used. In the first case the measured time (θ_{60}) in sec and the appropriate volume (V) in cu ft are inserted into the following equation which is an approximation based on Equation **212**:

$$\mathcal{R} = 0.049 \frac{V}{\theta_{60}}. \tag{226}$$

This approximation is quite accurate when the average absorption coefficient ($\overline{\alpha}$) is quite small. (Equation **226** may therefore be used in most hard or live rooms.)

If a calibrated sound source is operated under the same conditions as the sound source being tested, Equation **225** can be solved for $10 \log_{10} [(1/4 \pi x^2) + (4/\mathcal{R})]$ by inserting the known power level and measured pressure level for the calibrated source. Using this value of $10 \log_{10} [(1/4 \pi x^2) + (4/\mathcal{R})]$ and the measured sound pressure level for the source being tested, the power level can be calculated. The intermediate calculation of $10 \log_{10} [(1/4 \pi x^2) + (4/\mathcal{R})]$ can be omitted entirely as indicated by

$$PWL_{test\ unit} = PWL_{calibrated\ source} + SPL_{test\ unit} - SPL_{calibrated\ source}. \quad (227)$$

Equipment for measuring reverberation time accurately is costly. Obtaining and maintaining a calibrated sound source is probably less expensive.

Methods of determining sound power levels from in-duct measurements have not been perfected. If a good average of the sound pressure level in the duct could be determined, the sound power level could be calculated from the cross sectional area (A) in ft² and

$$PWL = SPL + 10 \log_{10} A - 10.5 - \Delta. \quad (228)$$

Hearing and Noise Criteria

The ear responds to effective sound pressures from approximately .0002 microbar (0 dB) to 200 microbar (120 dB) over a frequency range of approximately 20 Hz to 10,000 Hz. The auditory system functions both as a sound level meter and as an analyzer. The subjective responses to a sound are expressed in terms of loudness, pitch, and quality. Loudness is primarily determined by sound pressure but is also a function of

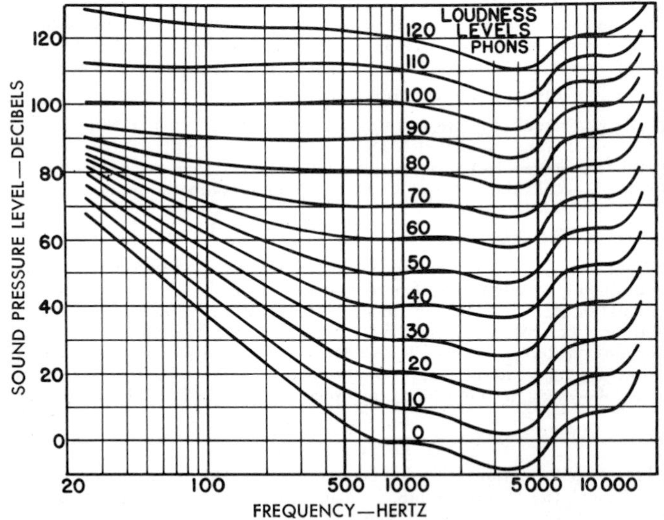

Figure 80—Loudness Levels of Pure Tones in a Free Field

Adapted from the data of H. Fletcher and W. A. Munson, Loudness, Its Definitions, Measurement and Calculation, *J. Acous. Soc. Am.* vol. 5, p. 82, 1933.

frequency. Pitch is essentially determined by frequency but is also affected by sound pressure. The units of pitch and loudness are the MEL and SONE respectively. Another unit, the PHON is used for loudness level.

The MEL, SONE, and PHON are all units of judgement as distinguished from units of measurement. It is not wise to ascribe a margin of error of less than 1 or 2 dB to any acoustical measurement. There are relationships between acoustical judgements and measurements but since they are statistical relationships large variations may be expected in some cases.

The loudness level of a pure tone in a free field may be determined from its frequency and sound pressure level using Figure 80. The loudness of a tone in PHONS is equal to the sound pressure level in dB(C) of a 1000 cps tone which to the average listener sounds as loud as does the tone being measured. Figure 80 and similar data for various band widths rather than pure tones are based on the average subjective response of numerous individuals. The threshold of hearing, on the average, corresponds to the loudness contour line marked 0 PHONS. The thresholds of discomfort and of pain are commonly listed as 120 and 140 dB(C) sound pressure levels respectively.

The loudness level of two or more tones combined is *not* the sum of the individual loudness levels. The loudness values for well separated sounds are additive on the SONE scale. The loudness of a pure tone in SONES can be determined from its loudness level in PHONS using Figure 81.

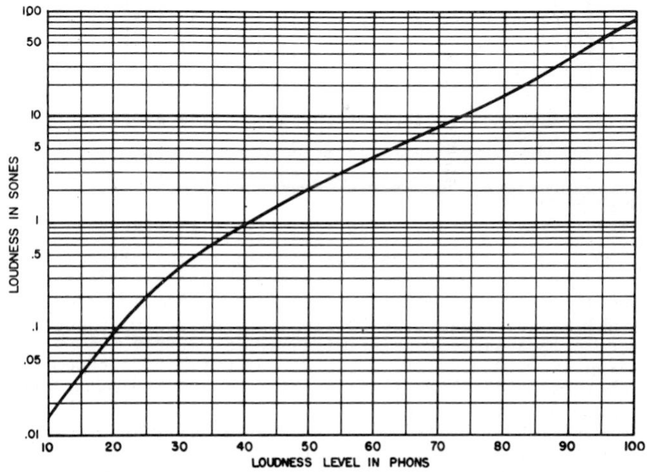

Figure 81—Loudnesses of Pure Tones in a Free Field

Adapted from the data of H. Fletcher and W. A. Munson, Loudness, Its Definitions, Measurement and Calculation, *J. Acous. Soc. Am.* vol. 5, p. 82, 1933.

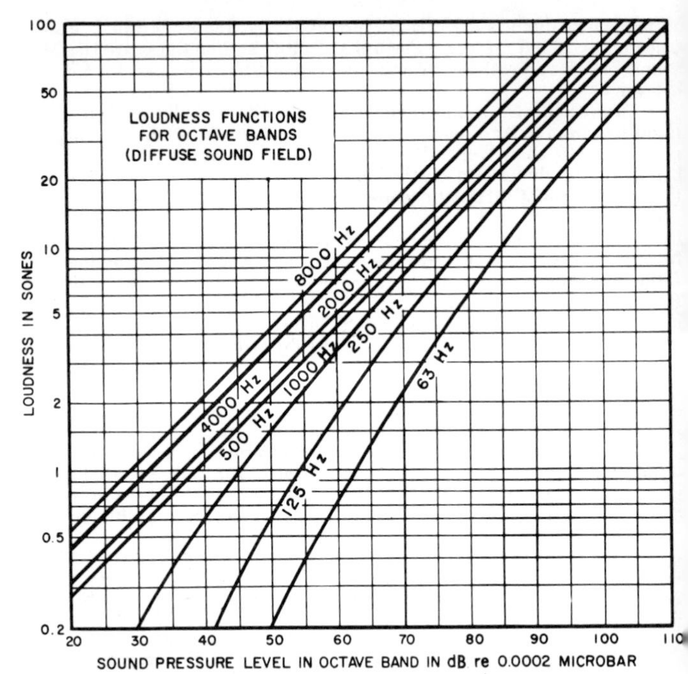

Figure 82—Loudness Levels for Octave Band Spectrums

Adapted from the data of C. M. Harris, "Handbook of Noise Control," McGraw-Hill Book Co., Inc., New York, 1957, p. 5-12.

There are various methods in use for predicting the loudness level of a broad band noise from sound spectrum measurements. The most frequently used method employs a chart similar to that of Figure 82 from which loudness values in SONES corresponding to the sound pressure level in each octave band are determined. The sum of all such values except the loudest is multiplied by 0.3 and added to the loudest value. The corresponding loudness level is the sound pressure level at 1000 Hz which can be read from Figure 82.

The sensitivity of most people to a change in sound pressure level is about 1 dB at a loudness level of about 50 PHONS. Even larger changes are not perceptible at lower levels.

Masking occurs when one sound is rendered inaudible by another's presence. In the case of broad band noises the strong noise will mask out the weaker one if there is a difference in sound pressure level of about 6 dB or more. It can be observed from Figure 78 that such a difference means that the increase above the higher level due to the lower will be 1 dB or less. In the case of pure tones the ear becomes more selective and masking therefore more difficult.

A pure tone can be detected if its sound pressure level exceeds the RMS level of a rather narrow band of the background noise regardless of noise outside that band width. This band width is approximately 50 hertz below 1000 Hz. At higher frequencies, the level of the tone must exceed the level of a somewhat wider band to be detectable.

When two tones have nearly the same frequency, beats (i.e., rising and falling of the noise level) will occur due to wave interference. The beat frequency will be equal to the difference in frequency of the two tones. Figure 83 indicates the most annoying beat frequency for a range of frequencies and the lower limit of beat frequencies to avoid annoyance. When two broad band noises are produced there is a danger that a beat will be set up if an appreciable portion of the energy in each is contained in a narrow band and if the two individual bands have nearly the same frequency.

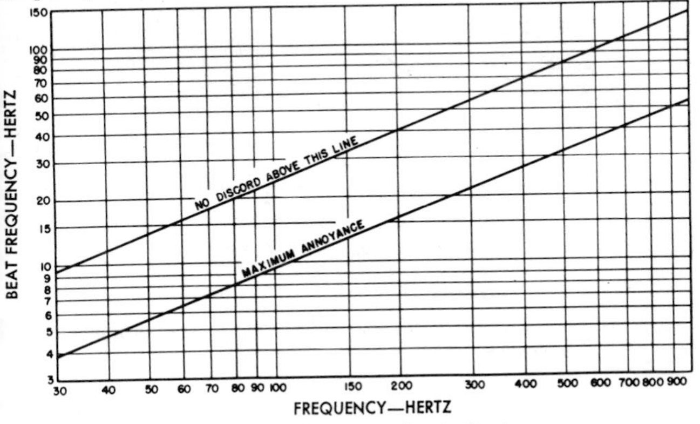

Figure 83—Annoyance Due to Beats

The acceptability of a background noise depends on the communication requirements (i.e., whether speech, music, or other) as well as the loudness spectrum of the noise in the listening area. Even without background noise a room may be acoustically unsuitable for certain kinds of communication. The reverberation time (θ_{60}) and room volume (V) can be used as a criterion of acceptability for a given kind of communication. Reverberation time is a function of room constant as indicated in Equation 226. In Figure 84 the optimum room constants ($\mathcal{R}$) are plotted vs. room volume for various kinds of communication. This chart is based on the specific relationship between surface (S) and volume (V) as indicated in the insert. Lines for dead and live rooms are also shown based on the average absorption coefficients indicated.

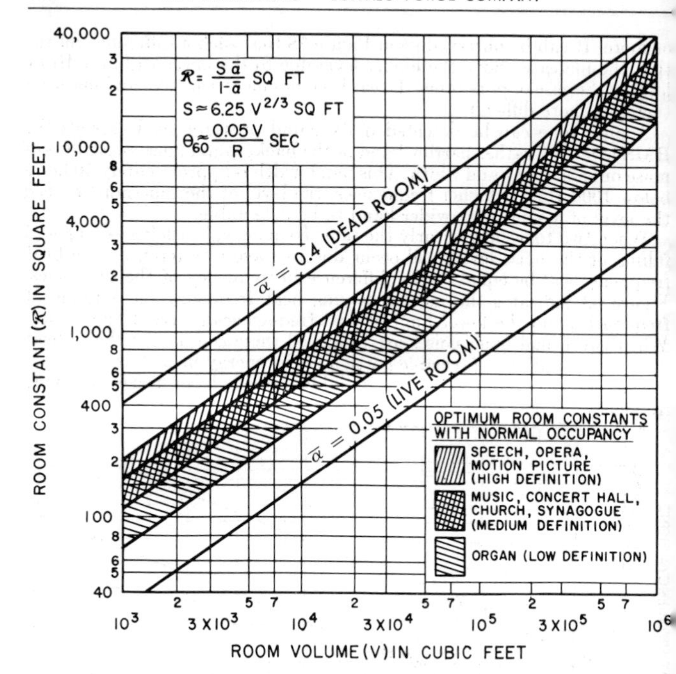

Figure 84—Optimum Room Constants

Adapted from the data of L. L. Beranek, "Acoustics," McGraw-Hill Book Co., Inc., New York, 1954, pp. 316 and 426.

TABLE 51—SPEECH INTERFERENCE LEVELS

In dB re 0.0002 microbar

These levels barely permit reliable conversation at the distances and voice levels indicated

Distance, ft, between source and listener	Normal voice level, dB	Raised voice level, dB
0.5	71	77
1	65	71
2	59	65
3	55	61
4	53	59
5	51	57
6	49	55
12	43	49

Adapted from the data of C. M. Harris, "Handbook of Noise Control," McGraw-Hill Book Co., Inc., New York, 1957, p. 𝒥-11.

Other acoustical criteria include speech interference levels, damage risk levels, and various other "noise criteria" based on surveys of acceptability for normal use.

The speech interference level is the average of the octave band sound pressure levels in the three bands where most of the sounds which contribute to speech intelligibility occur. These are the 1000, 2000, and 4000 Hz bands. Suggested maximum permissible speech interference levels, measured when the room is not in use, are listed in Table 51.

Damage risk levels are listed in Table 52 for various exposures to continuous sounds. None of the octave band sound pressure levels can be exceeded without risk of hearing damage. Corresponding maximum "A" network sound levels are also listed in dB(A).

TABLE 52—DAMAGE RISK LEVELS

In dB re 0.0002 microbar

Duration per Day	"A" Network	Octave Band Center Frequency—Hz						
		125	250	500	1000	2000	4000	8000
8 hr	86	96	92	88	86	85	85	86
4 hr	88	103	96	91	88	86	85	87
2 hr	95	110	101	94	91	88	87	90
1 hr	103	118	107	99	95	91	90	95
30 min	111	126	114	105	100	95	93	99
15 min	120	135	122	112	106	99	98	104
7 min	127	135	135	122	114	105	104	111
3 min	131	135	135	134	124	113	111	120
< 1.5 min	134	135	135	135	134	124	121	130

One exposure per day

Adapted from the data of A. P. G. Peterson and E. E. Gross, Jr., "Handbook of Noise Measurement," General Radio Co., West Concord, Mass., 1967, p. 68.

One of the most widely used noise criteria is that given in the ASHRAE Guide, reproduced here in part. The recommended noise criteria (NC) for various types of spaces are given in Table 53. The corresponding octave band spectrums are drawn in Figure 85. The criteria are based in part on speech interference level (indicated by the NC number) and on a favorable relation between high and low frequency components. Recommended band pressure levels should not be exceeded under normal conditions. Normal conditions are those usually encountered at the time of occupancy except that measurement at the occupant location requires removal of the occupant. Fan and other equipment serving a space should not produce a noise spectrum in the space exceeding the recommended NC curve. Obviously the acoustical characteristics of the room and duct system as well as the fan must be considered. Fan equipment can also cause objectionable noise at neighboring locations due to transmission through the atmosphere. The various criteria may also be used to establish the maximum permissible band pressure levels under these conditions. In this case the various factors that affect sound propagation in open air should be considered.

A rule of thumb for relating sound level measurements to noise criteria is that $dB(A)$ will equal $NC - 6$ within plus or minus 2 dB.

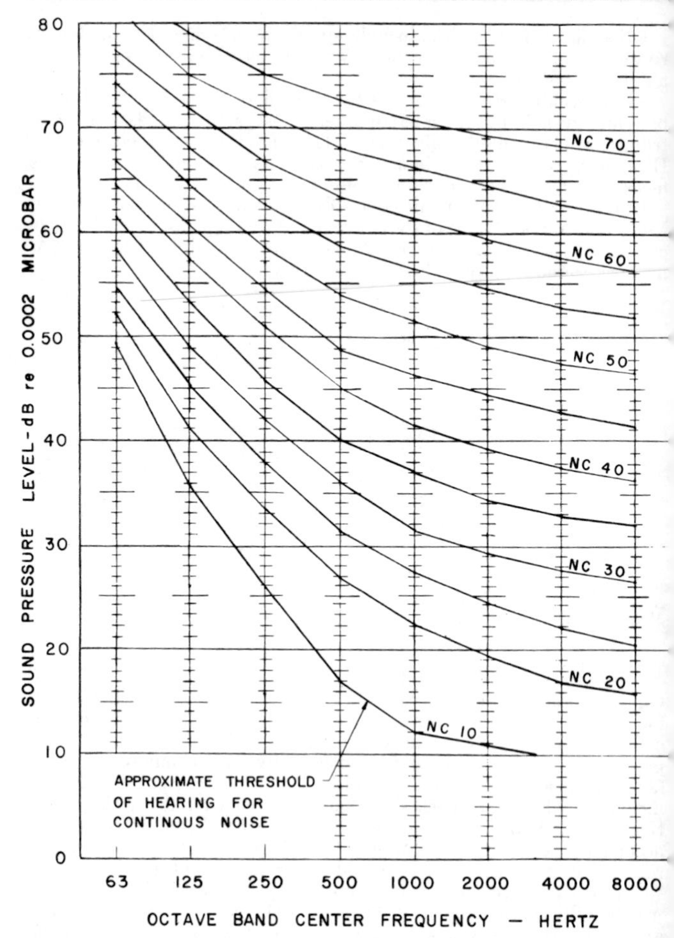

Figure 85—Recommended Noise Criteria

Refer to Table 53 for recommended NC number according to application. The sound pressure levels in the space under normal conditions (except unoccupied) should not exceed the corresponding curve values in any octave band.

Adapted from the data of ASHRAE Guide and Data Book, Systems, 1970, p. 498.

TABLE 53—RECOMMENDED NOISE CRITERIA

Mass Communication without Amplification	
Concert Halls	NC 20-25
Legitimate Theaters	NC 25-30
Conference Rooms	NC 25-35
School Rooms	NC 30-40
Churches and Courtrooms	NC 30-40
Mass Communication with Amplification	
Broadcast Studios	NC 15-20
Assembly Halls	NC 25-30
Motion Picture Theaters	NC 30-35
Individual Communication	
Homes, Apartments, and Hotels	NC 25-35
Hospitals and Libraries	NC 30-40
Private Offices	NC 30-35
General Offices	NC 40-45
Restaurants and Department Stores	NC 40-50
Coliseums	NC 50-60
Factories	NC 50-70

The recommended noise criteria are given as NC numbers. Corresponding octave band spectrums are given in Figure 85. The maximum sound pressure level in any band should not exceed the indicated value. The NC number also corresponds to the speech interference level in decibels.

Adapted from the data of ASHRAE Guide and Data Book, Systems, 1970, p. 497.

Noise Control

In order to determine whether the noise at a particular listener location or locations is acceptable according to one of the criteria discussed above it is necessary to study the transmission path or paths over which the noise will travel from the source or sources to the listener. There may be several sources contributing to the noise at any one location and several paths over which each noise may travel from its source to the listener.

Many of the principles of noise control may be determined by studying the relations involved in the measurement of sound power.

In a free field the noise level at any location is a function of distance (x) and directivity (Q). For each doubling of distance the sound pressure level will be decreased by 6 dB. If a source is highly directional it may be feasible to aim the noise in the direction which will produce the most noise in the least objectionable direction.

In a reverberant field the noise level can frequently be brought under control by room surface treatment. There will be an area close to the source where such treatment will do no good.

In either of the above cases the sound pressure level (SPL) at any listener location can be determined from the sound power level (PWL) and directivity factor (Q) of the source and the room constant ($\mathcal{R}$) using

$$SPL = PWL + 10 \log_{10} \left(\frac{Q}{4 \pi x^2} + \frac{4}{\mathcal{R}} \right) + 10.5 + \Delta. \qquad (229)$$

In a free field the room constant becomes infinitely large making ($4/\mathcal{R}$) insignificant compared to ($Q/4 \pi x^2$). Similarly in the reverberant field the distance (x) must be large enough to make ($Q/4 \pi x^2$) insignificant compared to ($4/\mathcal{R}$). A graphical solution of Equation 229 is given in Figure 86. Both chart and equation give the sound pressure level in dB relative to the sound power level for a source that can be considered a point.

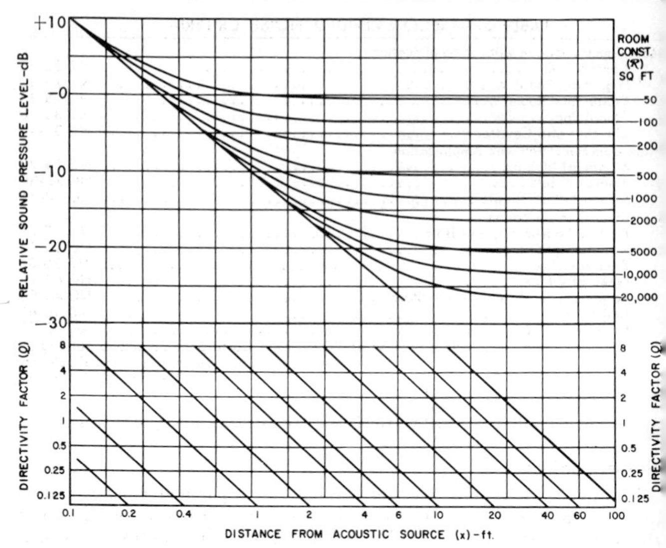

Figure 86—Sound Pressure Levels Relative to Sound Power Levels

Adapted from the data of L. L. Beranek, "Acoustics," McGraw-Hill Book Co., Inc., New York, 1954, pp. 317-319.

In open air the energy losses in the air itself may become significant for frequencies above 1000 Hz if appreciable distances are involved. The attenuation in dB may be determined from

$$\Delta\, SPL = 13.24\, \zeta\, x \tag{230}$$

for which the distance (x) is in feet and the energy attenuation constant (ζ) is obtained from Figure 77. Reflections by and absorption at the boundaries and refractions due to temperature gradient, wind, etc., generally serve to decrease the noise level below calculated levels at any outdoor location.

When a partition is located between a source and receiver, a transmission loss occurs. This loss depends on the frequency and the angle of incidence of the sound and on the construction and materials of the partition. An empirical relationship based on various materials and random incidence which expresses the average transmission loss ($\overline{TL}$) in dB in terms of the weight in lb per sq ft (W/A) of the partition is

$$\overline{TL} = 23 + 14.5 \log_{10} \frac{W}{A}\,. \tag{231}$$

For each doubling of mass the transmission loss is increased 4.4 dB. The transmission loss is greater at high frequencies than at low frequencies, increasing theoretically 6 dB per octave. When calculating the approximate transmission loss in each octave band the average transmission loss is generally assumed equal to that in the 500 Hz band and a 5 or 6 dB cumulative correction is made to each band. Some deviation must be expected both as regards average transmission loss and frequency distribution. Empirical values for many walls and floors have been tabulated by Harris.*

Transmission loss may be defined as 10 times the logarithm (to the base 10) of the ratio of the sound energy incident on a wall to the sound energy transmitted through that wall. The transmission loss for a wall constructed of several surfaces, each with a different individual transmission loss, can be determined from

$$TL_{1+2+\ldots+n} = 10\ log_{10}\left[\frac{S_1 + S_2 + \ldots + S_n}{\dfrac{S_1}{(10)^{\frac{TL_1}{10}}} + \dfrac{S_2}{(10)^{\frac{TL_2}{10}}} + \ldots + \dfrac{S_n}{(10)^{\frac{TL_n}{10}}}}\right]. \tag{232}$$

The transmission loss for a major opening is 0 dB at all frequencies. The transmission loss of a crack varies with its geometry but is quite small so that even small openings in an enclosure may have to be treated to achieve the desired noise control. The noise reduction or attenuation (ΔSPL) across a wall is the difference in sound pressure level at the two surfaces and may be determined from the transmission loss (TL), the area of the transmitting wall (S_w), and the room constant ($\mathcal{R}$) for the receiving space using

$$\Delta SPL = SPL_1 - SPL_2 = TL - 10\ log_{10}\left(\frac{1}{4} + \frac{S_w}{\mathcal{R}}\right). \tag{233}$$

In fan engineering most of the important noise sources are associated with airstreams and most of the transmission path is through those airstreams. Nevertheless it is important to examine the possibility of mechanical excitation and solid-borne noise.

Much of the sound energy in a duct radiates in the direction of air movement. The object of most noise control measures is to impede this flow of noise yet allow the air to pass freely. Some of the energy is transmitted to the duct material. That which is not absorbed or dissipated as heat is transmitted to the ambient air surrounding the duct. The sound pressure level outside the duct can be determined from Equation 233 and the sound pressure level inside the duct. In most cases a further reduction is required and an additional barrier such as a wall or ceiling must be installed. The sound pressure level on the duct side of this barrier can be determined from the characteristics of the enclosure including the proposed barrier. When the duct is quite close to the barrier it may be necessary to consider the direct radiation, in which case a cylindrical wave front can be assumed to radiate from the duct. Equation 233 can

*C. M. Harris, "Handbook of Noise Control," McGraw-Hill Book Co., Inc., New York, 1957, pp. 20-18—20-46.

then be used to determine the sound pressure level on the opposite side of the barrier. Besides being tedious, these calculations of the various sound pressure levels due to reflection and absorption effects involve numerous difficulties. The sound pressure level (SPL) in the duct in terms of the sound power level (PWL) of the source is

$$SPL = PWL - 10 \log_{10} A + 10.5 + \Delta, \tag{234}$$

assuming a plane wave of area (A) in ft^2 equal to the cross sectional area.

When computing radiation through a duct opening, reflection and absorption cannot be ignored. They are the means by which sound control is achieved. Another factor which also must be considered is the generation of noises in the various duct elements that always accompanies airflow.

The attenuation of bare ducts and ducts covered with thermo-insulation is given in Table 54. Even in the small sizes there will probably be a net generation of noise rather than a net attenuation in high velocity duct designs, i.e., around 5000 fpm.

TABLE 54—ATTENUATION OF BARE AND COVERED DUCTS

dB/ft.

Type	Size in.	Octave Band Center Frequency—Hz							
		63	125	250	500	1000	2000	4000	8000
Round	to 12	0.03	0.03	0.03	0.03	0.04	0.06	0.08	0.10
Rectangular	6 x 6	0.20	0.20	0.15	0.10	0.10	0.10	0.10	0.10
	24 x 24	0.20	0.20	0.10	0.05	0.05	0.05	0.05	0.05
	72 x 72	0.10	0.10	0.05	0.01	0.01	0.01	0.01	0.01

For ducts covered with thermal insulation use table values if round or twice table values if rectangular.

Adapted from the data of ASHRAE Guide and Data Book, Systems, 1970, p. 509.

When the inside of a duct is lined with acoustical material, and the major dimension of the section is only a fraction of the liner length (x) in ft, the attenuation (ΔSPL) may be estimated from the perimeter (P) in in., cross section (A) in sq in., and the absorption coefficient (α) using

$$\Delta SPL = 12.6 \frac{P}{A} x \alpha^{1.4}. \tag{235}$$

Figure 87 gives attenuation values per foot of duct lined with ½″ and 1″ acoustic material based on average center of band absorption coefficients.

Duct lining is usually most effective in the middle frequency range. The attenuation at high frequencies can be increased by incorporating elbows or miters in the system. Unlined bends reduce radiation by reflecting more power toward the source than is generated by the disturbance. The net attenuation due to lined and unlined elbows and miters may be estimated from Table 55.

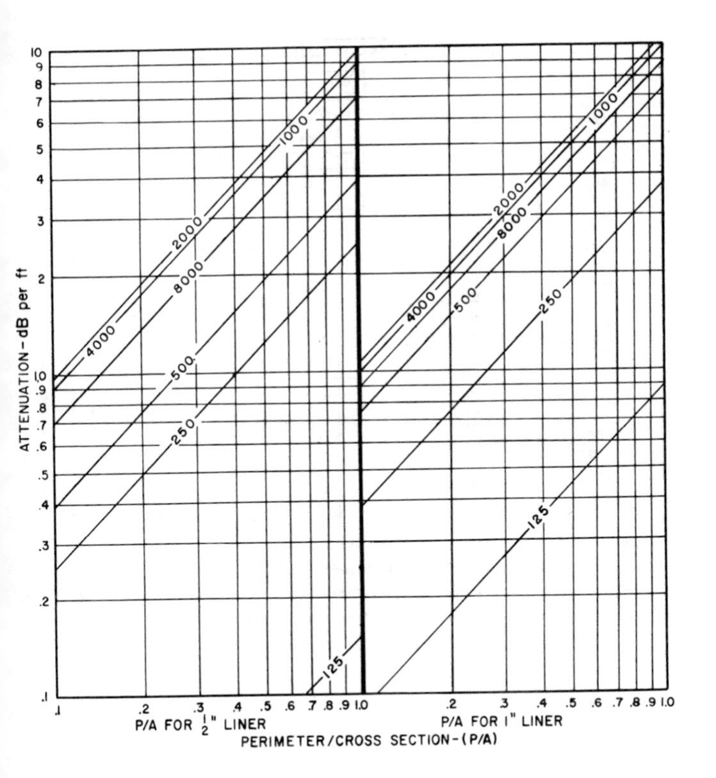

Figure 87—Attenuation Due to Lined Ducts

The sound power radiated down a duct divides at any divided flow fitting in proportion to the ratio of individual to total branch area $(A_1)/(A_1 + A_2 + .. + A_n)$. The difference between upstream and downstream sound power levels (ΔPWL) is expressed by

$$\Delta PWL = 10 \log_{10} \left(\frac{A_1}{A_1 + A_2 + .. + A_n} \right). \quad (236)$$

TABLE 55—ATTENUATION OF ELBOWS
dB

Type	Size in.	Octave Band Center Frequency—Hz							
		63	125	250	500	1000	2000	4000	8000
Curved Bend No Lining	5-10	0	0	0	0	1	2	3	3
	11-20	0	0	0	1	2	3	3	3
	21-40	0	0	1	2	3	3	3	3
	41-80	0	1	2	3	3	3	3	3
Miter No Lining	5 wide	0	0	0	1	5	7	5	3
	10 wide	0	0	1	5	7	5	3	3
	20 wide	0	1	5	7	5	3	3	3
	40 wide	1	5	7	5	3	3	3	3
Miter Upstream Lining	5 wide	0	0	0	1	5	8	6	8
	10 wide	0	0	1	5	8	6	8	11
	20 wide	0	1	5	8	6	8	11	11
	40 wide	1	5	8	6	8	11	11	11
Miter Downstream Lining	5 wide	0	0	0	1	6	11	10	10
	10 wide	0	0	1	6	11	10	10	10
	20 wide	0	1	6	11	10	10	10	10
	40 wide	1	6	11	10	10	10	10	10
Miter Complete Lining	5 wide	0	0	0	1	6	12	14	16
	10 wide	0	0	1	6	12	14	16	18
	20 wide	0	1	6	12	14	16	18	18
	40 wide	1	6	12	14	16	18	18	18

Curved bend data for either round or rectangular sections.

Miter data for rectangular sections without turning vanes.

Lining should be 10% of width and extend upstream or downstream at least 2 duct widths.

Lining need only be on sides. Width is between inside faces of lining.

Adapted from the data of ASHRAE Guide and Data Book, Systems, 1970, p. 509.

Not all of the power radiated to an opening leaves the duct. Some is radiated back and is called the end reflection loss. This loss can be determined from Figure 88. It is a function of frequency, size, and location relative to a wall as indicated on the chart.

Similar reflections occur at other discontinuities such as sudden expansions and contractions. The transmission loss for an expansion chamber will vary with the ratio of cross sectional area of the chamber to that of the inlet or exit pipe (A_e/A_p) and the ratio of the chamber length to wave length as given by Figure 89. The study of filters and mufflers is too broad to be covered here. A comprehensive treatment of the subject is given by Harris.*

*C. M. Harris, "Handbook of Noise Control," McGraw-Hill Book Co., Inc., New York, 1957, Chap. 21.

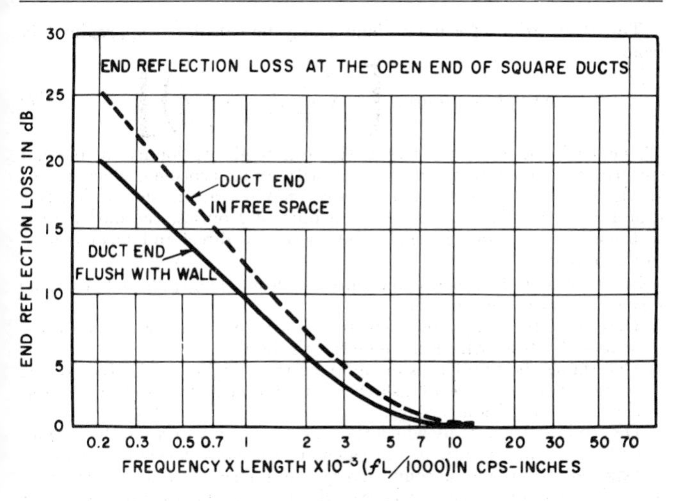

Figure 88—End Reflection Losses

Adapted from the data of ASHRAE Guide and Data Book, Systems and Equipment, 1967, p. 388.

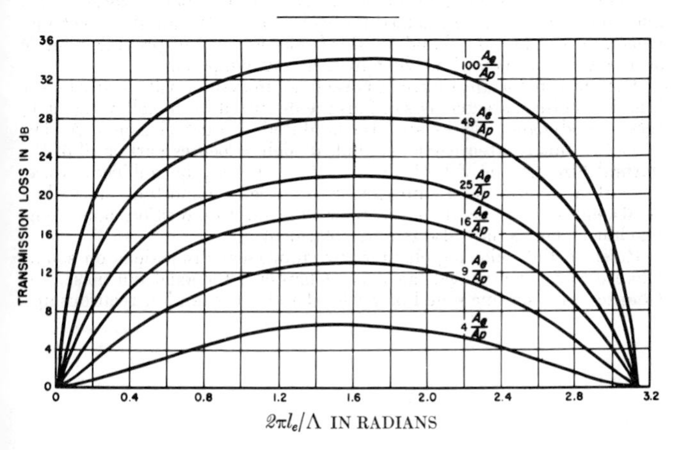

Figure 89—Attenuation Due to Expansion Chambers

Adapted from the data of C. M. Harris, "Handbook of Noise Control," McGraw-Hill Book Co., Inc., New York, 1957, p. *21*-16.

The attenuation of a lined plenum may be calculated approximately from

$$\Delta PWL = 10 \log_{10} \left[\frac{1}{A} \left(\frac{1}{\frac{\cos \beta}{2 \pi x^2} + \frac{1 - \alpha}{\alpha S}} \right) \right]. \qquad (237)$$

This equation includes the attenuation due to absorption by the plenum surface (S) having an acoustic lining with an absorption coefficient (α). It also includes the reduction in direct sound transmission which is a function of the distance (x) between inlet and outlet, the outlet cross sectional area (A), and the angle (β) between the direct and normal paths to the outlet.

Summarizing, the general procedure which should be followed in solving any noise control problem is—

1. Determine the sound power levels and directivity factors of all sources of noise by test or from manufacturer's data.
2. Determine the various listening areas that might be affected by the various sources and establish the allowable noise levels at these locations from applicable criteria.
3. Determine the paths by which the noise will travel to reach the listener or the listening locations and calculate the noise levels that may be expected taking into account divergence, reflection, and absorption.
4. If the expected noise levels exceed what can be tolerated consider whether means of reducing noise at the source, means of altering the transmission path, or means of otherwise protecting the listener are available or desirable.

Sound power levels and sound pressure levels, both expected and allowable, should be determined for each band of the audible spectrum. Generally the use of a band width of one octave will provide suitable accuracy for problems involving air handling equipment.

The most important source of noise in a fan system will usually be the fan. The noise characteristics of fans are discussed in the following chapters. Aerodynamic noises are also produced in duct elements. At low velocities this is often negligible, but at high velocities part or all of the natural attenuation of both ducts and bends may be nullified. Noises generated in grills and diffusers are especially important since duct treatment cannot be used for their control. Combustion noises and machinery noises may also require treatment.

Refer to the following chapters for additional discussions on sound: Chapter 6 for centrifugal fan noise, Chapter 7 for axial fan noise, and Chapter 8 for specific sound power level and other fan law relationships.

PART II
FANS

CHAPTER 6

CENTRIFUGAL FANS

Centrifugal fans of various descriptions constitute one of several types of turbomachinery which are used to transfer energy to a flowing fluid. Centrifugal fans are similar in many respects to both centrifugal pumps and centrifugal compressors. The principal distinction between these last two types of machines is that pumps handle liquids which are practically incompressible but compressors handle gases under such conditions that an appreciable change in density or compression results. Although fans also handle gases, the change in density is usually small enough that compressibility effects can be ignored. ASME test codes differentiate between fans and compressors according to density change. The point of division is a 7% density change which corresponds to about a 1.1 isentropic compression ratio.

The flow through centrifugal machines is principally radial in the region of energy transfer and is readily distinguished from the flow in axial flow machines. Axial flow fans are discussed in the next chapter, but many of the principles of energy transfer given below are applicable to all types of fans.

Energy Transfer

In the rotor of any turbomachine the axial, radial, and tangential components of the forces of the fluid particles on the rotor are associated with axial thrust, radial thrust, and torque respectively. Refer to page **271** for a discussion of thrust. The net torque is equal to the time rate of change in moment of momentum of the fluid between rotor inlet (Subscript 1) and rotor outlet (Subscript 2). The rate of energy transfer, or power (PW) for a constant rate of mass flow (m) is the product of torque and angular velocity (ω):

$$PW_E = \frac{m}{g_c}\,\omega\,(R_2\,V_{2tang} - R_1\,V_{1tang}) = \frac{m}{g_c}\,(U_2\,V_{2tang} - U_1\,V_{1tang}). \tag{238}$$

The product of radius (R) and tangential velocity (V_{tang}) is frequently called the "fluid whirl." The product of angular velocity and radius is the linear rotor velocity (U).

The tangential fluid velocity and the radial fluid velocity may be combined vectorially to obtain the absolute fluid velocity in the radial plane (V_{abs}). In like manner, the linear rotor velocity may be subtracted vectorially from the absolute fluid velocity to obtain the relative fluid velocity in the radial plane (V_{rel}). The net energy transfer per unit mass of fluid, or what is frequently called the total Euler head (H_E), may be determined from:

$$H_E = \frac{\omega}{g_c}(R_2 V_{2tang} - R_1 V_{1tang}) = \frac{1}{2g_c}[(V_{2abs}^2 - V_{1abs}^2) + (U_2^2 - U_1^2) + (V_{1rel}^2 - V_{2rel}^2)]. \quad (239)$$

The first equality states that the head a rotor should develop depends on the angular velocity, and the change in whirl between inlet and outlet. In the second equality the first term, $(V_{2abs}^2 - V_{1abs}^2)/2g_c$, is the change in absolute velocity head across the rotor due to kinetic energy change. The second term, $(U_2^2 - U_1^2)/2g_c$, is the change in pressure head due to centrifugal forces. The third term, $(V_{1rel}^2 - V_{2rel}^2)/2g_c$, is the change in pressure head due to the change in relative velocity through the rotor. The first term therefore represents the change of velocity pressure while the last two terms combined represent the change of static pressure.

The various forms of Equations 238 and 239 are convenient in analyzing the effect of design changes and the effect of different conditions of operation on an ideal machine. The sign convention employed here is that a positive value of PW or H means that power must be transmitted to the air or that head is developed by the rotor, respectively.

Energy transfer to the fluid due to shaft work can only take place within the impeller. The energy transformation involved in the conversion of velocity to static head which may take place in the casing or elsewhere should not be confused with the process of energy transfer.

The analysis of certain limiting flow situations may be helpful in the understanding of the energy transfer process. For the limiting case where flow is purely radial, i.e., $V_{2tang} = 0$ and $V_{1tang} = 0$, both the net power transmitted to and the head developed in the fluid must be zero. That this is so, is clearly indicated in Equations 238 and 239. For purely radial entry, i.e., for no inlet whirl, the theoretical power and head are determined exclusively by conditions at the discharge or outlet.

Another limiting situation is that of no flow, i.e., $m = 0$. No net power will be transmitted to the fluid in the absence of flow. Similarly, the relative velocity at either inlet or outlet will be zero. However, the linear rotor velocity and absolute fluid velocities will have finite values since the absolute fluid velocity must equal the linear rotor velocity in such situations. The head theoretically developed by a rotor at no flow will be twice that due to change of centrifugal forces alone, viz., $(U_2^2 - U_1^2)/g_c$. The kinetic energy portion is largely transformed, not into pressure energy, but into internal energy as a result of fluid friction, producing temperature rise rather than static pressure.

The density does not appear anywhere in the expression for theoretical head. Therefore, the head which an impeller will develop is independent of density. The conventional units are ft-lb of energy per lbm of fluid which is usually abbreviated to ft of fluid flowing.

Each type of fan utilizes in distinctly different proportions the various means of developing head. In axial flow fans the particles theoretically flow at constant radii so that $U_2 = U_1$ and there is no centrifugal effect. The various types of centrifugal fans are characterized by distinctly different heel-to-tip ratios as well as tip angles so that the proportion of developed head due to centrifugal effect varies. Fans with forwardly curved blades generally have very large heel-to-tip ratios and therefore produce less head due to centrifugal effect than fans with backwardly curved blades which generally have considerably smaller heel-to-tip ratios. Radial blade fans are produced with various heel-to-tip ratios, and the amount of head developed due to centrifugal effect varies accordingly. Mixed flow fans have a limited change in radius and therefore produce a limited amount of head by means of centrifugal effect. Cross flow fans employ radial in-flow and out-flow at the same radius, so the positive and negative centrifugal effects cancel.

Prerotation and Slip

The fluid approaching the inlet of a radial flow impeller will follow the path of least resistance. There will be a different path and a different value of the least resistance for each capacity. The minimum resistance occurs at the design capacity. With uniform axial approach the fluid particles must simply turn radially to enter the impeller at the design capacity. At any capacity off design the fluid particles must turn tangentially as well as radially in order to follow the path of least resistance.

The combination of purely radial absolute velocity and tangential linear rotor velocity produces a relative fluid velocity the tangential component of which is directed opposite to the rotation. The relative fluid angle can be determined vectorially. The heel of the blade should be curved forwardly at such an angle that the fluid can enter between blades without impact.

The heel angle can only be correct for one flow rate, that which is called the design capacity. At all other capacities the fluid has to acquire prerotation. There will be some impact loss and some additional fluid friction but the sum of the two must be the least possible for the actual flow rate. At capacities less than design the prerotation must be positive with respect to wheel rotation and at capacities over design the prerotation must be negative with respect to wheel rotation.

Ideally, at the design point the theoretical head and power should be as indicated by Equations 239 and 238. However, both the head developed and the power transmitted to the fluid are less than the theoretical values due to the phenomenon known as slip. The difference cannot be called a loss but more appropriately ineffectiveness or non-utilization since it would occur even with an ideal fluid. There are various theories for predicting slip, none of which agrees completely with empirical data so that none is entirely satisfactory. However, the net result is that the fluid leaves the impeller at a mean relative angle with the tangential direction which is less than the blade angle. Therefore, the impeller does not develop the full theoretical head nor transmit the full theoretical power. A reduction in head also occurs due to the real flow velocity gradients across the impeller channel. This is considerably smaller than that due to slip. Again, this is not a loss since it does not involve any energy input.

The spacing and discharge angle of the blades both influence the amount of slip. For a greater number of blades (n_{bl}) there is smaller spacing, more guidance is given the flow, and less slip results. Lower tip angles (β_2) give rise to less slip apparently because the mean path of the particles more nearly matches the blade shape. The reduction of head due to slip (ΔH_{slip}) is also a function of capacity and heel-to-tip ratio, but for simplicity

$$\Delta H_{slip} = \frac{U_2^2}{g_c}\left(\frac{K \pi \sin \beta_2}{n_{bl}}\right). \tag{240}$$

This approximate expression contains what is known as the Stodola correction and is generally valid only for long overlapping blades. According to Wislicenus* the correction factor (K) for a 90° tip and 12 blades is approximately 0.65. For a 40° tip and 16 blades, K is approximately 0.9. The corresponding difference in power transmitted to the fluid due to slip (ΔPW_{slip}) may be obtained by multiplying by the appropriate mass flow rate (m) as indicated by

$$\Delta PW_{slip} = \frac{m U_2^2}{g_c}\left(\frac{K \pi \sin \beta_2}{n_{bl}}\right). \tag{241}$$

Ideal Performance Characteristics

The ideal performance characteristics of a fan may be derived from the energy transfer and slip relationships given above. For simplicity the condition of no inlet whirl i.e., $V_{1tang} = 0$, will be assumed. The effects of controlled inlet whirl will be discussed under the heading, "Inlet Guide Vanes."

The expression for theoretical total head may be rewritten

$$H_E = \frac{U_2}{g_c}\left(U_2 - \frac{q}{A_{2rad}} \cot \beta_2\right) - \frac{U_1}{g_c}\left(U_1 - \frac{q}{A_{1rad}} \cot \beta_1\right). \tag{242}$$

This expression indicates the effect of volumetric capacity (q) and blade angle (β). The area (A_{rad}), through which the fluid must flow, is best described as that which is normal to the radial velocity component. The second term involving conditions at the inlet is zero, since zero inlet whirl is assumed. Subtracting the difference in head due to slip leaves the ideal head (H_i) taking into account slip, but ignoring reduction in head due to real flow velocity gradients and losses due to skin friction, turbulence, etc.:

$$H_i = \frac{U_2^2}{g_c}\left(1 - \frac{K \pi \sin \beta_2}{n_{bl}}\right) - \frac{U_2 \, q \cot \beta_2}{g_c A_{2rad}}. \tag{243}$$

The first term yields the theoretical shutoff head, including the effect of slip. Only a portion of this will appear as static head, the rest appearing as temperature rise. The second term expresses the effect of changes in capacity. For a given speed of rotation and wheel geometry the effect of capacity variation will depend on the curvature of the blade at the tip. For a 90⁰ tip angle the ideal head will be constant regardless of capacity since the cotangent of 90⁰ is zero. For a forwardly curved tip angle the ideal head will rise with increasing capacity since for angles over 90⁰ the cotangent becomes negative. For backwardly curved tip angles the ideal head will gradually fall with increasing capacity since the cotangent of angles below 90⁰ is positive.

*G. F. Wislicenus, "Fluid Mechanics of Turbomachinery," Dover Publications, Inc., New York, 1965, p. 280.

The variation of ideal power (PW_i) with capacity may be determined simply by noting that power is proportional to the product of head and mass flow rate:

$$PW_i = m\left[\frac{U_2^2}{g_c}\left(1 - \frac{K\ \pi\ sin\ \beta_2}{n_{bl}}\right) - \frac{U_2\ q\ cot\ \beta_2}{g_c\ A_2}\right]. \tag{244}$$

For radial tip fans the theoretical power is directly proportional to the capacity but for forwardly curved tips the theoretical power rises much more rapidly and for backwardly curved tips much less rapidly, even to the point where it may fall off with increasing capacity.

Typical performance characteristics based on ideal head and power are given in Figure 90, for the condition where there is no whirl at the rotor inlet.

Losses and Efficiencies

The actual power transmitted to the fluid and the actual head developed will both differ from the ideal as a result of various losses. These losses may be classified according to whether they affect head, power, or capacity.

Hydraulic efficiency (η_h) is the ratio of actual head (H) to ideal head (H_i). The hydraulic losses ($H_i - H$) result from skin friction and energy dissipation caused by change of direction or velocity in the impeller or in any other part of the machine. Because the main flow is generally turbulent the friction losses usually vary as the square of the velocity and therefore capacity. Shock losses are a minimum at the design point and increase as the capacity deviates therefrom.

The isentropic compression efficiency (η_c) as defined by Equation 166 is the ratio of the ideal to the actual work performed on a gas and is therefore similar to hydraulic efficiency. However, isentropic compression efficiency includes a thermodynamic effect which is absent in hydraulic efficiency. If the effects of temperature level and pressure ratio are removed from the concept of isentropic compression efficiency, the result is the polytropic compression efficiency (η_p). It can be deduced that the polytropic efficiency is a function of the polytropic exponent (n) and the isentropic exponent (γ) or

$$\eta_p = \frac{n}{n-1}\ \frac{\gamma - 1}{\gamma}. \tag{245}$$

Both the hydraulic efficiency (in the case of incompressible flow) and the polytropic compression efficiency (in the case of compressible flow) are measures of the perfection in the design of the flow passages.

Volumetric efficiency (η_v) is the ratio of the net volume flow rate (q) handled by the machine to the volume flow rate handled by the impeller (q_i). The leakage volume flow rate ($q_i - q$) passes through the clearance spaces between rotating and stationary parts to recirculate through the impeller. The volumetric efficiency is therefore a measure of the perfection in the design of the clearance spaces.

Mechanical efficiency (η_m) is the ratio of the power transmitted to the fluid (PW_i) and converted into useful output to the power applied to the shaft (PW). The mechanical losses ($PW - PW_i$) include the power loss due to disk friction as well as the mechanical losses in bearings, seals, etc.

Total efficiency (η_T) is the ratio of the theoretical air horsepower (AHP) to the brake horsepower (BHP). The total power losses ($BHP - AHP$) are due to skin friction, turbulence, leakage, and mechanical friction. Therefore

$$\eta_T = \eta_h \, \eta_v \, \eta_m = \eta_c \, \eta_v \, \eta_m. \tag{246}$$

Static efficiency (η_S) may be determined from the total efficiency and the ratio of fan static pressure (FSP) to fan total pressure (FTP) using

$$\eta_S = \eta_T \frac{FSP}{FTP}. \tag{247}$$

The total and static efficiencies provide information on over-all performance, i.e., for the entire fan including rotor, casing, etc. The difference is that the kinetic energy leaving the fan as represented by its outlet velocity head is considered available in the first case and is disregarded in the second.

Actual Performance Characteristics

The actual head-capacity relationship for the condition of no leakage can be derived from the ideal head-capacity relationship by subtracting the appropriate friction and shock losses for each capacity. The results of such calculations for each of three typical blade tip angles are illustrated in Figure 90. Similarly, the actual power-capacity relationships can be derived from the ideal by adding the power losses due to disk friction, bearings, etc. The effect of leakage in either case is approximately as if the zero capacity line were shifted to the right by a corresponding amount. This is also indicated in Figure 90.

The relationships shown for all three types were calculated as if each were to handle the same amount of air at design and develop the same head with equal total efficiencies. To further illustrate the differences Figure 91 was drawn showing the actual net heads superimposed on one chart and the actual powers superimposed on another. The variation of the various losses with capacity is also shown. The three types of fans for which these performance characteristics were drawn are not necessarily of the same size or speed. To produce the results shown, the backwardly curved design must have the highest tip speed and the forwardly curved design the lowest tip speed. At the design point and at other points off design the most stable operation as indicated by the slopes of the curves is obtained with the backwardly curved type (see page 268). Also, the power at capacities greater than design is least for the backwardly curved type. The power for this type tends to level off, and, if sufficiently low tip angles or appropriate inlet guide vanes are used, the power curve will actually droop as indicated by the dashed lines. This Limit-Load® type horsepower characteristic is quite desirable for closely motored fans on systems where capacity may increase due to lower than anticipated resistance. It will be noted that the forward curved type shows the lowest horsepower at shutoff, which characteristic is very desirable whenever there is considerable operation at reduced capacity.

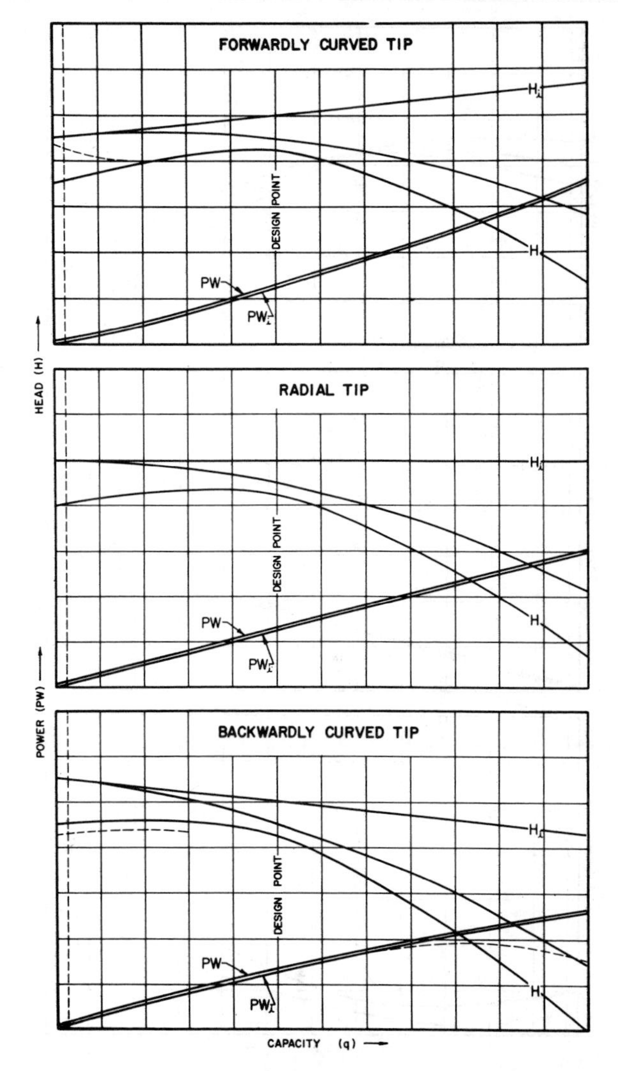

Figure 90—Theoretical Performance Characteristics for Centrifugal Fans

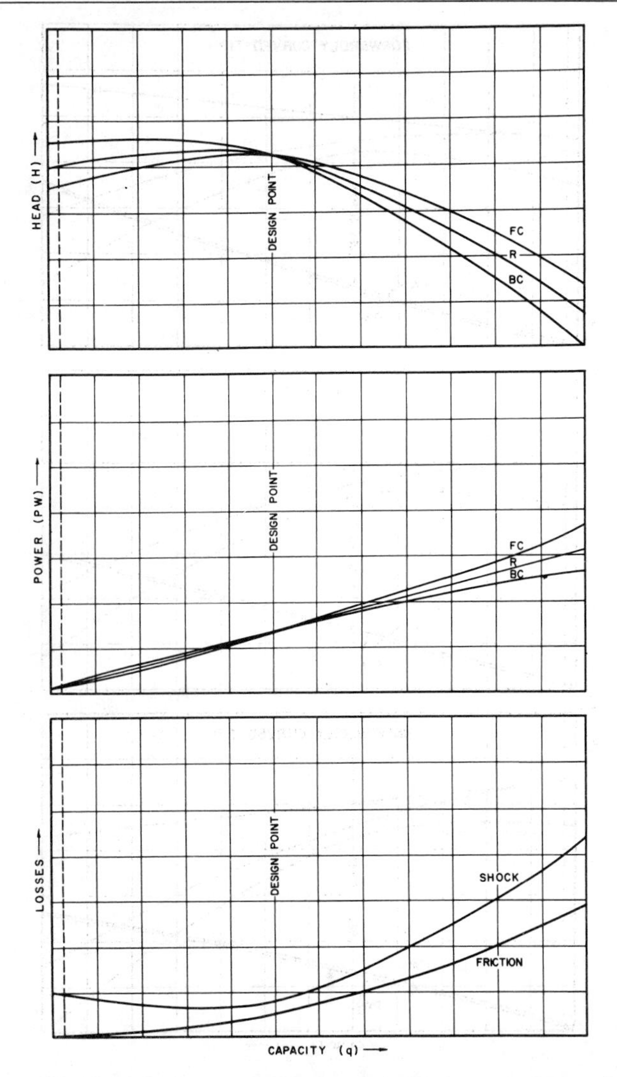

Figure 91—Theoretical Performance Characteristics for Centrifugal Fans

The dashed line curve at low capacity, indicated for the backwardly curved blade design, is for the flat backwardly inclined blade variation of this fan. The "break" in the curve is the result of a severe flow separation from a boundary in the blade passage. The solid line smooth curve is for a truly curved blade fan with identical tip angle. For equal tip angles the blade can only be curved by steepening the heel angle which in turn means that inlet guide vanes must be used (see page 212).

The usual head-capacity characteristic at low flows for forward curved designs appears as indicated by the dashed line. This is probably due to negative inlet whirl produced by back flow through the inlet of the wheel or rotor at these low capacities.

High relative Mach numbers lead to separation with a resultant loss of head and efficiency. However, in most fan applications the relative Mach number is quite low.

Theoretically, the net performance of a fan can be deduced by consideration of energy transfer, prerotation, slip, velocity gradient, and losses. Practically, however, there are so many secondary interactions that tests must be performed not only in the proof of a design but in its development as well. In the following paragraphs only the major considerations in the design of the various fan elements are discussed.

Over-all Design

There are two major design situations: (1) the design of an individual fan for specific requirements, and (2) the design of a line or several lines of fans for a range of requirements. Some aspects of the second situation will be discussed later, particularly with reference to specific speed and the fan laws. The design of an individual fan will be discussed here.

Forwardly curved tips provide the maximum head for given rotor size and backwardly curved tips the least. Because of the high percentage of head developed as kinetic energy or velocity head at the rotor outlet of a forwardly curved blade fan and because the conversion of velocity head to static head is inherently less efficient than the development of static head by centrifugal force, such fans are rather inefficient. Highest efficiencies are usually obtained with backwardly curved tips. Although first costs are usually lower with forward curved designs, operating costs are lower with backwardly curved designs. A compromise, viz., the use of a radial tip, may be indicated in many situations. Radial blades have greater strength against centrifugal force and are therefore used extensively on high pressure applications. Radial blades are also of simple shape and are therefore used in many situations where maintenance due to wear or unbalance might otherwise be a problem.

Assuming that the general type of centrifugal fan has been selected, the next step is to decide on an operating speed of rotation. Frequently the rotational speed may be specified or limited, due to direct connection to a prime mover. In general, economy due to reduction in size and improved hydraulic efficiency favors small, high-speed units. However, Reynolds number effects, particularly at the lower pressure ratios, favor larger, lower-speed units.

Having established a general type and speed, the design of an individual fan can be accomplished by estimating reasonable values of the various losses and the slip effect. Using blade angles close to the optimum established by experience, a preliminary value for the rotor diameter can be determined from the theoretical head capacity relationships. A method will be given below for determining the optimum inlet diameter. Once the tip and inlet diameters are fixed, the impeller design can be completed by calculating the necessary blade heel angles and streamlining the passages so as to minimize the losses. Inlet bells or cones should be streamlined as much as possible for the same reason. The discharge conditions, i.e., any requirement to gather the air for discharge through one or more openings and the need for conversion of energy will determine the casing design. The various losses may be re-estimated and adjustments made in the design as may be required. Any such design should be proved by tests.

Inlet Design

The velocity relative to the large diameter of the impeller inlet (V_{Irel}) is the vector sum of the absolute fluid velocity (V_{Iabs}) at that point and the linear rotor velocity (U_I). If there is no inlet whirl the absolute velocity will be purely axial (i.e., $V_{Iabs} = V_{Iax}$) so that

$$V_{Irel} = \sqrt{V_{Iax}^2 + U_I^2} = \sqrt{\left(\frac{4q/\pi}{D_I^2 - D_H^2}\right)^2 + \left(\pi D_I N\right)^2}. \quad (248)$$

There is an inlet diameter (D_I) for each combination of hub (or other obstruction) diameter (D_H), rotative speed (N), and volume flow rate (q) for which this relative velocity is a minimum. This is the optimum inlet diameter according to Shepherd.* A simple solution of Equation 248 for the optimum inlet diameter can be obtained either graphically or by trial and error. The optimum inlet diameter must be adjusted for the appropriate whirl, if any exists. If there is controlled inlet whirl the minimum relative velocity must be determined by means of vector construction.

The design velocity through the impeller inlet will be quite high. Some sort of converging passage is required to avoid a high shock loss at entrance. Even when the inlet is not free, but has connected duct work on the inlet side, the approach or duct velocity in all probability will be less than that through the impeller inlet.

From Chapter 3 it can be concluded that the entrance condition having the least coefficient of resistance is one of bell shape. The next best coefficient of resistance is obtained with a converging taper.

Normally, the clearance between the stationary inlet bell or cone and the impeller should be a minimum in order to minimize leakage. However, it is true that some designs employ slightly larger clearances in order to utilize the leakage flow to improve performance. It is possible to improve over-all efficiency in some cases even though the volumetric efficiency is reduced.

Impeller Design

All power that is transmitted to the fluid and converted into head is transmitted by the rotating blades. The number of blades should be

*D. G. Shepherd, "Principles of Turbomachinery," The Macmillan Co., New York, 1956, p. 227.

TABLE 56

USUAL NUMBER OF BLADES FOR VARIOUS TYPES OF CENTRIFUGAL FANS

Backwardly Curved Tip—single thickness.....	12-16
—airfoil shaped.....	8-12
Radial Tip—pressure blower type..........	10-20
—industrial exhauster type........	5-10
Forwardly Curved Tip....................	32-64

A smaller than optimum number of blades is frequently used in small sizes to facilitate manufacture. A larger than optimum number may be used in large sizes for structural reasons.

---

large in order to minimize the slip effect. On the other hand, since the blades form channels, through which the fluid must flow, their number should be comparatively small so that the mean hydraulic radius of the channels is approximately a maximum in order to minimize fluid friction.

The widths of the blades at the heel and tip, as they affect the channel areas (A_1 and A_2), influence the ideal head as indicated in Equations 242 and 243. The width of the blade at every point from heel to tip has an influence on the mean hydraulic radius and therefore on the friction losses through the impeller.

The effect of varying the tip angle has already been discussed. The optimum tip angle is given by Stepanoff* as 25^0. However, such low angles are rarely used in fan design. Excellent efficiencies are obtained with angles as high as 45^0 and the penalty for using 90^0 or radial tips is usually not more than about five points.

The optimum heel angle is that which allows the air to enter the impeller with minimum loss. The heels of the blades should be curved forward if they are to meet the air with minimum shock, regardless of tip curvature. When the inlet is small, very little is sacrificed by using a radial heel angle. Since the relative velocity varies with capacity, it also follows that the heel angle can only be correct for one capacity and that losses will increase rapidly at both higher and lower capacities.

The shape of the blade should be a smooth curve connecting the heel and tip. The flow may be improved by utilizing airfoil-shaped blades. Reduction of losses (especially at the heel) and therefore significant increases in efficiency have been achieved in this manner. The selection of a suitable airfoil section may be based on single airfoil theory with corrections for cascade effect or directly on rotating cascade tests where available.

Usually, consideration of structural vibrations alone requires that the blades be shrouded. In a fan the casing is not generally shaped to conform to the blade shape with minimum clearance. Shrouds are therefore important from a leakage standpoint as well. Except for secondary flow within a single channel, what leakage does occur is essentially radial from tip to heel through the clearance between the stationary and rotating inlets. The shape of the shroud on the inlet side should be such that the fluid can make the turn from axial to radial flow without separation, if

*A. J. Stepanoff, "Turboblowers," John Wiley & Sons, Inc., New York, 1955, pp. 66 and 232.

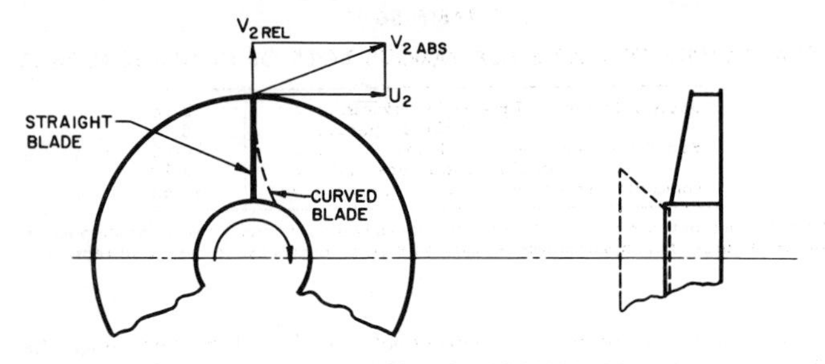

RADIAL DISCHARGE

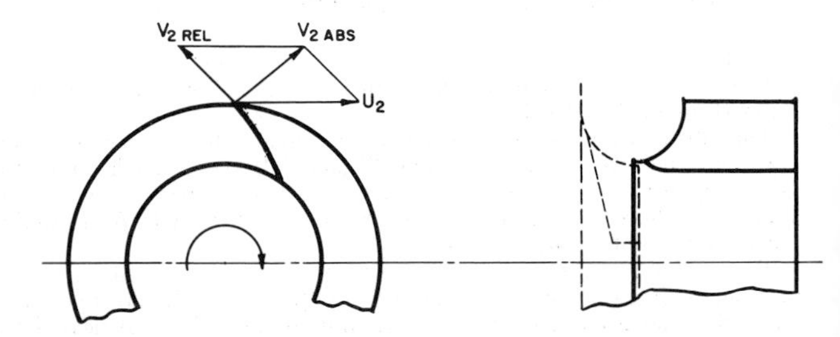

BACKWARD CURVED DISCHARGE

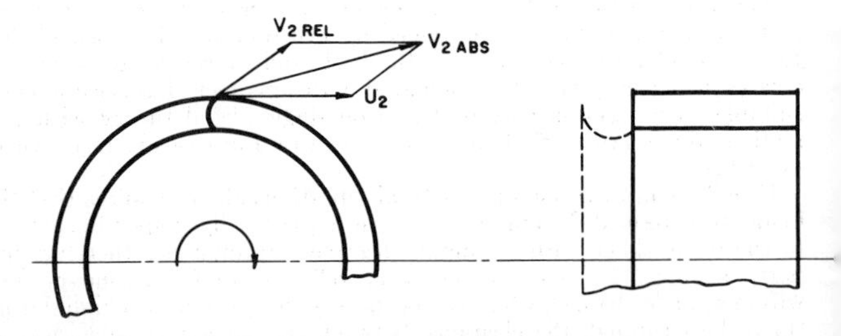

FORWARD CURVED DISCHARGE

Figure 92 —Blade Design for Backward, Radial, and Forward Tips

losses are to be minimized. If there is one factor which has led to the rapid development of airfoil bladed fans, it is the development of economical curved inlet shrouds. The well-curved inlet shroud makes it possible to realize the full advantage to be obtained with the use of airfoil blades. Before the advent of economical spinning and pressing to achieve the desired inlet shroud shapes, the only fans to successfully employ airfoil blades were of axial flow designs where such shrouds were not necessary.

Casing Design

The casing of a centrifugal fan must serve two functions. First, it must collect the air from the periphery of the wheel so that it may be discharged in the desired direction. Second, since a fairly large portion of the head developed appears at the impeller discharge as kinetic energy, the casing must convert a portion of this velocity head into static head. Both the transformation of energy and the collection of air even at constant velocity involve the loss of a portion of the total energy. The transformation of energy may be accomplished quite efficiently in a radial diffuser at the impeller periphery or in a conical diffuser located beyond the point of discharge after the fluid has been collected and directed to that point by some sort of scroll shaped casing. Both radial and conical diffusers require considerable space so that the processes of collection and diffusion are often attempted concurrently in fans. The sacrifice in efficiency involved in such an attempt is least with backwardly curved designs since here the amount of energy transformation required is the least. Diffuser vanes are seldom, if ever, used in fans since they impair efficiency at off design points and may even do so at design.

Casings are usually volute or scroll shaped. Centrifugal fan casings generally have straight parallel sides and a spiral shaped scroll. The point at which the scroll makes the closest approach to the impeller periphery is called the cutoff. Ideally the cutoff should be located at the diameter of the impeller, the increase in radius should be in proportion to the angular displacement, and the discharge plane should extend nearly radially from the point of cutoff. In practice the point of cutoff is always cut back so that there will be some clearance over the impeller tip. The cutoff clearance is quite critical in both generation of noise and efficiency. In practice the plane of discharge may be almost tangent to the point of cutoff so that in effect a portion of the impeller discharges directly into the outlet. The increase in radial dimension of the volute may be obtained approximately by a series of circular arcs rather than by a true spiral curve. Some designs may incorporate what is known as a drop outlet. All of these features are illustrated in Figure 93. The lower case letters indicate the scroll centers which may be uniform as shown, or expanding from a to d. The various scroll radii (R) should be selected so that the circular arcs merge into each other, forming a smooth continuous curve. As shown, the cutoff has been cut back from a point on top of the wheel through an arc of something just under 90^0. The amount of clearance over the cutoff is about 20% of the impeller diameter. Values as low as 5% may be used. The drop outlet is certainly less efficient than a diverging taper. The difference will approach that between abrupt and gradual enlargements as given in Chapter 3.

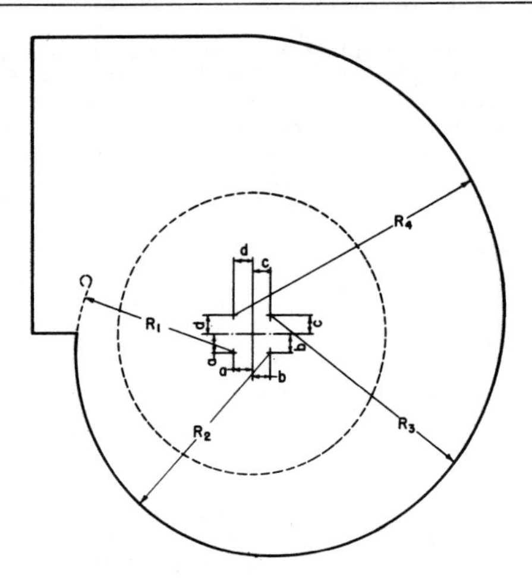

Figure 93—Scroll Design for Ventilating Fans

The width of the casing is usually appreciably greater than the tip width of the impeller. It usually exceeds the width of the impeller at the heel in order that the entire inlet bell may be contained within the width of the housing.

Inlet Guide Vanes

Either positive or negative inlet whirl can be produced with appropriately shaped guide vanes ahead of the impeller. Vanes curved in the direction of rotation produce positive whirl which reduces theoretical head and power. Counter-rotation vanes produce negative whirl with the opposite effect. This can be demonstrated in Equations 238 and 239 by substituting positive or negative values of tangential velocity. In either case the impeller blades should be curved forward at the heel to meet the incoming flow directly and minimize the losses at entrance. Smaller heel angles are required with counter rotation vanes, and steeper heel angles are needed when the vanes are curved in the direction of rotation. A proper heel angle for no inlet whirl falls somewhere in between. If two impellers, one intended for use with inlet vanes and the other intended for use without inlet vanes, are designed with the proper heel angle and other features so that hydraulic, volumetric, and mechanical efficiencies are the same, the difference in actual head and power will equal the difference in theoretical head and power.

There is no superiority in over-all efficiency of either an open inlet fan or one of the same type with fixed inlet vanes, if they are equally well designed. However, there are other advantages, particularly in backward curved designs. An open inlet fan is simpler in both blade shape and inlet

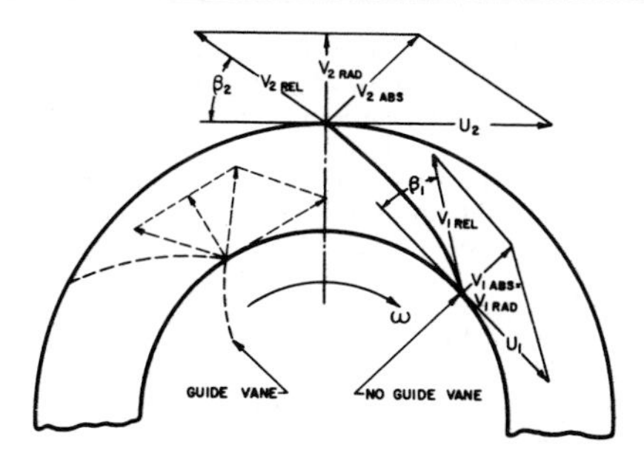

Figure 94 —Vector Diagram for Ventilating Fans With and Without Inlet Vanes

design. For the heel angle required, a perfectly flat backwardly inclined blade gives an acceptable tip angle. A fan with fixed inlet vanes has a curved blade which, with its steeper heel angle, makes it mechanically stronger than the flat blade. The inlet vanes serve as mechanical guards and as straighteners which reduce the effect of any adverse inlet whirl that might result from an accidental upstream disturbance. Most important of all, at reduced capacities the separation that occurs with flat blade designs is eliminated and a smooth unbroken head-capacity characteristic results instead. At capacities over design the Limit-Load® horsepower characteristic is accentuated when inlet vanes are used.

The over-all efficiency of straight radial blade fans may be improved by using inlet vanes to produce positive whirl. The fluid angle then more nearly matches the heel angle, reducing losses and improving efficiency.

The effectiveness of inlet vanes in changing theoretical head and power is limited with small inlet diameters. Inlet vanes are not generally used to produce negative whirl. The use of such "ramming" vanes narrows the operating range considerably.

Fixed inlet vanes are generally located as near the impeller inlet as possible. The effective discharge angle from the vane will be somewhat smaller than the actual angle for any finite number of vanes due to the inertia of the flowing air. As with slip in impellers, the number and angle of vanes influence the slip through inlet guide vanes. The entering edges of the vanes should be directed exactly upstream. In order to achieve the same degree of vane overlap from the center to the periphery of the inlet, the radius of curvature of the vane is gradually increased from the center outward, thus making the vane surface a portion of a cone.

Variable inlet vanes may be used to advantage whenever considerable operation at less than design capacity is required. If the fan is designed for fixed inlet vanes, variable vanes with the same effective curvature may be substituted without any appreciable sacrifice in peak efficiency. If the fan is designed with an open inlet, the variable vanes should be designed to produce the smallest possible effect on flow in the wide open position. In either case, gradual closure of the vanes should direct the flow more and more in the direction of rotation. The resulting changes in inlet whirl produce reductions in both power and head. Since, for a fan operating on a given system, reductions in head developed must be accompanied by reductions in capacity, power requirements at capacities less than design are always lower than the power required at design. The use of variable inlet vanes for capacity control leads to a further reduction of power. This additional reduction will nearly equal the theoretical amount due to increased inlet whirl at capacities near design. That is to say, the efficiency remains nearly constant for small capacity reductions. Under these conditions the change in capacity and the change in absolute velocity combine in such a way that the change in the direction of the relative velocity is practically negligible. At more greatly reduced capacities there is a significant change in the direction of the relative velocity. Even so, the change is not as great as if capacity were reduced without increased inlet whirl.

Variable inlet vanes may be used with forward, radial, or backward blade impellers to achieve better power reduction at reduced volume than with dampers which do not produce inlet whirl. Because of the shapes of their power-capacity curves, the greatest reduction is usually obtained with backwardly curved blades and the least with forwardly curved blades. For equal design efficiencies, the net horsepower for reduced capacities near design should be very nearly the same regardless of the type of impeller.

Noise Characteristics

Fan noise consists of a series of discreet tones superimposed on a broad band component. The former which may be called the rotational component may be traced to the process of energy transfer that also leads to the development of head. The latter which may be called the vortex component may be traced to the formation of turbulent eddies of one kind or another that usually lead to losses of head.

Each time a blade passes a point in the rotational path, an impulse is delivered to the air at that point. This impulse may be resolved into a large steady component and a series of very small oscillating components. The steady component produces head, the oscillating components produce rotational noise at discreet tones. The predominant tone of this rotational component of fan noise in centrifugal apparatus is usually that at the blade passing frequency. In very narrow blade designs, the higher harmonics may be of equal intensity. Widening the blades progressively weakens the higher harmonics.

Doubling the number of blades in any fan theoretically produces a cancellation of the odd harmonics and a doubling in strength of the even harmonics. Insofar as doubling the number of blades reduces the size of the fan required to produce the necessary head, the strength of the even harmonics will only be increased to a value somewhere between 1 and 2 times the original value. Tests on a one bladed propeller and the smaller but equivalent two bladed propeller indicate a factor of one. Tests on a 16 blade centrifugal and the equivalent 32 blade centrifugal indicate a factor very close to 2. Since the odd harmonics will definitely be eliminated, the sound power level of the fan could be reduced by as much as 3 dB if the even harmonics are not strengthened at all and if originally they represent one half of the total intensity, or by as little as 0 dB if the even harmonics are strengthened the full amount.

There are a number of factors which determine the optimum number of blades for each of the various types of centrifugal fans. These include the effect of number of blades on slip, fluid friction, structural strength, and cost as well as noise output. The net result is that noise considerations seldom control the number of blades.

Vortices can be created at the leading or trailing edges of the blades, along the sides of the blades, or at locations remote from the blades. In general, the size, rate of growth and decay, and point of origin and movement of these vortices will be random in nature and the noise resulting therefrom will have a broad band spectrum.

Streamlining the leading edges of the blades minimizes vortex formation at that location. At the design capacity, both thin blades with rounded edges and thick blades with airfoil sections are quite effective in reducing vortex formation. The airfoil shaped blade may have some advantage, particularly when the leading edge angle does not match the entering flow angle across the entire width of the blade.

Large eddies may be formed in the blade passages due to flow separation from a boundary. The greatest benefit to be derived from the use of airfoil shaped blades is that of reducing separation. This is somewhat offset from a noise standpoint by the decrease in the optimum number of blades compared to that for thin blades. Von Kármán vortex streets will be shed from the trailing edges because of their finite thicknesses. The thickness of the blade apparently has very little effect in centrifugal fans.

Whenever two masses of air meet with a finite relative velocity, turbulence results. The discharge from the impeller and the previously collected streams join in such fashion. The degree of turbulence depends upon the degree of perfection of the design.

The sound power level curve for a backwardly curved thin bladed centrifugal fan is shown in Figure 95 together with other performance characteristics. This curve is typical of that for all centrifugal fan types. The over-all shape of the sound power level curve indicates that the sound power output of a fan is a function of both capacity and pressure. Tests indicate that sound power outputs are proportional to the capacity ratio multiplied by the square of the pressure ratio, all other conditions being equal. Conditions off design are certainly not equal to those at design as is indicated by the shape of the specific sound power level curve. Refer to Chapter 8 for a discussion of specific sound power level. The spectrum for a centrifugal fan may be approximated in most cases by subtracting 9, 7, 5, 7, 10, 13, 20, and 29 dB from the over-all level to obtain the levels in the first through eighth octave bands, respectively, provided the blade passing frequency falls in the third band. A slight readjustment of values is needed if the blade passing frequency falls in any other band.

The speed of sound so greatly exceeds the air speed in most fans that the noise is propagated upstream and down with equal facility. The acoustical impedances of the inlet and outlet openings are so nearly equal that in most cases the sound power radiated through the outlet can safely

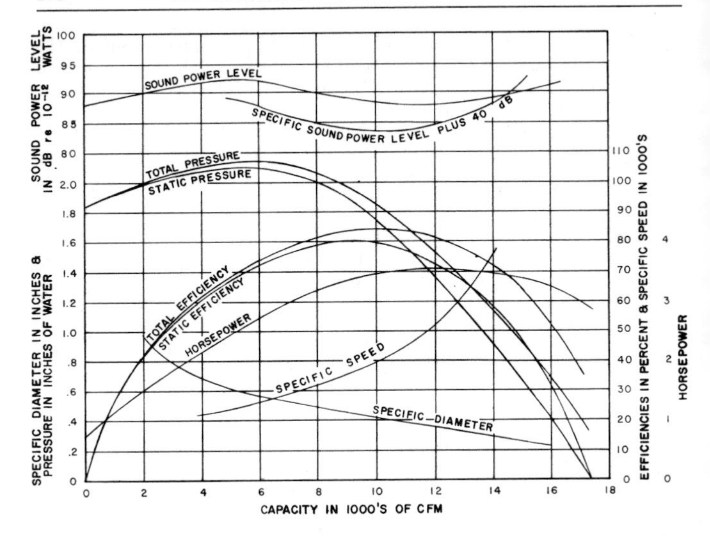

Figure 95—Typical Constant Speed Performance Curves for Ventilating Fans

---

be assumed to be equal to that radiated through the inlet. The transmission through the casing walls is so small by comparison that when the total sound power output of a fan is measured the portions radiated through the outlet and inlet are each reported as one half of that total. The corresponding sound power levels are therefore each 3 dB less than the total sound power level. To estimate the level of the sound power output through the casing, subtract the amount given in Table 57 from the total sound power level.

The equations in Chapter 5 can be used to estimate the sound pressure levels at various locations from sound power level ratings. For locations for which the fan can be considered a point source, Equation 229 would be appropriate. For locations very close to a large fan, Equation 234 which is based on a plane wave, might be best. The noise emanating from a fan cannot be considered to diverge very much until after it travels at least one opening diameter in the case of inlet or outlet noise, or one casing diameter for casing noise.

TABLE 57—CORRECTIONS FOR NOISE THROUGH CASING

Casing Thickness	14 ga	12 ga	10 ga	8 ga	¼	⅜	½	¾
Correction —dB	16	18	19	20	22	25	27	30

CHAPTER 7

AXIAL FLOW FANS

As the name implies the direction of the flow through an axial flow fan is predominantly axial, i.e., parallel to the axis of rotation. Ideally there is no component of velocity in the radial direction. There must be an increase in the tangential component if energy is to be transferred from the impeller to the air.

Many of the principles of energy transfer and design as given in the previous chapter on centrifugal fans are applicable to axial flow fans. There are some points of difference but before discussing them it is convenient to name certain dimensions. The nomenclature outlined below may differ from that used by some other authors because there is no general agreement on the method of specifying angularity. The method used here is to specify angularity from a tangential reference line unless otherwise noted. Some designers prefer to use an axial reference line.

Nomenclature

Figure 96 is a cylindrical section through an axial flow fan blade. Typical vector diagrams for conditions at the leading (subscript 1) and trailing (subscript 2) edge planes are also shown.

The distance between the leading and trailing edges is the chord length (x_c). The distance along the cylindrical arc between corresponding points on two successive blades is the pitch length (x_p).

The distance from the chord line to the mean thickness line is the camber (y_b). The camber will vary with chordwise position (x_b). The thickness of the blade (y_t) may be constant or may vary with chordwise position (x_t). The positions of maximum camber and maximum thickness need not necessarily coincide.

The blade angle (β) at any position along the chord is that formed by the line which is tangent to the mean thickness line and a reference line which is drawn in the tangential direction, i.e., parallel to the direction of rotation. The blade setting or stagger angle (γ) is formed by the chord line and a similar reference line.

The fluid angle (α) at any position is that formed by the relative velocity vector (V_{rel}) and the linear rotor velocity vector (U).

A constant annular area is required to produce a constant axial component (V_{ax}) of the absolute velocity as indicated on the vector diagrams.

The purely axial absolute velocity (V_{abs}) on the leading edge vector diagram implies that there is no prerotation. The tangential component of the absolute velocity indicated for the trailing edge produces an appre-

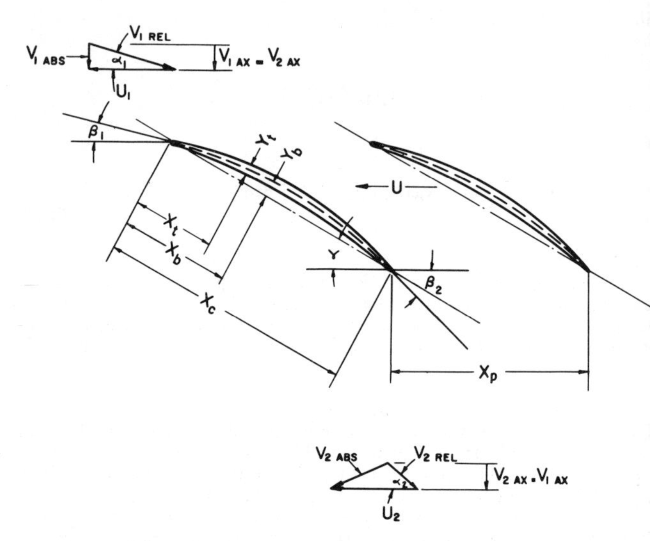

Figure 96—Blade Design and Nomenclature for Axial Flow Fans

ciable amount of fluid whirl. A discharge vane assembly may be used to transform this whirl energy into pressure energy.

The various lengths and angles may vary with radial position. The cylindrical section shown is for only one of many radial positions between the hub (subscript H) and tip (subscript T).

A rotor blade assembly preceded by or followed by a stator vane assembly constitutes a "stage."

Energy Transfer

As with centrifugal fans the axial and tangential components of the forces of the fluid particles on the rotor produce axial thrust and torque respectively. If there is no radial velocity component there is no radial force component and hence no radial thrust. Axial thrust is discussed in Chapter 11. The rate of energy transfer or the power (PW) involved in the production of torque is the same as for a centrifugal fan. Rewriting Equation 238 on the basis of axial flow, i.e., no radial components, produces

$$PW_E = m\,\frac{\omega R}{g_c}(V_{2tang} - V_{1tang}) = m\,\frac{\omega R}{g_c}\,V_{ax}\,(cot\;\alpha_1 - cot\;\alpha_2). \quad (249)$$

This equation expresses the power transmitted to a fluid flowing at a particular radius (R). Since different portions of the fluid will flow at different radii, the variation of mass flow rate (m) and the variation of the change in tangential velocity ($V_{2tang} - V_{1tang}$) must be taken into account. The fluid angles (α_1) and (α_2) may also vary with radius. The angular velocity (ω) and axial velocity (V_{ax}) may generally be assumed constant. The product (ωR) is the linear rotor speed (U).

The net energy transfer per unit mass of fluid or the Euler total head (H_E) for an axial flow fan may be derived as

$$H_E = \frac{\omega R}{g_c}(V_{2tang} - V_{1tang}) = \frac{V_{2abs}^2 - V_{1abs}^2}{2g_c} + \frac{V_{1rel}^2 - V_{2rel}^2}{2g_c}. \tag{250}$$

The theoretical head (H_E) developed will be the same in each portion of fluid only if the change in tangential velocity is inversely proportional to the radius. This relationship is one design criterion but not the only possible one.

The change in relative velocity produces an increase in static pressure across the impeller equal to the change in energy $(V_{1rel}^2 - V_{2rel}^2)/2g_c$, disregarding losses. There is no centrifugal effect without radial flow $(U_2^2 - U_1^2)/2g_c = 0$. The energy transfer is largely due to the change in absolute kinetic energy $(V_{2abs}^2 - V_{1abs}^2)/2g_c$.

If this kinetic energy appears as whirl at the rotor exit, stator discharge vanes may be used for its transformation to useful pressure energy. Such a stage is usually designed for axial inlet flow without inlet vanes.

Negative transformation may be accomplished with stator inlet vanes to produce inlet whirl. The rotor blades are then designed to provide axial discharge flow.

Vaneaxial fans are generally single stage machines with either inlet or discharge vanes. Compressors are generally multi-stage machines which do not necessarily employ purely axial velocity for any but the first and last stages. Tubeaxial fans are single stage machines without any guide vanes. Any energy transformation must take place without the benefit of guidance.

In the design of a single stage vaneaxial fan it is convenient to assume a purely axial velocity entering and leaving the stage. To produce the necessary change in whirl some sort of vortex flow must be superimposed on the axial flow through the stage.

The choices available are the free vortex pattern and various forced vortex patterns. Fans have frequently been designed for free vortex flow which produces constant head, i.e., the same total head in each particle regardless of radius ($H_{r1} = H_{r2}$). The full forced vortex or solid rotation which produces constant dimensionless head, i.e., the same total head per unit of peripheral velocity squared in each particle ($g_c H_{r1}/U_{r1}^2 = g_c H_{r2}/U_{r2}^2$), is advocated by Stepanoff.*

Incidence and Deviation

The difference between the fluid and blade angles at the rotor entrance is called incidence ($\alpha_1 - \beta_1$). The difference between the blade and fluid angles at rotor exit is called deviation ($\beta_2 - \alpha_2$).

Incidence at the design capacity is a matter of design as discussed on

*A. J. Stepanoff, "Turboblowers," John Wiley & Sons, Inc., New York, 1955, p. 56.

page 225. Deviation is a function of the geometry of the blade as indi cated by

$$\beta_2 - \alpha_2 = K (\beta_2 - \beta_1) \sqrt{x_p/x_c}. \quad (251$$

The value of K, which relates the difference between the leading anc trailing edge angles $(\beta_2 - \beta_1)$ and the pitch-chord ratio (x_p/x_c) to devia tion varies with stagger angle and with blade form. Various methods o estimating K are listed by Shepherd*. One of these methods indicate: a value of 0.26 for circular arc blades with 30° stagger angle.

Deviation, like slip, is affected by any factor which influences flui guidance through the impeller.

When the fluid cannot accommodate itself to the guiding surfaces of a passage, separation occurs. The aeronautical term "stall" is sometime used to describe such a phenomenon in turbomachines. Stall may originat at only one portion of a blade when the incidence exceeds a certain value Rotating stall passes from one blade to the next and produces the sam net effect as if it occurred continuously on only one blade. Pronounce separation is accompanied by appreciable circulatory flow.

Performance Characteristics

The ideal performance characteristics of an axial flow fan can be derive from the various energy transfer relations. The theoretical total hea (H_E) is exactly as given by Equation 242 for centrifugal fans. The idea total head (H_i) can be obtained from this by substituting the actual flui angles (α) for the blade angles (β). For the usual case of no controlle inlet whirl,

$$H_i = \frac{U^2}{g_c} - \frac{Uq \cot \alpha_2}{g_c A_{2ax}}. \quad (252$$

which indicates the effect of volume flow rate (q) and fluid angle (α_2). Th linear rotor velocity (U) varies with radial position. The area $(A_{2ax}$ through which the fluid must flow is the total annulus between hub an tip corrected for blade thickness. The ideal head at no flow or shutof according to Equation 252 is (U^2/g_c). The corresponding static pressure i never realized, first because some of the energy will appear as temperatur rise, and second because the losses involved in circulating around th blade, etc., reduce the head developed.

At design the ideal head will be appreciably less than at shut off. Thi fact is indicated in Equation 252 for fluid angles less than 90^0. The actua head will be less by an amount equal to the hydraulic losses.

At capacities over design, assuming the same fluid angle (α_2), the idea head indicated by Equation 252 is less than at design. The actual head i even smaller due to increased losses. Capacity increases are accompanie by negative prerotation or negative incidence or both. Both lead to a reduction in head.

At capacities under design the ideal head increases, but only unti stalling occurs. At this point the variation of fluid angle with capacit may have more influence on head production than the decrease in ca

* D. G. Shepherd, "Principles of Turbomachinery," The Macmillan Co., New York 1956, p. 406.

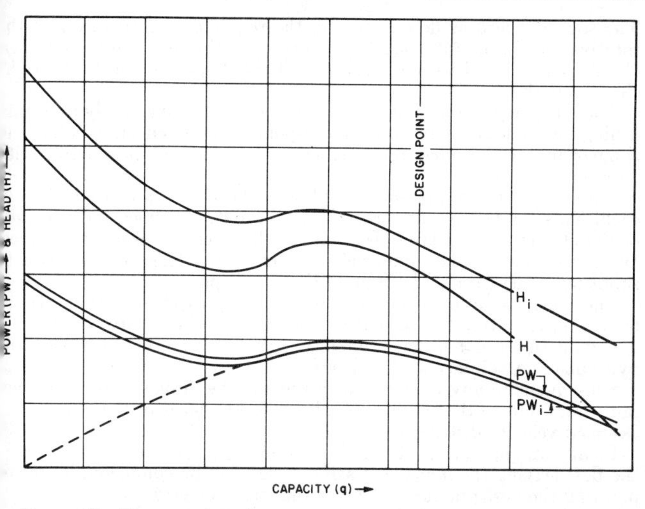

Figure 97—Theoretical Performance Characteristics for Axial Flow Fans

acity. Actual head-capacity characteristics frequently dip before rising
o the shutoff head.

The power-capacity characteristics of axial flow fans roughly parallel
he head-capacity curves as indicated by

$$PW_i = m\left(\frac{U^2}{g_c} - \frac{Uq \cot \alpha_2}{g_c\, A_{2ax}}\right). \tag{253}$$

The decrease in the bracketed term generally outweighs any increases
ı mass flow rate (m) over design, so ideal power (PW_i) decreases. At
apacities below that required to prevent stall the actual flow rate due to
irculating around the blade increases with head far faster than the net
ow rate decreases. This produces a rising characteristic towards shutoff.

)ver-all Design

As with centrifugal fans, only the design of an individual fan for a
pecific requirement will be treated here. The design of a line or several
nes of fans for a range of requirements will be discussed in the chapter
n fan laws. In addition, a single stage fan employing discharge vanes
ill be assumed.

The first step in design is to decide on a speed of operation. This may be
pecified or limited due to a requirement for direct connection to a prime
ıover. Reynolds number effects favor large low-speed units. Economy
ue to reduction in size favors small high-speed units.

Once the speed is selected the next step is to establish a reasonable trial
ze on the basis of past experience or by a trial and error method or both.

The specific speed as determined by the required performance and th rotative speed is useful in establishing the hub-tip ratio and the number chordal length, and various angles of the blades, all of which affect th size required.

The adequacy of the trial size may be checked conveniently by estab lishing the blade geometry at the corresponding mean effective radius an comparing the expected performance, based on empirical data, wit requirements.

Empirical data are presented as plots of head (Ψ) and capacity (Φ coefficients against specific speed (N_s). All three are defined and discusse in the chapter on fan laws. The data itself covers a variety of designs Where possible the data published by various investigators was used t supplement the data of the Buffalo Forge Company.

The need for adjustments of the trial design can be established a least approximately by calculating the ideal head-capacity relationshi including an estimated deviation effect and by correcting for reasonabl hydraulic and volumetric efficiencies.

Subsequent to any necessary adjustments the design at several othe radii from hub to tip may be completed on the basis of the required o assumed velocity distribution.

Finally an appropriate stator vane assembly can be designed to matc the flow leaving the impeller. Casing design can be completed by incor porating the best practical inlet and diffuser geometry.

The above procedure is detailed in the following paragraphs on design After a reasonable design is established it should be proved by tests.

Design Radii

The mean effective radius (R_m) of an axial flow fan may be defined a that radius which divides the flow into two equal parts. Assuming a uni form axial velocity across the section the mean radius in terms of ti and hub radii (R_T and R_H) is

$$R_m{}^2 = \frac{R_T{}^2 + R_H{}^2}{2} = \frac{R_T{}^2}{2}\left[1 + \left(\frac{R_H}{R_T}\right)^2\right]. \qquad (254$$

The mean effective radius as defined above is used in the calculation o the head and capacity coefficients which appear below. The head gener ated at the mean effective radius is equal to the total integrated hea whether free vortex or solid rotation flow is assumed.

Experience indicates that there is an optimum hub-tip ratio (R_H/R_T for each value of specific speed (N_s). High ratios are required for hig pressure fans and low ratios are required when only low heads are to b developed. The relationship between optimum hub-tip ratio and specifi speed is indicated in Figure 98. A range of values is shown since there i also some variation with the number and solidity of the blades.

The specific speed (N_s) can be determined from the required capacit (q), total head (H), and rotative speed (N). These values together wit the mean effective radius and hub-tip ratio also determine the head an capacity coefficients (Ψ and Φ):

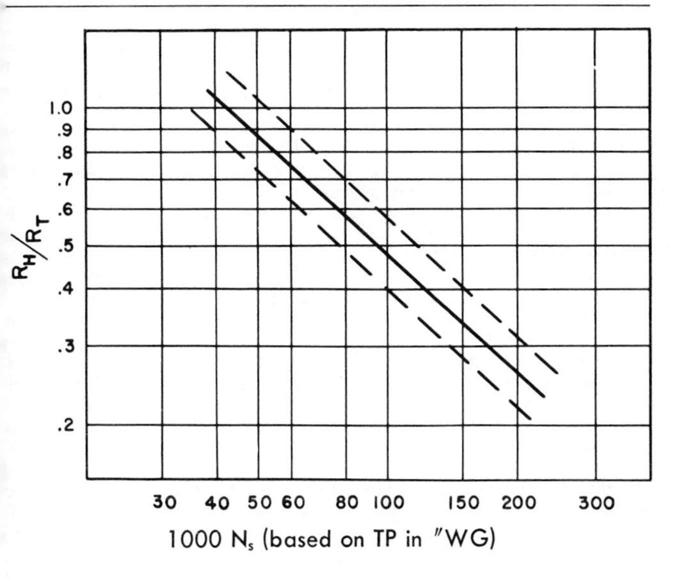

Figure 98—Optimum Hub-Tip Ratios for Axial Flow Fans

$$\Phi_m = \frac{\dfrac{q}{\pi\,(R_T^2 - R_H^2)}}{2\,\pi\,N\,R_m} = \frac{q}{4\,\pi^2\,N\,R_m^3}\left[\frac{1 + \left(\dfrac{R_H}{R_T}\right)^2}{1 - \left(\dfrac{R_H}{R_T}\right)^2}\right] \text{ and} \quad (255)$$

$$\Psi'_m = \frac{g_c\,H}{(2\,\pi\,N\,R_m)^2} = \frac{g_c\,H}{4\,\pi^2\,N^2\,R_m^2}. \quad (256)$$

Any consistent set of units may be used to determine the values of these dimensionless groups. Blockage due to blade thickness has been disregarded in Equation 255.

Preliminary values of these coefficients may be obtained for a trial value of R_m. Equation 254 may be used with the hub-tip ratio corresponding to the required specific speed to determine the hub and tip radii.

Number and Solidity of Blades

The optimum number of blades (n_{bl}) is also a function of specific speed. An approximation of the optimum number may be determined from the hub and tip radii as indicated by

$$n_{bl} = \frac{6\ R_H}{R_T - R_H} = \frac{6\ \dfrac{R_H}{R_T}}{1 - \dfrac{R_H}{R_T}}. \tag{257}$$

The solidity of the blades as indicated by the ratio of the chord length to the blade spacing (x_c/x_p) more or less determines the capacity per revolution at design for a given blade angle. The blade spacing or pitch (x_p) is simply the circumference at a particular radius $(2\pi\ R)$ divided by the number of blades (n_{bl}). The chord length of the blade (x_c) is the distance between the leading and trailing edges at the same radius.

From an aerodynamic standpoint the chord length should increase from hub to tip. From a structural standpoint the reverse is preferred. As a compromise, many designers employ an almost constant chord over the entire blade length.

The blade spacing increases from hub to tip. A pitch-chord ratio near unity is frequently employed at the mean effective radius. Very good efficiencies have been obtained with pitch-chord ratios of 4:1 or higher.

The effect of pitch-chord ratio on capacity is included in Figure 99. This chart indicates a preferred value of $(\Phi x_p/x_c)_m$ for each value of specific speed (N_s).

Some variation from the preferred value can be tolerated. The chart is based entirely on the performance of rather conventional designs of vaneaxial fans without prerotation. The pitch-chord ratio (x_p/x_c) cor-

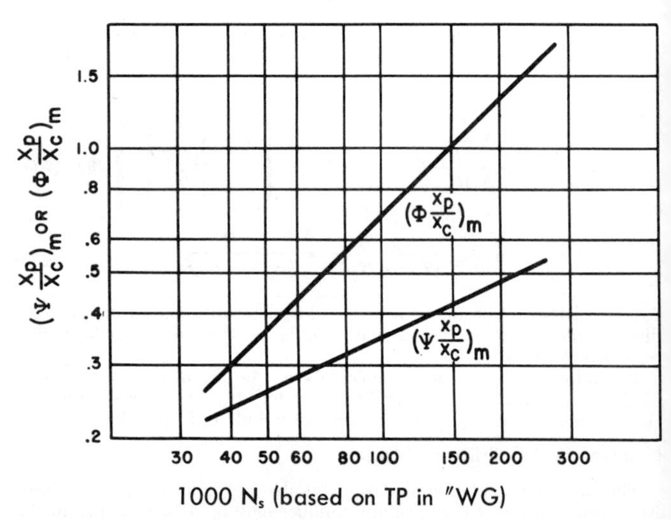

Figure 99—Mean Head and Capacity Coefficients for Axial Flow Fans

responding to the required capacity coefficient (Φ) and the chart values of $(\Phi x_p/x_c)_m$ can be determined by simple algebra.

The optimum values of $(\Psi x_p/x_c)_m$ are also plotted vs specific speed (N_s) in Figure 99. The pitch-chord ratio $(x_p/x_c)_m$ corresponding to the required head coefficient and the chart value of $(\Psi x_p/x_c)_m$ must agree with that calculated from $(\Phi x_p/x_c)_m$. Although some variation can be tolerated without sacrificing efficiency, any appreciable discrepancy between the two calculated values of $(x_p/x_c)_m$ generally indicates that a different trial value for the mean effective radius should be investigated.

Decreasing pitch-chord ratio (i.e., closer blade spacing) improves fluid guidance and therefore within limits increases head. This effect is indicated in Figure 99. Relative guidance is also a function of the discharge blade angle.

Blade Angles

Axial flow blades are generally designed on the basis of a uniform axial component of velocity across the annulus for the entire blade passage. With no inlet guide vanes there will be no prerotation at the design point. The blades may be twisted in various ways to produce different vortex flow patterns including those necessary to give constant head or constant dimensionless head along the radius.

The leading edge blade angles (β_1) should be designed to match the fluid angles (α_1) at the rotor inlet. Occasionally a slight positive incidence will be desirable on a fan with a solidity less than unity in order to obtain the maximum possible head. Small values of negative incidence are sometimes incorporated in the design of a fan with a solidity greater than unity so that the danger of stall will be reduced.

The linear rotor velocity (U) varies directly as the radius. Therefore the relative velocity (V_{1rel}) increases and the fluid angle (α_1) decreases with radius from hub to tip. If the blade angles (β_1) are to match the fluid angles at entrance, the leading edge of the blade must be twisted accordingly.

The trailing edge blade angle $(\beta_2)_m$ at the mean effective radius must be designed to produce the required head. This angle may be determined from the theoretical fluid angle $(\alpha_2)_m$ based on Equation 252 and the expected deviation $(\beta_2 - \alpha_2)$ from Equation 251. It may also be determined from experimental data such as that in Figure 100. The value of $(\beta_2)_m$ may be obtained from the chart value of $(\beta_2 - \beta_1)_m$ and the required value of $(\beta_1)_m$. Figure 100 includes the effect of fluid deviation which may explain the spread in camber values at higher head coefficients. The discharge angles at other radii may be determined by constructing the appropriate velocity triangles.

Free vortex design requires that the product of the tangential component of the absolute velocity (V_{tang}) times the radius (R) be constant along the blade from hub to tip at both inlet and outlet. The resulting constant change in whirl leads to a constant head (H) generation at all radii. Figure 100 is based principally on designs of this type.

Solid rotation design requires that the quotient of the tangential component of the absolute velocity divided by the radius be constant along the radius. The change in whirl and therefore the head generation is

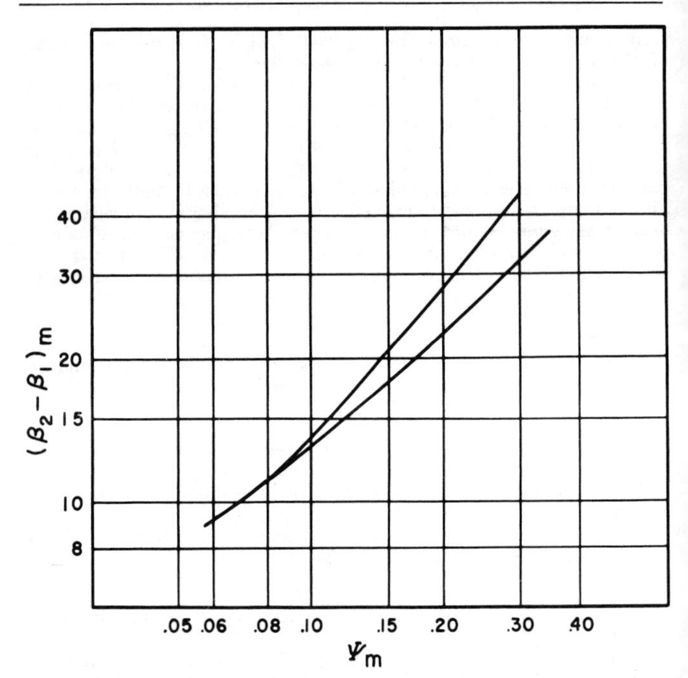

Figure 100—Mean Camber for Axial Flow Fans

proportional to the square of the radius. This leads to a constant dimensionless head (Ψ') at all radii.

Various other designs which are based on other forced vortex patterns are also used.

The performance of a fan can be altered by changing the blade setting or stagger angle (γ). Increased stagger produces an equal increase in inlet and discharge angles and therefore an increase in capacity without affecting head. With limited changes the efficiency is practically constant. The change in capacity is proportional to the change in the tangent of the inlet angle (β_1).

Blade Profile

The inlet angles (β_1), discharge angles (β_2), and the chord length (x_c) at various radii may be determined from the preceding data.

The mean thickness line of the blade should be a smooth curve whose tangents form the necessary angles with the direction of rotation at the leading and trailing edges.

Various combinations of circular and parabolic arcs are used for the mean line. One convenient method of construction is to locate the point of maximum camber $(x_b)_{max}$ at the same chordwise position as the intersection of the two tangents mentioned above. The amount of the maximum camber $(y_b)_{max}$ should be one half the displacement of the intersection above the chord. Numerous other tangent lines can be constructed by dividing the edge tangents into a number of equal segments and connecting corresponding points by straight lines.

The blade profile should generally be as thin and as polished as possible. Streamlined airfoil shaped sections are usually used although thin sheets of constant thickness are often employed with good results.

Most good airfoils have about the same thickness (y_t) variation with chordwise position. The maximum thickness may be located 30 to 50 per cent of the chord from the leading edge. The maximum thickness is generally of the order of 10% of the chord. The leading edge should be rounded to provide tolerance to variation in incidence. Ideally the trailing edge should be tapered to a point. For structural reasons this too is rounded. The maximum thickness may be increased toward the hub for the same reason, especially if the chord is not decreased toward the tip.

Discharge Vane and Casing Design

The discharge vanes transform the kinetic energy produced by the impeller in the form of whirl into more useful pressure energy. To make this transformation efficiently, the air discharged from the impeller must be guided through a gradual turn until the tangential component is eliminated. If the resulting axial velocity is still too high a diffuser may be employed for additional energy transformation. The discharge vanes and diffuser are sometimes combined. The entrance angles of the discharge or diffuser vanes should match the fluid angles at the impeller exit within a few degrees. The exit angles should be 90^0 (i.e., axial) at all radii. The axial distance between the blades and the vanes should be roughly 10% of the tip diameter. Closer spacing may be preferred for operation at the design point only. Larger spacings are preferred when operation at capacities other than design is contemplated. The wider spacing allows more time for the air to adjust itself for any difference in fluid and vane entrance angles. The number of vanes and their length are related for good design. The solidity at the mean effective radius should be near unity. The number should also be selected to provide a reasonable hydraulic radius. Vane length at the hub may be somewhat shorter than at the tip to compensate for the closer spacing.

The casing itself should be cylindrical over the blades. The clearance at this point should be the minimum practical value in order to limit leakage. Radial running clearances of about 0.001 inches per inch of impeller OD are frequently used where both the impeller and the housing can be machined. The use of larger clearances involves a sacrifice in efficiency.

Additional guiding surfaces are required inside the casing. They should provide a smooth transition between the annular passage over the hub and the cylindrical or other shaped passages both upstream and downstream. Streamlined stationary nose pieces or tail pieces or both, supported by vanes, may be used to house the bearings or other drive elements. One

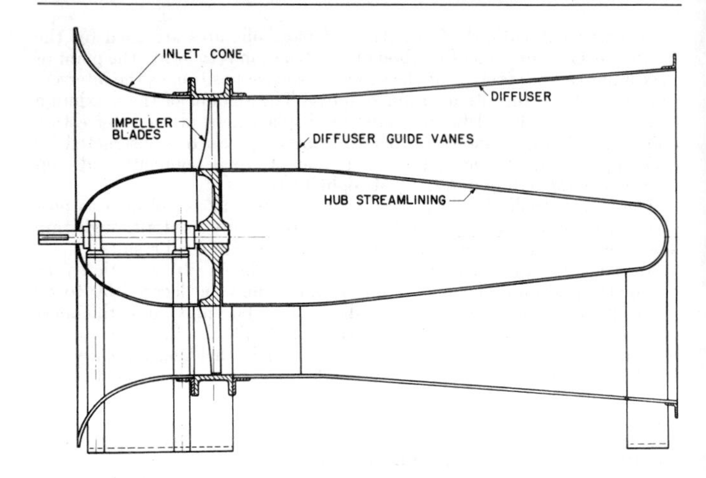

Figure 101 —Casing Design for Fully Streamlined Vaneaxial Fans

or the other of these devices may be incorporated on the rotor assembly.

Inlet bells or diffuser cones may be required for efficient operation depending on inlet and outlet conditions.

Noise Characteristics

The noise characteristics of axial flow fans are very similar to those of centrifugal fans. Refer to Chapter 6 for details on the latter. The division of fan noise into rotational tones and broad band vortex components applies to both types.

In axial flow apparatus the predominant tone of the rotational component may be one of the higher harmonics rather than the fundamental blade passing frequency, if the fan is used to develop appreciable pressure.

Increases in the number of blades generally have more effect on axial fan noise since the total number of blades is usually less than for a centrifugal fan. The number of blades should differ from the number of guide vanes to prevent strengthening of the fundamental tone or the major harmonics even though certain product frequencies are created thereby.

The effects of streamlining on leading edge vortices and side separation eddies are the same for both axials and centrifugals. The effect of trailing edge thickness is more pronounced in axials. There may be a noticeable increase in noise if the wake from one blade is cut by succeeding blades.

The sound power level curve for a vaneaxial fan is shown in Figure 101 together with other performance characteristics. This curve is typical for all axial flow fan types. The overall shape of the curve is slightly different from that for a centrifugal, consistent with the difference in pressure-

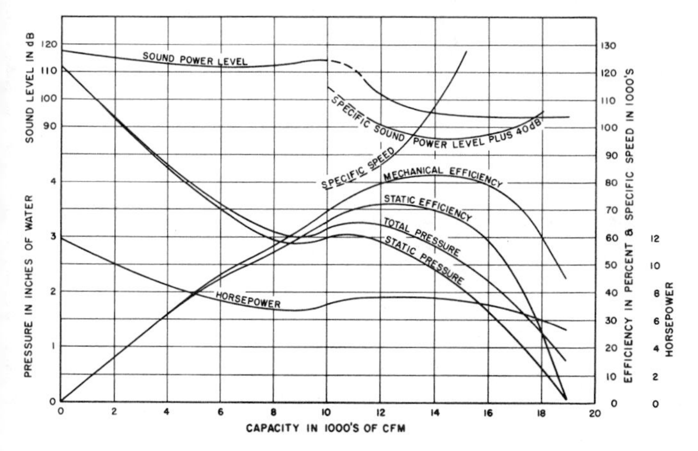

Figure 102 —Typical Constant Speed Performance Curves for Vaneaxial Fans

capacity curves. The specific sound power level curves are substantially the same—both indicating a minimum at the best efficiency point. The spectrum for a high pressure vaneaxial fan may be approximated in most cases by subtracting 18, 15, 8, 5, 5, 8, 18, and 27 dB from the over-all level to obtain the levels in the first through eighth octave bands, respectively. The corresponding values for a low pressure propeller fan are 5, 5, 7, 9, 15, 18, 25 and 30 dB.

CHAPTER 8

FAN LAWS

The fan laws relate the performance variables for any homologous series of fans. The variables involved are fan size ($SIZE$), rotative speed (RPM), gas density (δ), capacity (CFM), fan total pressure (FTP), horsepower (HP), sound power level (PWL), and efficiency (η).

The fan laws are the mathematical expression of the fact that when two fans are both members of a homologous series their performance curves are homologous. At the same "point of rating," i.e., at similarly situated points of operation, efficiencies are equal. The ratios of all the other variables are interrelated.

The ten fan laws given in Table **58** can be used to predict the performance of any fan when test data for a fan of the same series is available. The subscript a denotes that the variable is for the fan under consideration. The subscript b indicates that the variable is for the tested fan.

Fan Law Number 1 predicts the effect of changing size, speed, or density on capacity, pressure, power, and sound power level. For convenience density is always shown as an independent variable and sound power level is always shown as a dependent variable. Of the remaining five variables, a different pair is shown as the independent variable in each of the ten laws. Fan static pressure or fan velocity pressure may be substituted for fan total pressure.

Fan Law Restrictions

Before the fan laws can be used to predict the performance of a fan at any point of rating, it is necessary to have test data for a fan of the same series at the same point of rating. If test data are lacking, the methods for predicting performance which are outlined in the preceding chapters on Centrifugal and Axial Flow Fans must be employed instead of the fan laws.

The use of the fan laws is restricted to cases where the linear dimensions of the fan under consideration are all proportional to the corresponding dimensions of the fan for which test data are available. The proportionality factor is the size ratio. In the fan laws any convenient dimension may be used for "SIZE."

Another restriction is that the fluid velocities in the fan under consideration must be proportional to the corresponding velocities in the tested fan. The proportionality factor is the ratio of peripheral speeds for any pair of similarly situated points on the rotors. Such a condition is established if the two fans have the same point of rating.

TABLE 58—FAN LAWS 1 through 5

For all Fan Laws: $\eta_a = \eta_b$ and $(\text{pt. of rtg.})_a = (\text{pt. of rtg.})_b$

No.	Dependent Variables		Independent Variables					
1a	CFM_a	$= CFM_b$	$\times$	$\left(\frac{SIZE_a}{SIZE_b}\right)^{3}$	$\times$	$\left(\frac{RPM_a}{RPM_b}\right)^{1}$	$\times$	$\left(1\right)$
1b	FTP_a	$= FTP_b$	$\times$	$\left(\frac{SIZE_a}{SIZE_b}\right)^{2}$	$\times$	$\left(\frac{RPM_a}{RPM_b}\right)^{2}$	$\times$	$\left(\frac{\delta_a}{\delta_b}\right)$
1c	HP_a	$= HP_b$	$\times$	$\left(\frac{SIZE_a}{SIZE_b}\right)^{5}$	$\times$	$\left(\frac{RPM_a}{RPM_b}\right)^{3}$	$\times$	$\left(\frac{\delta_a}{\delta_b}\right)$
1d	PWL_a	$= PWL_b$	$+ 70 \log_{10}$	$\left(\frac{SIZE_a}{SIZE_b}\right)$	$+ 50 \log_{10}$	$\left(\frac{RPM_a}{RPM_b}\right)$	$+ 20 \log_{10}$	$\left(\frac{\delta_a}{\delta_b}\right)$
2a	CFM_a	$= CFM_b$	$\times$	$\left(\frac{SIZE_a}{SIZE_b}\right)^{2}$	$\times$	$\left(\frac{FTP_a}{FTP_b}\right)^{1/2}$	$\times$	$\left(\frac{\delta_b}{\delta_a}\right)^{1/2}$
2b	RPM_a	$= RPM_b$	$\times$	$\left(\frac{SIZE_b}{SIZE_a}\right)^{1}$	$\times$	$\left(\frac{FTP_a}{FTP_b}\right)^{1/2}$	$\times$	$\left(\frac{\delta_b}{\delta_a}\right)^{1/2}$
2c	HP_a	$= HP_b$	$\times$	$\left(\frac{SIZE_a}{SIZE_b}\right)^{2}$	$\times$	$\left(\frac{FTP_a}{FTP_b}\right)^{3/2}$	$\times$	$\left(\frac{\delta_b}{\delta_a}\right)^{1/2}$
2d	PWL_a	$= PWL_b$	$+ 20 \log_{10}$	$\left(\frac{SIZE_a}{SIZE_b}\right)$	$+ 25 \log_{10}$	$\left(\frac{FTP_a}{FTP_b}\right)$	$- 5 \log_{10}$	$\left(\frac{\delta_a}{\delta_b}\right)$
3a	RPM_a	$= RPM_b$	$\times$	$\left(\frac{SIZE_b}{SIZE_a}\right)^{3}$	$\times$	$\left(\frac{CFM_a}{CFM_b}\right)^{1}$	$\times$	$\left(1\right)$
3b	FTP_a	$= FTP_b$	$\times$	$\left(\frac{SIZE_b}{SIZE_a}\right)^{4}$	$\times$	$\left(\frac{CFM_a}{CFM_b}\right)^{2}$	$\times$	$\left(\frac{\delta_a}{\delta_b}\right)$
3c	HP_a	$= HP_b$	$\times$	$\left(\frac{SIZE_b}{SIZE_a}\right)^{4}$	$\times$	$\left(\frac{CFM_a}{CFM_b}\right)^{3}$	$\times$	$\left(\frac{\delta_a}{\delta_b}\right)$
3d	PWL_a	$= PWL_b$	$- 80 \log_{10}$	$\left(\frac{SIZE_a}{SIZE_b}\right)$	$+ 50 \log_{10}$	$\left(\frac{CFM_a}{CFM_b}\right)$	$+ 20 \log_{10}$	$\left(\frac{\delta_a}{\delta_b}\right)$
4a	CFM_a	$= CFM_b$	$\times$	$\left(\frac{SIZE_a}{SIZE_b}\right)^{4/3}$	$\times$	$\left(\frac{HP_a}{HP_b}\right)^{1/3}$	$\times$	$\left(\frac{\delta_b}{\delta_a}\right)^{1/3}$
4b	FTP_a	$= FTP_b$	$\times$	$\left(\frac{SIZE_b}{SIZE_a}\right)^{4/3}$	$\times$	$\left(\frac{HP_a}{HP_b}\right)^{2/3}$	$\times$	$\left(\frac{\delta_a}{\delta_b}\right)^{1/3}$
4c	RPM_a	$= RPM_b$	$\times$	$\left(\frac{SIZE_b}{SIZE_a}\right)^{5/3}$	$\times$	$\left(\frac{HP_a}{HP_b}\right)^{1/3}$	$\times$	$\left(\frac{\delta_b}{\delta_a}\right)^{1/3}$
4d	PWL_a	$= PWL_b$	$- 13.3 \log_{10}$	$\left(\frac{SIZE_a}{SIZE_b}\right)$	$+ 16.6 \log_{10}$	$\left(\frac{HP_a}{HP_b}\right)$	$+ 3.3 \log_{10}$	$\left(\frac{\delta_a}{\delta_b}\right)$
5a	$SIZE_a$	$= SIZE_b$	$\times$	$\left(\frac{CFM_a}{CFM_b}\right)^{1/2}$	$\times$	$\left(\frac{FTP_b}{FTP_a}\right)^{1/4}$	$\times$	$\left(\frac{\delta_a}{\delta_b}\right)^{1/4}$
5b	RPM_a	$= RPM_b$	$\times$	$\left(\frac{CFM_b}{CFM_a}\right)^{1/2}$	$\times$	$\left(\frac{FTP_a}{FTP_b}\right)^{3/4}$	$\times$	$\left(\frac{\delta_b}{\delta_a}\right)^{3/4}$
5c	HP_a	$= HP_b$	$\times$	$\left(\frac{CFM_a}{CFM_b}\right)^{1}$	$\times$	$\left(\frac{FTP_a}{FTP_b}\right)^{1}$	$\times$	$\left(1\right)$
5d	PWL_a	$= PWL_b$	$+ 10 \log_{10}$	$\left(\frac{CFM_a}{CFM_b}\right)$	$+ 20 \log_{10}$	$\left(\frac{FTP_a}{FTP_b}\right)$	$+ 0 \log_{10}$	$\left(\frac{\delta_a}{\delta_b}\right)$

FAN LAWS 6 through 10—TABLE 58

For all Fan Laws: $\eta_a = \eta_b$ and (pt. of rtg.)$_a$ = (pt. of rtg.)$_b$

No.	Dependent Variables			Independent Variables				
6a	$SIZE_a$	$= SIZE_b$	$\times$	$\left(\frac{CFM_a}{CFM_b}\right)^{1/3}$	$\times$	$\left(\frac{RPM_b}{RPM_a}\right)^{1/3}$	$\times$	(1)
6b	FTP_a	$= FTP_b$	$\times$	$\left(\frac{CFM_a}{CFM_b}\right)^{2/3}$	$\times$	$\left(\frac{RPM_a}{RPM_b}\right)^{4/3}$	$\times$	$\left(\frac{\delta_a}{\delta_b}\right)^{1}$
6c	HP_a	$= HP_b$	$\times$	$\left(\frac{CFM_a}{CFM_b}\right)^{5/3}$	$\times$	$\left(\frac{RPM_a}{RPM_b}\right)^{4/3}$	$\times$	$\left(\frac{\delta_a}{\delta_b}\right)^{1}$
6d	PWL_a	$= PWL_b$	$+ 23.3 \log_{10}$	$\left(\frac{CFM_a}{CFM_b}\right)$	$+ 26.6 \log_{10}$	$\left(\frac{RPM_a}{RPM_b}\right)$	$+ 20 \log_{10}$	$\left(\frac{\delta_a}{\delta_b}\right)$
7a	$SIZE_a$	$= SIZE_b$	$\times$	$\left(\frac{FTP_a}{FTP_b}\right)^{1/2}$	$\times$	$\left(\frac{RPM_b}{RPM_a}\right)^{1}$	$\times$	$\left(\frac{\delta_b}{\delta_a}\right)^{1/2}$
7b	CFM_a	$= CFM_b$	$\times$	$\left(\frac{FTP_a}{FTP_b}\right)^{3/2}$	$\times$	$\left(\frac{RPM_b}{RPM_a}\right)^{2}$	$\times$	$\left(\frac{\delta_b}{\delta_a}\right)^{3/2}$
7c	HP_a	$= HP_b$	$\times$	$\left(\frac{FTP_a}{FTP_b}\right)^{5/2}$	$\times$	$\left(\frac{RPM_b}{RPM_a}\right)^{2}$	$\times$	$\left(\frac{\delta_b}{\delta_a}\right)^{3/2}$
7d	PWL_a	$= PWL_b$	$+ 35 \log_{10}$	$\left(\frac{FTP_a}{FTP_b}\right)$	$- 20 \log_{10}$	$\left(\frac{RPM_a}{RPM_b}\right)$	$- 15 \log_{10}$	$\left(\frac{\delta_a}{\delta_b}\right)$
8a	$SIZE_a$	$= SIZE_b$	$\times$	$\left(\frac{HP_b}{HP_a}\right)^{1/4}$	$\times$	$\left(\frac{CFM_a}{CFM_b}\right)^{3/4}$	$\times$	$\left(\frac{\delta_a}{\delta_b}\right)^{1/4}$
8b	RPM_a	$= RPM_b$	$\times$	$\left(\frac{HP_a}{HP_b}\right)^{3/4}$	$\times$	$\left(\frac{CFM_b}{CFM_a}\right)^{5/4}$	$\times$	$\left(\frac{\delta_b}{\delta_a}\right)^{3/4}$
8c	FTP_a	$= FTP_b$	$\times$	$\left(\frac{HP_a}{HP_b}\right)^{1}$	$\times$	$\left(\frac{CFM_b}{CFM_a}\right)^{1}$	$\times$	(1)
8d	PWL_a	$= PWL_b$	$+ 20 \log_{10}$	$\left(\frac{HP_a}{HP_b}\right)$	$- 10 \log_{10}$	$\left(\frac{CFM_a}{CFM_b}\right)$	$+ 0 \log_{10}$	$\left(\frac{\delta_a}{\delta_b}\right)$
9a	$SIZE_a$	$= SIZE_b$	$\times$	$\left(\frac{HP_a}{HP_b}\right)^{1/2}$	$\times$	$\left(\frac{FTP_b}{FTP_a}\right)^{3/4}$	$\times$	$\left(\frac{\delta_a}{\delta_b}\right)^{1/4}$
9b	RPM_a	$= RPM_b$	$\times$	$\left(\frac{HP_b}{HP_a}\right)^{1/2}$	$\times$	$\left(\frac{FTP_a}{FTP_b}\right)^{5/4}$	$\times$	$\left(\frac{\delta_b}{\delta_a}\right)^{3/4}$
9c	CFM_a	$= CFM_b$	$\times$	$\left(\frac{HP_a}{HP_b}\right)^{1}$	$\times$	$\left(\frac{FTP_b}{FTP_a}\right)^{1}$	$\times$	(1)
9d	PWL_a	$= PWL_b$	$+ 10 \log_{10}$	$\left(\frac{HP_a}{HP_b}\right)$	$+ 10 \log_{10}$	$\left(\frac{FTP_a}{FTP_b}\right)$	$+ 0 \log_{10}$	$\left(\frac{\delta_a}{\delta_b}\right)$
10a	$SIZE_a$	$= SIZE_b$	$\times$	$\left(\frac{HP_a}{HP_b}\right)^{1/5}$	$\times$	$\left(\frac{RPM_b}{RPM_a}\right)^{3/5}$	$\times$	$\left(\frac{\delta_b}{\delta_a}\right)^{1/5}$
10b	CFM_a	$= CFM_b$	$\times$	$\left(\frac{HP_a}{HP_b}\right)^{3/5}$	$\times$	$\left(\frac{RPM_b}{RPM_a}\right)^{4/5}$	$\times$	$\left(\frac{\delta_b}{\delta_a}\right)^{3/5}$
10c	FTP_a	$= FTP_b$	$\times$	$\left(\frac{HP_a}{HP_b}\right)^{2/5}$	$\times$	$\left(\frac{RPM_a}{RPM_b}\right)^{4/5}$	$\times$	$\left(\frac{\delta_a}{\delta_b}\right)^{3/5}$
10d	PWL_a	$= PWL_b$	$+ 14 \log_{10}$	$\left(\frac{HP_a}{HP_b}\right)$	$+ 8 \log_{10}$	$\left(\frac{RPM_a}{RPM_b}\right)$	$+ 6 \log_{10}$	$\left(\frac{\delta_a}{\delta_b}\right)$

Still other restrictions on the ranges of sizes and speeds may necessitate the use of correction factors. These include size factors and compressibility factors. The validity of the fan laws within these limitations has been verified by test.

Similarity

The fan laws may be derived by various methods of reasoning. Close examination of the theoretical expressions for head and power will lead to the correct conclusions. Dimensional analysis may also be employed. Various texts present these methods in various ways. Complete similarity in any case requires geometric, kinematic, and dynamic similarity.

Geometric similarity requires not only the linear proportionality mentioned above but complete angular equality and no omission or addition of parts. Theoretically, both roughnesses and thicknesses should be proportional to size. Fortunately, considerable variations can be tolerated without invalidating the fan laws. However, the effects of any compromise in geometric similarity should be thoroughly investigated in any case.

Kinematic similarity requires the proportionality of corresponding fluid velocities to peripheral speed. Therefore, capacities should be proportional to peripheral speed times size squared.

Dynamic similarity requires that the fluid forces throughout the fan under consideration be proportional to the corresponding fluid forces throughout the tested fan. The constant of proportionality is the ratio of what may be called the inertia forces for two similarly located fluid particles. The inertia force of a fluid on a unit area is proportional to the mass density and to the velocity squared.

The most important force in the fluid insofar as a fan is concerned is the pressure force. The requirement that the ratio of pressure forces equal the ratio of inertia forces leads directly to the fan laws as given in Table 58.

The somewhat less important forces in the fluid include those due to elasticity, viscosity, gravity, and surface tension. The ratio of the inertia force to the force corresponding to each of these fluid properties leads to the Mach, Reynolds, Froude, and Weber numbers respectively. The equality of these dimensionless groups is a requirement of dynamic similarity. Only the first two are of much importance in fans. The fan laws are based on incompressible flow with equal Mach and Reynolds numbers at corresponding points. If there is any significant variation of either, a correction factor must be applied to the fan laws.

Model Testing and Size Effect

The fan laws indicate that the performance of a full size fan can be predicted exactly from a test of a smaller size model. The accuracy of such predictions is sufficient for most engineering applications. Complete similarity, however, does require that the Reynolds numbers be equal. A considerable variation in Reynolds number can be tolerated only if complete turbulence exists in each case. Significant effects accompany any variation at lower Reynolds numbers.

Three factors determine the Reynolds number of a fan passage: the size of the passage, the velocity, and the kinematic viscosity of the fluid.

In some types of model testing, the effect of changing size can be nullified by adjusting the kinematic viscosity either through a change in fluids or a change in temperature. This is not usually practicable with fans.

The results obtained from model tests will be somewhat conservative. For this reason published data on fans should either be based on tests of the actual size or stepped up from model tests but not stepped down from tests involving larger size fans.

A model, to comply with the requirements for geometric similarity, should have the same relative roughness and relative clearances as the full size fan. Both are difficult to achieve in practice since the full size fan will generally incorporate the minimum practical roughness and clearances.

The effect of increased relative roughness is to increase hydraulic losses and, therefore, lower over-all efficiency. If the precise Reynolds numbers and relative roughnesses for all portions of the flow passages could be evaluated, Figure 27 could be used to estimate their effect on hydraulic losses.

Increases in relative clearance produce increased leakage and, therefore, decreased overall efficiencies. If the pressure heads across the leakage channels can be evaluated, the effect of changes in relative clearance can be determined.

The effects listed above will vary from one series of fans to another so that any general formulations for correcting fan law predictions cannot possibly be correct in all cases. A very approximate expression for the effect of fan size (*SIZE*) on static efficiency (η_S) is

$$\frac{1 - (\eta_S)_a}{1 - (\eta_S)_b} = 0.5 + 0.5\left(\frac{SIZE_b}{SIZE_a}\right)^{0.2}. \qquad (258)$$

This expression is based on tests of only one series of fan. The Reynolds number ratio should be substituted for the size ratio in cases involving different fluid velocities or different fluid viscosities. Two similar fans, each required to develop the same pressure, must operate with equal velocities regardless of size.

The above considerations on leakage and hydraulic losses suggest that predictions from model tests based on the fan laws alone would indicate a higher rotative speed for a full size fan than is actually necessary. Such is usually the case.

Compressibility

The fan laws indicate that the performance of a high pressure fan can be predicted from test data on a low pressure fan and vice versa. Even assuming that Reynolds number and size effects are negligible, correction will still be needed. Complete dynamic similarity requires equal Mach numbers. High pressures require higher velocities than low pressures when identical fluids are involved. This leads to a difference in Mach numbers.

When the Mach numbers are both considerably smaller than unity, the need for fan law corrections is due to the difference in volume change through the fans. This is frequently called compressibility effect. The magnitude of this effect increases with increased differences in pressure development between the test fan and the fan under consideration. The effect is negligible for differences of about 10 inches water gage or so. To ignore the effect in any case involving high pressure predictions from low pressure tests is conservative as will be apparent shortly.

Mach numbers vary throughout the impeller. When they approach unity at any point, critical conditions develop as discussed in Chapter 3. Since the flow rate becomes limited, the condition is usually described as choking. The performance of turbomachines operated at higher and higher speeds gradually departs more and more from the fan laws due to choking. Choking is due to locally high velocities regardless of pressure. Such effects may be significant with small high speed equipment but in most fan engineering they can be ignored.

Compressibility effects are due to differences in the pressure developed regardless of velocity. Compressibility factors may be derived from basic hydraulic and thermodynamic considerations.

The basic hydraulic formula for the power (PW) delivered to an incompressible fluid flowing through the machine in terms of the volume rate (CFM) in cfm or any other units and the pressure developed ($P_2 - P_1$) in consistent units is

$$PW = CFM\,(P_2 - P_1). \tag{259}$$

The corresponding thermodynamic expression for polytropic compression in terms of the entering and leaving volumes (CFM_1 and CFM_2) and pressures (P_1 and P'_2) is

$$PW = \frac{CFM_2\,P'_2 - CFM_1\,P_1}{n - 1} + CFM_2\,P'_2 - CFM_1\,P_1. \tag{260}$$

The polytropic exponent (n) may be determined from Equation 245. The absolute discharge pressure (P'_2) for compressible flow will be higher than that for incompressible flow if power, capacity at inlet, and pressure at inlet are equal.

It is generally assumed that the fan laws apply to the inlet volumes (CFM_1). This will be assumed in the following even though there are some strong arguments favoring the use of discharge volumes (CFM_2).

A compressibility factor (K_p) may be used to relate the pressures developed in the two cases:

$$(P_2 - P_1) = (P'_2 - P_1)\,K_p. \tag{261}$$

By setting the right hand portions of Equations 259 and 260 equal to each other, it can be shown after considerable algebraic manipulation that

$$K_p = \frac{\dfrac{n}{n-1}\left[\left(\dfrac{P_2}{P_1}\right)^{\frac{n-1}{n}} - 1\right]}{\left(\dfrac{P_2}{P_1} - 1\right)}. \tag{262}$$

Although either gage or absolute pressures may be used in Equation 261 only absolute pressures may be inserted into Equation 262. Note too that the incompressible values of the discharge pressure should be used although the correction factor is usually so small that it will make little

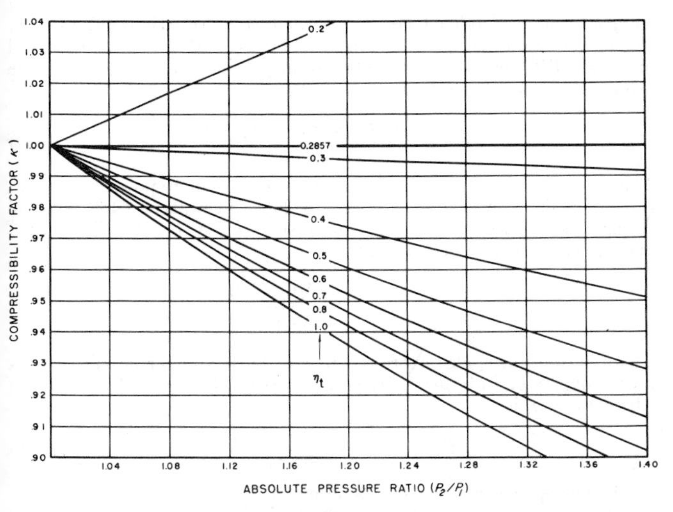

Figure 103—Compressibility Corrections for Fan Laws

Adapted from the data of Test Code for Air Moving Devices, AMCA Standard, 210-67, 1967, pp. 24-25.

---

difference whether incompressible or compressible values are used. Figure 103 is a graphical solution of Equations 262 and 245.

If the fan laws are used to predict compressible flow performance from incompressible flow test data, the capacity and power will be correct but the fan total, velocity, and static pressures must be adjusted as follows:

$$FTP' = FTP/K_p, \tag{263}$$

$$FVP' = FVP/(2K_p - 1), \text{ and} \tag{264}$$

$$FSP' = FTP' - FVP'. \tag{265}$$

The prime mark signifies a compressible flow value. The compressibility factor may be determined from Figure 103. Since the absolute pressure ratio depends on the compressible flow performance which depends on the compressibility factor, a method of successive approximations must be employed. The actual value of total efficiency (η_T) will be the same for compressible and incompressible flow. However, because capacity and power are the same and the fan total pressure is higher for compressible flow, the apparent total efficiency (η'_T) is higher. That is, it would appear that there is a greater output for a given input. This is not true.

Horsepower Formulas

Equations 259 and 260 give the power output of a fan for the incompressible and compressible flow cases. The latter can be simplified by using the compressibility factor (K_p) as defined in Equations **261** and **262**. For power input (HP) in hp, inlet capacity (CFM) in cfm, inlet total pressure (TP_1) in ″WG, and outlet total pressure (TP'_2) in ″WG, the compressible flow formula is

$$HP = \frac{CFM_1\ (TP'_2 - TP_1)\ K_p}{6356\ \eta_T}. \tag{266}$$

The total efficiency (η_T) is the ratio of power output to power input and the conversion constant (*6356*) was developed in Equation 158. For the special case where the flow is incompressible, $K_p = 1$ and $TP'_2 = TP_2$, and the corresponding equation is

$$HP = \frac{CFM_1\ (TP_2 - TP_1)}{6356\ \eta_T}. \tag{267}$$

This relationship is also expressed in Fan Law Number 5c. The horsepower, expressed in terms of fan static pressure ($SP_2 - TP_1$) and static efficiency (η_S), is

$$HP = \frac{CFM_1\ (SP_2 - TP_1)}{6356\ \eta_S}. \tag{268}$$

The horsepower may also be determined from the weight rate of flow (w) in lb per min and the total heads (H) in ft of fluid using

$$HP = \frac{w\ (H_2 - H_1)}{33000\ \eta_T}. \tag{269}$$

The fluid density enters into the weight rate of flow in Equation **269** and into the pressure (equivalent head) in Equation 267.

Equivalent Total Pressure

The fan laws are based on the premise that a fan will develop the same head in feet of fluid flowing regardless of the fluid, all other conditions being equal. This implies that the pressure developed will vary directly with density.

The use of the fan laws can sometimes be simplified by employing a device which can be called equivalent total pressure. Equivalent static pressures may also be used. The term "equivalent" indicates that there are two sets of density conditions involved. One must be that for the actual fan (subscript a) and the other must be that for the base fan (subscript b) for which fan performance is known. These subscripts are the same as those used in the table of fan laws. Equivalent total pressure (ETP) is, therefore, the base fan total pressure (FTP_b) corresponding to the actual fan total pressure (FTP_a) taking into account the difference in density (δ), i.e.,

$$ETP = FTP_b = FTP_a \left(\frac{\delta_b}{\delta_a}\right). \tag{270}$$

The similarity laws apply to systems as well as to fans so that, all other conditions being equal, the pressure required to maintain a certain flow rate through a system will vary directly with density. For kinematic similarity the volume (not weight) flow rate must be constant in both cases.

Unit Capacity

Unit capacity may be defined as the capacity that a certain size fan will handle when it develops a pressure of one inch water gage. The unit capacity and the corresponding speed of rotation will vary from one point of rating to another and from size to size. For any size fan of a particular series, there will be only one unit capacity for each point of rating.

Fan Law Number 2a may be used to determine unit capacity. Using subscript b to denote the base conditions which are known by test and subscript a to denote conditions at the same point of rating but at a pressure of one inch water gage, the unit capacity is equal to CFM_a and FTP_a is unity. When size is constant

$$unit\ capacity = CFM_a = \frac{CFM_b}{\left(FTP_b \frac{\delta_a}{\delta_b}\right)^{1/2}} = \frac{CFM_b}{ETP_b^{1/2}}. \qquad (271)$$

Curves of unit capacity versus efficiency are quite useful in determining the range of ratings for which one series of fan may be superior to another and vice versa. The best series of fans, assuming sizes are the same for each, is that which shows the highest efficiency at the appropriate value of unit capacity ($q/\sqrt{p}$).

Curves of unit capacity versus capacity are useful in preparing multi-rating tables for fans. The appropriate point of rating may be determined by noting the conditions at the appropriate value of $q/\sqrt{p}$. Horsepower can be determined from the appropriate efficiency in Equation 267 or 268. Speed can be determined from Fan Law Number 3a since pressure is known to vary as the capacity squared, as required in Fan Law Number 3b. With size constant

$$RPM_a = RPM_b \frac{CFM_a}{CFM_b}. \qquad (272)$$

The usual multi-rating tables are made up for certain values of pressure so that Fan Law Number 2 may be used to determine the variation of capacity, speed, and horsepower with size after a table is completed for the base size.

Specific Speed and Specific Size

Specific speed may be defined as the rotative speed at which a hypothetical fan of specific size would be required to operate in order to develop a pressure of one inch water gage at a capacity of one cfm. The specific speed will vary from one point of rating to another but for any given design there will be only one specific speed for each point of rating including that at best efficiency.

Fan Law Number 5 may be used to determine both the size and speed of this hypothetical fan. Using subscript a to denote the hypothetical

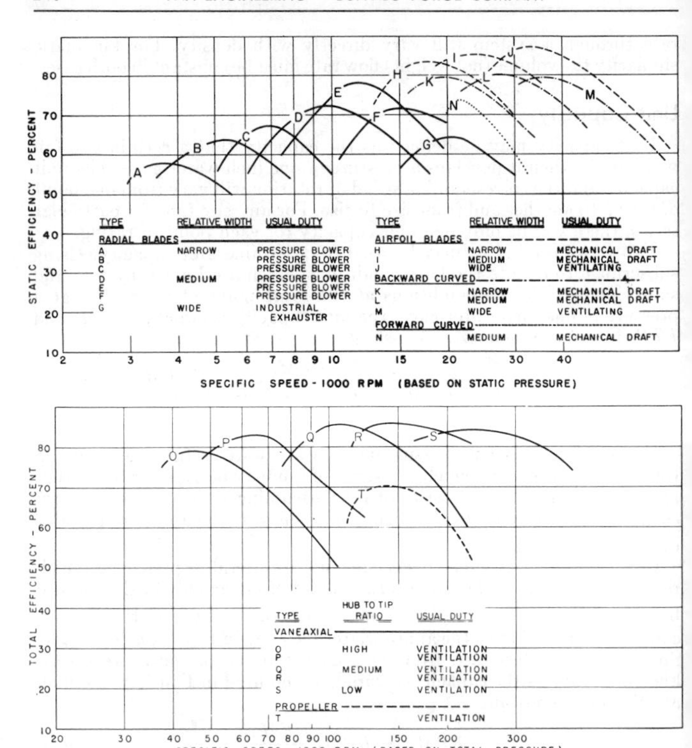

Figure 104 —Specific Speed Ranges for Various Types of Fans

conditions and subscript b to denote the base conditions, the specific speed (N_s) is equal to RPM_a and both CFM_a and FTP_a are unity. The density ratio may be eliminated by employing equivalent total pressures so that

$$N_s = RPM_a = \frac{(RPM_b)\ (CFM_b)^{1/2}}{(ETP_b)^{3/4}}. \tag{273}$$

The specific size, sometimes called specific diameter (D_s), is equal to $SIZE_a$ so that

$$D_s = SIZE_a = \frac{(SIZE_b)\ (ETP_b)^{1/4}}{(CFM_b)^{1/2}}. \tag{274}$$

Both specific speed and specific size may be based on fan static pressure as well as fan total pressure.

The fact that there is only one value of specific speed at best efficiency regardless of size for any one design of fan is of particular significance. Evidence of this was given in the preceding chapter on Axial Flow Fans. This fact may be utilized to advantage in choosing the best type of fan for a given combination of capacity, pressure, and speed. Figure 104 is a composite plot of static efficiency versus specific speed for various types of centrifugal fans and total efficiency versus specific speed for various types of axial flow fans. The values shown are typical for the descriptions listed regardless of make.

Additional details on the uses of specific speed and specific size as aids to selection are given in Chapter 13.

Head and Capacity Coefficients

Although the fan laws as listed in Table 58 are useful for comparisons, they do not give specific design dimensions. As a matter of fact, Fan Law Number 1 indicates that capacity varies as the cube of any linear dimension. Additional experience indicates that three separate linear dimensions are involved; two must be cross sectional dimensions which form a flow area and the other must be a diameter which when linked to rotative speed forms a linear velocity. In the same way, Fan Law Number 1 indicates that pressure varies as the square of any linear dimension. Both dimensions must be diameters and each must be linked to rotative speed.

These concepts are useful in making slight modifications to a design. Reducing the diameter produces an approximately proportional decrease in capacity. A decrease in pressure approximately proportional to the square of the diameter ratio is also produced. Power will be reduced approximately as the cube of the diameter ratio. Any slight increase in the width of a centrifugal impeller will produce a corresponding increase in capacity and power but no appreciable effect on pressure. The situation with regard to axials is somewhat more complex since changes in the flow area can only be accomplished by changes in diameter.

Dimensionless capacity and head coefficients can be derived from Fan Laws Number 1a and 1b, respectively, by placing all the variables for one condition in a single fraction. These coefficients can be made more significant if $SIZE^3$ is interpreted as flow area times diameter in the first case and if $SIZE^2$ is interpreted as diameter squared in the second. Units must be consistent dimensionally. For capacities (CFM) in cfm and pressures (FTP) in ″WG, speeds (RPM) in rpm, linear dimensions ($SIZE$) in ft, densities (δ) in lbm per cu ft, and a conversion factor (g_c) in ft-lbm per lb-min² should be used. Linear rotor velocities (U) in fpm, fluid velocities (V) in fpm, and heads (H) in ft-lb/lbm should be used.

The dimensionless capacity coefficient (Φ) is

$$\Phi = \frac{CFM_a}{SIZE_a{}^3 \times RPM_a} = \frac{V}{U}. \tag{275}$$

The dimensionless head coefficient (Ψ) is

$$\Psi = \frac{5.192\ FTP_a\ g_c}{\delta_a \times SIZE_a{}^2 \times RPM_a{}^2} = \frac{Hg_c}{U^2}. \tag{276}$$

In the above formulas it is necessary to specify the diameter upon which the linear rotor velocity is based. This is usually taken as the mean effective diameter in axial flow fans and the tip diameter in centrifugal fans.

Sound Power Level and the Fan Laws

The ratio of the sound power levels for two similar fans can be predicted from the fan laws. This characteristic like the other dependent variables is given in terms of a different pair of independent variables in each of the ten laws. The fans must have the same point of rating and both must have good balance, good bearings, etc. Complete test data on one of the fans must be available.

The noise spectrums for any two fans at the same point of rating may be considered similar in most cases. The ratio of the sound powers at any pair of corresponding frequencies will equal the ratio of the over-all sound powers. Corresponding frequencies may be the two blade frequencies or any two harmonics thereof. If the rotative speeds and, therefore, the blade frequencies are equal, the fan laws may be used to predict the sound power levels in each of the standard octave bands provided the corresponding test data is available. If rotative speeds are not equal, only the over-all sound power level can be predicted. The spectrum can be determined only approximately in such cases.

Test data on sound power level will usually be based on measurements of the total noise radiated from the inlet and outlet (and the casing, which is usually only a small percentage of the total power). If the inlet and outlet have the same size and shape, there is a good chance that the noises radiated in the two directions will be equal. This is approximately true even in centrifugal fans having round inlets and rectangular outlets.

Fan Law Number 1d indicates that the ratio of sound power outputs varies as the seventh power of the size ratio, the fifth power of the speed ratio, and the square of the density ratio. These relationships have been verified by Madison and Graham* in the Buffalo Forge Company laboratory.

The physical significance of these relationships may be better understood by referring to Fan Law Number 5. This indicates that sound power outputs are proportional to the capacity ratio times the square of the pressure ratio. These relationships suggest that fan noise may be divided into two parts, one which accompanies flow and another which accompanies pressure development. Such a division helps to explain the shape of the normal sound power level-capacity characteristics for both axial flow and centrifugal fans.

The effect of density on sound power level as given in the fan laws is limited to the noise generation phase. The effect on transmission through air must be considered separately.

Specific Sound Power Level

Specific sound power level may be defined as the sound power level

*R. D. Madison and J. B. Graham, Fan Noise Variation with Changing Fan Operation, *Trans.* ASHAE, vol. 64, pp. 319-340, 1958.

which would be produced by a fan of specific size operating at its specific speed and developing a pressure of one inch water gage at a capacity of one cfm. A similar expression based on 10,000 cfm and called either specific K or specific sound power level plus 40 dB is sometimes used. Specific sound power levels will vary from one point of rating to another but for any given design there will be only one specific sound power level for each point of rating. There will be a minimum value of specific sound power level occurring at or very near the best efficiency point.

Fan Law Number 5 may be used to determine the sound power level as well as the size and speed of this hypothetical fan. Using subscript a to denote the hypothetical conditions and subscript b to denote the base conditions, the specific sound power level (PWL_s) is equal to PWL_a and both CFM_a and FTP_a are unity:

$$PWL_s = PWL_a = PWL_b - 10 \log_{10} (CFM_b \times FTP_b^2). \qquad (277)$$

Specific sound power levels may be based on either fan static pressure or fan total pressure.

The significance of specific sound power level lies in the fact that actual sound power levels (PWL) may be calculated quite simply from the specific sound power level (PWL_s) at the point of rating from the required capacity (CFM) and pressure (FTP) alone without the need for precalculating the size and speed:

$$PWL = PWL_s + 10 \log_{10} (CFM \times FTP^2). \qquad (278)$$

Since the second term on the right is constant for a given requirement, the difference in sound power levels for two different points of rating can be determined simply by subtracting the specific sound power level for one from the specific sound power level for the other.

The actual sound power level-capacity characteristic of a fan shows very little variation over a large range of capacities. A specific sound power level-capacity characteristic better illustrates that for minimum noise fans should be rated at the best efficiency point.

Two completely different types of fans may be compared quite easily from an over-all noise standpoint simply by comparing their specific sound power levels. The difference in actual sound power levels of two fans picked for the best point of rating in each case will equal the difference in specific sound power levels. The noise spectrums may vary considerably depending on the number of blades and the rotative speeds of each.

CHAPTER 9

FAN TESTING

The exact performance characteristics of a fan can only be determined by tests. The principle of energy transfer can be used to estimate performance in the early stages of design but the effects of slip or deviation are rarely estimated accurately from theory alone nor are the various losses. The fan laws can be used within limits to predict performance but only after a fan of the same series has been tested. Tests are therefore always required to prove a design.

The performance of any fan will be affected by any condition which disturbs the fluid approaching the inlet. For this reason the true capabilities of a fan can only be determined under controlled conditions, as on a test block. Ideally the flow approaching the fan should be steady and have a velocity across the channel which is as nearly uniform as possible. Test block conditions may also be specified to include definite inlet disturbances.

Field tests are considered less reliable than laboratory tests because the flow patterns at the measuring stations are usually less uniform and often unsteady. It is seldom possible to test a fan in the field at more than one point of rating. If a fan is forced to operate "off design," due to poorly estimated system resistance, the operating efficiency may be considerably lower than anticipated.

Test Codes

Various engineering societies and industrial organizations throughout the world have published fan test codes and several groups are contemplating new codes. The most widely used codes in the United States are those published by the Air Moving and Conditioning Association (AMCA). These include AMCA Standard 210-67 covering all aspects of performance except sound and AMCA Standard 300-67 covering sound performance. Both are laboratory test codes which contain provisions for simulating numerous installation and operating variables. Details regarding instruments and apparatus are specified. Rules concerning measurements, calibration corrections, reduction of data, conversion from test to specified conditions, and presentation of results are provided.

The American Society of Mechanical Engineers (ASMF) has published a fan test code which is similar to AMCA Standard 210-67. This document, ASME PTC 11-1946, has been out of print for some time. A complete revision is planned which will include provisions for field testing as well as laboratory testing.

The American Society of Heating, Refrigerating and Air-Conditioning Engineers (ASHRAE) has a fan test code, which is quite similar to

AMCA Standard 210-67, under consideration for adoption as ASHRAE Standard 51-70. ASHRAE Standard 36-62, Measurement of Sound Power Radiated from Heating, Refrigerating and Air-Conditioning Equipment, can be used for fans. This standard differs from AMCA Standard 300-67 in its provisions for pure tone measurements.

The International Organization for Standardization (ISO) is working on a test code which will contain provisions for laboratory, field, and sound testing.

Test codes provide a convenient starting point for performance specifications and contractual agreements. In some cases it may be more convenient for all parties concerned if exceptions are taken to certain code provisions. This is quite legitimate since fan test codes are not instruments of law. However, since most of the provisions of these test codes are necessary to insure accuracy of measurement and reproducibility of results, caution is advised when exceptions are contemplated.

The following discussions on measurements, calculations, and test setups are in general agreement with the provisions of the 1967 AMCA test codes, except where noted otherwise.

Test Setups

The test setup should employ a duct arrangement similar to that intended for the actual installation. The test setup should also be chosen for operation at the intended point of rating.

There are two general types of test setups: (1) those which utilize an auxiliary fan to provide for operation at or near free delivery even when the resistances through the measuring elements are high and (2) those which do not utilize an auxiliary fan.

Four general duct arrangements are possible: (1) both inlet and discharge ducts, (2) inlet duct only, (3) discharge duct only, and (4) neither discharge nor inlet duct.

When both inlet and discharge ducts are contemplated on the actual installation, the test setup may incorporate a similar arrangement or an inlet bell fitted to the inlet connection may be substituted for the inlet duct as shown in Figure 105A. (A good inlet bell will produce the same flow conditions as a straight inlet duct.) When measurements must be made in both ducts, suitable calming lengths and straighteners must be provided in each. Inlet ducts should be sized within $+12\frac{1}{2}\%$ or $-7\frac{1}{2}\%$ of the fan inlet area. Outlet ducts should be within $+7\frac{1}{2}\%$ and $-12\frac{1}{2}\%$ of the fan outlet area.

If either an inlet duct or a discharge duct is to be used without the other, a similar duct arrangement may be employed in the test setup. The above remarks on duct sizes, calming lengths, and straighteners also apply to these cases. See Figures 105A and 105B.

In any test setup utilizing one or more ducts, performance can be determined from pressure measurements in those ducts. The point of

FIG. 105A TEST SETUP WITH DISCHARGE DUCT ONLY (Pitot Traverse shown)

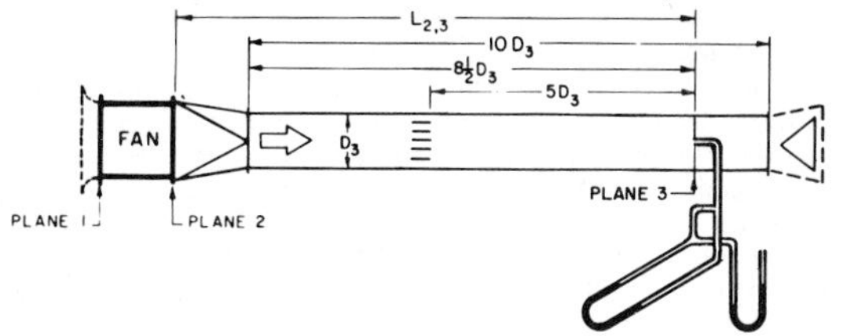

FIG. 105B TEST SETUP WITH INLET DUCT ONLY (Pitot Traverse shown)

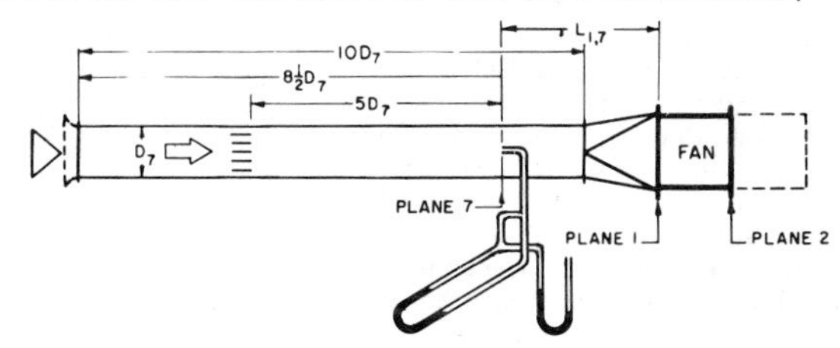

FIG. 105C TEST SETUP WITH DISCHARGE CHAMBER (Multiple Nozzles shown)

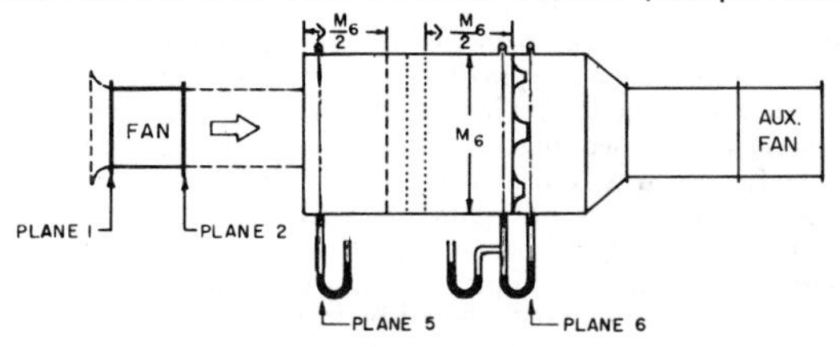

FIG. 105D TEST SETUP WITH INLET CHAMBER (Venturi or Duct Nozzle shown)

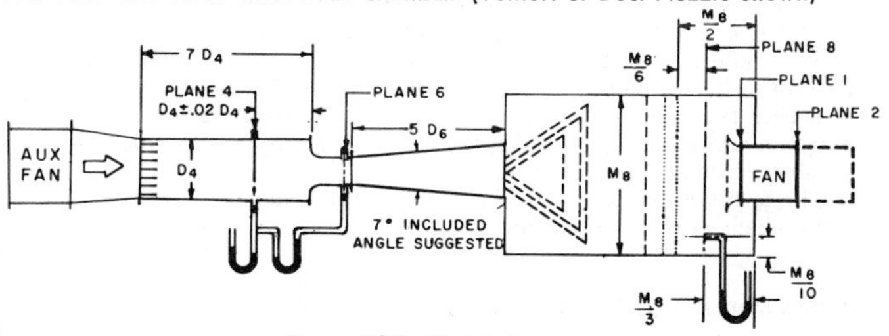

Figure 105—Test Setups

Adapted from the data of Standard Test Code for Air Moving Devices, AMCA Standard 210-67, 1967, pp. 9-18.

rating can be varied by throttling at the end of either duct with symmetrical devices such as nozzles, orifice plates, perforated plates, adjustable cones, or flat plates.

When no ducts are contemplated, the condition can be simulated by mounting the fan in a wall of a test chamber. To vary the point of rating, a variable speed (or variable inlet vane) auxiliary fan may be used to supply air to the chamber at different pressures. A suitable pitot traverse measuring station can be inserted between the supply fan and the chamber. This arrangement permits the measurement of performance at or near free delivery since the auxiliary fan supplies the energy necessary to overcome the resistance through the measuring section. Such an arrangement can also be used where only a short run of duct, connected to the fan, is contemplated.

The low capacities of small size fans cannot always be measured accurately by pitot tube tests. Better accuracy can usually be obtained by using flow nozzles if appreciable exit velocities can be generated. The pressure required to produce these velocities may be supplied by the test fan or by an auxiliary fan if the test fan is not capable. In the first case the nozzles may be located at the end of the test duct. Suitable approach conditions must be provided. When an auxiliary fan is employed, a series of nozzles in a chamber may be set up permanently as shown in Figure 105C. Variations in point of rating are produced by plugging and unplugging various combinations of nozzles. Alternatively, a single nozzle or nozzle Venturi may be inserted in a duct between the auxiliary fan and the chamber as shown in Figure 105D.

Figures 105A to 105D give the principal dimensions for various test setups. Additional combinations are possible, e.g., either the pitot traverse or the multiple nozzles can be used with an inlet chamber. Specific numbers are assigned to various sections or planes of reference as indicated.

If a fan is to be furnished with bearings it should be tested on its own shaft and bearings after a suitable "run in" period. Inlet and outlet should be unobstructed except for bearings and supports and any other appurtenances such as screens or dampers which are specified. Inlet bells and discharge cones, if contemplated, should be in place.

The fan may have to be rotated to provide a suitable discharge on the test block. The relative position of inlet boxes, if any, to the discharge should not be changed, since this may affect performance.

The room in which the test is conducted should be free from any air currents which might produce an effect on fan performance. Whenever it is necessary to discharge the air into another room, provisions for air entry should be made. An adequate whirl free supply of uniform density air should be available to the fan.

The acoustic properties of the room will determine the type of sound tests which can be performed.

Measurement of Fan Capacity

Fan capacity is the volume rate of flow expressed at inlet conditions (CFM_1). The flow rate may be measured by means of a pitot traverse in either the inlet or discharge duct. Measurements can also be made in a duct quite remote from the fan provided any leakage, to or from atmosphere, is prevented. The measured volume (CFM_x) must be multiplied by the ratio of the density at the measuring station (δ_x) to the density at inlet (δ_1):

$$CFM_1 = CFM_x \left(\frac{\delta_x}{\delta_1}\right). \tag{279}$$

Capacity is not measured directly. In a pitot traverse, velocity pressures are measured. Refer to Figures 28, 29, and 30 for standard pitot tube construction, standard pitot tube marking, and standard straightener, respectively. Twenty velocity pressure readings are required to determine the capacity at a single point of rating. Two 10-point pitot traverses, at 90° to each other, should be made. The velocity pressure corresponding to the average velocity may be determined from the 20 readings, each corrected for gage calibration (VP_{x1}, VP_{x2}, . . , VP_{x20}) by squaring the average of the square roots as indicated by

$$VP_x = \left(\frac{\sqrt{VP_{x1}} + \sqrt{VP_{x2}} + \ldots + \sqrt{VP_{x20}}}{20}\right)^2. \tag{280}$$

The actual capacity at the measuring station (CFM_x) may be determined from the area (A_x), density (δ_x), and the velocity pressure (VP_x), using

$$CFM_x = 1096.7\ A_x \sqrt{\frac{VP_x}{\delta_x}}. \tag{281}$$

In methods involving orifices or nozzles, etc., static pressure differences are measured. Details on instrumentation, location of reading points, calibration, etc., are given in Chapter 3.

Measurement of Fan Pressure

The total pressure developed by a fan (FTP) is the algebraic difference between the gage total pressures at inlet (TP_1) and outlet (TP_2):

$$FTP = TP_2 - TP_1. \tag{282}$$

When ducts are connected to both inlet and outlet both total pressures must be measured. If there is no inlet duct the gage total pressure at the inlet is assumed to be zero. If there is no discharge duct the gage total pressure at the outlet is assumed to be equal to the velocity pressure corresponding to the average velocity through the outlet.

The velocity pressure of the fan (FVP) is defined as the velocity pressure corresponding to the average velocity through the outlet (VP_2).

The static pressure of the fan (FSP) is the difference between the total and velocity pressures of the fan:

$$FSP = FTP - FVP. \tag{283}$$

It is important to note that the fan static pressure is not equal to the difference in static pressures at inlet (SP_1) and outlet (SP_2). This can be demonstrated by using the appropriate substitutions based on the above definitions:

$$FSP = TP_2 - TP_1 - VP_2 = SP_2 - TP_1. \tag{284}$$

The total pressures at the measuring stations must be measured simultaneously with the velocity pressures used in determining capacity. Two 10-point traverses at 90° to each other are required for both inlet and discharge measurements. The average total pressure (TP_x) is the arithmetic average of the individual total pressure readings (TP_{x1}, TP_{x2}, . . , TP_{x20}) each corrected for gage calibration:

$$TP_x = \left(\frac{TP_{x1} + TP_{x2} + .. + TP_{x20}}{20}\right). \tag{285}$$

Alternatively, static pressures may be averaged from traverse readings or by using piezometer rings. Total pressures are then calculated by adding the appropriate velocity pressure.

The total pressure at the fan inlet (TP_1) or outlet (TP_2) will differ from that at the measuring station in the corresponding duct by an amount equal to the friction through the duct and straighteners if any:

$$TP_2 = TP_3 + \left(f\,\frac{L + 4D}{D}\right)_{2,\,3} VP_3 \text{ and} \tag{286}$$

$$TP_1 = TP_7 + \left(f\,\frac{L}{D}\right)_{1,\,7} VP_7. \tag{287}$$

The codes stipulate that a friction factor of .02 may be used and that a standard straightener is equivalent to four diameters of round duct. There is some evidence that the straightener loss is quite a bit higher.

Details on instrumentation, calibration, etc. are discussed in Chapter 3.

Measurement of Fan Horsepower

Fan horsepower is the brake horsepower (BHP) required to drive the fan on its own shaft and bearings, if any are to be furnished with the fan. Fan horsepower does not include any transmission loss resulting from the use of belt drives, couplings, or variable speed or other devices. Various prime movers may be used on the test block. Many may also serve as the means of measuring brake horsepower. In field testing there is seldom any choice but to use the prime mover which is installed.

Electric dynamometers are essentially electric motors with both armature and field mounted so that they will revolve about the same shaft. An arm is attached to the field and a restraining force applied at the opposite end. If the speed of rotation (RPM) in rpm, the restraining force (F) in pounds, and the distance from the center of rotation to the point of application of the force (l) in inches are measured, the brake horsepower can be determined from

$$BHP = \frac{2\,\pi\,F\,l\,(RPM)}{12 \times 33{,}000}. \tag{288}$$

TABLE 59 — DYNAMOMETER CONSTANTS FOR CONVENIENT ARM LENGTHS

Arm Length l	Dynamometer Constant $(2\pi l)/(12 \times 33000)$
6.3025″	1/10000
10.5042″	1/6000
12.6050″	1/5000
15.7563″	1/4000
21.0080″	1/3000
31.5126″	1/2000

Some convenient lengths (l) and the corresponding values of $(2\pi l)/(12 \times 33{,}000)$ are listed in Table 59.

The restraining force (F_x) on the arm may be measured with a yardarm type balance or a dial type scale. If the weight of the arm is not perfectly counterbalanced (by means of a counterweight on the stator) the measured force will have to be corrected. This correction, called tare (F_x'), can be determined by running the dynamometer without load at the proper speed and noting the scale reading. The corrected force (F) may be smaller or greater than the measured force depending on whether there is positive or negative tare, so that

$$F = F_x \pm F_x'. \tag{289}$$

The arm should be in exactly the same position for each reading. When dial type scales are used the deflection may become so great that an adjustment will be required. Such an adjustment is never required with a yardarm type balance that always returns the arm to the same position.

Calibration tests are not generally required for electric dynamometers. By measuring tare at the proper speed the effects of bearing and windage losses may be cancelled out. Electrical connections must be completely flexible and the bearings should be in good condition and well lubricated.

Fan horsepower may also be determined by measuring the electrical input to a calibrated electric motor. Calibration tests are performed with some form of absorption dynamometer. If the electrical input is measured in terms of amps and volts and the corresponding efficiency is determined from the calibration, the brake horsepower of the fan if driven by a direct current motor can be calculated from

$$BHP = \frac{(amps)\ (volts)\ (eff)}{746}. \tag{290}$$

When alternating current motors are used the actual power will differ from the apparent power indicated by the amps and volts. Power factor (Pf) is the ratio of actual to apparent power for single phase or three phase AC motors.

For single phase AC motors,

$$BHP = \frac{(amps)\ (volts)\ (eff)\ (Pf)}{746}. \tag{291}$$

For three phase AC motors,

$$BHP = \frac{\sqrt{3}\ (amps)\ (volts)\ (eff)\ (Pf)}{746}. \tag{292}$$

A wattmeter may be used to determine the actual power input without the necessity of measuring amps, volts, and power factor separately. For 3-phase current the 2 wattmeter method of measuring power or a polyphase wattmeter should be used.

In a torsion meter, the torque (τ) is measured by means of a strain gage element bonded to the transmission shaft. A separate prime mover is required. Fan horsepower can be determined from the torque in pound-inches and speed in rpm from

$$BHP = \frac{2\,\pi\,(RPM)\,\tau}{33000\,(12)}. \tag{293}$$

In field testing a fan driven by an uncalibrated prime mover, reasonable values of motor or engine efficiency based on manufacturer's tests of similar models should be used. The accuracy of the results will usually be adequate for most engineering applications.

Measurement of Fan Speed

During the course of a test determination, fan speed should be maintained constant. The 1967 AMCA code stipulates that three readings of speed and power input should be taken if the speed is regulated within plus or minus ½% or within 2 rpm. Otherwise simultaneous readings of speed and power must be made for each pressure reading.

A line frequency stroboscopic tachometer may be used with a marked disc on the end of the dynamometer shaft to assist in regulating speed. Speed control may be achieved by regulating the resistance connected to the field, or both the field and armature resistances, depending on dynamometer design.

The actual measurement of speed can be accomplished with various types of direct connected tachometers or by various stroboscopic methods. Stroboscopic methods are almost essential on low power fans where the drag of any other type of tachometer might slow down the apparatus.

Every reasonable precaution should be taken to prevent slippage of the revolution counter when a counter and timer method is used.

A stroboscopic tachometer, with a variable oscillator, may be adjusted so that the light flashes at the rotative speed. When this condition is obtained an identifiable point on the rotating assembly will appear stationary in space. The speed may then be read directly from the calibrated scale. A stroboscopic tachometer on line current will flash at line frequency. If the speed being measured is equal to line frequency divided by an integral number, a single identifiable point will appear as that number of equally spaced but stationary points. The speed of rotation will then be line frequency divided by the number of images that appear. For a 60 cycle current:

$$RPM = \frac{3600}{no.\ of\ images}. \tag{294}$$

Measurement of Air Density

In order to accurately determine performance by test, the density of the air entering the fan and the density at the measuring stations must be determined. In addition it should be ascertained that the air density is uniform across all sections. This will be so if there is substantially no temperature stratification at the point where the air enters the test system, (i.e., fan inlet or duct inlet). Test codes specify that the temperature difference at this point shall not exceed 4°F (preferably 2°F).

The density of entering or ambient air can be determined from measured wet- and dry-bulb temperatures and barometric readings using the psychrometric density chart in Figure 12. Wet-bulb temperatures in ducts cannot be measured accurately due to velocity effects. Since the absolute humidity will be constant, such densities (δ_x) can be computed from the ambient density (δ_a) and the temperature and pressure ratios with

$$\delta_x = \delta_a \left(\frac{T_a}{T_x}\right) \left(\frac{b_x}{b_a}\right). \tag{295}$$

The barometer in the duct (b_x) can be computed by adding the measured gage pressure (converted to inches of mercury, i.e., $SP_x/13.6$) to the ambient barometer (b_a). Both the ambient (T_a) and duct temperatures (T_x) should be in degrees Rankine.

Measurement of Sound Power Level

The sound test code published by AMCA in 1967 specifies procedures based on the use of a calibrated sound source in a semi-reverberant room. Sound power levels in each of the eight octave bands are calculated on the basis of Equation **227** and corrected for end reflection. Various test setups, simulating different types of installations, may be used. No procedures are given for measuring directivity or pure tones.

Refer to Chapter 5 for discussions on the measurement of sound levels, sound pressure levels, and sound power levels. Corrections for background level, non-standard air, and end reflection are also given.

Before sound testing, the fans should be checked for balance and alignment. Background noises should be eliminated. Motors and bearings sometimes contribute to false readings.

Test Results

Test conditions may differ from conditions expected in actual operation. Differences in density due to differences in temperature or pressure are almost certain to occur unless the tests are conducted in an environmental test chamber. The test may be conducted with a model and the test speed may be higher or lower than contemplated for the actual installation. In any event results may be compared with requirements by utilizing the fan laws and corrections for compressibility and size effect if appropriate. Convenient forms for recording readings, calculations and converted results are given in Figures 106-108.

Compressibility Corrections

The calculations outlined in Figure 108 lead to actual results at the test conditions (subscript a) of size, speed, and density and expected results at the specified operating conditions (subscript b). The conversion of resul from one set of conditions to the other, by means of the fan laws a indicated, ignores compressibility. Such an approach is only justified whe the fan pressures in each case are of the same order of magnitude.

Compressibility corrections should be made whenever the pressu developed under test conditions (FTP_a) differs significantly from the fa pressure expected under actual conditions (FTP_b). There will be signi icant differences if the test fan (model or prototype) is operated at different tip speed than that expected for the proposed installation.

The results of any test include a compressibility effect. That is, th measured performance of a fan handling any gas is somewhat better tha the performance which would be measured if the fan handled an incom pressible fluid (all other conditions being equal). For the same rate flow entering the fan and the same transfer of energy within the fan, th pressure developed in a compressible fluid must be greater than th produced in an incompressible fluid. The compressibility factor (K_p), a explained in Chapter 8, relates the actual pressures to their correspondi incompressible values (indicated by a prime mark) as follows:

$$FTP_a' = FTP_a (K_p)_a, \quad (29$$

$$FVP_a' = FVP_a/[2\,(K_p)_a - 1], \textit{ and} \quad (29$$

$$FSP_a' = FTP_a' - FVP_a'. \quad (29$$

The compressibility factor $(K_p)_a$ can be determined from the total pre sure developed on test (FTP_a) and the corresponding total efficienc $(\eta_T)_a$ using Figure 103. Since $(\eta_T)_a$ depends on $(K_p)_a$, as indicated b Equation 266, it may be necessary to use a method of successive approx mations similar to that outlined below.

$$FTP_b' = FTP_a' \times \left(\frac{RPM_b \times SIZE_b}{RPM_a \times SIZE_a}\right)^2 \times \frac{\delta_b}{\delta_a}, \quad (29$$

$$FVP_b' = FVP_a' \times \left(\frac{RPM_b \times SIZE_b}{RPM_a \times SIZE_a}\right)^2 \times \frac{\delta_b}{\delta_a}, \textit{ and} \quad (30$$

$$FSP_b' = FSP_a' \times \left(\frac{RPM_b \times SIZE_b}{RPM_a \times SIZE_a}\right)^2 \times \frac{\delta_b}{\delta_a}. \quad (30$$

In order to determine the pressures which could actually be measure at the specified conditions another compressibility factor $(K_p)_b$ must b calculated and used in:

$$FTP_b = FTP_b'/(K_p)_b, \quad (30$$

$$FVP_b = FVP_b'\,[2\,(K_p)_b - 1], \textit{ and} \quad (30$$

$$FSP_b = FTP_b - FVP_b. \quad (30$$

The value of $(K_p)_b$ cannot be determined directly from Figure 103 sin it depends on the value of FTP_b and $(\eta_T)_b$, both of which are known only approximately. Two successive approximations will generally yield a sufficiently accurate value of $(K_p)_b$. The first approximation $(K_p)_b'$ can be obtained from the computed incompressible total pressure (FTP_b') and the corresponding total efficiency $(\eta_T)_b'$. This first approximation can be used to obtain a second approximation of the fan pressure (FTP_b'') which can then be used with the corresponding total efficiency $(\eta_T)_b''$ to determine the second approximation $(K_p)_b''$. This second approximation can usually be used for the final value $(K_p)_b$ in Equations 302-304.

The fan capacity or flow rate at inlet conditions and the fan horsepower are not affected by compressibility. The fan laws may be applied to these two variables without correction. The flow rate at discharge conditions can be computed, at least approximately, after determining a reasonable value for the polytropic exponent.

BUFFALO FORGE CO. EXP. FILE NO. X-________ DATE________

GENERAL DATA

TEST PER AMCA 210 FIG. 1.1 USING DYNAMOMETER

PHYSICAL DATA

FAN: TYPE________ SIZE________ ARRANGEMENT________

WHEEL________

OUTLET________ X________ AREA (A_2)________

DUCT: CONNECTED TO DISCHARGE BY TRANSFORMATION PIECE

DIAMETER (D_3)________ AREA (A_3)________

LENGTH ($L_{2,3}$)________ FRICTION $(f\frac{L}{D})_{2,3}$________

DYNAMOMETER: MAKE________ RATING________

TARE________ ARM (ℓ)________ $K = \frac{2\pi\ell}{33000 \times 12}$________

CALIBRATIONS

BAROMETER: MAKE________ CORRECTION________

TOTAL PRESSURE (TP) MANOMETER________

VELOCITY PRESSURE (VP) MANOMETER________

	BEFORE TEST								AFTER TEST							
HOOK																
TP																
HOOK																
VP																

THERMOMETERS MAKE________ CERTIFIED CALIBRATED

STRATIFICATION CHECK________

OTHER DATA

PERFORMANCE CURVE________ RESULTS (FORM 4056)________

READINGS (FORM 4057)________ CALIBRATION CORRECTION (FORM 4058)________

FORM 4055 BY________

Figure 106—Test Form—General Data

BUFFALO FORGE CO. EXP. FILE NO. X-__________ DATE __________

TEST READINGS

AMCA FIG. 1.1 TEST DYNAMOMETER TEST

SPEED HELD AT______ RPM STROBOSCOPICALLY

DET.	1		2		3		4		5		6		7		8		9		10	
PT.	TP_3	VP_3	TP_3	VP_3	TP_3	VP_3	TP_3	VP_3	TP_3	VP_3	TP_3	VP_3	TP_3	VP_3	TP_3	VP_3	TP_3	VP_3	TP_3	VP_3
1																				
2																				
3																				
4																				
5																				
6																				
7																				
8																				
9																				
10																				
11																				
12																				
13																				
14																				
15																				
16																				
17																				
18																				
19																				
20																				
	F_X	F*	F_X	F*	F_X	F*	F_X	F*	F_X	F*	F_X	F*	F_X	F*	F_X	F*	F_X	F*	F_X	F*
1																				
10																				
20																				
	b_1	b_1°	b_1	b_1°	b_1	b_1°	b_1	b_1°	b_1	b_1°	b_1	b_1°	b_1	b_1°	b_1	b_1°	b_1	b_1°	b_1	b_1°
1																				
10																				
20																				
	t_1	t'_1	t_1	t'_1	t_1	t'_1	t_1	t'_1	t_1	t'_1	t_1	t'_1	t_1	t'_1	t_1	t'_1	t_1	t'_1	t_1	t'_1
1																				
10																				
20																				
	t_3	RPM	t_3	RPM	t_3	RPM	t_3	RPM	t_3	RPM	t_3	RPM	t_3	RPM	t_3	RPM	t_3	RPM	t_3	RPM
1																				
10																				
20																				

* TARE _______ LB'S. SUBTRACTED ° BAR CALIBRATION_______"HG. SUBTRACTED

FORM-4057 READINGS BY ____________________

Figure 107—Test Form—Readings

BUFFALO FORGE CO. EXP. FILE NO. X-__________ DATE __________

CALCULATIONS & RESULTS

AMCA FIG. 1.1 TEST $A_2 =$ __________ $A_3 =$ __________ $\left(f\frac{L+4D}{D}\right)_{2,3} =$ __________

DYNAMOMETER TEST K = __________ NO COMPRESSIBILITY

DETERMINATION NO.	1	2	3	4	5	6	7	8	9	10
CALCULATIONS & ACTUAL RESULTS FOR _____ $SIZE_a$ AT RPM_a & δ_a AS LISTED										
t_1 (ARITH. AVG.)										
t'_1 (ARITH. AVG.)										
b_1 (ARITH. AVG.)										
δ_1 (FROM FIG. 12) $= \delta_a$										
t_3 (ARITH. AVG.)										
TP_3 (ARITH. AVG.)										
VP_3 (RMS AVG.)										
$SP_3 = TP_3 - VP_3$										
$b_3 = b_1 + SP_3/13.6$										
$\delta_3 = \delta_1 (T_1/T_3)(b_3/b_1)$										
$V_3 = 1096.5\sqrt{VP_3/\delta_3}$										
$CFM_3 = V_3 \times A_3$										
$\Delta TP_{2,3} = (f L/D)_{2,3}\, VP_3$										
$FTP = TP_3 + \Delta TP_{2,3} = FTP_a$										
$FVP = VP_3 (A_3/A_2)^2 (\delta_3/\delta_2) = FTP_a$										
$FSP = FTP - FVP = FSP_a$										
$CFM_1 = CFM_3 (\delta_3/\delta_1) = CFM_a$										
RPM (ARITH. AVG.) $= RPM_a$										
F (ARITH. AVG.)										
$BHP = K \times W \times RPM = BHP_a$										
PREDICTED RESULTS FOR _____ $SIZE_b$ AT _____ RPM_b & _____ δ_b BY FAN LAWS										
CFM BY FAN LAW 1_a										
FTP BY FAN LAW 1_b										
FVP BY FAN LAW 1_b										
FSP BY FAN LAW 1_b										
BHP BY FAN LAW 1_c										
$\eta_T = CFM_b \times FTP_b / 6356\, BHP_a$										
$\eta_S = \eta_T \times FSP_b / FTP_b$										

FORM 4056 CALCULATIONS BY ____________________

Figure 108—Test Form—Calculation and Results

CHAPTER 10

FAN SYSTEMS

Fan systems may consist of any combination of fans, duct elements, heat exchangers, air cleaners, or other equipment through which all or part of the total flow must pass.

Open systems have at least one intake and one discharge opening. Closed systems form a loop and have no such openings.

Supply and exhaust systems were described in Chapter 4. Some of the problems of system design and fan selection such as the effects of multiple branches were discussed. In this chapter additional problems of fan-system matching will be examined.

Fan and System Matching

Fan performance must match system requirements. The only possible operating points are those where the system characteristic intersects the fan characteristic. At such points the pressure developed by the fan exactly matches the system resistance and the flow through the system equals the fan capacity. If the flow rate is not equal to specifications, either the fan characteristic must be altered (by a change in speed, size, or whirl) or the system characteristic must be changed (by altering components or damper settings).

Graphical methods of determining the points of intersection are often quite valuable in the analysis of fundamental principles but too tedious for routine fan selection. The non-graphical methods of selection explained in Chapter 13 all take into account the necessity for matching the fan and system characteristics.

If more than one fan serves a system, their combined characteristics must be used to determine the capacity and other performance characteristics of the system.

In any case fan characteristics should be based on the gas density at the proposed fan location. System characteristics must be based on the individual densities in each of the system components. The over-all system resistance is equal to the sum of the pressure losses for the individual components along any one flow path as discussed in Chapter 4. Several interesting situations develop when the density varies within a system.

System Characteristics

The over-all resistance to flow through a system will vary with capacity. This variation can be shown graphically by plotting the pressure-capacity characteristics in the same manner that fan characteristics are presented.

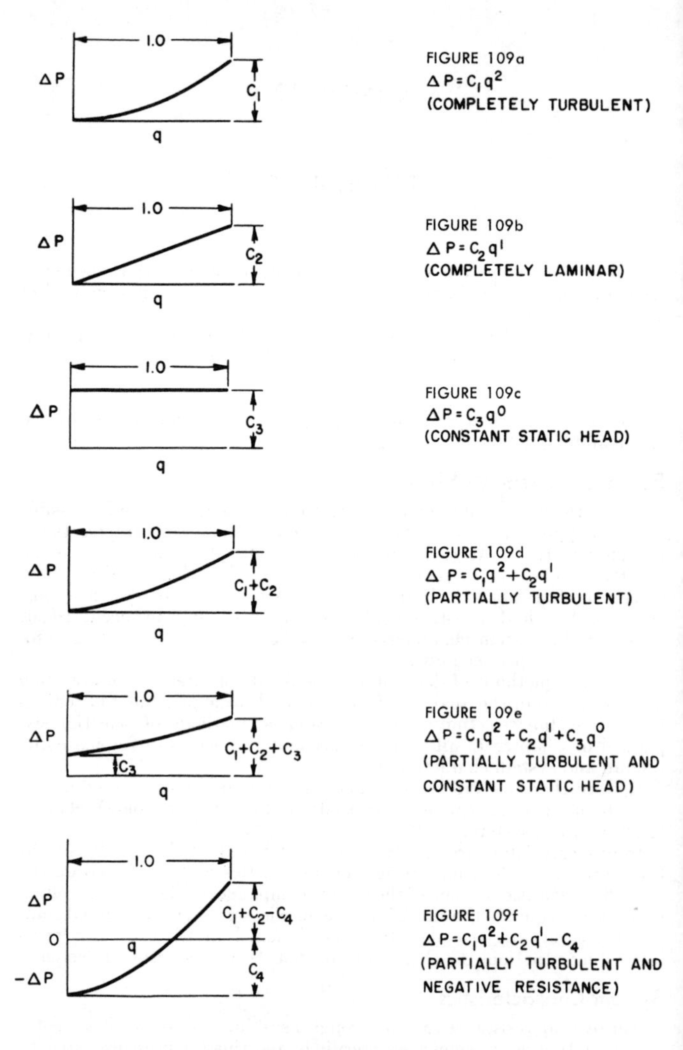

Figure 109—System Resistance Curves

The variation of pressure drop (ΔP) with capacity (q) may also be expressed algebraically:

$$\Delta P = C_1 q^2 + C_2 q + C_3 - C_4. \qquad (305)$$

This equation divides the pressure drop into four parts. The first part varies as the square of the capacity. The second part varies as the first power of the capacity. The third and fourth parts are both independent of capacity but opposite in sign. The coefficients (C_1, etc.) are constant for a given system handling a given fluid regardless of flow rate. For certain system components only one of the four coefficients may be of finite value. For other system components two or more of the four coefficients may be of finite value. The most notable example of the latter is a duct with partially turbulent flow for which C_1 and C_2 are both larger than zero and the net exponent on capacity is something between 1 and 2. This is rather clearly demonstrated in Equation 146.

For any component, through which the flow is completely turbulent, only C_1 exceeds zero. Abrupt expansions and hard bends or elbows are typical examples of devices whose resistances vary as the square of the capacity.

Components must have completely laminar flow if only C_2 is to exceed zero. The flow through some low velocity fabric filters meets this description.

The static head which must be exceeded if a gas is to flow into a column of liquid at a given depth may be considered as a resistance for which only C_3 is of finite value. The resistances of various bubbling devices may be considered independent of flow rate. The pressure (or vacuum) required by other devices may also be independent of flow rate.

There is no such thing as negative resistance. However, in certain systems the fan or fans may be assisted by some reaction or device which maintains a pressure at the intake or a vacuum at the discharge. In these situations C_4 will have a finite value.

Figure 109 illustrates the variation of system resistance with capacity for several situations as marked. The pressure drops at unit capacity are equal to the values of the coefficients as indicated.

Two-Fan Systems

There are various reasons for using more than one fan on a system. Supply and exhaust fans are used in ventilation to avoid excessive pressure buildup in the space being served. Forced and induced draft fans are used to maintain a specified draft over the fire. Two fans may fit the available space better than one larger fan. Capacity control by means of various fan combinations may be more economical than other control methods. Multi-stage arrangements may be necessary when pressure requirements exceed the capabilities of a single-stage fan. Standby fans are frequently required to insure continuous operation.

When two fans are used they may be located quite remotely from each other or they may be so close as to share shaft and bearings or even casings. Double width, double inlet fans are essentially two fans in parallel in a common housing. Multi-stage blowers are in effect two or more fans in series in the same casing. Fans may also be in series but at opposite ends of the system. Parallel arrangement fans may have almost any amount of their operating resistance in common. At one extreme the fans may have common inlet and discharge plenums. At the other extreme the fans may both have considerable individual duct work of equal or unequal resistance.

Fans in series must all handle the same amount of gas by weight measurements, assuming no losses or gains between stages. The combined total pressure will be the sum of the individual fan total pressures. The velocity pressure of the combination may be defined as the pressure corresponding to the velocity through the outlet of the last stage. The static pressure for the combination is the difference between its total and velocity pressures and is therefore not equal to the sum of the individual fan static pressures. The volumetric capacities will differ whenever the inlet densities vary from stage to stage. Compression in one stage will reduce the volume entering the next if there is no re-expansion between the two. As with any fan the pressure capabilities are also influenced by density.

The combined total pressure-capacity characteristic for two fans in series can be drawn by using the volumetric capacities of the first stage for abscissas and the sum of the appropriate total pressures for ordinates. Due to compressibility the volumetric capacities of the second stage will not equal the volumetric capacities of the first stage. The individual total pressures must be chosen accordingly before they are combined. If the gas can be considered incompressible, the pressures for the two stages may be read at the same capacity. In the area near free delivery it may be necessary to estimate the negative pressure characteristics of one of the fans in order to combine values at the appropriate capacity.

Fans in parallel must all develop sufficient pressure to overcome the losses in any individual duct work, etc., as well as the losses in the common portions of the system. When such fans have no individual duct work but discharge into a common plenum, their individual velocity pressures are lost and the fans should be selected to produce the same fan static pressures. If fan velocity pressures are equal, the fan total pressures will be equal in such cases. When the fans do have individual ducts but they are of equal resistance and joined together at equal velocities, the fans should be selected for the same fan total pressures. If fan velocity pressures are equal, fan static pressures will be equal in this case. If the two streams join together at unequal velocities, there will be a transfer of energy from the higher velocity stream to the lower velocity stream. The fans serving the lower velocity branch can be selected for a correspondingly lower total pressure. The other fan must be selected for a correspondingly higher total pressure than would be required if velocities were equal.

The combined pressure-capacity curves for two fans in parallel can be plotted by using the appropriate pressures for ordinates and the sum of the corresponding capacities for abscissas. Such curves are meaningful only when a combined system curve can be drawn. In the area near shutoff it may be necessary to estimate the negative capacity characteristics of one of the fans in order to combine values at the appropriate pressure.

Figure 110 illustrates the combined characteristics of two fans with

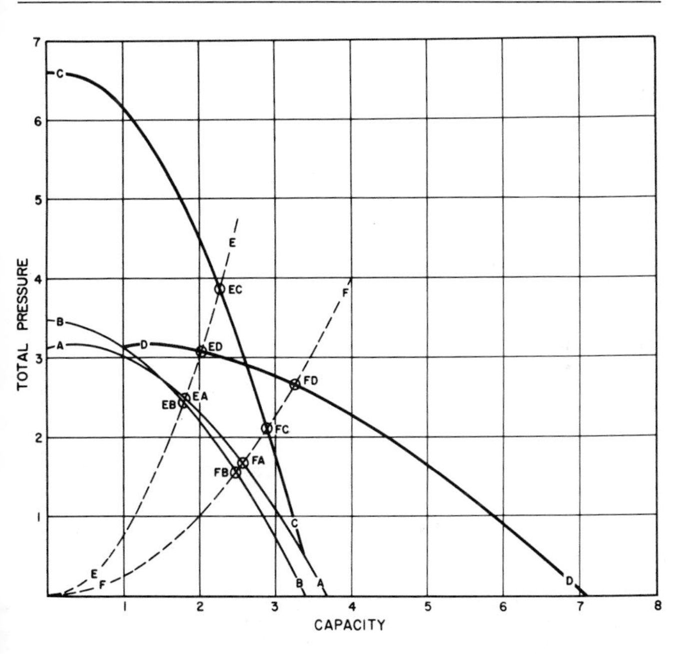

Figure 110—Combined Performance of Fans in Series and Parallel

---

slightly different individual characteristics (A-A and B-B). The combined characteristics are shown for the two fans in series (C-C) and in parallel (D-D). Only total pressure curves are shown. This is always correct for series arrangements but may introduce slight errors for parallel arrangements. An incompressible gas has been assumed. The questionable areas near shutoff or free delivery have been omitted. Two different system characteristics (E-E and F-F) have been drawn on the chart. With the two fans in series, operation will be at point EC or FC if the fan is on System E or F respectively. Parallel arrangement will lead to operation at ED or FD. Single fan operation would be at the point indicated by the intersection of the appropriate fan and system curves provided the effect of an inoperative second fan were negligible. Some sort of bypass is required around an inoperative fan in series whereas an inoperative fan in parallel need only be dampered shut. Parallel operation yields a higher capacity than series operation on System F but the reverse is true on System E. For the type of fan and system characteristics drawn there is only one possible point of operation for any arrangement.

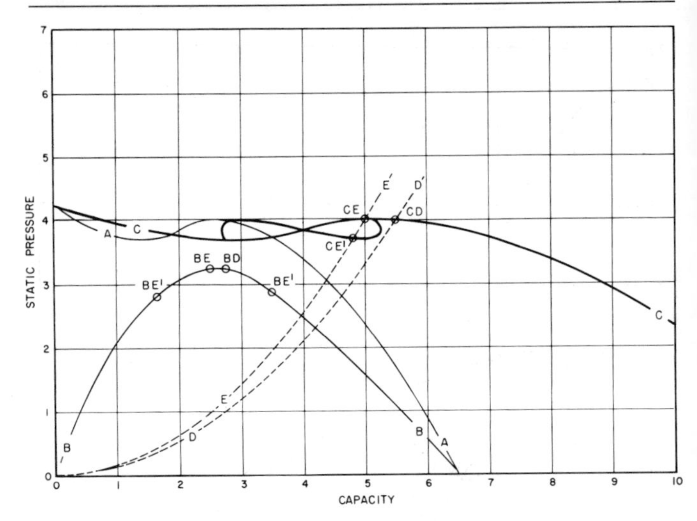

Figure 111—Forwardly Curved Tip Fans in Parallel

An interesting situation develops when characteristics are of more complicated shape. Figure 111 is drawn for two identical forward curved type fans in parallel with a common discharge plenum. Static pressures are used in this chart. However, more important is the fact that a very complex combined curve results due to the characteristic dip in the fan pressure curve. Each fan has pressure and efficiency characteristics as shown by the curves A-A and B-B respectively. The combined curve (C-C) is drawn by plotting all the possible combinations of capacity at each pressure value. A single curve results except in the area just to the left of the peak. This would not be of concern except that it is an area very close to the best efficiency point. If the system resistance were estimated as in curve D-D the expected point of operation would be CD and the expected efficiency for the fan would be as indicated by BD. If for some reason the estimate of system resistance should be wrong and the actual system characteristic was as in curve E-E two points of operation are possible, namely CE and CE′. Nothing is wrong with point CE as indicated by the efficiency at BE. However, due to slight differences in individual system resistance, the fans will usually operate to produce the combined performance indicated at CE′. When this happens one fan will be overloaded and the other underloaded, both operating at poor efficiencies as indicated by the two points BE′. The unbalance may be reversed quite easily with the result that the load shifts from one fan to the other. One or both driving motors may be damaged if the overload is severe enough.

Systems with Mass or Heat Exchange

If the air passing through a system is heated or cooled, its density will be decreased or increased respectively and assuming no change of mass its volume rate will be increased or decreased accordingly. The resistance of any component should be calculated for the actual gas density, volume, and velocity through it. The over-all system resistance is the sum of these individual resistances along any one flow path.

The mass rate of flow may be different at various locations. Multiple intakes or outlets have been discussed in Chapter 4. The mass rate may also vary due to a change of state as when water is evaporated into a gas stream. Conversely, water vapor may be condensed out of an air-vapor mixture. Additional gas may be generated as in any combustion process. In any case it is necessary to determine the rate of mass gain or loss from the appropriate relation for the physical or chemical process involved. The actual densities, volumes, and velocities should be used to determine individual resistances, after which over-all resistances can be determined by simple addition.

The fan for any system including one with mass or heat exchange must develop enough pressure to overcome the system resistance. This pressure requirement is the same regardless of fan location. The best fan location based on horsepower requirements is at the point where the inlet volume will have the smallest possible value. Naturally, the fan will have to be downstream from all intakes on exhaust systems and upstream from all discharge openings on supply systems. Volume flow rate varies inversely with density when the mass flow rate is constant. Volume flow rate is proportional to weight flow when density is constant. Both density and weight flow may vary, in which case volume flow will vary accordingly.

The difference in horsepower requirements for different fan locations can be calculated from either Equation 267 or 269. Both yield the same results. For constant system resistance the pressure required of the fan ($TP_2 - TP_1$) will be constant regardless of location. The head required of the fan ($H_2 - H_1$) will vary with density and therefore with location. If there are no losses or gains, the weight flow (w) will be constant regardless of location. The volume flow (CFM) will vary with position as noted above. In any event the fan location requiring the least horsepower assuming constant efficiency is that place where the density is greatest.

When only temperature changes are involved, it is convenient to refer to these alternate locations as the "cold fan location" or the "hot fan location." In addition to requiring the least horsepower the "cold fan" will be a smaller size than the "hot fan" if both are the same type selected for the same point of rating. To produce the same pressure with lighter gas the "hot fan" must operate at a higher tip speed. The "hot fan" will have a higher temperature rise ($T_2 - T_1$) as indicated by Equation 167 since the inlet temperature (T_1) will be higher and the pressure ratio (P_2/P_1) will be constant. The extra energy for this extra heating occasions the higher horsepower.

Closed Systems

In any system, open or closed, the temperature of the air is increased as it passes through the fan. In a closed system the air recirculates back to the fan so that its temperature is raised repeatedly. Eventually the losses through the duct walls will exactly balance the energy input to the system. Under equilibrium conditions, the temperature rise through the fan equals the temperature drop around the rest of the system. The equilibrium temperatures can be calculated using the amount of surface, the surface coefficients, etc. in the appropriate heat transfer equations. A similar situation occurs when the dampers on a fan are completely closed and operation is at the shutoff condition.

The exact values of pressure are not always determinate in closed systems. If there is a major opening to atmosphere, the pressure at that point will be atmospheric even if there is no flow through the opening. The pressures at other locations around the system can then be figured accordingly. In a tightly closed system there may be a panel which is flexible enough to allow equalization of internal and external pressures. If not, the pressures will fluctuate so much at any location that measurement becomes difficult or impossible.

Closed systems can be pumped up or down to any pressure by means of an auxiliary compressor or vacuum pump. Fans for circulating the gas within the system must be selected for the appropriate density. The pressures throughout the system may be calculated with reference to the pressure at the pressurizing connection.

Capacity Control

If a fan system must operate over a range of capacities, some means of adjusting either the fan characteristics or the system characteristics must be provided.

System characteristics can be altered by inserting additional resistance or by providing alternative flow paths. Gradual adjustment can be provided with movable dampers either in the main passage or in the bypass.

Fan characteristics may be modified by changing the fan itself, its rotative speed of by altering the inlet whirl. Gradual adjustment is usually possible within the limits of the device used whether it be a variable speed motor or transmission or a variable inlet vane. Step-by-step adjustment is possible with multi-speed motors and multiple fan arrangements.

The choice of a specific control method should be based on an economic evaluation. Before such an evaluation can be made, it is necessary to estimate the operating times at various capacities. Each of the available methods entails a loss in efficiency over most if not all of its operating range. The most inefficient methods are usually the least expensive to install originally. Only a power-cost evaluation will indicate the best method on the basis of both first and operating costs.

The effects of various methods of capacity control on fan operation are illustrated in Figure 112. All curves are drawn for the same fan (a backward curve centrifugal) operating at the same full load speed. The system resistance varies as the square of the capacity.

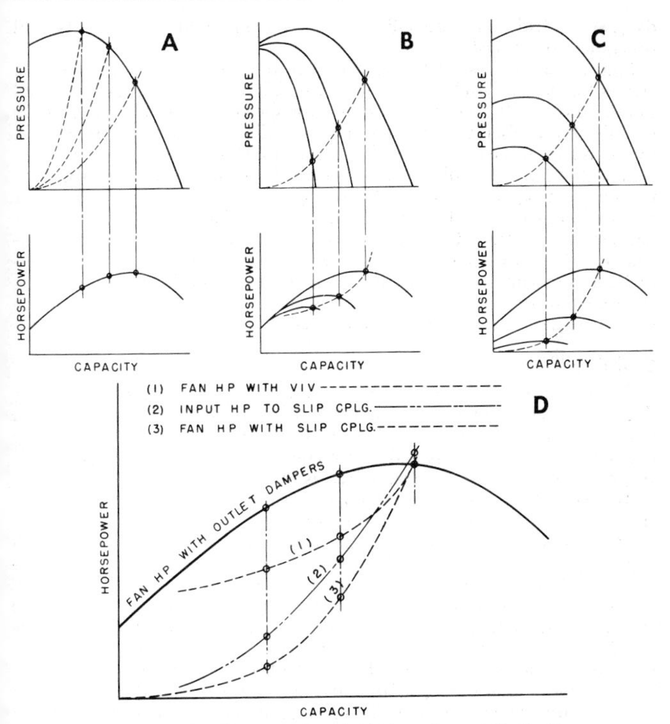

Figure 112—Horsepowers for Various Control Methods

Figure 112A is drawn for damper control. The pressure required of the fan is higher at reduced ratings than at design because the damper increases system resistance. The dotted system curves include this increase which also varies as the square of the capacity. The horsepowers at one-half and three-fourths load are less than at full load because of the nature of the fan characteristics. This would not be true if the characteristics of an axial fan were used instead of those for a centrifugal fan.

Figure 112B is drawn for variable inlet vane control. Three fan curves are drawn for three different positions or settings of the variable inlet vanes. The horsepowers required by the fan at reduced capacities fall between those for damper control and those for speed control.

Figure 112C is drawn for speed control. Instead of three system curves, three fan curves are drawn, one each at full, three-fourths and one-half speeds. There is also a horsepower curve for each speed. The horsepowers at reduced capacities are less than the corresponding horsepowers for damper control since fan efficiency is constant and no elements add resistance to the system.

Figure 112D shows the horsepower relations for all three methods. The curves for damper and vane control are exactly as in Figures 112A and 112B; however, two curves are shown for speed control. The extra curve includes the inefficiency of a hydraulic coupling used as a variable speed transmission. It, therefore, represents the input to the transmission rather than to the fan as for all the other curves. This curve indicates that there is a range of capacities near full load where inlet vane control is superior to speed control on a horsepower input basis. The simplicity of a duct damper gives it the advantage in first cost. Variable inlet vanes are considerably less expensive than most methods of speed control. Speed control does have additional advantages when considerable operation at less than maximum speed is expected. The accompanying reduction in noise and increase in life may also be appreciable.

Stability

The flow through a system and its fan will normally be steady. If the fluctuations occasioned by a temporary disturbance are quickly damped out, the fan system may be described as having a "stable" operating characteristic. If the unsteady flow continues after the disturbance is removed, the operating characteristic is "unstable."

To insure stable operation the slopes of the pressure-capacity curves for the fan and system should be of opposite sign. Almost all systems have a positive slope, i.e., the pressure requirement or resistance increases with capacity. Therefore, for stable operation the fan curve should have a negative slope. Such is the case at or above the design capacity.

When the slopes of the fan and system characteristics are of opposite sign, any disturbance tending to produce a temporary decrease in flow is nullified by the increase in fan pressure. When the slopes are of the same sign, any tendency to decrease flow is strengthened by the resulting decrease in fan pressure. When fan and system curves coincide over a range of capacities, the operating characteristics are extremely unstable. Even if the curves exactly coincide at only one point, the flow may vary over a considerable range.

There may or may not be any obvious indications of unstable operation. The pressure and power fluctuations that accompany unsteady flow may be so small and rapid that they cannot be detected by any but the most sensitive of instruments. Less rapid fluctuations may be detected on the ordinary instruments used in fan testing. The changes in noise which occur with each change in flow rate are easily detected by ear as individual beats if the beat frequency is below about 10 cycles per second. (Refer to Figure 83 for a more precise set of limits on discord.) In any event the over-all noise level will be higher with unsteady flow than with steady flow.

The conditions which accompany unsteady flow are variously described as pulsations, resonant surging, pumping, etc. Since these conditions only occur when the operating point is to the left of maximum pressure on the fan curve, this peak is frequently referred to as the surge point or pumping limit.

The beat frequency or frequency of pulsation can frequently be calculated by considering the system to be a Helmholz resonator. If the system consists of a large cross section duct connected to a fan by means of a small cross section duct, the frequency f may be computed from

$$f = \frac{c}{2\pi}\sqrt{\frac{S}{LV}}. \tag{306}$$

For such a "concentrated" volume system the cross sectional area (S) and length (L) are those of the small cross section connecting duct. This may be likened to the neck of a resonator. The volume (V) of the large cross section duct which may be compared with the main chamber of a resonator must be relatively large. Actually, best results are obtained when the fan wheel's circumference is added to the length of the small duct and any transformation piece to obtain the length (L). The speed of sound (c) in standard dry air is 1125 fps so that $c/2\pi$ is 178 fps for this condition.

If the system consists of an equal "distributed" volume, i.e., the duct work connected to the fan has practically uniform cross section, the neck condition should be based on the fan outlet area (S) and a length (L) equal to the circumference of the wheel plus the length of any transformation piece. In such cases the frequency f will be somewhat greater than that indicated by Equation 305. An increase of up to 57% may be expected depending on how perfectly the volume is distributed.

Pulsation may be prevented by rating the fan to the right of the surge point. Fans are usually selected on this basis but it is sometimes necessary to reduce the volume delivered to a value below that at the surge point.

Volume reduction will not always lead to pulsation. On one series of tests by Heath and Elliot* no pulsations were detected unless the fan pressure exceeded about 9″ WG. It is quite probable that incipient pulsations were damped out. Damping effect depends on the system volume.

If the required capacity is less than that at the pumping limit, pulsation can be prevented in various ways all of which in effect provide a negatively sloping fan curve at the actual operating point. To accomplish this effect the required pressure must be less than the fan capabilities at the required capacity. One method is to bleed sufficient air so that actual operation is beyond the pumping limit. Other possible methods are the use of speed or vane control for volume reduction. In either of these cases, the point of operation on the new fan curve must be to the right of the new surge point. Although in the section on "Capacity Control" dampers were considered a part of the system, they may also be considered a part of the fan if located in the right position. Accordingly, pulsations may be eliminated in a supply system if the damper is on the inlet of the blower. Similarly, dampering at the outlet of the exhauster will control pulsation in exhaust systems.

Another condition frequently referred to as instability is associated with flow separation in the blade passages of a rotor and is evidenced by slight discontinuities in the performance curve. There may be a small range of capacities at which two distinctly different pressures may be

*W. R. Heath and W. R. Elliot, Control and Prediction of Pulsation Frequency in a Duct System, *Trans. ASME*, J. Appl. Mech., Dec. 1946, Vol. 13, No. 4, pp. A291-3.

developed depending on which of the two flow patterns exists. Such a condition usually occurs at capacities just to the left of peak efficiency.

The range of speeds over which a compressor may operate may be limited by choking, that is, the increase in flow rate as predicted by the fan laws cannot be obtained and the slope of the high-speed pressure-capacity characteristic approaches infinity. Choking is not usually a problem with fans.

Mutual Influence of Fan and System

Fan performance data are generally based on tests wherein the air approaches the inlet with a uniform velocity, free of whirl. Duct element losses except where noted otherwise are based on similar flow conditions. The effects of prerotation on fan performance were discussed in Chapters 6 and 7. The effects of one elbow on another were listed briefly in Chapter 3.

Elbows, unless provided with adequate turning vanes or splitters, produce uneven velocity patterns that may persist for considerable distances in subsequent straight ducts. Non-uniform inlet velocities may in themselves alter fan performance since different portions of the impeller will be loaded differently. Non-uniform velocities may produce whirls in the inlet flow which also affect fan performance. To prevent adverse effects every reasonable precaution should be taken to insure uniform flow from all elbows.

Inlet boxes are special elbows which are frequently furnished with fans. Their principal purpose may be to turn the air or to provide a means of excluding the bearings from the air stream. Fan performance should be based on tests with boxes in place if they are to be furnished. This is not always practical. The total inlet box loss which includes the effect on fan performance as well as elbow loss will be of the order of one inlet velocity head. The exact value will depend on both fan and box design. The relative direction of inlet box entry and fan discharge may also have an effect, particularly when forward curved blade designs are involved. The highest loss usually occurs when the air entry is from the direction opposite (180°) the direction of discharge. The least loss usually occurs with the entry from the same direction (0°) as the discharge although an angularity of 90° is not much worse. A rectangular box with an axial depth of approximately 50% of the fan inlet diameter and a width of approximately three times the depth will be quite suitable. A splitter plate in the plane of the shaft extending from the closed end of the box out toward the shaft is recommended to prevent any adverse effects due to whirl. The axial depth may be tapered gradually to minimize effects of uneven velocity.

The velocity pattern at fan discharge will vary with design. Performance data are usually based on tests with a straight discharge duct. If an elbow is located quite close to the discharge, there may be some loss in fan performance due to a reduction in static pressure regain. The loss through the elbow may be affected by an uneven velocity pattern. If the velocity along the inside radius of the elbow is higher than that along the outside radius, the loss will be higher than normal. The loss will be less than normal if velocity is higher along the outside radius than along the inside radius.

CHAPTER 11

FAN MECHANICS

The mechanical design of a fan should provide the various parts with adequate strength and stability to withstand the forces expected during all phases of operation. Both steady state inertial and vibrational forces should be considered as well as fluid forces. The operating conditions and expected life should be clearly defined. Maintenance and manufacturing requirements should be anticipated.

The forces which may act on the various fan parts will be discussed first. Discussions on stress and strength follow. These are followed by short dissertations on balancing and other mechanical considerations.

Torque and Thrust Forces

As noted in Chapter 6 the axial, radial, and tangential components of the forces of the fluid on the rotor lead to axial thrust, radial thrust, and torque, respectively. In some analyses, it is most convenient to consider the corresponding pressure components, but in other cases it is simpler to consider the component forces directly.

The tangential forces react on the blades in the direction opposite rotation. They are transmitted as torque to the driving shaft. The forces may be transmitted through a hub, or through a back plate or spider and hub, to the driving shaft. If the difference in pressure across each portion of blade could be determined, the corresponding tangential forces could be calculated. The total tangential force (F_{tang}) can be determined from the total mass flow (m) and the effective change in tangential velocity through the rotor (ΔV_{tang}):

$$F_{tang} = \frac{m}{g_c} \Delta V_{tang}. \qquad (307)$$

The force per blade can be determined by simple division. The radius (r) at which this force may be considered to act can be determined from the torque (τ):

$$r = \frac{\tau}{F_{tang}}. \qquad (308)$$

The torque in inch-pounds may be calculated from the horsepower (HP) and speed (RPM) from

$$\tau = \frac{63030\ HP}{RPM}. \qquad (309)$$

The axial forces react on all parts of the rotor in both directions. Only the unbalanced axial forces produce axial thrust which must be taken by a thrust bearing to the foundation through the bearing supports. The distribution of pressure due to fan action may or may not be unbalanced in the axial direction depending on rotor design. The resultant axial thrust, if any, always tends to move the rotor in the direction of the inlet. A fan will not produce thrust if the pressure distribution is balanced. This is usually the case for double inlet fans.

In an axial flow fan the total axial thrust or net axial force (F_{ax}) in pounds may be calculated approximately from

$$F_{ax} = 5.192\ FTP \frac{\pi D_T^2}{4}, \tag{310}$$

where the fan total pressure (FTP) is in inches water gage and the impeller tip diameter (D_T) is in feet.

In a single inlet centrifugal fan the total axial thrust may be calculated approximately from

$$F_{ax} = 5.192\ FSP \frac{\pi D_I^2}{4} K, \tag{311}$$

where the fan static pressure (FSP) is in inches water gage and the impeller inlet diameter (D_I) is in feet. The value of the proportionality constant (K) may be assumed to be about 1.0 whenever the gage pressure inside the fan housing is positive (blower applications), the impeller is completely shrouded (inlet shroud and back plate), and the shaft will allow some leakage flow (no stuffing box). If the gage pressure in the housing is negative (exhauster application), the shaft hole is tightly sealed, or both, the value of K may be assumed to be approximately 2.0. If the impeller is completely open (paddle wheel) there will be practically no net thrust. If the impeller has only one shroud (cone wheel) the value of K will be somewhat higher than for a completely shrouded impeller.

Axial thrust may be reduced or even reversed by building fins on the outside of the back plate. Such fins can be designed to equalize the pressure with very little flow and only a small power increase. Balancing holes in the back plate or a balancing chamber such as are frequently employed on high pressure single suction pumps could also be used but are seldom justified.

The change in momentum occasioned by the change in direction at the inlet of a centrifugal fan also produces axial thrust. This thrust (F'_{ax}) tends to move the impeller in the direction opposite the inlet and may be calculated from the mass flow rate (m) and the axial approach velocity (V'_{ax}) using

$$F'_{ax} = \frac{m}{g_c} V'_{ax}. \tag{312}$$

This momentum thrust is usually negligible compared to the pressure thrust.

The distribution of forces within a fan due to an externally applied vacuum or pressure may or may not be unbalanced. Usually this pressure or vacuum can be considered to act only on the cross sectional area of the shaft and then only if one end extends through the casing to a region of atmospheric pressure. The resulting thrust may be directed toward or away from the inlet depending on the direction of the shaft extension and whether there is a pressure or vacuum.

There are no radial components of the forces of the fluid particles on the rotor in an axial flow fan when there are no radial velocity components. In a centrifugal fan the radial forces will be perfectly balanced if the pressures at all points on the impeller discharge are equal. Reasonably uniform pressures are obtained with volute type housings over most of the usual operating range. Since the volute is only correct at design, non-uniformity and therefore radial thrust increases with increased departure from the best efficiency point of rating. Any unbalanced radial thrust acting on the rotor must be taken by the journal bearings to the foundation through the bearing supports.

Unbalanced pressure forces acting on the casing in any direction must be taken by foundation bolts. A down blast fan will tend to push itself upward but the weight of the unit is usually sufficient to hold it in place. A single inlet fan will slide in the direction of the inlet unless restrained by friction or by some other force. Unbalanced torque will cause the unit to rotate in the direction opposite rotation unless restrained.

Centrifugal Force

Any particle of mass rotating about any point except its own center of gravity has an acceleration toward the center of rotation equal to the linear velocity squared (U^2) divided by the radius (R). The restraining force known as centripetal force, which is equal to the product of this acceleration and the mass (M) must be directed toward the center of rotation. The reaction of the mass on its restraints must be equal and act in the opposite direction to the restraining force. This force, known as centrifugal force (F), may be calculated from

$$F = \frac{M\,U^2}{g_c\,R} = \frac{M\,R\,N^2}{2934}, \tag{313}$$

where the speed of rotation (N) is in rpm, F is in lb, M is in lbm, and R is in ft.

Centrifugal forces are important in the mechanical design of a fan in two rather distinct ways.

First, there is a group of internal forces. The centrifugal forces of the individual particles of any member must be restrained by the adjoining particles. This induces both radial and tangential stresses in the member or even adjoining members. Adequate strength must be provided to prevent failure.

Second, there is a possibility of a net external force. The centrifugal force of the entire rotor is the same as if its whole mass were concentrated at the center of gravity. If the center of rotation coincides with the center of mass there will be no external force. Any force developed because of a difference in these two centers will be transmitted to the bearings. The observable reaction will be one of vibration. The direction of the force will change continuously due to rotation. Equation 313 indicates that a small mass at a large radius is sufficient to balance a large mass at a small radius.

Vibratory Forces and Critical Speeds

In any elastic system there are certain operating speeds at which dangerous vibrations are likely to occur. These critical speeds correspond to the various natural frequencies of vibration of the system components. Fans should be designed so that operating speeds will differ from critical speeds by a safe amount. This usually means operation below the first critical but may mean operation between two criticals.

There are two types of vibrations—forced and free. An elastic body will vibrate freely at one or more of its natural frequencies if its equilibrium is momentarily disturbed by an external force. The motion will gradually die down due to damping. If an external force is applied repeatedly, an elastic body will vibrate at the frequency of the external excitation whether this coincides with a natural frequency or not. Resonance occurs when the excitation frequency coincides with one of the natural frequencies. Large amplitude vibrations accompany resonance unless there is considerable damping in the system.

The free vibrations of an elastic body may consist of an infinite number of different particle motions. Among these various modes of vibration there are certain principal ones wherein all the particle motions are at the same frequency and follow a precise pattern.

The principal modes of vibration which are of most concern are those which occur at the lowest frequencies. It is convenient to classify these modes of vibration according to their numerical order and the direction of vibration relative to the principal axis of the part or member. The direction of oscillation may be longitudinal, lateral, or angular. Longitudinal vibrations are seldom serious in fan parts. Most fan parts may be considered as either beams or plates. Lateral vibrations lead to bending. Angular vibrations lead to torsion. The first bending mode may have a higher or lower frequency than the first torsional mode depending on the geometry and the material of the part.

The forces which produce vibration may result from the motion of the parts themselves or from unbalance. If there is no damping, even the slightest unbalance may cause dangerously large amplitude vibrations at a critical speed. Damping forces arise due to air friction and internal friction in the vibrating structure. With normal damping a well balanced fan will easily pass through a critical whereas an unbalanced fan might not. Damping causes the vibration amplitude to lag behind the exciting force at speeds below critical as noted under "Balancing."

There are various methods of calculating the critical speeds of rotating shafts. In simple systems with concentrated loads the natural frequency of lateral vibration (f) in Hz or the critical speed (N_{cr}) in rpm can be calculated from the static deflection of the shaft (y) in inches using

$$N_{cr} = 60\,f = \frac{60}{2\,\pi}\sqrt{\frac{g}{y}} = \frac{187.7}{\sqrt{y}}. \qquad (314)$$

For uniform loads the deflection should be modified as indicated in Table 60. This relationship between critical speed and deflection is shown graphically in Figure 113 by the solid line. Any speed below 80% of the critical is usually considered safe in fan shaft design.

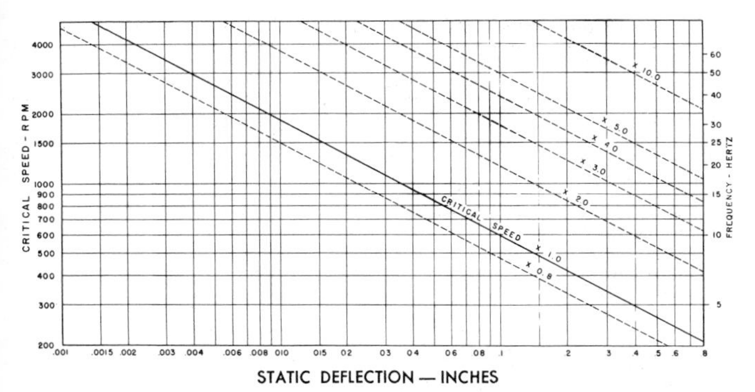

Figure 113—Critical Speed vs Static Deflection

Any deflection of the bearings should be included with the shaft deflection when calculating critical speeds. Bearing flexibility may be different in different directions.

The static deflections due to the mass of the shaft and any concentrated masses, but not those due to any uni-directional force such as belt pull, should be calculated as if the shaft position were horizontal even if it happens to be vertical. The formula is strictly correct only for those cases where the mass of the system can be considered concentrated at a single point and the static deflection is calculated at that point. Approximate results can be obtained for other systems by totalling the deflections under each load. Table 60 lists the deflection equations for beams with various types of loads.

Improved accuracy can be obtained in the more complicated cases by using Rayleigh's method which involves the equation

$$N_{cr} = 187.7 \sqrt{\frac{W_1 y_1 + W_2 y_2 + \ldots + W_n y_n}{W_1 y_1^2 + W_2 y_2^2 + \ldots + W_n y_n^2}}. \qquad (315)$$

In using Rayleigh's method it is necessary to determine the total deflections (y_1, etc.) under each of the loads. These deflections result not only from the load at that location, but all other loads as well. The first approximation based on static loads (W_1, etc.) is usually within 1% of the correct value. This can be improved by recalculating the deflections using the dynamic loads ($W_1\,y_1$, etc.).

Dunkerley's equation may also be employed, i.e.,

$$\frac{1}{N_{cr}^2} = \frac{1}{N_1^2} + \frac{1}{N_2^2} + \ldots + \frac{1}{N_n^2}. \qquad (316)$$

In this equation the actual critical speed (N_{cr}) is given in terms of the critical speed (N_1, etc.) for each mass (M_1, etc.) in the absence of all others.

TABLE 60—SHEAR, MOMENT, AND DEFLECTION FORMULAS

Support and Loading Diagrams	Reaction, Vertical Shears, and Constraining Moments	Bending Moments and Maximum Bending Moments
Cantilever, End Load 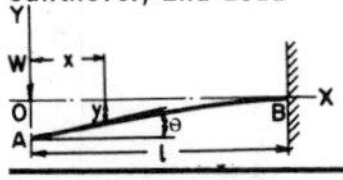	$R_2 = +W$	$M = -Wx$
	$V = -W$	Max $M = -Wl$ (at B)
Cantilever, Unif. Load 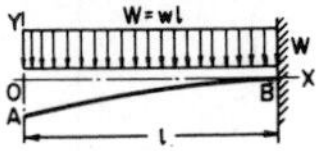	$R_2 = +W$	$M = -\frac{1}{2}\frac{W}{l}x^2$
	$V = -\frac{W}{l}x$	Max $M = -\frac{1}{2}Wl$ (at B)
End Supports, Ctr. Load 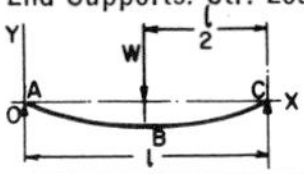	$R_1 = +\frac{1}{2}W$; $R_2 = +\frac{1}{2}W$	$M' = +\frac{1}{2}Wx$; $M'' = +\frac{1}{2}W(l-x)$
	$V' = +\frac{1}{2}W$; $V'' = -\frac{1}{2}W$	Max $M = +\frac{1}{4}Wl$ (at B)
End Supports, Int. Load 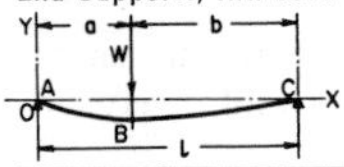	$R_1 = +W\frac{b}{l}$; $R_2 = +W\frac{a}{l}$	$M' = +W\frac{b}{l}x$; $M'' = +W\frac{a}{l}(l-x)$
	$V' = +W\frac{b}{l}$; $V'' = -W\frac{a}{l}$	Max $M = +W\frac{ab}{l}$ (at B)
End Supports, Unif. Load 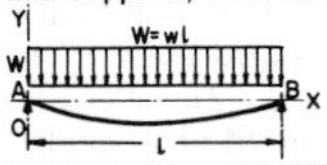	$R_1 = +\frac{1}{2}W$; $R_2 = +\frac{1}{2}W$	$M = \frac{1}{2}W\left(x - \frac{x^2}{l}\right)$
	$V = \frac{1}{2}W\left(1 - \frac{2x}{l}\right)$	Max $M = +\frac{1}{8}Wl\left(\text{at } x = \frac{1}{2}l\right)$
Fixed Ends, Ctr. Load 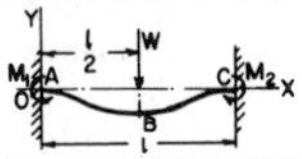	$R_1 = \frac{1}{2}W$; $M_1 = \frac{1}{8}Wl$	$M' = \frac{1}{8}W(4x - l)$; $M'' = \frac{1}{8}W(3l - 4x)$
	$V' = +\frac{1}{2}W$; $V'' = -\frac{1}{2}W$	Max $M = \pm\frac{1}{8}Wl$ (+ at B, − at A & C)
Fixed Ends, Int. Load 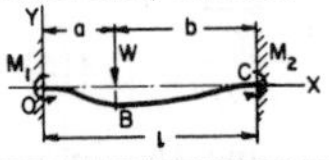	$R_1 = \frac{Wb^2}{l^3}(3a + b)$; $M_1 = W\frac{ab^2}{l^2}$	$M' = -W\frac{ab^2}{l^2} + R_1x$
	$V' = R_1$; $V'' = R_1 - W$	Max poss. $M = \frac{4}{27}Wl\left(\text{when } a = \frac{1}{3}l\right)$
Fixed Ends, Unif. Load 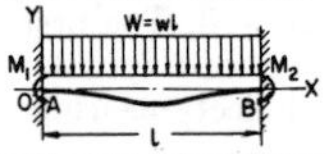	$R_1 = \frac{1}{2}W$; $M_1 = \frac{1}{12}Wl$	$M = \frac{1}{2}W\left(x - \frac{x^2}{l} - \frac{1}{6}l\right)$
	$V = \frac{1}{2}W\left(1 - \frac{2x}{l}\right)$	Max $M = -\frac{1}{12}Wl$ (at A & B)

W = load in lb
R = reaction in lb
M = moment in in.-lb
V = vertical shear in lb
x = distance in in.
l = length of beam in in.
a = length in in.
b = length in in.

Adapted from data of R. J. Roark, "Formulas for Stress and Strain," McGraw-Hill Book Co., Inc., New York, 1965, pp. 104-113.

FOR BEAMS WITH TRANSVERSE LOADS—TABLE 60

Deflections, Maximum Deflections, and End Slopes

$y = -\frac{1}{6}\frac{W}{EI}(x^3 - 3l^2 x + 2l^3)$ $\theta = +\frac{1}{2}\frac{Wl^2}{EI}$ (at A)

Max $y = -\frac{1}{3}\frac{Wl^3}{EI}$ (at A) (× 1.000 for use in Eq. 314)

$y = -\frac{1}{24}\frac{W}{EIl}(x^4 - 4l^3x + 3l^4)$ $\theta = +\frac{1}{6}\frac{Wl^2}{EI}$ (at A)

Max $y = -\frac{1}{8}\frac{Wl^3}{EI}$ (at A) (× 0.645 for use in Eq. 314)

$y = -\frac{1}{48}\frac{W}{EI}(3l^2x - 4x^3)$ $\theta = -\frac{1}{16}\frac{Wl^2}{EI}$ (at A)

Max $y = -\frac{1}{48}\frac{Wl^3}{EI}$ (at B) (× 1.000 for use in Eq. 314)

$y' = -\frac{1}{6}\frac{Wbx}{EIl}[2l(l - x) - b^2 - (l - x)^2]$ $\theta = -\frac{1}{6}\frac{W}{EI}\left(bl - \frac{b^3}{l}\right)$ (at A)

Max $y = -\frac{1}{27}\frac{Wab}{EIl}(a + 2b)\sqrt{3a(a + 2b)}$ $\left(\text{at } x = \sqrt{\frac{1}{3}a(a + 2b)} \text{ if } a > b\right)$

$y = -\frac{1}{24}\frac{Wx}{EIl}(l^3 - 2lx^2 + x^3)$ $\theta = -\frac{1}{24}\frac{Wl^2}{EI}$ (at A)

Max $y = -\frac{5}{384}\frac{Wl^3}{EI}\left(\text{at } x = \frac{1}{2}l\right)$ (× 0.789 for use in Eq. 314)

$y' = -\frac{1}{48}\frac{W}{EI}(3lx^2 - 4x^3)$

Max $y = -\frac{1}{192}\frac{Wl^3}{EI}$ (at B) (× 1.000 for use in Eq. 314)

$y' = \frac{1}{6}\frac{Wb^2x^2}{EIl^3}(3ax + bx - 3al)$

Max $y = -\frac{2}{3}\frac{W}{EI}\frac{a^3b^2}{(3a + b)^2}\left(\text{at } x = \frac{2al}{3b + a} \text{ if } a > b\right)$

$y = \frac{1}{24}\frac{Wx^2}{EIl}(2lx - l^2 - x^2)$

Max $y = -\frac{1}{384}\frac{Wl^3}{EI}\left(\text{at } x = \frac{1}{2}l\right)$ (× 0.766 for use in Eq. 314)

y = deflection in in. θ = slope in radians
E = modulus of elasticity in psi I = moment of section in in.^{4}
Prime means valid from A to B—double prime from B to C.
Constraining moments, loads, and reactions positive as shown.
Bending moments positive when clockwise. V & y positive when upward.
If beam is turned end for end, lengths a & b can be interchanged.

In addition to the primary critical speed caused by unbalance, a secondary critical can be observed at one-half the speed of the first in some applications. This effect is occasionally due to unbalance and gravity, but more often it is due to a non-uniform flexibility of the shaft. Such a condition might result from a keyway or flat spot on the shaft.

Shaft criticals due to torsional vibrations are rarely encountered in fans. The natural frequency (f) of a simple torsional system may be determined from the modulus of rigidity (G), the polar moment of inertia (J) of the shaft cross section, the length (l) of the shaft, and the mass moment of inertia (I_{m1}, etc.) of the concentrated masses in the appropriate equation. For the case where two masses are connected by a uniform shaft,

$$f = \frac{1}{2\,\pi}\sqrt{\frac{G\,J}{l}\left(\frac{I_{m1} + I_{m2}}{I_{m1}\,I_{m2}}\right)}. \tag{317}$$

For the case where the moment of inertia (I_{m2}) of one of the masses is so large compared to the other that the corresponding end of the shaft may be considered fixed.

$$f = \frac{1}{2\,\pi}\sqrt{\frac{G\,J}{l\,I_{m1}}}. \tag{318}$$

More complicated systems require more elaborate computations. The methods are outlined in most texts on vibration.

The various plates and beams which comprise a fan all have critical speeds. As with shafts, only the simpler cases will be discussed here. The lowest natural frequencies generally occur with cantilever beams. The blades of unshrouded wheels fall in this category. Shrouding may raise the natural frequency to several times the unshrouded value.

The lowest natural frequency (f) of a uniform cantilever beam in bending may be determined from the modulus of elasticity (E) of the beam material, the second moment (I) of the beam cross section about the principal axis, the length (l) of the beam, and its weight per unit length (w) using

$$f = \frac{3.52}{2\,\pi}\sqrt{\frac{g\,E\,I}{w\,l^4}}. \tag{319}$$

The natural frequency of an identical beam fixed at both ends (instead of one) is 6.4 times higher than indicated by Equation 319. The lowest natural frequency of a ring with radius (r) is

$$f = 2.68\sqrt{\frac{g\,E\,I}{w\,r^4}}. \tag{320}$$

Torsional and coupled torsional-bending vibrations also can be induced. In many cases the inherent stiffness of a part is increased by the spring action due to centrifugal force.

Stresses, Strains, and Other Design Considerations

The forces acting on a fan part may tend to bend, twist, tear, or crack it or any part to which the forces can be transmitted. To prevent failure the stresses induced in the various parts must be limited to a safe value.

Breakage is not the only criterion of failure. In some cases elastic deformation must be limited while in others a certain amount of plastic deformation can be tolerated if it simply results in a redistribution of stress. Both the short time and long time effects of stress must be considered.

Margins of safety must be provided to allow for variations in the strength of the material, dimensional tolerances, and any uncertainties regarding operation. The maximum expected stresses must be calculated. This may be accomplished by applying stress concentration factors to the calculated average stress. The ultimate strength, yield strength, fatigue strength, elastic limit, proportional limit, or any other appropriate property of the material may be used together with an appropriate margin of safety to determine the maximum allowable stress.

Some elementary facts about stress calculations are listed here for convenience. The average tensional stress (s) in a tension member may be computed from the cross sectional area (A) at the expected plane of separation and the force component (F) acting along a line perpendicular to that area, using

$$s = \frac{F}{A}. \tag{321}$$

Compressive stresses are also normal stresses but are directed opposite to tensile stresses. Bending stresses (s) in a beam are a particular distribution of tensile and compressive stresses across the section. Such stresses are of zero magnitude at the neutral axis. This axis may or may not coincide with the centroidal axis depending on the curvature of the beam. The stress in any fibre of a straight beam may be computed from the bending moment (M), the second moment of the cross section about the neutral axis (I), and the distance (y) of the fiber from the neutral axis, using

$$s = \frac{M\,y}{I}. \tag{322}$$

Shear stresses may be induced by any load parallel to the section. Direct shear (V) produces an average stress (s_s) over the cross sectional area (A) of

$$s_s = \frac{V}{A}. \tag{323}$$

Torque (τ) produces shear stresses (s_s). For a circular shaft with polar moment of inertia (J) the stress at any radius (r) is

$$s_s = \frac{\tau\,r}{J}. \tag{324}$$

The properties of various sections are tabulated in Table 61.

The second moments of area (I_x) are about the horizontal centriodal axis ($x-x$) shown in Table 61. The second moment of area about any parallel axis at a distance (y) is greater by an amount equal to Ay^2. The second moment of any composite section is the total for all the individual sections about the same axis. The stresses induced in the part may be due to more than one force. The maximum combined stress must not exceed the maximum allowable.

TABLE 61—PROPERTIES OF SECTIONS

SECTION	$I_x = AK^2$	$J = I_x + I_y$	A	$K = \sqrt{\frac{I}{A}}$
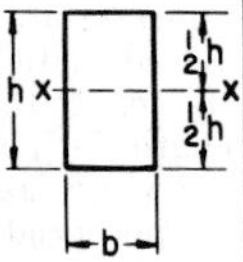 Rectangle (h × b; x–x at $\frac{1}{2}h$)	$\frac{bh^3}{12}$	$\frac{bh(b^2+h^2)}{12}$	bh	$\frac{h}{\sqrt{12}}$
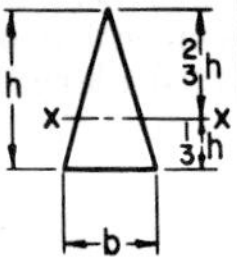 Triangle (h × b; x–x at $\frac{2}{3}h$ from apex, $\frac{1}{3}h$ from base)	$\frac{bh^3}{36}$	—	$\frac{bh}{2}$	$\frac{h}{\sqrt{18}}$
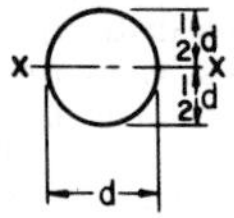 Solid circle (d; x–x at $\frac{1}{2}d$)	$\frac{\pi d^4}{64}$	$\frac{\pi d^4}{32}$	$\frac{\pi d^2}{4}$	$\frac{d}{4}$
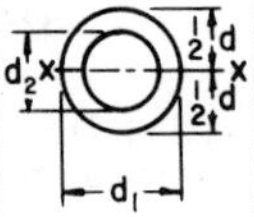 Hollow circle (d_1, d_2; x–x at $\frac{1}{2}d$)	$\frac{\pi(d_1^4-d_2^4)}{64}$	$\frac{\pi(d_1^4-d_2^4)}{32}$	$\frac{\pi(d_1^2-d_2^2)}{4}$	$\sqrt{\frac{(d_1^2+d_2^2)}{16}}$
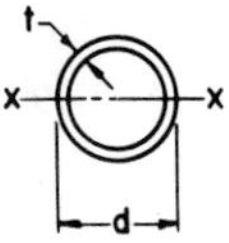 Thin ring (d, t; x–x)	$\frac{\pi d^3 t}{8}$	$\frac{\pi d^3 t}{4}$	$\pi d t$	$\frac{d}{\sqrt{8}}$

The basic parts of a fan rotor may be classified as either rotating discs, beams, plates, or shells. The stresses induced in these members are largely due to centrifugal force. This is particularly the case for blades, hubs, and shrouds. Shafts must be capable of withstanding both bending and torque loads. Bearing systems must be able to take both axial and radial thrust loads. Casings, gaskets, and seals must be designed for pressure loads.

Except for any critical speed operation the maximum stresses are induced either in starting or at maximum speed. Damaging stresses may be produced if an excessive starting torque is impressed on the rotor. However, if a fan is designed for safe operation at the maximum speed it will usually be satisfactory for use with a normal-starting-torque motor.

There is no practical way to design a part for operation at a critical speed. The only practicable solutions are to change the critical speed by altering the design or to change the operating speed. The following remarks are of most concern in calculating stresses at maximum speed conditions.

The stresses induced in fan blades are primarily due to the centrifugal force of the blade itself. The resultant force acts radially through the center of gravity of the blade insofar as the tensile and bending stresses induced at the root of an axial flow type of blade are concerned. Since such a blade is set at an angle to the plane of rotation, a twisting moment will also be produced. In order to determine its magnitude, the distribution of the particles of mass and their centrifugal force components which produce the twisting couple must be taken into account. The forces associated with torque and thrust react on the blades to produce bending and twisting of an axial blade. The resulting stresses should be combined with those produced by centrifugal force.

Centrifugal fan blades are subjected to the same kinds of forces as axial fan blades. However, their shapes and the methods of restraint may vary considerably. Straight radial blades are best suited to resist bending in the radial direction due to centrifugal force because of the high second moments of their sections in that direction. They are relatively weak under torque. In any case, a blade may be considered as a beam subjected to a rather complex transverse loading. Edges terminating at a shroud can generally be assumed as fixed, others as free ends or edges. Backward curved blades are stronger than backward inclined flat blades.

In some fans, blades are mounted on spider arms. The arms must withstand the centrifugal forces imposed by their own rotation and those forces transmitted from the blade. These forces may produce tensile, bending, or twisting stresses.

Shrouds and hubs can frequently be treated as rotating discs or composite discs. Both radial and tangential stresses are induced in such members by rotation. The maximum self-induced stress in a circular disc of uniform thickness can be determined from the properties of the material, the speed, and the radii. The maximum radial stress (s_r) occurs at $\sqrt{R_o R_i}$. Its magnitude is

$$Max\ s_r = \frac{3 + \nu}{8} \frac{\delta}{386} \left(\frac{2 \pi N}{60} \right)^2 (R_o^2 + R_i^2). \qquad (325)$$

The maximum tangential stress (s_t) occurs at the perimeter of the hole, if any, (R_i). Its magnitude is

$$Max\ s_t = \frac{1}{4}\frac{\delta}{386}\left(\frac{2\ \pi\ N}{60}\right)^2 [(3+\nu)\ R_o^2 + (1-\nu)\ R_i^2]. \qquad (326)$$

For stresses in psi the speed (N) must be in rpm, the density (δ) in pounds per cubic inch, and the inside radius (R_i) and outside radius (R_o) in inches. Poisson's ratio (ν) is dimensionless. Values are listed in the appendix for certain materials. Other loads must be carried by the shrouds, including the centrifugal forces of the blades and the pressure of any shrink fit that may exist at the operating speed. Various methods are employed to determine the combined stress distribution for the many shroud shapes that are used on fans.

Fan shafts must be able to withstand the stresses occasioned by the torque and the bending moments. A shaft designed to operate below the first critical speed will usually have sufficient strength against bending and torque. Nevertheless, the situation should be examined, particularly on low speed equipment with necked down shafts at the bearings. A maximum bending moment or moments occur at the support or supports for cantilever and simply supported beams, respectively. The maximum shear stress (s_s) is related to the shaft diameter (d) or its section modulus (J/r) and the loads according to

$$\frac{\pi\ d^3}{16} = \frac{J}{r} = \frac{\sqrt{(K_M\ M)^2 + (K_\tau\ \tau)^2}}{max\ s_s}. \qquad (327)$$

The normal bending moment (M) and the torque (τ) must be adjusted for any possible shock conditions. The bending moment factor (K_M) should be between 1.5 and 3.0 and the torque factor (K_τ) between 1.0 and 3.0 depending on how suddenly the load can be applied. Values of $\pi\ d^3/16$ are listed in Table 62.

TABLE 62—VALUES OF $\pi d^3/16$ FOR SHAFTS

in in.^{3}

Dia.	1″	2″	3″	4″	5″	6″	7″	8″	9″	10″
0	0.196	1.571	5.301	12.57	24.54	42.41	67.35	100.5	143.1	196.4
1/16	0.236	1.723	5.639	13.16	25.47	43.75	—	—	—	—
1/8	0.280	1.884	5.992	13.78	26.43	45.12	71.02	105.3	149.2	203.8
3/16	0.329	2.055	6.359	14.42	27.41	46.51	—	—	—	—
1/4	0.384	2.236	6.740	15.07	28.41	47.93	74.82	110.3	155.4	211.4
5/16	0.444	2.428	7.136	15.75	29.44	49.39	—	—	—	—
3/8	0.510	2.630	7.548	16.44	30.49	50.87	78.76	115.3	161.8	219.3
7/16	0.583	2.843	7.975	17.16	31.56	52.38	—	—	—	—
1/2	0.663	3.068	8.416	17.89	32.66	53.92	82.83	120.6	168.3	227.3
9/16	0.749	3.304	8.877	18.65	33.79	55.49	—	—	—	—
5/8	0.843	3.551	9.352	19.42	34.94	57.09	87.04	126.0	175.1	235.5
11/16	0.944	3.811	9.845	20.22	36.12	58.72	—	—	—	—
3/4	1.052	4.083	10.35	21.04	37.33	60.38	91.39	131.5	182.0	243.9
13/16	1.169	4.368	10.88	21.88	38.56	62.08	—	—	—	—
7/8	1.294	4.666	11.42	22.75	39.82	63.80	95.89	137.3	189.1	252.5
15/16	1.428	4.977	11.99	23.63	41.10	65.56	—	—	—	—

Fan bearings must be able to take the loads due to the dead weight, unbalance, and thrust of the rotor assembly. In addition, they must be able to operate at the intended speed without excessive heating. Various methods are used to estimate the temperature rise in sleeve and anti-friction bearings, both of which are used on fans.

When the heat dissipation by natural convection from the pillow block or other type of bearing housing is not adequate, some form of forced cooling is necessary. Small fan wheels called heat slingers, mounted on the shaft between a hot fan casing and the bearing, promote cooling by increasing the circulation of air over the bearing and by providing additional heat dissipation surface on the shaft itself. Pillow blocks may be provided with internal passages for the circulation of cooling water or even cooling air. Lubricating oil may be circulated through an external cooler. Most plain journal bearings are furnished with self-aligning and ring-oiling features. If the bearings are water cooled, the connections for the water should be flexible. Even though self-aligning features are built into the bearings, special precautions should be made to line up the original installation as perfectly as possible. Ring-oiling will provide adequate lubrication if the proper level is maintained in the reservoir and peripheral shaft speeds are not excessive. At high shaft speeds, forced or drop feed may be advisable. Hydrostatic oil lift is not required if a good quality bearing material is employed. The material must be capable of running dry for a short period after the shaft is started from rest. Different babbitts and bronzes have different load capabilities.

As a rule of thumb, the diametral clearance between the journal and bearing should be approximately 0.001 inches per inch of shaft diameter, plus 0.002 inches. Axial clearance in thrust bearings generally ranges from .008 to .012 inches. The clearance, together with speed, load, and viscosity, determines the coefficient of friction. With a clearance ratio of 0.001 and a ZN/P of 200, a coefficient of 0.01 can be expected. Increasing the viscosity (Z) in centipoises, increasing the speed (N) in rpm, decreasing the bearing pressure (P) in psi on the projected area, or decreasing the clearance increases the coefficient of friction, and vice versa. In starting on a rather greasy surface the coefficient may range from 0.08 to 0.14. If the bearing is perfectly dry the coefficient may range from 0.25 to 0.40.

By contrast anti-friction bearings have a coefficient of from 0.001 to 0.002 exclusive of any rubbing seals. Higher values should be expected during starting. In any case, bearing friction usually represents a very small percentage of the total requirement for fan horsepower. Anti-friction bearings must also be selected with loads, speeds, and heat dissipation in mind.

Any type of bearing must be protected from excessive vibration, heat, dirt, and moisture. Any rotor unbalance will produce vibrations in the bearing. Bearing supports should be isolated from the fan casing if it is hot. Adequate seals should prevent the entry of dirt or moisture as well as the loss of lubricant. Bearings in a high velocity air stream may require provisions to balance the internal and external pressure to prevent entry of foul air.

Mechanical Testing

Various mechanical tests may be performed on a fan or its parts, eithe to provide a basis for design calculations or to verify them. Spin test may be performed to determine the buckling speed of a blade, the burstin speed of a shroud, or a critical speed of any part. Shake tests may also b used to determine natural frequencies of vibration. Shock tests are fre quently required by military specifications.

In testing a particular part to destruction, it may be necessary t strengthen the restraining parts to prevent their failure. Non-destructiv spin testing may be used to prove a design for a certain speed. Over-spee tests may be required to establish a minimum margin of safety or as substitute for a high temperature test.

A vacuum test pit is a convenient tool for spin testing. The one illus trated in Figure 114 is made of heavy steel and reinforced concrete an has a vacuum pump capable of providing an absolute pressure of fift microns (0.050 mm Hg or 0.00197″ Hg). The horsepower requirements c the air turbine neglecting bearing friction are thereby reduced to les than 1/15,000 of that required to drive the impeller at standard atmos pheric pressure. The heavy construction and underground pit arrange ment provide adequate protection against flying parts.

Strain gages or brittle lacquer coatings may be applied to unloaded fa parts and suitable techniques employed to obtain a measure of the strain produced under load. The corresponding stress loads can then be cal culated.

Figure 114—Vacuum Spin Test Pit

Static and Dynamic Balancing

Fan rotors, particularly those operating at high speeds must be "balanced." Balancing is accomplished by adjusting the distribution of mass so that the center of mass more nearly coincides with the center of rotation. The amount of unbalance which can be tolerated varies with the speed and total mass of the rotor, the mass and transmissibility of the supporting structure, etc. Unbalance can be specified in any units such as ounce-inches which represent the product of weight and radius. The usual measure of unbalance effects is the vibration displacement of the bearings. A convenient unit of measurement is the one-thousandth part of an inch or "mil." The operating conditions for various speeds and vibration displacements have been described by Holtzclaw for mechanical draft fans. This data which is given in Table 63 agrees rather closely with the data of Rathbone.*

TABLE 63

VIBRATION DISPLACEMENTS FOR VARIOUS OPERATING CONDITIONS

In mils

RPM	Smooth	Fair	Rough	Very Rough
600	2	4	8	15-20
900	1.5	2.75	6	8-10
1200	1	2	4.5	6-8
1800	0.75	1.5	3.5	5-7
3600	0.4	0.7	2.5	4-5

Adapted from the data of J. P. Holtzclaw, Proper Fan Installation Reduces Operating and Maintenance Costs, *Power*, Mar. 1947.

It is important to distinguish between static and dynamic unbalance. In Figure 115 a rotating impeller is idealized as two axially separated discs on a shaft between bearings. Centrifugal forces are shown as vectors. The "A" portion of the figure depicts a statically unbalanced condition. The vibration displacement will be greater at the left-hand bearing than at the right-hand bearing. If the impeller were not rotating, it would tend to assume a position with the unbalanced mass at the bottom. Static unbalance can be corrected by adding a single balancing weight at the proper distance on the opposite side of the impeller as in either the "B" or "C" portions of the figure. The method of "B" is best as will be evident shortly.

The "C" portion of the figure depicts a dynamically unbalanced condition. The vibration displacements at the two bearings will be of the same magnitude if the impeller is statically balanced as shown. These displacements will be in opposite directions. Dynamic unbalance can only be corrected by adding a balancing couple as shown in the "D" portion of the figure. The planes of correction need not necessarily coincide with the planes of unbalance, but there must be two correction planes whenever there is dynamic unbalance.

The amount and location of the required balancing weights (one for static unbalance—two for dynamic unbalance) can be determined with a piece of chalk, an assortment of detachable weights, a good sense of touch, and a little patience.

---

*T. C. Rathbone, Vibration Tolerance, *Power Plant Engineering*, Nov. 1939.

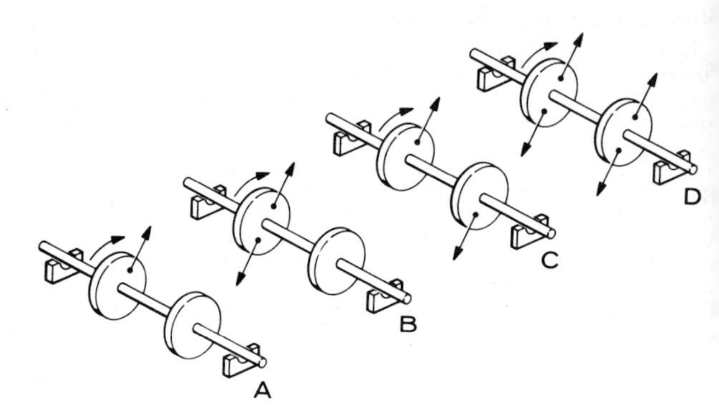

Figure 115—Static and Dynamic Unbalance

Any unbalance will produce a displacement of the shaft that ca usually be observed by "chalking the shaft." This displacement will b fixed with reference to the rotor and will, therefore, rotate with referenc to a fixed point in space. If a piece of chalk or the like is held at a fixe point so that it just touches the rotating shaft, it will leave a mark at th high spot. If the fan is perfectly balanced, the mark will extend all th way around. The greater the unbalance, the shorter the mark or lin will be. The center of the line would be at the same angular position as th unbalanced weight except for lag. The amount of lag will vary dependin on the ratio of operating speed to critical speed and the amount of damp ing in the system. At critical speed the angle of lag is 90°. Below critica speed the angle gradually approaches 0°. Above critical speed lag ma approach 180°. For most fan designs the lag will range from 15° to 45°

When a fan is out of balance statically, but not dynamically as i Figure 115 "A," the chalk marks at both bearings will be located at th same angular position relative to some point on the rotor. The amounts o displacement as indicated by the lengths of the marks will only be th same if the unbalance occurs midway between the bearings. To correc static unbalance a single trial weight should be located opposite th heavy spots. The correct angular and lateral positions can be estimate from an analysis of the chalk marks. If the estimated angular position i correct but the weight too small, rechalking will produce a longer line i the same angular position. If the weight is too great, the center of th line will shift 180°. If the weight is just right, the line will extend all th way around the shaft. If the angular position is not exactly correct th center of the line will shift accordingly.

To correct dynamic unbalance two equal trial weights should be lo cated in substantially the same manner as that indicated above. The tw inlet shrouds of a double inlet fan will normally be chosen as the planes of correction. The balance weights should be located with reference to the chalk marks at the nearest bearing in each case. If there is no static unbalance these marks will be 180° from each other and about equal in length.

There are certain routine matters which should be checked before field balancing should be attempted. The wheel should be undamaged and free from dirt or other foreign matter. The fit between wheel and shaft should be tight. The shaft should not be bent and bearings should be in good condition. Drives and motors should be perfectly aligned. Foundation bolts should be properly tightened.

If the chalk marks extend all the way around the shaft but a considerable vibration persists, the trouble can usually be traced to weak foundations. Such a resonant condition can be corrected by reinforcing the supports, adding mass, or both.

If a rotor is properly balanced at the factory, there is usually no need for field balancing. Obviously, damage in shipment or erection may alter the balance. If a fan is exposed to hot gases, there may be some relative motion between parts due to partial stress relief. Uneven erosion or corrosion will also alter balance.

Various techniques all requiring more elaborate instrumentation can be employed to eliminate all or part of the trial and error element in balancing.

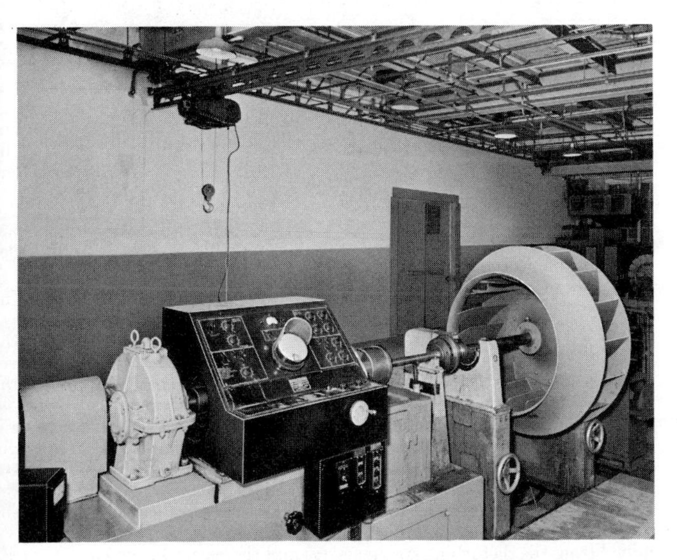

Figure 116—Dynamic Balancing—Impeller on Mandrel

Figure 117—Dynamic Balancing—Complete Rotor

Shop balancing is usually performed on special balancing machines for production and other reasons. Two such machines are illustrated in Figures 116 and 117. In the first, a wheel intended for an over-hung arrangement is mounted on a mandrel. In the second, the wheel is mounted on its own shaft. In both cases, the supports are flexibly mounted to provide sufficient sensitivity so that operation at only a fraction of the intended speed is sufficient for accurate balancing. Unless the rotor is quite flexible, sensitive low-speed balancing is perfectly satisfactory. The principles of operation of the various designs of dynamic balancing machines are given in textbooks on vibration.

Vibration Isolation

Vibrations may be induced in a fan by unbalanced centrifugal forces or by aerodynamic forces. The full force will be transmitted to the supporting structure if the fan is rigidly mounted. The forces transmitted may be smaller or greater if the fan is flexibly mounted. The transmission can be reduced if the inertia of the moving system is used to oppose the vibrating force or couple.

The ratio of transmitted force to impressed force is called "transmissibility." Ignoring any damping, the transmissibility (TR) may be determined from the disturbing frequency (f) and the natural frequency (f_n) of the mounted system using

$$TR = \frac{1}{\left(\frac{f}{f_n}\right)^2 - 1}. \qquad (328)$$

The natural frequency of the system may be determined from the static deflection (y) according to

$$f_n = \frac{1}{2\pi}\sqrt{\frac{g}{y}}. \qquad (329)$$

Equation 328 indicates that transmissibility will be unity when the ratio of disturbing frequency to natural frequency equals the square root of two. Transmissibility will be less than unity for higher values of this ratio, and greater than unity for lower values. A much more complicated expression is required to define conditions where damping cannot be ignored. The same general conclusions can be drawn in any case. Isolation can only be achieved when the ratio f/f_n exceeds the square root of two. Amplification results for any other case. Damping reduces amplification or isolation. The former is important when passing through a critical speed ($f/f_n = 1.0$). Reduction in isolation due to damping is relatively unimportant since compensation by increasing f/f_n is usually feasible.

Vibration mounts for a fan should be designed with both the fan and installation in mind. In any case the fan should have the best practical balance. Assuming for the moment that any fan, regardless of the total mass involved, will be balanced to the same degree of perfection (i.e., a certain unbalance in ounce-inches) fan speed will determine the magnitude of the disturbing force as well as its frequency. In many cases slow-speed fans do not need any vibration mounts at all. The need for isolation increases as the possibility of transmitting an annoying vibration increases. Such is the case when the supporting structure is relatively light or when there is a relatively direct connecting path to a sensitive area. Upper story installations require better isolation than basement installations. Sound studios require better isolation than industrial areas. Experience seems to indicate that transmissibility, as calculated from Equation 328, should be reduced to 0.20 if any vibration mounts are to be employed at all. Vibration tolerances will frequently place the maximum transmissibility at 0.10 or even lower.

The materials generally used for vibration mounts are steel springs, rubber-in-shear, and cork. Cork or a similar material may be employed in sheets under direct loads since it will compress. Rubber, being practically incompressible, is usually bonded to two steel parts and loaded in shear. Steel springs are loaded directly in compression. Snubbers may be required to prevent swaying.

A number of isolators are generally required for support. They should be distributed according to the distribution of load. The load may be due to thrust forces as well as to the dead weight of the equipment. The deflections must be uniform if a level is to be maintained. This can be accomplished by varying the durometer of rubber, the sheet area of cork, or the spring constant of a spring.

The amount of the deflection should be chosen to give the proper natural frequency according to Equation 329. This in turn will depend on the disturbing frequency and the allowable transmissibility according to Equation 328. In general steel springs are required for speeds below about 700 rpm and may be used at any speed. Rubber-in-shear may be used for speeds above 700 rpm, but in many cases steel springs will be required to limit the transmissibility to an acceptable value. Cork may be used for speeds above 1200 rpm with a similar proviso.

It is especially important that a fan and its driving motor be mounted on a common rigid base. If isolation is required, it should be provided between the base and the supports so that the base rather than the isolators must withstand the belt pull. Whenever the vibration mounts must be incorporated in hangars, a fail-safe design should be employed. The additional mass of the base will serve to limit the amplitude of vibration of a system, but will not alter the magnitude of the forces transmitted.

Short circuits must be prevented. Flexible connections must be used between the fan and any duct work on either inlet or outlet. Canvas is usually used for this purpose in ventilating systems. The fans and air conditioning cabinets and the like may be separately isolated or the entire apparatus treated as a single unit. If the latter, steam and water lines, etc. must not be allowed to transmit the vibrations to the building structure.

If vibration isolation is not attempted, the fan or fan unit should be balanced as perfectly as possible. As indicated above, the more mass under the fan the smaller will be the amplitude of vibration. As a rule of thumb, a mass of concrete two to three times the weight of the fan and drive should be used.

Standard Designations and Arrangements

The fan industry through AMCA has devised certain standard designations for rotation, discharge, inlet box position, drive arrangement, and motor position.

The method of specifying rotation is to view the fan from the drive side and indicate whether clockwise or counterclockwise. The drive side of a single inlet centrifugal fan is considered to be the side opposite the inlet even in those rare cases where actual drive location may be on the inlet side. It is necessary to specify which of the drives is used for reference on dual-drive arrangements. The rotation of a propeller or axial flow fan is usually immaterial and a matter of individual design. There is no official designation of drive sides for axial fans so that if it is necessary to specify rotation, the direction from which the fan is viewed should also be specified.

The method of specifying discharge position is indicated in Figure 118. If it is intended that the fan be suspended from the ceiling or a side wall, discharge should be specified as if the fan were floor mounted. The intended mounting arrangement should also be given. An angular measure is required for angular positions.

The various drive arrangements have been assigned a number as indicated in Figure 119. Designations for axials are not official but are consistent with standards for centrifugals. The official arrangement numbers are reserved for fans with bearings on the housing or subbase as appropriate. Pedestal mounted bearings can be furnished in some arrangements. When small fans are involved arrangements involving a bearing in the inlet should be avoided.

The method of specifying inlet box position is to view the fan from the drive side (same as for rotation) and indicate the position of the intake opening. Angularity may be specified as shown in Figure 120.

The various motor positions have been assigned a letter designation as indicated in Figure 121.

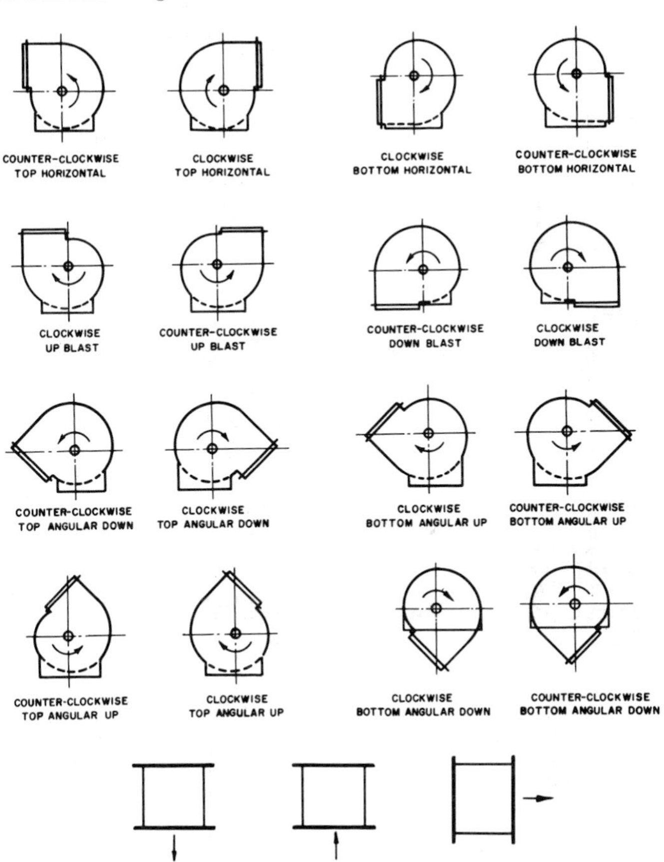

Figure 118—Standard Rotation and Discharge Designations

Adapted from the data of Designations for Rotation and Discharge of Centrifugal Fans, AMCA Standard 2406-66, 1966.

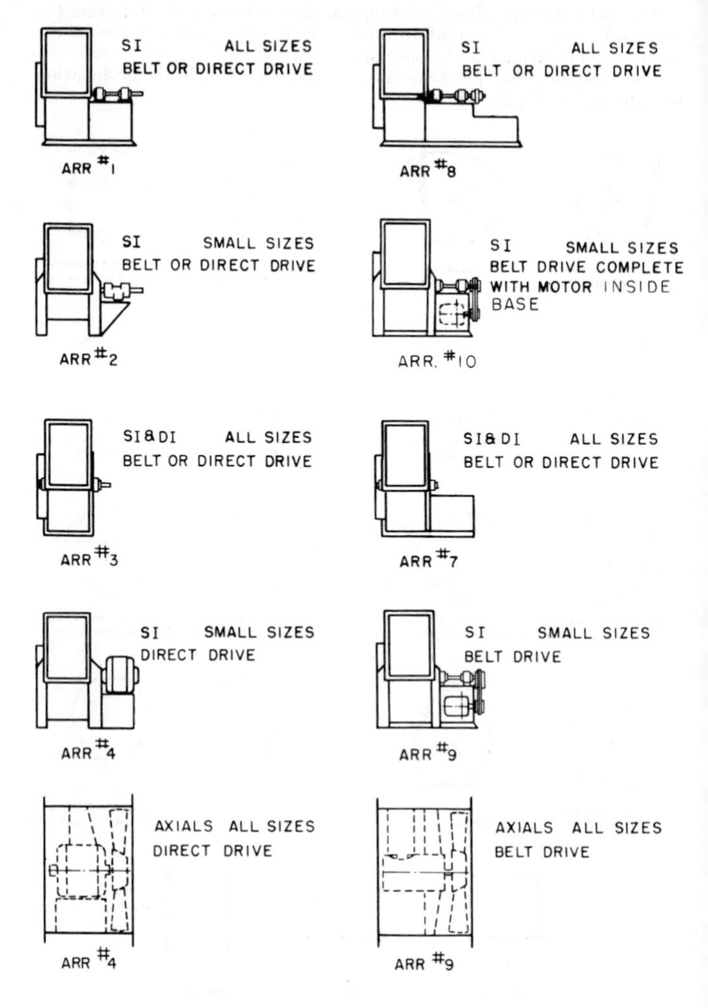

Figure 119—Standard Drive Arrangements

Adapted from the data of Drive Arrangement for Centrifugal Fans, AMCA Standard 2404-66, 1966.

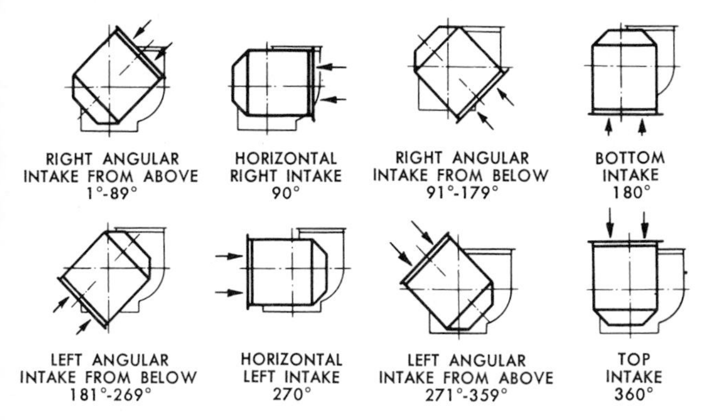

Figure 120—Standard Inlet Box Positions

Adapted from the data of Inlet Box Position for Centrifugal Fans, AMCA Standard 2405-66, 1966.

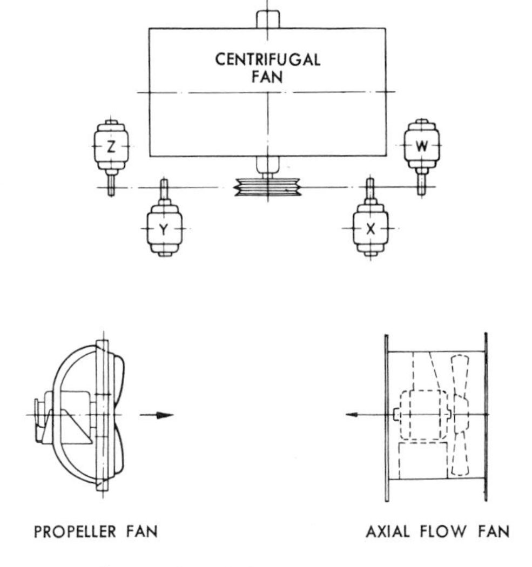

Figure 121—Standard Motor Positions

Adapted from the data of Motor Positions for Belt or Chain Drive Centrifugal Fans, AMCA Standard 2407-66, 1966.

CHAPTER 12

FAN MOTORS AND DRIVES

Most fans are driven by an electric motor either indirectly through a V-belt drive or directly through a flexible coupling. Other types of prime movers or other types of transmission elements may be more suitable for a particular application. Some of the more important aspects of a fan as a load are considered below, after which prime movers and transmission elements are briefly discussed.

Load Characteristics of a Fan

A suitable motor and drive can frequently be selected for a fan on the basis of full-load horsepower and speed alone. However, in some cases it will be necessary to examine the starting characteristics for the fan-drive combination. Breakaway torque, speed-torque relations, flywheel effect, acceleration time, temperature effects, and other considerations may be important.

From Fan Law No. 1c, the air horsepower of a fan varies as the cube of the speed if density and point of rating remain constant. Accordingly, the torque required varies as the square of the speed. Except for bearing friction the torque requirement would be zero at standstill, increasing gradually with increasing speed. This is a very desirable load characteristic since all of the motor torque is available for starting at standstill and a very large percentage is available for acceleration at other speeds.

The breakaway torque (τ_o) is usually only a very small percentage of a fan's full-load torque. The numerical value for a journal bearing of radius (R) can be calculated from the coefficient of static friction (f_o) and the normal force (F) on the bearing, using

$$\tau_o = f_o \, F \, R. \tag{330}$$

Refer to page 283 for the range of values for the dimensionless coefficient of static friction. Any consistent units can be used for the other variables. For a constant normal force the friction torque will gradually decrease as journal speed is increased until the coefficient of friction equals the equilibrium value for sliding friction. A typical speed-torque curve for a fan is given in Figure 122. The comparative values of breakaway and full-load torque will vary with design.

Comparatively high normal forces can be produced by belt drives so that some low starting torque motors are limited to direct drives as will be pointed out in the discussion on fractional horsepower motors.

The flywheel effect of a fan rotor is its mass moment of inertia about the axis of rotation. This polar moment of inertia is commonly expressed

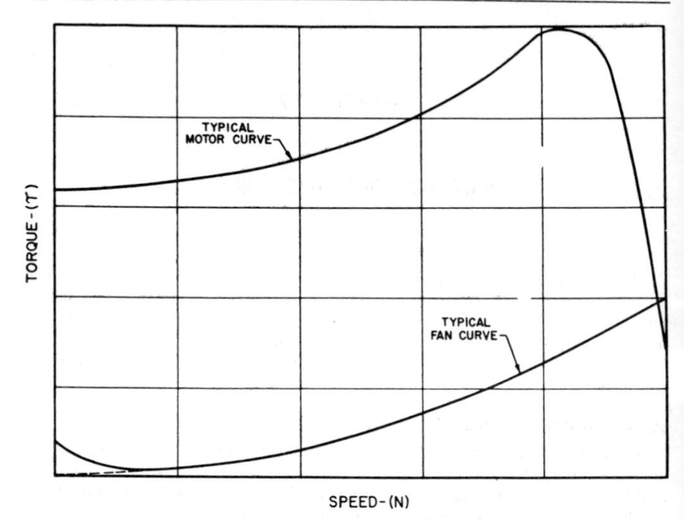

Figure 122—Typical Speed—Torque Curves

in weight units and designated "WK^2." The moment of inertia of a particle is the product of its mass and the square of its distance from the axis. The moment of inertia of a group of particles is the algebraic sum of the individual moments of inertia. The square root of the combined moment of inertia divided by the square root of the total mass is the radius of gyration (K) of the combined mass. The polar moments of inertia and radii of gyration for some common bodies are given in Table 64. Most fan elements can be considered to be composed of one or more of the bodies listed.

The radius of gyration of a fan rotor will generally be between 65% and 75% of the tip radius. By comparison a solid disc's radius of gyration is 70.7% of its outer radius.

The energy (E) in ft-lb stored in a rotating body is related to the flywheel effect (WK^2) in lb-ft² and to the rotative speed (N) in rpm according to

$$E = \frac{W}{2\,g}\left(\frac{2\,\pi\,K\,N}{60}\right)^2 = \frac{WK^2\,N^2}{5880}. \tag{331}$$

A corresponding amount of energy must be supplied by the driving motor in accelerating a fan rotor from rest to the speed N. The same amount of energy must be dissipated in decelerating a fan rotor from the speed N to rest. The time required to accomplish acceleration or deceleration is often important. This time (θ) in sec may be calculated from the initial and final speeds (N_1 and N_2) in rpm, the appropriate flywheel effect (WK^2) in

TABLE 64—FLYWHEEL EFFECTS FOR CYLINDERS AND PRISMS

BODY	WEIGHT W	RADIUS OF GYRATION K	FLYWHEEL EFFECT WK^2
l, r; CG & POLAR AXIS	$\pi r^2 l \delta$	$\frac{r}{\sqrt{2}}$	$\frac{\pi r^4 l \delta}{2}$
l, r_o, r_i; CG & POLAR AXIS	$\pi(r_o^2 - r_i^2) l \delta$	$\sqrt{\frac{r_o^2 + r_i^2}{2}}$	$\frac{\pi(r_o^4 - r_i^4) l \delta}{2}$
l, b, h; CG & POLAR AXIS	$bhl\delta$	$\sqrt{\frac{b^2 + h^2}{12}}$	$\frac{(b^3h + bh^3) l \delta}{12}$
l, b, h, x; CG AXIS; POLAR AXIS	$bhl\delta$	$\sqrt{\frac{b^2+h^2}{12} + x^2}$	$\left(\frac{b^3h + bh^3}{12} + bhx^2\right) l \delta$

lb-ft², and the torque (τ) in lb-ft available for acceleration or deceleration as the case may be, using

$$\theta = \frac{WK^2\,(N_1 - N_2)}{308\,\tau}. \tag{332}$$

If the driving (or retarding) torque is produced at the same speed as that at which the fan rotates, the WK^2 may be calculated about either the driver or driven axis with equal results. However, if the speeds differ the results must differ, since a given amount of energy is involved regardless of which axis is used for reference. The equivalent WK^2 or flywheel effect of the rotor referred to the motor axis ($WK^2{}_m$) may be determined from the flywheel effect of the rotor referred to its own axis ($WK^2{}_f$) and the ratio of fan to motor speeds squared $(N_f/N_m)^2$ as indicated by

$$WK^2{}_m = WK^2{}_f \left(\frac{N_f}{N_m}\right)^2. \tag{333}$$

The torque required by the fan to accelerate the air and any frictional torque are retarding torques. In starting, the torque developed by the motor at any speed must exceed the retarding torque if the rotor is to be accelerated. The speed-torque curves of different motors vary considerably. If the speed-torque curves for the motor and load (air and friction), both referred to the same axis, are drawn to the same scale as in Figure 122, the average available torque may be estimated as the average distance between them, over the range from zero to full speed, or over whatever other speed range might be of interest. The area between the two curves divided by the length along the speed axis will yield the average available torque for acceleration.

Acceleration time may be an important factor in motor design. Acceleration and deceleration times may be important factors in volume control.

If in decelerating the retarding torque is considered to be produced exclusively by the air load, that is, no friction or external braking, the decelerating time may be computed from

$$\theta = \frac{WK^2}{1.61 \times 10^6} \left[\frac{N_1^2 \, (N_1 - N_2)}{N_2 \, HP_1} \right]. \tag{334}$$

And if in addition to that produced by the air load, a retarding torque (τ_f) is imposed by bearing friction

$$\theta = \frac{WK^2}{1.61 \times 10^6} \frac{N_1^3}{HP_1 \, C_1} \left[tan^{-1} \left(\frac{N_1}{C_1} \right) - tan^{-1} \left(\frac{N_2}{C_1} \right) \right], \tag{335}$$

where

$$C_1 = \sqrt{\frac{\tau_f \, N_1^3}{5252 \, HP_1}}. \tag{336}$$

If an additional constant braking torque is applied, it can be added to the friction torque in Equation 336.

In some applications a fan may be expected to handle relatively hot gas under normal operating conditions, but relatively cold gas during start-up. As indicated by the fan laws, the power requirements of a fan increase in proportion to any increase in fluid density if the fan and system are otherwise unchanged. Motor and drive must be selected accordingly. With a centrifugal fan, it may be possible to damper back towards shutoff, thereby reducing power requirements during cold operation. Such a procedure when an axial flow type is involved is not practicable, but a bypass which allows a point of rating nearer free delivery can sometimes be used in such cases.

Ambient air conditions must also be considered in motor and drive selections. These may differ from the conditions of the air handled by the fan. High temperatures may limit the load carrying ability considerably. High velocity in some air-over applications makes higher outputs possible.

Prime Movers

There are various heat engines and other devices which may be used to drive a fan. Electric motors are generally used unless a more economical source of energy than electric power is available. Steam-engine drives are pretty much a thing of the past. Air and gas turbines have very limited fields of application.

Portable and emergency fan units are frequently driven by an internal combustion engine. Not all fans are designed for this kind of service. The torque pulses are generally more severe than for any other type of prime mover.

Certain fans, such as those installed in bomb shelters, may require pedals or hand cranks for emergency operation. Human-power drives are frequently employed on blowers for charcoal grills and backwoods forges.

Steam-turbine drives have various fields of application. One of the most attractive turbine drive situations occurs when high-pressure steam is available and low pressure steam is required for heating or process work. A turbine may be employed as a reducing valve in such cases. Turbine drives may be the only practical solution when high-speed operation is required. Speed reducers are generally required on low-speed applications since turbines are essentially high-speed machines. Speed control is easily accomplished by throttling the steam supply.

Electric motors are most conveniently discussed under two headings—Fractionals and Integrals. In either case the characteristics of the power supply must be determined. In most cases, power will be of the alternating-current type and voltage, frequency, and number of phases should be specified. If direct current is available voltage should be checked. The characteristics of the load (fan and any drive elements) together with power company restrictions on starting current as well as economic considerations will determine the type of motor and control which should be selected.

Integral Horsepower Electric Motors

Polyphase, usually three-phase, alternating-current motors are almost always used on fan applications requiring more than one horsepower. Direct-current motors are used on some fan applications and single-phase motors are only available in the smaller ratings.

There are several electrical types of polyphase motors, but only two are generally used for driving fans. These are the non-synchronous induction motors known as the squirrel-cage and wound-rotor types. Both are self-starting, but special starting controls are needed in many applications in order to limit starting time to acceptable values. Both types operate with very little slip at rated load.

Slip may be defined as the difference between synchronous speed and operating speed. Per cent slip is usually referred to synchronous speed as a basis of calculation. Synchronous speed (N_{syn}) is a function of the current frequency (f) and the number of poles (n_{poles}) as indicated by

$$N_{syn} = \frac{120 f}{n_{poles}}. \tag{337}$$

The squirrel-cage type takes its name from the rotor construction. Among the various standard designs the one designated as Design B is usually employed on fan loads. This is the "production" motor and it is suitable for continuous operation at rated load. Starting current is relatively low (about 600% of full-load), but frequent starts should be avoided. The starting torque (100% of full-load or higher) is usually more than adequate for most fans, but starting ability should be checked as discussed on page 305.

Squirrel-cage motors are essentially constant-speed machines. Multiple speed operation is possible if a special winding or windings are used. A single "consequent-pole" winding may be reconnected to give two speeds in the ratio of 2:1. The lower of the two speeds is obtained by reversing the connections to alternate poles which as a "consequence" induces additional intermediate poles. In most fan applications a 4:3 or 3:2 speed ratio may be more suitable than a 2:1 ratio. Two separate windings are required for the 4:3 and 3:2 ratios, but even this is usually less expensive than an adjustable-speed motor or drive. Multi-speed motors with variable torque characteristics will generally be capable of handling fan loads if sized for the high-speed power requirement, since motor horsepower varies as the square of the speed and fan horsepower varies as the cube of the speed on most systems.

Wound-rotor motors are also known as slip-ring motors. The general purpose or continuous rated type as distinguished from the intermittent rated type is used for fans principally where an adjustable-speed motor is desired. Speed reduction below 50% is not generally recommended since the fan load falls off so fast and control at low loads becomes difficult. The polyphase winding of the rotor is connected to an adjustable external resistance through slip rings and brushes. Top speed and efficiency are about the same as for the squirrel-cage motor, but the cost is higher. Starting torque and starting current can be controlled by adjusting external resistance.

Adjustable-speed a-c and d-c motor drives are available which will provide stepless speed control. Speed range, efficiency, and cost should be carefully considered. High slip at full load will lower efficiency to unacceptable values in many cases.

The National Electrical Manufacturers Association (NEMA) has adopted numerous standards concerning dimensions, ratings, enclosures, insulation, and other design data. These standards promote interchangeability, thereby facilitating motor specification and application.

In the integral horsepower ratings, frame sizes are given as three-digit numbers. The first two digits are four times the shaft center line height in inches of a standard foot-mounted motor. The last digit is a code number for certain mounting dimensions of the foot itself. Suffixal letters U, T, and S are indicative of certain shaft dimensions. The letters C and D indicate face and flange mounted types which will also have feet unless round frames are specified. Standard NEMA dimensions for polyphase-induction motors are tabulated in Table 65. Refer to Figure 123 for lettered dimensions of foot-mounted motors.

The horsepower ratings which can be built into any particular frame vary with the characteristics of the power source, i.e., volts, etc.; the design of the motor, i.e., Design B, etc.; the number of poles or speed; the type of enclosure; and other factors. The standard NEMA ratings for a limited number of combinations are indicated in Table 66.

Motor enclosures fall into two broad categories—open and totally-enclosed. Drip-proof and splash-proof machines are open motors with varying degrees of protection as indicated roughly by their names. They

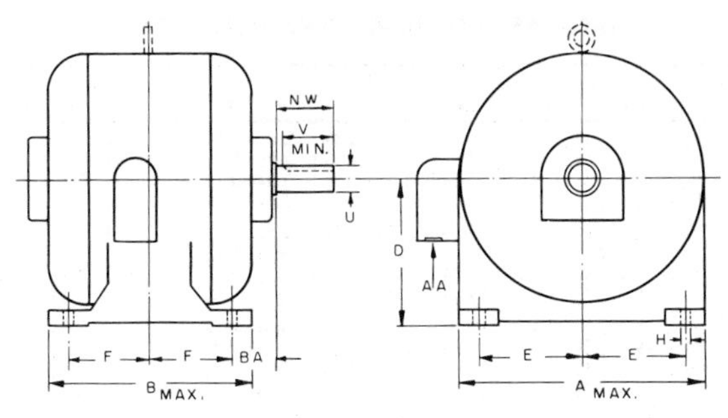

Figure 123—Standard NEMA Dimensions

Adapted from the data of Motor Standards, NEMA, 1969, p. 18.

---

should not be used if the ambient air contains anything which might be harmful to the interior of the motor. Weather-protected machines and machines with encapsulated windings provide additional protection for the windings against adverse atmospheric conditions. Both are open motors. There are also various sub-classifications for totally-enclosed motors. Total enclosures prevent the free exchange of air between inside and outside but are not airtight. Totally-enclosed fan-cooled (TEFC) machines have an integral-cooling fan outside the enclosure, but within a protective shield which also serves to direct the air over the enclosure. Totally-enclosed non-ventilated (TENV) machines do not have an integral fan so that a considerably larger frame is required, except in air-over applications or in some of the smaller ratings even without air-over. Air-over motors (TEAO) have not been assigned standard frame sizes, but, in effect, utilize standard frames for higher than standard ratings. Totally-enclosed motors can be furnished with special features for severe-duty applications, e.g., cast iron construction instead of aluminum or steel.

The National Electric Code classifies various fire and explosion hazards by divisions, classes, and groups. Explosion-proof and dust ignition-proof motors are available for hazardous environments. Explosion-proof motors are designed to withstand an internal explosion without rupturing and to prevent the ignition of vapor surrounding the motor by quenching any flames before they can pass through the sealing joints. Dust ignition-proof motors are designed to exclude ignitable amounts of dust and to prevent ignition of accumulations on or near the motor. Both are totally-enclosed motors.

Motor winding insulation systems are classified according to the temperature at which normal service life can be expected. Table 67 lists the maximum temperatures for which the various classes of insulation are suitable. The maximum temperature is the sum of the ambient temperature, the measurable temperature rise above ambient, and hot spot allow-

TABLE 65—STANDARD NEMA DIMENSIONS

Frame No.	Key	A max	B max	D	E	F	BA	H	N-W	U	V Min	AA Min
143T	3/16 x 3/16 x 1 3/8	7	6	3 1/2	2 3/4	2	2 1/4	11/32	2 1/4	7/8	2	3/4
145T	3/16 x 3/16 x 1 3/8	7	6	3 1/2	2 3/4	2 1/2	2 1/4	11/32	2 1/4	7/8	2	3/4
182T	1/4 x 1/4 x 1 3/4	9	6 1/2	4 1/2	3 3/4	2 1/4	2 3/4	13/32	2 3/4	1 1/8	2 1/2	3/4
184T	1/4 x 1/4 x 1 3/4	9	7 1/2	4 1/2	3 3/4	2 3/4	2 3/4	13/32	2 3/4	1 1/8	2 1/2	3/4
213T	5/16 x 5/16 x 2 3/8	10 1/2	7 1/2	5 1/4	4 1/4	2 3/4	3 1/2	13/32	3 3/8	1 3/8	3 1/8	1
215T	5/16 x 5/16 x 2 3/8	10 1/2	9	5 1/4	4 1/4	3 1/2	3 1/2	13/32	3 3/8	1 3/8	3 1/8	1
254T	3/8 x 3/8 x 2 7/8	12 1/2	10 3/4	6 1/4	5	4 1/8	4 1/4	17/32	4	1 5/8	3 3/4	1 1/4
256T	3/8 x 3/8 x 2 7/8	12 1/2	12 1/2	6 1/4	5	5	4 1/4	17/32	4	1 5/8	3 3/4	1 1/4
284T	1/2 x 1/2 x 3 1/4	14	12 1/2	7	5 1/2	4 3/4	4 3/4	17/32	4 5/8	1 7/8	4 3/8	1 1/2
284TS	3/8 x 3/8 x 1 7/8	14	12 1/2	7	5 1/2	4 3/4	4 3/4	17/32	3 1/4	1 5/8	3	1 1/2
286T	1/2 x 1/2 x 3 1/4	14	14	7	5 1/2	5 1/2	4 3/4	17/32	4 5/8	1 7/8	4 3/8	1 1/2
286TS	3/8 x 3/8 x 1 7/8	14	14	7	5 1/2	5 1/2	4 3/4	17/32	3 1/4	1 5/8	3	1 1/2
324T	1/2 x 1/2 x 3 7/8	16	14	8	6 1/4	5 1/4	5 1/4	21/32	5 1/4	2 1/8	5	2
324TS	1/2 x 1/2 x 2	16	14	8	6 1/4	5 1/4	5 1/4	21/32	3 3/4	1 7/8	3 1/2	2
326T	1/2 x 1/2 x 3 7/8	16	15 1/2	8	6 1/4	6	5 1/4	21/32	5 1/4	2 1/8	5	2
326TS	1/2 x 1/2 x 2	16	15 1/2	8	6 1/4	6	5 1/4	21/32	3 3/4	1 7/8	3 1/2	2
364T	5/8 x 5/8 x 4 1/4	18	15 1/4	9	7	5 5/8	5 7/8	21/32	5 7/8	2 3/8	5 5/8	3
364TS	1/2 x 1/2 x 2	18	15 1/4	9	7	5 5/8	5 7/8	21/32	3 3/4	1 7/8	3 1/2	3
365T	5/8 x 5/8 x 4 1/4	18	16 1/4	9	7	6 1/8	5 7/8	21/32	5 7/8	2 3/8	5 5/8	3
365TS	1/2 x 1/2 x 2	18	16 1/4	9	7	6 1/8	5 7/8	21/32	3 3/4	1 7/8	3 1/2	3
404T	3/4 x 3/4 x 5 5/8	20	16 1/4	10	8	6 1/8	6 5/8	13/16	7 1/4	2 7/8	7	3
404TS	1/2 x 1/2 x 2 3/4	20	16 1/4	10	8	6 1/8	6 5/8	13/16	4 1/4	2 1/8	4	3
405T	3/4 x 3/4 x 5 5/8	20	17 3/4	10	8	6 7/8	6 5/8	13/16	7 1/4	2 7/8	7	3
405TS	1/2 x 1/2 x 2 3/4	20	17 3/4	10	8	6 7/8	6 5/8	13/16	4 1/4	2 1/8	4	3
444T	7/8 x 7/8 x 6 7/8	22	18 1/2	11	9	7 1/4	7 1/2	13/16	8 1/2	3 3/8	8 1/4	3
444TS	5/8 x 5/8 x 3	22	18 1/2	11	9	7 1/4	7 1/2	13/16	4 3/4	2 3/8	4 1/2	3
445T	7/8 x 7/8 x 6 7/8	22	20 1/2	11	9	8 1/4	7 1/2	13/16	8 1/2	3 3/8	8 1/4	3
445TS	5/8 x 5/8 x 3	22	20 1/2	11	9	8 1/4	7 1/2	13/16	4 3/4	2 3/8	4 1/2	3
447T	7/8 x 7/8 x 6 7/8	22	24	11	9	10	7 1/2	13/16	8 1/2	3 3/8	8 1/4	3
447TS	5/8 x 5/8 x 3	22	24	11	9	10	7 1/2	13/16	4 3/4	2 3/8	4 1/2	3
182	3/16 x 3/16 x 1 3/8	9	6 1/2	4 1/2	3 3/4	2 1/4	2 3/4	13/32	2 1/4	7/8	2	3/4
184	3/16 x 3/16 x 1 3/8	9	7 1/2	4 1/2	3 3/4	2 3/4	2 3/4	13/32	2 1/4	7/8	2	3/4
213	1/4 x 1/4 x 2	10 1/2	7 1/2	5 1/4	4 1/4	2 3/4	3 1/2	13/32	3	1 1/8	2 3/4	3/4
215	1/4 x 1/4 x 2	10 1/2	9	5 1/4	4 1/4	3 1/2	3 1/2	13/32	3	1 1/8	2 3/4	3/4
254U	5/16 x 5/16 x 2 3/4	12 1/2	10 3/4	6 1/4	5	4 1/8	4 1/4	17/32	3 3/4	1 3/8	3 1/2	1
256U	5/16 x 5/16 x 2 3/4	12 1/2	12 1/2	6 1/4	5	5	4 1/4	17/32	3 3/4	1 3/8	3 1/2	1
284U	3/8 x 3/8 x 3 3/4	14	12 1/2	7	5 1/2	4 3/4	4 3/4	17/32	4 7/8	1 5/8	4 5/8	1 1/4
286U	3/8 x 3/8 x 3 3/4	14	14	7	5 1/2	5 1/2	4 3/4	17/32	4 7/8	1 5/8	4 5/8	1 1/4
324U	1/2 x 1/2 x 4 1/4	16	14	8	6 1/4	5 1/4	5 1/4	21/32	5 5/8	1 7/8	5 3/8	1 1/2
324S	3/8 x 3/8 x 1 7/8	16	14	8	6 1/4	5 1/4	5 1/4	21/32	3 1/4	1 5/8	3	1 1/2
326U	1/2 x 1/2 x 4 1/4	16	15 1/2	8	6 1/4	6	5 1/4	21/32	5 5/8	1 7/8	5 3/8	1 1/2
326S	3/8 x 3/8 x 1 7/8	16	15 1/2	8	6 1/4	6	5 1/4	21/32	3 1/4	1 5/8	3	1 1/2
364U	1/2 x 1/2 x 5	18	15 1/4	9	7	5 5/8	5 7/8	21/32	6 3/8	2 1/8	6 1/8	2
364US	1/2 x 1/2 x 2	18	15 1/4	9	7	5 5/8	5 7/8	21/32	3 3/4	1 7/8	3 1/2	2
365U	1/2 x 1/2 x 5	18	16 1/4	9	7	6 1/8	5 7/8	21/32	6 3/8	2 1/8	6 1/8	2
365US	1/2 x 1/2 x 2	18	16 1/4	9	7	6 1/8	5 7/8	21/32	3 3/4	1 7/8	3 1/2	2
404U	5/8 x 5/8 x 5 1/2	20	16 1/4	10	8	6 1/8	6 5/8	13/16	7 1/8	2 3/8	6 7/8	2
404US	1/2 x 1/2 x 2 3/4	20	16 1/4	10	8	6 1/8	6 5/8	13/16	4 1/4	2 1/8	4	2
405U	5/8 x 5/8 x 5 1/2	20	17 3/4	10	8	6 7/8	6 5/8	13/16	7 1/8	2 3/8	6 7/8	2
405US	1/2 x 1/2 x 2 3/4	20	17 3/4	10	8	6 7/8	6 5/8	13/16	4 1/4	2 1/8	4	2
444U	3/4 x 3/4 x 7	22	18 1/2	11	9	7 1/4	7 1/2	13/16	8 5/8	2 7/8	8 3/8	2 1/2
444US	1/2 x 1/2 x 2 3/4	22	18 1/2	11	9	7 1/4	7 1/2	13/16	4 1/4	2 1/8	4	2 1/2
445U	3/4 x 3/4 x 7	22	20 1/2	11	9	8 1/4	7 1/2	13/16	8 5/8	2 7/8	8 3/8	2 1/2
445US	1/2 x 1/2 x 2 3/4	22	20 1/2	11	9	8 1/4	7 1/2	13/16	4 1/4	2 1/8	4	2 1/2

Adapted from the data of NEMA Standards Publication, 1969, MG1-11.31.a.

TABLE 66—STANDARD NEMA FRAME ASSIGNMENTS

Polyphase, 60 Hertz, 575 Volts or Less

HP	RPM 3600	RPM 1800	RPM 1200	RPM 900
	Design B Squirrel-Cage Open Class B Insul.—1.15 Service Fac.			
½	—	—	—	143T
¾	—	—	143T	145T
1	—	143T	145T	182T
1½	143T	145T	182T	184T
2	145T	145T	184T	213T
3	145T	182T	213T	215T
5	182T	184T	215T	254T
7½	184T	213T	254T	256T
10	213T	215T	256T	284T
15	215T	254T	284T	286T
20	254T	256T	286T	324T
25	256T	284T	324T	326T
30	284TS	286T	326T	364T
40	286TS	324T	364T	365T
50	324TS	326T	365T	404T
60	326TS	364TS*	404T	405T
75	364TS	365TS*	405T	444T
100	365TS	404TS*	444T	445T
125	404TS	405TS*	445T	—
150	405TS	444TS*	—	—
200	444TS	445TS*	—	—
250	445TS	—	—	—

HP	RPM 3600	RPM 1800	RPM 1200	RPM 900
	Design B Squirrel-Cage TEFC Class B Insul.—1.00 Service Fac.			
½	—	—	—	143T
¾	—	—	143T	145T
1	—	143T	145T	182T
1½	143T	145T	182T	184T
2	145T	145T	184T	213T
3	182T	182T	213T	215T
5	184T	184T	215T	254T
7½	213T	213T	254T	256T
10	215T	215T	256T	284T
15	254T	254T	284T	286T
20	256T	256T	286T	324T
25	284TS	284T	324T	326T
30	286TS	286T	326T	364T
40	324TS	324T	364T	365T
50	326TS	326T	365T	404T
60	364TS	364TS*	404T	405T
75	365TS	365TS*	405T	444T
100	405TS	405TS*	444T	445T
125	444TS	444TS*	445T	—
150	445TS	445TS*	—	—
200	447TS	447TS*	—	—
250	447TS	—	—	—

HP	Design B Squirrel-Cage Open			
1	—	182	184	213
1½	182	184	184	213
2	184	184	213	215
3	184	213	215	254U
5	213	215	254U	256U
7½	215	254U	256U	284U
10	254U	256U	284U	286U
15	256U	284U	324U	326U
20	284U	286U	326U	364U
25	286U	324U	364U	365U
30	324S	326U	365U	404U
40	326S	364U	404U	405U
50	364US	365U*	405U	444U
60	365US	404US*	444U	445U
75	404US	405US*	445U	—
100	405US	444US*	—	—
125	444US	445US*	—	—
150	445US	—	—	—

HP	Design B Squirrel-Cage TENV			
1	—	182	184	213
1½	182	184	213	215
2	213	213	215	254U
3	215	215	254U	256U

HP	Design B Squirrel-Cage TEFC			
1	—	182	184	213
1½	182	184	184	213
2	184	184	213	215
3	184	213	215	254U
5	213	215	254U	256U
7½	215	254U	256U	284U
10	254U	256U	284U	286U
15	256U	284U	324U	326U
20	286U	286U	326U	364U
25	324U	324U	364U	365U
30	326S	326U	365U	404U
40	364US	364U	404U	405U
50	365US	365US*	405U	444U

HP	General Purpose Wound Rotor			
1	—	—	—	225
1½	—	—	—	254
2	—	224	225	254
3	—	225	254	284
5	—	254	284	324
7½	—	284	324	326
10	—	324	326	365
15	—	326	365	404
20	—	364	404	405

*When motors are to be used with V-belt drives, correct frame size is frame size shown but with suffix letter S omitted. Suffix letter S implies short shaft for direct-coupled service.

Adapted from the data of Motor Standards, NEMA, 1969, pp. 16-17.

TABLE 67—TEMPERATURE STANDARDS FOR CONTINUOUS DUTY POLYPHASE INDUCTION MOTORS

Class of Insulation	Enclosure	Service Factor	Ambient Temp.	Temperature Rise		Maximum Temperature
				Max. Meas. by Resist.	Hot Spot Allowance	
B	Open	1.15*	40°C	90°C†	0°C	130°C
	TEFC	1.00	40°C	80°C	10°C	130°C
	TENV	1.00	40°C	85°C	5°C	130°C
F	Open	1.15*	40°C	115°C†	0°C	155°C
	TEFC	1.00	40°C	105°C	10°C	155°C
	TENV	1.00	40°C	110°C	5°C	155°C
H	Open	—	—	—	—	—
	TEFC	1.00	40°C	125°C	15°C	180°C
	TENV	1.00	40°C	135°C	5°C	180°C

*1.15 Service Factor or higher based on HP and RPM:

HP	3600	1800	1200	900
1/20-1/8	1.40	1.40	1.40	1.40
1/6-1/3	1.35	1.35	1.35	1.35
1/2	1.25	1.25	1.25	1.15
3/4	1.25	1.25	1.15	1.15
1	1.25	1.15	1.15	1.15
1-1/2-200	1.15	1.15	1.15	1.15

†—At Service Factor Load

Adapted from the data of Motor Standards, NEMA, 1969, p. 12.

---

ance. The latter varies with type of enclosure. Should winding temperature exceed the maximum the insulation system will age and deteriorate prematurely.

Temperature rise may be measured by thermocouple, etc. or by resistance. The resistance method involves a determination of winding resistance at two distinctly different conditions of thermal equilibrium. The "cold" resistance (R_c) may be measured whenever the motor has been at rest for a sufficient time to insure equilibrium. The ambient temperature (t_c) at that time must also be measured. The "hot" resistance (R_h) should be measured immediately after the motor has been shut down from a loaded run of sufficient duration to insure equilibrium. The ambient temperature (t_h) at the time of shutdown must also be measured. Because of the unavoidable delay involved in disconnecting power lines and connecting measuring instruments, "hot" resistance is usually obtained by graphical extrapolation using several measurements and their delay periods. The temperature rise (ΔT) may be determined after ambient temperature measurements (t_c and t_h) are converted to inferred absolute temperatures (T_c' and T_h') using

$$\Delta T = T_c'\left(\frac{R_h}{R_c}\right) - T_h'. \tag{338}$$

Because the linear relationship between resistance and temperature does not extend all the way to absolute zero, inferred absolute temperatures must be used. For 100% conductivity copper $T_c' = 234.5 + t_c$ and $T_h' = 234.5 + t_h$ where all temperatures are in °C. The temperature of inferred zero resistance for 100% conductivity copper is −234.5 °C. Resistance measurements yield an average temperature rise, hence a hot spot allowance is necessary to prevent overheating. Thermometer measurements generally yield even lower temperature rises than resistance measurements.

If the motor is expected to operate at high altitudes, the allowable temperature rise should be reduced to compensate for the reduction in cooling efficiency due to the reduction in density. That is, a motor rated for operation at elevations up to 3300 feet cannot operate at full load at higher elevations without overheating. However, a motor selected for a fan which is rated for sea level conditions will not overheat at any higher elevation because the fan horsepower requirement decreases faster than the motor capability (unless the point of operation is changed).

The standard ambient temperature for motor design is 40°C (104°F). If the ambient temperature is expected to exceed 40°C, the temperature rise should be reduced a corresponding amount by appropriate design measures, such as additional cooling, or de-rating. That is, a motor rated for operation in a 40° C ambient cannot be operated in higher ambients at full load without over-heating. However, a motor selected for a fan which is rated for the same air temperature as the motor ambient will not overheat at lower temperatures because motor capability increases faster than fan load (unless the point of operation is changed). This can be important if cold starts are required. Consideration should be given to providing overload protection which is directly responsive to winding temperature. Such inherent overload protection will allow the motor to start a cold fan and will prevent overheating at all temperatures. The alternatives include amperage limiting which might restrict cold starts or compromise overheating protection.

The open drip-proof motor having a service factor greater than 1.0 may

---

TABLE 68—EFFECTS OF VOLTAGE VARIATION ON OPERATING CHARACTERISTICS

Characteristic	90% Voltage		110% Voltage	
	2 & 4 pole	6 pole & up	2 & 4 pole	6 pole & up
Starting Torque	−19%	−19%	+23%	+23%
Starting Current	−11%	−11%	+11%	+11%
Full Load Speed	−1%	−1%	+½%	+½%
Full Load Current	+11%	−2%	−6%	+7%
Temp. Rise at FL	+6°C	−5°C	−3°C	+10°C
Efficiency —FL	−1.2%	+1.0%	+0.4%	−2.0%
— ¾ FL	−0.7%	+1.5%	−0.2%	−3.5%
— ½ FL	+0.4%	+3.0%	−1.0%	−5.0%
Power Factor —FL	+1%	+8%	−3%	−8%
— ¾ FL	+3%	+8%	−5%	−8%
— ½ FL	+5%	+8%	−8%	−7%
Magnetic Noise	Decrease Slightly		Increase Slightly	

Data are for General-Purpose Induction Motors and are approximate only.

be overloaded continuously. If it is operated at the name plate voltage and frequency, horsepower ratings may be exceeded 15% or more as indicated by the service factors in Table 67. When overloaded the speed, efficiency, and power factor may be different from that at rated load. Starting torque and starting current will be the same.

NEMA standards provide that a motor shall operate successfully even if the combined variation of voltage and frequency from rated is plus or minus 10% (provided frequency variation does not exceed plus or minus 5%). The effects of supply variation on certain operating characteristics are given in Table 68. Standard voltages for motors at 60 Hz are 200, 230, 460, and 575 volts, and 220 and 380 volts at 50 Hz.

NEMA provides limits on minimum pitch diameter and maximum width of sheaves which can be mounted on a motor as indicated in Table 69.

There are no published limits on the size and weight of fan rotor which can be mounted directly on a motor shaft. If the weight of the impeller (W) in lb and the distance (l) in in. from the edge of the motor bearing to the center of gravity of the impeller are specified the motor manufacturer will be able to size the motor shaft properly. An approximate rule of thumb solution for the size of the motor shaft (d) in in. for a 3600 rpm Arrangement 4 fan is

$$d = 0.24\,(Wl^2)^{1/4}. \tag{339}$$

NEMA had adopted certain values of effective load (WK^2) which large standard motors should be able to accelerate without injurious temperature rise. Rule of thumb values for smaller motors are 2.25 lb-ft^2 per horsepower rating for 3600 rpm motors, 13.5 lb-ft^2 per horsepower rating for 1800 rpm motors, 37.5 lb-ft^2 per horsepower for 1200 rpm motors, and 80.0 lb-ft^2 per horsepower for 900 rpm motors. These rules give maximum allowable load (WK^2) in lb-ft^2 referred to the motor axis. If these values are not exceeded, the motor should be suitable for immediate re-starting after a false start or after a power interruption. Sufficient time must be allowed before any subsequent starts so that the motor temperature can return to rated temperature. Theoretically, the thermal capacity of any motor should be checked against the connected WK^2. Practically, however, the motors built in frame 447T or smaller are always capable of starting a "normal" fan load without overheating. "Abnormal" or unusually high WK^2 fan loads may occur if the fan handles very light gas or is very much oversized. Safe stall times for large (i.e., 4,000 hp to 250 hp) induction motors are of the order of four to twenty seconds and vary with design. Safe acceleration times are somewhat longer because of improved ventilation compared to that for a motor at standstill.

Starters for induction motors may be classified as either full-voltage, reduced-voltage, or part-winding types. All must provide overload protection as well as means for energizing and de-energizing the motor circuits.

Full-voltage or "across-the-line" starters are the simplest and least expensive. Most motors can withstand the application of full-voltage at standstill. Most fans are designed to withstand the corresponding acceleration forces. Unfortunately, the starting currents are frequently high

TABLE 69—STANDARD NEMA V-BELT LIMITATIONS

Frame Number	Horsepower at Full-Load Speed						V-belt Sheave	
	Synchronous RPM						Min. Diam.	Max. Width
	3600	1800	1200	900	720	600		
143T	1 ½	1	¾	½	—	—	2.2″	4 ¼″
145T	2-3	1 ½-2	1	¾	—	—	2.4″	4 ¼″
182T	3	3	1 ½	1	—	—	2.4″	5 ¼″
182T	5	—	—	—	—	—	2.6″	5 ¼″
184T	—	—	2	1 ½	—	—	2.4″	5 ¼″
184T	5	—	—	—	—	—	2.6″	5 ¼″
184T	7 ½	5	—	—	—	—	3.0″	5 ¼″
213T	7 ½-10	7 ½	3	2	—	—	3.0″	6 ½″
215T	10	—	5	3	—	—	3.0″	6 ½″
215T	15	10	—	—	—	—	3.8″	6 ½″
254T	15	—	7 ½	5	—	—	3.8″	7 ¾″
254T	20	15	—	—	—	—	4.4″	7 ¾″
256T	20-25	—	10	7 ½	—	—	4.4″	7 ¾″
256T	—	20	—	—	—	—	4.6″	7 ¾″
284T	—	—	15	10	—	—	4.6″	9″
284T	—	25	—	—	—	—	5.0″	9″
286T	—	30	20	15	—	—	5.4″	9″
324T	—	40	25	20	—	—	6.0″	10 ¼″
326T	—	50	30	25	—	—	6.8″	10 ¼″
364T	—	—	40	30	—	—	6.8″	11 ½″
364T	—	60	—	—	—	—	7.4″	11 ½″
365T	—	—	50	40	—	—	8.2″	11 ½″
365T	—	75	—	—	—	—	9.0″	11 ½″
404T	—	—	60	—	—	—	9.0″	14 ½″
404T	—	—	—	50	—	—	9.0″	14 ¼″
404T	—	100	—	—	—	—	10.0″	14 ¼″
405T	—	—	75	60	—	—	10.0″	14 ¼″
405T	—	100	—	—	—	—	10.0″	14 ¼″
405T	—	125	—	—	—	—	11.5″	14 ¼″
444T	—	—	100	—	—	—	11.0″	16 ¾″
444T	—	—	—	75	—	—	10.5″	16 ¾″
444T	—	125	—	—	—	—	11.0″	16 ¾″
444T	—	150	—	—	—	—	—	16 ¾″
445T	—	—	125	—	—	—	12.5″	16 ¾″
445T	—	—	—	100	—	—	12.5″	16 ¾″
445T	—	150	—	—	—	—	—	16 ¾″
445T	—	200	—	—	—	—	—	16 ¾″
182	1 ½	1	¾	½	—	—	2 ¼″	3″
184	3	2	1 ½	¾	—	—	2 ½″	3″
213	5	3	2	1 ½	1	—	2 ½″	3 ½″
215	7 ½	5	3	2	1 ½	1	3″	3 ½″
254U	10	7 ½	5	3	2	1½	3″	5 ½″
256U	15	10	7 ½	5	3	2	3 ¾″	6 ¾″
284U	20	15	10	7 ½	—	—	4 ½″	7 ¾″
286U	25	—	—	—	—	—	4 ½″	7 ¾″
286U	—	20	—	10	5	3	4 ½″	9 ¾″
324U	—	25	15	—	7 ½	5	4 ½″	9 ¾″
326U	—	30	20	15	10	7½	5 ¼″	11″
364U	—	40	25	20	15	10	6″	11″
365U	—	50	30	25	—	—	6 ¾″	12″
404U	—	60	—	—	—	—	7 ½″	12″
404U	—	—	40	30	20	15	6 ¾″	13″
405U	—	75	—	—	—	—	9″	13″
405U	—	—	50	40	25	20	8 ¼″	13″
444U	—	100	—	—	—	—	10″	17″
444U	—	—	60	50	30	25	9″	17″
445U	—	125	—	—	—	—	11″	17″
445U	—	—	75	60	40	30	10″	17″

Adapted from the data of Motor Standards, NEMA, 1960, p. 13 and 1969, MG1-14.43a.

enough to produce voltage drops that cause light flicker or magnetic devices to "drop out." Power companies, therefore, have restrictions on the size of the motor which may be started across the line.

Reduced-voltage starting lowers the starting current. It also reduces the starting torque as indicated in Table 68. There are various methods including auto-transformer, resistance, and reactance methods which may be used to start squirrel-cage motors. Wound-rotor motors can be started with very low starting current by the proper selection of resistance during starting. Several circuit switchings may be required for either type of motor where current restrictions are severe.

Part-winding starting may be possible on motors built for dual-voltage operation. Such motors have two similar sections of winding in each phase. Low-voltage operation requires the sections be connected in parallel and high-voltage operation requires a series connection. A standard dual-voltage motor may be used with the proper connection for part-winding starting on the lower voltage. Special internal connections are required for part-winding starting on the higher voltage. In part-winding starting, full voltage power is connected to either ⅔ or ½ of the windings. Subsequently, full voltage is applied to the balance of the windings. Current inrush is limited during starting by the higher resistance which results from using only part of the windings. Whether a fan will be accelerated to full speed on the first step depends on the torque characteristics of the fan and motor and the inertia of the fan. Higher starting torques are available from ⅔ part-windings than from ½ part-windings. If full acceleration is not achieved on the first step there will be another current inrush on the second step equal to the full-voltage starting current corresponding to the motor speed.

Fractional Horsepower Electric Motors

Single-phase alternating-current motors are almost always used on fan applications requiring less than one horsepower. Polyphase and direct-current motors are available in this range, but rarely used.

From an electrical standpoint, there are essentially four types of single-phase motors which are suitable for driving fans. They are designated as shaded-pole, permanent-split capacitor, split-phase, and capacitor-start motors. All are basically single-speed motors. With suitable internal or external modifications, operation at two or even more speeds is possible. Each type employs a squirrel-cage rotor, a main field winding, and some sort of auxiliary winding. Rotor designs differ, contributing to differences in locked-rotor torque and slip at normal operating speeds. Main windings are usually four-pole, but may be two-, six-, or even eight-pole design. Auxiliary windings are required to make the motor self-starting. Such a winding may be deactivated after it performs the starting function or it may remain active at all speeds.

There are various physical and mechanical modifications or alternatives possible in each type. Standards involving frame size, mounting arrangement, and enclosure parallel those for integral horsepower motors. Fractional frame sizes are sixteen times the shaft center line height of a standard foot-mounted motor. Single-phase motors develop a pulsating torque so that resilient mountings are preferred on many applications. In some instances, a footless motor is preferred so as to minimize air resistance. In any air-over application a totally-enclosed motor should be employed to prevent gumming of the windings. Total enclosure is particularly important on those types which employ a centrifugal switch. Some motors are listed as definite-purpose, fan and blower motors. Many general-purpose motors may also be used on fan applications. Some fans are equipped with a special-purpose motor designed for the precise requirements of the application, taking into account the cooling effect of any air passing over the motor, the number of starts, hours of operation, etc.

Shaded-pole motors are the least expensive of the four types usually used to drive a fan. They are inherently very low efficiency (about 30%), high slip (about 14%), low locked-rotor torque (about 60% of full-load) machines with comparatively high starting current. Starting is achieved by inducing a current in the short-circuited auxiliary winding which is angularly displaced from the main winding. Two such windings are needed if the motor must be reversible. The starting winding is energized at all speeds leading to low efficiency and low power factor. Relatively high resistance rotors are required to develop as much starting torque as these motors do. This promotes high slip so that the rated speeds of four-pole and six-pole, 60 Hz motors are 1550 and 1050 rpm, respectively. This type of motor is not generally used if the fan requirements exceed 1/6 or 1/4 horsepower since low efficiency leads to high operating currents and, therefore, large wire sizes, high heat generation, and high operating costs. All ratings are usually built in NEMA frame 42 or 48 or their equivalents. The starting torque is not sufficient to overcome the breakaway torque of a belt-driven fan so that these motors are limited to direct-connected fans of reasonable weight. Speed can be adjusted by reducing the effective voltage. This can be accomplished by winding extra coils and taps into the main field or by adding impedance externally as with a series choke. In either case, three or four speed steps can be controlled with a simple selector switch.

Permanent-split capacitor motors are slightly more expensive than shaded-pole motors. They have medium efficiency (about 50%), fairly high slip (about 10%), low starting torque (about 60% of full-load), and relatively low starting and running currents compared to shaded-pole motors. Both the main winding and starting winding are distributed whereas in shaded-pole motors salient-pole windings are usually used. Angular displacement of the magnetic field used by the auxiliary winding is achieved by incorporating a capacitor in series with the auxiliary winding. This starting circuit is in parallel with the main winding and is energized at all speeds, but, with the proper capacitor, reasonable efficiency and good power factor are achieved. Rated speeds of four-pole and six-pole, 60 Hz motors are 1625 and 1075 rpm, respectively. This type of motor is not generally used if the fan requirement exceeds about 1/3 horsepower. All ratings are usually built in the equivalent of NEMA frame 42 or 48. The low starting torque of these motors limits their use to direct connected fans. Two-speed operation can be obtained by incorporating two windings on the motor and using a double-pole, double-throw switch. Three or four speed steps can be controlled with a selector switch and series choke or tapped-wound motor arrangement. The direction of rotation can be reversed by reversing the leads.

Split-phase motors are also built with distributed main and auxiliary windings. The angular displacement of the starting field is achieved by utilizing a very high resistance auxiliary winding. In order to prevent this winding from burning out, it must be deactivated as soon after the starting function is achieved as possible. A centrifugal switch is usually used to open the starting circuit at about 75% of rated speed. No capacitors are employed. These motors have a comparatively high efficiency (about 65%), low slip (about 4%), medium starting torque (about 100 to 275% of full-load), and comparatively high starting currents (about 600% of full-load). Comparatively low resistance rotors are employed promoting low slip. Rated speeds for two-, four-, six- and eight-pole, 60 Hz operation are about 3450, 1725, 1140, and 850 rpm, respectively. This type of motor is generally used for fan requirements up to ½ horsepower. These ratings are usually built in the equivalent of NEMA frame 48 or 56. Starting torque is adequate for most belt-driven fans. The four-pole motor is usually selected for belt-driven applications. Two-speed motors standardized for four-pole/six-pole speeds are controllable with a single-pole, double-throw switch.

Capacitor-start motors are essentially split-phase motors with a capacitor in series with the starting winding. Starting current is limited considerably by the use of the capacitor so that considerable starting torque (about 250 to 400% of full-load) can be built into these motors. The excess starting torque is usually unimportant as far as a fan load is concerned, but this type of motor must frequently be used to prevent light flicker, etc. Capacitor motors are generally used for ½ to ¾ horsepower fan requirements. They are built in NEMA frame 56 or its equivalent. Slip is about the same as for the split-phase motor and efficiencies are equal or higher. The capacitors themselves are usually mounted in a box, usually in a pigaback position on top of the motor. The starting circuit is de-energized by means of a centrifugal switch just as in the split-phase motor.

Transmission Elements

There are various machine elements which may be used to transmit mechanical power from the prime mover to the fan. If the motor speed matches the fan speed, some form of direct connection may be in order. If the motor speed differs from the fan speed, an indirect connection through belts, chains, or gears is indicated. Variable-speed prime movers may be used in either case. Alternatively the transmission may include a variable-speed device.

Shaft couplings may serve several purposes. They provide for disconnection as well as connection. They may provide sufficient flexibility to protect shafts and bearings against misalignment, shock loads, or torsional vibration. Special designs may include slip or over-running features to protect one shaft or the other against overload. Variable-speed designs are also available.

Rigid couplings are rarely used because small amounts of lateral and angular misalignment are almost unavoidable.

Flexible couplings are built in a variety of designs. Flexibility can be achieved by using flexible material such as rubber, flexible shapes such as springs, or sliding joints. Every reasonable precaution should be taken to obtain and maintain good alignment even though a flexible coupling is provided. The extent to which a flexible coupling will alter vibration characteristics or protect against shock varies from one design to another. The rating data for a flexible couple may be presented in various ways. Torque transmitting ability is usually expressed as horsepower per 100 rpm. Speed and bore limitations will be listed. Service factors for various load/prime-mover combinations may be listed separately or incorporated in the capacity ratings.

Flexible couplings transmit power through parts in mechanical contact, cushioned in some cases by a film of lubricant. The flexibility permits light oscillations, but no further relative rotation so that driven speed always equals driver speed.

Hydraulic couplings transmit power without any mechanical contact of parts. The input power is used to drive the "impeller" which applies the force needed to accelerate the fluid. The fluid in turn decelerates in the "runner" applying the forces necessary to drive the output shaft and connected load. There is always some relative rotation or slip between the impeller and runner. The minimum slip may range from 2% to 5% of the input-shaft speed. The output-shaft speed can be controlled down to about 20% of input-shaft speed on fan-type loads. As a practical operating procedure, supplementary damper control is recommended below about 30% speed because otherwise response time is rather high when decelerating. Control is achieved by adjusting the amount of fluid in the working circuit. A pump delivers fluid from a sump through a cooler to the impeller. The amount of fluid in the working circuit is usually adjusted by "trimming" the level in a rotating chamber with a "scoop" device. The power to drive the pump and overcome bearing friction is usually called "fixed horsepower loss," since it remains constant for a constant input speed. In addition there will be a "slip horsepower loss" which is a function of the input and output speeds and the fan horsepower as indicated by

$$Slip\ HP\ loss = \left(\frac{Motor\ RPM - Fan\ RPM}{Fan\ RPM}\right) Fan\ HP. \qquad (340)$$

The fraction represents the slip referred to the fan speed. The slip horsepower loss as a per cent of fan horsepower is equal to the per cent slip. Maximum slip loss, for loads which vary as the cube of the speed occurs at ⅔ speed and is approximately 15% of the full-speed fan horsepower. Input horsepower is the sum of the load and losses as indicated by

$$Input\ HP = Fan\ HP + Slip\ HP\ loss + Fixed\ HP\ loss. \qquad (341)$$

A comparison of various volume control methods including speed control is given on page **266**.

Variable-speed devices, known as magnetic drives or eddy-current couplings, are available which also operate on the slip-coupling principle.

Slip losses can be calculated in the manner indicated above. Fixed losses will be due to windage, etc., in an air-cooled device or pumping, etc., in a liquid-cooled machine. Control is obtained by adjusting the strength of the excitation producing the magnetic field. This field is rotated mechanically rather than electrically, but it drives the rotor just as in an induction motor.

In both fluid and magnetic drives the absence of any mechanical connection reduces the transmission of torsional vibration or shock loads. Starting characteristics are also improved. Although such considerations are important, the principal reason for employing a slip coupling is to provide variable-speed control with a constant-speed motor where such a combination is more economical than a variable-speed prime mover.

Hydroviscous couplings, which employ a series of grooved disks attached alternately to the driver and driven shafts, are also used as fan drives. Output speed is controlled by adjusting the spacing between disks. Fan speed can be made equal to motor speed by forcing the disks together in a "locked up" position. Slip loss is the same as for any slip device except it is zero at "lock up."

Indirect drives may serve several purposes. They permit the motor to be located in various positions relative to the fan. They also provide for a wide choice of fan speeds even though the choice of motor speeds is limited.

The vast majority of indirect drives are of the V-belt type. Very few flat-belt drives are used on fans. Positive drives of the timing-belt or chain and sprocket varieties are used occasionally. Choice is usually based on first cost although maintenance and operating cost may be important. Both chain and belt drives transmit power by increasing tension in one of the connecting legs (and reducing tension in the other). The net tension force (F) in lb may be determined from the horsepower (HP) transmitted and the belt speed (V) in fpm from

$$F = \frac{33000\, HP}{V}. \tag{342}$$

Friction drives like the flat- or V-belt types require an initial tension to prevent the belt from slipping. This produces an additional load on both the fan and motor bearings at standstill and a consequent increase in breakaway torque. The net tension when transmitting power will be the same as for a positive drive with the same pitch diameter.

The speed ratio of an indirect drive is usually calculated directly from the pitch-diameter ratio. This calculation gives an exact value for a positive drive, but only an approximate value for a friction drive since creep and slip will cause a reduction in driven speed. Experimentally determined values of creep are of the order of 1 to 2%. The reduction in speed due to slip may also be about 1 to 2% on heavily loaded drives so that the combined speed loss may be as high as 4%. A corresponding loss of power will result. The frictional force which must be overcome in pulling a V-belt from its groove results in additional power loss as does any friction within the belt itself. The over-all efficiency of a V-belt drive may be about 95%. By comparison a good quality roller chain may be 98% to 99% efficient, and silent chain and flat-belt efficiencies will fall in between.

Rating tables for V-belts usually list the allowable horsepower per belt for various combinations of driver sheave, driven sheave, and motor speeds. Correction factors for arc of contact and belt length are tabulated for standard belt lengths. The smallest sheave should not be smaller than the minimum value listed for the belt section involved. This limitation reflects both the poor life and poor efficiency of highly flexed belts. Limitations on belt speed reflect the need for balancing and a reduction in load carrying ability due to centrifugal force.

The driver sheave limits adopted by NEMA and presented in Table 69 reflect the fact that belt pull is inversely proportional to sheave size for constant torque. Although first cost and space limitations favor small sheaves, maintenance and operating costs may be reduced with larger sheaves.

Take-up and installation allowances are generally provided in motor base design. New belts should not be stretched over the sheaves so that motor movement toward the fan should be made possible during replacement installation. Adjustment of center distance in the opposite direction must be possible in order to periodically take up the slack produced by stretching under load.

Variable-pitch sheaves make possible a limited (about 25%) fan speed adjustment. Both stationary and in-motion control types are available. The variable-pitch sheave will be least expensive if chosen for the high-speed shaft. This is usually the motor shaft in fan applications. Motor position must be adjustable within the range required by any adjustable pitch drive.

CHAPTER 13

FAN SELECTION

In the majority of fan applications it is neither necessary nor desirable to design a completely new fan for the specific job requirements. Standard designs are available in each of the various aerodynamic types of fans. Numerous sizes are offered in arrangements and types of construction suitable for a wide range of applications. Therefore, fan selection is usually a matter of choosing the best size and type from those available.

Fan selection is a procedure which begins with the specification of requirements and ends with the evaluation of alternative possibilities. Of the many fans which may be capable of satisfying a particular capacity and pressure requirement, the best selection is the one that does the job most economically. First costs, operating costs, and maintenance costs must all be considered.

The methods of rating given in this chapter are based on the fan laws. Many of the equations are taken directly from Chapter 8.

Specification of Requirements

A fan specification should give the fan supplier all of the pertinent information regarding performance, service, evaluation, arrangement, etc., so that the best selection can be offered. Most of the important items are listed in Table 70. Explanatory notes are given for many of these items in the following paragraphs.

The number of fans and their aerodynamic type are items which should only be specified after comparing the various possibilities. Refer to Chapter 10 for discussion on the use of two fans in series or in parallel. Refer to Chapters 6 and 7 for discussions of the various aerodynamic types.

The type of service for which the fan is intended should be specified to warn the supplier of any unusual conditions. In some instances a duct layout should be included with the specifications. In any case the sizes of the connecting duct work should be indicated.

The capacity of the fan must be specified by the system designer. Due to the nature of the application the designer may find it convenient to calculate the capacity as a weight rate of flow. Fan capacity is usually expressed as a volume rate of flow and is commonly specified in cubic feet per minute at inlet conditions. This means that to determine the appropriate fan capacity in *CFM*, divide the weight rate of flow in pounds per minute by the inlet density in pounds per cubic foot:

$$CFM = \frac{lb\ per\ min\ flowing}{lb\ per\ cu\ ft\ at\ inlet}. \qquad (343)$$

TABLE 70—GENERAL FAN SPECIFICATIONS

General
- Number of Fans ________
- Aerodynamic Type ________
- Size of Connecting Ductwork ________
- Service ________

Capacity of Each Fan—Specify Maximum and Reduced Ratings
- CFM at Inlet or lb/hr ________

Fan Pressure at Each Capacity
- Inches Water Gage ________
- State whether Static or Total ________
- Indicate Distribution between Inlet and Outlet ________

Gas Composition and Conditions at Each Capacity
- Name or Gas Analysis ________
- Molecular Weight or Specific Gravity Referred to Air ________
- Ambient Barometer in "Hg or Elevation in ft ________
- Temperature at Inlet in °F ________
- Relative Humidity in % ________
- Dust Loading through Fan ________

Power Evaluation Factors
- Expected Life in yr ________
- Expected Operation at Each Rating in hr/yr ________
- Power Rate in $/kW-hr ________
- Demand Charge in $/kW or $/hp ________

Physical Data
- Number of Inlets ________
- Type of Drive ________
- Arrangement Number ________
- Direction of Entry for Inlet Boxes ________
- Rotation, Discharge, and Motor Position ________

Construction Details
- Appurtenances ________
- Special Materials ________
- Type and Mounting of Bearings ________

Motor Data
- Electrical Characteristics ________
- Type and Enclosure ________

If an adjustable flow rate is contemplated the minimum capacity and any intermediate capacities at which power requirements are to be evaluated should also be specified.

The fan pressure requirement for each capacity must be specified by the system designer. The fan must develop enough pressure: (1) to accelerate the air or gas from the velocity at the entrance to that at the exit of the system, (2) to overcome any difference in pressure between entrance and exit, and (3) to overcome the friction and shock losses encountered throughout the system. The entrance to the system must be considered to be a quiescent point upstream of the physical opening if the system draws from atmosphere or from a plenum. The exit is the plane of the physical opening discharging to atmosphere.

Either fan total pressure (*FTP*) or fan static pressure (*FSP*) can be specified. Using the definitions given in the chapter on fan testing (Page 249)

$$FTP = TP_2 - TP_1 \text{ and} \tag{344}$$

$$FSP = SP_2 - TP_1 \tag{345}$$

where the subscripts *1* and *2* refer to fan inlet and fan outlet conditions.

Denoting system entrance and exit by subscripts e and x

$$TP_1 = SP_e + VP_e + \Delta TP_{e-1} \text{ and} \quad (346)$$

$$TP_2 = SP_x + VP_x + \Delta TP_{2-x}. \quad (347)$$

Combining Equations 344, 346, and 347 yields

$$FTP = \Delta TP_{e-x} + \Delta VP_{e-x} + \Delta SP_{e-x} \quad (348)$$

which gives the fan total pressure in terms of the friction and shock losses (ΔTP_{e-x}), the net acceleration loss (ΔVP_{e-x}), and the pressure difference (ΔSP_{e-x}). In most fan applications (VP_e), (SP_e), and (SP_x) are all zero gage pressures and Equation 348 reduces to

$$FTP = \Delta TP_{e-x} + VP_x \quad (349)$$

which states that the fan total pressure is equal to the sum of the friction, shock, and exit losses. Under the same conditions

$$FSP = \Delta TP_{e-x} + VP_x - VP_2. \quad (350)$$

If the fan has no discharge ductwork or if the fan and system outlet areas are equal, $VP_2 = VP_x$ and

$$FSP = \Delta TP_{e-x} \text{ or} \quad (351)$$

fan static pressure equals the sum of the friction and shock losses. This equation should not be used if there is an appreciable difference between (VP_x) and (VP_2).

The distribution of pressure between inlet and outlet as obtained from Equations 346 and 347 should be given as this will affect the inlet density and, therefore, the performance of the fan. Suitable margins should be included in the specified pressures and capacities.

The sum of the total pressure losses through the system should include an allowance for any elements required to connect the fan to the system. This will be a negligibly small amount unless the size of the fan opening differs greatly from the size of the connected duct work.

The performance of a fan is a function of the density of the air or gas at the fan inlet. The inlet density not only determines the volumetric capacity for a specified weight rate of flow, but the pressure which the fan is able to develop as well. The factors which affect density and should therefore be specified are the barometer, temperature, and relative humidity at the inlet, as well as the name or composition of the gas. The ambient barometer and the gage pressure at the fan inlet may be specified in lieu of the inlet barometer.

The composition of the gas and information about any entrained material (dust loading, etc.) should be specified so that the fan supplier can offer the best selection based on any previous experience.

Whenever the gas composition and conditions are not specified, the fan supplier usually assumes air at standard conditions. Standard conditions for the fan industry are dry air at 70°F and 29.92″ Hg barometer. The density corresponding to these conditions is 0.075 lb per cu ft. Other industries have different standards. If the fan requirements are specified in terms of another industry's standards, both the actual and standard conditions should be given in detail. In other words, if the weight rate of flow corresponding to a certain number of standard cfm is required, sufficient information to determine both the actual and standard density should be listed.

If power requirements are going to be evaluated by the user, as they should be to obtain the best selection, the fan supplier should be advised of the method of evaluation. The usual method is to reduce the expected cost of power during the useful life of the equipment to the present value of an annuity sufficient to yield the annual expenditure. The annual expenditure will depend on the power rate and the expected operating schedule during the life of the equipment, as well as the power requirements at the various operating conditions. The size of the hypothetical investment will depend on the expected life and the rate of interest which could be obtained. Accordingly, the cost of the expected operation reduced to present value ($Oper\ \$_{RPV}$) may be determined from the power rate ($\$/kW\text{-}hr$) and the expected annual power consumption ($kW\text{-}hr/yr$), using

$$Oper\ \$_{RPV} = \frac{\$}{kW\text{-}hr}\ \frac{kW\text{-}hr}{yr}\left[\frac{1-(1+i)^{-n}}{i}\right]. \tag{352}$$

The bracketed factor which is the present value of an annuity to yield one dollar annually for (n) years if invested at (i) rate of interest may be determined from any standard interest table.

Inefficiency may be penalized by charging the fan a flat amount for each horsepower or kilowatt required. In the power generation industry such a demand charge which reflects the loss of power available for sale at peak load may be applied in addition to any operating charge based on the cost of fuel.

Operating costs as determined by Equation 352 or any other method should be added to the first costs and expected maintenance costs for each possible selection. The best selection is the fan having the lowest total cost. Maintenance costs are not as readily determined as first and operating costs. In many cases maintenance costs can be assumed equal for alternate selections. All pertinent engineering factors should be examined to justify any such assumptions.

The items listed under "Physical Data" and "Construction Details" should be specified because the user is usually in a better position than is the supplier to decide such issues. Certain of these items, like rotation and discharge, have no influence on cost. Other items, like arrangement number and appurtenances, may have great influence on first cost but no effect on the size and type of fan which should be selected. Still other items, like the number of inlets and type of drive, largely determine the size and type of fan which should be selected.

If there is no connecting duct work on the inlet side of the fan, either a single or double inlet fan can be used in many cases. The first cost is generally lowest for the double inlet fan in such cases, particularly when relatively large quantities and low pressures are involved. Double fans require less head room, but more floor space than a single inlet fan for the same rating. Single inlet fans are generally favored for high-pressure, low-capacity ratings. The advantages of providing only one inlet connection rather than two are obvious. If direct-connected speeds are required the type of fan which can be offered will depend on whether single or double inlet is specified.

Direct-drive specifications limit the fan speeds to available motor speeds, and this in turn limits the number of possible fan selections. It is quite unlikely that a standard size fan will be able to satisfy performance requirements exactly at a direct connected speed. Accordingly, either requirements must be relaxed or a non-standard fan must be used. The performance of a standard fan can sometimes be changed sufficiently by modifying wheel diameter or width. At other times an odd sized fan may be furnished. When warranted an entirely new design may be furnished. Direct drives generally require less maintenance and involve less power transmission loss than belt drives.

Belt-drive specifications make a large number of fan selections possible. Any standard size fan may be used. The most economical motor can generally be used even if its speed does not match the fan speed. Should requirements be altered slightly after installation, it will usually be a comparatively easy and inexpensive matter to change the belt drive. The total first cost of fan motor and drive usually favors belt drives below about 200 hp and direct drives above that figure.

The standard designations for arrangement number, direction of entry for inlet boxes, rotation, discharge, and motor position are given in Chapter 11. Arrangements with the impeller mounted between bearings are generally less expensive than those with overhung impellers. In the smaller size fans arrangements with bearings in the inlet are generally avoided because a closely situated bearing may block an appreciable portion of the inlet. Overhung impeller arrangements are frequently used to protect the bearings whenever the fan must handle hot, dirty, or corrosive gas. The alternative is to use inlet boxes and increase the center distance between bearings accordingly. Overhung pulleys or sheaves are preferred for easy maintenance, but jack shafts may be required on some larger drives.

Various appurtenances may be required including vibration isolation bases, belt guards, drains, access or inspection doors, flanged connections, inlet screens, stack bracing, *evasés*, stuffing boxes, shaft seals, heat slingers, outlet dampers, and variable inlet vanes.

Standard fans are usually steel plate products. However, certain standard lines are cast iron housed. Under certain conditions special materials or special methods of construction may be justified. Where corrosion resistance is required the materials of construction should be specified by the user, if possible. Several classes of spark resistant construction are generally available. Abrasion resistance is very difficult to achieve in a fan. Additional thicknesses of material or special materials or both may be specified. Center line support may be required to maintain alignment when high temperature gases are handled. Special materials may be required to prevent rapid oxidation at elevated temperatures. Refer to Chapter 22.

Certain fan lines are normally furnished with anti-friction bearings, others with sleeve bearings. Any preference should be specified together with details on lubrication system, cooling mediums, and type of mounting.

The type of motor, its enclosure, etc., should be specified, particularly if furnished by the user. In any case the electrical characteristics should be listed.

Selecting the Proper Size and Type of Fan

Theoretically, almost any size fan of any type could conceivably be used to satisfy the maximum requirements of a particular job. Practical engineering and economic considerations reduce the possibilities to a relatively narrow range of sizes and a few types.

The suitability of a particular type of fan depends more on the relationships between the various performance requirements than on their exact values. This is particularly true if the speed is specified. In such cases the specific speed may be calculated, and the types of fans which exhibit a reasonable efficiency at this condition may be determined from a chart such as that in Figure 104.

Certain types or designs of fans are designated according to their usual field of application. There are ventilating fans, mechanical draft fans, industrial exhausters, and pressure blowers, with sub-classifications in each case.

Ventilating fans are designed for clean air service at normal temperatures. Some heavy-duty ventilating fans may be used for more severe conditions. Both centrifugal and axial designs are available. Centrifugal types may have either backwardly or forwardly curved blades. Maximum efficiencies are obtained with the former, particularly when airfoil shaped blades are used. Forwardly curved blade types are used when space and price are more important than efficiency. Belt drives are normally used so that any rating can be obtained with a standard size fan. Axial flow fans will generally be considerably smaller and less expensive than centrifugals. Some of these advantages may be lost if noise considerations require extensive treatment. Propeller fans are usually designed for free delivery operation, but may be used up to one inch static pressure in some cases.

Mechanical draft fans are those fans which are designed for forced draft, induced draft, gas recirculating, primary air, and similar service. Mechanical draft fans are generally similar to heavy-duty ventilating fans. Additional features are incorporated as specified by the public utilities companies and other users. Because direct connection is usually specified, many basic designs are required in order to provide maximum efficiency over the wide range of specific speeds usually encountered. Temperatures and dust loadings may be comparatively high.

Industrial exhausters are designed for various kinds of industrial service. In most cases efficiency is sacrificed for the sake of simplicity and ruggedness. Belt drives are usually employed. In many highly erosive or corrosive applications the impellers and other parts are considered expendable. In other cases a considerable effort is made to extend the life of such parts by using special materials. Whenever stringy material must be passed through the fan, a centrifugal type with "cone" or "open" wheel should be used. The heels of the blades should be shaped so that material will slide off due to centrifugal force and there should be no shrouds to prevent this sliding off. When sticky materials must be handled, the amount of internal surface should be minimized as is done in axial types designed for spray booth duty.

Pressure blowers must be designed to withstand the high tip speeds required to produce high pressures. The impeller is frequently mounted directly on the motor shaft. If not, some other form of direct drive is usually employed. Therefore, numerous designs are required to provide maximum efficiency for all ratings.

After determining the type or types of fans that are suitable for an application, it is necessary to determine the best size fan in each type. There is only one size fan in each type that will operate at the point of maximum efficiency for any given rating. This optimum size fan must be operated at a certain speed to produce the required rating. A smaller sized fan could be selected that would have to operate at higher speed or a larger sized fan could be selected that would have to operate at lower speed. In either case efficiency would be lower than that for the optimum size.

Fans which rate to the right of peak efficiency may be called undersized fans, and those which rate to the left of peak efficiency may be called oversized fans. To the left means lower capacity and to the right means higher capacity on the base curve. Oversized fans are hard to justify unless future increases in capacity are contemplated. Occasionally, the required operating speed of an oversized fan will match a motor speed. Slightly undersized fans are usually selected because optimum sizes are rarely standard sizes. Ratings slightly to the right of peak efficiency are usually more stable, i.e., have steeper slopes than those at or to the left of peak efficiency. Sometimes a fan which is considerably undersized will be the best choice. In such cases, the additional operating costs occasioned by the lower efficiency must be offset by the savings in first cost or some other engineering or economic factor.

Rating Fans from Test Curves

A fan rating is a statement of fan performance at one point of operation. A complete rating includes all of the variables that enter into the fan laws, namely: capacity, pressure, gas density, fan size, speed, horsepower, sound power level, and efficiency.

Rating a fan is any procedure based on the fan laws which permits the determination of some of the above variables if others are given. For instance, rating a fan may involve the calculation of speed, horsepower, and sound power level for a given size of fan at a given capacity, pressure, and gas density. In another instance, rating a fan may involve the calculation of fan size, horsepower, and sound power level for a given combination of speed, capacity, pressure, and gas density.

Two methods of rating fans for a given capacity, pressure, and density are outlined below. The first, which may be called the equivalent air method, starts with a given (or assumed) fan size and leads to the determination of the corresponding speed and horsepower. The second, which may be called the specific speed method, starts with a given (or assumed) fan speed and leads to the determination of size and horsepower.

In both methods it is necessary to have a test curve for a fan of the same type as that being considered. If the density (δ_b) for which this base curve was drawn differs from the actual density (δ_a) for which a fan is to be selected, the rated static pressure (FSP) must be converted to equivalent static pressure (ESP):

$$ESP = FSP\left(\frac{\delta_b}{\delta_a}\right). \tag{353}$$

Alternatively, equivalent total pressure can be calculated if the rating is given in terms of fan total pressure. If the equivalent air method is used and the size ($SIZE_a$) of the fan being rated differs from the base size ($SIZE_b$), the actual capacity (CFM) must be converted to equivalent capacity ($ECFM$):

$$ECFM = CFM\left(\frac{SIZE_b}{SIZE_a}\right)^2. \tag{354}$$

The next step in the equivalent air method is to determine the point of rating on the base curve. The point of rating capacity ($PRCFM$) and point of rating static pressure ($PRSP$) may be determined by trial and error from the following relationship:

$$\frac{ESP}{PRSP} = \left(\frac{ECFM}{PRCFM}\right)^2. \tag{355}$$

A slide rule may be used to establish the point of rating. Set the hairline over the value of $ECFM$ on the "D" scale. Adjust the "B" scale until the proper value for ESP is also under the hairline. Maintaining this relationship between "B" and "D" scales, move the hairline until the values

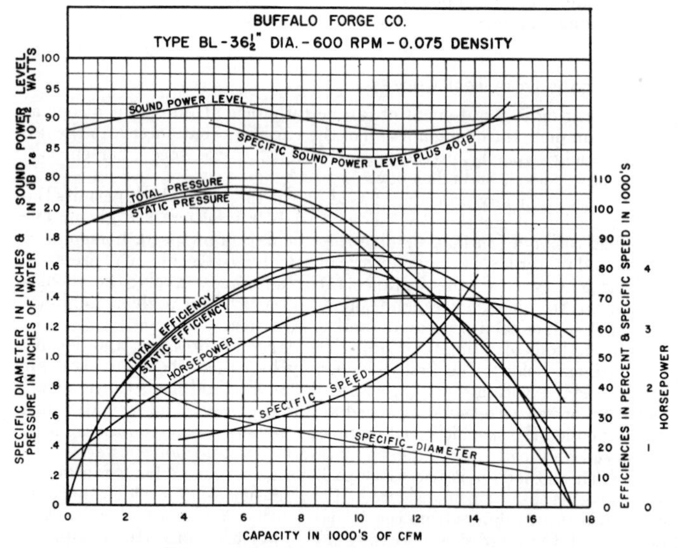

Figure 124—Typical Fan Test Curves—BL

on "B" and "D" scales correspond to a point on the *CFM-SP* base curve. This is the point of rating. To determine the rated speed (RPM_a), insert the base speed (RPM_b) into

$$RPM_a = RPM_b \left(\frac{ECFM}{PRCFM}\right) \left(\frac{SIZE_b}{SIZE_a}\right). \tag{356}$$

To determine the actual horsepower (HP_a), note the static efficiency (η_S) at the point of rating and insert into

$$HP_a = \frac{CFM\ (FSP)}{6356\ \eta_S}. \tag{357}$$

Example 12 illustrates the equivalent air method of rating using Figure 124 as a base curve.

EXAMPLE 12. Equivalent Air Method of Rating

Given: Base performance for a specific design according to Figure **124**. Standard wheel diameters for this design include: 36½", 40¼", 44½", 49", and 54¼".

Required: Pick a standard fan to deliver 30,000 cfm of air against 5" static pressure. Conditions at the fan inlet are 100°F dry-bulb, 75°F wet-bulb, and 29.5" Hg barometer.

Solution: First calculate inlet density and equivalent static pressure. Note that base curve is drawn for standard air with .075 lb/cu ft density.

$\delta_a = .0693$ *lb/cu ft from Figure 12.*

$ESP = 5 \times \dfrac{.075}{.0693} = 5.41''$ *WG from Eq. 353.*

Select a trial size, calculate equivalent air, and determine point of rating. Note that base curve is drawn for 36½" wheel diameter.

$SIZE_a = 44\frac{1}{2}''$ *trial size.*

$ECFM = 30000 \left(\dfrac{36\frac{1}{2}}{44\frac{1}{2}}\right)^2 = 20200$ *cfm from Eq. 354.*

$PR = 10900$ *cfm @ 1.57" SP from base curve.*

Calculate speed and horsepower. Note that base curve is drawn for 600 rpm and that static efficiency at point of rating is 77%.

$RPM_a = 600 \left(\dfrac{20200}{10900}\right) \left(\dfrac{36\frac{1}{2}}{44\frac{1}{2}}\right) = 911$ *rpm from Eq. 356.*

$HP_a = \dfrac{30000 \times 5}{6356 \times .77} = 30.7$ *hp from Eq. 357.*

Select the next size smaller and the next size larger for trial and determine ratings.

$SIZE_a = 40\frac{1}{4}''$ *trial size.*

$ECFM = 30000 \left(\dfrac{36\frac{1}{2}}{40\frac{1}{4}}\right)^2 = 24700$ *cfm*

$SIZE_a = 49''$ *trial size.*

$ECFM = 30000 \left(\dfrac{36\frac{1}{2}}{49}\right)^2 = 16750$ *cfm*

$PR = 12150\ cfm\ @\ 1.31''$ $\qquad$ $PR = 9630\ cfm\ @\ 1.80''$

$$RPM_a = 600\left(\frac{24700}{12150}\right)\left(\frac{36\frac{1}{2}}{40\frac{1}{4}}\right) = 1105\ rpm \qquad RPM_a = 600\left(\frac{16700}{9630}\right)\left(\frac{36\frac{1}{2}}{49}\right) = 775\ rpm$$

$$HP_a = \frac{30000 \times 5}{6356 \times .715} = 33.0\ hp \qquad HP_a = \frac{30000 \times 5}{6356 \times .797} = 29.6\ hp$$

Note that the larger fan must run slower and the smaller fan faster than the original trial size. The horsepower requirements are all fairly close to 30 hp. Even allowing for a 3% power loss in the belt drive, the 40¼″ fan could be driven by a 30 HP motor without exceeding normal service factor of a 1.15SF motor (1.03 × 33.0 = 34.0, 1.15 × 30.00 = 34.5). The cost of the extra power and the reduction in motor life should be evaluated against the savings in first cost for the smaller fan.

Assuming that the fan is expected to operate 7500 hr/yr for 20 years and that power costs will average 6 mills/kW-hr, while interest rates average 4%, the present value of the difference in cost for power to drive the 33.0 hp and 30.7 hp fans can be determined. Assuming equal motor and drive efficiencies, the power difference is .746 (33.0-30.7) or 1.72 kilowatts. The cost of the extra power for one year is .006 (1.72) (7500) or $77.50. The present value of an annuity which would yield this amount for 20 years if invested at 4% may be determined using interest tables or Equation 352 as $77.50 (13.59) or $1052.00. This will more than pay for the difference in first cost of the fans without even considering the reduction in motor life.

The first step in the specific speed method is to calculate the equivalent static pressure using Equation 353. The next step is to calculate the value of the specific speed (N_s) corresponding to the required speed (RPM_a), capacity (CFM), and equivalent static pressure (ESP):

$$N_s = \frac{RPM_a\,(CFM)^{1/2}}{(ESP)^{3/4}}. \tag{358}$$

The point of rating may be determined directly if a specific speed curve is drawn on the base curve. Simply read the capacity ($PRCFM$) corresponding to the value of specific speed for the required conditions.

The required size ($SIZE_a$) may be determined by inserting the base size ($SIZE_b$) and base speed (RPM_b) into

$$SIZE_a = SIZE_b\left(\frac{CFM}{PRCFM} \times \frac{RPM_b}{RPM_a}\right)^{1/3}. \tag{359}$$

Alternatively, the required size may be determined by reading the value of the specific size (D_s) for the point of rating and inserting in

$$SIZE_a = D_s\,\frac{CFM^{1/2}}{ESP^{1/4}}. \tag{360}$$

To determine the rated horsepower (HP_a) note the static efficiency (η_S) and insert into Equation 357.

EXAMPLE 13. Specific Speed Method of Rating

Given: Same base performance curve as for Example 12. Wheel diameters established by job requirements.

Required: Pick a fan for the same requirements and conditions as in Example 12 but fan to be direct connected to a squirrel-cage, 60 Hz, induction motor.

Solution: First calculate inlet density and equivalent static pressure as before. From Example 12,

$\delta_a = .0693$ *and* $ESP = 5.41''\ WG.$

Select a trial motor speed and calculate the corresponding specific speed for the requirements.

$RPM_a = 1170$ *rpm trial value*

$$N_s = 1170\,\frac{(30000)^{1/2}}{(5.41)^{3/4}} = 57100 \text{ from Eq. 358.}$$

Determine point of rating on base curve and evaluate suitability of trial speed.

$PR = 12500$ *cfm from base curve.*

Since the static efficiency at this point is only 69.5%, try the next lower motor speed which will require a bigger size fan and therefore will move point of rating to the left.

$RPM_a = 880$ *rpm trial value.*

$$N_s = 880\,\frac{(30000)^{1/2}}{(5.41)^{3/4}} = 42900 \text{ from Eq. 358.}$$

$PR = 10600$ *cfm from base curve.*

The static efficiency at this point is 78%, which seems high enough to warrant further investigation.

Determine the corresponding size and horsepower. Note that the base curve is drawn for 600 rpm and 36½" wheel diameter.

$$SIZE_a = 36\tfrac{1}{2}\left(\frac{30000}{10600} \times \frac{600}{880}\right)^{1/3} = 45\tfrac{1}{2}'' \text{ from Eq. 359.}$$

$$HP_a = \frac{30000 \times 5}{6356 \times .78} = 30.3 \text{ hp from Eq. 357.}$$

Select the next lower motor speed for trial and determine size and rating.

$RPM_a = 700$ *rpm trial value.*

$$N_s = 700\,\frac{(30000)^{1/2}}{(5.41)^{3/4}} = 34200 \text{ from Eq. 358.}$$

$PR = 8600$ *cfm.*

$$SIZE_a = 36\tfrac{1}{2}\left(\frac{30000}{8600} \times \frac{600}{700}\right)^{1/3} = 52\tfrac{1}{2}'' \text{ from Eq. 359.}$$

$$HP_a = \frac{30000 \times 5}{6356 \times .80} = 29.5 \text{ hp from Eq. 357.}$$

Evaluating on the same basis as that used in Example 12, the present value of the savings in operating costs would be .746 (30.3 − 29.5) (.006) (7500) (13.59) or $365.00. This will probably not be enough to pay for the difference in first cost since both fan and motor will be more expensive for the low-speed rating.

If the point of rating on the base curve has been determined by either the equivalent air or specific speed method, the corresponding sound power level (PWL_b) can be read from the base curve. Fan law 1d as written below can then be used to calculate the actual sound power level (PWL_a):

$$PWL_a = PWL_b + 70 \log_{10}\left(\frac{SIZE_a}{SIZE_b}\right) + 50 \log_{10}\left(\frac{RPM_a}{RPM_b}\right) + 20 \log_{10}\left(\frac{\delta_a}{\delta_b}\right). \quad (361)$$

Alternatively, the specific sound power level (PWL_s) can be read directly at the point of rating and used in

$$PWL_a = PWL_s + 10 \log_{10} (CFM \times FSP^2). \quad (362)$$

In either case the distribution of sound power level in the various octave bands can be approximated using data similar to that shown in Table 71. Such data should be obtained by actual tests for the type of fans involved.

EXAMPLE 14. Over-all Noise Rating

Given: Same base performance curve as for Examples 12 and 13.

Required: Determine noise ratings for the fans selected in Examples 12 and 13.

Solution: Read the sound power levels on the base curve at the point of rating capacity for each fan. For instance, for the 44½″, PWL_b is 88.0 dB.

Calculate the actual sound power level.

$$PWL_a = 88.0 + 70 \log_{10}\left(\frac{44\frac{1}{2}}{36\frac{1}{2}}\right) + 50 \log_{10}\left(\frac{911}{600}\right) + 20 \log_{10}\left(\frac{.0693}{.075}\right).$$

$$PWL_a = 88.0 + 70\ (.085) + 50\ (.181) + 20\ (-\ .033).$$

$$PWL_a = 88.0 + 6.0 + 9.1 - 0.7 = 102.4 \text{ dB from Eq. 361.}$$

Tabulating for all the fan selections:

$SIZE_a$	44½″	40¼″	49″	45½″	52½″
PWL_b	88.0 dB	88.1 dB	88.7 dB	88.1 dB	89.4 dB
Size corr.	6.0 dB	2.9 dB	8.9 dB	6.7 dB	11.0 dB
Speed corr.	9.1 dB	13.3 dB	5.5 dB	8.3 dB	3.3 dB
Dens. corr.	−0.7 dB	−0.7 dB	−0.7 dB	−0.7 dB	−0.7 dB
PWL_a	102.4 dB	103.6 dB	102.4 dB	102.4 dB	103.0 dB
Say	102 dB	104 dB	102 dB	102 dB	103 dB

Alternate Solution: Read the specific sound power levels at the point of rating capacity for each fan on the base curve. For instance, for the 44½″

fan the point of rating PWL_s is 83.7 − 40 or 43.7 dB. Calculate the sound power level.

$PWL_a = 43.7 + 10 \log_{10} (30000 \times 5^2)$.

$PWL_a = 43.7 + (5.87)$.

$PWL_a = 43.7 + 58.7 = 102.4$ *dB from Eq. 362.*

Tabulating for all the fan selections

$SIZE_a$	44½″	40¼″	49″	45½″	52½″
PWL_s	43.7 dB	44.9 dB	43.7 dB	43.6 dB	44.4 dB
Corr.	58.7 dB	58.7 dB	58.7 dB	58.7 dB	58.7 dB
PWL_a	102.4 dB	103.6 dB	102.4 dB	102.3 dB	103.1 dB
Say	102 dB	104 dB	102 dB	102 dB	103 dB

TABLE 71

OCTAVE BAND DISTRIBUTION OF SOUND POWER LEVEL FOR TYPE BL FANS

Table Values are the corrections to be applied to over-all sound power level

Blade Frequency Range in Hz	OCTAVE BAND—Center Frequency Hz							
	63	125	250	500	1000	2000	4000	8000
75 to 150	−8	−4	−6	−6	−10	−13	−22	−29
150 to 300	−8	−6	−4	−6	−10	−13	−22	−29
300 to 600	−8	−6	−6	−4	−6	−12	−22	−29

$$\text{Blade Frequency in Hz} = \frac{RPM \times \text{number of blades}}{60}$$

EXAMPLE 15. Octave Band Ratings

Given: Octave Band Distribution per Table 71.

Required: Determine octave band distribution of sound power level for 44½″ fan selected in Example 14 if it has 16 blades.

Solution: Read the appropriate octave band distribution factors from Table 71 and apply to over-all values to determine sound power level spectrum.

$$\text{Blade frequency} = \frac{911 \times 16}{60} = 243 \text{ Hz}.$$

Octave Band

Freq.	63	125	250	500	1000	2000	4000	8000
Over-all Level	102	102	102	102	102	102	102	102
Dist. Corr.	−8	−6	−4	−6	−10	−13	−22	−29
Band Level	94	96	98	96	92	89	80	73

Rating Fans From Published Data

Rating data is generally published in the form of tables or charts for each size fan of a given type. The average user commonly finds such pres-

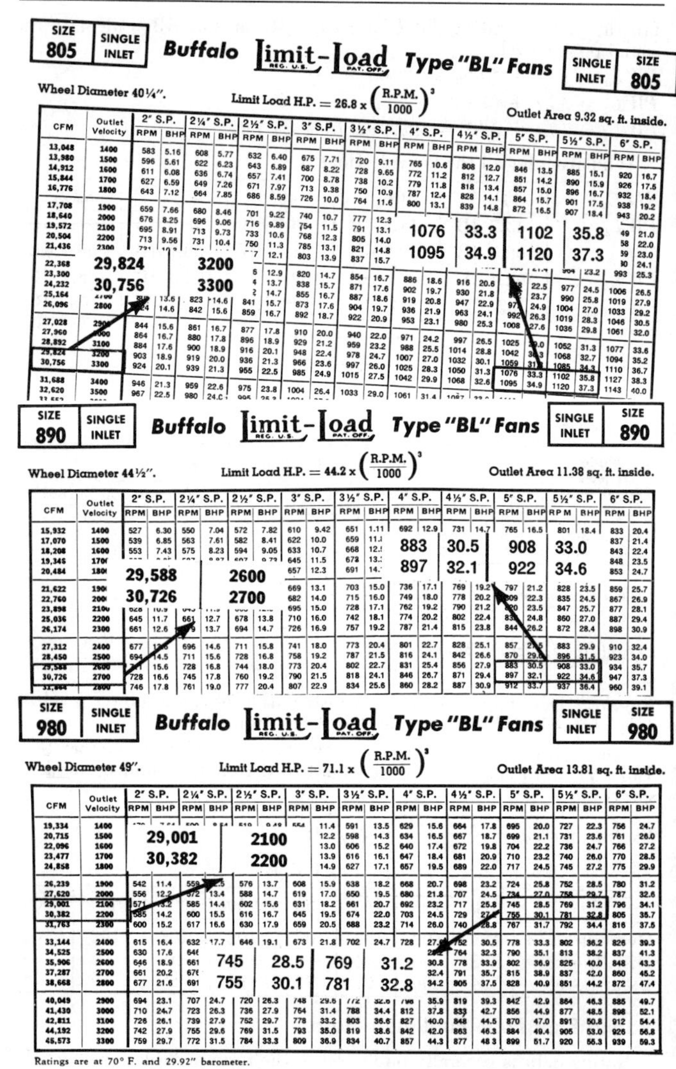

SIZE 805 — SINGLE INLET — Buffalo Limit-Load Type "BL" Fans — SINGLE INLET — SIZE 805

Wheel Diameter 40¼". Limit Load H.P. $= 26.8 \times \left(\frac{\text{R.P.M.}}{1000}\right)^3$ Outlet Area 9.32 sq. ft. inside.

CFM	Outlet Velocity	2" S.P.		2¼" S.P.		2½" S.P.		3" S.P.		3½" S.P.		4" S.P.		4½" S.P.		5" S.P.		5½" S.P.		6" S.P.	
		RPM	BHP	RPM	BHP	RPM	BHP	RPM	BHP	RPM	BHP	RPM	BHP	RPM	BHP	RPM	BHP	RPM	BHP	RPM	BHP
13,048	1400	583	5.16	608	5.77	632	6.40	675	7.71	720	9.11	765	10.6	808	12.0	846	13.5	885	15.1	920	16.7
13,980	1500	596	5.61	622	6.23	643	6.89	687	8.22	728	9.65	772	11.2	812	12.7	851	14.2	890	15.9	926	17.5
14,912	1600	611	6.08	636	6.74	657	7.41	700	8.78	738	10.2	779	11.8	818	13.4	857	15.0	896	16.7	932	18.4
15,844	1700	627	6.59	649	7.26	671	7.97	713	9.38	750	10.9	787	12.4	828	14.1	864	15.7	901	17.5	938	19.2
16,776	1800	643	7.12	664	7.85	686	8.59	726	10.0	764	11.6	800	13.1	839	14.8	872	16.5	907	18.4	943	20.2
17,708	1900	659	7.66	680	8.46	701	9.22	740	10.7	777	12.3	[illegible]	[illegible]	[illegible]	[illegible]	[illegible]	[illegible]	[illegible]	[illegible]	[illegible]	21.0
18,640	2000	676	8.25	696	9.06	716	9.89	754	11.5	791	13.1	[illegible]	[illegible]	[illegible]	[illegible]	[illegible]	[illegible]	[illegible]	[illegible]	[illegible]	22.0
19,572	2100	695	8.91	713	9.73	733	10.6	768	12.3	805	14.0	[illegible]	[illegible]	[illegible]	[illegible]	[illegible]	[illegible]	[illegible]	[illegible]	[illegible]	23.0
20,504	2200	713	9.56	731	10.4	750	11.3	785	13.1	821	14.8	[illegible]	[illegible]	[illegible]	[illegible]	[illegible]	[illegible]	[illegible]	[illegible]	[illegible]	24.1
21,436	2300	[illegible]	[illegible]	[illegible]	[illegible]	[illegible]	12.1	803	13.9	837	15.7	[illegible]	[illegible]	[illegible]	[illegible]	[illegible]	21.4	964	23.2	993	25.3
22,368	2400	[illegible]	[illegible]	[illegible]	[illegible]	[illegible]	12.9	820	14.7	854	16.7	886	18.6	916	20.6	[illegible]	22.5	977	24.5	1006	26.5
23,300	2500	[illegible]	[illegible]	[illegible]	[illegible]	[illegible]	13.7	838	15.7	871	17.6	902	19.7	930	21.8	[illegible]	23.7	990	25.8	1019	27.9
24,232	[illegible]	[illegible]	[illegible]	[illegible]	[illegible]	[illegible]	14.7	855	16.7	887	18.6	919	20.8	947	22.9	[illegible]	24.9	1004	27.0	1033	29.2
25,164	[illegible]	[illegible]	13.6	823	14.6	841	15.7	873	17.6	904	19.7	936	21.9	963	24.1	992	26.3	1019	28.3	1046	30.5
26,096	2800	[illegible]	14.6	842	15.6	859	16.7	892	18.7	922	20.9	953	23.1	980	25.3	1008	27.6	1036	29.8	1061	32.0
27,028	2900	844	15.6	861	16.7	877	17.8	910	20.0	940	22.0	971	24.2	997	26.5	1025	[illegible]	1052	31.3	1077	33.6
27,960	3000	864	16.7	880	17.8	896	18.9	929	21.2	959	23.2	988	25.5	1014	28.8	1042	[illegible]	1068	32.7	1094	35.2
28,892	3100	884	17.6	900	18.9	916	20.1	948	22.4	978	24.7	1007	27.0	1032	30.1	1059	[illegible]	1085	34.3	1110	36.7
29,824	3200	903	18.9	919	20.0	936	21.3	966	23.6	997	26.0	1025	28.3	1050	31.3	1076	33.3	1102	35.8	1127	38.3
30,756	3300	924	20.1	939	21.3	955	22.5	985	24.9	1015	27.5	1042	29.9	1068	32.6	1095	34.9	1120	37.3	1143	40.0
31,688	3400	946	21.3	959	22.6	975	23.8	1004	26.4	1033	29.0	1061	31.4	[illegible]	[illegible]						
32,620	3500	967	22.5	980	24.0	[illegible]	[illegible]														

SIZE 890 — SINGLE INLET — Buffalo Limit-Load Type "BL" Fans — SINGLE INLET — SIZE 890

Wheel Diameter 44½". Limit Load H.P. $= 44.2 \times \left(\frac{\text{R.P.M.}}{1000}\right)^3$ Outlet Area 11.38 sq. ft. inside.

CFM	Outlet Velocity	2" S.P.		2¼" S.P.		2½" S.P.		3" S.P.		3½" S.P.		4" S.P.		4½" S.P.		5" S.P.		5½" S.P.		6" S.P.	
		RPM	BHP	RPM	BHP	RPM	BHP	RPM	BHP	RPM	BHP	RPM	BHP	RPM	BHP	RPM	BHP	RPM	BHP	RPM	BHP
15,932	1400	527	6.30	550	7.04	572	7.82	610	9.42	651	1.11	692	12.9	731	14.7	765	16.5	801	18.4	833	20.4
17,070	1500	539	6.85	563	7.61	582	8.41	622	10.0	659	[illegible]	[illegible]	[illegible]	[illegible]	[illegible]	[illegible]	[illegible]	[illegible]	[illegible]	837	21.4
18,208	1600	553	7.43	575	8.23	594	9.05	633	10.7	668	[illegible]	[illegible]	[illegible]	[illegible]	[illegible]	[illegible]	[illegible]	[illegible]	[illegible]	843	22.4
19,346	[illegible]	[illegible]	[illegible]	[illegible]	[illegible]	[illegible]	[illegible]	645	11.5	672	[illegible]	[illegible]	[illegible]	[illegible]	[illegible]	[illegible]	[illegible]	[illegible]	[illegible]	848	23.5
20,484	[illegible]	[illegible]	[illegible]	[illegible]	[illegible]	[illegible]	[illegible]	657	12.3	691	[illegible]	[illegible]	[illegible]	[illegible]	[illegible]	[illegible]	[illegible]	[illegible]	[illegible]	853	24.7
21,622	[illegible]	[illegible]	[illegible]	[illegible]	[illegible]	[illegible]	[illegible]	669	13.1	703	15.0	736	17.1	769	19.2	797	21.2	828	23.5	859	25.7
22,760	[illegible]	[illegible]	[illegible]	[illegible]	[illegible]	[illegible]	[illegible]	682	14.0	715	16.0	749	18.0	778	20.2	[illegible]	22.3	835	24.5	867	26.9
23,898	2100	[illegible]	[illegible]	[illegible]	[illegible]	[illegible]	[illegible]	695	15.0	728	17.1	762	19.2	790	21.2	[illegible]	23.5	847	25.7	877	28.1
25,036	2200	645	11.7	661	12.7	678	13.8	710	16.0	742	18.1	774	20.2	802	22.4	[illegible]	24.8	860	27.0	887	29.4
26,174	2300	661	12.6	[illegible]	13.7	694	14.7	726	16.9	757	19.2	787	21.4	815	23.8	844	26.2	872	28.4	898	30.9
27,312	2400	677	[illegible]	696	14.6	711	15.8	741	18.0	773	20.4	801	22.7	828	25.1	857	[illegible]	883	29.9	910	32.4
28,450	2500	694	14.5	711	15.6	728	16.8	758	19.2	787	21.5	816	24.1	842	26.6	870	[illegible]	896	31.5	923	34.0
29,588	2600	[illegible]	15.6	728	16.8	744	18.0	773	20.4	802	22.7	831	25.4	856	27.9	883	30.5	908	33.0	934	35.7
30,726	2700	728	16.6	745	17.8	760	19.2	790	21.5	818	24.1	846	26.7	871	29.4	897	32.1	922	34.6	947	37.3
[illegible]	2800	746	17.8	761	19.0	777	20.4	807	22.9	834	25.6	860	28.2	887	30.9	912	33.7	937	36.4	960	39.1

SIZE 980 — SINGLE INLET — Buffalo Limit-Load Type "BL" Fans — SINGLE INLET — SIZE 980

Wheel Diameter 49". Limit Load H.P. $= 71.1 \times \left(\frac{\text{R.P.M.}}{1000}\right)^3$ Outlet Area 13.81 sq. ft. inside.

CFM	Outlet Velocity	2" S.P.		2¼" S.P.		2½" S.P.		3" S.P.		3½" S.P.		4" S.P.		4½" S.P.		5" S.P.		5½" S.P.		6" S.P.	
		RPM	BHP	RPM	BHP	RPM	BHP	RPM	BHP	RPM	BHP	RPM	BHP	RPM	BHP	RPM	BHP	RPM	BHP	RPM	BHP
19,334	1400	[illegible]	[illegible]	[illegible]	[illegible]	[illegible]	[illegible]	[illegible]	11.4	591	13.5	629	15.6	664	17.8	695	20.0	727	22.3	756	24.7
20,715	1500	[illegible]	[illegible]	[illegible]	[illegible]	[illegible]	[illegible]	[illegible]	12.2	598	14.3	634	16.5	667	18.7	699	21.1	731	23.6	761	26.0
22,096	1600	[illegible]	[illegible]	[illegible]	[illegible]	[illegible]	[illegible]	[illegible]	13.0	606	15.2	640	17.4	672	19.8	704	22.2	736	24.7	766	27.2
23,477	1700	[illegible]	[illegible]	[illegible]	[illegible]	[illegible]	[illegible]	[illegible]	13.9	616	16.1	647	18.4	681	20.9	710	23.2	740	26.0	770	28.5
24,858	1800	[illegible]	[illegible]	[illegible]	[illegible]	[illegible]	[illegible]	[illegible]	14.9	627	17.1	657	19.5	689	22.0	717	24.5	745	27.2	775	29.9
26,239	1900	542	11.4	559	[illegible]	576	13.7	608	15.9	638	18.2	668	20.7	698	23.2	724	25.8	752	28.5	780	31.2
27,620	2000	556	12.2	[illegible]	13.4	588	14.7	619	17.0	650	19.5	680	21.8	707	24.5	734	27.0	758	29.7	787	32.6
29,001	2100	571	[illegible]	585	14.4	602	15.6	631	18.2	661	20.7	692	23.2	717	25.8	745	28.5	769	31.2	796	34.1
30,382	2200	585	14.2	600	15.5	616	16.7	645	19.5	674	22.0	703	24.5	729	[illegible]	755	30.1	781	32.8	805	35.7
31,763	2300	600	15.2	617	16.6	630	17.9	659	20.5	688	23.2	714	26.0	740	[illegible]	767	31.7	792	34.4	816	37.5
33,144	2400	615	16.4	632	17.7	646	19.1	673	21.8	702	24.7	728	[illegible]	752	30.5	778	33.3	802	36.2	826	39.3
34,525	2500	630	17.6	[illegible]	[illegible]	[illegible]	[illegible]	[illegible]	[illegible]	[illegible]	[illegible]	[illegible]	[illegible]	764	32.3	790	35.1	813	38.2	837	41.3
35,906	2600	646	18.9	661	[illegible]	[illegible]	[illegible]	[illegible]	[illegible]	[illegible]	[illegible]	[illegible]	30.8	778	33.9	802	36.9	825	40.0	848	43.3
37,287	2700	661	20.2	[illegible]	[illegible]	[illegible]	[illegible]	[illegible]	[illegible]	[illegible]	[illegible]	[illegible]	32.4	791	35.7	815	38.9	837	42.0	860	45.2
38,668	2800	677	21.6	691	[illegible]	[illegible]	[illegible]	[illegible]	[illegible]	[illegible]	[illegible]	[illegible]	34.2	805	37.5	828	40.9	851	44.2	872	47.4
40,049	2900	694	23.1	707	24.7	720	26.3	748	29.6	772	32.6	796	35.9	819	39.3	842	42.9	864	46.3	885	49.7
41,430	3000	710	24.7	723	26.3	736	27.9	764	31.4	788	34.4	812	37.8	833	42.7	856	44.9	877	48.5	898	52.1
42,811	3100	726	26.1	739	27.9	752	29.7	778	33.2	803	36.6	827	40.0	848	44.5	870	47.0	891	50.8	912	54.4
44,192	3200	742	27.9	755	29.6	769	31.5	793	35.0	819	38.6	842	42.0	863	46.3	884	49.4	905	53.0	926	56.8
45,573	3300	759	29.7	772	31.5	784	33.3	809	36.9	834	40.7	857	44.3	877	48 3	899	51.7	920	55.3	939	59.3

Ratings are at 70° F. and 29.92" barometer.

Figure 125—Typical Multi-Rating Table—BL

entations more convenient than test curves of a single size. Some of the typical methods of presenting rating data and examples of their use are illustrated below.

Multi-rating tables are probably the most common type of published data. Portions of three pages from a typical multi-rating table are illustrated in Figure 125. Such tabulations are almost always based on standard air. To use such a table, enter with the required CFM and ESP and read the RPM and BHP on the appropriate line in the appropriate column. If the requirements do not match the listed values of CFM or ESP exactly, linear interpolations will give accurate results. The table value of RPM is the required operating speed. The table value of BHP must be multiplied by the ratio of actual density to standard density to obtain the required operating horsepower. Example 16 illustrates the use of such tables.

EXAMPLE 16. Multi-Rating Table Selection

Given: Multi-Rating Table for a specific design according to Figure 125.

Required: Pick a fan to deliver 30000 cfm of air against 5″ static pressure. Conditions at the fan inlet are 100°F dry-bulb, 75°F wet-bulb, and 29.5″ Hg barometer.

Solution: Calculate inlet density and equivalent static pressure. Note that the tables are drawn up for standard air.

$\delta_a = .0693$ *lb/cu ft from Figure 12.*

$$ESP = 5 \times \frac{.075}{.0693} = 5.41'' \text{ WG from Eq. 353.}$$

Select a trial size and determine rating.

Examine table for size 805. Note that interpolation is required between 5″ and 5½″ and between 29824 cfm and 30756 cfm.

$$1076 + \left(\frac{5.41 - 5.00}{5.50 - 5.00}\right)(1102 - 1076) = 1076 + 21 = 1097,$$

$$1095 + \left(\frac{5.41 - 5.00}{5.50 - 5.00}\right)(1120 - 1095) = 1095 + 20 = 1115,$$

$$1097 + \left(\frac{30000 - 29824}{30756 - 29824}\right)(1115 - 1097) = 1097 + 3 = 1100 \text{ rpm}.$$

$$33.3 + \left(\frac{5.41 - 5.00}{5.50 - 5.00}\right)(35.8 - 33.3) = 33.3 + 2.1 = 35.4,$$

$$34.9 + \left(\frac{5.41 - 5.00}{5.50 - 5.00}\right)(37.3 - 34.9) = 34.9 + 2.0 = 36.9,$$

$$35.4 + \left(\frac{30000 - 29824}{30756 - 29824}\right)(36.9 - 35.4) = 35.4 + 0.3 = 35.7 \text{ hp}.$$

The required operating horsepower is less than the table value since the operating density is less than the standard density for which the table was prepared.

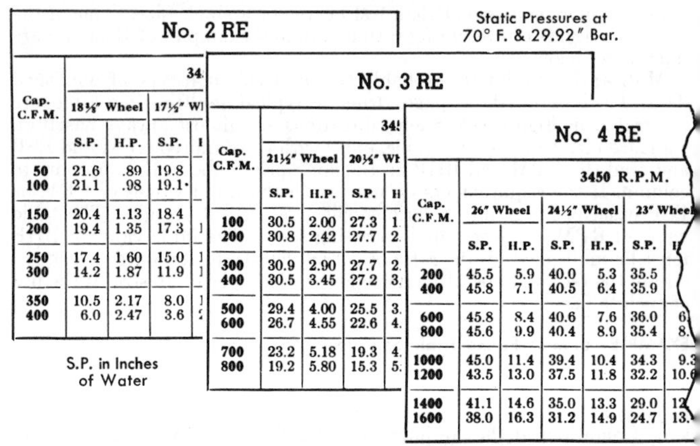

Static Pressures at 70° F. & 29.92" Bar.

No. 2 RE

Cap. C.F.M.	18⅜" Wheel S.P.	18⅜" Wheel H.P.	17½" Wheel S.P.
50	21.6	.89	19.8
100	21.1	.98	19.1
150	20.4	1.13	18.4
200	19.4	1.35	17.3
250	17.4	1.60	15.0
300	14.2	1.87	11.9
350	10.5	2.17	8.0
400	6.0	2.47	3.6

S.P. in Inches of Water

No. 3 RE

Cap. C.F.M.	21½" Wheel S.P.	21½" Wheel H.P.	20½" Wheel S.P.
100	30.5	2.00	27.3
200	30.8	2.42	27.7
300	30.9	2.90	27.7
400	30.5	3.45	27.2
500	29.4	4.00	25.5
600	26.7	4.55	22.6
700	23.2	5.18	19.3
800	19.2	5.80	15.3

No. 4 RE

3450 R.P.M.

Cap. C.F.M.	26" Wheel S.P.	26" Wheel H.P.	24½" Wheel S.P.	24½" Wheel H.P.	23" Wheel S.P.	23" Wheel H.P.
200	45.5	5.9	40.0	5.3	35.5	
400	45.8	7.1	40.5	6.4	35.9	
600	45.8	8.4	40.6	7.6	36.0	6.
800	45.6	9.9	40.4	8.9	35.4	8.
1000	45.0	11.4	39.4	10.4	34.3	9.3
1200	43.5	13.0	37.5	11.8	32.2	10.6
1400	41.1	14.6	35.0	13.3	29.0	12
1600	38.0	16.3	31.2	14.9	24.7	13.

Figure 126—Typical Multi-Rating Table—RE

24" Design 53 Belt-Air

Motor H.P.	Free Delivery CFM	RPM	DB	1/10" S.P. CFM	RPM	DB	1/8" S.P. CFM	RPM	DB	1/4" S.P. CFM	RPM	DB	3/8" S.P. CFM	RPM	DB
1/4	5,350	735	61.8	4,400	709	63.5									
1/3	5,900	810	64.1	5,160	790	65.6	4,900	783	66.0						
1/2	6,750	930	66.7	6,200	915	68.2	5,920	900	68.4	4,620	870	67.8			
3/4	7,700	1,060	69.5	7,220	1,050	70.6	7,050	1,040	70.9	6,120	1,020	71.5	4,750	980	70.4
1	8,470	1,170	71.7	8,000	1,140	72.3	7,850	1,135	72.5	7,120	1,130	73.5	6,000	1,090	73.0
1-1/2	9,650	1,330	74.5	9,300	1,325	77.3	9,180	1,320	75.2	8,670	1,310	76.3	7,750	1,280	76.
2													9,100	1,420	78.5

30" Design 53 Belt-Air

Motor H.P.	Free Delivery CFM	RPM	DB	1/10" S.P. CFM	RPM	DB	1/8" S.P. CFM	RPM	DB	1/4" S.P. CFM	RPM	DB	3/8" S.P. CFM	RPM	DB
1/4	7,200	511	61.5												
1/3	7,950	565	62.7	6,400	538	64.3									
1/2	9,100	648	65.6	7,900	621	67.1	7,480	620	67.4						
3/4	10,350	737	68.3	9,500	720	70.0	9,100	710	70.2	6,980	680	69.4			
1	11,300	812	70.4	10,600	793	71.6	10,200	780	71.9	8,680	770	72.2			
1-1/2	12,900	923	73.2	12,300	900	74.0	12,100	900	74.4	10,900	890	75.2	9,200	865	74.
2	14,200	1,020	75.4	13,800	1,010	76.0	13,500	990	76.2	12,500	983	77.2	11,000	960	77.2
3													13,800	1,115	79.7

36" Design 53 Belt-Air

Motor H.P.	Free Delivery CFM	RPM	DB	1/10" S.P. CFM	RPM	DB	1/8" S.P. CFM	RPM	DB	1/4" S.P. CFM	RPM	DB	3/8" S.P. CFM	RPM	DB
1/4	9,250	378	59.5												
1/3	10,200	418	61.7												
1/2	11,600	480	64.6	9,380	453	66.3	8,680	450	66.1						
3/4	13,200	547	67.3	11,500	528	69.2	11,000	523	69.6						
1	14,600	600	69.5	13,200	590	71.2	12,600	577	71.3	9,450	562	70.3			
1-1/2	16,600	682	72.2	15,500	673	73.4	15,000	665	73.7	12,800	652	74.2			
2	18,200	752	74.4	17,300	740	75.1	16,900	730	75.5	15,000	720	76.2	12,300	693	75.5
3	20,600	854	77.1	20,000	844	77.7	19,600	842	78.0	18,400	835	79.1	16,200	813	79.0

Figure 127—Typical Multi-Rating Table—Belt-Air

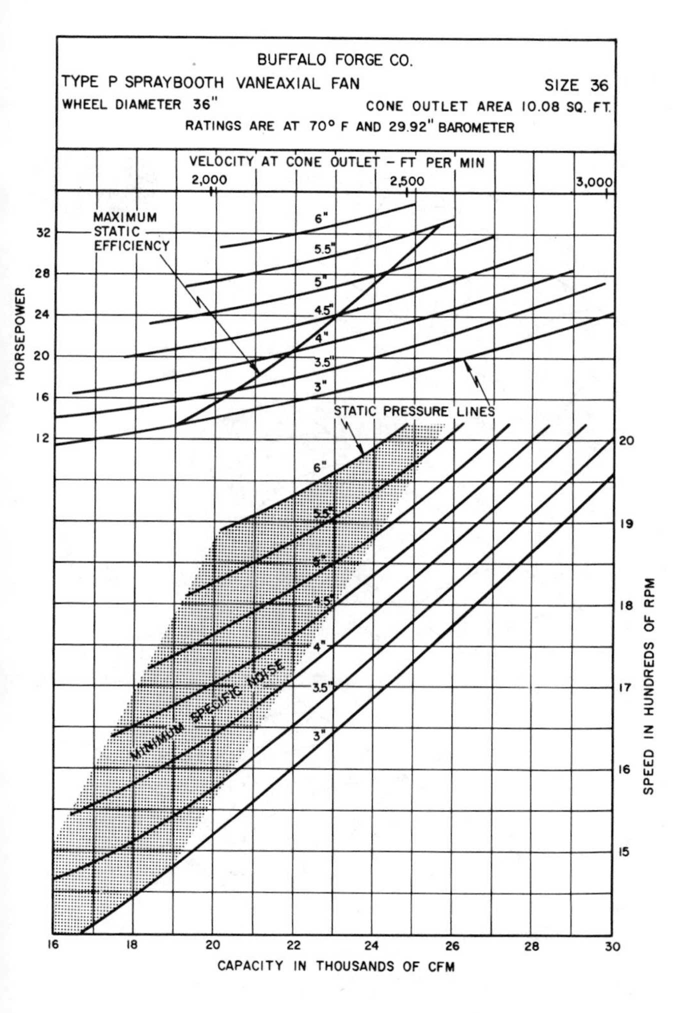

Figure 128—Typical Multi-Rating Chart—P Spray Booth

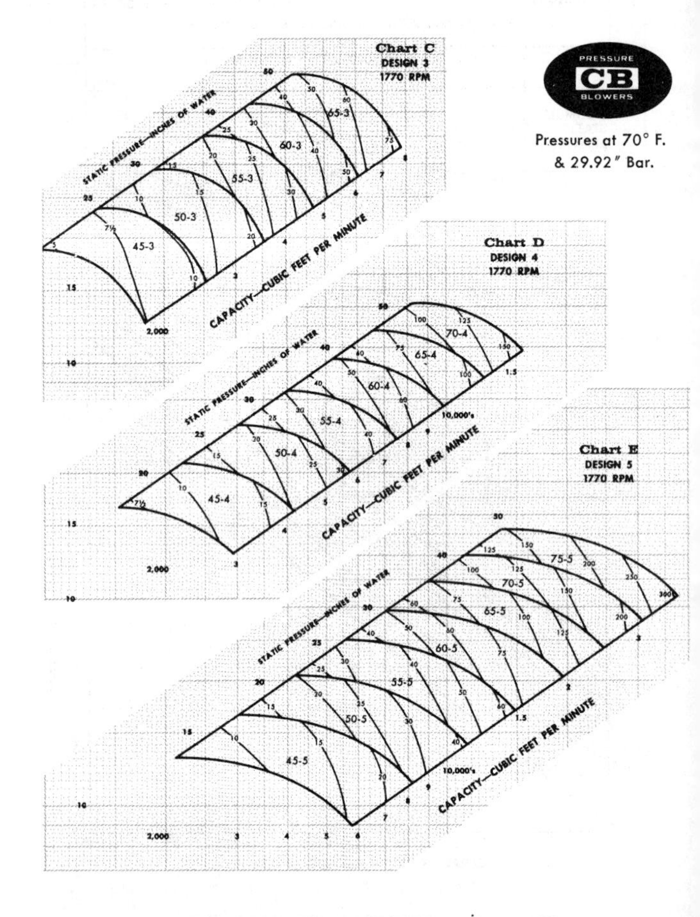

Figure 129—Typical Multi-Rating Chart—CB

$$35.7\left(\frac{.0693}{.075}\right) = 33.0\ hp.$$

Performing similar interpolations for the other two sizes shown in Figure 125 and tabulating results:

SIZE 805	SIZE 890	SIZE 980
1100 rpm	909 rpm	773 rpm
35.7 hp @ .075	33.2 hp @ .075	31.9 hp @ .075
33.0 hp @ .0693	30.7 hp @ .0693	29.5 hp @ .0693

These results agree with the results obtained by the equivalent air method, within a fraction of 1%, as they should since Figure 125 is based on the data in Figure 124. Refer to Example 12 for an evaluation of these selections.

Various other types of multi-rating tables can be compiled. Some list the pressures and horsepowers for various capacities at one or more direct connected motor speeds. Figure 126 illustrates such a table for three sizes of one particular fan design. Others list the capacities and speeds for various pressures with fully loaded motors. Figure 127 illustrates this type of table for three sizes of another particular fan design.

There are also various types of multi-rating curves which can be constructed. One type is illustrated in Figure 128 which shows the performance of one size fan only. Similar charts must be constructed for any other sizes for which the performance is to be published. To use a chart of this type find the intersection of the required CFM and ESP in each group of curves. Read the speed opposite the lower intersection and the horsepower opposite the upper intersection. Correct the horsepower for density as in the example on multi-rating tables.

Various other types of multi-rating curves can be constructed which show the performance of one or more sizes of fans of a given type.

Figure 129 illustrates a portion of a single-speed, zone-type, multi-rating chart. Each zone is marked with the size of fan which could be used to satisfy any of the ratings within the boundaries of the zone. The upper and lower curved boundaries respectively are the performance curves of the largest and smallest impellers which can be used in each size. To use such a chart enter with the rated capacity and equivalent static pressure and note the fan size. Also note the position of the equivalent rating with respect to the various horsepower lines. The required horsepower can be determined by multiplying the interpolated chart value by the ratio of actual density to standard density. The required speed is the speed for which the chart is drawn.

Figure 130 illustrates another type of multi-rating chart which can be used to determine the rating for any standard size fan in the particular line for which the chart is drawn. To use the chart locate the point corresponding to the actual CFM and the square root of the equivalent static pressure. Draw a straight line through this point and the origin. Note the intersection with the various horizontal lines for each size. Also note the values of f_N and η_S on the vertical line passing through that intersection. Insert these values into the appropriate speed and horsepower formulas also given on the chart. Example 17 illustrates the use of this chart.

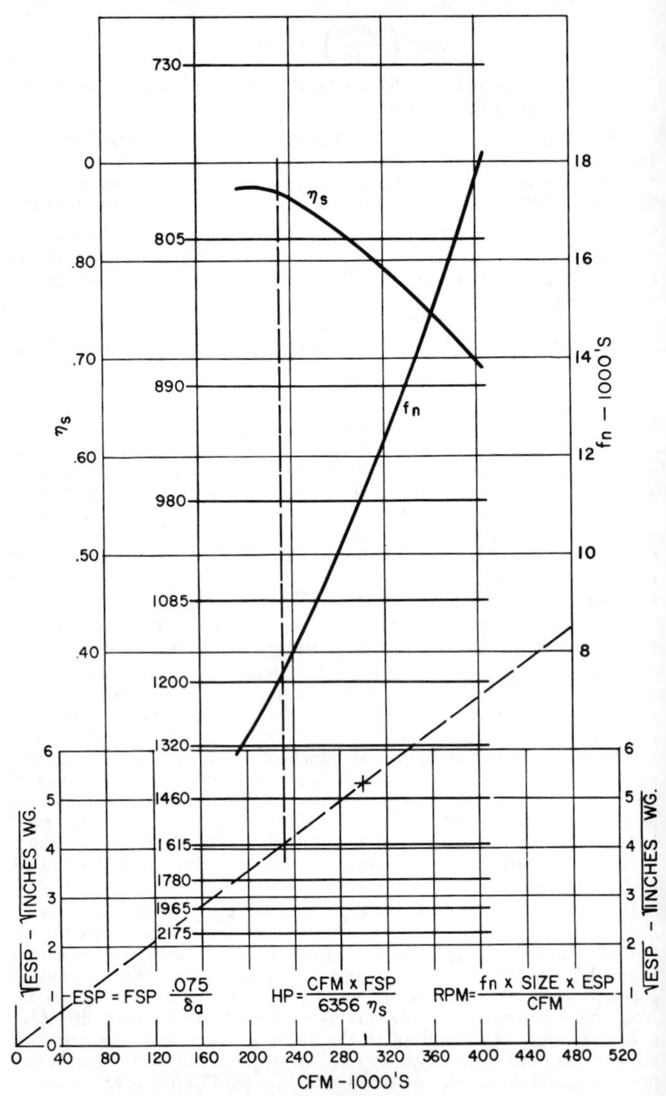

Figure 130—Typical Multi-Rating Chart—BA

EXAMPLE 17. Multi-Rating Chart Selection

Given: Multi-Rating Chart for a specific design according to Figure 130.

Required: Pick a fan to deliver 300,000 cfm of gas against 20″ static pressure. Conditions at the fan inlet are 300°F, 29.0″ Hg, and 1.04 SG.

Solution: Calculate inlet density, equivalent static pressure, and the square root of equivalent static pressure. Note that the chart is drawn for standard air.

$$\delta_a = .075\ (1.04) \left(\frac{530}{760}\right) \left(\frac{29.0}{29.92}\right) = .0527\ lb/cu\ ft.$$

$$ESP = 20.0 \left(\frac{.075}{.0527}\right) = 28.5.$$

$$\sqrt{ESP} = 5.34.$$

Spot point corresponding to 300,000 and 5.34. Draw a straight line between spotted point and origin. Note that this line intersects several size lines. If maximum efficiency is desired, note that 1615 size line is intersected almost directly below the point of maximum efficiency (actually 87.0%). Similarly, note value of the speed factor directly above the intersection (7.550 × 1000). Calculate speed and HP.

$$RPM_a = \frac{7550 \times 1615 \times 28.5}{300{,}000} = 1155\ rpm.$$

$$HP_a = \frac{300{,}000 \times 20.0}{6356 \times .87} = 1086\ hp.$$

PART III

FAN APPLICATIONS

CHAPTER 14

VENTILATION

The purpose of any general ventilation system is to promote the health, comfort, and well being of the occupants of the space served. This objective is accomplished by controlling the thermal conditions, or the amounts of contaminants, or both, in the atmospheric environment. The human occupancy itself produces chemical vitiation, sensible and latent heat, odors, and organisms. Industrial or other activity within a space may also produce gaseous or particulate contaminants as well as undesirable thermal conditions.

The methods of ventilating discussed in this chapter may all be broadly classified as "dilution" methods. This principle of ventilation simply involves the removal of an amount of heated or otherwise contaminated air and the substitution of an equal amount of relatively uncontaminated or "fresh" air.

Ventilation is truly a part of air conditioning, and the principles given here apply to systems which can be described by either name. Similarly, industrial ventilation is often used as a broad title covering both dilution and local exhaust systems. The reader is referred to Chapter 15 for further data on air conditioning, Chapter 17 for more information on local exhaust, and Chapter 21 for details on blast cooling of equipment or products.

Design Principles

The human body exhibits a fortunate tolerance to limited amounts of a contaminant, no matter how toxic. Because of this tolerance, the principle of dilution may be applied economically to a wide range of contaminating substances. The cost of equipment is roughly proportional to the volume rate of air flow required for ventilation. In addition, whenever winter outdoor air is used, tempering provisions must be made to prevent drafts, freeze-up of equipment, etc. For these reasons, the designer should evaluate auxiliary methods which may range from purification of recirculated air to medical screening of more susceptible persons. Whenever dilution ventilation is employed, one must recognize individual variations among human beings. The air-conditioning engineer strives to satisfy the largest possible percentage of occupants. The industrial hygienist attempts to prevent ill effects in any worker. Nevertheless, in the first case, at any given time there may be some complaints of too hot or too cold, no matter how well designed the system. Similarly, in the second case, it is likely that a small percentage of workers will not be able to tolerate small concentrations of contaminant, unnoticed by the vast majority.

The principle of dilution is easy to comprehend in the case of a single gaseous or particulate contaminant. If the tolerance limit is one part in one-hundred, then one-hundred parts of fresh air must be supplied for each part of contaminant released in the space. For instance, if a contaminant were generated at the rate (*CGR*) of 100 units per minute, and if the limit of human tolerance or maximum allowable concentration (*MAC*) were 2 units per 1000 cu ft, then the required ventilation rate (*CFM*) would be 100/2 or 50 times 1000, or 50,000 cfm. A formula expressing the dilution principle may be given as:

$$CFM = \frac{CGR \text{ in any units per min}}{MAC \text{ in same units per cu ft}}. \qquad (363)$$

When there are two or more contaminants released simultaneously, the one with the greatest ventilation requirement should be used as the basis of design.

Heat, odors, and bacteria, as well as industrial contaminants, may be controlled by dilution ventilation. Other air-conditioning or industrial-ventilation procedures may be more appropriate in individual cases as discussed below.

Heat Control

The sources of heat in a space, in addition to whatever heat is intentionally supplied are the human occupants themselves and any mechanical, chemical, or other processes which may be carried on there. The metabolic process will yield an amount of heat dependent on the size and body structure of the individual, physical activity, age, sex, health, nutrition, and climate. Table 72 lists total, sensible, and latent heat dissipation rates for various activities. Additional energy may be expended as useful work. Thermal efficiency for humans ranges from 20 to 30%. The total energy liberated as heat from any mechanical or chemical process may be derived from a knowledge of fuel consumption, efficiencies, etc. Likewise heat gains or losses from external sources by whatever means should be reckoned.

The physiological response of the human body to thermal stimuli affects both the subjective feeling of "comfort" and the health and well being of the individual. The human body can adapt to a diverse range of environmental conditions, as well as physical activities. For both comfort and health, the temperature of the deep-body tissues must be maintained at relatively constant values. The processes by which heat is dissipated from the body include evaporation, convection, and radiation. The process of evaporation may involve insensible perspiration or sweating. Convection and radiation regulation is accomplished by variations in skin temperature resulting from changes in subsurface blood flow and actual changes in total blood volume. Changes in muscular activity and posture, whether voluntary or involuntary, also serve to regulate the heat loss of the body. Some of these bodily adaptations can be accomplished almost instantaneously, but others may take several weeks. Instances of the latter, such as changes in blood volume and certain glandular activity account for the process known as acclimatization. A feeling of comfort will exist whenever the heat regulating mechanisms can maintain body

TABLE 72—HEAT DISSIPATION RATES

Activity	Metabolic Rate	Sensible Heat	Latent Heat
	Btu Per Hour	Btu Per Hour	Btu Per Hour
Basal	291	145	145
Seated at Rest	384	225	159
Reading Aloud (Seated)	420	225	195
Standing at Rest	431	225	206
Hand Sewing (Seated)	441	225	216
Knitting 23 Stitches per Minute on Sweater	462	225	237
Dressing and Undressing	468	225	243
Tailor	482	225	257
Singing	486	225	261
Office Worker Moderately Active	490	225	265
Light Work Standing	549	225	324
Typewriting Rapidly	558	225	333
Ironing with 5 lb. Iron	570	225	345
Dishwashing—Plates, Bowls, Cups, and Saucers	600	225	375
Clerk Moderately Active Standing at Counter	600	225	375
Book Binder	626	225	401
Shoemaker	661	225	436
Sweeping Bare Floor 38 Strokes per Minute	672	229	443
Pool Player	680	230	450
Walking 2 mph., Light Dancing	761	250	511
Light Metal Worker (at Bench)	862	277	585
Painter of Furniture (at Bench)	876	280	596
Carpenter	954	307	647
Restaurant Serving	1000	325	675
Pulling Weight	1041	335	708
Walking 3 mph.	1050	339	711
Walking 4 mph., Active Dancing, Roller Skating	1390	452	938
Walking Down Stairs	1444	467	977
Stone Mason	1490	485	1005
Bowling	1500	490	1010
Man Sawing Wood	1800	590	1210
Swimming	1986	—	—
Running 5.3 mph.	2268	—	—
Walking 5 mph.	2330	—	—
Walking Very Fast 5.3 mph.	2580	—	—
Walking Upstairs	4365	—	—
Maximum Exertion Different People	3000-4800	—	—

Adapted from the data of W. L. Fleisher, A. E. Stacey, Jr., F. C. Houghten and M. B. Ferderber, M.D., Air Conditioning in Industry, *Trans. ASHVE*, vol. 45, pp. 59-110, 1939, p. 85.

---

temperature without noticeable strain. Sweating is by far the chief mechanism by which the body adjusts to high-temperature environments. Just as a certain amount of sweating is required during physical exertion, so, too, a certain amount is required under exposure to high-temperature conditions. Whenever the body cannot dissipate heat at the required rate, the storage of heat begins with its attendant rise in deep-tissue temperature. The dangers to health under these conditions range from heat cramps to heat exhaustion, and, ultimately, to heat stroke. The effect of clothing ranges from insulation against cold to shielding against radiant heat. The marked sensations of the body encountered when passing from an equilibrium state corresponding to a given environment into a considerably warmer or cooler environment has frequently been

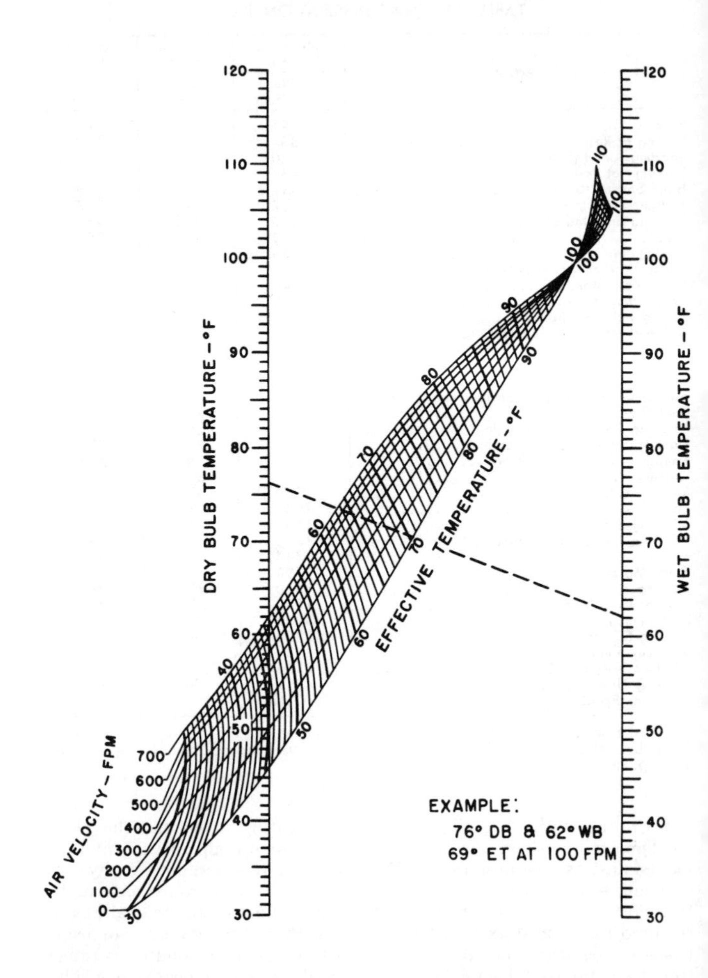

Figure 131—Effective Temperatures—at rest

Adapted from the data of C. P. Yaglou and W. E. Miller, Effective Temperature with Clothing, *Trans. ASHVE*, vol. 31, pp. 89-99, 1925.

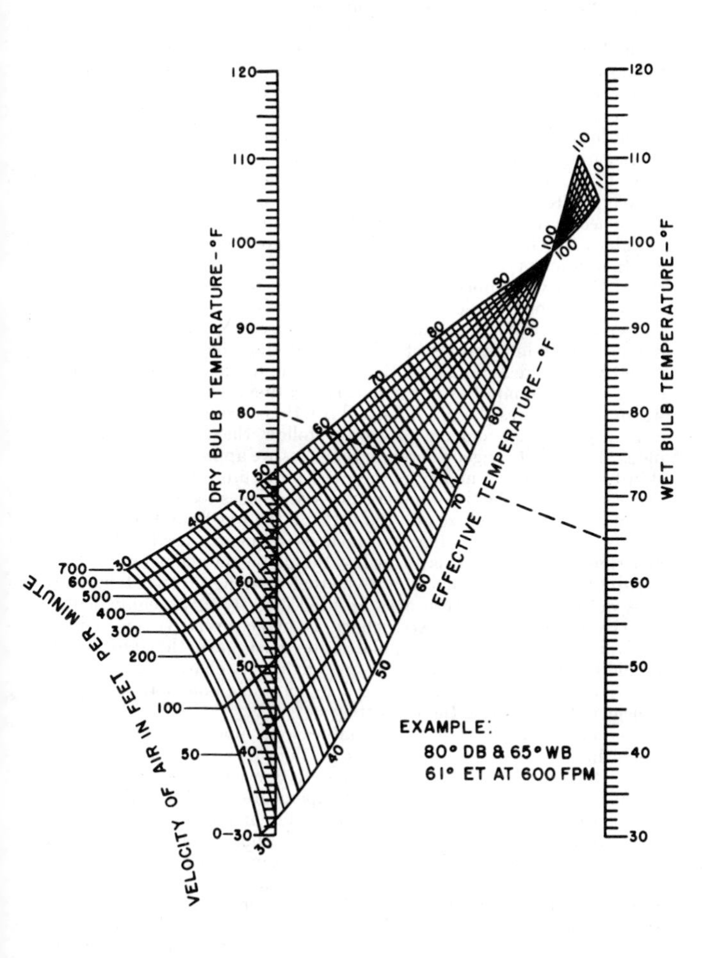

Figure 132—Effective Temperatures—light work

Adapted from the data of C. P. Yaglou, Comfort Zones for Men at Rest and Stripped to the Waist, *Trans. ASHVE*, vol. 33, pp. 165-179, 1927.

labeled "shock." Even though rapid physiological adjustments are necessary under such conditions, research studies reveal no harmful effects to normal subjects or even subjects with heart disease. During the period before thermal equilibrium is accomplished, some feelings of discomfort may occur. Cognizance of the fact that rapid changes in environmental temperature do not cause deleterious effects upon health has led to the use of lower inside-summer-design temperatures.

Research reveals that various combinations of temperature, humidity, velocity, and radiation effects produce the same degree of comfort. "Effective temperature" and other environmental indices have been developed in recognition of this fact. These indices vary in the number of variables which they take into account and the manner in which the combination is assigned a numerical value. Each index has some limitations. Effective temperature, which is probably the most widely used index, does not include any radiant heat effect beyond that associated with the experimental chamber actually used. In addition, results are based on first impressions of subjects entering the chamber, and it has recently been demonstrated that this unduly magnifies the warming effect of high humidities in the normal heating and ventilating range. In warm atmospheres the physiological reactions produced by temperature, humidity, and air movement closely follow the effective temperature index. In the hot range, where the temperature approaches or exceeds the skin temperature, humidity is the most important of the environmental factors, and the effective-temperature scale places too much emphasis on the dry-bulb temperature and too little on the wet-bulb. One approximation of the effect of radiation which is frequently used, although not experimentally verified, is to utilize the globe thermometer reading instead of the dry-bulb temperature when determining effective temperature. The wet-bulb temperature may be used directly or an equivalent wet-bulb read from a psychrometric chart. To make this latter conversion, the equivalent state and the original state must have the same absolute humidity. Figures 131 and 132 are alignment charts for determining effective temperatures. Differences in clothing and activity must be considered when using these charts.

The assumption that in a comfortable environment humidity variations are of little consequence and that sensations of warmth and comfort are associated mainly with heat loss by radiation and convection led to the development of the "operative-temperature" index. Although the formula for operative temperature is quite complex, a close approximation can be obtained by averaging the dry-bulb and the mean radiant temperatures. Some conclusions resulting from its use are quite interesting. For instance, in a room where the six surfaces exert equal effect and where the air movement is moderate, an operative temperature of 70° results when there is one outside wall at 55° and where the other five surfaces as well as the air are at 71½°. Similarly, with two cold walls at 55°, the air and other surface temperatures must be 73°.

A "heat-stress" index has been developed in an attempt to evaluate the endurance of workers expending energy in different amounts in relation to globe temperature, dry-bulb, humidity, and air speed. This index has no application in the comfort range.

The British have developed an "equivalent-temperature" and an 'equivalent-warmth" index, both of which reflect their somewhat dif-erent standard of comfort. A similar French index is called "resultant emperature." These and other indices all have limitations and are not liscussed here in order to avoid confusion.

Due to the variability of weather, occupancy, and other factors, a entilation system alone serving a space will seldom, if ever, supply ptimum comfort conditions. This can only be accomplished with a com-lete air-conditioning system, of which ventilation will be a necessary art. Nevertheless, ventilation is used by itself to promote more com-ortable conditions than would otherwise exist. Heating and ventilating ystems are often designed without specifically evaluating the additional osts and benefits of complete air conditioning. However, the economic dvantages of complete, year-round air conditioning are being increas-ngly demonstrated and should be investigated.

Industrial heat relief, in addition to preventing the various manifesta-ions of heat stress, has for its aim the reduction of accidents and errors, as vell as increases in efficiency. Although undocumented, the following ffective temperatures, corrected for radiant effects, can be considered imiting for the conditions outlined:

80°F corrected ET—limit for heavy, manual work.
85°F corrected ET—limit for light, manual work.
90°F corrected ET—approximately ½ of time spent resting.
65°F corrected ET—accidents tend to increase below this value.

Figure 132 shows the effect of velocity on effective temperature up to 700 feet per minute. The practical limiting value of velocity is considered o be 700 to 800 feet per minute. However, there have been recorded nstances where velocities of 3000 feet per minute or more have been equested by workers. Small jets at velocities such as these have been sed on an intermittent basis.

In industrial heat relief it is frequently possible to employ shielding r insulation, or both, around a particularly hot spot. Insulation can be conomically justified to a certain degree on steam generators, dryers, tc., on the basis of reducing heat losses. Radiant shielding has been lemonstrated to be particularly effective in providing heat relief economi-ally. It is not unusual to expect 90° or lower shield surface temperatures n 65°F rooms when the furnace so shielded has a surface temperature of pproximately 300°. To attempt the same measure of relief with ventila-ion alone would be foolhardy indeed. For maximum effectiveness, hielding should be supported independently of the structure being hielded. In addition, if properly located, the natural draft created by the eated air column may also be used to promote comfort.

If shielding and natural ventilation do not produce the desired degree f comfort, spot cooling or blast cooling can be used. Blast cooling is only ffective when the worker himself has some measure of control over the last. In this regard, directional control by louvers, swing mounting, etc., r some sort of on-off control, all have merits. Cooling blasts can fre-quently be treated without resorting to complete air conditioning. Evapo-ative cooling is very popular and can be used to great advantage in educing effective temperatures in many applications.

Odor Control

The principal sources of objectionable odors are those resulting fron smoking or from bodily processes. The ventilation requirement to kee the concentration of odoriferous matter below objectionable limits ex ceeds that required to prevent chemical vitiation, but is generally les than the total amount of conditioned air required for the heating or cool ing load. For instance, the normal breathing rate of a person at rest i approximately 1/4 CFM and under maximum exertion rises to 3½ CFM The corresponding oxygen consumption is approximately 4/100ths of th breathing rate. Oxygen content may drop from the normal 21% to 15% without change in respiratory process or even awareness of the reductio Minimum ventilation to prevent odor buildup is 5 CFM per non-smoke and 25 CFM per smoker. Recommended values are usually 50% higher

The smelling process begins with a molecular diffusion of the odorou substance, which then goes into solution with the mucous coating on th olfactory membrane arousing the sense of smell by some chemical actio on the olfactory hairs. The sensitivity of these organs is greatest whe the nose is neither too dry nor too wet and is therefore dependent o relative humidity. Only the strongest of several simultaneous odors ca be perceived, which explains the "masking" of odors. However, th sudden appearance of new odors can be quickly detected, and, althoug the olfactory sense is soon fatigued, the breathing of fresh air revives th full sense of smell in very short order. The intensity of the sensatio varies as the logarithm of the concentration. There is a lower limit of con centration, or a threshold value, below which odors are imperceptible Some typical substances and threshold values are listed in Table 73.

In the case of industrial odorants, it is often impractical to attemp dilution below threshold values. However, where figures on threshol concentrations are available, the ventilation requirement can be com puted from this value, using the dilution formula on page 349.

TABLE 73—ODOR THRESHOLD CONCENTRATIONS

Substance	Parts Per Million	Lb Per Million Cu Ft of Air
Carbon Tetrachloride	71.8	28.62
Ammonia	53.0	2.34
Phosgene	5.6	1.44
Sulphur Dioxide (Water Soluble)	4.0	0.46
Chlorine (Water Soluble)	3.5	0.64
Acrolein	1.8	0.26
Amyl Acetate	1.0	0.34
Carbon Bisulphide	0.77	0.15
Phenol	0.306	0.074
Cresol	0.200	0.056
Hydrogen Sulfide	0.180	0.016
Ozone	0.050	0.006
Pyridine (Burning Tobacco)	0.0123	0.0025
Iodoform	0.0016	0.0018
Valeric Acid (Body Odor)	0.00013	0.00005
Ethyl Mercaptan	0.00026	0.00004
Butyric Acid	0.00006	0.00001

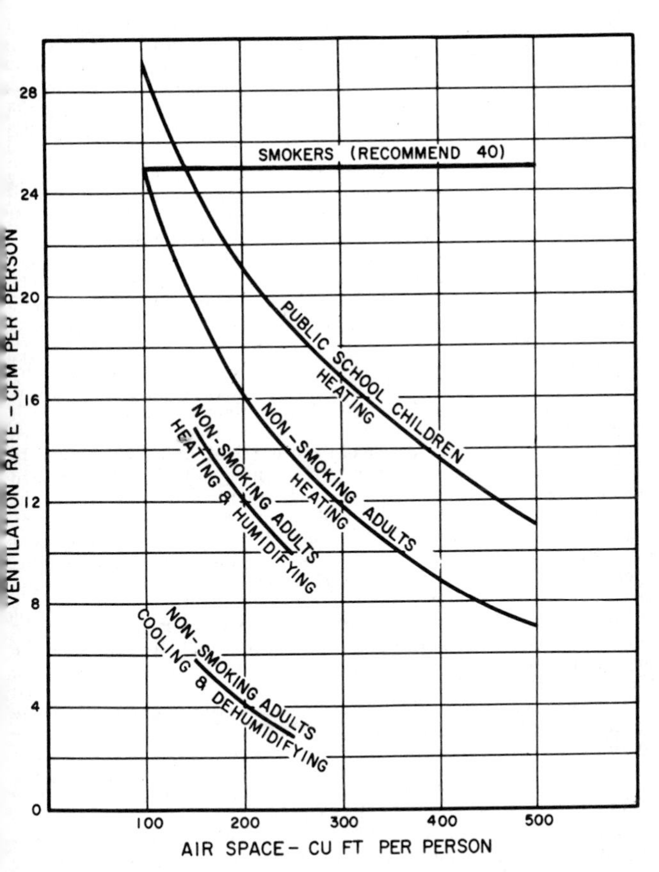

VALUES LISTED ARE MINIMUMS FOR SEDENTARY OCCUPANTS OF AVERAGE SOCIO-ECONOMIC STATUS. VALUES SHOULD BE ADJUSTED FOR DIFFERENCES IN STATUS OR ACTIVITY.

Figure 133—Minimum Ventilation Rates

Adapted from the data of C. P. Yaglou, E. C. Riley, and D. I. Coggins, Ventilation Requirements, *Trans. ASHVE*, vol. 42, pp. 133-162, 1936, p. 156, and of C. P. Yaglou, Ventilation Requirements for Cigarette Smoke, *Trans. ASHVE*, vol. 61, pp. 25-32, 1955, p. 31.

The concentration of body odors in a space depends on the amount of air space allowed per person, the personal hygiene of the occupants, and their activity. The subjective response of any occupant to any particular odor depends upon the concentration, the thermal conditions in the atmosphere, and his sensitivity as a receiver. The chart in Figure 133 gives a graphical representation of some of the factors affecting ventilation requirements.

The nature of odors suggests that complaints can be eliminated by masking them with stronger, more agreeable odors; counteracting them by adding a combining odor; or removing them entirely, either by absorption, adsorption, or chemical reaction; as well as by diluting them.

Air washers can be effective on water soluble vapors, gases, and fumes. However, most odorous substances are not especially water soluble. The use of water or any solvent presents a problem regarding the ultimate disposal of the contaminated solution often approaching the seriousness of the original problem.

Most odors encountered in air conditioning are readily retained by activated carbon which, unlike many other adsorbents, greatly prefers organic substances to H_2O. "Activated" carbon is treated so that it presents an immense surface per unit volume of material and is so oriented that it can retain a large fraction of its own weight, up to 55% in fact. In air-conditioning work, the carbon cells are used to their full extent and then replaced by fresh cells. The used cells are usually reactivated at the factory, although in commercial applications, such as solvent recovery, regenerating units are applied at the job site. In addition to the process of adsorption, activated carbon may remove contaminants by promoting chemical reactions between the sorbed substances. Activated-carbon adsorbers are available in plates and canisters of various sorts.

The use of purification equipment such as activated carbon reduces the ventilation requirement. The cost of such equipment, together with the increased horsepower or operating costs due to the pressure drop across that equipment and the value of the heat liberated, should be evaluated against the savings accrued by reducing outdoor-air requirements. These savings include the reduction in heating and cooling load made possible by the recirculation of air and the attendant reduction in operating costs. It should be noted that, although activated carbon removes most of the odors associated with tobacco smoke, the actual particulate matter should be filtered, or precipitated, separately.

Odor is probably more closely associated with freshness of air than almost any other quality. However, temperature, humidity, and air movement also play an important part. High air temperatures around the head produce the impression of stuffiness. Variability of air movement increases the sensation of freshness. Environments with warmer walls and cooler air have generally been found more pleasant and fresher than those of equal warmth with wall temperatures similar to, or lower than, the air temperature.

"Air-conditioning-coil odors" are rather rare, but when they do occur, they produce violent complaints, since the odors are extremely foul and disturbing. Such odors are released, after a period of intensive selective buildup, possibly as a result of fluctuating operating conditions. Limited research would indicate that of the usual materials, when coil odors are a problem, aluminum is first, tinned copper second, and bare copper third in desirability. Chromatized and phosphatized all-aluminum coils gave by far the best results. Similar treatments to aluminum-finned copper coils produced desirable results. Experience indicates that latent heat removal contributes significantly, but that a dripping coil is better than one which is merely wet.

Bacteria Control

It is impractical to maintain sanitary conditions in a space by ventilation alone. The estimated 500 cfm of pure air per person required is prohibitive. The majority of bacteria found in the air are relatively harmless, so that a significant reduction in bacteria content of the air does not necessarily imply control of air-borne disease. Significant amounts of bacteria can be eliminated by simple filtering, precipitation, or use of air washers. This is true apparently because a large percentage of micro-organisms are dust borne. However, recontamination will occur if concentrated buildups are allowed in the spray water. Germicidal action may be obtained from the use of ultraviolet radiation or introduction of various chemicals into the air from sprays, etc. However, it is the current consensus of medical and public health associations that there is no justification for employing methods of air disinfection in homes, offices, or places of ordinary public congregation. Hospitals, on the other hand, must do everything possible to prevent transport of infection from one area to another.

Industrial Contaminant Control

Almost any mechanical or chemical operation is a possible source of atmospheric contamination. Human systems have a tolerance to almost all materials, but, if the limiting concentration is exceeded, effects are produced ranging from minor irritation to ultimate death. Industrial hygienists classify dusts as irritants, toxic dusts, fibrosis-producing dusts, inert dusts, allergy-producing dusts, and fever-producing substances, and they classify gaseous substances as asphyxiants, irritants, inorganic or organometallic gases, and volatile drugs and drug-like substances. Fortunately, research and experience have provided sufficient information to establish maximum allowable concentrations which, if not exceeded, will allow the average worker to be exposed for the normal working day without significant harmful effects. Values of maximum allowable concentration (*MAC*) and lower explosive limits (*LEL*) for typical substances may be found in Table 74 together with ventilation requirements per pint or pound. A larger list of maximum allowable concentration and lower explosive limits may be found in the reference. If the rate of generation or evolution is known and a *MAC* or *LEL* value can be obtained, then the amount of ventilation required may be obtained from the following formulas:

$$CFM = \frac{386.7 \times lb\ of\ Solvent\ per\ min \times 10^6 \times K}{Molecular\ wt.\ of\ Solvent \times MAC\ in\ ppm}, \text{ and} \quad (364)$$

$$CFM = \frac{386.7 \times lb\ of\ Solvent\ per\ min \times 10^2 \times K}{Molecular\ wt.\ of\ Solvent \times LEL\ in\ \%}. \quad (365)$$

The factor K in the above formulas indicates that a factor of safety must be applied, depending on the possibilities for isolated concentrations in specific localities due to drafts, obstructions, etc. The value of K is also dependent upon the ultimate danger represented by the substance itself. Safety factors of from 3 to 12 have been required in various instances.

An industrial ventilating system may consist simply of a wall fan exhausting from a space to the outside. The use of such means to produce control over a wide area necessarily means that large quantities of air must be exhausted. The alternative, a local exhaust system, requires far less capacity, although hoods, ducts, etc., must be used. Refer to Chapter 17.

TABLE 74—DILUTION AIR VOLUMES FOR VAPORS

Liquid	MAC	Air Req'd to Dilute to MAC‡		LEL	Flash Point
	ppm	ft³/pint evap.	ft³/lb evap.	% Vol.	°F
Acetone	1000	5,500	6,650	2.55	15
Amyl acetate	100	27,200	29,800	1.1	80
Iso-amyl alcohol	100	37,200	43,900	1.2	115
Benzol	25	Not Recommended		—	(12)
n-Butanol (butyl alcohol)	100	44,000	52,200	1.45	110
n-Butyl acetate	150	20,400	22,200	1.39	90
Butyl cellosolve	50	61,600	65,600	—	165
Carbon disulfide	20	Not Recommended		1.25	−22
Carbon tetrachloride	25	Not Recommended		—	—
Cellosolve	200	20,800	21,500	2.6	120
Cellosolve acetate	100	29,700	29,300	1.71	135
Chloroform	50	Not Recommended		—	—
1-2 Dichloroethane	100	Not Recommended		6.2	65
1-2 Dichloroethylene	200	26,900	20,000	9.7	(43)
Dioxane	100	47,300	43,900	—	54
Ethyl acetate	400	10,300	11,000	2.18	30
Ethyl alcohol	1000	6,900	8,400	3.28	(55)
Ethyl ether	400	9,630	13,100	—	—
Gasoline	Requires Special Consideration			1.3	(−50)
Methyl alcohol	200	49,100	60,500	6.72	60
Methyl acetate	200	25,000	26,100	3.15	20
Methyl butyl ketone	100	33,500	38,700	—	—
Methyl cellosolve	25	Not Recommended		—	115
Methyl cellosolve acetate	25	Not Recommended		—	140
Methyl ethyl ketone	200	22,500	26,900	—	(30)
Methyl iso-butyl ketone	100	32,300	38,700	—	(73)
Methyl propyl ketone	200	19,000	22,400	—	60
Naptha (coal tar)	100	30,000-38,000	40,000-50,000	—	(100)
Naptha (petroleum)	500	6,000-7,000	8,000-10,000	—	—
Nitrobenzene	1	Not Recommended		1.8	(190)
Iso-Propyl alcohol	400	13,200	16,100	2.02	60
Propyl acetate	200	17,500	18,900	1.78	60
Iso-Propyl ether	500	5,700	7,570	—	−15
Stoddard solvent	500	6,000-7,000	8,000-10,000	—	—
Tetrachloroethane	5	Not Recommended		—	—
Tetrachloroethylene	100	39,600	23,400	—	—
Toluol (toluene)	200	19,000	21,000	1.27	45
Trichloroethylene	100	45,000	29,400	—	—
Xylol (xylene)	100	33,000	36,400	1.0	75

‡The tabulated dilution air quantities must be multiplied by the selected K value.

Adapted from the data of Committee on Industrial Ventilation, "Industrial Ventilation," American Conference of Governmental Industrial Hygienists, 1970, p. 2-2.

Night-Air Cooling

The daily variation in air temperature in many localities provides a "heat sink" of a sort. Wherever night-air temperatures are significantly lower than daytime temperatures during hot spells, or summer weather, a significant reduction in room temperature can be effected by judicious use of attic fans. In a typical residence without attic fans, the room temperature as well as the outside temperature rises gradually throughout the course of the day up to about 4:00 P.M. As the sun sets, air temperatures will fall rapidly on the outside. Inside, however, due to the mechanism of time lag in heating, the room temperature will not fall nearly as fast. This heat soaking into the living spaces from the structure maintains uncomfortable conditions, even though the outside air may be quite comfortable. This effect may persist into the late hours of the night, or even carry over until after sunrise and the next heating cycle. If, however, an attic fan is placed in operation when the outside temperature begins to fall rapidly, the inside temperature can be made to closely approach that of the outside, provided, of course, that sufficient air is moved throughout the spaces. If the fan is shut off when the outside temperature begins to rise again and the space kept reasonably closed with blinds pulled during the day, an additional benefit results during the ensuing day, due also to the mechanism of time lag. A particularly effective method of using an attic fan for maximum comfort in a two-story residence is to arrange window openings so that air is drawn in through the various downstairs living areas only during early evening hours to produce maximum comfort there and subsequently opening the upstairs windows so as to concentrate the cooling effect in the upper sleeping quarters later during the evening and night. Capacities are usually based on changing the air in all living spaces once every minute in areas such as southern U.S.A., once every minute and one half in northern U.S.A.

During the heat of the day, attic temperatures may range to or upwards of 140°F. Daytime attic ventilation can reduce this effect which is due to solar radiation. Consequently, some attic fans are installed to provide cross-ventilation of attics only, while others are installed in such a manner as to provide cross-ventilation during the day and normal, living-space ventilation during night-air cooling hours. Some experimenters report no benefit from operating an attic fan to remove this high-temperature air. Since the stagnant air film tends to act as insulation, the attic temperature would decrease if a fan were operated, but the insulation value of the air film would also decrease. Lack of other thermal resistance between attic and second floor might make this important.

The cooling effect of the increased air motion from an attic fan must also be considered. Some users will even tolerate an increase in temperature resulting from the use of an attic fan during the day in order to appreciate the effects of increased air motion.

Since propeller fans are generally employed for attic-fan duty, it is important that discharge air be allowed free access to the outside. Velocities through louvers and screens should not exceed 1000 fpm.

Infiltration and Natural Ventilation

Infiltration is the leakage of air through the various cracks and interstices which occur in building construction. The force which causes infiltration is a pressure difference, which may be the result of wind, or a difference in inside and outside temperatures, more commonly referred to as stack effect. These same forces may produce natural ventilation through windows, doors, or other openings provided for the purpose. In any case, the flow rate may be estimated by calculating the areas available for both inflow and outflow, and determining the velocities by equating the driving force with the frictional resistance.

Assuming equal areas on windward and leeward sides, the flow rate can be calculated from the expression

$$q = EAV, \tag{366}$$

where the air flow (q) is in cfm, the free area of inlet openings (A) is in square feet, the wind velocity (V) is in feet per minute (which equals miles per hour times 88), and the effectiveness (E) of the openings may be assumed as 0.5 to 0.6 for perpendicular winds and 0.25 to 0.3 for diagonal winds.

The determination of the net free area through interstices and around window sash would be, to say the least, tedious. The values in Table 75 are more convenient to use.

The stack effect which may be produced within a building by a column of air which is warm relative to the outside temperature may be estimated from the expression,

$$q = 10A\sqrt{H(t_i - t_o)}, \tag{367}$$

where the air flow (q) is in cfm; the area of inlets or outlets (A), whichever is smaller, is in square feet; the height of building between inlets and outlets (H) is in feet; the average indoor temperature (t_i) is in °F; and the average outdoor temperature (t_o) is in °F.

The assumed equal areas of inlets and outlets provides maximum flow per unit area. Air flow may be increased by increasing one over the other, but not in proportion to the additional area. The chart in Figure 134 may be used to determine the increase.

When both wind and thermal forces act to produce flow the combined result is not the simple sum of the two individually-estimated quantities. The actual flow under such conditions can be approximated from Figure 135.

In addition to the items enumerated above, there are numerous other factors which influence both infiltration and natural ventilation. The natural variability of winds and the effects of other structures, trees, etc., all affect the flow rate. Although infiltration is generally undesirable from the standpoint of increases in either heating or cooling loads, human chemical requirements, that is O_2 supply and CO_2 removal, are usually satisfied by infiltration unless the building is unusually tight. In well built structures, infiltration alone will not supply sufficient ventilation to dilute odors or produce thermal benefits. On the other hand, given sufficient openings, normal wind velocities are sufficient to produce amazingly high flow rates. For instance, a ten mile per hour wind will

TABLE 75—INFILTRATION

THRU WALLS—CFH/SQ FT	Wind Velocity—MPH					
	5	10	15	20	25	30
Frame Construction*						
Corrugated iron siding	7.00	21.00	36.00	52.00	68.00	85.00
Wood siding, paper, sheathing, lath and plaster	.02	.07	.13	.18	.23	.26
Masonry—13″ brick‡						
Porous brick—good work.—plain	.60	1.90	4.00	6.60	9.60	12.80
Porous brick—good workmanship—3 coats oil paint	.40	1.50	3.00	4.90	6.90	9.30
Hard brick—poor workmanship—1 coat cold water paint	.20	.80	1.80	3.00	4.50	6.10
Porous brick—good workmanship—furring, lath and plaster	.04	.11	.22	.38	.54	.74

THRU WINDOWS and DOORS CFH/FT OF CRACK	Wind Velocity—MPH					
	5	10	15	20	25	30
Wood Windows⊙						
Around frame in wood frame wall	2.00	6.00	11.00	17.00	23.00	30.00
Around frame in uncalked mas. wall	3.00	8.00	14.00	20.00	27.00	35.00
Around frame in calked masonry wall	.50	1.50	2.60	3.80	4.80	5.80
Wood Windows—Double Hung—Unlocked⊙						
Around sash—average fit—plain	5.00	15.00	29.00	43.00	58.00	74.00
Around sash—avg. fit—weathstrip	2.00	7.00	13.00	19.00	26.00	33.00
Around sash—poor fit—plain	25.00	63.00	100.00	137.00	176.00	220.00
Around sash—poor fit—weathstrip	4.00	13.00	23.00	35.00	48.00	61.00
Wood Windows—Casement						
Around Sash—plain	40.00	81.00	121.00	162.00	202.00	242.00
Around Sash—weatherstripped	1.90	3.70	5.60	7.40	9.30	11.20
Metal Windows§						
Around frame—steel mullions	8.00	16.00	28.00	44.00	63.00	84.00
Around frame—steel framing	14.00	30.00	52.00	76.00	105.00	133.00
Metal Windows—Double Hung§						
Around sash—plain	20.00	47.00	74.00	104.00	137.00	171.00
Around sash—weatherstripped	7.00	19.00	32.00	46.00	60.00	76.00
Metal Windows—Casement§						
Around ventilator—avg. industrial pivoted	52.00	108.00	180.00	244.00	310.00	380.00
Around ventilator—avg. architectural projected	24.00	52.00	88.00	118.00	155.00	190.00
Around ventilator—avg. residential	12.00	32.00	54.00	77.00	102.00	125.00
Doors⊕						
Around frame in wood frame wall	2.00	6.00	11.00	17.00	23.00	30.00
Around frame in uncalked mas. wall	3.00	8.00	14.00	20.00	27.00	35.00
Around frame in calked mas. wall	.50	1.50	2.60	3.80	4.80	5.80
Around door—1/16″ crack, 1/16″ clearance	57.00	114.00	159.00	227.00	284.00	341.00
Around door—1/8″ crack, 1/16″ clearance	86.00	171.00	257.00	342.00	428.00	514.00
Around door—weatherstripped	2.10	4.20	6.20	8.30	10.80	12.50

*Adapted from the data of G. L. Larson, D. W. Nelson, and C. Braatz, Air Infiltration through Various Types of Wood Frame Construction, *Trans. ASHVE*, vol. 36, pp. 397-428, 1930, pp. 400 and 402.

‡Adapted from the data of G. L. Larson, D. W. Nelson, and C. Braatz, Air Infiltration through Various Types of Brick Wall Construction, *Trans. ASHVE*, vol. 36, pp. 99-122, 1930, pp. 110 and 111.

⊙Adapted from the data of G. L. Larson, D. W. Nelson, and R. W. Kubasta, Air Infiltration through Double Hung Wood Windows, *Trans. ASHVE*, vol. 37, pp. 571-604, 1931, p. 599.

§Adapted from the data of J. E. Emswiler and W. C. Randall, The Weathertightness of Rolled Section Steel Windows, *Trans. ASHVE*, vol. 34, pp. 527-546, 1928, pp. 528 and 530.

⊕Adapted from the data of C. C. Schrader, Further Data on Infiltration of Air through Building Openings, *Trans. ASHVE*, vol. 31, pp. 85-88, 1925.

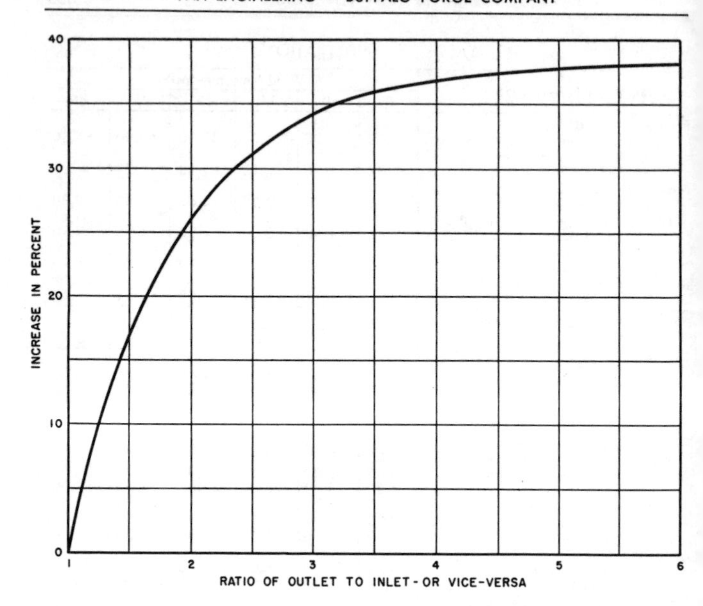

Figure 134—Effect of Opening Size on Natural Ventilation

Adapted from the data of W. C. Randall and E. W. Conover, Predetermining the Airation of Industrial Buildings, *Trans. ASHVE*, vol. 37, pp. 605-618, 1931, p. 609.

---

produce a 100,000 cfm flow rate with only ten 4′ x 5′ inlet openings. The main difficulty arises in attempting to utilize these large flow rates to the best advantage. Structural and architectural requirements often preclude any possibility of good distribution. In addition, the required manual manipulation of controls needed to offset the variations due to natural causes can be a burden, particularly in industry.

Whenever it is desired to utilize the natural stack effect resulting from furnace operation, etc., wind forces should be used to assist whenever possible. Since a negative pressure region is created on the roof at the windward side, heat generating equipment should be located at this side. Similarly, the roof over such equipment should be higher than the surrounding roofs, if at all possible. This not only makes possible a greater difference in height between inlet and outlet openings, but also provides for a wind-jump even when not located on the windward end.

As pointed out in Chapter 4, caution must be exercised in using trained arrows when sketching ventilation systems. Suction openings tend to draw equally from all directions, whereas pressure openings tend to produce a flow axis perpendicular to the plane of the opening. Although

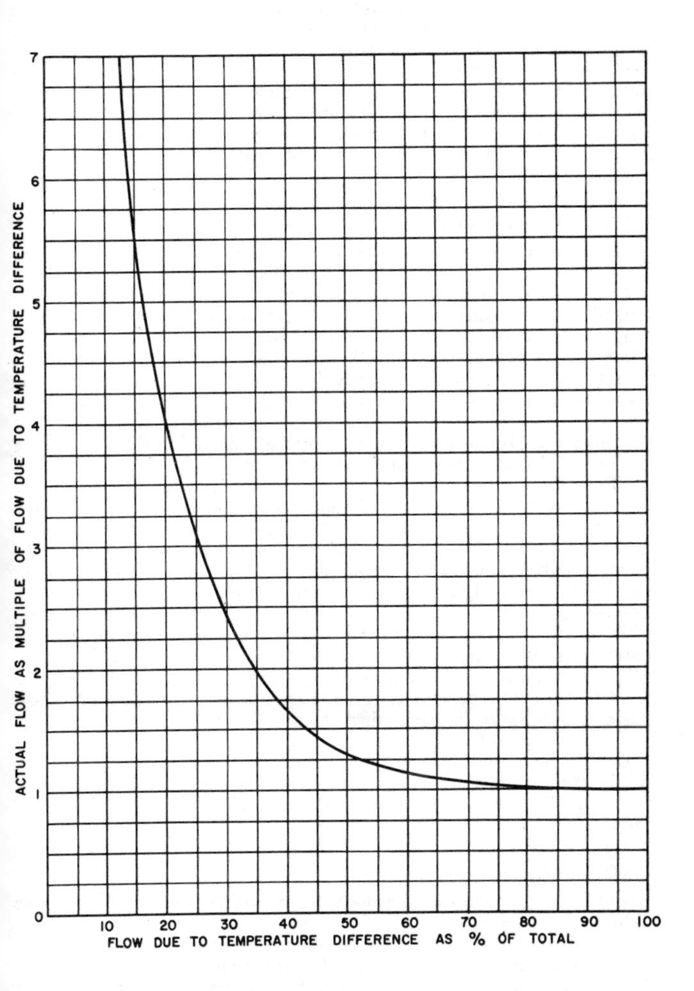

Figure 135—Combined Wind and Stack Effects

Adapted from the data of W. C. Randall and E. W. Conover, Predetermining the Airation of Industrial Buildings, *Trans. ASHVE*, vol. 37, p. 612.

short-circuiting is a real danger, when both inlet and outlet openings are directly in line, bending of the supply stream is quite difficult when both openings are in the same plane. On this basis the designer can utilize roof openings for both supply and exhaust, provided he utilizes the positive and negative pressure areas correctly. Numerous designs of non-powered roof ventilators are available which utilize the forces of nature in varying degrees. In selecting such apparatus, the designer should consider not only the protection afforded against inclement weather, but the effectiveness in utilizing wind forces.

Mechanical Ventilation

Although natural ventilation is often quite successful, the advantages of continuous ventilation regardless of weather and positive control often make mechanical ventilation quite attractive. Such systems may utilize fans of any type with or without ductwork. Fans, grilles, nozzles, etc., should be located to utilize or be assisted by the natural forces whenever possible. Specifically, however, this equipment should be located and sized in such a manner as to provide the desired air flow in only the desired areas. Exhaust openings should be hooded, baffled, and located as close as possible to the area to be exhausted. For further discussion of this, see Chapter 17. In locating air entry ports, consideration should be given to possible contamination from other sources.

Whether natural or mechanical means are used to exhaust air from a space, a corresponding amount of make-up air is required. The principal advantage in using a fan unit for this purpose lies in its ability to provide the necessary heat under controlled conditions, thereby eliminating objectionable drafts due to infiltration which would otherwise result. Roof ventilators employing make-up air heating provisions have proven very popular on industrial applications. Such roof units, generally speaking, utilize space which would not otherwise be used. Depending on the fans involved, such units may or may not be suitable for systems with ductwork.

The advantages of recirculating room air in many cases are quite obvious. As has been pointed out, the cost of purifying such air, if required, should be evaluated against the savings due to reduction in heating and cooling loads.

Another advantage in using mechanical ventilation lies in the possibility of pressurizing the space, thereby promoting better conditions by preventing the infiltration of dust, dirt, and moisture, along with infiltration air.

Specific Applications

Some of the more interesting characteristics of various unusual systems are enumerated below.

Vehicular tunnel systems have several distinctive features. Innumerable variations have been used, depending on the length of the tunnel and the arrangement of the traffic lanes. For relatively long tunnels, the "transverse" method has proven quite satisfactory. In this method, supply air is fed to all locations in the tunnel through a large passage under the roadbed. A similar exhaust passage is located above the road-

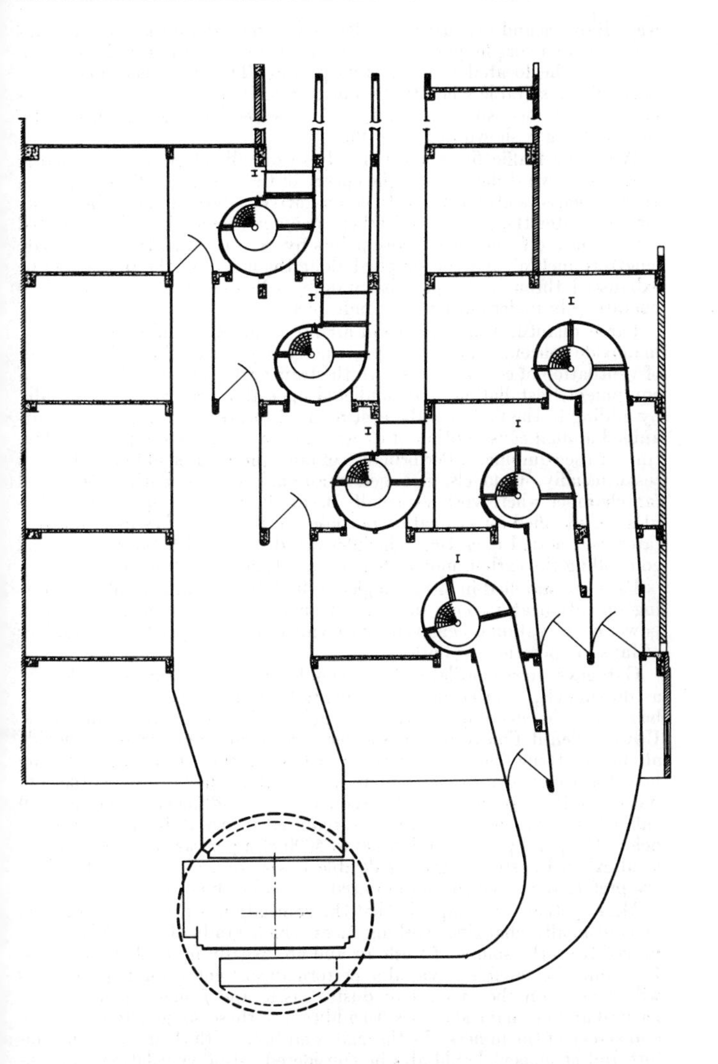

Figure 136 —Vehicular Tunnel Ventilation Building

way. Blowers and exhausters are located in special ventilation buildings which serve a specific portion of the tunnel. In most tunnels these buildings must be located near the two portals. The transverse method is particularly suitable when traffic must be maintained in both directions either simultaneously or alternately. A cross section of a typical ventilation building is shown in Figure 136.

Wherever traffic flows continuously in one direction as is frequently the case in twin-tube tunnels, the energy of the moving traffic in inducing air flow is frequently utilized. In comparatively short tunnels, the supply air may enter the portals and other openings provided and the vitiated air is removed from one or more points by exhaust fans. In intermediate length tunnels air may be supplied along the length of the tunnel and be exhausted through the portals. Standby exhaust fans are required to operate only under emergency conditions.

Large quantities of ventilation air are required to dilute the carbon monoxide concentration to 2½ parts per 10,000 parts of air. The amount of ventilation of course varies with the traffic rate. The combined costs of equipment, installation, and predicted operation are evaluated, usually by adding to the first cost the cost reduced to present value of the guaranteed annual consumption of electrical energy during the probable lifetime of the equipment. Performance of fan equipment should be based on tests, usually of models, arranged in an enclosure simulating the actual fan chamber where vortices usually occur. Preliminary operating schedules are specified for evaluation purposes on the basis of estimated traffic rates, but actual operating schedules are determined by measuring and controlling the carbon monoxide concentration in the tunnel.

Fans are supplied in either single- or dual-drive arrangements facilitating operation at various speeds. Adequate ventilation with maximum power conservation is achieved by varying either the speed or the number of fans in operation, or both.

Garages require ventilation to prevent buildup of carbon monoxide, just as do tunnels. Ventilation requirements for parking facilities should be based on the maximum possible number of moving and idling cars. Upward ventilation results in a lower concentration of carbon monoxide at the breathing line, as well as a lower temperature above the breathing line, for which reasons it is to be preferred to downward ventilation. Assuming the carbon monoxide production of an idling car to be 25 to 50 cubic feet per hour, the ventilation required to maintain concentrations below 1½ parts per 10,000 is 2800 to 5600 cfm per car. In service areas, local exhaust systems utilizing flexible hoses connected to the tailpipes are preferred and sometimes required by local ordinance.

Mine systems are unique in that the ventilation is principally required at continually changing working faces which gradually are further removed from the source of fresh air and are usually in dead-end pockets. Fans must be capable of variable performance. Ventilation requirements will depend on the amount of dusts, gases, and fumes resulting from natural and mechanical causes. In addition to these dangers to the health and safety of the miners, the thermal conditions with their effect on comfort and efficiency should also be considered. Mine ventilation, particularly for deep mines, must recognize the geo-thermogradient which may range from 1° per 100 feet to 1° per 200 feet, depending upon geological and meteorological conditions. Mine fans frequently incorporate features making it possible to reverse the flow of air. This, together with a system for controlling the course of air through the mine itself, is of tremendous value in preventing the spread of fumes, etc., in case of fire.

Power-plant ventilation is slightly unusual in that the mechanical draft equipment itself may be used to produce ventilation to a degree and the open grill-work floor structure of most central stations provides huge natural draft potentials. Even so, additional mechanical ventilation is often required. Local confined areas or hot spots may require more ventilation than can be provided naturally. Proper positioning or sizing of inlet openings may not always be possible.

Animal shelters should be designed to effect maximum productivity consistent with cost. In addition, building maintenance is greatly reduced if excessive moisture is prevented. In dairy barns and similar applications the exhaust should be taken from points approximately 18″ above the floor. A rule of thumb for sizing natural draft flues is to provide a cross-sectional area equal to 170 times the number of thousands of pounds in the total weight of the animals, divided by the square root of the difference in elevation in feet between the points where fresh air enters and foul air leaves. In sizing fans a figure of 50 to 60 cfm of air per cow or its equivalent is often used.

Although the above-mentioned special applications seldom incorporate heating or air-conditioning provisions, most other systems invariably incorporate one or both. Additional data may be obtained in the following chapter on winter and summer air conditioning.

CHAPTER 15

WINTER AND SUMMER AIR CONDITIONING

The purpose of any air-conditioning system is to control the conditions within a space for the benefit of the persons, products, or process equipment which may occupy the space. Air conditioning in its modern sense encompasses the processes of heating and humidifying, as well as cooling and dehumidifying. In addition to controlling temperature and humidity by thermodynamic means, a complete air-conditioning system should be capable of controlling contamination due to dust, odor, pollen, etc.

The principal methods discussed here involve sufficiently treating a quantity of air that, when it is introduced into a room and mixed with the air in that room, the desired conditions are maintained. The thermodynamic processes are of major interest in this chapter. Contaminant control is discussed in Chapter 14.

Design Principles

Any analysis of the advantages of air conditioning ultimately leads to economic considerations. Economic comparisons and judgments dictate the choice between complete and partial air conditioning, as well as between various systems or components. Commercial establishments often find that they must have both winter and summer air conditioning to attract customers. Similarly, some business establishments find ample economic justification for complete air conditioning in increased efficiency, decreased absenteeism, etc. Historically, air conditioning was first used industrially where the quality of the product, efficiency of the process, or life of the equipment, or all three, demanded control of atmospheric conditions. Although the cost of complete air conditioning may be an appreciable percentage of the total cost for the building, the yearly cost compared to annual salaries ranges from approximately 1% for applications such as office buildings to approximately 4% for such applications as schools. There is considerable evidence that efficiency gains of several times these values result from air conditioning for both office and factory workers. Additional advantages accrue from reduced absenteeism and turnover, reduced cleaning, decorating, and maintenance costs, as well as from other intangible benefits due to a more healthful and inviting atmosphere.

Fan systems range from those providing air for ventilation only to those providing air that is conditioned to satisfy all of the thermodynamic requirements. All incorporate provisions to distribute air so as to absorb the load, be it ventilation, thermodynamic, or both. Individual units may be located in the spaces served or in central stations established to serve several areas. Different combinations of the two are frequently utilized. Direct radiation is also utilized in combination with various air systems. The number of variations and combinations is so great that only representative systems will be discussed here.

System components include various types of sensible and latent heat transfer devices, filters, dampers, and other control equipment, as well as fans. Various factory built assemblies are available, as are individual components for field erection.

DESIGN PROCEDURE

In general, owing to the large number of variables, each air-conditioning job should be considered unique and treated individually. However, it is not usually possible or desirable to completely evaluate more than two or three alternate systems for any given job. Engineering judgment, based on experience, rather than detailed calculations is usually employed to cull out all others.

Preliminary to the actual design of an air-conditioning system, the availability of and use charges for various services, including fuels, electric power, water, sewers, and equipment space, should be examined. The choice of heating and refrigeration plants is beyond our scope here, but to a degree is dependent upon the air-conditioning-system design and vice versa. The factors which should be considered include the advantages and disadvantages of (1) the various heat transfer mediums, (2) the different degrees of centralization, (3) the flexibility and reliability of the equipment, and (4) the expense of installation and operation.

The usual design procedure involves establishing the various extreme conditions in order to select equipment with capabilities sufficient to insure satisfactory full-load operation. In doing so, however, one must be careful to provide safeguards to prevent over-conditioning during part-load operation. In considering details of this procedure, zoning, design conditions, loads, systems, and equipment are discussed in the order listed.

Zoning

The probabilities for a completely satisfactory air-conditioning job increase rapidly as the size of the space and number of occupants decrease. The relative cost of the installation also increases. Although the desirability of individual room control has always been apparent, it is only in recent years that this element of complete air conditioning has been accomplished more often than not.

In the discussions of fan systems, page **408**, it will be noticed that certain systems are designed for multiple-zone operation. Those systems which are not so designed may still be used to satisfy multiple-zone requirements by applying them as individual systems to the individual zones. The choice will depend on the economics of the situation.

There are a number of criteria which are used to establish zones of substantially uniform air-conditioning requirements. Generally speaking, these criteria are based on similarities of occupancy, exposure, or construction. The basis of these various criteria is the load influencing effect of each. The choice of one or a combination of criteria should reflect the magnitude of this influence. It is obvious, for instance, that equipment which produces large quantities of heat should be located in a different area from that used for a sales room or general offices. It is often desirable to separately zone the last two mentioned spaces. Briefly then, separate zones are indicated wherever there is sufficient difference in either duration or density of occupancy or type of activity therein.

The action of the sun and wind produces different load requirements in different areas of a building, depending on the exposure. Although clouds may hide the sun and various factors cause winds to vary in direction, both the sun and the wind can frequently be relied upon to produce an effect which would make it generally advisable to zone one section of a building differently from another. Both effects may be modified by the influence of surrounding buildings or other structures.

The experienced designer may often be able to zone a small building intelligently by simply noting the usage and weather influences on a layout, but a more detailed analysis of the individual loads involved, taken in various trial combinations for various times during the course of the day, is usually in order. The magnitude and times of peak occupancy and the amount of glass and the degree of shading are often controlling factors.

Large buildings are frequently divided into two major zones, one of which, the "interior," has no outside exposure, and the other or "exterior" includes the periphery and topmost story. Tall buildings may be further zoned by grouping several stories together. These items constitute a sort of criteria based on construction.

Whenever central fan systems are used, particularly for multi-story buildings, compound zoning may be in order. That is, it may be economically advisable to provide more than one central system, each capable of multi-zone operation, in order to satisfy the individual requirements of the various spaces on a particular exposure, etc. A single refrigeration-heating plant may serve several central fan systems or several individual fan systems. There may also be occasions when it will be desirable to zone the refrigeration-heating plant system as well. A wise engineering choice requires a complete economic evaluation.

Design Conditions

In Chapter 14, the effects of temperature, humidity, air motion, and radiation on comfort were discussed at length. The designer should choose a combination of these factors which will produce the optimum conditions for the space under consideration. Research studies indicate that optimum effective temperatures are 71° in summer and 68° in winter, but some factors not included in these studies should be considered before establishing inside design conditions.

The seasonal difference results partly from acclimatization and partly from a difference in attire. Any appreciable variation in clothing habits would change the optimum conditions.

The "effective temperature" of various combinations of temperature, humidity, and velocity is arbitrarily defined as the saturated air temperature which produces the same sensory effect. However, the use of saturated air is certainly not recommended. As a matter of fact, effective temperature research was principally conducted in the middle relative-humidity range.

The two effective-temperature charts presented in Chapter 14 list differences in activity and clothing. In addition, it appears that women on the average prefer a 1° higher effective temperature than men and similarly that persons over 40 prefer a 1° higher effective temperature than those under 40.

The studies of effective-temperature were conducted in rooms wherein the surrounding surfaces were approximately at the temperature of the air. Any difference in wall temperature, or, for that matter, surrounding temperature due to crowds, etc., should be taken into account.

Inside winter dry-bulbs of 70°F are usually specified for those spaces occupied by sedentary adults. Temperatures in the vicinity of 65° are usually specified for factory spaces and 60° or lower for gymnasiums and the like. Temperatures above 70° may be specified for some special-purpose hospital rooms, etc. However, it is not at all unusual to maintain a thermostat setting at a temperature considerably different from the specified indoor design. It should be expected, based on the effective-temperature index, that thermostats will be set as high as 75° when there is no particular humidity control during winter.

During summer when complete air conditioning is provided, controls are usually set to maintain conditions at 75° dry-bulb and 50% relative humidity. It is usual, however, to design for somewhat higher dry-bulb temperatures. Conditions can then be maintained at the lower thermostatic setting only to the point where the equipment must operate continuously. Beyond this point, temperatures will exceed the thermostat setting. Table 76 lists some pertinent information about inside design conditions.

TABLE 76—INTERIOR DESIGN CONDITIONS

Conditions	ET, °F	DB, °F	RH, %	AV, fpm
Optimum Winter Conditions	68	73	42	25
Optimum Summer Conditions	71	76	51	25
Common Winter Conditions	68	76	25	—
Unusual Winter Design—practical applications	66	70	50	—
Usual Summer Design—practical applications	74	80	51	—
Common Summer Design—short occupancy	75	82	49	—
Common Summer Design—ample peak capacity	72	78	50	—

Corrections:

Sex—Women desire 1.0°ET higher than men.

Age—Over 40 group desires 1.0°ET higher than under 40.

Activity—Factories 60-65, gymnasium 55-60 usual winter DB.

Location—Add 1.0°ET for each 5° latitude below 40° latitude.

Clothing—Seasonal variation above reflects mainly clothing differences.

Adapted from the data of W. Bruce, "Man and His Thermal Environment," A report to the Division of Building Research, National Research Council of Canada, 1953.

Table 77 lists winter and summer design temperatures for various locations throughout the world. The outdoor design temperatures listed are not highs or lows that have been recorded but statistical quantities as explained in the notes. More extreme temperatures can be expected during a normal winter or summer. Based on 2160 hours in the three winter months there will be approximately 22 hours at or below the 99% value and 54 hours at or below the 97½% value. Based on 2928 hours in the four summer months there will be approximately 30, 75, and 150 hours at or above the 1%, 2½%, and 5% values respectively. If there are no compensating factors, equipment selected for these design values will not maintain inside design conditions under more extreme conditions.

The selection of outdoor design conditions should be based on consideration of the consequences of under-conditioning and factors such as heat capacity of the structure, the hours of occupancy, and the nature of the occupants. ASHRAE suggests that the "Low" value be used if the structure has low heat capacity, is not insulated, or is occupied during the coldest part of the day. The "99%" value might be used for structures with moderate heat capacity, some internal load, and daytime occupancy. The "97½%" value can frequently be used for massive, institutional buildings with little glass.

The summer design conditions may be adjusted to give the approximate 1%, 2½%, or 5% level for the hottest season in 10 or 50 years by adding the difference between the 5% and 2½% levels or the 5% and 1% levels respectively. For example, the 2½% levels for Buffalo, N. Y. for the hottest season in 50 years would be 86 + (88 − 83), or 91 dry-bulb and 71 + (72 − 70), or 73 wet-bulb approximately.

If there is no station listed in the immediate vicinity of the proposed installation, the data for the nearest station can be adjusted as follows:

1—Add 1°F to dry-bulb for each 200 ft decrease in elevation.

2—Add 1°F to wet-bulb for each 500 ft decrease in elevation.

3—Add 2°F to dry-bulb and 1° to wet-bulb if installation is surrounded by buildings and streets and weather station is downwind of foliage.

4—Add 2°F to dry-bulb and 1° to wet-bulb if installation is inland and weather station is downwind of large bodies of water.

A 15 mph wind is generally assumed in winter heat loss calculations, as was done for the winter condition portions of Tables 80 and 81. The ASHRAE suggests that a somewhat lower value could often be used in most localities and that it should be based on the average wind velocity for that specific area. Table 78 provides a means of correcting transmission calculations. In summer a 7½ mph wind might be considered average, and this value has been assumed in the summer condition portions of Tables 80 and 81.

The effect of the sun is usually ignored for winter design and its approximate maximum effect accounted for in summer design. These are justifiable assumptions for maximum design. However, both the reflection of winter sunlight from snow or other light surfaces and the shading of the summer sun due to clouds and neighboring buildings are important considerations as they might affect part-load operations, zoning, etc.

TABLE 77—WINTER and SUMMER DESIGN TEMPERATURES IN °F

Station		Winter[3]			Summer[4]					
City or Airport[1]	Elev.[2] ft.	Low	Dry-Bulb 99%	Dry-Bulb 97½%	Dry-Bulb 1%	Dry-Bulb 2½%	Dry-Bulb 5%	Wet-Bulb 1%	Wet-Bulb 2½%	Wet-Bulb 5%
UNITED STATES OF AMERICA										
Alabama										
Alexander City	660	12	16	20	96	94	93	79	78	77
Anniston AP	599	12	17	19	96	94	93	79	78	77
Auburn	730	17	21	25	98	96	95	80	79	78
Birmingham AP	610	14	19	22	97	94	93	79	78	77
Decatur	580	10	15	19	97	95	94	79	78	77
Dothan AP	321	19	23	27	97	95	94	81	80	79
Florence AP	528	8	13	17	97	95	94	79	78	77
Gadsden	570	11	16	20	96	94	93	78	77	76
Huntsville AP	619	8	13	17	97	95	94	78	77	76
Mobile AP	211	21	26	29	95	93	91	80	79	79
Mobile CO	119	24	28	32	96	94	93	80	79	79
Montgomery AP	195	18	22	26	98	95	93	80	79	78
Selma-Craig AFB	207	18	23	27	98	96	94	81	80	79
Talladega	565	11	15	19	97	95	94	79	78	77
Tuscaloosa AP	170	14	19	23	98	96	95	81	80	79
Alaska										
Anchorage AP	90	−29	−25	−20	73	70	67	63	61	59
Barrow	22	−49	−45	−42	58	54	50	54	51	48
Fairbanks AP	436	−59	−53	−50	82	78	75	64	63	61
Juneau AP	17	−11	− 7	− 4	75	71	68	66	64	62
Kodiak	21	4	8	12	71	66	63	62	60	58
Nome AP	13	−37	−32	−28	66	62	59	58	56	54
Arizona										
Douglas AP	4098	13	18	22	100	98	96	70	69	68
Flagstaff AP	6973	−10	0	5	84	82	80	61	60	59
Fort Huachuca AP	4664	18	25	28	95	93	91	69	68	67
Kingman AP	3446	18	25	29	103	100	97	70	69	69
Nogales	3800	15	20	24	100	98	96	72	71	70
Phoenix AP	1117	25	31	34	108	106	104	77	76	75
Prescott AP	5014	7	15	19	96	94	91	67	66	65
Tucson AP	2584	23	29	32	105	102	100	74	73	72
Winslow AP	4880	2	9	13	97	95	92	66	65	64
Yuma AP	199	32	37	40	111	109	107	79	78	77
Arkansas										
Blytheville AFB	264	6	12	17	98	96	93	80	79	78
Camden	116	13	19	23	99	97	96	81	80	79
El Dorado AP	252	13	19	23	98	96	95	81	80	79
Fayetteville AP	1253	3	9	13	97	95	93	77	76	75
Fort Smith AP	449	9	15	19	101	99	96	79	78	77
Hot Springs N. Pk.	710	12	18	22	99	97	96	79	78	77
Jonesboro	345	8	14	18	98	96	95	80	79	78
Little Rock AP	257	13	19	23	99	96	94	80	79	78
Pine Bluff AP	204	14	20	24	99	96	95	81	80	79
Texarkana AP	361	16	22	26	99	97	96	80	79	78
California										
Bakersfield AP	495	26	31	33	103	101	99	72	71	70
Barstow AP	2142	18	24	28	104	102	99	73	72	71
Blythe AP	390	26	31	35	111	109	106	78	77	76
Burbank AP	699	30	36	38	97	94	91	72	70	69
Chico	205	23	29	33	102	100	97	71	70	69
Concord	195	27	32	36	96	92	88	69	67	66
Covina	575	32	38	41	100	97	94	73	72	71
Crescent City AP	50	28	33	36	72	69	65	61	60	59
Downey	116	30	35	38	93	90	87	72	71	70
El Cajon	525	26	31	34	98	95	92	74	73	72

See Footnotes at end of table.

TABLE 77 (Cont.) **UNITED STATES OF AMERICA**

Station		Winter[3]			Summer[4]					
City or Airport[1]	Elev.[2] ft.	Low	Dry-Bulb		Dry-Bulb			Wet-Bulb		
			99%	97½%	1%	2½%	5%	1%	2½%	5%
El Centro AP	−30	26	31	35	111	109	106	81	80	79
Escondido	660	28	33	36	95	92	89	73	72	71
Eureka/Arcata AP	217	27	32	35	67	65	63	60	59	58
Fairfield-Travis AFB	72	26	32	34	98	94	90	71	69	67
Fresno AP	326	25	28	31	101	99	97	73	72	71
Hamilton AFB	3	28	33	35	89	85	81	71	68	66
Laguna Beach	35	32	37	39	83	80	77	69	68	67
Livermore	545	23	28	30	99	97	94	70	69	68
Lompoc, Vand. AFB	552	32	36	38	82	79	76	65	63	61
Long Beach AP	34	31	36	38	87	84	81	72	70	69
Los Angeles AP	99	36	41	43	86	83	80	69	68	67
Los Angeles CO	312	38	42	44	94	90	87	72	70	69
Merced-Castle AFB	178	24	30	32	102	99	96	73	72	70
Modesto	91	26	32	36	101	98	96	72	71	70
Monterey	38	29	34	37	82	79	76	64	63	61
Napa	16	26	31	34	94	92	89	69	68	67
Needles AP	913	27	33	37	112	110	107	76	75	74
Oakland AP	3	30	35	37	85	81	77	65	63	62
Oceanside	30	33	38	40	84	81	78	69	68	67
Ontario	995	26	32	34	100	97	94	72	71	70
Oxnard AFB	43	32	35	37	84	80	78	70	69	67
Palmdale AP	2517	18	24	27	103	101	98	70	68	67
Palm Springs	411	27	32	36	110	108	105	79	78	77
Pasadena	864	31	36	39	96	93	90	72	70	69
Petaluma	27	24	29	32	94	90	87	70	68	67
Pomona CO	871	26	31	34	99	96	93	73	72	71
Redding AP	495	25	31	35	103	101	98	70	69	67
Redlands	1318	28	34	37	99	96	93	72	71	70
Richmond	55	28	35	38	85	81	77	66	64	63
Riverside-March AFB	1511	26	32	34	99	96	94	72	71	69
Sacramento AP	17	24	30	32	100	97	94	72	70	69
Salinas AP	74	27	32	35	87	85	82	67	65	64
San Bernardino, N. AFB	1125	26	31	33	101	98	96	75	73	71
San Diego AP	19	38	42	44	86	83	80	71	70	68
San Fernando	977	29	34	37	100	97	94	73	72	71
San Francisco AP	8	32	35	37	83	79	75	65	63	62
San Francisco CO	52	38	42	44	80	77	73	64	62	61
San Jose AP	70	30	34	36	90	88	85	69	67	65
San Luis Obispo	315	30	35	37	89	85	82	65	64	63
Santa Ana AP	115	28	33	36	92	89	86	72	71	70
Santa Barbara CO	100	30	34	36	87	84	81	67	66	65
Santa Cruz	125	28	32	34	87	84	80	66	65	63
Santa Maria AP	238	28	32	34	85	82	79	65	64	63
Santa Monica CO	57	38	43	45	80	77	74	69	68	67
Santa Paula	263	28	33	36	91	89	86	72	71	70
Santa Rosa	167	24	29	32	95	93	90	70	68	67
Stockton AP	28	25	30	34	101	98	96	72	70	69
Ukiah	620	22	27	30	98	96	93	70	69	67
Visalia	354	26	32	36	102	100	97	73	72	70
Yreka	2625	7	13	17	96	94	91	68	66	65
Yuba City	70	24	30	34	102	100	97	71	70	69
Colorado										
Alamosa AP	7536	−26	−17	−13	84	82	79	62	61	60
Boulder	5385	− 5	4	8	92	90	87	64	63	62
Colorado Springs AP	6173	− 9	− 1	4	90	88	86	63	62	61
Denver AP	5283	− 9	− 2	3	92	90	89	65	64	63
Durango	6550	−10	0	4	88	86	83	64	63	62
Fort Collins	5001	−18	− 9	− 5	91	89	86	63	62	61
Grand Junction AP	4849	− 2	8	11	96	94	92	64	63	62

TABLE 77 (Cont.) **UNITED STATES OF AMERICA**

Station		Winter[3]			Summer[4]					
City or Airport[1]	Elev.[2] ft.	Low	Dry-Bulb 99%	Dry-Bulb 97½%	Dry-Bulb 1%	Dry-Bulb 2½%	Dry-Bulb 5%	Wet-Bulb 1%	Wet-Bulb 2½%	Wet-Bulb 5%
Greeley	4648	−18	− 9	− 5	94	92	89	65	64	63
La Junta AP	4188	−14	− 6	− 2	97	95	93	72	71	69
Leadville	10177	−18	− 9	− 4	76	73	70	56	55	54
Pueblo AP	4639	−14	− 5	− 1	96	94	92	68	67	66
Sterling	3939	−15	− 6	− 2	95	93	90	67	66	65
Trinidad AP	5746	− 9	1	5	93	91	89	66	65	64
Connecticut										
Bridgeport AP	7	− 1	4	8	90	88	85	77	76	75
Hartford, Brainard Fld.	15	− 4	1	5	90	88	85	77	76	74
New Haven AP	6	0	5	9	88	86	83	77	76	75
New London	60	0	4	8	89	86	83	77	75	74
Norwalk	37	− 5	0	4	91	89	86	77	76	75
Norwich	20	− 7	− 2	2	88	86	83	77	76	75
Waterbury	605	− 5	0	4	90	88	85	77	76	75
Windsor Locks, Br. Fld.	169	− 7	− 2	2	90	88	85	76	75	73
Delaware										
Dover AFB	38	8	13	15	93	90	88	79	78	77
Wilmington AP	78	6	12	15	93	90	87	79	77	76
District of Columbia										
Andrews AFB	279	9	13	16	94	91	88	79	77	76
Washington Nat. AP	14	12	16	19	94	92	90	78	77	76
Florida										
Belle Glade	16	31	35	39	93	91	90	80	79	79
Cape Kennedy AP	16	33	37	40	90	89	88	81	80	79
Daytona Beach AP	31	28	32	36	94	92	91	81	80	79
Fort Lauderdale	13	37	41	45	91	90	89	81	80	79
Fort Myers AP	13	34	38	42	94	92	91	80	80	79
Fort Pierce	10	33	37	41	93	91	90	81	80	79
Gainesville AP	155	24	28	32	96	94	93	80	79	79
Jacksonville AP	24	26	29	32	96	94	92	80	79	79
Key West AP	6	50	55	58	90	89	88	80	79	79
Lakeland CO	214	31	35	39	95	93	91	80	79	78
Miami AP	7	39	44	47	92	90	89	80	79	79
Miami Beach CO	9	40	45	48	91	89	88	80	79	79
Ocala	86	25	29	33	96	94	93	80	79	79
Orlando AP	106	29	33	37	96	94	93	80	79	78
Panama City, Tyn. AFB	22	28	32	35	92	91	90	81	80	80
Pensacola CO	13	25	29	32	92	90	89	82	81	80
St. Augustine	15	27	31	35	94	92	90	81	80	79
St. Petersburg	35	35	39	42	93	91	90	81	80	79
Sanford	14	29	33	37	95	93	92	80	79	79
Sarasota	30	31	35	39	93	91	90	80	80	79
Tallahassee AP	58	21	25	29	96	94	93	80	79	79
Tampa AP	19	32	36	39	92	91	90	81	80	79
West Palm Beach AP	15	36	40	44	92	91	89	81	80	80
Georgia										
Albany, Turner AFB	224	21	26	30	98	96	94	80	79	78
Americus	476	18	22	25	98	96	93	80	79	78
Athens	700	12	17	21	96	94	91	78	77	76
Atlanta AP	1005	14	18	23	95	92	90	78	77	76
Augusta AP	143	17	20	23	98	95	93	80	79	78
Brunswick	14	24	27	31	97	95	92	81	80	79
Columbus, Lawson AFB	242	19	23	26	98	96	94	80	79	78
Dalton	720	10	15	19	97	95	92	78	77	76
Dublin	215	17	21	25	98	96	93	80	79	78
Gainesville	1254	11	16	20	94	92	89	78	77	76
Griffin	980	13	17	22	95	93	90	79	78	77

TABLE 77 (Cont.) **UNITED STATES OF AMERICA**

Station		Winter[3]			Summer[4]					
City or Airport[1]	Elev.[2] ft.	Low	Dry-Bulb		Dry-Bulb			Wet-Bulb		
			99%	97½%	1%	2½%	5%	1%	2½%	5%
La Grange	715	12	16	20	96	94	92	79	78	77
Macon AP	356	18	23	27	98	96	94	80	79	78
Marietta, Dobbins AFB	1016	12	17	21	95	93	91	78	77	76
Moultrie	340	22	26	30	97	95	93	80	79	78
Rome AP	637	11	16	20	97	95	93	78	77	76
Savannah-Travis AP	52	21	24	27	96	94	92	81	80	79
Valdosta-Moody AFB	239	24	28	31	96	94	92	80	79	78
Waycross	140	20	24	28	97	95	93	80	79	78
Hawaii										
Hilo AP	31	56	59	61	85	83	82	74	73	72
Honolulu AP	7	58	60	62	87	85	84	75	74	73
Kaneohe	198	58	60	61	85	83	82	74	73	73
Wahiawa	215	57	59	61	86	84	83	75	74	73
Idaho										
Boise AP	2842	0	4	10	96	93	91	68	66	65
Burley	4180	−5	4	8	95	93	89	68	66	64
Coeur d'Alene AP	2973	−4	2	7	94	91	88	66	65	63
Idaho Falls AP	4730	−17	−12	−6	91	88	85	65	64	62
Lewiston AP	1413	1	6	12	98	96	93	67	66	65
Moscow	2660	−11	−3	1	91	89	86	64	63	61
Mountain Home AFB	2992	−3	2	9	99	96	93	68	66	64
Pocatello AP	4444	−12	−8	−2	94	91	88	65	63	62
Twin Falls AP	4148	−5	4	8	96	94	91	66	64	63
Illinois										
Aurora	744	−13	−7	−3	93	91	88	78	77	75
Belleville, Scott AFB	447	0	6	10	97	95	92	79	78	77
Bloomington	775	−7	−1	3	94	92	89	79	78	77
Carbondale	380	1	7	11	98	96	94	80	79	78
Champaign/Urbana	743	−6	0	4	96	94	91	79	78	77
Chicago, Midway AP	610	−7	−4	1	95	92	89	78	76	75
Chicago, O'Hare AP	658	−9	−4	0	93	90	87	77	75	74
Chicago, CO	594	−5	−3	1	94	91	88	78	76	75
Danville	558	−6	−1	4	96	94	91	79	78	76
Decatur	670	−6	0	4	96	93	91	79	78	77
Dixon	696	−13	−7	−3	93	91	89	78	77	76
Elgin	820	−14	−8	−4	92	90	87	78	76	75
Freeport	780	−16	−10	−6	92	90	87	78	77	75
Galesburg	771	−10	−4	0	95	92	89	79	78	76
Greenville	563	−3	3	7	96	94	92	79	78	77
Joliet AP	588	−11	−5	−1	94	92	89	78	77	75
Kankakee	625	−10	−4	1	94	92	89	78	77	76
La Salle/Peru	520	−9	−3	1	94	93	90	78	77	76
Macomb	702	−5	−3	1	95	93	90	79	78	77
Moline AP	582	−12	−7	−3	94	91	88	79	77	76
Mt. Vernon	500	0	6	10	97	95	92	79	78	77
Peoria AP	652	−8	−2	2	94	92	89	78	77	76
Quincy AP	762	−8	−2	2	97	95	92	80	79	77
Rantoul, Chanute AFB	740	−7	−1	3	94	92	89	78	77	76
Rockford	724	−13	−7	−3	92	90	87	77	76	75
Springfield AP	587	−7	−1	4	95	92	90	79	78	77
Waukegan	680	−11	−5	−1	92	90	87	77	76	75
Indiana										
Anderson	847	−5	0	5	93	91	88	78	77	76
Bedford	670	−3	3	7	95	93	90	79	78	77
Bloomington	820	−3	3	7	95	92	90	79	78	76
Columbus, Baka. AFB	661	−3	3	7	95	92	90	79	78	76
Crawfordsville	752	−8	−2	2	95	93	90	79	77	76

TABLE 77 (Cont.) UNITED STATES OF AMERICA

Station		Winter[3]			Summer[4]					
City or Airport[1]	Elev.[2] ft.	Low	Dry-Bulb		Dry-Bulb			Wet-Bulb		
			99%	97½%	1%	2½%	5%	1%	2½%	5%
Evansville AP	381	1	6	10	96	94	91	79	78	77
Fort Wayne AP	791	−5	0	5	93	91	88	77	76	75
Goshen AP	823	−10	−4	0	92	90	87	77	76	74
Hobart	600	−10	−4	0	93	91	88	78	76	75
Huntington	802	−8	−2	2	94	92	89	78	76	75
Indianapolis AP	793	−5	0	4	93	91	88	78	77	76
Jeffersonville	455	3	9	13	96	94	91	79	78	77
Kokomo	790	−6	0	4	94	92	89	78	76	75
Lafayette	600	−7	−1	3	94	92	89	78	77	76
La Porte	810	−10	−4	0	93	91	88	77	76	74
Marion	791	−8	−2	2	93	91	88	78	76	75
Muncie	955	−8	−2	2	93	91	88	78	77	75
Peru, Bunk. Hill AFB	804	−9	−3	1	91	89	86	77	76	74
Richmond AP	1138	−7	−1	3	93	91	88	78	77	75
Shelbyville	765	−4	2	6	94	92	89	78	77	76
South Bend AP	773	−6	−2	3	92	89	87	77	76	74
Terre Haute AP	601	−3	3	7	95	93	91	79	78	77
Valparaiso	801	−12	−6	−2	92	90	87	78	76	75
Vincennes	420	−1	5	9	96	94	91	79	78	77
Iowa										
Ames	1004	−17	−11	−7	94	92	89	79	78	76
Burlington AP	694	−10	−4	0	95	92	89	80	78	77
Cedar Rapids AP	863	−14	−8	−4	92	90	87	78	76	75
Clinton	595	−13	−7	−3	92	90	87	78	77	76
Council Bluffs	1210	−14	−7	−3	97	94	91	79	78	76
Des Moines AP	948	−13	−7	−3	95	92	89	79	77	76
Dubuque	1065	−17	−11	−7	92	90	87	78	76	75
Fort Dodge	1111	−18	−12	−8	94	92	89	78	77	75
Iowa City	645	−14	−8	−4	94	91	88	79	77	76
Keokuk	526	−9	−3	1	95	93	90	79	78	77
Marshalltown	898	−16	−10	−6	93	91	88	79	77	76
Mason City AP	1194	−20	−13	−9	91	88	85	77	75	74
Newton	946	−15	−9	−5	95	93	90	79	77	76
Ottumwa AP	842	−12	−6	−2	95	93	90	79	78	76
Sioux City AP	1095	−17	−10	−6	96	93	90	79	77	76
Waterloo	868	−18	−12	−8	91	89	86	78	76	75
Kansas										
Atchison	945	−9	−2	2	97	95	92	79	78	77
Chanute AP	977	−3	3	7	99	97	95	79	78	77
Dodge City AP	2594	−5	3	7	99	97	95	74	73	72
El Dorado	1282	−3	4	8	101	99	96	78	77	76
Emporia	1209	−4	3	7	99	97	94	78	77	76
Garden City AP	2882	−10	−1	3	100	98	96	74	73	72
Goodland AP	3645	−10	−2	4	99	96	93	71	70	69
Great Bend	1940	−5	2	6	101	99	96	77	76	75
Hutchinson AP	1524	−5	2	6	101	99	96	77	76	75
Liberal	2838	−4	4	8	102	100	99	74	73	71
Manhattan, Ft. Riley	1076	−7	−1	4	101	98	95	79	78	77
Parsons	908	−2	5	9	99	97	94	79	78	77
Russell AP	1864	−7	0	4	102	100	97	78	76	75
Salina	1271	−4	3	7	101	99	96	78	76	75
Topeka AP	877	−4	3	6	99	96	94	79	78	77
Wichita AP	1321	−1	5	9	102	99	96	77	76	75
Kentucky										
Ashland	551	1	6	10	94	92	89	77	76	75
Bowling Green AP	535	1	7	11	97	95	93	79	78	77
Corbin AP	1175	0	5	9	93	91	89	79	77	76
Covington AP	869	−3	3	8	93	90	88	77	76	75

TABLE 77 (Cont.) **UNITED STATES OF AMERICA**

Station		Winter[3]			Summer[4]					
City or Airport[1]	Elev.[2] ft.	Low	Dry-Bulb		Dry-Bulb			Wet-Bulb		
			99%	97½%	1%	2½%	5%	1%	2½%	5%
Hop'ville, Cam. AFB	540	4	10	14	97	95	92	79	78	77
Lexington AP	979	0	6	10	94	92	90	78	77	76
Louisville AP	474	1	8	12	96	93	91	79	78	77
Madisonville	439	1	7	11	96	94	92	79	78	77
Owensboro	420	0	6	10	96	94	92	79	78	77
Paducah AP	398	4	10	14	97	95	94	80	79	78
Louisiana										
Alexandria AP	92	20	25	29	97	95	94	80	80	79
Baton Rouge AP	64	22	25	30	96	94	92	81	80	79
Bogalusa	103	20	24	28	96	94	93	80	79	78
Houma	13	25	29	33	94	92	91	81	80	79
Lafayette AP	38	23	28	32	95	93	92	81	81	80
Lake Charles AP	14	25	29	33	95	93	91	80	79	79
Minden	250	17	22	26	98	96	95	81	80	79
Monroe	78	18	23	27	98	96	95	81	81	80
Natchitoches	120	17	22	26	99	97	96	81	80	79
New Orleans AP	3	29	32	35	93	91	90	81	80	79
Shreveport AP	252	18	22	26	99	96	94	81	80	79
Maine										
Augusta AP	350	−13	− 7	− 3	88	86	83	74	73	71
Bangor, Dow AFB	162	−14	− 8	− 4	88	85	81	75	73	71
Caribou AP	624	−24	−18	−14	85	81	78	72	70	68
Lewiston	182	−14	− 8	− 4	88	86	83	74	73	71
Millinocket AP	405	−22	−16	−12	87	85	82	74	72	70
Portland AP	61	−14	− 5	0	88	85	81	75	73	71
Waterville	89	−15	− 9	− 5	88	86	82	74	73	71
Maryland										
Baltimore AP	146	8	12	15	94	91	89	79	78	77
Baltimore CO	14	12	16	20	94	92	89	79	78	77
Cumberland	945	0	5	9	94	92	89	76	75	74
Frederick AP	294	2	7	11	94	92	89	78	77	76
Hagerstown	660	1	6	10	94	92	89	77	76	75
Salisbury	52	10	14	18	92	90	87	79	78	77
Massachusetts										
Boston AP	15	− 1	6	10	91	88	85	76	74	73
Clinton	398	− 8	− 2	2	87	85	82	75	74	72
Fall River	190	− 1	5	9	88	86	83	75	74	73
Framingham	170	− 7	− 1	3	91	89	86	76	74	73
Gloucester	10	− 4	2	6	86	84	81	74	73	72
Greenfield	205	−12	− 6	− 2	89	87	84	75	74	73
Lawrence	57	− 9	− 3	1	90	88	85	76	74	72
Lowell	90	− 7	− 1	3	91	89	86	76	74	72
New Bedford	70	3	9	13	86	84	81	75	73	72
Pittsfield AP	1170	−11	− 5	− 1	86	84	81	74	72	71
Sp'field, West. AFB	247	− 8	− 3	2	91	88	85	76	74	73
Taunton	20	− 9	− 4	0	88	86	83	76	75	74
Worcester AP	986	− 8	− 3	1	89	87	84	75	73	71
Michigan										
Adrian	754	− 6	0	4	93	91	88	76	75	74
Alpena AP	689	−11	− 5	− 1	87	85	82	74	73	71
Battle Creek AP	939	− 6	1	5	92	89	86	76	74	73
Benton Harbor AP	649	− 7	− 1	3	90	88	85	76	74	73
Detroit Met. CAP	633	0	4	8	92	88	85	76	75	74
Escanaba	594	−13	− 7	− 3	82	80	77	73	71	69
Flint AP	766	− 7	− 1	3	89	87	84	76	75	74
Grand Rapids AP	681	− 3	2	6	91	89	86	76	74	73
Holland	612	− 4	2	6	90	88	85	76	74	73

TABLE 77 (Cont.) **UNITED STATES OF AMERICA**

City or Airport[1]	Elev.[2] ft.	Winter[3] Low	Winter[3] Dry-Bulb 99%	Winter[3] Dry-Bulb 97½%	Summer[4] Dry-Bulb 1%	Summer[4] Dry-Bulb 2½%	Summer[4] Dry-Bulb 5%	Summer[4] Wet-Bulb 1%	Summer[4] Wet-Bulb 2½%	Summer[4] Wet-Bulb 5%
Jackson AP	1003	−6	0	4	92	89	86	76	75	74
Kalamazoo	930	−5	1	5	92	89	86	76	75	74
Lansing AP	852	−4	2	6	89	87	84	76	75	73
Marquette CO	677	−14	−8	−4	88	86	83	73	71	69
Mt. Pleasant	796	−9	−3	1	89	87	84	75	74	73
Muskegon AP	627	−2	4	8	87	85	82	75	74	73
Pontiac	974	−6	0	4	90	88	85	76	75	73
Port Huron	586	−6	−1	3	90	88	85	76	74	73
Saginaw AP	662	−7	−1	3	88	86	83	76	75	73
Sault Ste. Marie AP	721	−18	−12	−8	83	81	78	73	71	69
Traverse City AP	618	−6	0	4	89	86	83	75	73	72
Ypsilanti	777	−3	−1	5	92	89	86	76	74	73
Minnesota										
Albert Lea	1235	−20	−14	−10	91	89	86	77	76	74
Alexandria AP	1421	−26	−19	−15	90	88	85	76	74	72
Bemidji AP	1392	−38	−32	−28	87	84	81	73	72	71
Brainerd	1214	−31	−24	−20	88	85	82	74	73	72
Duluth AP	1426	−25	−19	−15	85	82	79	73	71	69
Fairbault	1190	−23	−16	−12	90	88	85	77	75	74
Fergus Falls	1210	−28	−21	−17	92	89	86	75	74	72
International Falls AP	1179	−35	−29	−24	86	82	79	72	69	68
Mankato	785	−23	−16	−12	91	89	86	77	75	74
Minn./St. Paul AP	822	−19	−14	−10	92	89	86	77	75	74
Rochester AP	1297	−23	−17	−13	90	88	85	77	75	74
St. Cloud AP	1034	−26	−20	−16	90	88	85	77	75	73
Virginia	1435	−32	−25	−21	86	83	80	73	71	69
Willmar	1133	−25	−18	−14	91	88	85	77	75	73
Winona	652	−19	−12	−8	91	89	86	77	76	74
Mississippi										
Biloxi, Keesler AFB	25	26	30	32	93	92	90	82	81	80
Clarksdale	178	14	20	24	98	96	95	81	80	79
Columbus AFB	224	13	18	22	97	95	93	79	79	78
Greenville AFB	139	16	21	24	98	96	94	81	80	79
Greenwood	128	14	19	23	98	96	94	81	80	79
Hattiesburg	200	18	22	26	97	95	94	80	79	78
Jackson AP	330	17	21	24	98	96	94	79	78	78
Laurel	264	18	22	26	97	95	94	80	79	78
McComb AP	458	18	22	26	96	94	93	80	79	79
Meridian AP	294	15	20	24	97	95	94	80	79	78
Natchez	168	18	22	26	96	94	93	80	80	79
Tupelo	289	13	18	22	98	96	95	80	79	78
Vicksburg CO	234	18	23	26	97	95	94	80	80	79
Missouri										
Cape Girardeau	330	2	8	12	98	96	94	80	79	78
Columbia AP	778	−4	2	6	97	95	92	79	78	77
Farmington AP	928	−2	4	8	97	95	93	79	78	77
Hannibal	489	−7	−1	4	96	94	91	79	78	77
Jefferson City	640	−4	2	6	97	95	93	79	78	77
Joplin AP	982	1	7	11	97	95	93	79	78	77
Kansas City AP	742	−2	4	8	100	97	94	79	77	76
Kirksville AP	966	−13	−7	−3	96	94	91	79	78	77
Mexico	775	−7	−1	3	96	94	91	79	78	77
Moberly	850	−8	−2	2	96	94	91	79	78	77
Poplar Bluff	322	3	9	13	98	96	94	80	79	78
Rolla	1202	−3	3	7	97	95	93	79	78	77
St. Joseph AP	809	−8	−1	3	97	95	92	79	78	77
St. Louis AP	535	−2	4	8	98	95	92	79	78	77
St. Louis CO	465	1	7	11	96	94	92	79	78	77

TABLE 77 (Cont.) **UNITED STATES OF AMERICA**

Station		Winter[3]			Summer[4]					
City or Airport[1]	Elev.[2] ft.	Low	Dry-Bulb		Dry-Bulb			Wet-Bulb		
			99%	97½%	1%	2½%	5%	1%	2½%	5%
Sedalia, Whitem. AFB	838	−2	4	9	97	94	92	79	77	76
Sikeston	318	4	10	14	98	96	94	80	79	78
Springfield AP	1265	0	5	10	97	94	91	78	77	76
Montana										
Billings AP	3567	−19	−10	−6	94	91	88	68	66	65
Bozeman	4856	−25	−15	−11	88	85	82	61	60	59
Butte AP	5526	−34	−24	−16	86	83	80	60	59	57
Cut Bank AP	3838	−32	−23	−17	89	86	82	65	63	61
Glasgow AP	2277	−33	−25	−20	96	93	89	69	67	65
Glendive	2076	−28	−20	−16	96	93	90	71	69	68
Great Falls AP	3664	−29	−20	−16	91	88	85	64	63	61
Havre	2488	−32	−22	−15	91	87	84	66	64	63
Helena AP	3893	−27	−17	−13	90	87	84	65	63	61
Kalispell AP	2965	−17	−7	−3	88	84	81	65	63	62
Lewiston AP	4132	−27	−18	−14	89	86	83	65	63	62
Livingston AP	4653	−26	−17	−13	91	88	85	63	62	61
Miles City AP	2629	−27	−19	−15	97	94	91	71	69	68
Missoula AP	3200	−16	−7	−3	92	89	86	65	63	61
Nebraska										
Beatrice	1235	−10	−3	1	99	97	94	78	77	76
Chadron AP	3300	−21	−13	−9	97	95	92	72	70	69
Columbus	1442	−14	−7	−3	98	96	93	78	76	75
Fremont	1203	−14	−7	−3	99	97	94	78	77	76
Grand Island AP	1841	−14	−6	−2	98	95	92	76	75	74
Hastings	1932	−11	−3	1	98	96	94	77	75	74
Kearney	2146	−14	−6	−2	97	95	92	76	75	74
Lincoln CO	1150	−10	−4	0	100	96	93	78	77	76
McCook	2565	−12	−4	0	99	97	94	74	72	71
Norfolk	1532	−18	−11	−7	97	95	92	78	76	75
North Platte AP	2779	−13	−6	−2	97	94	90	74	73	72
Omaha AP	978	−12	−5	−1	97	94	91	79	78	76
Scottsbluff AP	3950	−16	−8	−4	96	94	91	70	69	67
Sidney AP	4292	−15	−7	−2	95	92	89	70	69	67
Nevada										
Carson City	4675	−4	3	7	93	91	88	62	61	60
Elko AP	5075	−21	−13	−7	94	92	90	64	62	61
Ely AP	6257	−15	−6	−2	90	88	86	60	59	58
Las Vegas AP	2162	18	23	26	108	106	104	72	71	70
Lovelock AP	3900	0	7	11	98	96	93	65	64	62
Reno AP	4404	−2	2	7	95	92	90	64	62	61
Reno CO	4490	8	12	17	94	92	89	64	62	61
Tonopah AP	5426	2	9	13	95	92	90	64	63	62
Winnemucca AP	4299	−8	1	5	97	95	93	64	62	61
New Hampshire										
Berlin	1110	−25	−19	−15	87	85	82	73	71	70
Claremont	420	−19	−13	−9	89	87	84	74	73	72
Concord AP	339	−17	−11	−7	91	88	85	75	73	72
Keene	490	−17	−12	−8	90	88	85	75	73	72
Laconia	505	−22	−16	−12	89	87	84	74	73	72
Manchester, G. AFB	253	−11	−5	1	92	89	86	76	74	73
Portsmouth, P. AFB	127	−8	−2	3	88	86	83	75	73	72
New Jersey										
Atlantic City CO	11	10	14	18	91	88	85	78	77	76
Long Branch	20	4	9	13	93	91	88	77	76	75
Newark AP	11	6	11	15	94	91	88	77	76	75
New Brunswick	86	3	8	12	91	89	86	77	76	75

TABLE 77 (Cont.) **UNITED STATES OF AMERICA**

Station		Winter[3]			Summer[4]					
City or Airport[1]	Elev.[2] ft.	Low	Dry-Bulb		Dry-Bulb			Wet-Bulb		
			99%	97½%	1%	2½%	5%	1%	2½%	5%
Paterson	100	3	8	12	93	91	88	77	76	75
Phillipsburg	180	1	6	10	93	91	88	77	76	75
Trenton CO	144	7	12	16	92	90	87	78	77	76
Vineland	95	7	12	16	93	90	87	78	77	76
New Mexico										
Alamagordo, H. AFB	4070	12	18	22	100	98	96	70	69	68
Albuquerque AP	5310	6	14	17	96	94	92	66	65	64
Artesia	3375	9	16	19	101	99	97	71	70	69
Carlsbad AP	3234	11	17	21	101	99	97	72	71	70
Clovis AP	4279	2	14	17	99	97	95	70	69	68
Farmington AP	5495	−3	6	9	95	93	91	66	65	64
Gallup	6465	−13	−5	−1	92	90	87	64	63	62
Grants	6520	−15	−7	−3	91	89	86	64	63	62
Hobbs AP	3664	9	15	19	101	99	96	72	71	70
Las Cruces	3900	13	19	23	102	100	97	70	69	68
Los Alamos	7410	−4	5	9	88	86	83	64	63	62
Raton AP	6379	−11	−2	2	92	90	88	66	65	64
Roswell, Walker AFB	3643	5	16	19	101	99	97	71	70	69
Santa Fe CO	7045	−2	7	11	90	88	85	65	63	62
Silver City AP	5373	8	14	18	95	93	91	68	67	66
Socorro AP	4617	6	13	17	99	97	94	67	66	65
Tucumcari AP	4053	1	9	13	99	97	95	71	70	69
New York										
Albany AP	277	−14	−5	0	91	88	85	76	74	73
Albany CO	19	−5	1	5	91	89	86	76	74	73
Auburn	715	−10	−2	2	89	87	84	75	73	72
Batavia	900	−7	−1	3	89	87	84	75	74	72
Binghamton CO	858	−8	−2	2	91	89	86	74	72	71
Buffalo AP	705	−3	3	6	88	86	83	75	73	72
Cortland	1129	−11	−5	−1	90	88	85	75	73	72
Dunkirk	590	−2	4	8	88	86	83	75	74	72
Elmira AP	860	−5	1	5	92	90	87	75	73	72
Geneva	590	−8	−2	2	91	89	86	75	73	72
Glens Falls	321	−17	−11	−7	88	86	83	74	72	71
Gloversville	770	−12	−6	−2	89	87	84	75	73	71
Hornell	1325	−15	−9	−5	87	85	82	74	72	71
Ithaca	950	−10	−4	0	91	88	85	75	73	72
Jamestown	1390	−5	1	5	88	86	83	75	73	72
Kingston	279	−8	−2	2	92	90	87	76	74	73
Lockport	520	−4	2	6	87	85	82	75	74	72
Massena AP	202	−22	−16	−12	86	84	81	75	74	72
Newburg-Stew. AFB	460	−4	2	6	92	89	86	78	76	74
NYC-Central Park	132	6	11	15	94	91	88	77	76	75
NYC-Kennedy AP	16	12	17	21	91	87	84	77	76	75
NYC-LaGuardia AP	19	7	12	16	93	90	87	77	76	75
Niagara Falls AP	596	−2	4	7	88	86	83	75	74	73
Olean	1420	−13	−8	−3	87	85	82	74	72	71
Oneonta	1150	−13	−7	−3	89	87	84	74	72	71
Oswego CO	300	−4	2	6	86	84	81	75	74	72
Plattsburg AFB	165	−16	−10	−6	86	84	81	74	73	71
Poughkeepsie	103	−6	−1	3	93	90	87	77	75	74
Rochester AP	543	−5	2	5	91	88	85	75	74	72
Rome-Griffiss AFB	515	−13	−7	−3	90	87	84	76	74	73
Schenectady	217	−11	−5	−1	90	88	85	75	73	72
Suffolk County AFB	57	4	9	13	87	84	81	76	75	74
Syracuse AP	424	−10	−2	2	90	87	85	76	74	73
Utica	714	−12	−6	−2	89	87	84	75	73	72
Watertown	497	−20	−14	−10	86	84	81	75	74	72

TABLE 77 (Cont.) **UNITED STATES OF AMERICA**

Station		Winter[3]			Summer[4]					
City or Airport[1]	Elev.[2] ft.	Low	Dry-Bulb		Dry-Bulb			Wet-Bulb		
			99%	97½%	1%	2½%	5%	1%	2½%	5%
North Carolina										
Asheville AP	2170	8	13	17	91	88	86	75	74	73
Charlotte AP	735	13	18	22	96	94	92	78	77	76
Durham	406	11	15	19	94	92	89	78	77	76
Elizabeth City AP	10	14	18	22	93	91	89	80	79	78
Fay'ville, Pope AFB	95	13	17	20	97	94	92	80	79	78
Goldsboro, S-J. AFB	88	14	18	21	95	92	90	80	79	78
Greensboro AP	897	9	14	17	94	91	89	77	76	75
Greenville	25	14	18	22	95	93	90	81	80	79
Henderson	510	8	12	16	94	92	89	79	78	77
Hickory	1165	9	14	18	93	91	88	77	76	75
Jacksonville	24	17	21	25	94	92	89	81	80	79
Lumberton	132	14	18	22	95	93	90	81	80	79
New Bern AP	17	14	18	22	94	92	89	81	80	79
Raleigh/Durham AP	433	13	16	20	95	92	90	79	78	77
Rocky Mount	81	12	16	20	95	93	90	80	79	78
Wilmington AP	30	19	23	27	93	91	89	82	81	80
Winston-Salem AP	967	9	14	17	94	91	89	77	76	75
North Dakota										
Bismarck AP	1647	−31	−24	−19	95	91	88	74	72	70
Devil's Lake	1471	−30	−23	−19	93	89	86	73	71	69
Dickinson AP	2595	−31	−23	−19	96	93	90	72	70	68
Fargo AP	900	−28	−22	−17	92	88	85	76	74	72
Grand Forks AP	832	−30	−26	−23	91	87	84	74	72	70
Jamestown AP	1492	−29	−22	−18	95	91	88	75	73	71
Minot AP	1713	−31	−24	−20	91	88	84	72	70	68
Williston	1877	−28	−21	−17	94	90	87	71	69	67
Ohio										
Akron/Canton AP	1210	− 5	1	6	89	87	84	75	73	72
Ashtabula	690	− 3	3	7	89	87	84	76	75	74
Athens	700	− 3	3	7	93	91	88	77	76	75
Bowling Green	675	− 7	− 1	3	93	91	88	77	75	74
Cambridge	800	− 6	0	4	91	89	86	77	76	75
Chillicothe	638	− 1	5	9	93	91	88	77	76	75
Cincinnati CO	761	2	8	12	94	92	90	78	77	76
Cleveland AP	777	− 2	2	7	91	89	86	76	75	74
Columbus AP	812	− 1	2	7	92	88	86	77	76	75
Dayton AP	997	− 2	0	6	92	90	87	77	75	74
Defiance	700	− 7	− 1	1	93	91	88	77	76	74
Findlay AP	797	− 6	0	4	92	90	88	77	76	75
Fremont	600	− 7	− 1	3	92	90	87	76	75	74
Hamilton	650	− 2	4	8	94	92	90	78	77	76
Lancaster	920	− 5	1	5	93	91	88	77	76	75
Lima	860	− 6	0	4	93	91	88	77	76	75
Mansfield AP	1297	− 7	1	3	91	89	86	76	75	74
Marion	920	− 5	1	6	93	91	88	77	76	75
Middletown	635	− 3	3	7	93	91	88	77	76	75
Newark	825	− 7	− 1	3	92	90	87	77	76	75
Norwalk	720	− 7	− 1	3	92	90	87	76	75	74
Portsmouth	530	0	5	9	94	92	89	77	76	75
Sandusky CO	606	− 2	4	8	92	90	87	76	75	74
Springfield	1020	− 3	3	7	93	90	88	77	76	75
Steubenville	992	− 2	4	9	91	89	86	76	75	74
Toledo AP	676	− 5	1	5	92	90	87	77	75	74
Warren	900	− 6	0	4	90	88	85	75	74	73
Wooster	1030	− 7	− 1	3	90	88	85	76	75	74
Youngstown AP	1178	− 5	1	6	89	86	84	75	74	73
Zanesville AP	881	− 7	− 1	3	92	89	87	77	76	75

TABLE 77 (Cont.) **UNITED STATES OF AMERICA**

Station		Winter[3]			Summer[4]					
City or Airport[1]	Elev.[2] ft.	Low	Dry-Bulb		Dry-Bulb			Wet-Bulb		
			99%	97½%	1%	2½%	5%	1%	2½%	5%
Oklahoma										
Ada	1015	6	12	16	102	100	98	79	78	77
Altus AFB	1390	7	14	18	103	101	99	77	76	75
Ardmore	880	9	15	19	103	101	99	79	78	77
Bartlesville	715	−1	5	9	101	99	97	79	78	77
Chickasha	1085	5	12	16	103	101	99	77	76	75
Enid-Vance AFB	1287	3	10	14	103	100	98	78	77	76
Lawton AP	1108	6	13	16	103	101	98	78	77	76
McAlester	760	7	13	17	102	100	98	79	78	77
Muskogee AP	610	6	12	16	102	99	96	79	78	77
Norman	1109	5	11	15	101	99	97	78	77	76
Oklahoma City AP	1280	4	11	15	100	97	95	78	77	76
Ponca City	996	1	8	12	102	100	97	78	77	76
Seminole	865	6	12	16	102	100	98	78	77	76
Stillwater	884	2	9	13	101	99	97	78	77	76
Tulsa AP	650	4	12	16	102	99	96	79	78	77
Woodward	1900	−3	4	8	103	101	98	76	74	73
Oregon										
Albany	224	17	23	27	91	88	84	69	67	65
Astoria AP	8	22	27	30	79	76	72	61	60	59
Baker AP	3368	−10	−3	1	94	92	89	66	65	63
Bend	3599	−7	0	4	89	87	84	64	62	61
Corvallis	221	17	23	27	91	88	84	69	67	65
Eugene AP	364	16	22	26	91	88	84	69	67	65
Grants Pass	925	16	22	26	94	92	89	68	66	65
Klamath Falls AP	4091	−5	1	5	89	87	84	63	62	61
Medford AP	1298	15	21	23	98	94	91	70	68	66
Pendleton AP	1492	−2	3	10	97	94	91	66	65	63
Portland AP	21	17	21	24	89	85	81	69	67	66
Portland CO	57	21	26	29	91	88	84	69	68	67
Roseburg AP	505	19	25	29	93	91	88	69	67	65
Salem AP	195	15	21	25	92	88	84	69	67	66
The Dalles	102	7	13	17	93	91	88	70	68	67
Pennsylvania										
Allentown AP	376	−2	3	5	92	90	87	77	75	74
Altoona CO	1468	−4	1	5	89	87	84	74	73	72
Butler	1100	−8	−2	2	91	89	86	75	74	73
Chambersburg	640	0	5	9	94	92	89	76	75	74
Erie AP	732	1	7	11	88	85	82	76	74	73
Harrisburg AP	335	4	9	13	92	89	86	76	75	74
Johnstown	1214	−4	1	5	91	87	85	74	73	72
Lancaster	255	−3	2	6	92	90	87	77	76	75
Meadville	1065	−6	0	4	88	86	83	75	73	72
New Castle	825	−7	−1	4	91	89	86	75	74	73
Philadelphia AP	7	7	11	15	93	90	87	78	77	76
Pittsburgh AP	1137	−1	5	9	90	87	85	75	74	73
Pittsburgh CO	749	1	7	11	90	88	85	75	74	73
Reading CO	226	1	6	9	92	90	87	77	76	75
Scranton/Wilkes-B.	940	−3	2	6	89	87	84	75	74	73
State College	1175	−3	2	6	89	87	84	74	73	72
Sunbury	480	−2	3	7	91	89	86	76	75	74
Uniontown	1040	−1	4	8	90	88	85	75	74	73
Warren	1280	−8	−3	1	89	87	84	75	73	72
West Chester	440	4	9	13	92	90	87	77	76	75
Williamsport AP	527	−5	1	5	91	89	86	76	75	74
York	390	−1	4	8	93	91	88	77	76	75
Rhode Island										
Newport	20	1	5	11	86	84	81	75	74	73
Providence AP	55	0	6	10	89	86	83	76	75	74

TABLE 77 (Cont.) **UNITED STATES OF AMERICA**

Station		Winter[3]			Summer[4]					
City or Airport[1]	Elev.[2] ft.	Low	Dry-Bulb		Dry-Bulb			Wet-Bulb		
			99%	97½%	1%	2½%	5%	1%	2½%	5%
South Carolina										
Anderson	764	13	18	22	96	94	91	77	76	75
Charleston AFB	41	19	23	27	94	92	90	81	80	79
Charleston CO	9	23	26	30	95	93	90	81	80	79
Columbia AP	217	16	20	23	98	96	94	79	79	78
Florence AP	146	16	21	25	96	94	92	80	79	78
Georgetown	14	19	23	26	93	91	88	81	80	79
Greenville AP	957	14	19	23	95	93	91	77	76	75
Greenwood	671	15	19	23	97	95	92	78	77	76
Orangeburg	244	17	21	25	97	95	92	80	79	78
Rock Hill	470	13	17	21	97	95	92	78	77	76
Spartanburg AP	816	13	18	22	95	93	90	77	76	75
Sumter-Shaw AFB	291	18	23	26	96	94	92	80	79	78
South Dakota										
Aberdeen AP	1296	−29	−22	−18	95	92	89	77	75	74
Brookings	1642	−26	−19	−15	93	90	87	77	75	74
Huron AP	1282	−24	−16	−12	97	93	90	77	75	74
Mitchell	1346	−22	−15	−11	96	94	91	77	76	74
Pierre AP	1718	−21	−13	− 9	98	96	93	76	74	73
Rapid City AP	3165	−17	− 9	− 6	96	94	91	72	71	69
Sioux Falls AP	1420	−21	−14	−10	95	92	89	77	75	74
Watertown AP	1746	−27	−20	−16	93	90	87	76	74	73
Yankton	1280	−18	−11	− 7	96	94	91	78	76	75
Tennessee										
Athens	940	10	14	18	96	94	91	77	76	75
Bristol-Tri City AP	1519	6	11	16	92	90	88	76	75	74
Chattanooga AP	670	11	15	19	97	94	92	78	78	77
Clarksville	470	6	12	16	98	96	94	79	78	77
Columbia	690	8	13	17	97	95	93	79	78	77
Dyersburg	334	7	13	17	98	96	94	80	79	78
Greenville	1320	5	10	14	93	91	88	76	75	74
Jackson AP	413	8	14	17	97	95	94	80	79	78
Knoxville AP	980	9	13	17	95	92	90	77	76	75
Memphis AP	263	11	17	21	98	96	94	80	79	78
Murfreesboro	608	7	13	17	97	94	92	79	78	77
Nashville AP	577	6	12	16	97	95	92	79	78	77
Tullahoma	1075	7	13	17	96	94	92	79	78	77
Texas										
Abilene AP	1759	12	17	21	101	99	97	76	75	74
Alice AP	180	26	30	34	101	99	97	81	80	79
Amarillo AP	3607	2	8	12	98	96	93	72	71	70
Austin AP	597	19	25	29	101	98	96	79	78	77
Bay City	52	25	29	33	95	93	91	81	80	79
Beaumont	18	25	29	33	96	94	93	81	80	79
Beeville	225	24	28	32	99	97	96	81	80	79
Big Spring AP	2537	12	18	22	100	98	96	75	73	72
Brownsville AP	16	32	36	40	94	92	91	80	80	79
Brownwood	1435	15	20	25	102	100	98	76	75	74
Bryan AP	275	22	27	31	100	98	96	79	78	78
Corpus Christi AP	43	28	32	36	95	93	91	81	80	80
Corsicana	425	16	21	25	102	100	98	79	78	77
Dallas AP	481	14	19	24	101	99	97	79	78	78
Del Rio, Laughl. AFB	1072	24	28	31	101	99	98	79	77	76
Denton	655	12	18	22	102	100	98	79	78	77
Eagle Pass	743	23	27	31	106	104	102	80	79	78
El Paso AP	3918	16	21	25	100	98	96	70	69	68
Fort Worth AP	544	14	20	24	102	100	98	79	78	77
Galveston AP	5	28	32	36	91	89	88	82	81	81

TABLE 77 (Cont.) **UNITED STATES OF AMERICA**

Station		Winter[3]			Summer[4]					
City or Airport[1]	Elev.[2] ft.	Low	Dry-Bulb		Dry-Bulb			Wet-Bulb		
			99%	97½%	1%	2½%	5%	1%	2½%	5%
Greenville	575	13	19	24	101	99	97	79	78	78
Harlingen	37	30	34	38	96	95	94	80	80	79
Houston AP	50	23	28	32	96	94	92	80	80	79
Houston CO	158	24	29	33	96	94	92	80	80	79
Huntsville	494	22	27	31	99	97	96	80	79	78
Kileen-Gray AFB	1021	17	22	26	100	99	97	78	77	76
Lamesa	2965	7	14	18	100	98	96	74	73	72
Laredo AFB	503	29	32	36	103	101	100	79	78	78
Longview	345	16	21	25	100	98	96	81	80	79
Lubbock AP	3243	4	11	15	99	97	94	73	72	71
Lufkin AP	286	19	24	28	98	96	95	81	80	79
McAllen	122	30	34	38	102	100	98	80	79	78
Midland AP	2815	13	19	23	100	98	96	74	73	72
Mineral Wells AP	934	12	18	22	102	100	98	78	77	76
Palestine CO	580	16	21	25	99	97	96	80	79	78
Pampa	3230	0	7	11	100	98	95	73	72	71
Pecos	2580	10	15	19	102	100	97	72	71	70
Plainview	3400	3	10	14	100	98	95	73	72	71
Port Arthur AP	16	25	29	33	94	92	91	81	80	80
San Angelo, Gdfl. AFB	1878	15	20	25	101	99	97	76	75	74
San Antonio AP	792	22	25	30	99	97	96	77	77	76
Sherman-Perrin AFB	763	12	18	23	101	99	97	79	78	77
Snyder	2325	9	15	19	102	100	97	75	74	73
Temple	675	18	23	27	101	99	97	79	78	77
Tyler AP	527	15	20	24	99	97	96	80	79	78
Vernon	1225	7	14	18	103	101	99	77	76	75
Victoria AP	104	24	28	32	98	96	95	80	79	79
Waco AP	500	16	21	26	101	99	98	79	78	78
Wichita Falls AP	994	9	15	19	103	100	98	77	76	75
Utah										
Cedar City AP	5613	−10	−1	6	94	91	89	65	64	62
Logan	4775	−7	3	7	93	91	89	66	65	63
Moab	3965	2	12	16	100	98	95	66	65	64
Ogden CO	4400	−3	7	11	94	92	89	66	65	64
Price	5580	−7	3	7	93	91	88	65	64	63
Provo	4470	−6	2	6	96	93	91	67	66	65
Richfield	5300	−10	−1	3	94	92	89	66	65	64
St. George CO	2899	13	22	26	104	102	99	71	70	69
Salt Lake City AP	4220	−2	5	9	97	94	92	67	66	65
Vernal AP	5280	−20	−10	−6	90	88	84	64	63	62
Vermont										
Barre	1120	−23	−17	−13	86	84	81	73	72	70
Burlington AP	331	−18	−12	−7	88	85	83	74	73	71
Rutland	620	−18	−12	−8	87	85	82	74	73	71
Virginia										
Charlottsville	870	7	11	15	93	90	88	79	77	76
Danville AP	590	9	13	17	95	92	90	78	77	76
Fredericksburg	50	6	10	14	94	92	89	79	78	76
Harrisonburg	1340	0	5	9	92	90	87	78	77	76
Lynchburg AP	947	10	15	19	94	92	89	77	76	75
Norfolk AP	26	18	20	23	94	91	89	79	78	78
Petersburg	194	10	15	18	96	94	91	80	79	78
Richmond AP	162	10	14	18	96	93	91	79	78	77
Roanoke AP	1174	9	15	18	94	91	89	76	75	74
Staunton	1480	3	8	12	92	90	87	78	77	75
Winchester	750	1	6	10	94	92	89	78	76	75

TABLE 77 (Cont.) **UNITED STATES OF AMERICA**

Station		Winter[3]			Summer[4]					
City or Airport[1]	Elev.[2] ft.	Low	Dry-Bulb		Dry-Bulb			Wet-Bulb		
			99%	97½%	1%	2½%	5%	1%	2½%	5%
Washington										
Aberdeen	12	19	24	27	83	80	77	62	61	60
Bellingham AP	150	8	14	18	76	74	71	67	65	63
Bremerton	162	17	24	29	85	81	77	68	66	65
Ellensburg AP	1729	− 5	2	6	91	89	86	67	65	63
Everett-Paine AFB	598	13	19	24	82	78	74	67	65	63
Kennewick	392	4	11	15	98	96	93	69	68	66
Longview	12	14	20	24	88	86	83	68	66	65
Moses Lake, Lar. AFB	1183	−14	− 7	− 1	96	93	90	68	66	65
Olympia AP	190	15	21	25	85	83	80	67	65	63
Port Angeles	99	20	26	29	75	73	70	60	58	57
Seattle-Boeing Fld	14	17	23	27	82	80	77	67	65	64
Seattle CO	14	22	28	32	81	79	76	67	65	64
Seattle-Tacoma AP	386	14	20	24	85	81	77	66	64	63
Spokane AP	2357	− 5	− 2	4	93	90	87	66	64	63
Tacoma-McCd AFB	350	14	20	24	85	81	78	68	66	64
Walla Walla AP	1185	5	12	16	98	96	93	69	68	66
Wenatchee	634	− 2	5	9	95	92	89	68	66	64
Yakima AP	1061	− 1	6	10	94	92	89	69	67	65
West Virginia										
Beckley	2330	− 4	0	6	91	88	86	74	73	72
Bluefield AP	2850	1	6	10	88	86	83	74	73	72
Charleston AP	939	1	9	14	92	90	88	76	75	74
Clarksburg	977	− 2	3	7	92	90	87	76	75	74
Elkins AP	1970	− 4	1	5	87	84	82	74	73	72
Huntington CO	565	4	10	14	95	93	91	77	76	75
Martinsburg AP	537	1	6	10	96	94	91	78	77	76
Morgantown AP	1245	− 2	3	7	90	88	85	76	74	73
Parkersburg CO	615	2	8	12	93	91	88	77	76	75
Wheeling	659	0	5	9	91	89	86	76	75	74
Wisconsin										
Appleton	742	−16	−10	− 6	89	87	84	75	74	72
Ashland	650	−27	−21	−17	85	83	80	73	71	69
Beloit	780	−13	− 7	− 3	92	90	87	77	76	75
Eau Claire AP	888	−21	−15	−11	90	88	85	76	74	72
Fond du Lac	760	−17	−11	− 7	89	87	84	76	74	73
Green Bay AP	683	−16	−12	− 7	88	85	82	75	73	72
La Crosse AP	652	−18	−12	− 8	90	88	85	78	76	75
Madison AP	858	−13	− 9	− 5	92	88	85	77	75	73
Manitowoc	660	−11	− 5	− 1	88	86	83	75	74	72
Marinette	605	−14	− 8	− 4	88	86	83	74	72	70
Milwaukee AP	672	−11	− 6	− 2	90	87	84	77	75	73
Racine	640	−10	− 4	0	90	88	85	77	75	73
Sheboygan	648	−10	− 4	0	89	87	84	76	74	72
Stevens Point	1079	−22	−16	−12	89	87	84	75	73	71
Waukesha	860	−12	− 6	− 2	91	89	86	77	75	74
Wausau AP	1196	−24	−18	−14	89	86	83	74	72	70
Wyoming										
Casper AP	5319	−20	−11	− 5	92	90	87	63	62	60
Cheyenne AP	6126	−15	− 6	− 2	89	86	83	63	62	61
Cody AP	5090	−23	−13	− 9	90	87	84	61	60	59
Evanston	6860	−22	−12	− 8	84	82	79	58	57	56
Lander AP	5563	−26	−16	−12	92	90	87	63	62	60
Laramie AP	7266	−17	− 6	− 2	82	80	77	61	59	58
Newcastle	4480	−18	− 9	− 5	92	89	86	68	67	66
Rawlins	6736	−24	−15	−11	86	84	81	62	61	60
Rock Springs AP	6741	−16	− 6	− 1	86	84	82	58	57	56
Sheridan AP	3942	−21	−12	− 7	95	92	89	67	65	64
Torrington	4098	−20	−11	− 7	94	92	89	68	67	66

TABLE 77 (Cont.) **CANADA**

Station		Winter[3]			Summer[4]					
City or Airport[1]	Elev.[2] ft.	Low	Dry-Bulb		Dry-Bulb			Wet-Bulb		
			99%	97½%	1%	2½%	5%	1%	2½%	5%
CANADA										
Alberta										
Calgary AP	3540	−30	−29	−25	87	85	82	66	64	63
Edmonton AP	2219	−30	−29	−26	86	83	80	69	67	65
Grande Prairie AP	2190	−44	−43	−37	84	81	78	66	64	63
Jasper CO	3480	−38	−32	−28	87	84	81	66	64	63
Lethbridge AP	3018	−31	−31	−24	91	88	85	68	66	64
McMurray AP	1216	−44	−42	−39	87	84	81	69	67	65
Medicine Hat AP	2365	−33	−30	−26	96	93	90	72	69	67
Red Deer AP	2965	−38	−33	−28	88	86	83	67	65	64
British Columbia										
Dawson Creek	2200	−47	−40	−35	84	81	78	66	64	63
Fort Nelson AP	1230	−43	−44	−41	87	84	81	66	64	63
Kamloops CO	1150	−15	−16	−10	97	94	91	71	69	68
Nanaimo CO	100	16	17	20	81	78	75	66	64	62
New Westminster CO	50	12	15	19	86	84	82	68	66	65
Penticton AP	1121	0	− 1	3	94	91	88	71	69	68
Prince George AP	2218	−38	−37	−31	85	82	79	68	65	63
Prince Rupert CO	170	9	11	15	73	71	69	62	60	59
Trail	1400	− 3	− 2	3	94	91	88	70	68	67
Vancouver AP	16	13	15	19	80	78	76	68	66	65
Victoria CO	228	20	20	23	80	76	72	64	62	60
Manitoba										
Brandon CO	1200	−36	−29	−26	90	87	84	75	73	71
Churchill AP	115	−43	−40	−38	79	75	72	68	66	63
Dauphin AP	999	−35	−29	−26	89	86	83	74	72	70
Flin Flon CO	1098	−38	−40	−36	85	81	78	71	69	67
Portage la Prairie AP	867	−28	−25	−22	90	87	84	75	74	72
The Pas AP	894	−41	−35	−32	85	81	78	73	71	69
Winnipeg AP	786	−31	−28	−25	90	87	84	75	74	72
New Brunswick										
Campbellton CO	25	−20	−18	−14	87	84	81	74	71	69
Chatham AP	112	−17	−15	−10	90	87	84	74	71	69
Edmundston CO	500	−29	−20	−16	84	81	78	75	72	70
Fredericton AP	74	−19	−16	−10	89	86	83	73	70	68
Moncton AP	248	−16	−12	− 7	88	85	82	74	71	69
Saint John AP	352	−15	−12	− 7	81	79	77	71	68	66
Newfoundland										
Corner Brook CO	40	− 9	−10	− 5	84	81	79	69	68	66
Gander AP	482	− 5	− 5	− 1	85	82	79	69	68	66
Goose Bay AP	144	−28	−27	−25	86	81	77	69	67	65
St. John's AP	463	1	2	6	79	77	75	69	68	66
Stephenville	44	− 4	− 6	− 1	79	76	74	69	68	66
Northwest Territories										
Fort Smith AP	665	−51	−49	−46	85	83	80	67	65	64
FrobisherBay AP	68	−45	−45	−42	63	59	56	—	—	—
Inuvik	75	−54	−50	−48	80	77	75	63	61	60
Resolute AP	209	−52	−49	−47	54	51	49	—	—	—
Yellowknife AP	682	−51	−49	−47	78	76	74	65	63	62
Nova Scotia										
Amherst	63	−15	−10	− 5	85	82	79	72	70	68
Halifax AP	136	− 4	0	4	83	80	77	69	68	67
Kentville CO	50	− 8	− 4	0	86	83	80	72	70	69
New Glasgow	317	−16	−10	− 5	84	81	79	72	70	68
Sydney AP	197	− 3	0	5	84	82	80	72	70	68
Truro CO	77	−17	−12	− 7	84	81	79	72	70	69
Yarmouth AP	136	2	5	9	76	73	71	69	68	67

TABLE 77 (Cont.) **CANADA**

Station		Winter[3]			Summer[4]					
City or Airport[1]	Elev.[2] ft.	Low	Dry-Bulb		Dry-Bulb			Wet-Bulb		
			99%	97½%	1%	2½%	5%	1%	2½%	5%
Ontario										
Belleville CO	250	−15	−11	−7	89	86	84	77	75	73
Chatham CO	600	−1	3	6	92	90	88	77	75	74
Cornwall	210	−22	−14	−9	89	86	84	77	75	74
Fort William AP	644	−31	−27	−23	86	83	80	72	70	68
Hamilton	303	−2	0	3	91	88	86	77	75	73
Kapuskasing AP	752	−37	−31	−28	87	84	81	73	71	69
Kenora AP	1345	−33	−31	−28	86	83	80	75	73	71
Kingston CO	300	−16	−10	−7	85	82	80	77	75	73
Kitchener	1125	−11	−3	1	88	85	83	76	75	74
London AP	912	−9	−1	3	90	88	86	76	75	74
North Bay AP	1210	−27	−21	−17	87	84	82	71	70	69
Oshawa	370	−11	−5	−2	90	87	85	77	75	73
Ottawa AP	339	−21	−17	−13	90	87	84	75	74	73
Owen Sound	597	−9	−5	−1	87	84	82	74	72	71
Peterborough CO	648	−20	−13	−9	90	87	85	76	74	73
St. Catharines CO	325	1	2	5	91	88	86	77	75	73
Sarnia	625	−6	2	6	92	90	88	76	74	73
Sault Ste. Marie CO	675	−21	−20	−15	88	85	83	72	70	68
Sudbury	850	−25	−20	−15	89	86	84	72	70	69
Timmins CO	1100	−37	−33	−28	90	87	84	73	71	69
Toronto AP	578	−10	−3	1	90	87	85	77	75	73
Windsor AP	637	−1	4	7	92	90	88	77	75	74
Prince Edward Island										
Charlottetown AP	186	−11	−6	−3	84	81	79	72	70	68
Summerside AP	78	−10	−8	−3	84	81	79	72	70	68
Quebec										
Bagotville	536	−35	−26	−22	88	84	81	72	71	69
Chicoutimi CO	150	−31	−24	−20	87	83	80	72	71	69
Drummondville CO	270	−26	−18	−13	88	85	82	76	74	72
Granby	550	−23	−17	−12	87	84	82	76	74	72
Hull	200	−21	−17	−13	90	87	84	75	74	73
Mégantic AP	1362	−27	−20	−16	84	81	78	75	73	71
Montréal AP	98	−20	−16	−10	88	86	84	76	74	73
Québec AP	245	−25	−19	−13	86	82	79	75	73	71
Rimouski	117	−18	−16	−12	78	74	71	71	69	68
St. Jean	129	−21	−15	−10	87	85	83	76	74	73
St. Jérome	310	−30	−18	−13	87	84	82	76	74	73
Sept Iles AP	190	−29	−27	−22	80	78	75	66	64	63
Shawinigan	306	−27	−20	−15	88	85	83	76	74	72
Sherbrooke CO	595	−25	−18	−13	87	84	81	75	73	71
Thetford Mines	1020	−25	−19	−14	86	83	80	75	73	71
Trois Rivières CO	200	−30	−18	−13	88	85	82	76	74	72
Val d'Or AP	1108	−37	−31	−27	88	85	82	72	71	69
Valleyfield	150	−20	−14	−9	87	85	83	76	74	73
Saskatchewan										
Estevan AP	1884	−32	−30	−25	93	89	86	75	73	71
Moose Jaw AP	1857	−33	−32	−27	93	89	86	73	71	69
North Battleford AP	1796	−33	−33	−29	90	86	83	71	69	67
Price Albert AP	1414	−45	−41	−35	88	84	81	72	70	68
Regina AP	1884	−38	−34	−29	92	88	85	73	71	69
Saskatoon AP	1645	−37	−34	−30	90	86	83	71	69	67
Swift Current AP	2677	−31	−29	−25	93	89	86	72	70	68
Yorkton AP	1653	−38	−33	−28	89	85	82	74	72	70
Yukon Territory										
Whitehorse AP	2289	−45	−45	−42	78	75	72	62	60	59

TABLE 77 (Cont.)

MEXICO, CENTRAL AMERICA WEST INDIES AND ATLANTIC ISLANDS

Station		Winter[3]			Summer[4]					
City or Airport[1]	Elev.[2] ft.	Low	Dry-Bulb		Dry-Bulb			Wet-Bulb		
			99%	97½%	1%	2½%	5%	1%	2½%	5%
MEXICO										
Mexico D.F. Mexico City	7575	33	37	39	83	81	79	61	60	59
Jalisco Guadalajara	5105	35	39	42	93	91	89	68	67	66
Nuevo Leon Monterey	1732	31	38	41	98	95	93	79	78	77
Vera Cruz Vera Cruz	184	55	60	62	91	89	88	83	83	82
Yucatan Merida	72	56	59	61	97	95	94	80	79	77
CENTRAL AMERICA										
British Hondura Belize	17	55	60	62	90	90	89	82	82	81
El Salvador San Salvador	2238	51	54	56	98	96	95	77	76	75
Guatemala Guatemala City	4855	45	48	51	83	82	81	69	68	67
Honduras Tegucigalpa	3094	44	47	50	89	87	85	73	72	71
Nicaragua Managua	135	62	65	67	94	93	92	81	80	79
Panama & Canal Zone Panama City	21	69	72	73	93	92	91	81	81	80
WEST INDIES AND ATLANTIC ISLANDS										
Bahamas Nassau	11	55	61	63	90	89	88	80	80	79
Bermuda Kindley AFB	129	47	53	55	87	86	85	79	78	78
Cuba Guantanamo Bay	21	60	64	66	94	93	92	82	81	80
Havana	80	54	59	62	92	91	89	81	81	80
Dominican Republic Santo Domingo	57	61	63	65	92	90	88	81	80	80
Greenland Nassarssuaq	85	−23	−12	− 8	66	63	61	56	54	52
Haiti Port au Prince	121	63	65	67	97	95	93	82	81	80
Iceland Reykjavik	59	8	14	17	59	58	56	54	53	53
Martinique Fort de France	13	62	64	66	90	89	88	81	81	80
Puerto Rico San Juan	82	65	67	68	89	88	87	81	80	79
Trinidad Port of Spain	67	61	64	66	91	90	89	80	80	79

TABLE 77 (Cont.) **SOUTH AMERICA**

Station		Winter[3]			Summer[4]					
City or Airport[1]	Elev.[2] ft.	Low	Dry-Bulb		Dry-Bulb			Wet-Bulb		
			99%	97½%	1%	2½%	5%	1%	2½%	5%
SOUTH AMERICA										
Argentina										
Buenos Aires	89	27	32	34	91	89	86	77	76	75
Córdoba	1388	21	28	32	100	96	93	76	75	74
Tucuman	1401	24	32	36	102	99	96	76	75	74
Bolivia										
La Paz	12001	28	31	33	71	69	68	58	57	56
Brazil										
Belem	42	67	70	71	90	89	87	80	79	78
Belo Horizonte	3002	42	47	50	86	84	83	76	75	75
Brasilia	3442	46	49	51	89	88	86	76	75	75
Curitiba	3114	28	34	37	86	84	82	75	74	74
Fortaleza	89	66	69	70	91	90	89	79	78	78
Porto Alegre	33	32	37	40	95	92	89	76	76	75
Recife	97	67	69	70	88	87	86	78	77	77
Rio de Janeiro	201	56	58	60	94	92	90	80	79	78
Salvador	154	65	67	68	88	87	86	79	79	78
São Paulo	2608	36	42	46	86	84	82	75	74	74
Chile										
Punta Arenas	26	22	25	27	68	66	64	56	55	54
Santiago	1706	27	32	35	90	89	88	71	70	69
Valpariso	135	39	43	46	81	79	77	67	66	65
Columbia										
Baranquilla	44	66	70	72	95	94	93	83	82	82
Bogotá	8406	42	45	46	72	70	69	60	59	58
Cali	3189	53	57	58	84	82	79	70	69	68
Medellin	4650	48	53	55	87	85	84	73	72	72
Equador										
Guayaquil	20	61	64	65	92	91	89	80	80	79
Quito	9446	30	36	39	73	72	71	63	62	62
French Guiana										
Cayenne	20	69	71	72	92	91	90	83	83	82
Guyana										
Georgetown	6	70	72	73	89	88	87	80	79	79
Paraguay										
Asunción	456	35	43	46	100	98	96	81	81	80
Peru										
Lima	394	51	53	55	86	85	84	76	75	74
Surinam										
Paramaribo	12	66	68	70	93	92	90	82	82	81
Uruguay										
Montevideo	72	34	37	39	90	88	85	73	72	71
Venezuela										
Caracas	3418	49	52	54	84	83	81	70	69	69
Maracaibo	20	69	72	73	97	96	95	84	83	83

TABLE 77 (Cont.) **EUROPE**

Station		Winter[3]			Summer[4]					
City or Airport[1]	Elev.[2] ft.	Low	Dry-Bulb		Dry-Bulb			Wet-Bulb		
			99%	97½%	1%	2½%	5%	1%	2½%	5%
EUROPE										
Austria										
Vienna	644	−2	6	11	88	86	83	71	69	67
Azores										
Lajes (Terceira)	170	42	46	49	80	78	77	73	72	71
Belgium										
Brussels	328	13	15	19	83	79	77	70	68	67
Bulgaria										
Sofia	1805	−2	3	8	89	86	84	71	70	69
Czechoslavakia										
Prague	662	3	4	9	88	85	83	66	65	64
Denmark										
Copenhagen	43	11	16	19	79	76	74	68	66	64
Finland										
Helsinki	30	−11	−7	−1	77	74	72	66	65	63
France										
Lyon	938	−1	10	14	91	89	86	71	70	69
Marseilles	246	23	25	28	90	87	84	72	71	69
Nantes	121	17	22	26	86	83	80	70	69	67
Nice	39	31	34	37	87	85	83	73	72	72
Paris	164	16	22	25	89	86	83	70	68	67
Strasbourg	465	9	11	16	86	83	80	70	69	67
Germany										
Berlin	187	6	7	12	84	81	78	68	67	66
Hamburg	66	10	12	16	86	76	73	68	66	65
Hannover	561	7	16	20	82	78	75	68	67	65
Mannheim	359	2	8	11	87	85	82	71	69	68
Munich	1729	−1	5	9	86	83	80	68	66	64
Gibraltar										
Gibraltar	11	38	42	45	92	89	86	76	75	74
Greece										
Athens	351	29	33	36	96	93	91	72	71	71
Thessalonika	78	23	28	32	95	93	91	77	76	75
Hungary										
Budapest	394	8	10	14	90	86	84	72	71	70
Ireland										
Dublin	155	19	24	27	74	72	70	65	64	62
Shannon	8	19	25	28	76	73	71	65	64	63
Italy										
Milan	341	12	18	22	89	87	84	76	75	74
Naples	220	28	34	36	91	88	86	74	73	72
Roma	377	25	30	33	94	92	89	74	73	72
Netherlands										
Amsterdam	5	17	20	23	79	76	73	65	64	63
Norway										
Bergen	141	14	17	20	75	74	73	67	66	65
Oslo	308	−2	0	4	79	77	74	67	66	64
Poland										
Kraków	723	−2	2	6	84	81	78	68	67	66
Warsaw	394	−3	3	8	84	81	78	71	70	68

TABLE 77 (Cont.) **EUROPE, AFRICA**

Station		Winter[3]			Summer[4]					
City or Airport[1]	Elev.[2] ft.	Low	Dry-Bulb		Dry-Bulb			Wet-Bulb		
			99%	97½%	1%	2½%	5%	1%	2½%	5%
Portugal										
Lisbon	313	32	37	39	89	86	83	69	68	67
Rumania										
Bucharest	269	− 2	3	8	93	91	89	72	71	70
Spain										
Barcelona	312	31	33	36	88	86	84	75	74	73
Madrid	2188	22	25	28	93	91	89	71	69	67
Valencia	79	31	33	37	92	90	88	75	74	73
Sweden										
Stockholm	146	3	5	8	78	74	72	64	62	60
Switzerland										
Zurich	1617	4	9	14	84	81	78	68	67	66
United Kingdom										
Belfast	24	19	23	26	74	72	69	65	64	62
Birmingham	535	21	24	27	79	76	73	66	64	63
Cardiff	203	21	24	27	79	76	73	64	63	62
Edinburgh	441	22	25	28	73	70	68	64	62	61
Glasgow	85	17	21	24	74	71	68	64	63	61
London	149	20	24	26	82	79	76	68	66	65
U. S. S. R.										
Archangel	22	−29	−23	−18	75	71	68	60	58	57
Kaliningrad	23	− 3	1	6	83	80	77	67	66	65
Kiev	600	−12	− 5	1	87	84	81	69	68	67
Kharkov	472	−19	−10	− 3	87	84	82	69	68	67
Kuibyshev	190	−23	−19	−13	89	85	81	69	67	66
Leningrad	16	−14	− 9	− 5	78	75	72	65	64	63
Minsk	738	−19	−11	− 4	80	77	74	67	66	65
Moscow	505	−19	−11	− 6	84	81	78	69	67	65
Odessa	214	− 1	4	8	87	84	82	70	69	68
Rostov on Don	159	− 9	− 2	4	90	87	84	70	69	68
Tbilisi	1325	12	18	22	87	85	83	68	67	66
Volgograd	136	−21	−13	− 7	93	89	86	71	70	69
Yugoslavia										
Belgrade	453	4	9	13	92	89	86	74	73	72
				AFRICA						
Algeria										
Algiers	194	38	43	45	95	92	89	77	76	75
Congo										
Brazzaville	1043	54	60	62	93	92	91	81	81	80
Kinasha (Leopoldville)	1066	54	60	62	92	91	90	81	80	80
Stanleyville	1370	65	67	68	92	91	90	81	80	80
Ethiopia										
Addis Ababa	7753	35	39	41	84	82	81	66	65	64
Asmara	7628	36	40	42	83	81	80	65	64	63
Ghana										
Accra	88	65	68	69	91	90	89	80	79	79
Ivory Coast										
Abidjan	65	64	67	69	91	90	88	83	82	81
Kenya										
Nairobi	5971	45	48	50	81	80	78	66	65	65
Liberia										
Monrovia	75	64	68	69	90	89	88	82	82	81

TABLE 77 (Cont.) **AFRICA, ASIA**

Station		Winter[3]			Summer[4]					
City or Airport[1]	Elev.[2] ft.	Low	Dry-Bulb		Dry-Bulb			Wet-Bulb		
			99%	97½%	1%	2½%	5%	1%	2½%	5%
Libya										
Bengasi	82	41	46	48	97	94	91	77	76	75
Madagascar										
Tananarive	4531	39	43	46	86	84	83	73	72	71
Morocco										
Casablanca	164	36	40	42	94	90	86	73	72	70
Nigeria										
Lagos	10	67	70	71	92	91	90	82	82	81
Senegal										
Dakar	131	58	61	62	95	93	91	81	80	80
Somalia										
Mogadiscio	39	67	69	70	91	90	89	82	82	81
South Africa										
Capetown	55	36	40	42	93	90	86	72	71	70
Johannesburg	5463	26	31	34	85	83	81	70	69	69
Pretoria	4491	27	32	35	90	87	85	70	69	68
Sudan										
Khartoum	1279	47	53	56	109	107	104	77	76	75
Tanzia										
Dar es Salaam	47	62	64	65	90	89	88	82	81	81
Tunisia										
Tunis	217	35	39	41	102	99	96	77	76	74
United Arab Republic										
Cairo	381	39	45	46	102	100	98	76	75	74

ASIA

Station	Elev. ft.	Low	99%	97½%	1%	2½%	5%	1%	2½%	5%
Aden										
Aden	10	63	68	70	102	100	98	83	82	82
Afghanistan										
Kabul	5955	2	6	9	98	96	93	66	65	64
Burma										
Mandalay	252	50	54	56	104	102	101	81	80	80
Rangoon	18	59	62	63	100	98	95	83	82	82
Cambodia										
Phnom Penh	36	62	66	68	98	96	94	83	82	82
Ceylon										
Columbo	24	65	69	70	90	89	88	81	80	80
China										
Chungking	755	34	37	39	99	97	95	81	80	79
Shanghai	23	16	23	26	94	92	90	81	81	80
Hong Kong										
Hong Kong	109	43	48	50	92	91	90	81	80	80
India										
Ahmenabad	163	49	53	56	109	107	105	80	79	78
Bangalore	3021	53	56	58	96	94	93	75	74	74
Bombay	37	62	65	67	96	94	92	82	81	81
Calcutta	21	49	52	54	98	97	96	83	82	82
Madras	51	61	64	66	104	102	101	84	83	83
Nagpur	1017	45	51	54	110	108	107	79	79	78
New Delhi	703	35	39	41	110	107	105	83	82	82

TABLE 77 (Cont.) ASIA

Station		Winter[3]			Summer[4]					
City or Airport[1]	Elev.[2] ft.	Low	Dry-Bulb		Dry-Bulb			Wet-Bulb		
			99%	97½%	1%	2½%	5%	1%	2½%	5%
Iran										
Abadan	7	32	39	41	116	113	110	82	81	81
Meshed	3104	3	10	14	99	96	93	68	67	66
Tehran	4002	15	20	24	102	100	98	75	74	73
Iraq										
Baghdad	111	27	32	35	113	111	108	73	72	72
Mosul	730	23	29	32	114	112	110	73	72	72
Israel										
Jerusalem	2485	31	36	38	95	94	92	70	69	69
Tel Aviv	36	33	39	41	96	93	91	74	73	72
Japan										
Fukuoka	22	26	29	31	92	90	89	82	80	79
Sapporo	56	−7	1	5	86	83	80	76	74	72
Tokyo	19	21	26	28	91	89	87	81	80	79
Jordan										
Amman	2548	29	33	36	97	94	92	70	69	68
Korea										
Pyongyang	186	−10	−2	3	89	87	85	77	76	76
Seoul	285	−1	7	9	91	89	87	81	79	78
Lebanon										
Beirut	111	40	42	45	93	91	90	78	77	76
Malaysia										
Kuola Lumpur	127	67	70	71	94	93	92	82	82	81
Penang	17	69	72	73	93	93	92	82	81	80
Singapore	33	69	71	72	92	91	90	82	81	80
Nepal										
Katmandu	4388	30	33	35	89	87	86	78	77	76
Pakistan										
Chittagong	87	48	52	54	93	91	89	82	81	81
Karachi	13	45	49	51	100	98	95	82	82	81
Lahore	702	32	35	37	109	107	105	83	82	81
Peshwar	1164	31	35	37	109	106	103	81	80	79
Saudi Arabia										
Dhahran	80	39	45	48	111	110	108	86	85	84
Jedda	20	52	57	60	106	103	100	85	84	83
Riyadh	1938	29	37	40	110	108	106	78	77	76
Syria										
Damascus	2362	25	29	32	102	100	98	72	71	70
Taiwan										
Tainan	70	40	46	49	92	91	90	84	83	82
Taipei	30	41	44	47	94	92	90	83	82	81
Thailand										
Bangkok	39	57	61	63	97	95	93	82	82	81
Turkey										
Adana	82	25	33	35	100	97	95	79	78	77
Ankara	2825	2	9	12	94	92	89	68	67	66
Istanbul	59	23	28	30	91	88	86	75	74	73
Izmir	16	24	27	29	98	96	94	75	74	73

TABLE 77 (Cont.) **ASIA, EAST INDIES, PACIFIC ISLANDS, AUSTRALIA**

Station		Winter[3]			Summer[4]					
City or Airport[1]	Elev.[2] ft.	Low	Dry-Bulb		Dry-Bulb			Wet-Bulb		
			99%	97½%	1%	2½%	5%	1%	2½%	5%
U. S. S. R.										
Alma Ata	2543	−18	−10	− 6	88	86	83	69	68	67
Krasnoyarsk	498	−41	−32	−27	84	80	76	64	62	60
Petropavlovsk	286	− 9	− 3	0	70	68	65	58	57	56
Sverdlovsk	894	−34	−25	−20	80	76	72	63	62	60
Tashkent	1569	− 4	3	8	95	93	90	71	70	69
Vladivostok	94	−15	−10	− 7	80	77	74	70	69	68
Viet Nam										
Da Nang	23	56	60	62	97	95	93	86	86	85
Hanoi	53	46	50	53	99	97	95	85	85	84
Saigon	30	62	65	67	93	91	89	85	84	83
EAST INDIES AND PACIFIC ISLANDS										
Indonesia										
Djakarta	26	69	71	72	90	89	88	80	79	78
Kupang	148	63	66	68	94	93	92	81	80	80
Makassar	61	64	66	68	90	89	88	80	80	79
Medan	77	66	69	71	92	91	90	81	80	79
Palembang	20	67	70	71	92	91	90	80	79	79
Surabaya	10	64	66	68	91	90	89	80	79	79
New Guinea										
Manokwari	62	70	71	72	89	88	87	82	81	81
Point Moresby	126	62	67	69	92	91	90	80	80	79
New Zealand										
Auckland	140	37	40	42	78	77	76	67	66	65
Christ Church	32	25	28	31	82	79	76	68	67	66
Wellington	394	32	35	37	76	74	72	66	65	64
Philippines										
Manila	47	69	73	74	94	92	91	82	81	81
AUSTRALIA										
New South Wales										
Sydney	138	38	40	42	89	84	80	74	73	72
Northern Territory										
Alice Springs	1795	28	34	37	104	102	100	75	74	72
Darwin	88	60	64	66	94	93	91	82	81	81
Queensland										
Brisbane	137	39	44	47	91	88	86	77	76	75
South Australia										
Adelaide	140	36	38	40	98	94	91	72	70	68
Victoria										
Melbourne	114	31	35	38	95	91	86	71	69	68
Western Australia										
Perth	210	38	40	42	100	96	93	76	74	73

FOOTNOTES

[1]Stations listed with CO letter designations are city office locations surrounded by buildings and streets. Stations listed without letter designations are semi-rural locations which are usually comparable with airport (AP) and air force base (AFB) locations.

[2]Ground elevations of 1964 stations are listed.

[3]The winter design dry-bulbs listed under Low are the medians of the coldest temperatures recorded each year for periods of up to 30 years for the U.S. stations and the average

(*Footnotes for Table 77 continued next page.*)

Footnotes for Table 77 (cont.)

annual minimum for the Canadian and other stations. The values listed under 99% and 97½% are the hourly temperatures which were equalled or exceeded the listed percentage of hours during December, January, and February for the U. S. stations or during January only for Canadian stations. The coldest three months were selected for the other stations.

[4]The summer design dry-bulbs and wet-bulbs are the hourly temperatures which were equaled or exceeded 1%, 2½%, or 5% of the hours during June, July, August, and September for the U. S. stations or during July only for Canadian stations. The warmest four months were selected for the other stations.

Adapted from the data of Handbook of Fundamentals, ASHRAE, 1967, pp. 373-392.

TABLE 78—TRANSMISSION COEFFICIENT CONVERSIONS FOR VARIOUS WIND VELOCITIES

In Btu per hr-ft^2-°F

U for 15 MPH	*U* for 0 to 30 MPH WIND VELOCITIES						*U* for 7½ MPH
	0	5	10	20	25	30	
0.05	0.05	0.05	0.05	0.05	0.05	0.05	0.05
0.06	0.06	0.06	0.06	0.06	0.06	0.06	0.06
0.07	0.07	0.07	0.07	0.07	0.07	0.07	0.07
0.08	0.08	0.08	0.08	0.08	0.08	0.08	0.08
0.09	0.09	0.09	0.09	0.09	0.09	0.09	0.09
0.10	0.10	0.10	0.10	0.10	0.10	0.10	0.10
0.11	0.11	0.11	0.11	0.11	0.11	0.11	0.11
0.13	0.12	0.13	0.13	0.13	0.13	0.13	0.13
0.15	0.14	0.15	0.15	0.15	0.15	0.15	0.15
0.17	0.16	0.17	0.17	0.17	0.17	0.17	0.17
0.19	0.18	0.18	0.19	0.19	0.19	0.19	0.18
0.21	0.19	0.20	0.21	0.21	0.21	0.21	0.20
0.23	0.21	0.22	0.23	0.23	0.23	0.23	0.22
0.25	0.23	0.24	0.25	0.25	0.25	0.25	0.24
0.27	0.24	0.26	0.27	0.27	0.27	0.28	0.26
0.29	0.26	0.28	0.29	0.29	0.30	0.30	0.28
0.31	0.27	0.30	0.31	0.31	0.32	0.32	0.30
0.33	0.29	0.31	0.32	0.33	0.34	0.34	0.31
0.35	0.30	0.33	0.34	0.35	0.36	0.36	0.33
0.37	0.32	0.35	0.36	0.38	0.38	0.38	0.35
0.39	0.33	0.37	0.38	0.40	0.40	0.40	0.37
0.41	0.35	0.39	0.40	0.42	0.42	0.42	0.39
0.43	0.36	0.40	0.42	0.44	0.44	0.44	0.41
0.45	0.38	0.42	0.44	0.46	0.46	0.47	0.43
0.50	0.41	0.46	0.49	0.51	0.51	0.52	0.48
0.60	0.47	0.55	0.58	0.61	0.62	0.63	0.56
0.70	0.54	0.63	0.68	0.72	0.73	0.74	0.65
0.80	0.59	0.71	0.77	0.82	0.84	0.85	0.74
0.90	0.65	0.79	0.86	0.93	0.95	0.96	0.82
1.00	0.70	0.87	0.95	1.03	1.06	1.08	0.91
1.10	0.74	0.94	1.04	1.14	1.17	1.19	0.99
1.20	0.79	1.01	1.13	1.25	1.29	1.32	1.07
1.30	0.83	1.08	1.22	1.36	1.40	1.43	1.15

Adapted from the data of Handbook of Fundamentals, ASHRAE, 1967, p. 453.

Heating and Cooling Loads

To assist in the zoning of a structure, and as a necessary prerequisite for sizing and otherwise designing a complete system, the peak heating and cooling loads must be calculated. It is frequently necessary to calculate the peak load for the various zones and the total structure for various times of the day. Where central heating or refrigeration plants are utilized the peak demand on those plants is not necessarily the sum of the peak loads for all of the zones. Similarly, due to the phenomenon of thermal storage and temperature lag, the peak load for any given zone may not correspond, either in time or magnitude, to the instantaneous peak gain or loss of heat. There are numerous sources of heat gain or loss which must be considered in establishing loads.

The total occupancy load is the sum of the individual gains based on individual activity. As discussed in Chapter 14 and tabulated in Table 72 therein, human occupants produce both sensible and latent heat gains dependent upon their activity. This table on page **341** can be used to establish the rate of gain per person for any activity reasonably close to one described. For use in determining desirabilities of zoning, the total load should be determined for various times of the day, as well as for various "possible" zones.

Other internal sources of heat include lighting and electrical or steam appliances such as those listed in Table 79. These unit heat rates, when used in conjunction with the total number of units, will establish the sensible or latent heat gain or both due to that equipment. Chemical processes may be exothermic or endothermic. The heats of evolution of various farm produce in storage are listed in Table 121 in Chapter 21 in connection with cold storage applications. Appropriate allowances should be made for such loads. Whenever any of these internal loads is only intermittently active, a time weighted average should be used.

TABLE 79—HEAT GAINS DUE TO LIGHTING AND OTHER SOURCES

In Btu per hr

Source	Total Heat Gain
Lighting	
Fluorescent (including ballast)	4.09 per watt rating
Incandescent	3.41 per watt rating
Motor Driven Equipment	
Motor outside space	2544 per hp output
Motor inside space	2544 per hp input
Electrical Cooking Appliances*	
Not vented	1.70 per watt rating
Vented to outside	0.55 per watt rating
Gas Cooking Appliances*	
Not vented	500 per cu ft gas
Vented to outside	100 per cu ft gas
Meals*	50 per person

*Latent Heat may range from 25% to 75% of Total Heat

Adapted from the data of Handbook of Fundamentals, ASHRAE, 1967, pp. 496-500.

A transmission load exists whenever there is a difference in temperature between the air on one side of a wall and that on the other. Heat will naturally pass from the high-temperature air to the low-temperature air. The rate at which this heat will travel through the wall depends on the resistance it encounters. Natural convection serves to get the heat close to the wall, but it is usual to consider that a stagnant film of air exists right at the surface. The resistance of such films is reduced by increased air motion; consequently, a higher resistance is usually assigned to a surface on the inside in comparatively still air than for a surface on the outside. In air-conditioning work it is usual to assume still air on the inside, a 7½ mile per hour wind on the outside in summer, and a 15 mile per hour wind in winter. Tables 80 through 87 utilize air film resistances based on these conditions. In addition, the thermal conductivity and the thickness of the various building materials and insulation are also considered. The direction of heat flow, whether horizontal, vertically up, or vertically down, as it affects the conductance of any air spaces, is also considered. These tables list the over-all coefficient (U) for the transmission of heat through the air films, wall, insulation, etc., in Btu per hr per sq ft of surface. The proper value, when inserted into the convection heat transfer formula

$$TH = UA(t_o - t_i) \qquad (368)$$

with the appropriate area (A) in sq ft and temperature difference $(t_o - t_i)$ in °F, yields (TH) the transmission loss or gain (depending on the direction of heat flow) in Btu per hr. The area depends on the actual building dimensions, and the temperature difference should be based on the design inside (t_i) and outside (t_o) dry-bulb temperatures.

In summer design, a sun load must be figured since the maximum load usually occurs as a result of solar radiation. For glass surfaces the peak sun effect occurs at different times for the various exposures but produces an immediate load on the system in any case. Not so for opaque walls and roofs because thermal storage produces a temperature lag. Consequently, the time of maximum cooling load may differ appreciably from the time of maximum solar radiation intensity. The theoretical approach to the calculation of sun effect involves such considerations as solar altitude, azimuth, and declination, but the greatly simplified method, presented here, is of sufficient accuracy for most air-conditioning work. For the best accuracy refer to the data in the ASHRAE Handbook of Fundamentals which includes equations and coefficients for computer calculation of solar heat gain factors.

For relatively opaque surfaces, the effect of the sun may be estimated by utilizing the equivalent temperature differences (ETD) listed in Tables 88 and 89 in place of $(t_o - t_i)$ in the usual convection heat transfer formula. For transparent surfaces, heat gains per unit area are listed in Table 90. Here the heat gain is divided according to that which is transmitted directly through the glass by radiation, that which is absorbed, and that which is transmitted by convection and radiation owing to the temperature difference between the two surfaces. Various correction factors are listed in Table 91 which account for different types of glass and shading and deviations from indoor and outdoor design temperatures.

TABLE 80—TRANSMISSION COEFFICIENTS (*U*) FOR ROOFS & CEILINGS

In Btu per hr-ft²-°F

PITCHED ROOFS			Rafter Space				
			Unventilated—Uninsulated				Insulated
			Shingles				
			Asphalt		Tile	Wood	
			Sheathing				Any
			5/16″ ply	25/32″ wood		1 × 4 Strips	
Ceiling			Building Paper				
Finish	Backing	*R*	*.95*	*1.48*	*1.09*	*.87*	..
Upward Direction of Heat Flow (Winter Conditions)							
None	None	—	.57	.44	.53	.60	.66
None	Gyp. Bd. 3/8″	*.32*	.34	.29	.32	.35	.54
Plaster—lt. 1/2″	Gyp. lath 3/8″	*.64*	.30	.26	.29	.31	.46
Plaster—sd. 1/2″	Gyp. lath 3/8″	*.41*	.33	.28	.31	.34	.52
Plaster—lt. 3/4″	Metal lath	*.47*	.32	.27	.31	.33	.50
Plaster—sd. 3/4″	Metal lath	*.13*	.36	.30	.34	.37	.61
None	Insul. Bd. 1/2″	*1.43*	.25	.22	.24	.25	.34
Plaster—sd. 1/2″	Insul. Bd. lath	*1.52*	.24	.21	.23	.25	.33
Plaster—sd. 1/2″	Wood lath	*.40*	.33	.28	.31	.34	.52
Acous. Tile 1/2″	Gyp. Bd. 3/8″	*1.51*	.24	.21	.23	.25	.33
Acous. Tile 1/2″	Furring	*1.19*	.26	.23	.25	.27	.37
Acous. Tile 3/4″	Gyp. Bd. 3/8″	*2.10*	.21	.19	.20	.21	.26
Acous. Tile 3/4″	Furring	*1.78*	.23	.20	.22	.23	.30
Downward Direction of Heat Flow (Summer Conditions)							
None	None	—	.51	.40	.48	.53	.56
None	Gyp. Bd. 3/8″	*.32*	.30	.26	.29	.31	.47
Plaster—lt. 1/2″	Gyp. lath 3/8″	*.64*	.28	.24	.27	.28	.41
Plaster—sd. 1/2″	Gyp. lath 3/8″	*.41*	.29	.25	.28	.30	.45
Plaster—lt. 3/4″	Metal lath	*.47*	.29	.25	.28	.30	.44
Plaster—sd. 3/4″	Metal lath	*.13*	.32	.27	.31	.33	.52
None	Insul. Bd. 1/2″	*1.43*	.23	.20	.22	.23	.31
Plaster—sd. 1/2″	Insul. Bd. lath	*1.52*	.22	.20	.22	.23	.30
Plaster—sd. 1/2″	Wood lath	*.40*	.29	.26	.28	.30	.46
Acous. Tile 1/2″	Gyp. Bd. 3/8″	*1.51*	.22	.20	.22	.23	.30
Acous. Tile 1/2″	Furring	*1.19*	.24	.21	.23	.24	.34
Acous. Tile 3/4″	Gyp. Bd. 3/8″	*2.10*	.20	.18	.19	.20	.26
Acous. Tile 3/4″	Furring	*1.78*	.21	.19	.20	.21	.28

NOTE: Based on 15 mph outside winter (*.17*), 7½ mph outside summer (*.25*), still air inside (*.61 up—.92 down*), and air space if any (*.85 up—1.25 down*).

Adapted from the data of Handbook of Fundamentals, ASHRAE, 1967, p. 449.

TABLE 80 (Cont.)

TRANSMISSION COEFFICIENTS (*U*) FOR ROOFS & CEILINGS

In Btu per hr-ft²-°F

FLAT MASONRY ROOFS			Roofing (built-up over)					
			Concrete					
			Gravel Agg.			Lt. Wgt. Agg.		
Ceiling			4″	6″	8″	2″	3″	4″
Finish	Backing	*R*	*.32*	*.48*	*.64*	*2.22*	*3.33*	*4.44*
	Upward Direction of Heat Flow (Winter Conditions)							
None	None	—	.70	.63	.57	.30	.23	.18
None	Sus. Gp. Bd. ⅜″	*.32*	.38	.36	.34	.22	.18	.15
Plaster—lt. ½″	Sus. Gp. Bd. ⅜″	*.64*	.34	.32	.31	.21	.17	.14
Plaster—sd. ½″	Sus. Gp. Bd. ⅜″	*.41*	.37	.35	.33	.22	.18	.15
Plaster—lt. ¾″	Sus. Metal lath	*.47*	.36	.34	.33	.22	.17	.15
Plaster—sd. ¾″	Sus. Metal lath	*.13*	.41	.39	.37	.23	.18	.15
Acous. Tile ½″	Gyp. Bd. ⅜″	*1.51*	.26	.25	.24	.18	.15	.13
Acous. Tile ½″	Fur. or Chan.	*1.19*	.29	.27	.26	.19	.15	.13
Acous. Tile ¾″	Gyp. Bd. ⅜″	*2.10*	.23	.22	.21	.16	.14	.12
Acous. Tile ¾″	Fur. or Chan.	*1.78*	.25	.24	.23	.17	.14	.12
	Downward Direction of Heat Flow (Summer Conditions)							
None	None	—	.55	.51	.47	.27	.21	.17
None	Sus. Gp. Bd. ⅜″	*.32*	.30	.28	.27	.19	.16	.13
Plaster—lt. ½″	Sus. Gp. Bd. ⅜″	*.64*	.27	.26	.25	.18	.15	.13
Plaster—sd. ½″	Sus. Gp. Bd. ⅜″	*.41*	.29	.28	.26	.19	.15	.13
Plaster—lt. ¾″	Sus. Metal lath	*.47*	.28	.27	.26	.18	.15	.13
Plaster—sd. ¾″	Sus. Metal lath	*.13*	.31	.30	.29	.20	.16	.14
Acous. Tile ½″	Gyp. Bd. ⅜″	*1.51*	.22	.21	.20	.15	.13	.12
Acous. Tile ½″	Fur. or Chan.	*1.19*	.24	.23	.22	.16	.14	.12
Acous. Tile ¾″	Gyp. Bd. ⅜″	*2.10*	.19	.19	.18	.14	.12	.11
Acous. Tile ¾″	Fur. or Chan.	*1.78*	.21	.20	.19	.15	.13	.11

NOTE: Based on 15 mph outside winter (*.17*), 7½ mph outside summer (*.25*), still air inside (*.61 up—.92 down*), and air space if any (*.85 up—1.25 down*).

Adapted from the data of Handbook of Fundamentals, ASHRAE, 1967, pp. 445-446.

TABLE 80 (Cont.)

TRANSMISSION COEFFICIENTS (*U*) FOR ROOFS & CEILINGS

In Btu per hr-ft²-°F

FLAT WOOD OR METAL ROOFS			Rafter Construction					
			Roofing (built-up over)					
			Wood Deck			Wd. Fib. Slbs.		Metal Deck
Ceiling			21/32″	1 5/8″	2 5/8″	2″	3″	
Finish	Backing	*R*	*.98*	*2.03*	*3.23*	*3.6*	*5.4*	—
	Upward Direction of Heat Flow (Winter Conditions)							
None	None	—	.48	.32	.23	.21	.15	.90
None	Gyp. Bd. 3/8″	*.32*	.31	.23	.18	.17	.13	.44
Plaster—lt. 1/2″	Gyp. Bd. 3/8″	*.64*	.28	.22	.17	.16	.13	.38
Plaster—sd. 1/2″	Gyp. Bd. 3/8″	*.41*	.30	.23	.18	.17	.13	.42
Plaster—lt. 3/4″	Metal lath	*.47*	.29	.22	.18	.17	.13	.41
Plaster—sd. 3/4″	Metal lath	*.13*	.33	.24	.19	.18	.13	.48
Pl. or Plast. sd. 1/2″	Insul. Bd. 1/2″	*1.47*	.23	.18	.15	.14	.11	.29
Acous. Tile 1/2″	Gyp. Bd. 3/8″	*1.51*	.22	.18	.15	.14	.11	.29
Acous. Tile 1/2″	Furring	*1.19*	.24	.19	.16	.15	.12	.32
Acous. Tile 3/4″	Gyp. Bd. 3/8″	*2.10*	.20	.16	.14	.13	.11	.25
Acous. Tile 3/4″	Furring	*1.78*	.21	.17	.14	.14	.11	.27
	Downward Direction of Heat Flow (Summer Conditions)							
None	None	—	.40	.28	.21	.20	.14	.67
None	Gyp. Bd. 3/8″	*.32*	.25	.20	.16	.15	.12	.33
Plaster—lt. 1/2″	Gyp. Bd. 3/8″	*.64*	.23	.19	.15	.14	.11	.30
Plaster—sd. 1/2″	Gyp. Bd. 3/8″	*.41*	.24	.19	.16	.15	.12	.32
Plaster—lt. 3/4″	Metal lath	*.47*	.24	.19	.15	.15	.12	.31
Plaster—sd. 3/4″	Metal lath	*.13*	.26	.20	.16	.15	.12	.35
Pl. or Plast. sd. 1/2″	Insul. Bd. 1/2″	*1.47*	.19	.16	.13	.13	.10	.24
Acous. Tile 1/2″	Gyp. Bd. 3/8″	*1.51*	.19	.16	.13	.13	.10	.24
Acous. Tile 1/2″	Furring	*1.19*	.20	.17	.14	.13	.11	.26
Acous. Tile 3/4″	Gyp. Bd. 3/8″	*2.10*	.17	.15	.12	.12	.10	.21
Acous. Tile 3/4″	Furring	*1.78*	.18	.15	.13	.12	.10	.22

NOTE: Based on 15 mph outside winter (*.17*), 7½ mph outside summer (*.25*), still air inside (*.61 up—.92 down*), and air space if any (*.85 up—1.25 down*).

Adapted from the data of Handbook of Fundamentals, ASHRAE, 1967, pp. 447-448.

TABLE 81—TRANSMISSION COEFFICIENTS (*U*) FOR WALLS

In Btu per hr-ft²-°F

Over-all coefficients given for OUTSIDE WALLS without interior finishing. Insert values in Table 82 to obtain value with interior finish.

FRAME CONSTRUCTION		Sheathing						
		None	Bldg. Pap.	Ply-wood 5/16″	Gyp. Bd. 1/2″	Pap. & Wd. 25/32″	Insulation Board 1/2″	Insulation Board 25/32″
Exterior Finish	*R*	*.00*	*.06*	*.39*	*.45*	*1.04*	*1.32*	*2.06*
Asphalt Insul. Siding	*1.45*	.43	.42	.37	.36	.30	.28	.23
Wood Panels, 3/4″	*.94*	.56	.54	.46	.45	.35	.32	.26
Wood Shingles, 5/8″	*.87*	—	—	.47	.46	.36	.33	.26
Wood Siding, 5/8″	*.80*	.61	.58	.49	.48	.37	.34	.27
Plywood, 3/8″	*.47*	.76	.72	.58	.57	.42	.38	.30
Brick Veneer, 4″	*.44*	—	—	.60	.57	.43	.38	.30
Cut Stone Veneer, 4″	*.32*	—	—	.64	.62	.45	.40	.31
Asb. Cement Siding	*.21*	—	—	.69	.66	.48	.42	.32
Stucco, 1″	*.20*	—	—	.69	.67	.48	.42	.32
Asphalt Roll Siding	*.15*	—	—	.72	.69	.49	.43	.33
Met. Curtain—Flat Sheet	*neg.*	1.18	1.10	.81	.77	.53	.46	.34
Met. Siding—Not Flat	*neg.*	1.30†	—	.51*	.49*	.38*	.34*	.27*

Air space assumed @ 20°F and 1/4″ avg. (.73*).
†Corrugations, etc. 10% greater area than flat.

MASONRY WALLS				Facing (4″ unless otherwise specified)						
				No Add.	Cut Stone	Face Brick	8″ Slab Conc.	Conc. Block	Com. Brick	Cind. Block
Wall or Backing	Thk.	Cav.	*R*	*.00*	*.32*	*.44*	*.64*	*.71*	*.80*	*1.11*
Common Brick	4″	*.97*	*.80*	—	—	.33	—	.30	.29	.27
	4″	—	*.80*	.61	.48	.46	.42	.41	.39	.35
	8″	—	*1.60*	.41	.35	.33	.31	.31	.30	.27
	12″	—	*2.40*	.31	.27	.26	.25	.25	.24	.22
Hollow Clay Tile	4″	*.97*	*1.11*	—	—	.30	—	.27	.27	.25
	4″	—	*1.11*	.51	.42	.40	.37	.36	.35	.32
	8″	—	*1.85*	.37	.32	.31	.29	.28	.28	.26
	12″	—	*2.50*	.30	.27	.26	.24	.24	.24	.22
Concrete Block	4″	*.97*	*.71*	—	—	.34	—	.31	.30	.27
	4″	—	*.71*	.64	.51	.48	.43	.42	.41	.36
	8″	—	*1.11*	.51	.42	.40	.37	.36	.35	.32
	12″	—	*1.28*	.47	.39	.38	.35	.34	.33	.30
Cinder Block	4″	*.97*	*1.11*	—	—	.30	—	.27	.27	.25
	4″	—	*1.11*	.51	.42	.40	.37	.36	.35	.32
	8″	—	*1.72*	.39	.33	.32	.30	.30	.29	.26
	12″	—	*1.89*	.36	.32	.30	.29	.28	.27	.25
Light weight Block	4″	*.97*	*1.50*	—	—	.27	—	.25	.24	.23
	4″	—	*1.50*	.43	.36	.35	.32	.32	.31	.28
	8″	—	*2.00*	.35	.31	.30	.28	.27	.27	.25
	12″	—	*2.27*	.32	.28	.27	.26	.25	.25	.23
Poured Concrete	6″	—	*.48*	.75	.57	.53	—	.47	.45	.39
	8″	—	*.64*	.69	.52	.49	—	.43	.42	.37
Concrete or Stone	10″	—	*.80*	.61	—	—	—	—	—	—
	12″	—	*.96*	.55	—	—	—	—	—	—
Limestone/ Sandstone	16″	—	*1.28*	.47	—	—	—	—	—	—
	24″	—	*1.92*	.36	—	—	—	—	—	—

NOTE: Based on 1/2″ mortar (*.10*) between facing and backing, 15 MPH outside (*.17*); still air inside (*.68*).

Adapted from the data of Handbook of Fundamentals, ASHRAE, 1967, pp. 435-438.

TABLE 82—TRANSMISSION COEFFICIENTS—(*U*) FOR WALLS

In Btu per hr-ft^2-°F

Over-all coefficients given for INTERIOR FINISHES for various outside wall coefficients

Outside Wall Table 81		Type Lath and Plaster on Frame or Furring								Wood Panels on Frame		5/8″ Plaster on Masonry	
		Gypsum Lath			Metal Lath		Wood	1/2″ Ins. Bd.					
		NP	LWP	SP	LWP	SP	SP	NP	SP	3/4″	1/4″	LWP	SP
U	*R*	*.32*	*.64*	*.41*	*.47*	*.13*	*.40*	*1.43*	*1.52*	*.94*	*.31*	*.39*	*.11*
.22	*4.54*	.21	.19	.20	.20	.21	.20	.17	.16	.18	.21	.20	.22
.23	*4.35*	.21	.20	.21	.21	.22	.21	.17	.17	.19	.21	.21	.22
.24	*4.16*	.22	.21	.22	.22	.23	.22	.18	.18	.20	.22	.22	.23
.25	*4.00*	.23	.22	.23	.22	.24	.23	.18	.18	.20	.23	.23	.24
.26	*3.85*	.24	.22	.23	.23	.25	.24	.19	.19	.21	.24	.24	.25
.27	*3.70*	.25	.23	.24	.24	.26	.24	.20	.19	.22	.25	.24	.26
.28	*3.57*	.26	.24	.25	.25	.27	.25	.20	.20	.22	.26	.25	.27
.29	*3.45*	.26	.24	.26	.26	.28	.26	.20	.20	.23	.27	.26	.28
.30	*3.33*	.27	.25	.27	.27	.29	.27	.21	.21	.23	.27	.27	.29
.31	*3.23*	.28	.26	.27	.27	.30	.27	.21	.21	.24	.28	.28	.30
.32	*3.13*	.29	.27	.28	.28	.31	.28	.22	.21	.25	.29	.28	.31
.33	*3.03*	.30	.27	.29	.29	.32	.29	.22	.22	.25	.30	.29	.32
.34	*2.94*	.31	.28	.30	.29	.33	.30	.23	.22	.26	.31	.30	.33
.35	*2.86*	.31	.29	.31	.30	.33	.31	.23	.23	.26	.32	.31	.34
.36	*2.78*	.32	.29	.31	.31	.34	.31	.24	.23	.27	.32	.32	.35
.37	*2.70*	.33	.30	.32	.32	.35	.32	.24	.24	.27	.33	.32	.36
.38	*2.63*	.34	.31	.33	.32	.36	.33	.25	.24	.28	.34	.33	.37
.39	*2.56*	.35	.31	.34	.33	.37	.34	.25	.25	.29	.35	.34	.37
.40	*2.50*	.35	.32	.34	.34	.38	.34	.25	.25	.29	.36	.35	.38
.41	*2.44*	.36	.32	.35	.34	.39	.35	.26	.25	.30	.36	.35	.39
.42	*2.38*	.37	.33	.36	.35	.40	.36	.26	.26	.30	.37	.36	.40
.43	*2.32*	.38	.34	.37	.36	.41	.37	.27	.26	.31	.38	.37	.41
.45	*2.22*	.39	.35	.38	.37	.42	.38	.27	.27	.32	.39	.38	.43
.46	*2.17*	.40	.36	.39	.38	.43	.39	.28	.27	.32	.40	.39	.44
.47	*2.13*	.41	.36	.39	.38	.44	.39	.28	.27	.33	.41	.40	.45
.48	*2.08*	.42	.37	.40	.39	.45	.40	.28	.28	.33	.42	.40	.46
.49	*2.04*	.42	.37	.41	.40	.46	.41	.29	.28	.34	.43	.41	.47
.51	*1.96*	.44	.38	.42	.41	.48	.42	.29	.29	.34	.44	.42	.48
.52	*1.92*	.45	.39	.43	.42	.49	.43	.30	.29	.35	.45	.43	.49
.53	*1.89*	.45	.39	.43	.42	.50	.44	.30	.29	.35	.45	.44	.50
.54	*1.85*	.46	.40	.44	.43	.51	.44	.30	.30	.36	.46	.44	.51
.55	*1.82*	.47	.41	.45	.44	.51	.45	.31	.30	.36	.47	.45	.52
.56	*1.79*	.47	.41	.45	.44	.52	.46	.31	.30	.37	.48	.46	.53
.57	*1.75*	.48	.42	.46	.45	.53	.47	.31	.31	.37	.49	.47	.54
.58	*1.72*	.49	.42	.47	.46	.54	.47	.32	.31	.38	.49	.47	.55
.60	*1.67*	.50	.43	.48	.47	.56	.48	.32	.31	.38	.50	.49	.56
.61	*1.64*	.51	.44	.49	.47	.57	.49	.33	.32	.39	.51	.49	.57
.62	*1.61*	.52	.45	.50	.48	.58	.50	.33	.32	.39	.52	.50	.58
.64	*1.56*	.53	.46	.51	.49	.59	.51	.33	.32	.40	.53	.51	.60
.66	*1.52*	.54	.47	.52	.50	.61	.52	.34	.33	.41	.55	.52	.62
.67	*1.49*	.55	.47	.53	.51	.61	.53	.34	.33	.41	.56	.53	.63
.69	*1.45*	.56	.48	.54	.52	.63	.54	.35	.34	.42	.57	.54	.64
.72	*1.39*	.58	.49	.56	.54	.66	.56	.35	.34	.43	.59	.56	.67
.75	*1.33*	.60	.51	.57	.56	.68	.58	.36	.35	.44	.61	.58	.69
.76	*1.32*	.61	.51	.58	.56	.69	.58	.36	.35	.44	.61	.58	.70
.77	*1.30*	.62	.51	.59	.56	.70	.59	.37	.35	.45	.62	.59	.71
.81	*1.23*	.64	.53	.61	.59	.74	.61	.38	.36	.46	.65	.62	.75
1.10	*.91*	.81	.65	.76	.73	.96	.76	.43	.41	.54	.81	.77	.99
1.18	*.85*	.85	.67	.79	.76	1.02	.80	.44	.42	.56	.86	.80	1.04
1.30	*.77*	.92	.71	.85	.51	1.11	.85	.45	.44	.59	.93	.86	1.14

Code: NP = No Plaster. LWP = Lightweight Plaster. SP = Sand Plaster.

Adapted from the data of Handbook of Fundamentals, ASHRAE, 1967, pp. 435-440.

TABLE 83—TRANSMISSION COEFFICIENTS—(*U*) FOR INSULATION

In Btu per hr-ft²-°F

Value of U Without Insulation	Roof Insulation—Nominal Thickness						Batt or Fill—Actual Thickness			
	½″	1″	1½″	2″	2½″	3″	½″	1″	1½″	2″
	Actual Thickness Adjusted to R as follows						Fibrous Material R for k = .27			
	1.39	*2.78*	*4.17*	*5.26*	*6.67*	*8.33*	*1.85*	*3.70*	*5.55*	*7.40*
.08	.07	.07	.06	.06	.05	.05	.07	.06	.06	.05
.10	.09	.08	.07	.07	.06	.06	.08	.07	.06	.06
.12	.10	.09	.08	.07	.07	.06	.10	.08	.07	.06
.14	.12	.10	.09	.08	.07	.07	.11	.09	.08	.07
.16	.13	.11	.10	.09	.08	.07	.12	.10	.09	.07
.18	.14	.12	.10	.09	.08	.07	.14	.11	.09	.08
.20	.16	.13	.11	.10	.09	.08	.15	.12	.10	.08
.22	.17	.14	.12	.10	.09	.08	.16	.12	.10	.08
.24	.18	.14	.12	.11	.09	.08	.17	.13	.10	.09
.26	.19	.15	.12	.11	.10	.08	.18	.13	.11	.09
.28	.20	.16	.13	.11	.10	.08	.18	.14	.11	.09
.30	.21	.16	.13	.12	.10	.09	.19	.14	.11	.09
.32	.22	.17	.14	.12	.10	.09	.20	.15	.12	.10
.34	.23	.18	.14	.12	.10	.09	.21	.15	.12	.10
.36	.24	.18	.14	.12	.11	.09	.22	.15	.12	.10
.38	.25	.19	.15	.13	.11	.09	.22	.16	.12	.10
.40	.26	.19	.15	.13	.11	.09	.23	.16	.12	.10
.45	.28	.20	.16	.13	.11	.10	.25	.17	.13	.10
.50	.29	.21	.16	.14	.12	.10	.26	.18	.13	.11
.55	.31	.22	.17	.14	.12	.10	.27	.18	.14	.11
.60	.33	.22	.17	.14	.12	.10	.28	.19	.14	.11
.65	.34	.23	.18	.15	.12	.10	.29	.19	.14	.11
.70	.35	.24	.18	.15	.12	.10	.30	.20	.14	.11
.75	.37	.24	.18	.15	.13	.10	.31	.20	.15	.11
.80	.38	.25	.19	.15	.13	.10	.32	.20	.15	.12
.85	.39	.25	.19	.16	.13	.11	.33	.20	.15	.12
.90	.40	.26	.19	.16	.13	.11	.34	.21	.15	.12
1.00	.42	.26	.19	.16	.13	.11	.35	.21	.15	.12
1.10	.43	.27	.20	.16	.13	.11	.36	.22	.16	.12

Adapted from the data of Handbook of Fundamentals, ASHRAE, 1967, pp. 450-451.

TABLE 84—TRANSMISSION COEFFICIENTS—(*U*) FOR GLASS, ETC.

In Btu per hr-ft²-°F

VERTICAL GLASS SHEETS

Number of Sheets	One	Two			Three		
Air Space, inches	None	¼	½	1	¼	½	1
Outdoor exposure	1.13	0.61	0.55	0.53	0.41	0.36	0.34
Indoor exposure	0.75	0.50	0.46	0.45	0.38	0.33	0.32

HORIZONTAL GLASS SHEETS

	Heat Flow Up				Heat Flow Down			
Number of Sheets	One	Two			One	Two		
Air space, inches	None	¼	½	1	None	¼	½	1
Outdoor exposure	1.40	0.70	0.66	0.63	—	—	—	—
Indoor exposure	0.96	0.59	0.56	0.56	0.60	0.43	0.39	0.38

WALLS OF HOLLOW GLASS BLOCK

Description	Outdoor Exposure	Indoor Partition
5¾ × 5¾ × 3⅞ in. thick	0.60	0.46
7¾ × 7¾ × 3⅞ in. thick	0.56	0.44
11¾ × 11¾ × 3⅞ in. thick	0.52	0.40
7¾ × 7¾ × 3⅞ in. thick with glass fiber dividing the cavity	0.48	0.38
11¾ × 11¾ × 3⅞ in. thick with glass fiber dividing the cavity	0.44	0.36

APPROXIMATE APPLICATION FACTORS FOR WINDOWS

(Multiply Flat Glass *U* Values by These Factors)

Window Description	Single Glass		Double Glass		Windows With Storm Sash	
	Percent Glass	Factor	Percent Glass	Factor	Percent Glass	Factor
Sheets	100	1.00	100	1.00	—	—
Wood sash	80	0.90	80	0.95	80	0.90
Wood sash	60	0.80	60	0.85	60	0.80
Steel sash	80	1.00	80	1.20	80	1.00
Aluminum	80	1.10	80	1.30	80	1.10

SOLID WOOD DOORS

Nominal Thickness Inches	Actual Thickness Inches	*U* Exposed Door	*U* With Glass Storm Door
1	25/32	0.64	0.37
1¼	1 1/16	0.55	0.34
1½	1 5/16	0.49	0.32
1¾	1⅜	0.48	0.31
2	1⅝	0.43	0.28
2½	2⅛	0.36	0.26
3	2⅝	0.31	0.23

Adapted from the data of Handbook of Fundamentals, ASHRAE, 1967, p. 453.

TABLE 85—TRANSMISSION COEFFICIENTS (*U*) FOR FLOORS & CEILINGS

In Btu per hr-ft²-°F

FRAME CONSTRUCTION			Sub-Flooring					
			None	25/32″	25/32″ and Felt			
			Flooring					
Ceiling			None	None	½″ Cer. Tile	¾″ Hard	⅝″ Ply. & Tile	⅜″ Ins. & Tile
Finish	Backing	*R*	—	*.98*	*1.38*	*1.72*	*1.87*	*2.26*
Upward Direction of Heat Flow (Winter Conditions)								
None	None	—	—	.45	.38	.34	.31	.28
None	Gyp. Bd. ⅜″	*.32*	.65	.30	.27	.24	.23	.21
Plaster—lt. ½″	Gyp. lath ⅜″	*.64*	.54	.27	.24	.23	.21	.20
Plaster—sd. ½″	Gyp. lath ⅜″	*.41*	.61	.29	.26	.24	.22	.21
Plaster—lt. ¾″	Metal lath	*.47*	.59	.28	.26	.23	.22	.20
Plaster—sd. ¾″	Metal lath	*.13*	.74	.31	.28	.26	.24	.22
None	Insul. Bd. ½″	*1.43*	.38	.22	.20	.19	.18	.17
Plaster—sd. ½″	Insul. Bd. ½″	*1.52*	.36	.22	.20	.19	.18	.17
Plaster—sd. ½″	Wood lath	*.40*	.62	.29	.26	.24	.22	.21
Acous. tile ½″	Gyp. Bd. ⅜″	*1.51*	.37	.22	.20	.19	.18	.17
Acous. tile ½″	Furring	*1.19*	.41	.24	.22	.20	.19	.18
Acous. tile ¾″	Gyp. Bd. ⅜″	*2.10*	.30	.19	..18	.17	.16	.15
Acous. tile ¾″	Furring	*1.78*	.33	.21	.19	.18	.17	.16
Downward Direction of Heat Flow (Summer Conditions)								
None	None	—	—	.35	.31	.28	.26	.24
None	Gyp. Bd. ⅜″	*.32*	.46	.23	.21	.20	.18	.17
Plaster—lt. ½″	Gyp. lath ⅜″	*.64*	.40	.21	.20	.18	.17	.16
Plaster—sd. ½″	Gyp. lath ⅜″	*.41*	.44	.22	.21	.19	.18	.17
Plaster—lt. ¾″	Metal lath	*.47*	.43	.22	.20	.19	.18	.17
Plaster—sd. ¾″	Metal lath	*.13*	.51	.24	.22	.20	.19	.18
None	Insul. Bd. ½″	*1.43*	.31	.18	.17	.16	.15	.15
Plaster—sd. ½″	Insul. Bd. ½″	*1.52*	.30	.18	.17	.16	.15	.14
Plaster—sd. ½″	Wood lath	*.40*	.45	.22	.21	.19	.18	.17
Acous. tile ½″	Gyp. Bd. ⅜″	*1.51*	.30	.18	.17	.16	.15	.14
Acous. tile ½″	Furring	*1.19*	.33	.19	.18	.17	.16	.15
Acous. tile ¾″	Gyp. Bd. ⅜″	*2.10*	.25	.16	.15	.15	.14	.13
Acous. tile ¾″	Furring	*1.78*	.28	.17	.16	.15	.15	.14

NOTE: Based on still air both sides (*.61 up/.92 down*) air space if any 8″ (*.85 up/1.25 down*).

Adapted from the data of Handbook of Fundamentals, ASHRAE, 1967, p. 442.

TABLE 85 (Cont.)
TRANSMISSION COEFFICIENTS (*U*) FOR FLOORS & CEILINGS

In Btu per hr-ft²-°F

CONCRETE DECK CONSTRUCTION			Thickness of Deck					
			4″	8″	4″	4″	4″	4″
			Flooring					
Ceiling			Dk. Only	Dk. Only	⅛″ Tile	13/16″ Wood Block	Ply, Felt, Tile	Wood, Felt, Hdwd.
Finish	Backing	*R*	*.32*	*.64*	*.37*	*1.06*	*1.21*	*2.04*
Upward Direction of Heat Flow (Winter Conditions)								
None	None	—	.65	.54	.63	.44	.41	.31
Plaster—lt. ⅛″	None	*.08*	.62	.52	.60	.42	.40	.30
Acous. tile ½″	None	*1.19*	.37	.33	.36	.29	.28	.22
None	Susp. Gyp. ⅜″	*.32*	.37	.33	.36	.29	.28	.23
Plaster—lt. ½″	Susp. Gyp. ⅜″	*.64*	.33	.30	.33	.27	.26	.21
Plaster—sd. ½″	Susp. Gyp. ⅜″	*.41*	.36	.32	.35	.28	.27	.22
Plaster—lt. ¾″	Susp. metal lath	*.47*	.35	.31	.34	.28	.27	.22
Plaster—sd. ¾″	Susp. metal lath	*.13*	.40	.35	.39	.31	.29	.24
Acous. tile ½″	Susp. Gyp. ⅜″	*1.51*	.26	.24	.25	.22	.21	.18
Acous. tile ½″	Fur. or Chan.	*1.19*	.28	.26	.28	.23	.22	.19
Acous. tile ¾″	Susp. Gyp. ⅜″	*2.10*	.22	.21	.22	.19	.19	.16
Acous. tile ¾″	Fur. or Chan.	*1.78*	.24	.22	.24	.20	.20	.17
Downward Direction of Heat Flow (Summer Conditions)								
None	None	—	.46	.40	.45	.34	.33	.26
Plaster—lt. ⅛″	None	*.08*	.45	.39	.44	.34	.32	.26
Acous. tile ½″	None	*1.19*	.30	.27	.29	.24	.24	.20
None	Susp. Gyp. ⅜″	*.32*	.27	.25	.26	.22	.22	.18
Plaster—lt. ½″	Susp. Gyp. ⅜″	*.64*	.25	.23	.24	.21	.20	.17
Plaster—sd. ½″	Susp. Gyp. ⅜″	*.41*	.26	.24	.26	.22	.21	.18
Plaster—lt. ¾″	Susp. metal lath	*.47*	.26	.24	.25	.22	.21	.18
Plaster—sd. ¾″	Susp. metal lath	*.13*	.28	.26	.28	.23	.23	.19
Acous. tile ½″	Susp. Gyp. ⅜″	*1.51*	.20	.19	.20	.18	.17	.15
Acous. tile ½″	Fur. or Chan.	*1.19*	.22	.20	.22	.19	.18	.16
Acous. tile ¾″	Susp. Gyp. ⅜″	*2.10*	.18	.17	.18	.16	.16	.14
Acous. tile ¾″	Fur. or Chan.	*1.78*	.19	.18	.19	.17	.16	.14

NOTE: Based on still air both sides (*.61 up/.92 down*) air space if any 8″ (*.85 up/1.25 down*).

Adapted from the data of Handbook of Fundamentals, ASHRAE, 1967, pp. 443-444.

TABLE 86—TRANSMISSION COEFFICIENTS—(*U*) FOR PARTITIONS

In Btu per hr-ft²-°F

PARTITIONS			Surface Finish						
			One Side			Both Sides			
			NP	SP	LWP	NP	SP	LWP	Plaster Thickness
		R	*.00*	*.20 in.*	*.64 in.*	*.00*	*.20 in.*	*.64 in.*	
FRAME CONSTRUCTION									
Gypsum board or lath	⅜″	*.32*	.60	.56	.50	.34	.32	.28	½″
Wood lath	¼″	*.30*	—	.57	—	—	.32	—	½″
Insulation board	½″	*1.43*	.36	.35	—	.19	.19	—	½″
Metal lath	—	—	—	.67	.55	—	.39	.31	¾″
Plywood	¼″	*.31*	.60	—	—	.34	—	—	—
Plywood	⅜″	*.47*	.55	—	—	.31	—	—	—
Plywood	½″	*.63*	.50	—	—	.28	—	—	—
Wood panels	¾″	*.94*	.43	—	—	.24	—	—	—
Metal panels	—	—	.74	—	—	.43	—	—	—
MASONRY									
Common brick	4″	*.80*	.46	.44	.39	.46	.42	.34	⅝″
Concrete block	4″	*.71*	.48	.46	.40	.48	.43	.35	⅝″
Concrete block	8″	*1.11*	.40	.39	.35	.40	.37	.31	⅝″
Concrete block	12″	*1.28*	.38	.36	.33	.38	.35	.29	⅝″
Cinder block	3″	*.86*	.45	.43	.38	.45	.41	.33	⅝″
Cinder block	4″	*1.11*	.41	.39	.35	.41	.37	.31	⅝″
Cinder block	8″	*1.72*	.32	.31	.29	.32	.30	.26	⅝″
Cinder block	12″	*1.89*	.31	.30	.27	.31	.29	.25	⅝″
Light weight block	3″	*1.27*	.38	.36	.33	.38	.35	.30	⅝″
Light weight block	4″	*1.50*	.35	.34	.31	.35	.32	.27	⅝″
Light weight block	8″	*2.00*	.30	.29	.27	.30	.28	.24	⅝″
Light weight block	12″	*2.27*	.28	.27	.25	.28	.26	.23	⅝″
Hollow clay tile	3″	*.80*	.46	.44	.39	.46	.42	.34	⅝″
Hollow clay tile	4″	*1.11*	.41	.39	.35	.41	.37	.31	⅝″
Hollow clay tile	6″	*1.52*	.35	.33	.31	.35	.32	.27	⅝″
Hollow clay tile	8″	*1.85*	.31	.30	.28	.31	.29	.25	⅝″
Hollow gypsum tile	3″	*1.35*	.37	.35	.32	.37	.34	.29	⅝″
Hollow gypsum tile	4″	*1.67*	.33	.32	.29	.33	.31	.26	⅝″

NOTE: Based on still air both sides (*.68*).

NP = No Plaster. SP = Sand Plaster. LWP = Light Weight Plaster.

Adapted from the data of Handbook of Fundamentals, ASHRAE, 1967, pp. 438 & 441.

TABLE 87

TRANSMISSION RATES—(*TH*) FOR CONCRETE ON OR BELOW GRADE

BELOW GRADE (Based on U = 0.10, Temp. = 70° Inside)

Ground Temp.	Btu/hr per sq ft Floor	Btu/hr per sq ft Wall
40°F	3.0	6.0
50°F	2.0	4.0
60°F	1.0	2.0

ON GRADE—UNHEATED FLOORS in Btu/hr per ft—Exposed Edge

Outdoor Design	No Edge Insul. 	1″ Edge Insul. 
0 to −10°F	60	50
−10 to −20°F	65	55
−20 to −30°F	75	60

Outdoor Design	1″ Edge Insul. 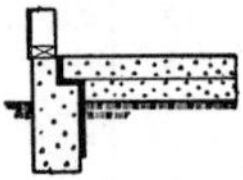	2″ Edge Insul. 
0 to −10°F	45	40
−10 to −20°F	50	45
−20 to −30°F	55	50

ON GRADE—HEATED FLOORS in Btu/hr per ft—Exposed Edge

Outdoor Design	1″ × 18″ Vert. Insul.	1″ × 12″ Vert. × 12″ Horiz. Insul.	2″ × 12″ Vert. × 12″ Horiz. Insul.
0 to −10°F	85	80	65
−10 to −20°F	95	90	75
−20 to −30°F	105	100	85

Adapted from the data of Handbook of Fundamentals, ASHRAE, 1967, pp. 460-461.

TABLE 88—ETD'S FOR SUN EFFECT ON ROOFS IN °F

ROOFS		SUN TIME								
		A.M.			P.M.					
Construction	Description	8	10	12	2	4	6	8	10	12
Roofs—Exposed to Sun										
Light	1″ Wood	12	38	54	62	50	26	10	4	0
Med. Lt.	2″ Concrete	6	30	48	58	50	32	14	6	2
Medium	2″ Gypsum	0	20	40	52	54	42	20	10	6
Med. Hvy.	4″ Concrete	0	20	38	50	52	40	22	12	6
Heavy	6″ Concrete	5	6	22	36	44	44	33	19	13
Roofs—Water Covered—Exposed to Sun										
Light	1″ Water	0	4	16	22	18	14	10	2	0
Heavy	1″ Water	−2	−2	−4	10	14	16	14	10	6
Any	6″ Water	−2	0	0	6	10	10	8	4	0
Roofs—Water Sprayed—Exposed to Sun										
Light	Sprays	0	4	12	18	16	14	10	2	0
Heavy	Sprays	−2	−2	2	8	12	14	12	10	6
Roofs in Shade										
Light	Shade	−4	0	6	12	14	12	8	2	0
Medium	Shade	−4	−2	2	8	12	12	10	6	2
Heavy	Shade	−2	−2	0	4	8	10	10	8	4

Basic Value Listed for:

1. Construction listed and normal finish.
2. Dark colored exterior.
3. August 1 in 40° N. latitude.
4. 20° outdoor degree range daily (95° max. 75° min. 84° mean).
5. 15° outdoor-indoor difference. 95° outside—80° room.

Corrections for other Conditions:

1. None for similar construction with or without 2″ insulation.
2. 55%/80% difference in values between sun and shade for light and medium colors.
3. None for hot months up to 50° latitude.
4. Add/subtract 1° ETD for each 2° less or greater than daily range.
5. Add/subtract 1° ETD for each 1° greater or less than outside-inside difference.

Adapted from the data of "Heating, Ventilating and Air Conditioning Guide," ASHRAE, 1960, pp. 190-191.

TABLE 89—ETD'S FOR SUN EFFECT ON WALLS IN °F

North Latitude Wall Facing	SUN TIME								
	A.M.			P.M.					
	8	10	12	2	4	6	8	10	12
Frame									
NE	22	24	14	12	14	14	10	6	2
E	30	36	32	12	14	14	10	6	2
SE	13	26	28	24	16	14	10	6	2
S	−4	4	22	30	26	16	10	6	2
SW	−4	0	6	26	40	42	24	6	2
W	−4	0	6	20	40	48	22	8	2
NW	−4	0	6	12	24	40	34	6	2
N (Shade)	−4	−2	4	10	14	12	8	4	0

Adapted from the data of "Heating, Ventilating and Air Conditioning Guide," ASHRAE, 1960, pp. 192-193.

(Table 89 continued on next page.)

TABLE 89 (Cont.) ETD'S FOR SUN EFFECT ON WALLS IN °F

North Latitude Wall Facing	SUN TIME								
	A.M.			P.M.					
	8	10	12	2	4	6	8	10	12
4 In. Brick or Stone Veneer and Frame									
NE	−2	24	20	10	12	14	12	10	6
E	2	30	31	14	12	14	12	10	6
SE	2	20	28	26	18	14	12	10	6
S	−4	−2	12	24	26	20	12	8	4
SW	0	0	2	12	32	36	34	10	6
W	0	0	4	10	26	40	42	16	6
NW	−4	−2	2	8	12	30	34	12	6
N (Shade)	−4	−2	0	6	10	12	12	8	4
8 In. Hollow Tile or 8 In. Cinder Block									
NE	0	0	20	16	10	12	14	12	8
E	4	12	24	26	20	12	14	14	10
SE	2	2	16	20	20	14	14	12	8
S	0	0	2	12	24	26	20	12	8
SW	2	2	2	6	12	26	30	26	8
W	4	4	4	6	10	18	30	32	18
NW	0	0	2	4	8	12	22	30	10
N (Shade)	−2	−2	−2	0	6	10	10	10	6
8 In. Brick or 12 In. Hollow Tile or 12 In. Cinder Block									
NE	2	2	10	16	14	10	10	10	10
E	8	8	14	18	18	14	14	14	12
SE	8	6	6	14	18	16	12	12	12
S	4	4	4	4	10	16	16	12	10
SW	8	6	6	8	10	12	20	24	20
W	8	6	6	8	10	14	20	24	24
NW	2	2	2	4	6	8	10	16	18
N (Shade)	0	0	0	0	2	6	8	8	6
12 In. Brick									
NE	8	8	8	8	10	12	12	10	10
E	12	12	12	10	12	14	14	14	14
SE	10	10	10	10	10	12	14	14	12
S	8	8	6	6	6	8	10	12	12
SW	10	10	10	10	10	10	10	12	14
W	12	12	12	10	10	10	10	12	16
NW	8	8	8	8	8	8	8	10	10
N (Shade)	4	2	2	2	2	2	2	4	6
8 In. Concrete or Stone or 6 In. or 8 In. Concrete Block									
NE	4	4	16	14	10	12	12	10	8
E	6	14	24	24	18	14	14	12	10
SE	6	6	16	18	18	14	12	12	10
S	2	2	4	12	16	18	14	10	8
SW	6	4	6	8	14	22	24	22	10
W	6	6	6	8	12	20	28	26	14
NW	4	4	4	4	6	12	20	22	8
N (Shade)	0	0	0	2	4	6	8	6	4
12 In. Concrete or Stone									
NE	6	6	6	14	14	10	10	12	10
E	10	8	10	18	18	16	12	14	14
SE	8	8	6	14	16	16	14	12	12
S	6	4	4	4	10	14	16	14	10
SW	8	8	6	6	8	10	18	20	18
W	10	8	8	10	10	12	16	24	22
NW	6	6	6	6	6	8	10	18	20
N (Shade)	0	0	0	0	2	4	6	8	6

Refer to Table 88 for Notes

TABLE 90—HEAT RATES (*TH*) FOR SUN EFFECT ON GLASS

In Btu per hr-ft²

40° N. Latitude—August 1—Clear Atmosphere

Sun Time	N	NE	E	SE	S	SW	W	NW	Hor.
RADIATION—⅛″ Common Window Glass									
6 AM	26	116	131	67	*7*	*6*	*6*	6	25
7	16	149	195	124	*11*	*10*	*10*	10	77
8	*14*	129	205	156	18	*12*	*12*	12	137
9	*15*	79	180	162	42	*14*	*14*	14	188
10	*16*	31	127	148	69	*16*	*16*	16	229
11	*17*	*18*	58	113	90	23	*17*	17	252
Noon	*17*	*17*	19	64	98	64	*19*	17	259
1 PM	*17*	*18*	58	113	90	23	*17*	17	252
2	*16*	31	127	148	69	*16*	*16*	16	229
3	*15*	79	180	162	42	*14*	*14*	14	188
4	*14*	129	205	156	18	*12*	*12*	12	137
5	16	149	195	124	*11*	*10*	*10*	10	77
6	26	116	131	67	*7*	*6*	*6*	6	25
7	3	7	6	2	*0*	*0*	*0*	0	1
CONVECTION—80° Indoor—Common Window Glass (outside temp. in parentheses)									
6 AM (74)	−5	−4	−4	−5	−5	−6	−6	−6	−5
7 (75)	−5	−2	−2	−3	−5	−5	−5	−5	−3
8 (77)	−3	0	1	0	−2	−3	−3	−3	0
9 (80)	0	2	4	3	1	0	0	0	3
10 (83)	3	4	6	6	5	3	3	3	8
11 (87)	8	8	10	11	10	9	8	8	13
Noon (90)	12	12	12	13	14	13	12	12	16
1 PM (93)	15	15	15	16	17	17	17	15	20
2 (94)	16	16	16	16	18	19	19	17	21
3 (95)	17	17	17	17	19	21	21	19	21
4 (94)	16	16	16	16	17	20	20	19	19
5 (93)	15	15	15	15	15	18	19	18	17
6 (91)	13	13	13	13	13	14	15	15	13
7 (87)	8	8	8	8	8	8	8	8	8
ABSORPTION—¼″ Heat Absorbing Plate Glass									
6 AM	4	16	18	9	1	1	1	1	3
7	2	24	30	20	2	2	2	2	11
8	2	22	33	25	2	2	2	2	21
9	2	16	30	29	8	3	3	3	32
10	3	5	25	27	14	3	3	3	37
11	3	3	12	21	18	3	3	3	42
Noon	3	3	3	15	19	12	3	3	45
1 PM	3	3	3	3	19	22	10	3	44
2	3	3	3	3	16	27	24	4	41
3	3	3	3	3	10	30	31	15	35
4	3	3	3	3	4	29	36	23	26
5	2	2	2	2	2	23	34	27	17
6	4	1	1	1	1	14	24	21	6
7	0	0	0	0	0	2	3	3	1

Italics indicate shaded glass.

Adapted from the data of "Heating, Ventilating and Air Conditioning Guide," ASHRAE, 1960, pp. 196-198.

TABLE 91—CORRECTIONS FOR SHADING, TYPE GLASS, ETC.

Glass Types and Combinations	Radiation	Convection	Absorption
Single Common Window	x1.00	x1.00	x .00
Single Regular Plate	x .87	x1.00	x .25
Single Heat Absorbent Plate	x .46	x1.00	x1.00
Double Common Window	x .85	x .60	x .10
Double Regular Plate	x .66	x .60	x .55
Outside Heat Absorb.—Inside Reg. Plate	x .37	x .60	x .75
Hammered	x.60-.80	x1.00	x .50
Hammered and Etched Both Sides	x.50-.75	x1.00	x .65
Hammered Heat Absorbent	x.20-.25	x1.00	x1.15
Hammered Heat Absorb. Etched 2 Sides	x.10-.20	x1.00	x1.40
Glass Block	x.25-.50	x.5-3.00	—
Shading (high no. in range for dark color, etc.)			
Canvas Awning—Sides open	x .25	—	—
Canvas Awning—Sides closed	x .35	—	—
Roller Shade—Fully drawn	x.41-.81	—	—
Roller Shade—Half Drawn	x.71-.91	—	—
Venetian Blind—45° slats	x.45-.75	—	—
Venetian Awning—45° slats	x .15	—	—
Shade Screen—40° Solar Altitude	x.15-.20	—	—
Temperature Deviation:			
Room Temperature—each degree below 80°F	Add following:		
Outside Temperature—each degree below 95°F	Subtract following:		
Single Flat or Rolled Figure Glass	1.0 Btu/hr/ft²		
Double Flat or Glass Block	0.5 Btu/hr/ft²		

Adapted from the data of "Heating, Ventilating and Air Conditioning Guide," ASHRAE, 1960, pp. 199-205.

Whenever outside conditions differ from those inside, a ventilation load must be considered. As discussed in Chapter 14, a certain amount of outside air will infiltrate through various cracks, etc., unless the pressure within is sufficient to offset the normal wind or stack effect or both. Even so, in order to pressurize a building there must be an outside air supply which exceeds the exhaust rate. In either case, then, there will be an outside air load. Sufficient heat must be supplied or extracted to bring this "ventilation air" to room temperature. The quantity of outside air mechanically supplied can be established by design. The quantity of infiltration air can be computed from the data in Chapter 14. Although in the latter case the air is actually heated or cooled to room temperature within the space, it is convenient to consider the outdoor air load separate from the room load in both cases. Once the state and rate of supply of outside air (CFM_o) are determined, the calculation of the sensible (SH_o) and latent (LH_o) loads due thereto may be calculated in Btu/hr from the following formulas:

$$SH_o = 1.087\ CFM_o\ (t_o - t_i), \quad and \tag{369}$$

$$LH_o = 4750\ CFM_o\ (H_o - H_i), \tag{370}$$

where t_o and t_i are outside and inside dry-bulb temperatures in °F respectively and H_o and H_i are the corresponding specific humidities in lb/lb dry air.

The diffusion of moisture through walls, etc., usually results in a negligibly small latent heat load. The following formula may be used to calculate this diffusion load (LH_d) when warranted:

$$LH_d = .0155\ A\ \Omega\ (e_o - e_i), \qquad (371)$$

where the vapor pressures of the outside and inside air (e_o and e_i) are in inches of Mercury and the permeance (Ω) of the specimen is in grains/sq ft-hr-in. Hg vapor pressure difference. Refer to Table 92 for values of Ω for various materials.

TABLE 92—WATER VAPOR PERMEANCES OF VARIOUS MATERIALS

In grains per hr-sq ft-″ Hg

Material	Thickness	Permeance
Air—Still	1″	126.
Concrete (plain)	1.5″	1.8
Concrete (2 coats asphalt)	1.5″	1.6
Felt—carpet 17 oz.	.056″	167.
30 lb Building felt, one sheet	.062″	1.8
Asphalt saturated rag 15 lb	.033-.038″	1.1-3.0
Tar saturated rag 15 lb	.030-.042″	5.7-38.6
Insulation:		
Rock Wool—loose	1.0″	25.6-230
Celotex vapor seal sheathing	.78″	2.0
Rock cork	.523″	3.0
Pressed corkboard	.905-.985″	2.3-2.7
Manufactured Boards:		
Fibreboard (plain)	1.06″	18.7
(Dipped asphalt one surface)	.633″	8.5
Masonite—Presdwood	.13″	10.7
Masonite—Presdwood tempered	.13″	4.8
Plasterboard	.37″	34.6
Plywood	.25″	3.7-4.5
Paint (Paint films only)		
Aluminum (on celotex)	1 coat	9.0
Aluminum (on pine)	1 coat	3.5
Aluminum (on pine)	2 coats	.5
Aluminum (on plaster)	2 coats	1.8
Aluminum (on plaster)	3 coats	.9
Asphalt (on concrete)	2 coats	14.4
Enamel (on pine)	1 coat	4.5
	2 coats	1.3
Flat white (on plywood)	2 coats	4.2
(on plaster)	2 coats	1.2-2.6
Paper		
Asbestos—14 lb	.28″	158.
Asphalt coated Kraft	.013″	.4-.7
Kraft—1 sheet	.004″	79.
Kraft—light waxed (2 lb)	.003-.004″	.1-1.2
Roofing—Base Sheet 39 lb	.076″	.3
Cap Sheet	.080″	.1
Tar Saturated sheathing—11 lb.	.032-.040″	12.3-18.6
Plaster on metal lath	½″	16.
Plaster on wood lath	½″	6.7
Wood Cedar (siding)	—	1.8
Pine	.496″	1.7
Spruce	.480″	2.0
Water Surface free standing	—	609.

Fan Systems

There are numerous systems which may be used to air condition a building. Various writers assign them different names and classify them in different groupings depending upon the individual interest involved. The method of classification outlined below highlights some of the principal differences from a fan application standpoint.

FAN SYSTEMS FOR AIR CONDITIONING

I—Individual Fan Systems for Single Zone Applications
- A. Remote or Unitary Systems
- B. Split or Combined Heating Systems

II—Central Fan Systems for Multiple Zone Applications
- A. Year 'round all-air systems
  1. Individual reheat systems
  2. Hot and cold deck systems
  3. Double duct systems
  4. Primary and secondary air systems
- B. Year 'round air-water systems
  1. Primary air and induction or fan-coil systems
  2. Primary air and heating-cooling panel systems

(Each of the terms used in this outline is defined or discussed below.)

As indicated in the outline, an individual fan system is used on applications where the entire area served is controlled as a single zone. This is perfectly satisfactory as long as the area has uniform load characteristics and provided the occupants are all satisfied with the same room conditions. As a matter of fact, for precise humidity control, small uniform load areas must be established and individual systems provided. At the other extreme there are applications where precision is not required even in temperature control and a single individual system will be satisfactory for a large area. Occasionally two or more complete systems will evaluate better than one. Sometimes the cost of duct runs can be reduced sufficiently to pay for the added cost of equipment. Not all of the equipment need be duplicated since heating and refrigeration can be piped from central plants to the fan-coil units.

Numerous distinctions can be made between remote fan systems and unitary systems designed for the same functions. The basic apparatus of either may be a completely integrated unit; however, a remote unit in general is larger and is designed for concealed use with duct work while a room unit generally has a sufficiently pleasing appearance for unconcealed use.

A "unit ventilator" is an under-the-window type of device built in unitary sizes suitable for schoolrooms, etc. The principal function of this type of equipment is to ventilate the space and cool it with outside air. A "ventilating unit" may be remotely located or it too may be installed in the space served. Since the area served is usually large, duct work may be required for the proper distribution of make-up air in either instance.

Although the major function of any ventilator is to bring in outside air, provisions must often be made for some heating. At the very least the outdoor air must be tempered to prevent freezing drafts, etc. When additional radiators or convectors are used to provide all or part of the required space heating, a split system is said to exist. A combined system is one where no direct radiation is used and the air is heated sufficiently to offset transmission losses.

Roof ventilators are increasingly popular due for the most part to their utilization of otherwise unused space. Make-up air and exhaust units are both available with propeller type fans. Centrifugal wheels are used in some exhaust units. Provisions may be made for split or combined heating control and recirculation of room air if warranted. Numerous wheel designs may be used for different pressure requirements. Ducts or diffusers or both may be attached. Weather protection is an essential feature of these designs.

Unit heaters and warm air furnaces may be applied to unitary and remote systems whose principal functions are to offset heat losses. Either may be gas, oil, or coal fired. Heaters may use steam, hot water, or electrical resistance elements. Although not specifically defined as such, a "unit heater" is commonly thought of as a propeller fan combination or at least a relatively compact centrifugal fan package without fresh air connections. "Heating units" are often ventilating units with fresh air provisions omitted. In many applications of both heaters and furnaces, no particular ventilation is provided other than from windows and infiltration.

Horizontal type unit heaters are usually suspended at a height of 7 or 8 feet and disposed at such locations that the blast provides a warm blanket over cold walls to minimize the chilling effects of radiation and infiltration. Depending upon outlet velocity, the influence of the ordinary unit may be felt for 50 to 100 feet. Most heaters are equipped with louvers on the outlet so that the blast direction can be controlled. A downward blow will be required whenever the unit must be mounted at a high level. Vertical type units are available in various designs.

Warm air heating of residential and commercial buildings can usually be described as perimeter heating if recently installed. With such systems the air is always introduced upward into the room, at or near the floor, usually under windows. The purpose is to blanket the cold walls and windows with warm air. In basementless structures the duct work under or imbedded in the floor serves to warm the floor. Loop systems have a continuous peripheral loop. Radial systems have a more extensive system of radial feeder ducts. Most systems use a network of small ducts and force the air through with a fan; however, some gravity system design data is still published.

The same distinctions apply between unitary and remote air conditioners. Most room units are self-contained whereas remote units more frequently have separate refrigeration. Self-contained units may have the economic advantage where it is desired to cool only a small portion of a structure or where direct radiation is used for heating, etc. The advantages and convenience of central refrigeration and heating become more pronounced with increased job size.

A central fan system is usually the most economical means of providing air conditioning to any space having two or more different load producing areas. Most multiple zone applications do not require precise humidity control as long as individual temperatures can be closely maintained.

There are numerous means of providing the required temperature control. Central fan systems may deliver all, or part of, the required heat transfer capacity to the spaces via the air. The remainder, if any, is usually carried by a stream of water. Either the air or water may be throttled for control purposes. Until recently, volume control of the air delivered to a space was rarely recommended, because of the possibility of resulting: (1) drafts and distribution problems, (2) poor ventilation, or (3) changing noise characteristics. Many of these problems have been solved.

A year 'round system must be capable of nullifying either net gains or net losses as required, often both simultaneously. Only cooling may be required in hottest weather, but in various amounts depending on variations in occupancy, cloud cover, etc. Similarly, various amounts of heating, but no cooling, may be required in coldest weather. However, in intermediate seasons heating may be needed to condition one room, and cooling may be needed to condition another. Therefore, any system for multiple zone applications requires two heat transfer mediums at some point in the system. In all systems, but some more than others, there will be occasions where heating capacity is nullified by cooling capacity. Although appearing uneconomical, this is the price that must be paid for individual room control. When comparing two systems on this basis, the difference in operating cost should be evaluated against the difference in control reliability.

With two mediums, the flow of one or both can be manipulated at the command of the individual space thermostats for temperature control. The various systems differ in the nature of these mediums and in the identity of the one(s) throttled.

Both mediums may possess a cooling potential when outside temperatures are above the room design temperature. If only one can be throttled, the cooling capacity of the other should not exceed the heat gain due to transmission else overcooling will result when there are no other gains. The heating and cooling potentials available at any outdoor air temperature must be as large as the greatest possible load in order to prevent any possible underconditioning. Overconditioning can be prevented by compensating any excess cooling with excess heating, and vice versa. For economy, such excesses should be avoided. The temperature of either the fixed quantity (primary) medium or the throttled (secondary) medium may be scheduled or reset according to outdoor temperature. This in effect matches its capacity to heat or cool to the loss or gain due to transmission and also makes for economical operation.

A primary air system is usually designed to operate in such a way that the primary air nullifies the variable transmission loss or gain. All other space loads are gains, the total value of which is potentially the same regardless of season or outdoor air temperature. The secondary medium must therefore be capable of nullifying any gain up to this total value at any time. When primary air is the only air supplied to the space, it must contain enough outdoor air to satisfy the ventilation requirements. If it is necessary, or desirable, to limit the room device to sensible cooling only, then all of the latent heat removal must be performed on the primary air. A primary air quantity of somewhere in the neighborhood of 25% of the quantity normally used in an all-air system will usually satisfy the ventilation requirements and be sufficient to allow for all of the latent heat removal. Primary air systems utilizing under-the-window units of either the induction or fan-coil types are frequently employed to satisfy the exterior zones of large buildings. This zone, usually limited to the outer 20′ or so, is subjected to practically uniform transmission effects around the entire periphery. The interior zone will have a cooling load the year round. Primary air systems using heating-cooling panels to nullify the remainder of the load are attractive simply because of the radiant compensation which is possible with such devices. Acoustical treatment and luminaires are often combined with the heat transfer panels in the ceiling offering economic advantages. The amount of primary air required for acceptable room air motion may be higher than for under-the-window unit systems. Both are air-water systems as indicated in the outline.

All-air systems may employ the primary air principle. If in such cases a constant temperature stream of secondary air is used, it must of course be throttled to satisfy individual spaces at anything but peak load. This is a disadvantage for reasons previously outlined. In cases, however, where a large interior zone exists, such as in block type buildings, interior zone air may be used for the secondary stream. Some of the inherent problems of volume control are minimized with such a scheme. There are several other all-air systems, in each of which all of the conditioning is applied to the supply air before it is introduced into the space. In an individual reheat system the supply air is conditioned in sufficient degree to satisfy any space with maximum cooling load (minimum heating load). Individual room control is achieved by reheating to the desired temperature. Some of the cooling capacity must be nullified at design conditions unless all zones have the same load (which is unlikely). Refrigeration plants must therefore be sized to a larger capacity for reheat systems than for any other since this excess cooling is required at design conditions. This requirement arises because the second medium must always have negative cooling capacity on reheat systems, whereas in other systems the second medium can be switched to positive cooling capacity when required by the occasion. The all-air alternative to either reheat or variable volume is temperature control produced by mixing two streams of air in such a way as to furnish a constant volume at the desired temperature. Both streams may be supplied at a temperature suitable for the worst condition of the moment. That is, the coldest stream of air need only be cold enough, if it alone is used, to condition the room with the maximum load for the outside air temperature prevailing. The warmest stream need not be any warmer than is required to offset the transmission loss. The two streams of air may be mixed at the discharge of the hot and cold deck apparatus or at the individual room or space. In the first case, individual ducts are required to serve the individual spaces, and for this reason the equipment is generally located near the spaces to be served. This means such systems must serve only relatively small areas. In the second case, a common double duct system serves the various spaces. This is a more economical arrangement than the first for systems having appreciable distances between equipment and occupied spaces.

Atmospheric cooling may be utilized to effect operating economies, during certain outdoor weather. If unlimited amounts of outdoor air could be supplied to a space, refrigeration would not be required for outdoor temperatures which are below room temperature. Unfortunately, it is not always possible to utilize outdoor air in this manner. The capacity of this air to cool depends on its amount as well as its temperature, and some systems cannot be designed to utilize a very large amount. Such is the case for primary air systems which are designed to handle only a small quantity of air.

Figures 137 to 143 illustrate many of the important considerations in multiple zone air-conditioning design.

Figure 137 is drawn for a typical building with several zones. It shows what might be called the minimum and maximum loads (per 1000 cfm) that the air-conditioning system must be capable of satisfying at each outside air temperature. It also shows the cooling capacity of various amounts of outside air at each outside temperature. Similar charts can be made for any building by following the procedure outlined below:

1. Calculate the effective transmission load at the summer design temperature. This is the actual transmission load if ventilation air is preconditioned before it is pumped into the space. If any outside air is pumped directly into the space, the corresponding ventilation load should be added to the transmission load.
2. Calculate the maximum sensible cooling load at the design temperature. This will include loads due to occupants, lighting, and sun effect as well as the effective transmission load.
3. Calculate the supply air quantity. This is the actual capacity of the supply fan or fans on an all-air system. It is a hypothetical capacity on an air-water system. Multiply the primary air rate by the ratio of the maximum sensible cooling load to be taken care of by both air and water to the maximum sensible cooling load to be taken care of by the air alone.
4. Divide both the maximum sensible cooling load and transmission load by the supply air quantity.
5. Plot the minimum load line. This is approximately a straight line passing through zero at an outdoor temperature equal to room design. This line must pass through the transmission load at the summer design temperature. (Figure 137 is based on an effective transmission load of 4000 Btu/1000 cfm at 95°F.)
6. Plot the maximum load line. This is approximately a straight line passing through the maximum sensible cooling load at the summer design temperature. This line will roughly parallel the minimum load line. (Figure 137 is based on a maximum load of 22000 Btu/1000 cfm at 95°F. This corresponds to a 20°F differential on an all-air system. If a higher differential was used, the general conclusions which could be drawn from Figures 138-143 would not be changed appreciably.)
7. Determine the amount of outside air which could be used for atmospheric cooling. This may range from 100% of the supply air quantity for an all-air system to around 25% for an air-water system.

8. Plot the atmospheric cooling lines for the maximum amount of outside air and for the minimum amount required for ventilation. These lines are straight lines passing through zero at an outside air temperature corresponding to room design. (Several lines are shown on Figure 137. The 100% line shows the maximum atmospheric cooling which can be obtained on an all-air system.)

Figures 138 through 143 are drawn for various systems as indicated in the titles. These charts illustrate many points about the methods of operation and the limitations of the various systems. The methods of control are the principal distinguishing features and are indicated at the top of each chart. Capacities are given per 1000 cfm of supply air as previously defined.

The two heavy lines define the limits of the system to heat or cool at any outside air temperature. The shaded area represents all the possible heating or cooling requirements at any outside air temperature. If the upper capacity line lies below the upper limit on load, overheating will result in any space whose load falls in the crosshatched area. Similarly, if the lower capacity line lies above the lower limit on load, overcooling will result in any space whose load falls in the crosshatched area.

The temperatures of each medium should be scheduled or reset according to outside temperature, as indicated at various points along the capacity lines.

Various changeover temperatures are indicated on the charts. There may be a complete changeover as in the air-water systems where the cold medium is changed to the hot and vice versa. Or there may be one or two outside temperatures at which the refrigeration plant is shut down in favor of atmospheric cooling or heating and vice versa.

Air-conditioning systems may also be described as either high- or low-velocity systems. An arbitrary dividing line near 2200 feet per minute has often been used. The distinction could also be made on the basis of the acoustical treatment each system requires for satisfactory operation. Except for the critical areas, only a short run of duct need be lined with acoustical material to adequately control sound in a low-velocity system. High-velocity systems require sound absorbers in the duct system and acoustical treatment of the terminal device. This additional control is necessitated by the increase in sound output of the fan (resulting from increased pressure requirements) and to the increase in regenerated duct noises. High-velocity duct work must withstand higher pressures and requires better fitting and sealing. However, the total weight of material is generally less than that for a low-velocity system. However, the principal advantage results from the size reduction as it affects building space. In existing construction the minimum reduction in usable space and in new construction the maximum reduction in story height are often of paramount importance and high-velocity systems should then be considered. The use of high velocity has proved economical on many double duct and primary air systems.

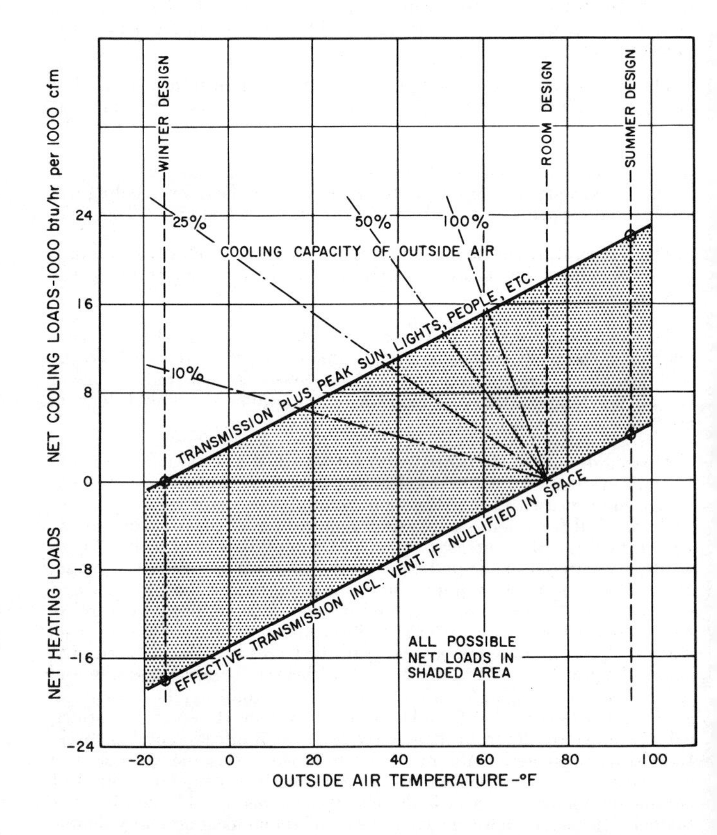

Figure 137—Net Space Loads vs Outdoor Temperature

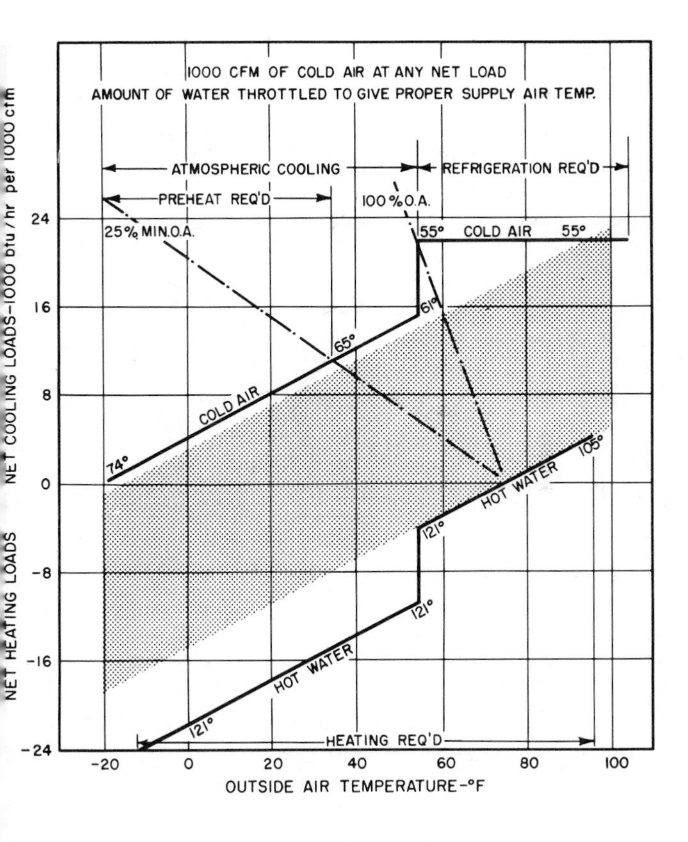

Figure 138—Operation of Individual Reheat System

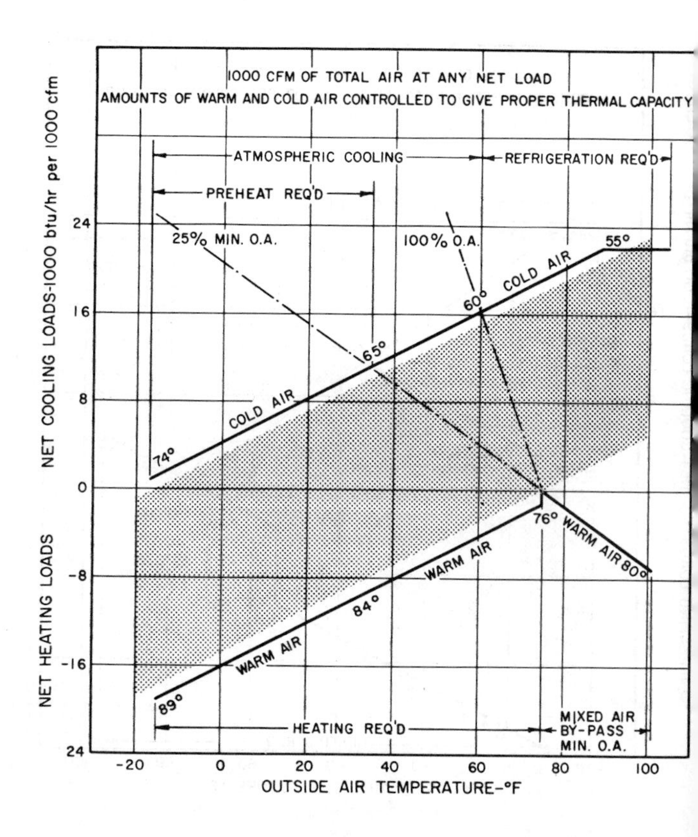

Figure 139—Operation of Double Duct System

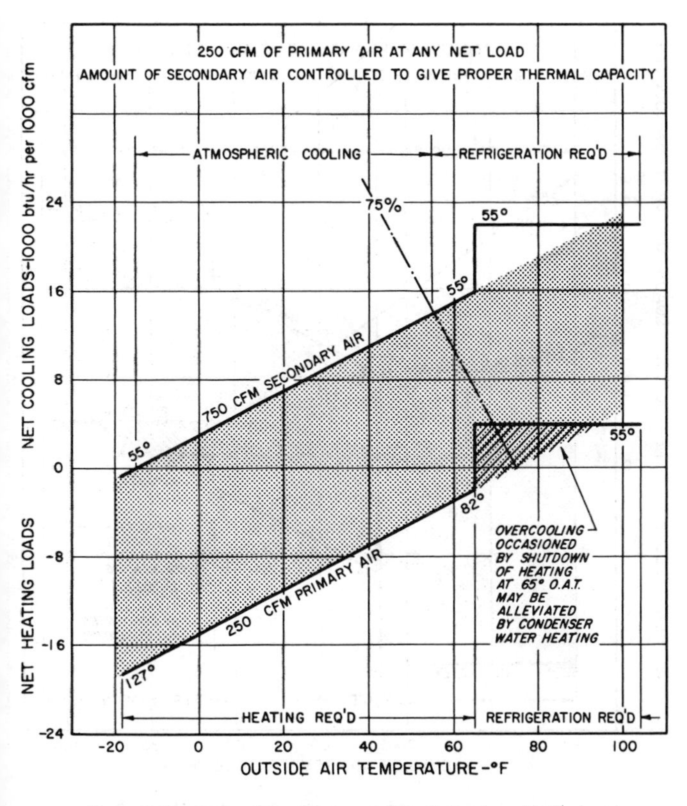

Figure 140—Operation of Primary Air—Secondary Air System

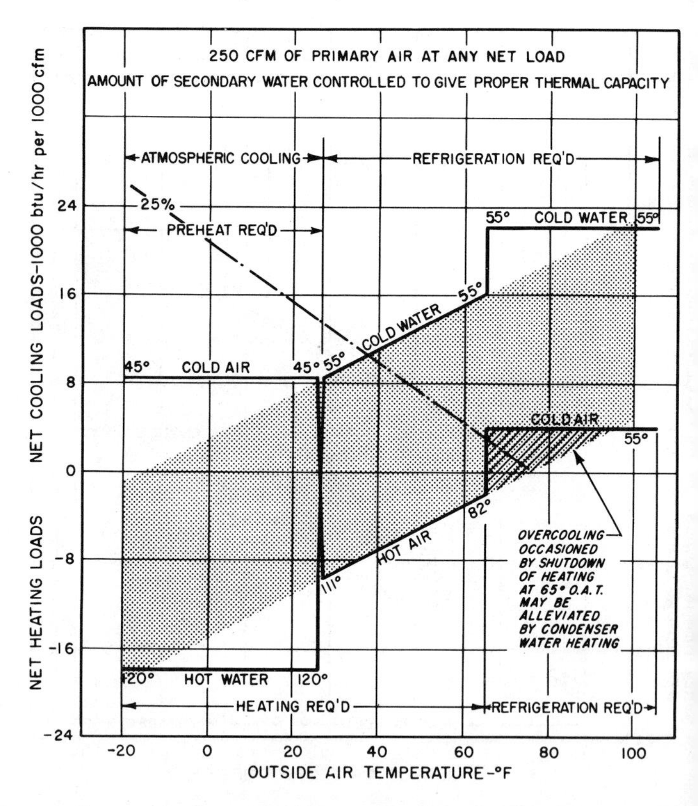

Figure 141—Operation of Primary Air—Secondary Water System

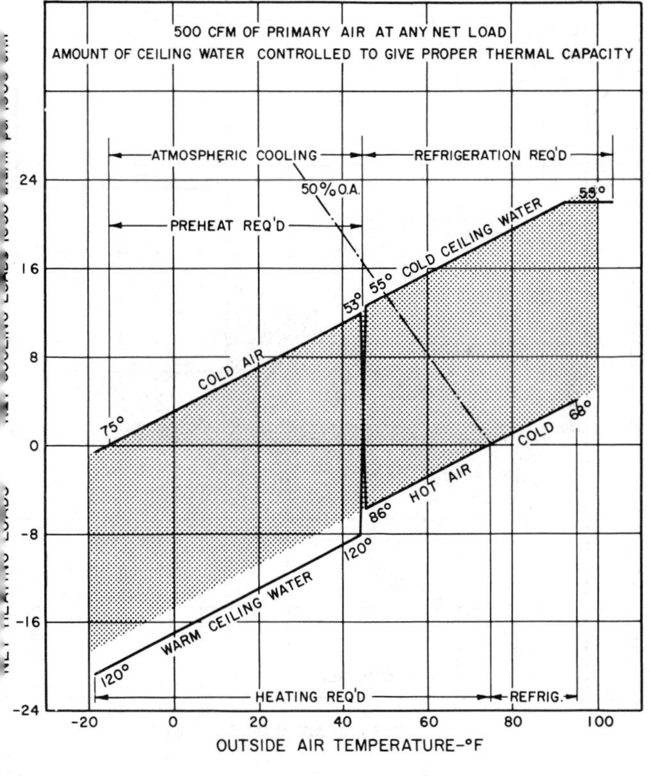

Figure 142—Operation of Primary Air—Radiant Panel System

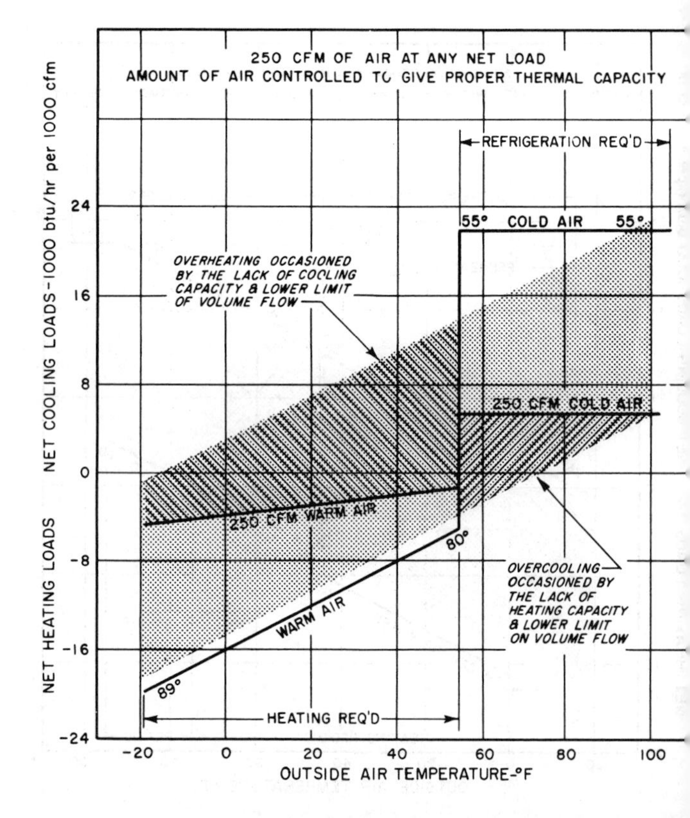

Figure 143—Operation of Variable Volume System

OPERATION OF FAN SYSTEMS

As has been seen above, the capacity of a system to heat or cool must exactly match the load at any instant to prevent overheating or overcooling. Automatic controls are the only means of producing satisfactory results, owing to the continuous variations that occur in most load producing factors. The capacity to heat, humidify, etc., can be matched to the part-load requirements by reducing the energy supplied to perform the function in question. Usually a sort of chain reaction is involved. For instance, an increase in outside temperature will produce in turn: a reduction in transmission loss, a slight rise in space temperature, a measurement of that rise by a thermostat, a signal to a valve, a reduction in steam consumption, and ultimately a decrease in the firing rate on the boiler. The flow of the heat transfer medium may actually be reduced as in the closing of a throttling valve or a portion may be bypassed and subsequently remixed with the main stream as in a mixing valve. In either case, the transfer rate of sensible or latent heat will be changed. The arrangement of coils, dampers, valves, etc., and the methods of detecting the need for a change in capacity are numerous. An examination of even a few combinations reveals many important aspects of control.

Some of the essential, or at least desirable, features for satisfactory control of conditions in a space can be summarized generally before investigating particular systems.

1. Changes in the net flow of supply air should be limited for reasons already mentioned.
2. A thermostat on the wall is preferred to other types of control, although it is often desirable to supplement such space controllers with outdoor or medium controllers or both.
3. Appreciable controller differentials will often have to be tolerated to limit short cycling and hunting.
4. Oversizing of coils, valves, etc. should be avoided since the range of effective valve positions, etc. is reduced thereby.
5. Commercially available dampers are not 100% airtight in their closed positions. Therefore, it is advisable to add a shutoff valve to any damper controlled coils.
6. Individual equipment is required for each zone if individual humidity control is desired. However, individual temperature control is usually sufficient for most comfort work, provided humidity is roughly maintained.
7. It is preferable to bypass return air rather than mixed air, or mixed air rather than outdoor air in order to minimize uncontrolled humidity effects.

Double Duct System

The system diagrammed in Figure 144 operates as follows:

1. Freeze-up protection—minimum outdoor air, maximum outdoor air, and exhaust air dampers close when the supply fan is turned off. A properly sized, non-freeze type, preheat coil should be used. A safety freeze-up protector (not shown) may also be used to cut out fans should some accident occur.

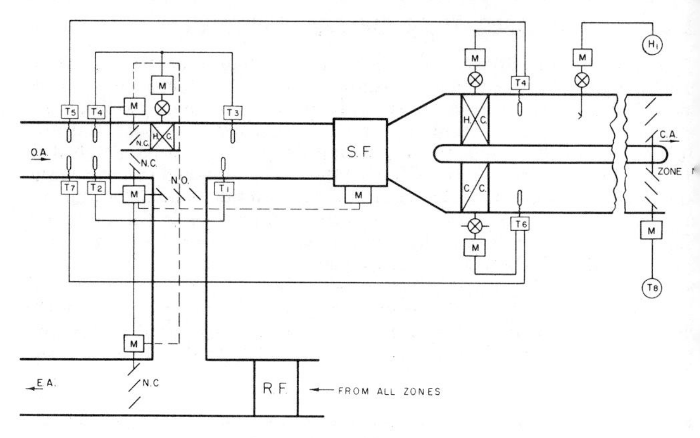

Figure 144—Double Duct System

---

2. Ventilation control—minimum outdoor air dampers are wide open whenever the supply fan is on.
3. Atmospheric cooling control—maximum outdoor air dampers are modulated by a mixed air controller **T-1** to provide the schedule of temperatures established by the outdoor compensator **T-2**.
4. Preheat control—the mixed air controller **T-3** modulates the valve on the preheat coil to maintain the schedule of temperatures established by the outdoor compensator **T-4**.
5. Humidification control—the humidistat **H-1** located in a representative space activates the humidifier as needed to maintain the setting.
6. Dehumidification control—no separate dehumidification control is shown. For this system, only the air passing through the cooling coil is dehumidified and that only incidental to cooling.
7. Heating control—the discharge controller **T-4** modulates the valve on the heating coil to maintain the schedule of temperatures established by the outdoor compensator **T-5**.
8. Cooling control—discharge controller **T-6** modulates the valve on the cooling coil to maintain the schedule of temperatures established by the outdoor compensator **T-7**.
9. Individual room temperature control—room thermostats **T-8**, etc., modulate the zone dampers or mixing device to maintain individual room settings.
10. Changeover control—for this system no provisions are shown for automatically starting the refrigeration plant, etc.

The above system may be described as either a hot and cold deck system or a double duct system. Both are year 'round, all-air systems suitable for multi-zone applications. Individual temperature control is provided by mixing two streams of air. Hot and cold deck zone dampers are arranged so that when one closes the other opens. High-velocity double duct systems employ various devices to provide similar mixing, and often total volume regulation and sound attenuation as well.

Numerous variations of the diagrammed system are possible, including the addition of a precooling coil to better control dehumidification of the outdoor air and the use of separate fans for each stream of air.

The parallel path arrangement with double ducts or even hot and cold deck apparatus provides two streams of air but not necessarily a constant volume total flow rate. Even if the pressure drops across the hot and cold decks are equalized and there is no other parallel resistance, a difference in total flow will develop on any change in damper position. For instance, if a resistance of ½″ is encountered by the air when all is passed through either the hot or cold deck, then there will be only ⅛″ resistance if half the air goes through each. In most hot and cold deck applications there is sufficient resistance through the ducts and other equipment that a ⅜″ differential will not produce an unbearable flow situation. This also depends on the steepness of the pressure characteristic of the fan.

With a high-velocity double duct system, however, the problem is magnified since the main trunks may be sized for 4″ loss with 100% flow. If each main handles only 50% flow, the resistance drops to 1″. With a single fan supplying both, the total flow could conceivably change a tremendous amount. Quite often the flow needs of one group of rooms will counterbalance those of another group. A more positive method of reducing the fluctuations is to measure any change in velocity in say the hot duct and reduce the temperature of that air to compensate. Figure 145 shows a modification based on this principle.

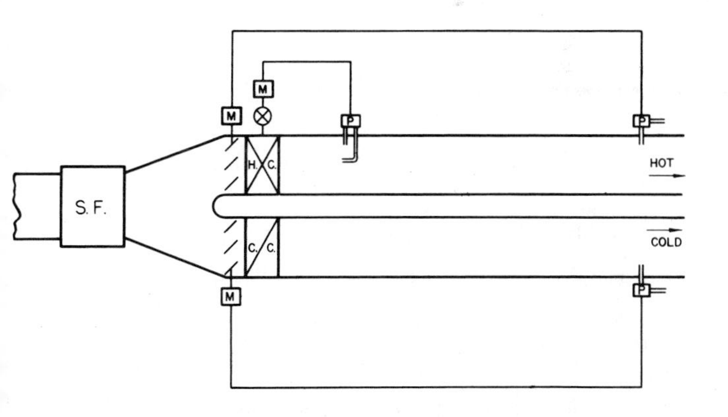

Figure 145—Static and Velocity Pressure Balancing

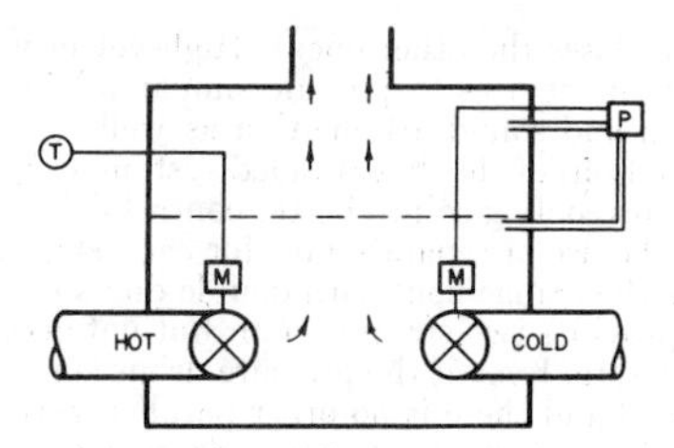

Figure 146—Double Duct Mixing Device

In addition to equalizing the total flow by the fan, the use of the above modification tends to reduce the pressure difference that must be accommodated by the terminal device itself. This difference may be further reduced by modulating an additional pair of dampers by means of individual static pressure controllers. This too is shown in Figure 145. Nevertheless, the possibility for some static pressure unbalance between hot and cold ducts persists at some terminal device locations. Numerous designs are utilized to make the terminal devices themselves capable of discharging a constant volume of air. The alternative is to use cold duct temperatures lower than design and hot duct temperatures higher than design. The various patented devices are all controlled by a space thermostat which modulates one of the valves to produce a change in discharge temperature. If that valve is on the hot duct, the cold duct valve is controlled independently to maintain constant flow. The pressure drop across an orifice, etc., may be used as a measure of the flow rate. Figure 146 diagrams a blender valve which incorporates these principles.

Reheat System

The system diagrammed in Figure 147 operates as follows:

1. Freeze-up protection—outdoor air and exhaust air dampers close when the supply fan is turned off. Preheat coils are full of steam whenever freezing air can enter them. (Coils must be properly sized to prevent overheating.)
2. Ventilation control—the system shown uses all outside air. Hence no control is needed.
3. Atmospheric cooling control—no control other than preheat is needed.
4. Preheat control—the preheat controller T-2 modulates the steam valve on preheat coil No. 2 to maintain a constant 65° leaving air temperature. The preheat coil should be selected for a temperature rise no greater than 30°. Outdoor controller T-1 should be set to put full steam on preheat coil No. 1 at 35°F.
5. Humidification control—the winter dew-point controller T-3 modulates the steam valve on the spray water heater to maintain its set point.

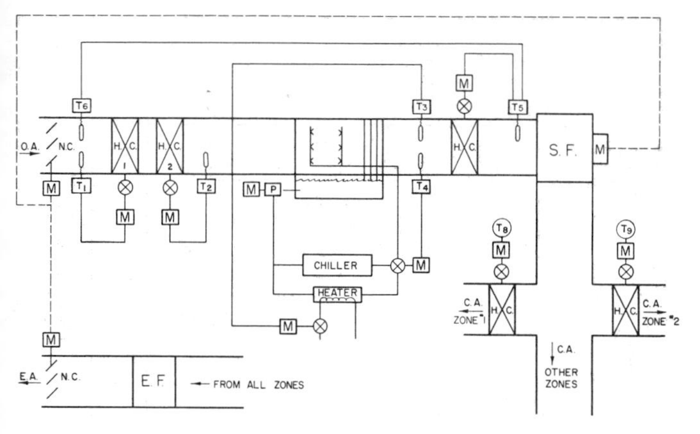

Figure 147—Individual Reheat System

6. Dehumidification control—the summer dew-point controller T-4 modulates the three way valve to provide the proper mixture of chilled and bypass water to maintain its set point.
7. Heating control—discharge controller T-5 modulates the valve on the heating coil to maintain the schedule of temperatures established by the outdoor compensator T-6.
8. Cooling control—no additional control beyond that for dehumidification is required.
9. Individual room temperature control—the room thermostats T-8, etc., modulate the valves on the reheat coils to maintain space temperature.
10. Changeover control—when refrigeration becomes available, it is necessary to cut out T-3 and cut in T-4. Automatic control for this or for starting the refrigeration machinery, etc., is not shown.

The above system may be described as an air washer system with dew-point control of humidity. It is a year 'round all-air system which provides individual temperature control with reheat coils.

The 100% outdoor air system diagrammed is typical of systems installed in operating suite applications in some of the larger hospitals.

A sprayed coil dehumidifier may be substituted for the air washer and an additional preheat coil inserted upstream in place of the water heater. Unless 100% outside air is required, return air may be utilized for preheat instead of multiple preheat coils as shown. On single zone applications return air can be used to supply the necessary reheat capacity.

Primary Air—Secondary Water System

The system diagrammed in Figure 148 operates as follows:

1. Freeze-up protection—outdoor air and exhaust air dampers close when the supply fan is turned off. The outdoor controller T-1 puts full

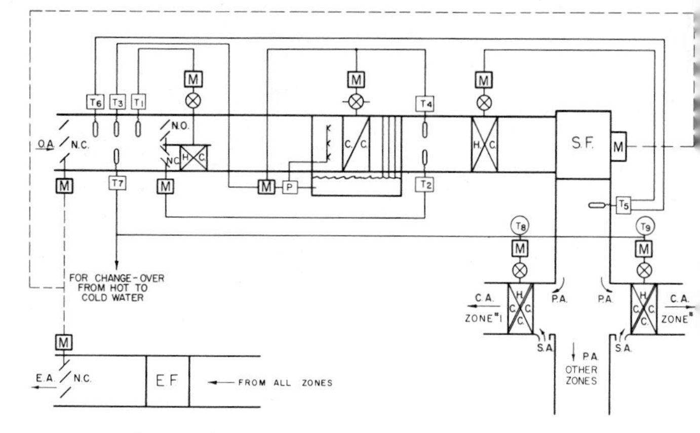

Figure 148—Primary Air—Secondary Water System

steam on the preheat coil when the temperature drops to the set point.

2. Ventilation control—all of the primary air comes from outside for the system as shown. This quantity should be chosen to equal or exceed the ventilation requirements.
3. Atmospheric cooling control—only the primary air quantity may be utilized for atmospheric cooling. To take advantage of even this amount, the primary air must be made the cold medium and the secondary water the warm medium at changeover.
4. Preheat control—the winter dew-point controller **T-2** modulates the face and bypass dampers on the preheat coil to maintain the dew-point setting.
5. Humidification control—the control of preheat in effect controls the dew point and therefore humidification. Outdoor wet-bulb controller **T-3** will shut off the pump when the wet-bulb temperature exceeds the set point in order to prevent overhumidification.
6. Dehumidification control—the summer dew-point controller **T-4** modulates the threeway valve on the chilled water coil to maintain its setting.
7. Heating control—the discharge controller **T-5** modulates the valve on the heating coil to maintain the schedule of temperatures established by the outdoor compensator **T-6**.
8. Cooling control—the only additional control beyond that for dehumidification is that when the valve is wide open on the cooling coil the sprays are turned on to give maximum sensible cooling. **T-4** must override **T-3** in this case.
9. Individual room temperature control—room thermostats **T-8** modulate the valves on individual room unit coils to maintain room settings.
10. Changeover control—as described outdoor controllers **T-3** and **T-6**

function to limit the authority of other controllers according to season. The summer-winter controller T-7 changes the water from hot to cold and reverses the action of the room thermostats T-8, etc., at their set points.

The above system may be described as a sprayed coil system with dew-point control of humidity. It is a year 'round air-water system suitable for multi-zone applications. Individual temperature control is provided by throttling the secondary water in the room units.

Many variations are possible, including the addition of return air connections and the substitution of an air washer or a non-sprayed coil with separate humidifier for the sprayed coil unit.

Return Air Bypass System

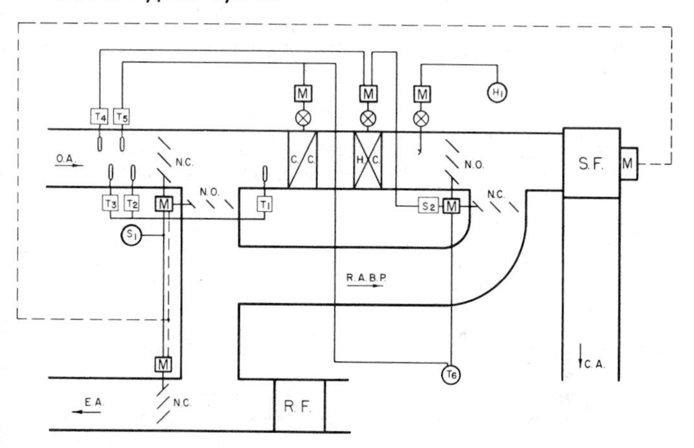

Figure 149—Return Air Bypass System

The system diagrammed in Figure 149 operates as follows:

1. Freeze-up protection—outdoor air and exhaust air dampers close when the supply fan is turned off or when the temperature at the safety low-limit controller T-1 is below its set point.
2. Ventilation control—minimum outdoor air damper opening is established by positioning the manual switch S-1.
3. Atmospheric cooling control—outdoor air damper is modulated by the winter controller T-2 according to its schedule of temperatures. Summer controller T-3 overrides T-2 to return damper to the minimum position when the temperature is above its set point.
4. Preheat control—preheat is provided by the return air.
5. Humidification control—the humidistat H-1 activates the humidifier as needed to maintain its setting.

6. Dehumidification control—no separate dehumidification control is shown for this system.
7. Heating control—the heating coil valve is modulated by the outdoor air controller T-4 according to its schedule. End switch S-2 on the face and bypass dampers closes the valve whenever the face damper is closed.
8. Cooling control—the valve on the cooling coil is wide open whenever the temperature at outdoor controller T-5 is above its set point.
9. Space temperature control—space thermostat T-6 modulates the face and bypass dampers to maintain its setting.
10. Changeover control—the summer-winter controller T-7 reverses the action of the face and bypass dampers and opens the valve on the cooling coil at its set point.

This system may be described as a return air bypass system. It is a year 'round, all-air system suitable only for single zone control. Many modifications are possible, including the substitution of mixed air or outdoor air for return air in the bypass. This system may also be modified to provide winter ventilation only, when radiation is available.

In the four systems diagrammed, various techniques of providing control for each function were used. Some of these are listed in Table 93.

Another function of an air-conditioning system not discussed with regard to each system but which may influence the design is that of night set-back and morning warm-up control. In addition to reducing the thermostatic settings by means of a timer or other device, the fan speed may be reduced (or stopped) if there is sufficient natural convection surface in the space (the outdoor air dampers closed, etc.). Elevated temperatures and the use of recirculated air only may be employed for quick warm up.

TABLE 93—CONTROL TECHNIQUES FOR AIR CONDITIONING FUNCTIONS

Function	Technique or Equipment, Etc.
Freeze-up protection	Non-freeze coils, full steam on coils, multiple preheat coils, or low limit and safety controls.
Ventilation control	100% outdoor air, minimum position control of outdoor air dampers, or minimum and maximum outdoor air damper control.
Atmospheric cooling	Mixed air control with outdoor compensation, or outdoor air control.
Preheat	Multiple preheat coils, face and bypass damper control on preheat coils, or return air control.
Humidification control	Dew point control or space humidistat control of air washer, sprayed coil, water spray, steam injection, or pan and coil.
Dehumidification control	Incidental to cooling only, dew point control, or space humidistat control.
Heating control	Discharge control with outdoor compensation, or outdoor air control.
Cooling control	Wild coil, discharge control with outdoor compensation, or dew point control.
Individual room temperature control	Throttling reheat coils, mixing two streams of air, modulating water in room units, or return air bypass control.
Changeover control	Outdoor air control.

These are by no means all the possible techniques or combinations that can be employed. The descriptions were primarily limited to the air handling equipment. The automatic controls used with the refrigeration machines, boilers, etc. must be coordinated with those used on the air handling equipment.

EQUIPMENT SELECTION

When selecting equipment for an air-conditioning system, each piece must be coordinated with every other. Various functional elements and controls are so interrelated that system performance may fall to the level of the poorest item, even if all others are top quality and properly selected.

The functions of circulating, heating, cooling, humidifying, dehumidifying, and purifying the air supplied to a conditioned space can each be performed by a wide variety of equipment designs. The control of conditions within the space may be subject to the limits imposed by the size or design of the individual functional element, by the size or design of the heating and refrigeration plant which may serve that element, or by the operating characteristics of the control system.

Oversizing is often as serious as undersizing from a functional standpoint, not to mention its economic undesirability.

Natural heating and cooling mediums are occasionally available. However, heating and refrigeration plants must be utilized in most cases. Refrigeration machines operate on the vapor-compression or absorption principle. The reverse cycle compression system or "heat pump" is being used increasingly, but the combustion of fuels is still the common source of heat. Condensing or evaporating mediums have attractive unit heat capacities, yet water, because of its low cost and ease of handling, is frequently used to transport the heating or cooling potential from the generating plant to the supply air coils.

Individual functional elements such as fans, coils, filters, etc., are generally available as factory-made units in standard sizes, so that selection amounts to choosing a unit with a capacity that closely matches the job requirements. When several possibilities exist, the choice should be made on the basis of an evaluation of first and operating costs.

Such factory-made components may be incorporated in the duct system during field erection, or a factory-assembled unit may be used. The choice generally depends on the comparative cost of field and factory labor. In the U.S. market the advantage may rest with the factory-assembled units for air capacities of 50,000 cfm or even higher. Fan-coil units do not generally exceed 50,000 cfm, but sprayed coil dehumidifiers complete with dampers and filters, etc., are often prebuilt or prefabricated for very high capacities. In addition to some pertinent details on fans, the equipment discussed in the following paragraphs includes humidifiers, air washers, coils, dehydrators, and controls.

Although no less a part of any complete air-conditioning system, detailed discussions are not given for ducts, terminal devices, odor controllers, and filters. Such discussions may be found in Chapters 3, 4, 14, and 23, respectively.

Fans

The energy for moving the air through an air-conditioning system may be provided by one or more fans. If only one fan is used, it is called "the supply fan." Such a fan may furnish the energy for exhaust or return air or both functions or a separate "exhaust fan," a separate "return air fan," or both may be used.

On a 100% outside air system the supply fan (SF) must pull the outside air (OA) into the system, push or pull it through the conditioning equipment, push the conditioned air (CA) into the space, and push the exhaust air (EA) out of the space. Figure 150a illustrates such a system and the corresponding pressure graphs. If the exhaust air openings are at all restricted, a considerable pressure must be built up in the space in order to force the exhaust air outside. A separate exhaust fan (EF) may be used to overcome this difficulty as illustrated in Figure 150b.

A single fan or fan unit may be used on a return air system as illustrated in Figure 150c. The same situation with regard to restricted exhaust openings exists as for Figure 150a. In addition, the return air portion of the duct work must be designed so that the losses equal those of the outside air and exhaust air portions. A separate return air fan (RF) may be used to overcome these difficulties as illustrated in Figure 150d.

In all of the systems diagrammed in Figure 150 the capacity of the supply fan (CFM_{SF}) may be considered equal to the required rate of supply of conditioned air (CFM_{CA}), and calculated from

$$CFM_{SF} = CFM_{CA} = \frac{SH_{room\ load}}{1.087\ (t_{CA} - t_{RA})}. \tag{372}$$

The supply rate is dependent on the sensible room load ($SH_{room\ load}$) in Btu/hr, the dry-bulb temperatures in °F of the supply air (t_{CA}) and the room or return air (t_{RA}).

The capacity of the exhaust fan (CFM_{EF}) in Figure 150b must equal that of the supply fan (CFM_{SF}), plus or minus any leakage (CFM_L) to or from the space due to infiltration or exfiltration:

$$CFM_{EF} = CFM_{SF} \pm CFM_L. \tag{373}$$

The capacity of the return air fan (CFM_{RF}) in Figure 150d should equal the supply rate minus the exhaust rate with corrections for infiltration or exfiltration:

$$CFM_{RF} = CFM_{SF} - CFM_{exh} \pm CFM_L. \tag{374}$$

In all the systems diagrammed in Figure 150 the fans should be selected to develop a total pressure corresponding to the differences in total pressure across them as indicated in the various diagrams. In every case the fan total pressure for the supply fan (FTP_{SF}) is equal to the sum of the total pressure losses ($\Sigma TP_{losses SF}$) from the outside air opening to the space plus the space pressure (TP_{space}):

$$FTP_{SF} = \Sigma\ TP_{losses SF} + TP_{space}. \tag{375}$$

The pressure required of the exhaust fan (FTP_{EF}) equals the sum of the losses from the space to the exhaust air opening ($\Sigma\ TP_{losses EF}$) minus the space pressure (TP_{space}):

$$FTP_{EF} = \Sigma\ TP_{losses EF} - TP_{space}. \tag{376}$$

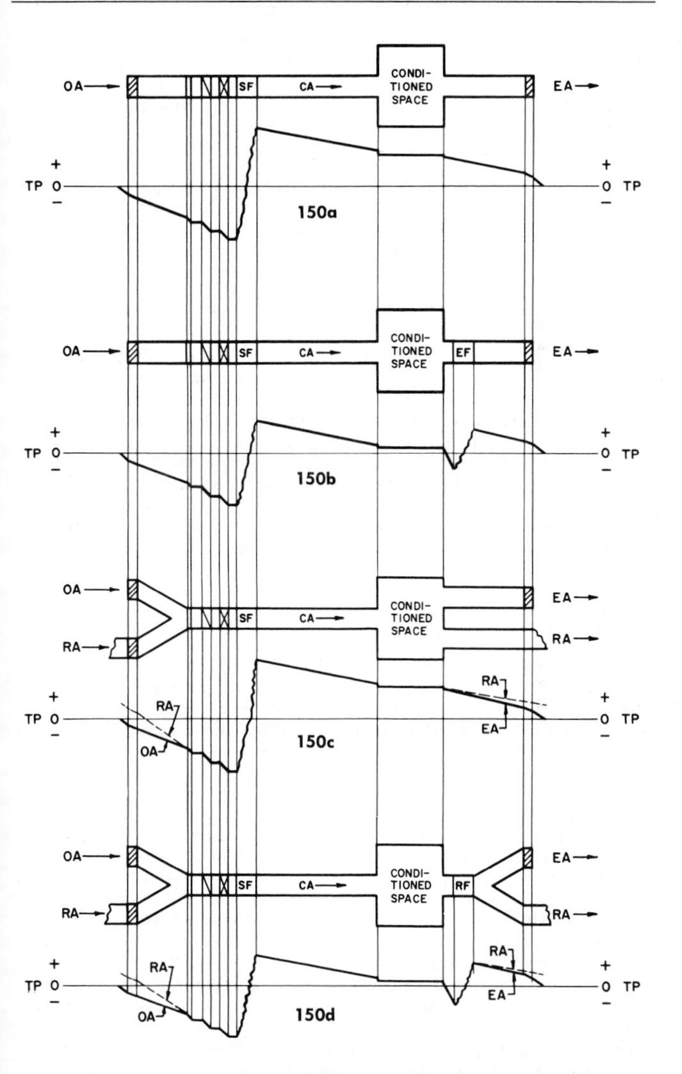

Figure 150—Supply, Exhaust, and Return Air Fan Systems

The pressure required of the return air fan (FTP_{RF}) equals the sum of the losses from the space to the exhaust air opening minus the space pressure, or it equals the sum of the losses from the space through the return line and back to the space ($\Sigma\ TP_{losses\,RF}$) minus the supply fan pressure (FTP_{SF}):

$$FTP_{RF} = \Sigma\ TP_{losses\,RF} - FTP_{SF}. \tag{377}$$

The supply fan may be located ahead of the conditioning coils in a blow-through arrangement or in the draw-through arrangement shown. Although the density may vary, the difference in fan requirements or performance is usually negligible on an air-conditioning system.

All types of fans have been employed on air-conditioning systems. The advantages and disadvantages of each type, as discussed in Chapter 13, generally apply to fans for air conditioning. Efficiency becomes more important as the job becomes larger. Stability and good paralleling characteristics are often essential. Belt drives are usually preferred to direct-connected motors. Flexible connections to duct work and even to power source should be provided, especially if resilient mountings are used. Quiet operation requires that vibration transmission through structural members be minimized by all these means. Air-borne noises are attenuated to some extent by duct work. Very little additional treatment is required for non-critical areas on low-velocity systems. Critical areas always require some sort of treatment to reduce noise to an acceptable level. High-velocity systems require extensive treatment, the amount depending on the level of fan noise and the natural attenuation of the duct work, etc.

Humidifiers

Moisture can be injected as steam directly into the air. This is usually accomplished in the supply unit or duct work, although industrially direct injection into room air is sometimes used. Some sensible heating of the air will result since the steam temperature will be higher than the air temperature. The exact amount of sensible heat can be calculated for any moisture addition using an enthalpy-humidity analysis. However, sufficiently accurate results are usually obtained by assuming a constant dry-bulb process.

Water can be evaporated into the air directly from pans by supplying the necessary heat with submerged coils. Here too some sensible heating will occur since the water temperature must be elevated above the air temperature. A generally safe assumption is that the sensible heating equals one-half the latent heating or one-third of the total heat.

Water can be sprayed directly into the air stream in limited quantities. The process may be considered adiabatic regardless of the water temperature if complete evaporation takes place. Consequently, sensible cooling will accompany the humidification. A constant wet-bulb process may therefore be assumed.

The pressure drop occasioned by any of these devices is negligibly small. Air washers and sprayed coils may also be used as humidifiers. They will be discussed in the next section.

Air Washers

When large quantities of finely divided water are sprayed into air the relation of the initial air state and spray water temperature determines whether heating, cooling, humidifying, or dehumidifying results. The process may be considered adiabatic if the water is recirculated and equilibrium obtained. In such cases the water assumes the wet-bulb temperature which remains constant and humidity is increased as dry-bulb is reduced. If heat is added to the spray water, humidification may be accompanied by an increase or decrease in dry-bulb depending upon the mean effective water temperature. If the water is cooled before spraying, the air will be cooled, but whether humidification or dehumidification results depends on whether the air is cooled below the dew point or not.

The contact-mixture analogy originally proposed by Carrier* may be used to explain the performance of air washers and sprayed or non-sprayed coils. This theory assumes that for both heat and vapor transfer the particles of the air may be divided into two groups, one of which contacts a hypothetical surface and the other bypasses or does not contact that surface. It is further assumed that the state of the contacted particles is that of "saturated air" at the temperature of the surface and that the end state of the air is a mixture of the bypassed portion at entering conditions and the contacted portion at the conditions described.

The ratio of non-contacted particles to total particles is frequently called the equivalent bypass factor (BPF). The hypothetical surface temperature is often referred to as the apparatus dew point (t_{ADP}). From the assumptions of the theory:

$$BPF = \frac{t_L - t_{ADP}}{t_E - t_{ADP}} = \frac{H_L - H_{ADP}}{H_E - H_{ADP}} = \frac{\Sigma_L - \Sigma_{ADP}}{\Sigma_E - \Sigma_{ADP}} \text{ or } \frac{i_L - i_{ADP}}{i_E - i_{ADP}}, \quad (378)$$

where t is the dry-bulb temperature, H is the absolute humidity, Σ is the sigma function, and i is the enthalpy. The subscripts L and E designate leaving and entering respectively. If $BPF = BPF_1$ for one unit, then $BPF = BPF_1$ for n units in parallel and $BPF = BPF_1{}^n$ for n units in series.

In a recirculated spray air washer the spray water assumes the wet-bulb temperature of the air. Under equilibrium conditions the wet-bulb and water temperatures are constant through the washer. The apparatus dew point or water temperature is easily measured, and the bypass factor easily determined from the entering and leaving temperature relationships. The values of BPF so determined are also valid when the sprays are heated or cooled.

The humidifying efficiency or cooling effect (η) of a recirculated spray air washer is defined as the ratio of dry-bulb reduction ($t_E - t_L$) to wet-bulb depression ($t_E - t'$). It can be shown that this is equal to one minus the bypass factor:

$$\eta = \frac{t_E - t_L}{t_E - t'} = 1 - \frac{t_L - t'}{t_E - t'} = 1 - BPF. \quad (379)$$

*W. H. Carrier, The Contact-Mixture Analogy Applied to Heat Transfer With Mixtures of Air and Water Vapor, *Trans. ASME*, vol. 59, pp. 49-53, 1937.

TABLE 94

BYPASS FACTORS FOR AIR WASHERS WITH RECIRCULATED SPRAYS

Buffalo Forge Company Washer		Length	Face Velocity or FV	Water Pressure or WP	Hum. Eff. η	ByPass Factor BPF
Type	Spray Pattern					
A	one bank with air	83″	500 fpm	20 psi	.70	.30
B	one bank with air	95″	500 fpm	20 psi	.70	.30
B	two banks, both with air	95″	500 fpm	20 psi	.90	.10
B	two banks opposed	95″	500 fpm	20 psi	.95	.05
C	one bank with air	56″	500 fpm	20 psi	.65	.35
H	two banks opposed	122″	500 fpm	35 psi	.97	.03

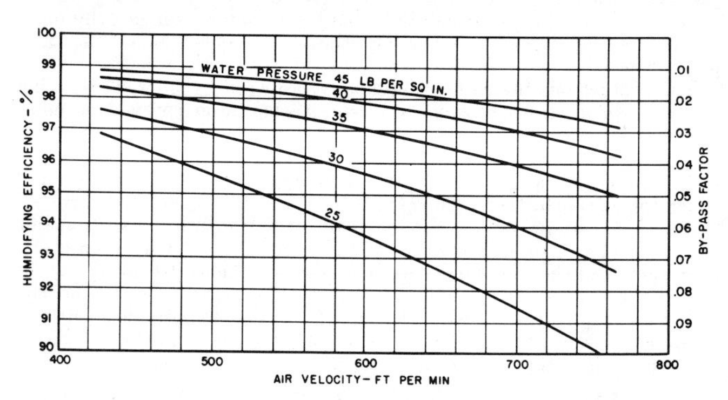

Figure 151—Humidifying Efficiencies of Air Washers

The performance of any recirculated spray air washer may be predicted from the operating characteristics, if such characteristics are related to either η or BPF. Table 94 gives η and BPF for several Buffalo Forge Company designs at certain specified conditions. Figure **151** shows the relation of η or BPF to face velocity and water pressure for one particular design.

Regardless of whether spray water is recirculated, heated, or cooled, there must be a heat balance. Assuming no loss to surroundings,

$$m_A(i_L - i_E) = m_W(WT_E - WT_L) + m_A \frac{(H_L - H_E)}{7000}(WT_E - 32), \text{ or} \tag{380}$$

$$m_A(\Sigma_L - \Sigma_E) = m_W(WT_E - WT_L), \tag{381}$$

where m_A and m_W are the mass flow rates of air and water respectively. The water temperatures are designated WT_E for entering and WT_L for leaving and other symbols are as previously defined. This formula simply verifies the constant wet-bulb—constant water temperature relationship for recirculated spray air washers. However, for hot or chilled water, it gives the equilibrium requirements.

Although the heat balance will give the water side requirements for ny air side requirements and vice versa, it is also necessary to relate erformance characteristics to operating characteristics. The bypass ıctor—apparatus dew point relationship is generally applicable but the umidifying efficiency concept is not, simply because the wet-bulb does ot remain constant when the water is either heated or chilled. The pparatus dew point will fall somewhere between the entering and leaving ater temperatures and will be quite close to the leaving temperature for w bypass factors. Although the bypass factor for any design may be efined for any combination of face velocity (FV) and water pressure WP), a trial value would have to be assumed for the ADP and checked hrough for assumed values of the operating variables FV and WP. To liminate the necessity for such a laborious procedure, AMCA in their ulletin 107 has related both design and operating variables to a "per-ormance factor." Portions of this bulletin are given in Figure 152. This ata was issued for dehumidifying air washers with a 12°F maximum ater temperature range.

The entering and leaving conditions are related to the performance actor (PF) by:

$$PF = \frac{(t_E' - WT_E) - (t_L' - WT_L)}{(t_E' - WT_E)}. \qquad (382)$$

The operating and design variables are related to performance factor y:

$$PF = PF_{base} \times F_V \times F_W \times F_P \times F_L \times F_H. \qquad (383)$$

The factors PF_{base}, F_V, F_W, etc., may be determined from Figure 152. The entering and leaving conditions may be established in relation to one nother by means of a heat balance. The corresponding performance actor can then be calculated from the appropriate temperatures using Equation 382. The operating variables may be manipulated to provide an qual value according to the Equation 383.

The published method does not provide for a leaving dry-bulb deter-mination, but once the entering and leaving wet-bulbs are known, the pparatus dew point can be calculated as the temperature correspond-ng to

$$\Sigma_{ADP} = \frac{\Sigma_L - BPF\,\Sigma_E}{1 - BPF}. \qquad (384)$$

f an exact value of BPF is not known, a close approximation may be btained by using one minus the performance factor instead. Given the pparatus dew point (t_{ADP}), entering dry-bulb (t_E), and bypass factor BPF), the leaving dry-bulb (t_L) can be determined from

$$t_L = BPF\, t_E + (1 - BPF)\, t_{ADP}. \qquad (385)$$

Heat exchangers for spray water are generally located outside the vasher. Shell and tube heat exchangers are used for chilling with various efrigerants or for heating with steam or hot water. An open type of eater known as an ejector may be used. Steam at approximately 5 psig s injected directly into the water on the suction side of the pump.

Humidification with heated sprays may eliminate the need for preheat oils. Instead of preheating to the desired wet-bulb and cooling along

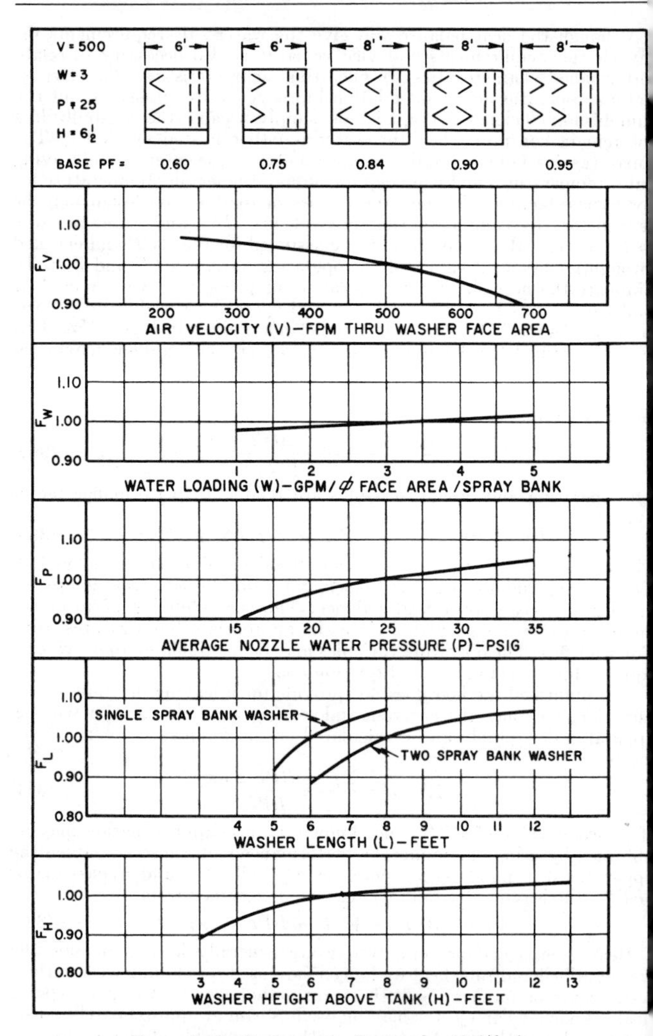

Figure 152—Performance Factors for Air Washers

Adapted from the data of Basic Data for Rating Air Washers, AMCA, Bul. 107, 194
(No longer in print.)

hat wet-bulb line with recirculated sprays, the same leaving conditions an be obtained directly, provided, of course, the air is tempered to prevent freezing. Reheating may be required in both cases for temperature control.

Unless the water is heated an appreciable amount, the dry-bulb temperature of the air is always lowered in an air washer. This evaporative cooling may be utilized on low wet-bulb occasions instead of refrigeration. Whenever dehumidification is required, the water must be chilled.

Air washers should always be equipped with screens and strainers to prevent fouling of the pump, piping, and nozzles. Provisions must be made to maintain the proper level in the tank, including make-up, overflow, and quick-fill connections. Humidifiers require make-up and dehumidifiers require overflow. Consequently, there are usually differences in the design. Eliminators, which are a series of corrugated plates, prevent entrained moisture from passing beyond the washer. The number of bends and lips, the angle, and the spacing, all influence the eliminator performance. Limiting face velocities depend on whether the eliminators are mounted for a vertical or a horizontal flow and on height if horizontal. Bent plate eliminator designs prevent carryover up to approximately 650 fpm FV. The most economical face velocity, particularly when dehumidifying, is approximately 500 fpm. Inlet baffles may be required on occasion to prevent loss of water out of the inlet due to turbulence or to the spray action itself. Special flooded eliminators are offered which provide scrubbing action with only limited humidification. Such an arrangement is usually operated continuously, but independently of the atomizing sprays which may be turned off in humid weather. Eliminator resistance varies with face velocity and design. Most effective bent plate eliminators have a resistance of approximately 0.2″ WG or more at 500 face velocity. Inlet baffles with slightly less than 0.1″ WG resistance perform satisfactorily. A spray may assist or resist the flow of air depending on its direction. The kinetic energy in the usual atomized spray amounts to approximately 0.1″ WG for a 3 gpm per square foot water loading at 500 face velocity.

High-velocity eliminators have been developed which make it possible to operate air washers at up to 1500-2000 fpm face velocity without carryover.

A discussion of air-conditioning coils follows, but it should be mentioned here that many of the advantages of both air washers and coils can be achieved by combining the two. Coils prevent contamination or loss of the heating or cooling medium. Sprays provide a means of humidifying, evaporative cooling, and washing the air. Sprayed coil units accomplish all these results utilizing a space generally smaller than required by an air washer but larger than needed for a non-sprayed coil.

Coils

Because the greatest resistance to heat transfer occurs in the air film, coils are designed with a larger surface area on the air side than on the medium side. The heating or cooling medium is delivered to the inside of the tubes and the outside of the tubes has extended fins over which the air is passed. Copper tubes are usually used with either copper or aluminum fins. However, other materials may be required for special applications. Ammonia attacks copper, and, therefore, steel is specified for this refrigerant. The bond between fin and tube is most important and the various designs differ principally in the manner of producing this bond. Copper fins are recommended whenever coils are sprayed. Solder coating of all copper coils provides metallic as well as mechanical bond between fin and tube. Different fin spacings may be offered. Air-conditioning coils may be designated according to the nature of the duty expected of them, or the medium for which they were designed, or some distinguishing constructional feature.

Heating coils may be expected to (1) temper the incoming air so that its temperature is above freezing, (2) preheat tempered air to facilitate humidification, or (3) reheat the humidified air for temperature control purposes. Tempering coils are not needed where return air is used, since there is sufficient heat therein to prevent freezing. Preheat coils may be employed in a dual role including the tempering duty. Reheating may be required after dehumidification as well as humidification. A heating system may use a single reheat coil to raise the temperature part way and booster coils in each space for final temperature control. Cooling coils may be required to dehumidify as well as cool.

For protection against freezing, (1) tempering coils should always have full steam pressure, hence should not be oversized and throttled; and (2) preheat coils which must be throttled for control purposes should be of a non-freeze design if freezing air can possibly get to the coil. Even if these provisions are made, devices to sense the temperature over the whole face of the coil and to close the outside air damper, should freezing conditions be approached, are considered by many to be very wise investments. A non-freeze type coil is constructed with a distributing device inside the tubes to theoretically keep every portion of the tubes supplied with live steam. Normally such a scheme gives good protection, but malfunction of traps or plugging of distributors could create a danger of freezing the condensate and subsequent damage. Unused chilled water coils may be protected in winter by draining them completely or by adding a suitable anti-freeze solution. Drained coils should be thoroughly blown out to remove trapped water. For hot water coils with anti-freeze, a corrosion inhibitor is necessary. Additional inhibitor will be required after a period of use at elevated temperatures. Anti-freeze solution has different properties than water has. These differences will affect coil and pump performance and therefore operating costs.

Air-conditioning coils are built with individual tubes arranged in one or more rows. The number of tubes in a row varies with individual design and size. The number of rows depends principally upon duty requirements.

Return bends may be used to connect any two tubes in a row or in two different rows. The extreme circuiting arrangements are (1) the case where all of the fluid passes through each tube in turn, and (2) the case where the fluid passing through any one tube does not pass through any other. For the same amount of working fluid and surface, the pressure drop in the first case is many, many times that of the second. The number of circuits equals the number of tubes in the latter case and is unity for the former. Between these extremes, numerous multiple circuit combinations are possible. Coils are made with the number of circuits equal to one-half, one, two, or three times the number of tubes in a row (across the face). The air always makes only one pass through the coils. In the usual air-conditioning applications the working fluid may make one or more passes across the path of the air. In the extremes, coils are either single-circuit, multiple-pass or single-pass, multiple-circuit arrangement.

The terms parallel flow, counter flow, and crossflow are also used to describe coils. All designs, as applied, have an element of crossflow, but the term is most appropriate for a multi-circuit, single-pass coil. Any multiple row, multi-pass coil can be arranged for either parallel or counter flow. If both air and working fluid enter at the same side, the arrangement is called parallel flow. Counter flow occurs for practical purposes whenever the air and working fluids enter at opposite ends. If the working fluid remains at constant temperature throughout, there is no practical difference between parallel and counter flow.

Steam coils are built with one or two rows of tubes. Standard coils may be single- or multiple-pass for either number of rows. Non-freeze coils cannot accurately be described as either single- or double-pass. The steam distributing tube which is centered inside the finned tube delivers steam to holes along its length. Condensate may be returned in either direction, although the usual arrangement has both connections on the same end. Unless the tubes are pitched in their own casing, the coil will have to be pitched properly to provide for condensate drainage. Proper trapping and other pertinent features are also essential, and manufacturers' recommendations should be followed. Most commercial coils have adequate provisions for expansion and contraction, but strains due to piping should be prevented.

The steam distributing feature of non-freeze coils also provides greater protection against temperature stratification in long tube lengths. Supply from both ends or vertical tube arrangements, where coils would otherwise be long and narrow, may also afford better distribution. The piping arrangement may not be as desirable in these last cases as in the first.

The exact sizing of steam coils is often a prerequisite to prevent overheating. Different combinations of fin or tube spacing are offered to provide economical selections.

Water coils are usually built in an even number of rows; although the last row may be unfinned, serving only to locate a return connection on the same end as the supply. Multiple circuits must be used to limit pressure losses. The various multi-pass circuits may be provided for either horizontal or vertical air flow. The tubes must be horizontal, and the return bends oriented properly for proper drainage. Proper orientation means different designs for different air directions. A removable header cover or covers may be provided to facilitate tube cleaning and positive drainage. Either hot or chilled water may be used. Brines must be conditioned or special materials used in coil construction where brines are to be used.

Direct-expansion coils are also built with multiple circuits to limit pressure drops. Multiple passes are used to simplify the distribution problem and to locate returns on the same end or side as supply. The refrigerant must be distributed uniformly to each circuit for efficient utilization of the surface. It is important that no liquid be returned; consequently coil selections are usually based on some definite amount of superheating of the vapor. Superheating requires much more surface than an equal amount of evaporation. If each circuit receives just the right amount of refrigerant, then superheating can be held to a minimum without floodback. Various distributor designs are in use on direct-expansion coils. The manifold or row type distributor utilizes a liquid level or hydrostatic head to achieve uniform distribution. This system requires accurate mounting and feed, and a feed that will not disturb the level. Pressure type distributors utilize the increase in velocity through an orifice and subsequent impingement to achieve uniform distribution. A somewhat higher pressure drop is encountered with this type compared to the others. This drop is not detrimental, since pressure reduction is required to obtain low temperatures anyway. The refrigerant, load, and suction temperature should be specified so that the orifice may be sized properly.

For any type of coil various sizes are generally offered as commercial standards. The basic convection heat transfer equation governs the selection of the proper coil. From

$$TH = UA \, \Delta \, t_m, \tag{386}$$

the load (TH) in Btu per hr that can be handled by a coil with a surface (A) in sq ft depends on the effective temperature head ($\Delta \, t_m$) in °F which exists between the air and the working fluid, and the transmission characteristic (U).

In the usual case the entering conditions for both the air and the heat transfer medium can be established by reference to design conditions. The leaving conditions and amounts of each are related to the load (TH) by

$$TH = m \, \Delta \, i, \tag{387}$$

where the weight (m) is in lb per hr and the enthalpy difference ($\Delta \, i$) is in Btu per lb. This expression yields:

$$SH = 1.087 \; CFM \; (t_L - t_E) \textit{ for air}, \tag{388}$$

$$TH = 4.45 \; CFM \; (i_L - i_E) \textit{ for air}, \tag{389}$$

$$TH = 500 \; GPM \; (WT_L - WT_E) \textit{ for water}, \tag{390}$$

$$TH = m\lambda \textit{ for steam or volatile refrigerants}. \tag{391}$$

By assuming a value for either the amount or the temperature/enthalpy difference in any case, the remaining unknowns may be resolved.

Once the limiting temperature conditions are established, the effective temperature head can be calculated for any flow pattern. Coil test data are evaluated on the basis of the log mean temperature difference, even though this expression is strictly correct only for constant U, true parallel, or true counter flow operations. An explanation of $\Delta \, t_m$ including formula and charts is given in Chapter 2. The inside and outside film coefficients in any case must be based on empirical data. The various fluid properties and velocities would have to be determined, as well as the physical data on the surface itself. The usual rating tables and charts simplify this problem by making the exact determination of intermediate factors unnecessary, and utilizing empirical data.

Most of the surface used in air-conditioning work may be selected for air face velocities ranging from 300 to 800 fpm with economical results. Due to shallower depth, heating coils are being selected at even higher velocities. The economic evaluation is essentially one of finding the selection for which first cost plus the present value of operating costs is a minimum. Obviously, higher velocities reduce surface requirements, but increase pressure drop. Similarly, coil depth influences refrigeration and coil costs. Cooling coil velocities may be limited to 500 fpm or less unless provisions can be made downstream to collect blown off water drops in a safe manner. Extended pans, low-velocity plenums, or eliminators may be used for this purpose. Since coils are usually not built to individual specifications, but are available with specific face areas, the usual selection procedure involves the equation of continuity as either

$$FA\ approx. = CFM \div FV\ approx.,\ or \tag{392}$$

$$FV\ actual = CFM \div FA\ actual. \tag{393}$$

There are several major differences between heating and cooling coil requirements. Dehumidification results whenever the surface temperature is below the dew point. Whereas with sensible heating or cooling all the heat must be transmitted through the air film, tube metal, and inside film, only the last two resist the flow of latent heat when condensation takes place on the surface. If, however, condensation occurs in the air stream as fog, the total heat must pass through the air film. Fogging occurs only when "saturated" air is further cooled. Cooling fluid temperatures are generally limited to those that will not cause icing of the coils. Otherwise, a reduction in heat transfer and air flow results, which cannot be tolerated. If dehumidification is desired, the coolant must be sufficiently cold to produce a surface temperature below the dew point. For a volatile refrigerant only one refrigerant condition will theoretically produce the required sensible to total heat ratio with a particular coil. The apparatus dew point may be considered the hypothetical surface temperature required to produce the desired leaving condition if the path of the process is considered a straight line through that temperature on the saturation curve. Since the surface temperature changes as the air proceeds through the coil, the actual process is not a straight line, but a pursuit curve of the instantaneous surface temperature at any point. When used with a bypass factor, the apparatus dew point is a valuable tool. The bypass factor expresses the fraction of air which can be considered to pass through a coil unaffected if the remainder is considered perfectly or totally conditioned.

The ADP-BPF method of rating direct-expansion coils in effect leads to a balancing of refrigerant and air side transmission. One such method utilizes two sets of factors, which we might call "*L*" and "*M*." If we assume a coil (face area and depth), the required refrigerant temperature, for any load and any capacity, can then be determined. To illustrate:

$$TH = \text{“}L\text{”} \times (i_E - i_{ADP})\ CFM,\ and \tag{394}$$

$$TH = \text{“}M\text{”} \times (t_{ADP} - t_R)\ FA, \tag{395}$$

where $TH = 4.45\ (i_E - i_L)\ CFM$ and other symbols are as previously defined.

TABLE 95—PERFORMANCE OF DIRECT EXPANSION COILS

"L" and "M" Factors—Series 80

Rows	1	2	3	4	5	6	7	8
"M" factor	420	840	1260	1680	2100	2520	2940	3360
"L" factor	1.48	2.45	3.07	3.47	3.78	4.05	4.19	4.28

Minimum Suction Temperatures to Prevent Frost—.°F

Leaving Wet-Bulb	Face Velocity—fpm			F & BP Dampers
	300	400	500	
45	32	32	32	32
50	32	32	32	32
55	32	31	30	32
60	27	26	25	32

Maximum Load per Distributor—Tons

Tube Face	12	15	18	21	24
Pressure Distributor	24	30	36	42	48

Adapted from the data of Direct Expansion Cooling Surface, Aerofin Corporation, Bul D-66, 1966.

The first expression can be solved for i_{ADP} by using the appropriate "L" value for any particular depth coil as listed in Table 95. The second expression can then be solved for the refrigerant temperature using the corresponding apparatus dew point (t_{ADP}) and "M" from Table 95.

It is not immediately obvious that the bypass factor is involved in the use of "L" and "M" factors. However, an examination of the definition will show that it is. A graphical solution for the leaving dry-bulb can be obtained on a psychrometric chart by drawing a straight line between the entering state and the apparatus dew point (plotted on the saturation curve). The leaving dry-bulb may be read at the intersection of this line with the leaving wet-bulb line.

The above analysis points up the major limitation of any device wherein sensible and latent heat are removed simultaneously. There are some sensible-total heat ratios which are impossible to satisfy in this manner. These can be discovered graphically on the psychrometric chart. If the entering and leaving conditions are connected by a straight line, and that line does not intersect the saturation curve, the sensible-total heat ratio cannot be satisfied directly. The remedy in such cases is to cool to the required dew point and reheat as required. The alternatives are to allow different room conditions than specified, or to reduce the fresh air load, or both. Room conditions can be specified with a sufficiently lower dry-bulb in many cases to offset the increase in space humidity and thereby maintain nearly the same effective temperature.

A graphical method, which utilizes an alignment chart in place of the "L" formula and the psychrometric charts, is illustrated in Figure 153. The required apparatus dew point may be obtained directly from the entering and leaving wet-bulbs and the bypass factor for any coil. The leaving dry-bulb can then be determined from the apparatus dew point and the entering dry-bulb. Since this completely defines the air side performance, it is only necessary to provide the indicated apparatus dew

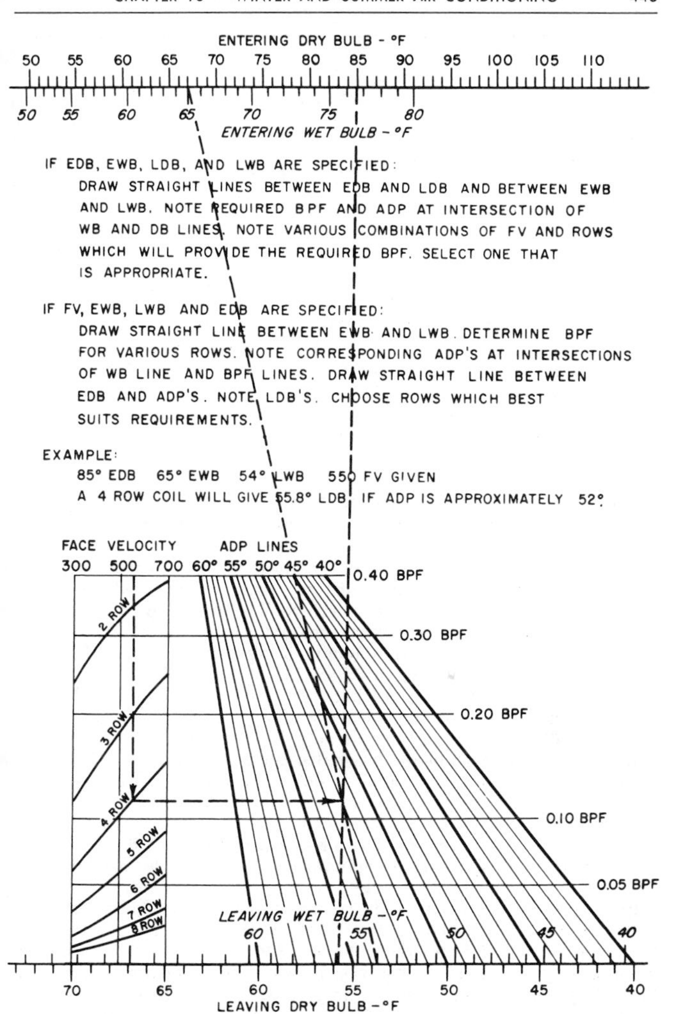
ENTERING DRY BULB - °F
50 55 60 65 70 75 80 85 90 95 100 105 110
50 55 60 65 70 75 80
ENTERING WET BULB - °F
IF EDB, EWB, LDB, AND LWB ARE SPECIFIED:
DRAW STRAIGHT LINES BETWEEN EDB AND LDB AND BETWEEN EWB AND LWB. NOTE REQUIRED BPF AND ADP AT INTERSECTION OF WB AND DB LINES. NOTE VARIOUS COMBINATIONS OF FV AND ROWS WHICH WILL PROVIDE THE REQUIRED BPF. SELECT ONE THAT IS APPROPRIATE.
IF FV, EWB, LWB AND EDB ARE SPECIFIED:
DRAW STRAIGHT LINE BETWEEN EWB AND LWB. DETERMINE BPF FOR VARIOUS ROWS. NOTE CORRESPONDING ADP'S AT INTERSECTIONS OF WB LINE AND BPF LINES. DRAW STRAIGHT LINE BETWEEN EDB AND ADP'S. NOTE LDB'S. CHOOSE ROWS WHICH BEST SUITS REQUIREMENTS.
EXAMPLE:
85° EDB 65° EWB 54° LWB 550 FV GIVEN
A 4 ROW COIL WILL GIVE 55.8° LDB IF ADP IS APPROXIMATELY 52°.
FACE VELOCITY
300 500 700
ADP LINES
60° 55° 50° 45° 40°
0.40 BPF
0.30 BPF
0.20 BPF
0.10 BPF
0.05 BPF
2 ROW
3 ROW
4 ROW
5 ROW
6 ROW
7 ROW
8 ROW
LEAVING WET BULB - °F
60 55 50 45 40
70 65 60 55 50 45 40
LEAVING DRY BULB - °F

Figure 153—Air Side Performance of Dehumidifying Coils

Adapted from the data of B. P. Morabito and W. Conroy, Here's a New, Quick Way to Select Chilled Water Coils, *Heating, Piping and Air Conditioning*, pp. 156-160, January, 1959. Original Copyright 1958, Carrier Corporation.

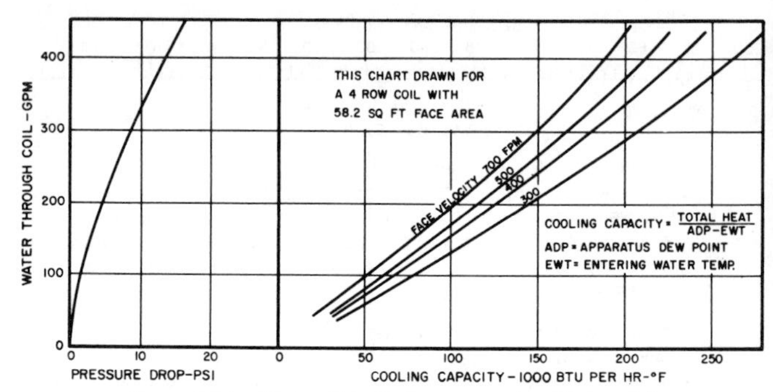

Figure 154—Water Side Performance of a Water Coil

Adapted from the data of B. P. Morabito and W. Conroy, Here's a New, Quick Way to Select Chilled Water Coils, *Heating, Piping and Air Conditioning*, pp. 156-160, January, 1959. Original Copyright 1958, Carrier Corporation.

---

point by proper selection of refrigerant temperature. For direct-expansion coils, the "M" factor expression can be used to solve for the appropriate t_R.

The ADP-BPF method can also be applied to chilled water coils. The air side determinations are identical to those for direct-expansion coils. The refrigerant side determinations are more complicated, since the refrigerant is not at constant temperature. The evaluation of water side performance involves water temperature and velocity and therefore water quantities and circuiting. Individual charts can be drawn for each particular coil, as exemplified in Figure 154.

A more general solution, with fewer charts, involves in effect an evaluation of the over-all coefficient (U). This may be expressed in terms of rows and face area rather than in actual surface area. The symbol (K) is used instead of (U) when units of Btu per hr-row-sq ft FA-°MED are employed. Figure 153 can be used to determine the apparatus dew point and bypass factor for any set of entering and leaving requirements. The numerous theoretical possibilities for coil selection will thereby be reduced to one or two practical cases. The air side performance will be fixed, so that it will only be necessary to manipulate the water side variables. The entering water temperature can be fixed to a limited extent, by relationship to apparatus dew point. The Aerofin Corporation suggests that the apparatus dew point will fall between the entering water temperature and leaving wet-bulb (.5 times the difference for Series 80 and .7 times the difference for Series 140). The rise in water temperature is generally limited by coil cost and pressure drop considerations to somewhere between 8 and 12 degrees. As pointed out by McFarlan* and Morabito**,

---

*A. I. McFarlan, Improved Zoning Betters Department Store Air Conditioning, *ASHRAE Journal*, December, 1959, pp. 37-40.
**B. P. Morabito, How Higher Cooling Coil Differentials Effect System Economies, *ASHRAE Journal*, August 1960, pp. 60-65.

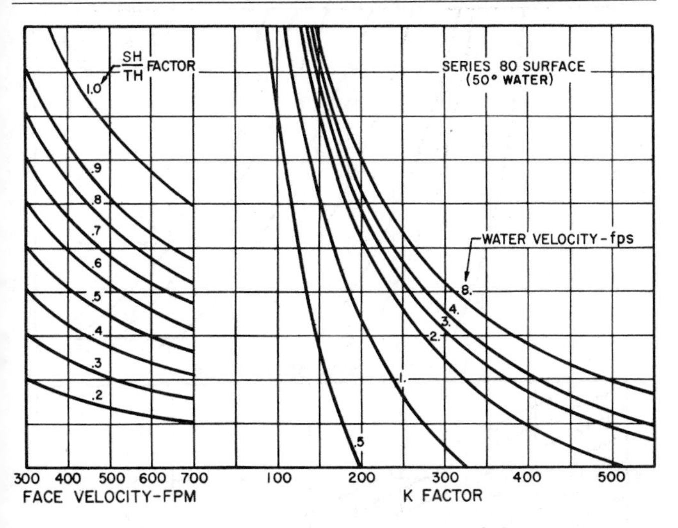

Figure 155—Performance of Water Coils

Adapted from the data of Water Coils for Cooling, Aerofin Corporation, Bul. C-58, 1958.

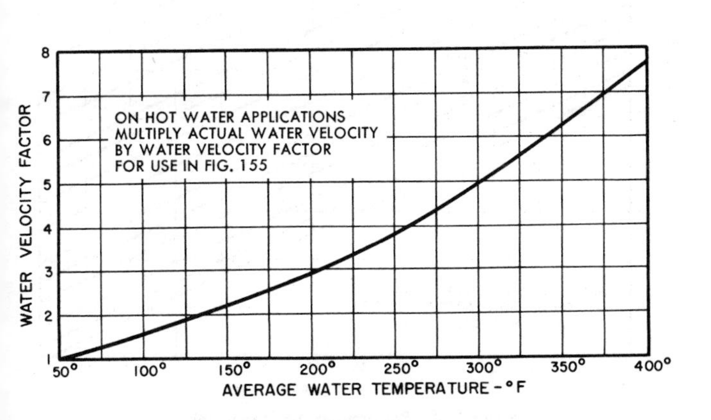

Figure 156—Hot Water Corrections

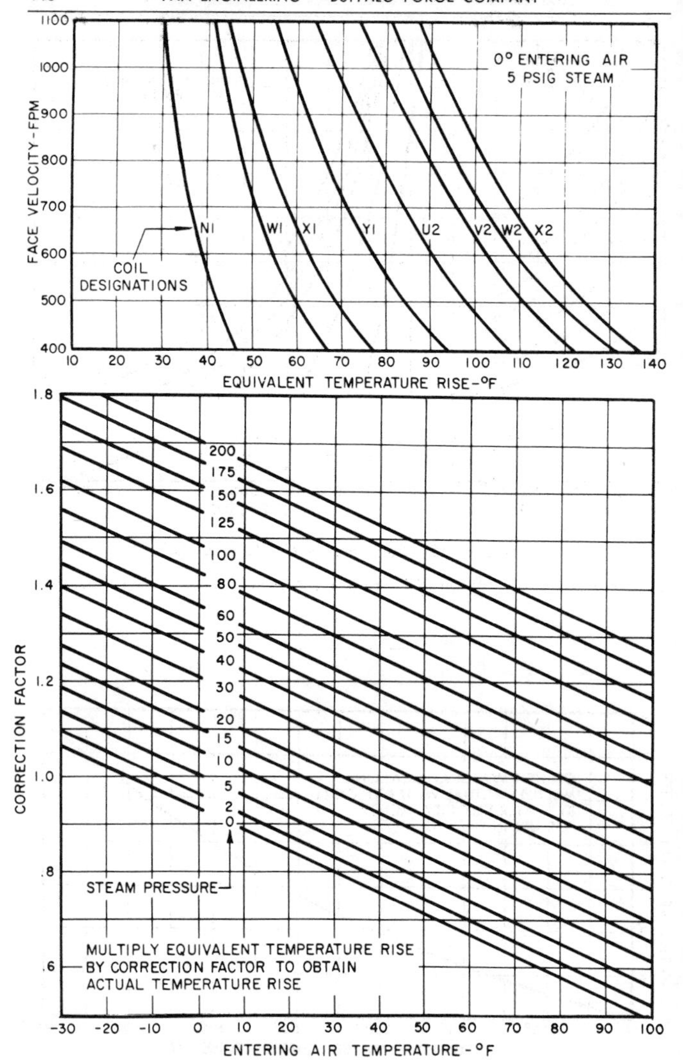

Figure 157—Performance of Steam Coils

Adapted from the data of Steam Heating Coils, Aerofin Corporation, Bul. B-58, 1958.

over-all system economies may dictate the use of higher cooling coil differentials. By establishing the entering water temperature and the water temperature rise, the leaving water temperature, MED, and GPM can be determined directly. Water velocities for various circuits or circuiting arrangements of the coil chosen can be figured and equivalent U or K values calculated. The choice of circuiting should be the one which matches the required surface to that available. The chart in Figure 155 shows K values for various air and water velocities for one type of water coil. The K value determined from this chart may be used to establish the number of rows required for a particular job, but only if the limitations as demonstrated by apparatus dew point and bypass factor are evaluated in some manner.

The same K factor chart may be used for hot water coils. Since the chart is based on approximately 50° water, and since the difference in properties of higher temperature water is appreciable, a correction factor chart is given in Figure 156. Since heating involves only sensible change, the apparatus dew point method is not applicable. Water temperatures and quantities should be established in relation to the heating plant and the required number of rows determined.

Steam coil ratings are perhaps the simplest to use. They are usually presented for each type of surface in terms of temperature rise versus face velocity for one combination of entering air temperature and steam pressure. By assuming a constant U (which is reasonable) the temperature rise for any other entering air and steam condition is proportional to the ratio of the difference between entering steam and air temperatures and the corresponding difference on which the chart is based. These ratios are usually tabulated as in Figure 157. The temperature rise data for various types of surface is also given in Figure 157 for 0° entering air and 5 psig steam.

Dehydration Equipment

Water vapor may be extracted by absorbent or adsorbent processes. In either case the heat released by condensation of the vapor raises the temperature of the air. Adsorbents, such as silica gel or activated alumina, are solid substances with submicroscopic pores capable of dehydrating air on physical contact. Absorbents are hygroscopic solutions such as lithium chloride and calcium chloride. The hygroscopic depression of either is the difference between its temperature and the saturation temperature corresponding to its water vapor pressure. Adsorbers convert the latent heat to sensible heat and approximately 20% additional sensible heating results from release of the "heat of wetting" and heat of reactivation. The path of the process in an absorber without external heat transfer more nearly follows a wet-bulb line. The effectiveness of each process is reduced as the desiccant water content is increased. Reactivation of solid beds makes intermittent operation necessary, unless parallel units are installed. Continuous operation of spray units is feasible, if the solution is circulated through a regenerator. Solution may be cooled in varying degrees and sprayed over different kinds of surface to produce a variety of leaving air conditions. However, economic advantages generally favor surface cooling and dehumidification. Whenever reheat must be employed or where the cost of electric power is high and the cost of gas or steam low, the advantage may shift to dehydration and sensible cooling.

Controls

The capacity of any piece of equipment so far discussed can be altered by some sort of throttling action. When conditions change, it is essential for comfort, etc., that the capacity of each element be matched to the new requirements. This can be accomplished by manipulating a damper or valve. Automatic means are generally used in preference to manual operation for reasons of accuracy, economy, and safety. If control is to be automatic, the damper or valve must be equipped with a motor or other actuator, which in turn responds to a signal from a controller that measures the need for a change. Thermostats, humidistats, and pressurestats may be used to sense changing conditions. The controller-actuator system may be designed to produce two position, multiple position, floating, or modulating action. On-off control and step control produce changes limited to definite increments. Floating control and proportioning control can produce damper or valve settings anywhere between minimum and maximum.

CONDENSATION

In many ways the water vapor in the air must be considered as a part of the mixture. However, in certain situations this water vapor can act independently of the air. The migration of moisture through porous materials depends only on the area (A), vapor pressure difference ($e_i - e_o$) between inside and outside, and the permeance (Ω) of the material. Equation 371 may be rewritten:

$$W/\theta = \Omega A (e_i - e_o), \qquad (396)$$

where the rate of moisture migration (W/θ) is expressed in any units consistent with those for Ω, A, and e.

Moisture will condense on any surface with a temperature lower than the dew point of the air to which it is exposed. Condensation will also occur within a porous media if the temperature and vapor pressure gradients are not compatible with continuity of vapor flow.

Surface condensation can be eliminated by adding insulation to uphold the surface temperature. For windows which are nonporous, double or triple glazing will provide adequate protection in most cases. Leaks, particularly around the inside pane, must be prevented. Figure 158 gives the maximum inside relative humidities which can be tolerated at any outside temperature without producing condensation on various types of windows at 50, 60, 70, or 80° inside temperatures.

The addition of insulation may cause condensation to occur within a wall unless a vapor barrier is used on the warm side. Various papers, foils, and even paints will provide protection, but only if properly applied, so that there will be no alternate paths for the vapor to follow. Physical damage may result if moisture formed within the wall finds a path to the inside wall. The insulating value of the wall may be reduced by the presence of moisture.

Condensation within walls will not always produce damaging results.

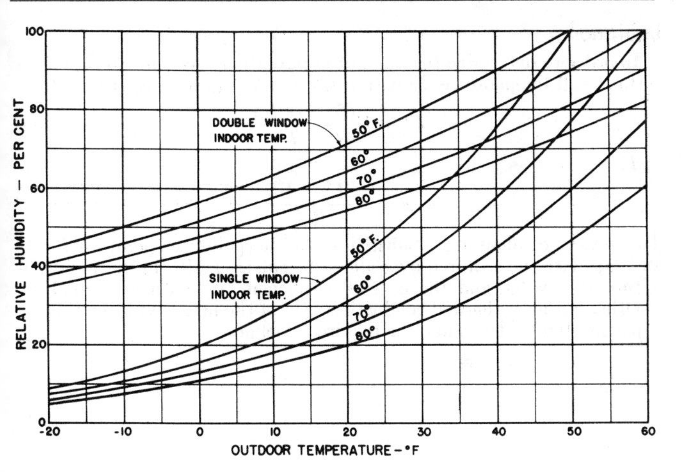

Figure 158—Condensation on Glass

Wood sheathing has considerable absorptive capacity. An annual cycle of wetting in winter and drying in summer may occur without exceeding the capacity of the material to hold the moisture it receives.

In some cases, venting of the outside portion of a wall so as to provide a path for outside air will control condensation. The loss of heat may be appreciable. Normally this method should be used in conjunction with a vapor seal.

The principal driving force behind moisture migration, vapor pressure difference, can be reduced by lowering the humidity. This can be accomplished by ventilation of the space. When a vapor barrier is used, ventilation is required to prevent excessive humidities. Normal infiltration is generally adequate in winter.

Condensation will occur on cold pipes and equipment unless insulated. Vapor seals must be employed to prevent the insulation from becoming saturated, especially whenever there will be no contemplated drying out period. As usual the seal should be on the warm side.

Surface Temperature

The temperature of a surface may be of interest, as we have seen, in problems on condensation or comfort. The same amount of heat must be transmitted through the surface film as through the entire wall. Using subscripts i, o, and w for inside, outside, and wall respectively:

$$AU\,(t_i - t_o) = A1.65\,(t_i - t_w),\ or \tag{397}$$

$$t_w = t_i - \frac{U}{1.65}\,(t_i - t_o). \tag{398}$$

Insulation

In order to determine the amount of insulation necessary to provide a certain wall temperature, Equation 397 and 75 can be used if rewritten:

$$U' = \frac{1.65\,(t_i - i_w)}{t_i - t_o}, \tag{399}$$

and

$$x = \frac{k\,(U - U')}{UU'}. \tag{400}$$

To prevent condensation, substitute the dewpoint temperature for t_w and calculate the required over-all coefficient (U') with insulation. Substitute this value and the over-all coefficient (U) without insulation, together with the thermal conductivity (k) of the proposed insulation, in Equation 400 to determine the required thickness.

CHAPTER 16

MECHANICAL DRAFT

The purpose of a mechanical draft system is to move air or gas through he furnace, boiler, or auxiliaries of a heat generator. The proper movenent of air or gas may be essential to efficient combustion or heat transfer r both. Draft systems may specifically provide energy for one or a combination of the following functions: (1) to supply the air required for ombustion, (2) to remove the products of combustion, (3) to deliver the uel to the burner, (4) to disperse the fuel, (5) to circulate the gases for etter heat transfer, (6) to propel molten ash, or even (7) to prevent eakage.

Of particular concern here are those systems employing fans to supply ll or part of the required energy. Natural draft is also discussed. Ejectors, hich are discussed in Chapter 22, are also used to provide draft.

esign Principles

There is probably no other fan application in which the economic ctors are given more study than in mechanical draft applications, articularly in the power generating field. The complete evaluation of perating expense and first cost of alternative fan selections is almost routine. The system designer first evaluates whether a fan should be used at ll and then selects the most economical one from available alternatives. t is often amazing to note the amount of fan power that can be justified r a steam generator.

Mechanical draft systems are generally classified as either forced draft, duced draft, primary air, overfire air, gas recirculating, or cyclone urner systems. Similar fans used on combustion systems outside of the ower generating field may bear the name of the application or process. ome typical examples are cement kiln fans, incinerator fans, waste heat ns, sintering fans, and hot gas fans.

The capacity requirements of any mechanical draft fan may be determined directly or indirectly from the thermal requirements of the ystem. That is, the heat generated will be determined by the amount and eating value of the fuel burned. The amounts of supply air and products f combustion also depend on the fuel burned. Excess air affects both the et heat release and the fan capacities. Fan pressure requirements depend n draft losses and the stack effect. For these reasons, various principles f combustion, together with specific data on various fuels, are given below.

TABLE 96—TYPICAL COAL ANALYSES AND HEATING VALUES

ASTM Rank		Typical Coal of Rank Listed	Per lb as received					Per lb Moisture and Ash Free					
			Proximate Analysis				HHV	Ultimate Analysis					HHV
Cl.	Gp.	State and County	H_2O	VM	FC	Ash	Btu	C	H_2	O_2	N_2	S	Btu
I	1	Pa., Schuylkill	2.0	1.8	86.2	10.0	13070	93.9	2.1	2.3	0.8	0.9	14850
I	2	Pa., Lackawanna	2.0	6.3	79.7	12.0	13000	93.5	2.6	2.3	0.9	0.7	15100
I	3	Va., Montgomery	3.0	10.5	66.5	20.0	11800	90.7	4.2	3.3	1.0	0.8	15320
II	1	W. Va., McDowell	3.0	16.3	75.7	5.0	14420	90.4	4.8	2.7	1.3	0.8	15670
II	1	Pa., Cambria	4.0	17.0	69.0	10.0	13430	89.4	4.8	2.4	1.5	1.9	15600
II	2	Pa., Somerset	3.0	20.4	66.0	10.0	13520	88.6	4.8	3.1	1.6	1.9	15540
II	2	Pa., Indiana	3.0	23.1	63.9	10.0	13600	87.6	5.2	3.3	1.4	2.5	15630
II	3	Pa., Westmoreland	3.0	30.3	55.7	11.0	13130	85.0	5.4	5.8	1.7	2.1	15260
II	3	Ky., Letcher; Pike	3.0	34.4	56.6	6.0	13800	85.2	5.4	7.0	1.6	0.8	15160
II	3	Oh., Jefferson	6.0	34.8	49.2	10.0	12450	82.2	5.5	7.7	1.7	2.9	14820
II	4	Ill., Saline; Perry	10.0	31.7	48.3	10.0	11610	80.6	5.4	10.3	1.7	2.0	14510
II	4	Ut., Carbon; Emery	8.0	36.6	43.4	12.0	11480	80.3	5.7	11.7	1.6	0.7	14350
II	5	Ill., Sangamon	14.0	34.3	39.7	12.0	10470	77.5	5.4	10.2	1.4	5.5	14160
III	1	Io., Polk	13.9	36.9	35.2	14.0	9660	65.8	7.7	16.8	1.2	8.5	13400
III	2	Col., Weld; Boulder	24.0	30.2	40.8	5.0	9200	75.0	5.1	17.9	1.5	0.5	12960
III	3	Wy., Campbell	24.0	30.0	36.0	10.0	8450	74.1	5.4	18.7	1.3	0.5	12800
IV	1	N.D., McLean; Morton	40.0	27.6	23.4	9.0	6330	72.4	4.7	18.6	1.5	2.8	12410

The ASTM D 388-38 Classification of coals by rank is outlined below:

Class, Group, and Name	*Dry Fixed Carbon or Moist Btu Limits*
I—1—Meta-Anthracite	98% or more DFC (Mineral Matter Free)
I—2—Anthracite	Between 92 and 98% DFC (MMF)
I—3—Semi-Anthracite	Between 86 and 92% DFC (MMF)
II—1—Low volatile Bituminous	Between 78 and 86% DFC (MMF)
II—2—Med. volatile Bituminous	Between 69 and 78% DFC (MMF)
II—3—High volatile A Bituminous	69% DFC & 14000 Btu or more (MMF)
II—4—High volatile B Bituminous	Between 13000 and 14000 Btu (MMF)
II—5—High volatile C Bituminous	Between 11000 and 13000 Btu (MMF)
III—1—Sub-bituminous A	Between 11000 and 13000 Btu (MMF)
III—2—Sub-bituminous B	Between 9500 and 11000 Btu (MMF)
III—3—Sub-bituminous C	Between 8300 and 9500 Btu (MMF)
IV—1—Lignite	Less than 8300 Btu (MMF)

Adapted from data of "Steam," The Babcock & Wilcox Company, 37 ed., 1963, pp. 2-7—2-9.

TABLE 97—TYPICAL SOLID FUEL ANALYSES AND HEATING VALUES

Type of Fuel	Per lb as Received					Per lb Moisture (but not ash) Free					
	Proximate Analysis				HHV Btu	Ultimate Analysis					HHV Btu
	H_2O	VM	FC	Ash		C	H_2	O_2	N_2	S	
Coke											
By-product	0.8	1.4	87.1	10.7	—	85.0	0.8	1.2	1.3	1.0	12690
Beehive	0.5	1.8	86.0	11.7	—	84.4	0.8	0.9	1.2	1.0	12527
Lo-temp.	0.0	9.8	83.5	6.7	—	84.2	3.2	3.2	1.9	0.8	14030
Lo-temp.	2.8	15.1	72.1	10.0	—	74.5	3.5	8.6	1.6	1.8	12600
Pitch	0.3	1.1	97.6	1.0	—	96.6	0.6	0.6	0.7	0.5	14097
Petroleum	1.1	7.0	90.7	1.2	—	90.8	3.3	3.1	0.8	0.8	15060
Fluid	0.3	—	—	0.3	—	87.0	2.4	3.2	1.6	5.2	14083
Fluid	0.3	6.8	92.6	0.3	—	—	—	—	—	5.1	14111
Wood											
Typical seasoned	24.0	65.5	9.5	1.0	—	37.9	7.2	53.8	0.1	0	6300
Charcoal	3.2	14.7	80.2	1.9	—	85.0	2.7	10.1	0.2	0.1	13530
Waste-redwood	50.4	40.9	8.6	0.1	—	26.5	8.5	64.8	0.1	0	4570
Waste-hemlock	57.9	31.3	9.9	0.9	—	21.2	8.9	69.0	0	0	3630
Waste-fir	35.9	52.5	11.1	0.5	—	33.5	8.0	57.9	0.1	0	5800
Hogged fuel-fir	47.2	42.9	8.9	1.0	—	—	—	—	—	—	4670
Sawdust-green	44.9	44.9	9.5	0.7	—	—	—	—	—	—	4910
Sawdust briquets	10.3	78.3	11.2	0.2	—	—	—	—	—	—	8130
Tanbark	71.8	22.4	4.5	1.3	—	14.2	9.6	74.9	0	0	2600
Straw, Typical	—	—	—	—	5000	—	—	—	—	—	6500
Corn, Shelled	—	—	—	—	7800	—	—	—	—	—	8500
Cottonseed Hulls	11.0	69.0	17.5	2.5	7100	—	—	—	—	—	—
Bagasse, Typical	52.0	40.2	6.1	1.7	4000	48.8	5.8	41.9	—	—	8340
Coke Breeze, Typical	7.3	2.3	79.4	11.0	11670	86.3	0.3	0.9	—	0.6	12600
Garbage, Typical	72.0	21.0	3.4	3.6	—	—	—	—	—	—	8800
Rubbish, Typical	7.5	59.5	13.0	20.0	—	—	—	—	—	—	6500
Peat											
Hamburg, Mich.	7.5	—	—	6.6	9090	—	—	—	—	0.3	10026
Rochester, N.H.	11.6	—	—	4.1	9083	—	—	—	—	0.2	10280
Westport, Conn.	12.7	—	—	4.1	8590	—	—	—	—	0.2	9839
New Durham, N.H.	6.1	—	—	17.9	7947	—	—	—	—	0.9	8460
New Fairfield, Conn.	9.6	—	—	7.9	7861	—	—	—	—	0.5	8698
Westport, Conn.	19.7	—	—	3.2	7691	—	—	—	—	0.2	9578
Cicero, N.Y.	14.6	—	—	7.4	7576	—	—	—	—	0.3	8869
Black Lake, N.Y.	8.7	—	—	16.6	7522	—	—	—	—	1.0	8237
Kittery, Maine	13.5	—	—	12.0	7319	—	—	—	—	1.9	8462
Greenland, N.H.	6.6	—	—	24.1	7186	—	—	—	—	1.0	7695
Madison, Wis.	7.0	—	—	18.8	6943	—	—	—	—	0.4	7628

Adapted from the data of T. Baumeister, "Mechanical Engineers' Handbook," McGraw-Hill Book Co., New York, 1958, pp. 7-17—7-20.

TABLE 98—TYPICAL GASEOUS FUEL ANALYSES AND HEATING VALUES

Type of Fuel Gas	Chemical Analysis—% by volume									LHV	HHV
	CO_2	O_2	N_2	CO	H_2	CH_4	C_2H_6	C_2H_4	C_6H_6	Btu/CF	Btu/CF
Natural, Pennsyl.*	—	—	0.8	—	—	83.4	15.8	—	—	1021	1129
Natural, So. Calif.*	0.7	—	0.5	—	—	84.0	14.8	—	—	—	1116
Natural, Ohio*	0.2	0.4	3.4	0.4	1.8	93.3	—	0.3	H_2S 0.2	—	964
Natural, Louis.*	—	—	5.0	—	—	90.0	5.0	—	—	—	1002
Natural, Okla.*	0.8	—	8.4	—	—	84.1	6.7	—	—	—	974
Coke Oven, Typical†	2.2	0.8	8.1	6.3	46.5	32.1	—	3.5	0.5	514	574
Blast Furnace, Lean*	14.4	—	56.4	23.3	2.4	0.1	—	—	H_2O 3.4	—	83.8
Blast Furnace, Rich*	11.1	—	56.4	26.6	2.4	0.1	—	—	3.4	—	94.3
Carbureted Water, Typ.†	3.0	0.5	2.9	34.0	40.5	10.2	—	6.1	2.8	508	550
Producer, Typ.†	4.5	0.6	50.9	27.0	14.0	3.0	—	—	—	153	163
Blue Water, Typ.†	5.4	0.7	8.3	37.0	47.3	1.3	—	—	—	262	287
Refinery Oil, Typ.†	0.1	1.0	—	1.2	13.1	23.3	21.7	39.6	—	—	1468
Oil Gas, Pacific Coast†	4.7	0.3	3.6	12.7	48.6	26.3	—	2.7	1.1	496	551
Coal Gas, Typical†	3.0	0.2	4.4	10.9	54.5	24.2	—	1.5	1.3	477	532
Butane, Commercial†	(C_4H_{10}—93.0 and C_3H_8—7.0) (after vaporization)									—	2522
Propane, Commercial†	(C_3H_8—100.0)									—	3261

*Adapted from the data of "Steam," The Babcock and Wilcox Company, 37 ed., 1963, pp. 3-A3 and 3-A5.

†Adapted from the data of T. Baumeister, "Mechanical Engineers' Handbook," McGraw-Hill Book Co., New York, 1958, pp. 7-32 and 7-33.

TABLE 99

TYPICAL PETROLEUM PRODUCT ANALYSES AND HEATING VALUES

Product	°API	SG @ 60°F	lb/gal	Ultimate Analysis					HHV Btu/lb
				C	H	S	N	O	
California crude	22.8	0.917	7.636	84.00	12.70	0.75	1.70	1.20	18910
Kansas crude	22.1	0.921	7.670	84.15	13.00	1.90	0.45	—	19130
Oklahoma crude	31.3	0.869	7.236	85.70	13.11	0.40	0.30	—	19502
Oklahoma crude	31.0	0.871	7.253	85.00	12.90	0.76	—	—	19486
Pennsylvania crude	42.6	0.813	6.769	86.06	13.88	0.06	0.00	0.00	19505
Texas crude	30.2	0.875	7.286	85.05	12.30	1.75	0.70	0.00	19460
Wyoming crude	31.5	0.868	7.228	—	—	—	—	—	19510
Mexican crude	13.6	0.975	8.120	83.70	10.20	4.15	—	—	18755
Gasoline	67.0	0.713	5.935	84.30	15.70	—	—	—	—
Gasoline	60.0	0.739	6.152	84.90	14.76	0.08	—	—	20750
Gasoline-benzene blend	46.3	0.796	6.627	88.30	11.70	—	—	—	—
Kerosene	41.3	0.819	6.819	—	—	—	—	—	19810
Gas oil	32.5	0.863	7.186	—	—	—	—	—	19200
Fuel oil (Mex.)	11.9	0.987	8.220	84.02	10.06	4.93	—	—	18510
Fuel oil (mid-continent)	27.1	0.892	7.428	85.62	11.98	0.35	0.50	0.60	19376
Fuel oil (Calif.)	16.7	0.955	7.956	84.67	12.36	1.16	—	—	18835

Adapted from the data of T. Baumeister, and L. S. Marks, "Standard Handbook of Mechanical Engineers," McGraw-Hill Book Co., New York, 1967, p. 7-22.

TABLE 100—HEAT VALUES OF PETROLEUM OILS

Deg API at 60°F	Density, lb per gal	High heat value at constant volume HHV, Btu		Low heat value at constant pressure LHV, Btu	
		Per lb	Per gal	Per lb	Per gal
10	8.337	18,540	154,600	17,540	146,200
20	7.787	19,020	148,100	17,930	139,600
30	7.305	19,420	141,800	18,250	133,300
40	6.879	19,750	135,800	18,510	127,300
50	6.500	20,020	130,100	18,720	121,700
60	6.160	20,260	124,800	18,900	116,400
70	5.855	20,460	119,800	19,020	112,500
80	5.578	20,630	115,100	19,180	107,000

Adapted from the data of T. Baumeister, and L. S. Marks, "Standard Handbook of Mechanical Engineers," McGraw-Hill Book Co., New York, 1967, p. 7-23.

Heat of Combustion

The heat of reaction, the chemical products, or both are the desired end result of any combustion process. The heat of combustion of any fuel can be determined by calorimeter tests. Typical calorific values are listed in Tables 96-100 for various fuels.

In the United States fuel is generally purchased on a higher heating value (*HHV*) basis. The lower heating value (*LHV*) is frequently used in Europe. The difference is the heat that would be released by the condensation of the water vapor formed from the burning hydrogen. Designating the weight of water vapor per pound of fuel which is formed from the burning hydrogen as $W_{wv\mathrm{H}}$ and assuming 1040 Btu/lb latent heat:

$$LHV = HHV - 1040\ W_{wv\mathrm{H}}. \qquad (401)$$

All values are referred to one pound of fuel, either as received or as otherwise noted.

The difference in higher heating values for fuel as received and for moisture free fuel is based on the difference in weight only. If wet fuel is fired, an additional correction should be made for the moisture that must be evaporated.

Dulong's formula may be used to determine the higher heating value of most coals and cokes from their ultimate analysis:

$$HHV = 14544\ W_{\mathrm{C}} + 62028\ W_{(\mathrm{H}\,-\,\mathrm{O}/8)} + 4050\ W_{\mathrm{S}}. \qquad (402)$$

The O/8 term is a correction factor applied to account for the hydrogen which is already combined with oxygen in the form of moisture in the fuel. The higher heating values calculated on this basis for hydrocarbon fuels such as wood may be low by 10% or more.

For computing *HHV* of petroleum oils the Bureau of Standards* recommends:

$$HHV = 22320 - 3780 \times SG. \qquad (403)$$

The heating values of gaseous fuels are best calculated from the values listed in Table 101 for the individual constituents.

*U. S. Bureau of Standards, Misc. Pub. No. 97, 1929.

TABLE 101—COMBUSTION CONSTANTS

No. Substance	Molecular weight	Density	Specific gravity	Heat of Combustion			
				Btu per cu ft		Btu per lb	
		Lb per cu ft	Air = 1.0	HHV	LHV	HHV	LHV
1. Carbon*	12.01	—	—	—	—	14093	14093
2. Hydrogen	2.016	0.0053	0.0696	325	275	61100	51623
3. Oxygen	32.000	0.0846	1.1053	—	—	—	—
4. Nitrogen (atm.)	28.016	0.0744	0.9718	—	—	—	—
5. Carb. monox.	28.01	0.0740	0.9672	322	322	4347	4347
6. Carb. dioxide	44.01	0.1170	1.5282	—	—	—	—
Paraffin series							
7. Methane	16.041	0.0424	0.5543	1013	913	23879	21520
8. Ethane	30.067	0.0803	1.0488	1792	1641	22320	20432
9. Propane	44.092	0.1196	1.5617	2590	2385	21661	19944
10. n-Butane	58.118	0.1582	2.0665	3370	3113	21308	19680
11. Isobutane	58.118	0.1582	2.0665	3363	3105	21257	19629
12. n-Pentane	72.144	0.1904	2.4872	4016	3709	21091	19517
13. Isopentane	72.144	0.1904	2.4872	4008	3716	21052	19478
14. Neopentane	72.144	0.1904	2.4872	3993	3693	20970	19396
15. n-Hexane	86.169	0.2274	2.9704	4762	4412	20940	19403
Olefin series							
16. Ethylene	28.051	0.0746	0.9740	1614	1513	21644	20295
17. Propylene	42.077	0.1110	1.4504	2336	2186	21041	19691
18. n-Butene	56.102	0.1480	1.9336	3084	2885	20840	19496
19. Isobutene	56.102	0.1480	1.9336	3068	2869	20730	19382
20. n-Pentene	70.128	0.1852	2.4190	3836	3586	20712	19363
Aromatic series							
21. Benzene	78.107	0.2060	2.6920	3751	3601	18210	17480
22. Toluene	92.132	0.2431	3.1760	4484	4284	18440	17620
23. Xylene	106.158	0.2803	3.6618	5230	4980	18650	17760
Miscell. gases							
24. Acetylene	26.036	0.0697	0.9107	1499	1448	21500	20776
25. Napthalene	128.162	0.3384	4.4208	5854	5654	17298	16708
26. Methyl alcohol	32.041	0.0846	1.1052	868	768	10259	9078
27. Ethyl alcohol	46.067	0.1216	1.5890	1600	1451	13161	11929
28. Ammonia	17.031	0.0456	0.5961	441	365	9668	8001
29. Sulfur*	32.06	—	—	—	—	3983	3983
30. Hydrog. sulfide	34.076	0.0911	1.1898	647	596	7100	6545
31. Sulfur dioxide	64.06	0.1733	2.264	—	—	—	—
32. Water vapor	18.016	0.0476	0.6215	—	—	—	—
33. Air	28.9	0.0766	1.0000	—	—	—	—

*Carbon and sulfur are considered as gases for molal calculations only.

COMBUSTION CONSTANTS—TABLE 101

Formula	For 100% Total Air mols per mol of combustible or cu ft per cu ft of combustible					For 100% Total Air lb per lb of combustible				
	Required for combustion		Flue Products			Required for combustion		Flue Products		
	O_2	Air	CO_2	H_2O	N_2	O_2	Air	CO_2	H_2O	N_2
C	1.0	4.76	1.0	—	3.76	2.66	11.53	3.66	—	8.86
H_2	0.5	2.38	—	1.0	1.88	7.94	34.34	—	8.94	26.41
O_2	—	—	—	—	—	—	—	—	—	—
N_2	—	—	—	—	—	—	—	—	—	—
CO	0.5	2.38	1.0	—	1.88	0.57	2.47	1.57	—	1.90
CO_2	—	—	—	—	—	—	—	—	—	—
CH_4	2.0	9.53	1.0	2.0	7.53	3.99	17.27	2.74	2.25	13.28
C_2H_6	3.5	16.68	2.0	3.0	13.18	3.73	16.12	2.93	1.80	12.39
C_3H_8	5.0	23.82	3.0	4.0	18.82	3.63	15.70	2.99	1.63	12.07
C_4H_{10}	6.5	30.97	4.0	5.0	24.47	3.58	15.49	3.03	1.55	11.91
C_4H_{10}	6.5	30.97	4.0	5.0	24.47	3.58	15.49	3.03	1.55	11.91
C_5H_{12}	8.0	38.11	5.0	6.0	30.11	3.55	15.35	3.05	1.50	11.81
C_5H_{12}	8.0	38.11	5.0	6.0	30.11	3.55	15.35	3.05	1.50	11.81
C_5H_{12}	8.0	38.11	5.0	6.0	30.11	3.55	15.35	3.05	1.50	11.81
C_6H_{14}	9.5	45.26	6.0	7.0	35.76	3.53	15.27	3.06	1.46	11.74
C_2H_4	3.0	14.29	2.0	2.0	11.29	3.42	14.81	3.14	1.29	11.39
C_3H_6	4.5	21.44	3.0	3.0	16.94	3.42	14.81	3.14	1.29	11.39
C_4H_8	6.0	28.59	4.0	4.0	22.59	3.42	14.81	3.14	1.29	11.39
C_4H_8	6.0	28.59	4.0	4.0	22.59	3.42	14.81	3.14	1.29	11.39
C_5H_{10}	7.5	35.73	5.0	5.0	28.23	3.42	14.81	3.14	1.29	11.39
C_6H_6	7.5	35.73	6.0	3.0	28.23	3.07	13.30	3.38	0.69	10.22
C_7H_8	9.0	42.88	7.0	4.0	33.88	3.13	13.53	3.34	0.78	10.40
C_8H_{10}	10.5	50.02	8.0	5.0	39.52	3.17	13.70	3.32	0.85	10.53
C_2H_2	2.5	11.91	2.0	1.0	9.41	3.07	13.30	3.38	0.69	10.22
$C_{10}H_8$	12.0	57.17	10.0	4.0	45.17	3.00	12.96	3.43	0.56	9.97
CH_3OH	1.5	7.15	1.0	2.0	5.65	1.50	6.48	1.37	1.13	4.98
C_2H_5OH	3.0	14.29	2.0	3.0	11.29	2.08	9.02	1.92	1.17	6.93
NH_3	0.75	3.57	—	1.5	3.32	1.41	6.10	—	1.59	5.51
			SO_2					SO_2		
S	1.0	4.76	1.0	—	3.76	1.00	4.29	2.00	—	3.29
H_2S	1.5	7.15	1.0	1.0	5.65	1.41	6.10	1.88	0.53	4.69
SO_2	—	—	—	—	—	—	—	—	—	—
H_2O	—	—	—	—	—	—	—	—	—	—
—	—	—	—	—	—	—	—	—	—	—

Adapted from the data of C. G. Segeler, Gas Engineers Handbook, The Industrial Press, New York, 1966, pp. 2/48, 2/52, 2/69, 2/84.

TABLE 102—COMBUSTION FORMULAS

Carbon (to CO)	$2C + O_2 \rightarrow 2CO + 4080$ Btu/lb C
Carbon (to CO_2)	$C + O_2 \rightarrow CO_2 + 14093$ Btu/lb C
Carbon Monoxide	$2CO + O_2 \rightarrow 2CO_2 + 4347$ Btu/lb CO (10013 Btu/lb C)
Hydrogen	$2H_2 + O_2 \rightarrow 2H_2O + 61100$* Btu/lb H
Sulphur (to SO_2)	$S + O_2 \rightarrow SO_2 + 3983$ Btu/lb S
Sulphur (to SO_3)	$2S + 3O_2 \rightarrow 2SO_3 + 4120$ Btu/lb S
Methane	$CH_4 + 2O_2 \rightarrow CO_2 + 2H_2O + 23879$* Btu/lb CH_4
Acetylene	$2C_2H_2 + 5O_2 \rightarrow 4CO_2 + 2H_2O + 21500$* Btu/lb C_2H_2
Ethylene	$C_2H_4 + 3O_2 \rightarrow 2CO_2 + 2H_2O + 21644$* Btu/lb C_2H_4
Ethane	$2C_2H_6 + 7O_2 \rightarrow 4CO_2 + 6H_2O + 22320$* Btu/lb C_2H_6
Hydrogen Sulphide	$2H_2S + 3O_2 \rightarrow 2SO_2 + 2H_2O + 7100$* Btu/lb H_2S

*HHV listed

Adapted from the data of "Steam," The Babcock & Wilcox Company, 37 ed., 1963, p. 4-3.

Air Required for Combustion

The theoretical oxygen requirements for the combustion of any fuel can be calculated from the appropriate chemical formula. Formulas for some of the common chemical reactions involving combustion are listed in Table 102. The numerical coefficients represent the molal relations of oxygen and combustible. For gases this gives the volumetric relationship as well. By using the appropriate molecular weights, the mass relationships can also be determined.

Oxygen requirements on both the volumetric and weight bases are listed for various substances in Table 101. Air requirements, based on the proportions of oxygen in air previously listed on page 3, are also shown.

For any specific fuel, the total dry air requirement (W_{da}) is the sum of the requirements for the individual constituents. This may be expressed as:

$$W_{da} = 11.53\, W_C + 34.34\, W_H + 4.29\, W_S + \ldots, \qquad (404)$$

where each term is referred to one pound of fuel and other terms may be used for any constituents not listed.

The air supplied for combustion will seldom, if ever, be dry. The amount of moisture may be determined from a psychrometric chart if sufficient data are known. The ambient absolute humidity (H_{amb}) of the supply air is quite variable, and a value of .013 pounds per pound of dry air is often assumed in combustion engineering. The amount of moisture supplied in the combustion air per pound of fuel may be expressed as the product of absolute humidity and the weight of dry air per pound of fuel, or:

$$H_{amb}\, W_{da} \approx .013\, W_{da}. \qquad (405)$$

TABLE 103—EXCESS AIR

Fuel	Type of Furnace or Burners	Excess Air %
Pulverized Coal	Completely water-cooled furnace for slag-tap or dry-ash-removal	15-20
	Partially water-cooled furnace for dry-ash-removal	15-40
Crushed Coal	Cyclone furnace-pressure or suction	10-15
Coal	Stoker-fired, chain-grate or traveling-grate	15-50
	Stoker-fired, underfeed	20-50
	Stoker-fired, spreader or W.C. vibrating grate	30-60
Fuel Oil	Oil burners, register-type	5-10
	Multifuel burners and flat-flame	10-20
Acid Sludge	Cone and flat-flame type burners, steam-atomized	10-15
Natural, Coke Oven, And Refinery Gas	Register-type burners	5-10
	Multifuel burners	7-12
Blast-furnace Gas	Intertube nozzle-type burners	15-18
Wood	Dutch-oven (10-23% through grates) and Hofft-type	20-25
Bagasse	All furnaces	25-35
Black Liquor	Recovery furnaces for kraft and soda-pulping processes	5-7

Adapted from the data of "Steam," The Babcock & Wilcox Company, 37 ed., 1963, p. 4-10.

Excess Air

The amount of air theoretically required will never produce complete combustion due to inadequate mixing before the constituents pass out the stack. This waste of fuel can be minimized or eliminated by using enough extra air to insure an adequate supply to each particle or parcel of combustible. The excess required will vary with the type of fuel and method of firing.

The amounts usually used are tabulated in Table 103. Referred to one pound of fuel, the dry excess air (W_{eda}) and total air supplied (W_{tda}) may be expressed as:

$$W_{eda} = W_{da} \times (\textit{Table 103 value}), \textit{ and} \tag{406}$$

$$W_{tda} = W_{da} \times (1 + \textit{Table 103 value}). \tag{407}$$

Although the use of excess air may eliminate one loss (unburned combustible), it produces another. It increases the mass of exit gases and since these are expelled at elevated temperatures, an increase in heat loss is involved. Every attempt should therefore be made to hold the excess air at that quantity just sufficient to eliminate unburned combustibles in the exit gases.

TABLE 104—TYPICAL SPECIFIC GRAVITIES FOR VARIOUS FLUE GASES

Fuel or Process	SG
Coal	1.04
Oil	1.00
Natural Gas	0.97
Wood	0.94
Bagasse	0.93
Lignite	0.97
Blast Furnace Gas	1.01
Black Liquor	0.93
Sintering	1.00

Products of Combustion

The chemical formulas of Table 102 and the data of Table 101 may be used to figure the volumes or weights of the various products of combustion. To these theoretical amounts must be added the excess air.

The total weight will equal the sum of the weights of product for each constituent in the fuel, plus the excess air. Referred to one pound of fuel, this may be expressed as:

$$W_{dg} = W_{\mathrm{CO_2}} + W_{\mathrm{SO_2}} + W_{\mathrm{N_2}} + W_{(\mathrm{N_2} + \mathrm{O_2})ea} + \ldots, \quad (408)$$

$$W_{dg} = 3.66\ W_{\mathrm{C}} + 2.00\ W_{\mathrm{S}} + 8.86 + W_{eda} + \ldots, \text{ and} \quad (409)$$

$$W_{wv} = 8.94\ W_{\mathrm{H}} + W_m + W_{tda}\ H_{amb}, \quad (410)$$

where W_m is the percent moisture in the fuel as received, if W_{H}, W_{C}, W_{S}, etc. are on the same basis. If, however, W_{H}, W_{C}, W_{S}, etc. are on a moisture and ash free basis, W_m as received must be corrected by dividing by the sum of the amount of fixed carbon and volatile matter expressed as decimals. The total weight of moist gas (W_{mg}) is simply the sum of the dry gas (W_{dg}) and water vapor (W_{wv}):

$$W_{mg} = W_{dg} + W_{wv}. \quad (411)$$

The volume of these products of combustion for any pressure and temperature may be calculated by utilizing the appropriate molal volume (volume of one mol.) and molecular weights:

$$Q_{mg} = Mol.\ Vol. \left(\frac{W_{\mathrm{CO_2}}}{44} + \frac{W_{\mathrm{SO_2}}}{64} + \frac{W_{eda}}{28.97} + \frac{W_{wv}}{18} + \ldots \right). \quad (412)$$

Once W_{mg} and Q_{mg} are determined, the density can be computed as the ratio of the two. The specific gravity of the gas referred to air at the same temperature and barometer may also be figured. Table 104 lists typical values of specific gravity for various flue gases. These values are sufficiently accurate for most fan specification purposes.

The absolute humidity in pounds per pound of dry gas of the exit gases may be determined from:

$$H_g = \frac{W_{wv}}{W_{dg}}. \quad (413)$$

Heat Losses in the Exit Gases

Some of the heating value of the fuel is lost to the atmosphere as sensible and latent heat in the products of combustion. The latent heat loss (LH) depends on the amount by which the water vapor in the flue gases exceeds that in the ambient air:

$$LH = 1040\, W_{dg}\,(H_g - H_{amb}). \tag{414}$$

The sensible loss depends on the extent to which the exit gas temperature (t_g) is elevated over ambient (t_{amb}). The sensible heat losses in the dry gas (SH_{dg}) and water vapor products (SH_{wv}) are:

$$SH_{dg} = 0.24\, W_{dg}\,(t_g - t_{amb}),\ and \tag{415}$$

$$SH_{wv} = 0.45\, W_{dg}\, H_g\,(t_g - t_{amb}). \tag{416}$$

The efficiency of combustion is 100 minus the sum of the heat losses in percent. Exit gas losses can be minimized by reducing the amount of water vapor or the temperature. The reduction that can be effected in either case is limited. The moisture formed by burning hydrogen is unavoidable. The moisture in fuels as received cannot be avoided in some cases either. Appreciable temperatures may be required either to prevent condensation or to produce the required natural draft as will be seen shortly.

Dew Point of the Products of Combustion

If the gases are cooled below the dew point in the air heater, economizer, or elsewhere, condensation will occur with damaging corrosion the probable result. This is even more damaging when condensation occurs in the presence of the products of combustion of sulfur. Unfortunately, the very presence of some of these products raises the dew-point temperature. Although the calculated dew point usually ranges around 100°F, tests have indicated values as high as 350°F. Apparently this phenomenon occurs due to a catalytic conversion of SO_2 to SO_3, followed by the formation of H_2SO_4. According to Coit* less than .01% H_2SO_4 by volume in flue gas containing 5% water vapor produces a dew point of 350°F. If no sulfuric acid can form and an exact dew point is desired, it can be read from a psychrometric chart at the value of humidity calculated with Equation 413.

Flue Gas Analysis

A quantitative chemical analysis of the flue gases is sufficient to permit calculation of the percent excess air. Such tests, plus fuel analyses and firing rates, provide enough information to calculate the flow rate for either supply air or products of combustion. Various principles are employed and numerous instruments available for measuring one or more of the gas constituents. The Orsat apparatus consists of a burette to measure gas volumes and appropriate reagents to absorb in turn CO_2, O_2, and CO. The change in volume is observed after each gas is absorbed and

*R. L. Coit, Sulphur Dew-Point Corrosion in Exhaust Gases, *Trans. ASME*, vol. 78, pp. 89-94, 1956.

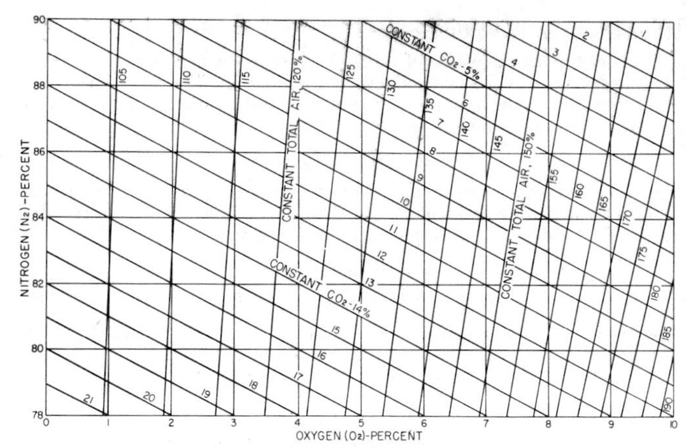

Figure 159—Total Air vs Orsat Readings

Adapted from the data of "Steam," The Babcock & Wilcox Company, 37 ed., 1963, p. 4-11.

---

the remainder is assumed to be N_2. The accuracy of the results of such tests depends largely on how truly representative is the sample or samples. If present, SO_2 is absorbed with the CO_2 and therefore causes an error. However, moisture has no effect.

The percent excess air may be determined by inserting the proper volumetric fractions (F) in:

$$\% \, EA = \frac{100\,(F_{O_2} - F_{CO}/2)}{(.21/.79)\,F_{N_2} - (F_{O_2} - F_{CO}/2)} \quad (417)$$

The chart in Figure 156 may also be used to determine the percent excess or total air.

The next two equations express the relations between the Orsat measurements and the weights of air and gas per pound of fuel. In:

$$W_{dg} = \frac{44\,F_{CO_2} + 28\,F_{CO} + 32\,F_{O_2} + 28\,F_{N_2}}{12\,F_{CO_2} + 12\,F_{CO}} \times W_C, \quad (418)$$

the numerator may be recognized as the apparent molecular weight of the dry gases. The denominator represents the molecular weight of the carbon portion of those same gases. Since both occupy the same volume under a single set of conditions, the fraction represents the weight of dry gases per pound of carbon burned. When multiplied by the percent carbon in the fuel, the net expression yields the weight of dry gases per pound of fuel.

Similarly, the numerator in the formula below represents the molecular weight of the air portion of those same gases, assuming that all of the nitrogen comes from the air and none from the fuel:

$$W_{da} = \frac{28 F_{N_2} \div 0.769}{12 F_{CO_2} + 12 F_{CO}} \times W_C = \frac{3.04 F_{N_2}}{F_{CO_2} + F_{CO}} \times W_C. \qquad (419)$$

Both formulas are valid regardless of moisture or hydrogen content of the fuel. However, the presence of SO_2 or unburned combustibles other than CO requires a different expression. The percent SO_2, being unobtainable with an Orsat anyway, is frequently ignored, and the equations are often used as given for approximate results.

The amount of water vapor per pound of fuel may be calculated as in Equation **410** and added to the weight of dry gases. The ambient moisture can be calculated from the humidity and added to the weight of dry air.

The weight of air supplied per pound of fuel may also be calculated from a mass balance. That is:

$$W_{ma} = W_{mg} + W_{ash} - 1. \qquad (420)$$

In all the preceding equations the weights of gas or air are for each pound of fuel fired. These unit weights multiplied by the firing rate give the total weight rates of gas or air flow. The volumetric rates of flow can be determined by using the following procedure. First, the density may be determined from the apparent molecular weight. Most of the intermediate calculations are performed in Equation **418**. The numerator of that expression is the apparent molecular weight of the dry gases. The apparent molecular weight of the moist gases is therefore:

$$Mol.\ wt._{mg} = \frac{W_{dg} + W_{wv}}{W_{dg} \div Mol.\ Wt._{dg} + W_{wv} \div 18} \qquad (421)$$

The density for any condition of temperature and pressure can be figured from the appropriate molal volume. The density for moist air (δ_{ma}) may be read from a psychrometric density chart or like the density of moist gas (δ_{mg}) it may be calculated from:

$$\delta_{ma} = \frac{Mol.\ Wt._{ma}}{Mol.\ Vol.},\ or \qquad (422)$$

$$\delta_{mg} = \frac{Mol.\ Wt._{mg}}{Mol.\ Vol.}. \qquad (423)$$

The volumetric flow rate, which is always of interest for fan work, is obtained by dividing the weight rate of flow by the density, thus:

$$CFM_{ma} = \frac{W_{ma}\, w_{fuel}}{60\, \delta_{ma}},\ or \qquad (424)$$

$$CFM_{mg} = \frac{W_{mg}\, w_{fuel}}{60\, \delta_{mg}}, \qquad (425)$$

where w_{fuel} is the firing rate in pounds per hour.

Stack Effect and Natural Draft

Any structure which confines a vertical column of gas is capable of producing a stack effect. The magnitude of that effect or the draft created at the base of the structure, if there is no flow, may be calculated from the difference in weight between the column of gas and a similar column of the ambient air or gas. Based on the average absolute temperature (T) in °R and the barometric pressure (b) in in. Hg, the theoretical draft (SP_{stack}) in in. WG for a chimney height (L) in ft is:

$$SP_{stack} = \frac{b \times 70.73}{5.192 \times 1545} L \left(\frac{Mol.\ Wt._{amb}}{T_{amb}} - \frac{Mol.\ Wt._{mg}}{T_{mg}} \right). \quad (426)$$

Frequently the molecular weight of the gas is assumed to be equal to that of ambient air for which the expression reduces to:

$$SP_{stack} = \frac{b\ L}{113.4} \left(\frac{28.97}{T_{amb}} - \frac{28.97}{T_{mg}} \right) = .2554\ b\ L \left(\frac{1}{T_{amb}} - \frac{1}{T_{mg}} \right). \quad (427)$$

The rate of gas flow that can be sustained by any stack effect depends on the energy losses which must be overcome, including the friction loss through the stack itself and the exit loss. These draft losses are discussed in the next few paragraphs. However, for chimney sizing purposes, a stack draft loss of 5% of the theoretical stack effect generally yields an economical diameter. Figure **160** gives the stack diameter on this basis for various flow rates. A trial diameter may be chosen from this chart. Next a trial height may be established for any desired stack effect from the data of Table **105**. Usually only the temperature at the inlet to the stack will be known. The temperature at the stack exit depends on the geometry of the stack as illustrated in Figure **161**. The trial diameter and height may be used to determine the exit gas temperature and the arithmetic average stack temperature may then be computed. The final stack height may be calculated from Equation **426** rearranged as follows:

$$L = \left(\frac{SP_{stack}}{0.95} \frac{113.4}{b} \right) \div \left(\frac{28.97}{T_{amb}} - \frac{Mol.\ Wt._{mg}}{T_{mg}} \right). \quad (428)$$

The calculated draft requirements (SP_{stack}) are frequently increased by 10% to provide a margin of safety. It may be necessary to modify the stack diameter to produce a stack flow loss of 5% or alternatively the 0.95 may be modified to suit conditions.

It is not readily apparent from the formula and charts, but when a boiler is located above sea level, the stack height requirements increase inversely as the square of the barometric pressure ratio relative to that at sea level, because the draft requirements increase inversely with the barometric ratio for the same weight flow (as is needed for combustion). To maintain the same percentage stack flow loss, the diameter must be varied inversely with the two-fifths power of the barometric pressure ratio:

$$L = \left(\frac{b_{SL}}{b_{amb}} \right)^2 \times L_{SL}, \text{ and} \quad (429)$$

$$D = \left(\frac{b_{SL}}{b_{amb}} \right)^{2/5} \times D_{SL}. \quad (430)$$

TABLE 105—STACK EFFECT PER 100 FEET OF HEIGHT

Assuming b = 29.92″ Hg and SG gas = 1.0

Avg. Flue Gas Temp.	Avg. Ambient Temperature			
	40°F	60°F	80°F	100°F
300°F	.52	.46	.41	.36
400°F	.64	.58	.53	.48
500°F	.73	.67	.62	.57
600°F	.81	.75	.69	.64
700°F	.87	.81	.76	.71
800°F	.92	.86	.81	.76

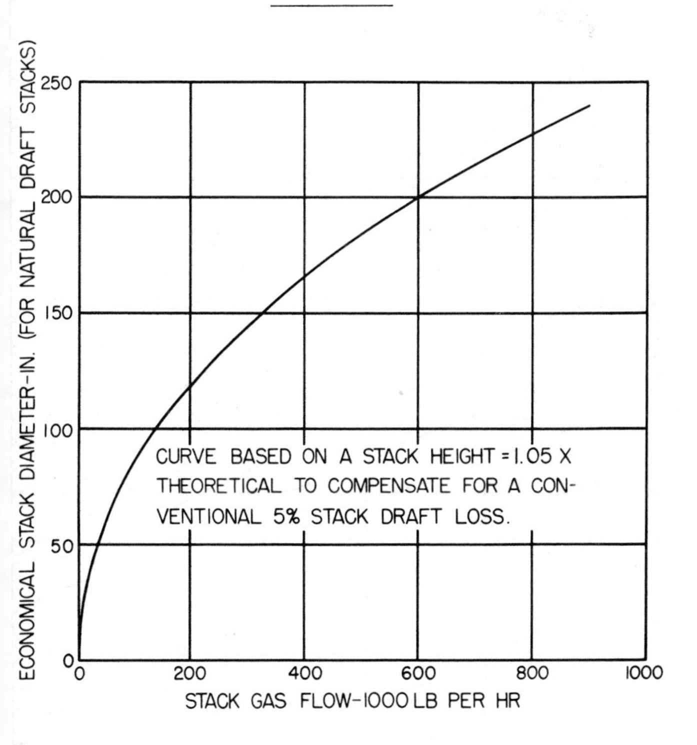

Figure 160—Economical Natural Draft Stack Diameters

Adapted from the data of "Steam," The Babcock & Wilcox Company, 37 ed., 1963, p. 5-7.

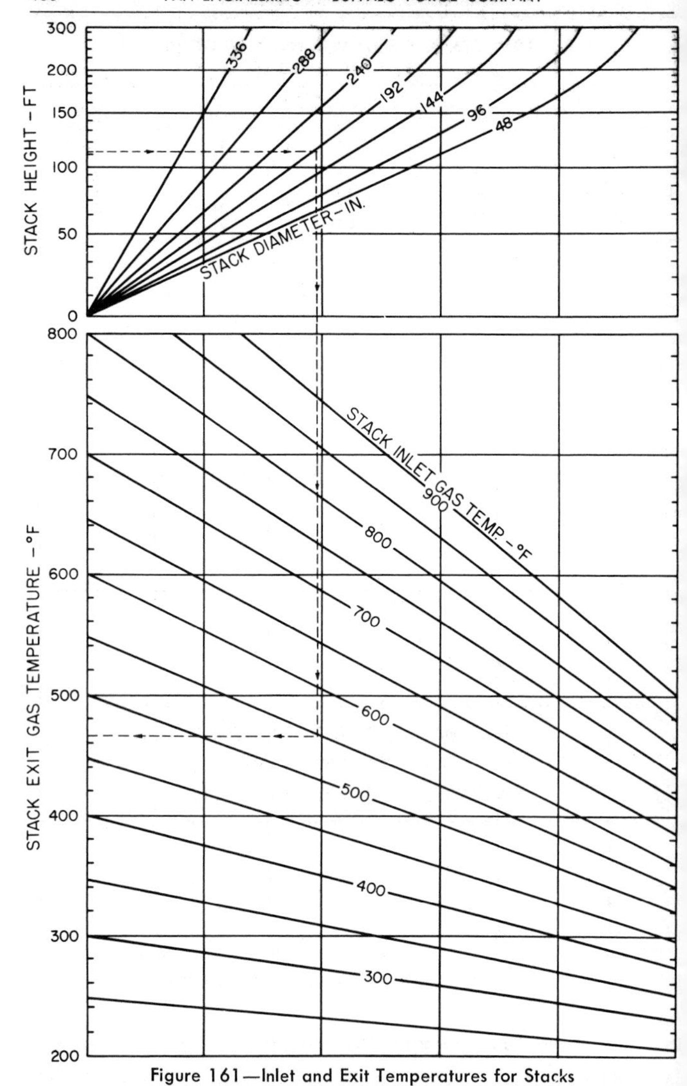

Figure 161—Inlet and Exit Temperatures for Stacks

Adapted from the data of "Steam," The Babcock & Wilcox Company, 37 ed., 1963, p. 5-6.

)raft Losses

The draft or energy provided by the stack or mechanical equipment or oth must be sufficient to overcome the losses occasioned by the flow of ases through the various boiler passes, etc. Balanced draft occurs at that ›cation where the pressure is equal to atmospheric pressure. Until ecently the design pressure in the furnace always was slightly less than tmospheric to insure that leakage would be inward. Today pressurized esigns are common, and the balanced draft point may be located close to r actually in the stack.

The actual draft losses of boiler elements are best determined by tests nder operating conditions. Fluctuations in flow patterns due to firing ariations or fouling affect draft losses even for identical ratings so that alculations of draft loss should usually be considered approximate only. Nevertheless, calculations are the only recourse on occasion, and the data f Chapter 3 will generally serve well.

Coursing through heat transfer apparatus the volumetric flow rate, for ir or gas, may change appreciably. During combustion, changes in both eat content and mass must be reckoned. A margin for fouling should lso be assigned.

Should there be a desire to check the pressure at any particular point, he internal stack effect must be computed, particularly for high boilers vith vertical passes.

The data of Chapter 3 are all based on constant flow volume. Provided he correct volume is used, such an approach will give satisfactory results or the loss through ducts, elbows, breaching, and stacks where the change n temperature is relatively small. The average volume may be based on he effective temperature (t_{eff}) with sufficient accuracy for most work. This can be calculated from the entering (t_{ent}) and leaving (t_{lvg}) temperatures:

$$t_{eff} = \frac{t_{ent} + 2t_{lvg}}{3}. \tag{431}$$

A friction factor (f) as determined from Figure **27** using roughness alues (ϵ) of .00015 for steel or .003 for brick or concrete may be used to etermine the pressure drop (ΔTP) in in. WG for round ducts, stacks, etc. f diameter (D) in ft and length or height (L) in ft for any flow rate CFM) in cfm:

$$\Delta TP = \frac{f}{2g}\frac{L}{D}\frac{\delta}{5.192}\left(\frac{CFM}{60} \times \frac{4}{\pi D^2}\right)^2 = \frac{f\,L\,\delta}{.7419\,D^5}\left(\frac{CFM}{1000}\right)^2. \tag{432}$$

The equivalent diameter based on constant capacity may be determined from the chart on page **107** for rectangular ducts.

The data on elbows, splitters, and turning vanes in Chapter 3 may be sed directly.

The friction (ΔTP) for turbulent flow of gases normal to a bank of ubes, N rows deep, may be calculated from the mass velocity (G) in lb er hr per sq ft and the density (δ) in lb per cu ft:

$$\Delta TP = \frac{f\,NG}{2.09 \times 10^8\,\delta}, \tag{433}$$

where $f = 0.20\ (DG/\mu)^{-0.15}$ for tubes in line and $f = 0.34\ (DG/\mu)^{-0.15}$ for staggered tubes. (Both cases are based on longitudinal and transverse pitch equal to twice the tube diameter (D) and G is based on the minimum free area either in the transverse or diagonal opening.)

The burner or wind box pressure requirements will vary with type, velocity, depth of fuel bed, etc.

The highest compartment pressure under a chain or traveling grate may be 3″ water gage or so. The burning characteristics at various portions of the grate are controlled by damper adjustment on the air supply to the compartments under those portions. Wind box pressures on underfeed stokers may be as high as 6″ water gage. Approximately 1″ water gage is required for each 10 pounds of coal per hour per square foot of grate.

The velocity of the primary air-fuel mixture at the tip of a pulverized fuel burner must exceed the speed of flame propagation in order to prevent flashback. For this reason and also to prevent settling, velocities of 2000 to 3000 feet per minute may be required at low ratings. Maximum velocities range from 4500 to 5500 feet per minute at the higher ratings. Secondary air velocities may range to 7500 feet per minute for circular types or to 12,000 for cross-tube type burners.

Secondary air velocities of 20,000 to 30,000 feet per minute may be used in cyclone furnaces.

Overfire air with jet velocities of 20,000 feet per minute may be provided to create turbulence on both overfeed and underfeed stoker furnaces.

The energy dissipated in producing turbulence, etc., may be calculated from the issuing velocity. Sufficient pressure must be provided ahead of the nozzle to increase the velocity (V) and overcome the friction of the nozzle itself. The Carnot-Borda coefficient may be expressed:

$$\Delta TP = \left(\frac{V_{jet} - V_{amb}}{1096.7}\right)^2 \delta, \tag{434}$$

and, if V_{amb} is negligible as at the top of the stack, $\Delta TP = VP$.

Equipment

A forced draft fan must deliver the necessary air for combustion plus excess air to insure complete combustion and must supply enough energy to overcome the losses of any auxiliaries, etc., up to the balanced draft point. This point may occur in the fuel bed or furnace when natural or induced draft is used to remove the products of combustion. For "pressurized" applications, the energy or pressure developed by the fan must be sufficient to overcome the losses through all of the equipment less whatever amount of stack draft that may be available. Test block ratings are frequently specified at 25% higher weight flow, 25% higher static pressure, and 25°F higher air temperature than net requirements.

An induced draft fan must remove the products of combustion, plus the excess air, and must supply enough energy to maintain the desired draft at the fire and overcome the succeeding losses less the natural draft available. The test block specifications are frequently increased over the net requirements 18% on flow, 25% on pressure, and 25°F on temperature. Even higher margins may be imposed on waste heat boilers.

An overfire air fan delivers combustion air over the fire to improve combustion efficiency and reduce smoking. The amount used is usually 5 to 10% of the total combustion air requirement and therefore reduces the forced draft fan capacity accordingly. The energy supplied must be sufficient to overcome any piping losses and provide the necessary turbulent mixing action. Pressures up to 30″ water gage may be required for high-velocity jets. (Overfire air may be supplied all or in part by the forced draft fan itself, or, in cases where only turbulence is required, a steam jet may be used.)

A primary air fan delivers some of the combustion air while transporting the fuel from the pulverizer to the burner. This air is usually taken from the forced draft supply after the air heater and consequently does not reduce the forced draft capacity requirements. The energy supplied by the fan must be sufficient to transport the material plus overcome the air losses less the energy delivered to it by the forced draft fan.

Gas recirculating fans redirect boiler gases, increasing the mass flow through various parts of the furnace, the superheaters, reheaters, and economizers. A variable amount is recirculated at low steam rates to control the reheat temperature. Up to 40% of the total gas flow may be recirculated at the lowest ratings. Proportionately less flow is used with increased ratings. The same system is used to temper the very hot gases o around 1900°F or below the fusion temperature of the ash. The amount of tempering gas may range to 20% of the total gas flow at the very highest ratings. The pressure developed by the recirculating gas fan must be sufficient to overcome the losses through the boiler passes and the recirculating duct work.

Cyclone burner fans provide all of the forced draft functions and additionally provide the energy to produce the cyclonic action in the burner and furnace. 15 to 20% of the combustion air is introduced tangentially as primary air through the burner, 75 to 80% of the total is introduced tangentially to the cyclone furnace, and 3 to 8% tertiary air is admitted at the center of the primary burner to prevent recirculation of fine coal.

Seal air fans may be used to provide air at sufficient pressure to prevent the escape of dirty air or gas from furnace or any auxiliary. Clean air is supplied to a chamber between the elements of a double seal so that it leaks both ways, that is, into the room and into the setting or machine. Sealing air may also be supplied by the forced draft fan on many installations.

Almost all large mechanical draft fans are provided in direct connected arrangements. Usually, electric motor drives are used. However, there is evidence of a recent returning interest in steam turbine drives. Depending on the expected part-load operation, either variable-speed or variable-inlet-vane control may evaluate best.

Double inlet, double width, Arrangement 3 fans are generally preferred. Induced draft fans are supplied with inlet boxes. Forced draft fans may also be supplied with inlet boxes or any one of a number of recirculating connections to temper the air to prevent condensation in the air heater.

Higher pressure fans, such as overfire air, primary air, and cyclone burner fans are frequently supplied in single inlet, Arrangement 8.

Testing

Seldom, if ever, will field conditions be as ideal for fan testing as they are on the test block. As has been shown, gas and fuel analyses and firing rate measurements will provide sufficient information to determine the approximate air and gas flows. Direct pressure measurements on both sides of any fan, together with barometric pressure, temperature, speed and power determinations complete the measurement of fan characteristics. However, it is usually preferable to measure the volume flow rate directly by means of a Pitot tube test rather than by Orsat analysis and fuel measurements. In both cases it is necessary to obtain as true an average as possible. This requires sampling at numerous locations across the test section. Even so, the test block in general provides better control of conditions, reducing stratification, etc., and therefore provides greater accuracy.

CHAPTER 17

LOCAL EXHAUST

The purpose of any local exhaust system is to eliminate what would otherwise be a hazard due to atmospheric contamination from some mechanical or chemical operation. The economic hazards of corrosion of plant and equipment as well as hazards to health and safety of workers are often controlled by local exhaust systems.

The specific method employed in any local exhaust system is to capture the contaminant at or near its source with a mass of air moving across all possible escape routes.

The alternate method of general or dilution ventilation aims to reduce the concentration of the contaminant below the danger point by introducing a larger mass of purer air and removing a corresponding amount of contaminated air from the general area. Assuming that all methods will give adequate control, the choice of one of the above possibilities or of otherwise eliminating the hazard should depend on an economic analysis. Local exhaust ventilation will give more positive control than dilution ventilation. Both systems will employ fans, and may utilize some sort of air cleaner or dust collector. The cost of these items can be reduced by minimizing the capacity (cfm of air) requirement. These savings will often pay for the added ductwork and hoods of the localized system.

The local exhaust methods outlined here are generally the same as those described in the more recent reference works on industrial ventilation. By following the general rules laid down, the reader should be able to design a system adequate to control almost any problem. However, since many states and municipalities have published safety codes governing the design, construction, and operation of such systems, applicable regulations should be consulted.

Design Principles

It is axiomatic that the best local exhaust system design will produce the required control in the most economical manner. The capacity of any local system greatly influences both the first and operating costs, so that the designer generally strives to reduce this quantity to a minimum. The capacity of the system is usually expressed in cfm.

Over the years data has been accumulated sufficient to establish a relation between the capacity required and certain dimensions of the machine itself or the enclosure used with the machine or operation. Such data are presented in Tables 106A and 106B for specific machines and operations. These operations most commonly involve dusts, mists, and fumes as the contaminants. In other cases, most notably those involving gases, vapors, and mists such as for an open-surface tank operation, a somewhat more involved, if not more scientific, method has been developed. This method takes into account the hazard potential of the specific material and its rate of evolution. By establishing the severity of the hazard and its rate of evolution according to the criteria in Table 108, a minimum control velocity can be determined from Table 109. If the control envelope area through which the control velocity must be effective can be established, the capacity requirement can be figured as the product of the two.

Dalla Valle* has determined the velocity contours in the vicinity of various exhaust openings. These findings can be simplified by noting that the flow of air or any fluid towards a restricted opening tends to be equal from all directions. From basic geometry it can be demonstrated that the surface area of a sphere varies as the square of the radius and that this is approximately so for a cylinder. Visualizing the control envelope as the surface of a sphere or cylinder whose radius is equal to the distance between the hood opening and the source of contaminant, some basic rules for reducing capacities to minimum values can be established.

Rule I—Enclose the contaminant as much as possible, and, where effectively surrounded, the plane area of all the openings may be used as the control envelope area. Canopies with as many as four open sides can be considered as enclosures and the control area figured as the plane area between the edge of the canopy and the edge of the equipment being served. The following formulas are usually used:

$$CFM = A\ V \text{ for plane openings in enclosures, and} \tag{435}$$

$$CFM = 1.4\ P\ D\ V \text{ for canopies,} \tag{436}$$

where the capacity (CFM) is in cfm, the plane area of opening (A) is in sq ft, the perimeter (P) of canopy (excluding any closed sides) is in ft, the vertical distance between canopy and equipment (D) is in ft, and the control velocity (V) is in fpm.

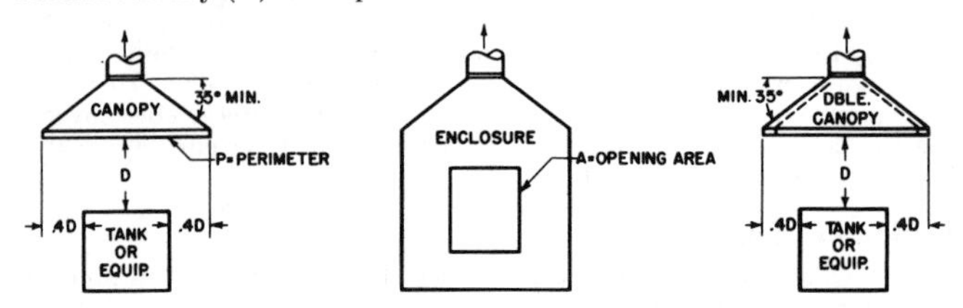

Figure 162—Canopy Hoods and Enclosures

Rule II—If it is not possible to use an enclosure or canopy, locate a lateral exhaust hood as close as possible to the source of contaminant. The required capacity can be determined from one of the following formulas:

$$CFM = (10\ x^2 + A)\ V \text{ for round or square opening hoods, and} \tag{437}$$

$$CFM = 3.7\ x\ L\ V \text{ for slot opening hoods,} \tag{438}$$

*J. M. Dalla Valle, "Exhaust Hoods," The Industrial Press, New York, 1945.

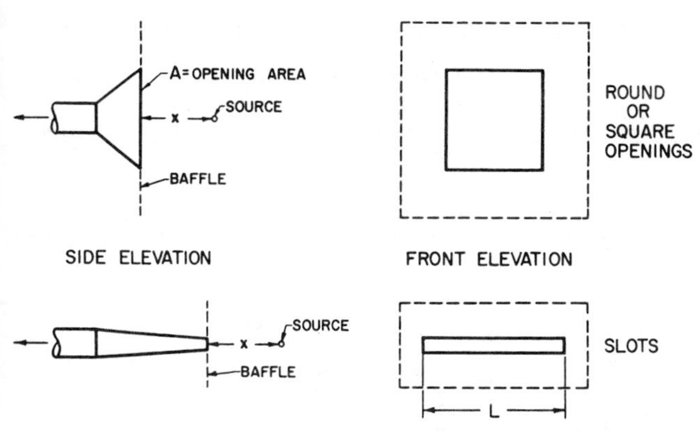

Figure 163—Lateral Exhaust Hoods

where the distance between the control envelope and the hood face (x) is in ft, the area of round or square opening (A) is in sq ft, and the length of slot (L) is in ft.

For lateral exhaust hoods the control velocity (V) must be obtained at the farthest point of contaminant release. The slot formula given above has been evaluated for specific tank geometries and the results listed in cfm per square foot of tank surface in Table 106D. This tabulated data may be easier to use than the formula.

Rule IIA—Use baffles wherever possible. If the source of contaminant is located completely to one side of the hood opening, the hood effectiveness can be concentrated on that side by proper baffling. Generally speaking, about one quarter of the control area behind the hood face is made inoperative. The following formulas take this into account:

$$CFM = 0.75\,(10\,x^2 + A)\,V \text{ for baffled round or square opening hoods, and} \tag{439}$$

$$CFM = 2.8\,x\,L\,V \text{ for baffled slot opening hoods.} \tag{440}$$

The principal factors affecting the requirement for control velocity are the air currents produced by the operation itself or by anything else. The velocity at which the contaminant is released is generally indicative of the attendant air currents but otherwise has little if any relationship to control velocity requirements. The data of Table 107 may be used to determine the range of values for any operation. By exercising a little engineering judgement the range can be narrowed down to a specific value. This value can then be used in the manner indicated in Tables 106C or D to determine the required capacity. Alternatively the data of Tables 108 and 109 may be used in the following manner to establish a control velocity. The Hazard Potential Rating (A, B, or C) can be determined on the basis of the maximum allowable concentration in parts per million for

TABLE 106—CAPACITIES REQUIRED FOR VARIOUS TYPES OF HOODS

A. MACHINE ENCLOSURES

Capacities listed in cfm per inch of machine dimension.

Active Machine Element	Typical Machine	CFM/In. Dia.	CFM/In. Width
Belt	Polisher or Sander	—	50-100
Disk or Wheel	Saw or Grinder	20-30	150-200
Drum	Sander or Jointer	—	20- 40

Above data is for rather close fitting enclosures where workpiece and active element are exposed but where particle velocity is directed into hood. Where machine and workpiece both are substantially enclosed, use 150 cfm/sq ft opening.

B. SPRAY BOOTHS, CABINETS, ETC.

Capacities listed in cfm per sq ft of booth opening.

Operation	Operator Outside	Operator Inside	Extra Large	Cabinet
Painting & Welding	150	100	75	—
Metalizing	200	125	—	—
Abrasive Blasting	—	—	—	500
Granite Cutting	—	200	—	500

Provide 80 fpm downdraft or 100 fpm cross draft past inside operator, even though a respirator is used.

C. CANOPY AND ENCLOSING HOODS

Contaminant	Remarks on Calculating cfm Capacity
Gases, Vapors, Mists	Use Table 109 velocity and appropriate area. Account for vapor liberated.
Smoke, Fumes	Use Table 107 or 109 velocity and appropriate area. Account for products of combustion.
Dusts	Use Table 107 velocity and appropriate area. Account for induced air flow.

D. LATERAL EXHAUST HOODS*

Capacities listed in cfm per sq ft of tank surface vs. control velocity.

	Control Velocity	Effective Tank Width ÷ Tank Length = W/L Ratio				
		0-0.09	0.1-0.24	0.25-0.49	0.5-0.99	1.0-2.0
Manifold on Tank ℄ or Hood Baffled	50	50	60	75	90	100
	75	75	90	110	130	150
	100	100	125	150	175	200
	150	150	190	225	260	300
Free Standing Tank Without Baffles or a ℄ Manifold	50	75	90	100	110	125
	75	110	130	150	170	190
	100	150	175	200	225	250
	150	225	260	300	340	375

1. Do not attempt $W/L > 2.0$. Avoid $W/L > 1.0$.
2. W = ½ tank width when a center line (℄) manifold is used.
3. W includes any set back of hood from edge of tank.
4. A baffle is a vertical plate that must extend to a height equal to the tank width. A wall close to the hood side of the tank is a perfect baffle.
5. The above table may be used for hoods along one side or two parallel sides of tank.

*Adapted from the data of American Standard Safety Code for Ventilation and Operation of Open-Surface Tanks, ASA, Z9.1—1951. (Revisions expected 1971.)

TABLE 107—RANGES OF CONTROL VELOCITY

Release of Contaminant	Typical Examples	Control Velocity
With negligible velocity	Most tank operations	50-100 fpm
With low velocity	Low pressure spraying. < 200 fpm conveyor transfer. Load—unload, mix, etc.	100-200 fpm
Actively generated	> 200 fpm conveyor transfer, shake-outs, screens, etc. Melting furnaces, etc.	200-500 fpm
With high velocity	Grinding, tumbling, abrasive cleaning.	500-2000 fpm

Adapted from the data of the Committee on Industrial Ventilation, "Industrial Ventilation," American Conference of Governmental Industrial Hygienists, Lansing, Mich., 1970, p. 4-5.

TABLE 108—HAZARD POTENTIAL AND RATE OF EVOLUTION CRITERIA

Hazard Poten.	Hygienic Standard		Flash Point	Rate Evo-lution	Liquid Temp-°F	°F Below Boil. Pt.	Relative Evapo-ration	Gas-sing
	Gas or Vapor	Mist						
A	0-100 ppm	0-100 μg/cu.m.	< 100°F	1	> 200	0-20	Fast	Fast
B	101-500 ppm	101-500 μg/cu.m.	100-200°F	2	150-200	21-50	Med.	Med.
C	> 500 ppm	> 500 μg/cu.m.	> 200°F	3	94-149	51-100	Slow	Slow
—	—	—	—	4	< 94	> 100	Nil	Nil

1. Hazard Potentials are listed for specific substances in the Reference.
2. μg/cu.m. = micrograms per cubic meter.
3. Information about rate of evolution is listed in the Reference.
4. In the absence of specific information, the following may be used:

Rate	Description	Complete Evaporation @ 70°F	Gassing Rate Examples
1	Fast	0-3 hours	Chrome Plating
2	Med.	3-12 hours	Pickling
3	Slow	12-50 hours	Tin Plating
4	Nil	> 50 hours	Copper Etching

Adapted from the data of American Standard Safety Code for Ventilation and Operation of Open-Surface Tanks, ASA, Z9.1—1951. (Revisions expected 1971.)

TABLE 109
MINIMUM CONTROL VELOCITIES FOR UNDISTURBED LOCATIONS

Hazard Potential and Rate of Evolution	Lateral Hoods	Enclosing and Canopy Hoods			
		1 open side	2 open sides	3 open sides	4 open sides
A-1, A-2, B-1	100	75	100	125	175
A-3, B-2, C-1	75	65	90	100	150
B-3, C-2	50	50	75	75	125
A-4, B-4, C-3 & 4	Adequate general room ventilation required				

1. Utilize velocity as indicated in Table 106C and 106D.
2. When cross drafts cannot be controlled by baffles, add the measured value to the above, considering the effect of direction as well as magnitude. In the absence of measurements, consider slight drafts as 25 fpm, moderate as 50 fpm, strong as 100 fpm, and very strong as 200 fpm.

Adapted from the data of American Standard Safety Code for Ventilation and Operation of Open-Surface Tanks, ASA, Z9.1—1951. (Revisions expected 1971.)

gases or vapors or in micrograms per cubic meter for mists, as indicated under Hygienic Standards in Table 108. Similarly, the fire or explosive hazard can be determined on the basis of flash point temperature. In the event both standards are applicable, the one yielding the higher hazard potential should be used.

In like manner, a classification for the Rate of Evolution (1, 2, 3, or 4) can be determined based on any of the four variables listed in the appropriate portion of Table 108. Although the actual temperature and the temperature differential relative to the boiling point provide rather clear cut standards, the items of evaporation and gassing are further discussed in the Notes. Once again, the rate classification should be the highest of any differing values.

The criteria in Table 108 have been developed specifically for open-surface tank operations involving a single hazardous substance. Where more than one substance is involved, the most demanding should be used as the criterion. As indicated in Table 106C, there is no reason that this data cannot be used for any application involving known gases, vapors, or mists, or even smoke or fumes, provided, of course, that appropriate data is available.

Air currents, which must be accounted for, may result from the fan action of the machine itself or from heating and ventilating equipment. Air currents may also result from the motions of operators and the material handled. Natural drafts due to thermal effects and window ventilation can also be serious. As a first rule the air currents should be measured wherever possible. Any drafts with unpredictable directional effects should be added directly to the control velocity as obtained from one of the Tables. Note 2 of Table 109 gives a rough guide for draft additions where measurements are not feasible.

To appreciate the driving forces involved in projecting hot air upwards when compared to normal control velocities, one needs only to calculate the theoretical velocity corresponding to the static draft. For instance, for a one foot high column of air at 80° with the surrounding air at 70°, a velocity of over 60 fpm theoretically results. Figure 164 shows the effect of both increased temperature differential and increased height. Although actual values will be somewhat less than the theoretical, it is obvious that the most practical approach is to utilize whatever upward velocity is produced by exhausting from directly above. Likewise, open air columns which can easily be affected by cross currents should be avoided by enclosing wherever possible.

It is also extremely desirable to enclose any process involving falling material, since large air masses can be set in motion due to both displacement and entrainment. Both entrainment and displacement will vary with the size of the stream and the height of fall. Hemeon* discusses these and thermal effects in considerable detail.

---

*W. C. L. Hemeon, "Plant and Process Ventilation," The Industrial Press, New York, 1963.

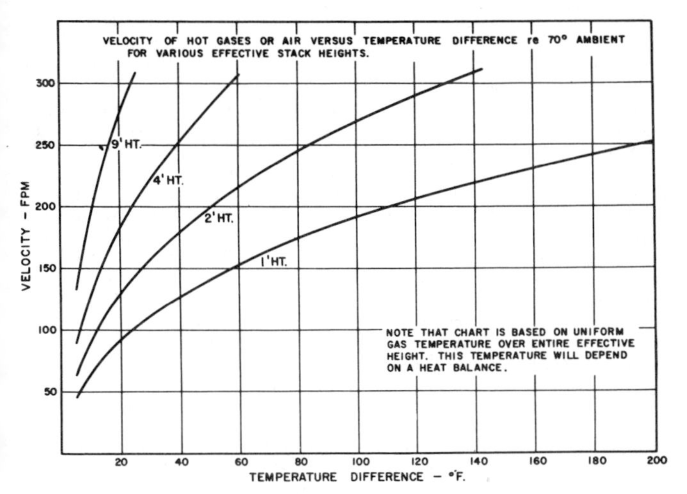

Figure 164 —Thermal Effects in Local Exhaust Ventilation

Hood Design

In the preceding paragraphs, capacity formulas were given for various types of hoods. In the following paragraphs, where applicable, comments on the entry losses and critical dimensions will be made regarding each hood type.

Plain openings or hoods which do not enclose the source of contaminant are often required in order to permit accessibility, etc., to the operation itself. In the interest of good design, it is necessary to locate this type of hood as close as possible to the source. It may take the form of a simple round duct opening, or it may consist of a more elaborate opening with a transformation to connect with the duct work. Hood entry losses will vary with the entry configuration and may be estimated from the data given for entrance losses in Chapter 3 on Fluid Flow. In brief, a re-entrant condition has a loss of from .85 to .95 velocity heads. A flanged duct end has an entry loss of approximately .50 velocity heads, giving a saving in pressure as well as in required capacity as previously outlined. A well-rounded or bell-mouthed entry has practically no loss. Refer to page 120 for exact data on converging entrances.

With all non-enclosing hoods it is necessary to determine a control velocity and the furthest point at which that control velocity must be effective, relative to the hood face. This point may be the furthest point on the actual source. In the case of contaminants with appreciable initial velocities, it is more likely that the contaminant will be propelled away from the hood at first and that the control velocity will have to be maintained at some greater distance. Because of the very sizable effect of temperature in producing high upward currents, non-enclosing hoods are not recommended for service under these conditions. In the event it is the only alternative, the hood should be located above the level of the source, and every possible effort made to prevent any side drafts from affecting the rising current of air. Even so, in cases such as these, it is not unusual that three or four times the actual volume of the hot current will need to be exhausted in order to effectively control contamination.

Slots are simply elongated plain openings, and the same entry loss data applies. A brief reflection on the nature of a slot will reveal that the capacity through the slot, rather than the velocity, is all important. For any appreciable length, a two-inch slot with 1000 fpm velocity will produce the same effect as a one-inch slot with 2000 fpm velocity. This reasoning assumes, of course, that the source of contaminant is several inches removed from the face of the slot. Similar reasoning will show that the use of baffles in the center of plain openings, essentially making peripheral slots, increases velocities effectively only in very close proximity to the opening. Nevertheless, some codes will specify a minimum slot velocity, and this value must be used. The proximity of a table top, floor, tank, or even the manifold itself will very often effectively form a flange around the slot opening. This increases the effectiveness and reduces the hood entry loss as discussed previously.

Canopies and enclosing hoods are related, differing principally only in the number of open sides. The use of the term "canopy" is usually restricted to those enclosures with three or four open sides. According to the principles already developed, it is always more desirable to enclose as fully as possible. The canopy portion of the hood should always extend beyond the edge of the tank or whatever the source of contamination. Authorities differ as to the amount of projection, and a value of .4 times the vertical distance between the top of the tank and the bottom of the canopy would seem conservative. This projection is required because of the effect of side drafts and also in the case of hot processes because of the expanding nature of the rising air current. Whenever the process itself produces a flow, due either to the liberation of a vapor, the formation of products of combustion, or thermal or induced flow effects, it is necessary to exhaust a volume equal to that produced, plus an additional amount sufficient to prevent contamination of the surroundings which might otherwise result from the balanced but still inward and outward stray currents.

Machine enclosures in general have been standardized and usually utilize the initial velocity imparted to the particle by the machine itself. For this reason, it is more convenient to specify the capacity required relative to some controlling machine dimension. Some state codes specify the number and size of pipes to be connected to the machine at specific locations. Booths and cabinets are specialized enclosures within which the operator usually performs the operation. A cabinet differs from a booth in that it is a complete enclosure, including a baffled air opening usually located at the top. The nature of the operations performed in booths may require that the operator wear a respirator. Control volumes are usually specified as so many cfm per square foot of booth opening to prevent the escape of contaminant beyond that opening; however, specified downdrafts or crossdrafts within the booth past the operator may also be listed in many codes.

System Design

The total system or fan capacity and the individual capacities of the branches are the appropriate summations of individual hood requirements. The total pressure required of the fan is the appropriate summation of hood entry, duct, elbow, collector, and exit losses for the longest run as discussed in Chapter 4.

In designing the duct work transportation of the contaminant must be provided without danger of settling out. Naturally, lower velocities will yield lower friction and shock losses. For gaseous contaminants, duct transport velocities of 1500-2500 feet per minute are generally used. For heavier contaminants duct velocities of 3000-5000 feet per minute are used. Duct sizes can be established on the basis of required volumes and velocities. Refer to Chapter 3 on Fluid Flow for individual friction and shock losses. As demonstrated in Chapter 4, wherever there is more than one branch, only the branch of greatest resistance (usually the longest run) need be figured and the loss in any other branch can be equalized by some form of dampering. It is not always wise in exhaust systems to utilize anything like a blast gate which might tend to form a pocket or otherwise accumulate material. Indeed, most codes outlaw blast gates whenever explosive material is involved. Although it is more laborious to design, a balanced system utilizes the materials involved to the best advantage and also avoids many of the dangers of plugging, erosion, and even explosions. An example of balanced system design is given in Chapter 4.

The reader is referred to Chapter 13 for details of fan selection. Industrial exhausters of the centrifugal type are specifically designed for local exhaust system duty. Different wheels are available when clean air, stringy material, or other material and air is handled by the fan. These are generally designated as: air wheel; open, cone, or long shavings wheel; and material wheel. Wear, spark, or corrosion resistant materials can, of course, be specified. Special axial flow fans have been standardized in a spray booth design which facilitates removal of accumulated paint, etc. These fans have large access doors and a minimum of interior surface which need be cleaned.

Various air cleaning devices are available as discussed in Chapter 23. Utilize the principles developed there for the selection of the proper size and type of air cleaning equipment.

The usual local exhaust system discharges to atmosphere. However, where the contaminant has been removed to a sufficient degree, recycling is sometimes used in order to conserve heat.

For any exhaust system to function properly, provisions must be made to replace the exhausted air. Unless make-up air provisions are made, either of two equally undesirable situations will develop. If the building construction allows, the required make-up air will enter untreated through the various holes and cracks available. For tighter building construction, the same situation will develop except that higher negative pressures will have to be produced within the building in order to produce flow through the slight openings. Consequently, the fan or fans will tend to back up on their performance curves. This will result in sub-design capacities at the various hoods with resulting spillage and contamination.

Sheet metal gauges, materials of construction, and other fabrication details are often specified by municipalities or states in their safety codes. Specific duct details can be found in Chapter 4.

Testing

The principles of flow and pressure measurement are outlined in Chapter 3. It may be necessary to measure the flow through each hood in order to properly balance a system; to determine whether it is functioning as intended, as required by law; or even to determine whether there are possibilities for extending the system.

The most popular method of estimating air flow through a hood is to measure the so-called hood suction in the branch pipe close to the hood and calculate the flow rate with the aid of a "coefficient of entry." The static suction reading is equal to the velocity pressure in the duct plus the hood entry loss. The coefficient of entry (C_e) is related to this negative static pressure (SP) reading and the velocity pressure (VP) in the duct branch according to the following formula:

$$C_e = \sqrt{\frac{VP}{SP}}. \tag{441}$$

This relationship is implied in Equation 151. Substituting .075 lb per cu ft for δ, this equation may be written for standard air conditions:

$$CFM = 4005\ C_e\ A\ \sqrt{SP}. \tag{442}$$

Accordingly, the flow (CFM) can be determined by measuring the hood suction (SP) in in. WG and the area (A) in sq ft if the coefficient of entry is known. The value of C_e may be obtained from Figure 61 for tapered hoods. The values for other types of hoods can be obtained from Table 110.

Some codes still specify the value for the static hood suction. When this is done without regard to the actual hood entry coefficient, it is obvious that the stipulation is made without regard to actual capacity. The only merit in this is the simplicity of having a single numerical value regardless of other variations.

TABLE 110—COEFFICIENTS OF ENTRY FOR HOODS

Belled Duct End	C_e = 0.97
Flanged Duct End	C_e = 0.82
Plain Duct End	C_e = 0.72
Square Edged Orifice	C_e = 0.60
Standard Grinder Hood	C_e = 0.78
Tapered Hoods	Refer to Figure 61

For Booths and Canopies use values for belled duct, flanged duct, or tapered hood as appropriate, provided the area at the face is at least twice the duct area.

CHAPTER 18

CONVEYING

The purpose of any conveying system is to transport material from one place to another. Air may be used as a conveying medium whenever the nature of the material is suitable. Most granular, crushed, or pulverized materials may be conveyed in pneumatic systems, although some of the finest materials are difficult to convey in this manner because they tend to become sticky or abrasive. At the other extreme, very large cardboard cartons have been successfully conveyed over long distances by means of air.

In any conveying system, energy is required to accelerate and lift the material and to overcome any losses due to friction. In pneumatic systems, the friction losses include those due to the sliding of the material along the walls of the ducts and elbows and those due to the forces within the air itself. The required energy may be supplied by a fan, blower, or compressor, or by some other type mechanical device, or the potential energy of the material itself may be utilized in some special cases.

Othmer* through Zenz has presented a detailed graphical analysis of the possible fluid-solids phases based on the various combinations of upward or downward air flow with upward, downward, or zero net solids flow as well as cocurrent air-solids horizontal flow. Most conveying applications for fans involve only dilute-phase, cocurrent, upward or horizontal, air-solids flow. This chapter is written accordingly except for a short closing section on the so called "fluidized" systems which may involve dense phases in either cocurrent or countercurrent air-solids flow.

The choice between a pneumatic system and a mechanical system should be based on a combined economical and functional analysis. Although a mechanical system involving buckets, belts, etc., will generally require less operating horsepower, its usually higher equipment, space, and maintenance costs often tip the balance toward an air system. Similarly, although an air system without the proper safeguards may plug on occasion, there are functional advantages, such as inherent self-cleaning and dust control characteristics, as well as attractive possibilities for drying, cooling, or otherwise processing en route.

Design Principles

Because conveying is more of an art than a science, the designer must exercise keen judgment in evaluating any functional advantages that one

*D. F. Othmer, "Fluidization," Reinhold Publishing Corporation, New York, 1956, Chapter 3, Graphical Analysis of Fluid-Solids Systems in the Process Industries by F. A. Zenz.

system may have over another. There are no hard and fast rules governing owning and operating costs which would facilitate an economic analysis. Therefore, good design may involve making several trial solutions and completely evaluating the functional and economic factors of each.

The designer should, of course, have full knowledge of the amount and nature of the material to be conveyed. The over-all path which the material must follow is often specified in great detail, but the designer, in the interests of good design, should attempt to eliminate any unnecessary elbows or bends.

The designer must determine the relative locations for the fan, feeder, and separator. There are three possibilities: the fan may be located upstream from the feeder, downstream from the separator, or in between the feeder and separator. The pressure at any point in the system will generally be greater than atmospheric on the discharge side of the fan and less than atmospheric on the suction side of the fan. To evaluate the alternative possibilities, such matters as wear and tear on the fan, damage to the material being transported, structural requirements to withstand the pressure forces, and the direction of leakage flow should be considered.

When the fan is located upstream from the feeder, it is spared any wear and tear due to material flow. The fan itself cannot cause any damage to the material, but the feeder may have to be carefully selected to avoid crushing or high-velocity impact. The entire system is generally under pressure. Although this makes it relatively easy to design to withstand the pressure forces, special precautions are required to insure tightness. Since leakage flow would be outward through any cracks or openings, tightness is required wherever a dust problem might otherwise result.

Various methods may be employed to feed the material into the system against the pressure that exists downstream from the fan. The screw feeder, illustrated in Figure 165D, effects a seal by compressing the material into a more solid mass and forces it into the pipe. The star or rotary valve, as illustrated in Figure 165E, effects a seal between the hopper above and the conveying pipe below. As the valve rotates the material drops into the upper chamber from the hopper and out of the lower into the conveying pipe. Any such mechanical device requires its own source of power, is subject to wear and tear, and may damage certain materials.

The pressure, downstream from the fan, may be reduced to a value below atmospheric pressure by using a venturi. The material can then be fed into the system from a hopper connected to the venturi throat as illustrated in Figure 165F. The velocity in the throat must be sufficiently high so that the static pressure regain equals the downstream pressure losses. High-velocity impact damages some materials. Venturi efficiencies are impaired by the turbulence produced by the material. Such a method is not generally suitable for long runs or high loadings.

When the fan is located downstream from the separator, it is spared most of the wear and tear due to material flow. Since no separator is perfect, some material will pass through to the fan. None of the material which is collected will be damaged by the fan. The pressure throughout the system will be less than atmospheric; consequently, there will be no

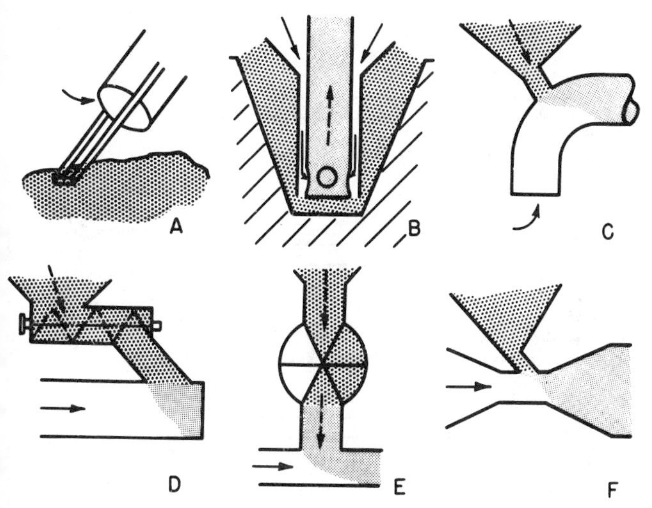

Figure 165—Methods of Feeding Material

danger of blow back at the feeder location. Any leakage flow will be inward. Whenever the run is long or the loading heavy, the separator will be subjected to considerable pressure forces. The cost of the separator may be increased if it must be designed for a high vacuum.

Many different methods may be employed to feed the material into a negative pressure system. In addition to the mechanical devices mentioned above, several simpler feeders can be used. The simple duct opening, illustrated in Figure 165A, is frequently used. A mechanical guard may be used to protect against plugging. If the material can be scraped into a pit, a concentric-tube feeder similar to that shown in Figure 165B may be used. The hopper-fed elbow, illustrated in Figure 165C, allows over-fed material to fall through to the floor.

When the fan is located between the feeder and the separator, the advantages of a negative pressure feeder location and positive pressure separator location are both achieved. All of the material must pass through the fan; consequently, wear and tear may be considerable. In addition, the material can be damaged by impact on the fan blades and scroll. In spite of these disadvantages, this method is frequently employed.

Several types of systems are illustrated by the line drawings in Figure 166. The first three are single pipe systems employing the three different fan locations discussed above. The last two systems involve multiple points of distribution or multiple sources of material as indicated.

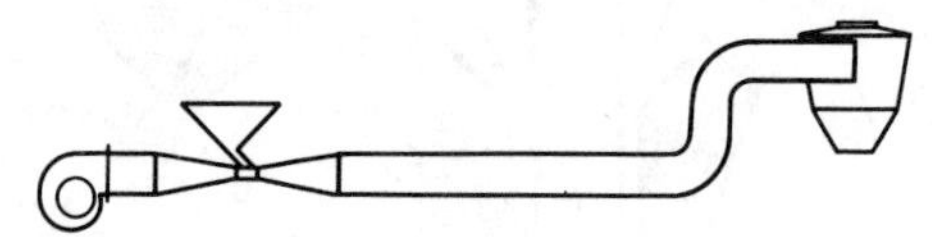

FAN UPSTREAM OF FEEDER—VENTURI FEEDER SHOWN

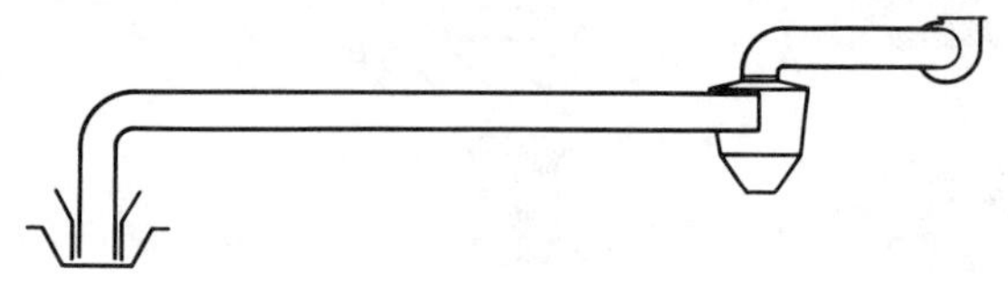

FAN DOWNSTREAM OF SEPARATOR—PIT FEEDER SHOWN

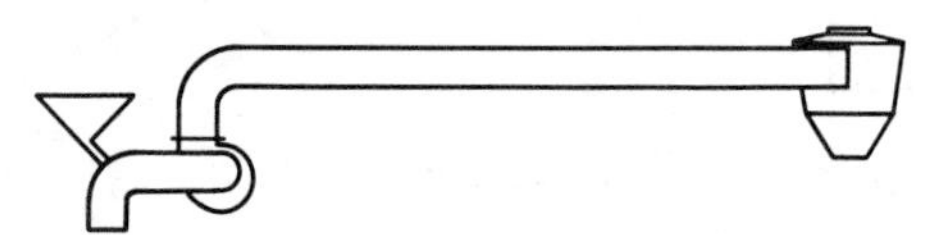

FAN BETWEEN FEEDER AND SEPARATOR—ELBOW FEEDER SHOWN

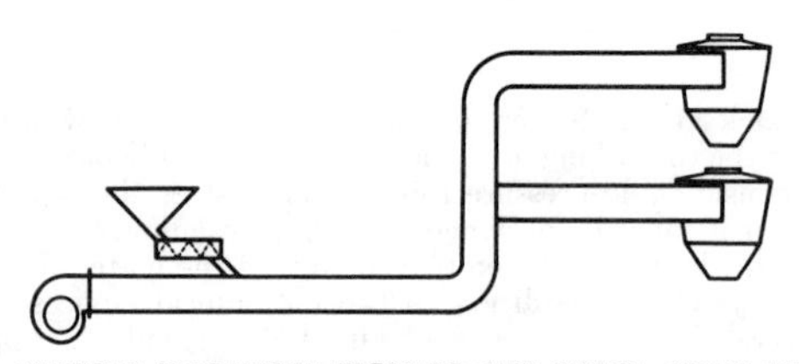

MULTIPLE DISTRIBUTION PRESSURE TYPE SYSTEM—SCREW FEEDER SHOWN

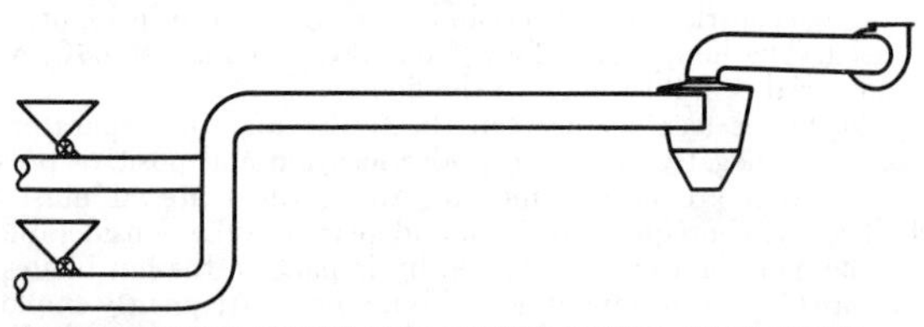

MULTIPLE SOURCE VACUUM TYPE SYSTEM—ROTARY VALVES SHOWN

Figure 166—Conveying Systems

Single pipe systems may plug on occasion. They can usually be unplugged very easily because they are essentially self-cleaning systems. Since the air will take the path of least resistance, any tendency to plug in one line of a multiple pipe system will be accentuated by the resulting reduction in flow. There is some evidence supporting the theory that unbalanced circuits and therefore plugging are reduced by using somewhat larger pipe size and relatively lower material loadings.

Material Loadings

After the general layout of a system has been established, the pipe must be sized. Various sizes may be used, but only one will give the most economical system. Consequently, several trial pipe sizes should be selected and evaluated.

There is a minimum transport velocity for each material so that the amount of air required will vary directly with the cross sectional area of the pipe. Therefore, the ratio of the weight flow of the material to that of the air will depend on the pipe size. This ratio, which is also called the material loading, is one of the most significant design parameters.

Standard industrial exhauster type fans can be utilized for material-to-air ratios up to 2:1 unless the conveying distances are unusually long. Standard pressure blowers of the centrifugal fan type can be used on material loadings as high as 5:1 or 6:1. Beyond this figure, either a combination of two fans in series, or a multi-stage blower, or some sort of positive displacement blower is generally required. For materials which tend to drift, Patterson* indicates the tendency is less with lower material-to-air ratios. Presumably, the relatively greater mass of air is better able to recapture any particles which settle out temporarily.

Once one or more pipe sizes are assumed, capacities and material loadings can be calculated. With a known velocity and pipe size, the equation of continuity can be used to determine the cfm of air. This, together with the density, adequately defines the rate of air flow. The pounds of material flow divided by the pounds of air flow for any consistent time interval gives the material loading. With these figures in hand, it is possible to calculate the pressure losses due to both air and material.

Design Velocities

An individual particle may be considered aerodynamically, and a "floating" velocity derived. The formula for a particle of any shape, in a vertical stream of air,

$$V_{floating} = \sqrt{\frac{2g}{f_D}\frac{\rho_p}{\rho_a}\frac{Volume}{Frontal\ Area}}, \qquad (443)$$

may be evaluated for a sphere-like particle

$$V_{floating} = \sqrt{\frac{4}{3}\frac{g}{f_D}\frac{\rho_p}{\rho_a}d_p}, \qquad (444)$$

where the floating velocity (V) is in ft per sec, the gravitational accelera-

*R. L. Patterson, Pulverized-Coal Transport Through Pipes, *Trans. ASME*, vol. 81 (1), pp. 43-54, 1959.

TABLE 111—CONVEYING VELOCITIES

in fpm

Material	fpm	Material	fpm
Castor Beans	5000	Paper	500
Cement	7000	Rags	450
Coal, powdered	4000	Rubber	450
Cork, ground	3000	Salt	550
Corn	5600	Sand	700
Cotton	4500	Sawdust, dry	300
Iron Oxide	6500	Shavings	350
Knots, blocks	5000	Wheat	580
Limestone, pulverized	5000	Wool	500
Oats	4500	Vegetable pulp, dry	450

tion (g) is in ft per sec per sec, the coefficient of drag (f_D) is dimension-less, the diameter of the particle (d_p) is in ft, and the densities of material (ρ_p) and air (ρ_a) are in any consistent units. This indicates that the weight, size, and shape of the particle influences the floating velocity. The coefficient of drag for a particle with sharp edges is comparatively independent of Reynolds number in the range usually encountered and for most shapes from thin flakes to cubes the value is close to 1.0. The drag coefficient for round bodies such as spheres and long cylinders varies with Reynolds number, but for the typical conveying application a value of 0.5 for spheres and 1.0 for cylinders may usually be justified. There is substantial experimental agreement with the above formula. However, it should be noted that irregularly shaped bodies, although normally tending to face broadside to the stream, do periodically turn, and for them the floating velocity will be a range of velocities. It should also be noted that floating velocity, strictly speaking, applies only to vertical pipes.

Although the relative velocity of material and air is equal to the floating velocity in a vertical pipe, this equality does not hold in a horizontal pipe. From the data of Gasterstadt* it would appear that

$$V_{relative} = V_{floating}\,(0.18 + 0.65 \times 10^{-4}\,V_{air}) \text{ for horizontal runs,} \quad (445)$$

where the various velocities are all in consistent units.

The material velocity is equal to the air velocity minus the relative velocity. The material velocity in a vertical pipe is usually somewhat less than that in a horizontal pipe. There is probably no mathematical expression with which a desirable material velocity for all materials can be calculated. The principal criterion is that the material velocity shall be sufficiently high that drifting is eliminated, or, at the very least, minimized. Even so, drifting will be allowed by some system designers because nothing can be done to avoid it completely. Some materials like coal have a critical moisture content above which drifting will occur. In such cases the designer must be satisfied to allow some accumulation in the system provided there is no consequent plugging. This is satisfactory in some cases, but it is obviously not satisfactory whenever there are strict contamination or sanitation requirements. Fortunately, many materials in their as-used condition do not exhibit this tendency to drift or stick. Other materials when properly controlled as to moisture content, etc., may be satisfactorily conveyed.

*M. Gasterstadt, Experimental Investigation of Pneumatic Conveying Process, *Zeitschrift des Vereines Deutscher Ingenieure*, vol. 68, No. 24, June 14, 1924.

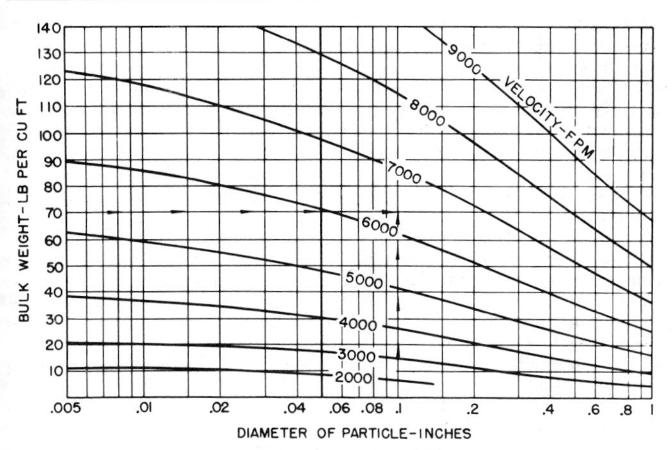

Figure 167—Conveying Velocities

The effect of material bulk on air velocity in a given pipe size may, for all practical purposes, be ignored. This may be better appreciated when one considers that even for a case where there are ten pounds of material per pound of air and where that material might weigh 100 pounds per cubic foot in a solid mass, this would affect the volume of one pound of air only by one-tenth of a cubic foot out of 13.3 cubic feet.

Some commonly accepted air velocities for conveying various materials are listed in Table 111. These figures usually include sufficient margin to avoid plugging. As a rule of thumb, materials with bulk weights ranging from 25 to 75 lbs per cu ft can be transported satisfactorily with an air velocity of 5000 fpm.

Madison assumed a relationship between bulk weight and material velocity to develop the chart in Figure 167.

Pressure Losses

The losses due to the flow of air through the various duct elements may be calculated from the data in Chapter 3. For straight duct runs, Figures 46 through 50 may be used. These charts are laid out for the usual heating and ventilating pipe. In the interests of reducing friction losses, as well as reducing the possibilities for drifting or plugging, considerably smoother pipe with fewer joints is usually used in conveying systems. Therefore, the necessary correction for smoothness should be applied to the duct friction charts. The roughness correction chart is on page 102. The friction charts are on pages 104 and 106.

One of the many reasons for employing a conveying system utilizing air is that it can conveniently go around corners where other systems can do so only with difficulty. Nevertheless, elbows are a source of considerable pressure loss, and their effects should be eliminated or minimized wherever possible. An easy bend with a radius ratio of five or six is usually used. The developed length of such an elbow usually amounts to approximately ten diameters, and this figure may be used for the pressure loss calculation. In addition to the above friction losses, there are shock losses occasioned by the change in direction or cross section of the ductwork. These include entrance losses (see page **119**), contractions and enlargements (see page **92**), divided-flow fittings (see page **121**), and sharp-bend elbows (see page **109**), as well as feeding devices, separators, and any process equipment.

In addition to the pressure required to produce the air flow through the system, energy must be provided: to accelerate the material as many times as necessary, to lift the material the required distance, and to overcome the frictional forces developed as the material slides along the bottom of horizontal ducts or the outside of elbows. This energy is put into the air by the fan and in turn is transmitted to the material as required. Bearing in mind that the sum of the potential and kinetic energy in a unit weight of fluid is equal to the total head in ft-lb per lb of that fluid, expressions can be developed for the various losses associated with the energy requirements of the material at certain stages.

The energy in ft-lb, available from one lb of air, is numerically equal to the total head in ft of air. Since the equivalent of one inch of water is 69.4 ft of air, the energy in a unit weight of air is 69.4 times its total pressure (TP) in inches water gage. The rate at which energy can be obtained from the air is equal to the weight rate of air flow (w_a) multiplied by 69.4 times the change in total pressure (TP). The rate at which energy must be used depends on the work done on the material. Dividing the rate at which work is done on the material by 69.4 times the weight rate of air flow gives the total pressure loss which must be suffered by the air.

The rate at which work is done in lifting a weight rate of material (w_m) in lb per unit time through a vertical distance (L) in ft is $w_m L$ in ft-lb per unit time. Accordingly, the total pressure (TP_L) in inches water gage which must be lost by the air is:

$$TP_L = \frac{w_m\,L}{69.4\,w_a} = \frac{RL}{69.4}, \tag{446}$$

where the ratio of material to air is designated by R. No allowance for friction is included in this expression.

Similarly, the rate at which work is done in accelerating the material to a given velocity (V_m) is $w_m\,V_m{}^2/2\,g$. The corresponding total pressure loss (TP_A) is:

$$TP_A = \frac{w_m\,V_m{}^2/2\,g}{69.4\,w_a} \approx R\,(VP). \tag{447}$$

The expression $V_m{}^2/(2\,g\,69.4)$ can be equated to the velocity pressure (VP) of the air, but only if the material velocity (V_m) is equal to the air velocity corresponding to VP. This loss is suffered by the air each time the material must be accelerated from rest to the velocity corresponding to VP. In addition to the original acceleration, there is always a reacceleration after each elbow, particularly after a lift. The estimation of material velocities throughout the system during the design stage requires very good judgment.

The work done in overcoming friction is equal to the frictional force (F_f), times the distance (d), over which it acts. The frictional force, of course, is equal to the normal force (F_n) multiplied by a coefficient of friction (f). This coefficient in turn depends upon whether the material is in motion or at rest. Coefficients of static friction based on measured angles of slide are listed in Table 112. Assuming as did Fischer* that the coefficient of sliding friction does not differ materially, we can calculate the frictional force provided we know the normal force. This normal force will vary depending on whether the weight due to gravity or the centrifugal force must be considered. Even if air separates each particle from the next, the total weight still must be borne by the duct in horizontal runs. Similarly, in elbows a normal force will be developed equivalent to the centrifugal force of the material rounding the bend. In general, the pressure required (TP_f) to overcome sliding friction may be expressed:

$$TP_f = \frac{F_f d}{69.4\, w_a} = \frac{f F_n d}{69.4\, w_a}. \tag{448}$$

The pressure required (TP_H) to move the material over a horizontal run of length (H) in ft is:

$$TP_H = \frac{f\, w_m H}{69.4\, w_a} = \frac{f\, RH}{69.4}. \tag{449}$$

Note that this loss is independent of velocity except through f.

The head required ($TP_{90°}$) in inches WG to move the material around any 90° bend is:

$$TP_{90°} = \frac{f\,(CF)\,d}{69.4\, w_a} \approx \pi f\, R\,(VP), \tag{450}$$

since the centrifugal force (CF) is equal to $w_m\, V_m^2/g\, r$ and the distance around the bend (d) is $\pi\, r/2$. The elbow radius (r) cancels out. Once again the expression $V_m^2/(2g\; 69.4)$ can be equated to the velocity pressure (VP) of the air only if the material velocity (V_m) equals the air velocity. They are not equal, but the error may be considered a margin of safety.

The pressure losses which must be suffered by the air to the material can be calculated only approximately from Equations 446, 447, 449, and 450. Equation 446 gives the exact requirement for lifting, but ignores any friction in the vertical run. Equation 447 gives the exact requirement for accelerating from rest to a particular velocity, but the value of the actual final velocity can not be predicted with great accuracy. Equations 449 and 450 would give the exact requirements for sliding friction if the coefficients could be evaluated precisely, but they cannot in most cases. Equations 449 and 450 ignore air friction effects. Nevertheless, when these equations are used with good judgment, practicable results can be obtained.

All four losses, due to material, vary directly with the material-to-air ratio. The vertical run loss is proportional to the lift and the horizontal run loss is proportional to the length of run. Elbow losses are proportional to the angle of bend, but independent of the radius of bend according to

*J. Fischer, Practical Pneumatic Conveyor Design, *Chemical Engineering*, pp. 114-118, June 2, 1958.

TABLE 112

COEFFICIENTS OF FRICTION FOR VARIOUS MATERIALS SLIDING ON STEEL

Material	(f)	(δ)
Alfalfa, ground	.6	15
Alumina, fine, granulated	.7	55
Anthracite Coal, broken of any size	.4	55
Bagasse, wet	1.0	4
Beans (See Coffee, Cocoa, Navy, Soy)		
Bituminous Coal, pulverized	.8	30
Borax, dehydrated, powdered	.8	75
Bran	.7	21
Brewers Grits	.4	33
Buckwheat	.5	34
Casein, granular	.6	40
Cinders	.7	42
Clover Seed	.5	48
Coal (See Anthracite, Bituminous)		
Cocoa Beans	.5	37
Cocoa Nibs	.5	32
Cocoanut meal	.8	32
Cocoanut, shredded	.5	25
Coffee beans, green	.5	42
Coffee, steel cut	.4	28
Coke, pulverized	.7	25
Corn, field (on cob)	.4	45
Corn, shelled	.4	45
Corn Flakes	.4	12
Corn Germ	.5	25
Corn Germ Flakes	.7	25
Corn Grits	.4	40
Cornmeal	.7	40
Cornmeal muffin mixture	1.0	28
Cotton Seed	.6	25
Cotton Seed meal	.7	33
Cryolite, ½″ to 200 mesh, crushed	.6	52
Dolomite, pulverized	.9	46
Farina	.6	44
Feldspar, pulverized	.8	55
Flax Seed, ground	.7	28
Flour	.6	37
Flour, prepared biscuit	.8	26
Flyash, powdered	.9	45
Fuller's Earth, raw	.7	42
Glass, Batch, average mix	1.0	100
Grass, blue, seed	.6	11
Gravel	.6	120
Gypsum	1.0	142
Hominy	.4	45
Iron Oxide Pigment	.8	25
Kalsomine, powder	.9	32
Limestone, pulverized	.9	85
Linseed meal	.6	27
Linseed, rolled	.7	25
Malt, dry	.4	32
Malt, spent dry	.5	10
Malt Sugar, ground	.6	35
Malt Sugar, unground	.6	30
Mica, ground	.7	13
Milk, powdered	1.0	40
Navy Beans	.4	54
Oats	.4	26
Oats, rolled	.5	18
Pablum	.6	9
Plaster of Paris, powdered	.8	50
Portland Cement	.8	95
Pumice, pulverized	1.0	40
Resin, synthetic, (from plant), crushed	.6	40
Resin and Wood Flour, powdered	.8	19
Rice	.4	50
Rubber, scrap, ground	.7	23
Salt, granulated	.6	81
Sand, coarse sized	.6	95
Sand, Core	.8	65
Sand, mine run	.7	105
Sand, very fine	.6	100
Sand, voids full of water	1.0	120
Seed (See Clover, Cotton, Flax, Grass, Timothy)		
Soap chips	.6	10
Soy Beans, crushed	.7	34
Soy Beans, flour	.8	27
Soy Beans, meal	.5	40
Soy Beans, split	.5	44
Soy Beans, whole	.4	47
Starch, lump and pelleted	.5	30
Starch, powdered	1.0	35
Starch, tablet, granular crystals	.4	40
Sulphur, pulverized	1.0	50
Timothy Seed	.5	36
Tobacco Stems, chopped, coarse	.4	16
Wheat	.4	48
Wheat Germ	.6	32
Wheat Germ, ground	.7	32
Wood chips, dry	.4	23
Wood sawdust, dry	.7	20
Wood sawdust, ground	1.0	20

f—dimensionless. δ—lb/cu ft average bulk density.

Adapted from the data of Weights of Various Substances, Stephans-Adamson Division of Borg-Warner Corporation, Aurora, Ill.

the above analysis. The suggested radius ratio of five or six is principally based upon reducing erosion and minimizing the shock losses suffered directly by the air. Acceleration and elbow losses are both related to the air velocity.

Fan Performance

In conveying systems, as in any other type of system, the operating characteristics may be determined by drawing the fan performance curves and the system resistance curves on the same graph. The point of operation is the point of intersection of the two capacity-pressure curves.

Figure 168 is drawn for a typical fan-system combination. The system resistance is shown for a wide range of air capacities when only air is passed through the system. The system resistance is shown for only a narrow range of air capacities when both air and material are passed through the system. Any extension of this curve toward zero air capacity would be misleading since the velocity would soon drop below the minimum necessary for transport.

The operating point when material is fed at the normal rate will be at A. If the material is fed at a lower rate, the operating point will gradually move to the right along the fan curve until it reaches B, at which point no material is fed into the system. Similarly, the operating point would move to the left of A if the feed rate were increased. The amount that the feed rate can be increased over design is limited by the resultant decrease in velocity, and attendant possibility of plugging. Point C is not an operating point, but the difference in pressure between A and C is that which must be developed to lift, accelerate, and slide the material along the ducts and elbows. The pressures at C and B are simply those which must be developed to move the corresponding amount of air through the system without any material.

When material is fed at the normal rate, but none passes through the fan, the operating horsepower will be at D. If the material is fed at a lower rate, the operating point will gradually move to the right along the fan curve until it reaches E, at which point no material is fed into the system. Less horsepower is required when material is conveyed than when only air is passed through the system. The point F represents the horsepower requirement when the conveyed material passes through the fan.

Whenever the material passes through the fan an increase in power requirements should be expected compared to that at the same capacity and speed with only air passing through the fan. Although the material-air mixture does not behave like a homogeneous fluid, the air-material horsepower can be predicted, but only approximately, by multiplying the air horsepower by the ratio of effective density to air density. The effective density is the total weight of the air and material divided by the volume of the mixture. The actual increase in horsepower will probably be less than predicted, particularly if the material has been accelerated before entering the fan. A rather large portion of the material will probably separate out of the air stream and be accelerated directly by the blades. Much of this energy will be lost when the material slides around the scroll, but in many cases there will be a residual velocity at the fan outlet.

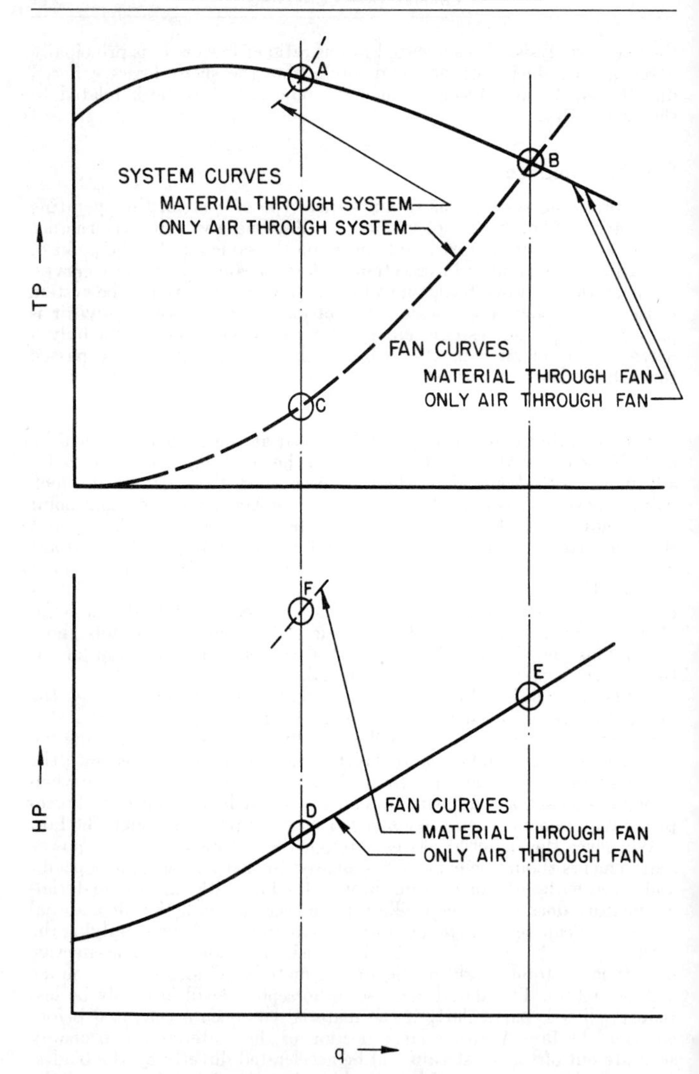

Figure 168—Fan and Conveying System Curves

Accordingly, the pressure required for acceleration at that point can be reduced. Conclusive evidence is lacking, but it is usually assumed that the pressure curve for a fan is not altered by the presence of material in the air. Density effects would tend to increase pressure, but turbulence and friction would have the opposite effect. In Figure 168, different power curves are shown for the two cases but the same pressure curve is shown whether material passes through the fan or not.

The industrial exhauster type of fan is generally used on conveying systems whenever it is capable of developing sufficient pressure. On rather short systems the pressure required for material-to-air ratios up to about 2:1 can usually be developed by a standard industrial exhauster. Various impeller designs are usually available. The standard material wheel is suitable for most applications. Extra-heavy construction may provide better service whenever appreciable amounts of material are expected to pass through the fan. "Open" or "cone" wheels are usually required whenever stringy materials must be conveyed through the fan. Granular materials do not present this problem.

Pressure blowers can be used on systems with material-to-air ratios up to 5:1 or 6:1. Above this value, two fans in series or a multi-stage blower may be required. These types are generally not suitable for applications where any appreciable amounts of material must pass through the fan itself.

System Design

Many of the important aspects of conveying system design have been discussed in the preceding paragraphs. Example 18 illustrates the application of the various formulas and principles of design.

In the example, the conveying air was discharged to atmosphere, as is usually the case. It is imperative that an adequate supply of air be provided. Frequently, the air can be obtained directly from outdoors. If for any reason indoor air must be used, provisions should be made for a make-up air supply to the building. Occasionally, a recycling arrangement will be economical, either because the material in the stream leaving the separator is too valuable to throw away or because it would cost too much to reduce the amount of discharge to an acceptable value as regards air pollution.

Systems should be designed to withstand the pressure forces that would result if the system plugged up with material. At such times the fan operates at or near "shut off." The peak pressure may be considerably higher than the normal operating pressure.

Drifting and plugging can sometimes be controlled by using kicker blocks or some other type of turbulator.

Elbows are frequently given special treatment to limit the erosive effects of the material. They may be lined or made of extra heavy material. Pipes are usually made with fewer and smoother joints than ventilating ducts.

Some conveying systems are designed to heat, dry, or otherwise process the material as it is being transported.

EXAMPLE 18. Conveying System

REQUIREMENTS

Conveying Rate: 20,000 lb/hr

Layout: Feeder, 50′ hor, 90° el, 50′ up, 90° el, 50′ hor, separator

Fan Location: Best position as determined by evaluation.

PROPERTIES OF MATERIAL

Bulk Weight: 50 lb/ft³ (25% voids)

Average Frontal Area: 0.032 in.²

Average Particle Volume: 0.004 in.³

Average Coefficient of Drag: 1.0

Average Coefficient of Friction on Steel: 0.4

VELOCITIES AND LOADINGS

Air Velocity: $V_a = 5000\ fpm\ (assumed)$

Floating Velocity: $V_f = 60\sqrt{\frac{2 \times 32.2}{1.0}\ \frac{50}{.75 \times .075}\ \frac{.004}{.032 \times 12}} = 1460\ fpm$

Relative Velocity: $V_r = 1460\ (0.18 + 0.65 \times .5000) = 740\ fpm$

Material Velocity: $V_m = 5000 - 1460 = 3540\ fpm\ (vertical)$
$V_m = 5000 - 740 = 4260\ fpm\ (horizontal)$
$V_m = 3400\ fpm\ lvg\ 3800\ fpm\ avg\ (1st\ el)$
$V_m = 2800\ fpm\ lvg\ 3100\ fpm\ avg\ (2nd\ el)$

Note: For 90° el, leaving velocity assumed to be .8 × entering velocity.

Material Rate: $w_m = 20{,}000/60 = 333\ lb/min$

Air Rate: $w_a = 5000 \times .075 \times .785 = 294\ lb/min\ (12''\ pipe)$
$w_a = 5000 \times .075 \times .349 = 131\ lb/min\ (8''\ pipe)$
$w_a = 5000 \times .075 \times .087 = 33\ lb/min\ (4''\ pipe)$

Material Loading: $R = 333/294 = 1.13\ (12''\ pipe)$
$R = 333/131 = 2.54\ (8''\ pipe)$
$R = 333/33 = 10.10\ (4''\ pipe)$

LOSSES DUE TO MATERIAL FLOW

Lift Losses: $TP_L = 1.13 \times 50/69.4 = 0.81''\ (12''\ pipe)$
$TP_L = 2.54 \times 50/69.4 = 1.83''\ (8''\ pipe)$
$TP_L = 10.10 \times 50/69.4 = 7.33''\ (4''\ pipe)$

Acceleration Losses: $\Delta VP = 1.13 - 0.00 = 1.13''\ (0\ to\ 4260\ fpm)$
$\Delta VP = 0.78 - 0.72 = 0.06''\ (3400\ to\ 3540\ fpm)$
$\Delta VP = 1.13 - 0.49 = \underline{0.64''}\ (2800\ to\ 4260\ fpm)$
$\Delta VP\ total = 1.83''$
$\Delta VP\ total + margin = 2.00''$
$TP_A = 1.13 \times 2.00 = 2.26''\ (12''\ pipe)$
$TP_A = 2.54 \times 2.00 = 5.08''\ (8''\ pipe)$
$TP_A = 10.10 \times 2.00 = 20.20''\ (4''\ pipe)$

Horizontal Losses: $TP_H = 1.13 \times .4 \times 100/69.4 = 0.65''\ (12''\ pipe)$
$TP_H = 2.54 \times .4 \times 100/69.4 = 1.46''\ (8''\ pipe)$
$TP_H = 10.10 \times .4 \times 100/69.4 = 5.81''\ (4''\ pipe)$

Elbow Losses: $VP = 0.90''$ *(avg 1st el)*
$VP = 0.60''$ *(avg 2nd el)*
$VP = 1.50''$
$TP_{2-90°} = 1.13 \times .4\ \pi\ 1.50 = 2.13''$ *(12″ pipe)*
$TP_{2-90°} = 2.54 \times .4\ \pi\ 1.50 = 4.78''$ *(8″ pipe)*
$TP_{2-90°} = 10.10 \times .4\ \pi\ 1.50 = 19.00''$ *(4″ pipe)*

LOSSES DUE TO AIR FLOW

Duct Losses: Very smooth pipe using *Fig. 46 and Fig. 47*

$$TP_d = \left(\frac{150 \times 12}{12} + 20\right) 1.56 \div (1.33 \times 57) = 3.50'' \text{ (12'' pipe)}$$

$$TP_d = \left(\frac{150 \times 12}{8} + 20\right) 1.56 \div (1.35 \times 51) = 5.55'' \text{ (8'' pipe)}$$

$$TP_d = \left(\frac{150 \times 12}{4} + 20\right) 1.56 \div (1.40 \times 43) = 12.20'' \text{ (4'' pipe)}$$

Other Losses: $TP_e = 0.00''$ *Bell Mouthed Entry*
$TP_x = 1.00''$ *Exit Loss (assumed)*
$TP_s = 2.00''$ *Separator (assumed)*
$TP_t = 3.00''$ *Total*

FAN REQUIREMENTS

Capacity: $CFM = 294 \div .075 = 3930$ *cfm std air (12″ pipe)*
$CFM = 131 \div .075 = 1750$ *cfm std air (8″ pipe)*
$CFM = 33 \div .075 = 435$ *cfm std air (4″ pipe)*

Pressure:
$FTP = 0.81 + 2.26 + 0.65 + 2.13 + 3.50 + 3.00 = 12.25''$ *(12″ pipe)*
$FTP = 1.83 + 5.08 + 1.46 + 9.78 + 5.55 + 3.00 = 21.70''$ *(8″ pipe)*
$FTP = 7.33 + 20.2 + 5.81 + 19.0 + 12.2 + 3.00 = 67.54''$ *(4″ pipe)*

Horsepower: Assuming 70% η_T for comparison (air only)
$BHP = 3930 \times 12.25 \div 6356 \times .70 = 10.8$ *hp (12″ pipe)*
$BHP = 1750 \times 21.70 \div 6356 \times .70 = 8.6$ *hp (8″ pipe)*
$BHP = 435 \times 67.54 \div 6356 \times .70 = 6.6$ *hp (4″ pipe)*

Selection: Industrial Exhauster Type *(12″ pipe)*
Pressure Blower Type *(8″ pipe)*
Pressure Blower Type (or Positive Pressure Blower) *(4″ pipe)*

EVALUATION

Refer to the section on "Principles of Design." Note that operating horsepowers decrease with duct size, as do piping costs, but that fan costs increase in spite of the lower capacity requirements. Also note that the higher speed, more refined types of fans or blowers required for high material loadings are less suitable for installations where the material or a part of it must pass through the fan itself.

"Fluidized" Systems

In a "fluidized" system the air flow primarily serves to activate or fluidize the solids. The energy required to effect transport may be provided in various ways.

In one type of system a fan is used to provide only the energy for activation and the force of gravity is utilized to transport the fluidized solids. In such an aerated gravity conveyor the equipment consists of a duct-like enclosure around some kind of porous membrane. The fluidized material flows down the inclined membrane effecting horizontal movement as well as vertical drop. Air is supplied upward through the membrane from a chamber. The amount of air required depends on the amount and nature of the material, which in turn depends on the dimensions of the system. The fan pressure required also depends on the amount and nature of the material.

In another type of system sufficient air is supplied for fluidization and a pump, generally one acting on the screw principle, is used to supply the energy for transport.

In still another type of system a fully compacted dense phase is obtained by restricting the motion of the particles with an orifice, valve, or expanded section of unfluidized solids at the exit, and the energy for solids transport is provided as pressure head at the entrance.

CHAPTER 19

AIR-COOLED HEAT EXCHANGERS

Heat exchangers are used to condition fluids, recover heat that might otherwise be wasted, or both. In air cooled exchangers the air is heated and the warmer fluid is cooled, or condensed, or both.

In evaporative equipment the latent heat of the air is increased and its sensible heat may be decreased or increased while the heat content of the warmer fluid is reduced. The evaporated moisture may come from the warm fluid itself, as in direct-contact apparatus; or, a separate water spray may be used, as in indirect-contact apparatus. In dry equipment, only the sensible heat of the air is increased.

The heated air may be discharged to atmosphere, utilized for combustion or for drying, or used directly to heat a space.

Water, brines, and oils are frequently air cooled for use in quenching and various other processes, or for engine or other machine cooling. Both dry and evaporative equipment are used to cool such liquids.

Refrigerant condensers may be considered air cooled on both direct and reverse cycles, i.e., on refrigeration and heat pump duty.

Solvent vapors are often condensed with air-cooled equipment for reuse.

Flue and other gases may be cooled using air in regenerative or recuperative equipment.

Fluidized beds of solid particles are frequently air cooled following a drying or other process which heats the material.

Air-blast cooling of non-fluid substances is discussed in Chapter 21.

Design Principles

Water is generally superior to air as a heat transfer medium because of its higher density and specific heat. However, its use may be restricted by law or ordinance, or the cost of providing and disposing of sufficient quantities may be prohibitive.

If the economics of the situation indicate that some form of air cooling is more desirable than water cooling, an evaluation of possible air-cooled alternatives must be made. The major functional considerations involve the choice between dry and evaporative apparatus and the choice of direct and indirect contact of the two fluids.

Direct-contact equipment includes cooling ponds, spray ponds, cooling towers and air washers. All depend on the evaporation of a relatively small portion of the fluid into the air to produce cooling. The evaporation and windage losses, though only a small percentage of the total flow, may represent an appreciable dollar amount depending on the unit value of the material. Cooling towers and ponds are invariably limited to water-cooling applications. Air washers are used to cool some more valuable solutions on occasion.

Indirect-contact equipment may be used with any fluid without loss or contamination. In "dry-coil" coolers and condensers, only sensible heat is transferred on the air side. In the usual "evaporative" coolers and condensers, latent heat transfer is effected by spraying water on the air side of the coil surface. Combination dry and evaporative cooling is possible; a spray chamber may be used to reduce the dry-bulb temperature of the air for a subsequent dry coil.

A wise engineering choice will be based on the most complete evaluation of pumping and equipment costs, for alternative types and sizes, that can be justified by the size of the cooling or condensing problem.

Except for natural-draft towers or ponds, the various methods of using air to cool, as outlined below, all incorporate fans as a vital part of the system. The equipment should be sized to perform as needed when outdoor weather conditions are at summer design values. The probability of more extreme weather and the possible consequences will influence the choice of design conditions. Winter operation should also be considered, and the required steps taken to prevent freeze-up, etc.

The data on evaporation, page **51**, can be utilized in the analysis of evaporative water cooling. Equations **67** and **68** may be used directly to determine the amount of water evaporated for a given set of circumstances, or it may be noted that the rate of evaporation (w_v), when multiplied by the latent heat of evaporation (λ), gives the cooling rate (LH) in Btu per hr.

For parallel flow of air and a flat water surface:

$$LH = S\,(95 + 0.425\,V)\,(e_w - e_a). \tag{451}$$

For transverse flow as over a wet-bulb:

$$LH = S\,(201 + 0.88\,V)\,(e_w - e_a). \tag{452}$$

The driving force is seen to be the difference in vapor pressure between that of the heated water (e_w) and that of the moisture in the air (e_a) expressed in inches of mercury. The influence of velocity (V) in ft per min is readily apparent, both in the formula and the chart on page **52**. The area (S) is the interfacial surface in sq ft. The determination of S is the principal difficulty in direct-contact apparatus, particularly when droplet surface rather than film surface is involved.

The data on convective heat transfer, pages **47-57**, can be utilized in the analysis of a dry-cooling process. The usual problem involves calculating the amount of surface necessary to do the required cooling job. The formulas for film coefficients, over-all coefficients, and mean temperature difference may be used directly.

Various simplified design methods are offered in the following discussions of specific apparatus.

Cooling Ponds and Spray Ponds

Cooling ponds are usually sized on the basis of negligible wind velocity or a value of $LH/S = 95\,(e_w - e_a)$. For water heated to 100° and a 65°F wet-bulb, this amounts to approximately 3.5 Btu per hr per sq ft of pond area per degree difference between the temperature of the heated water and the wet-bulb temperature of the air.

Spray ponds usually spray 50 gpm per nozzle at about 6 psig, producing a greatly increased cooling rate over that of a cooling pond due to the increase in exposed surface. A value of 130 Btu per hr per sq ft pond area per degree difference between temperature of heated water and wet-bulb temperature of the air is frequently used. Based on still air and temperatures assumed above, this figure indicates about 17 square feet of exposed surface per square foot of pond as calculated with Equation **452**.

Cooling Towers

Natural-draft cooling towers are classified as atmospheric or chimney types. Wind and stack effects, respectively, are utilized to provide the energy for ventilation. These effects are subject to weather influences so that performance is both variable and limited. Tower sizing should be based on some minimum wind as well as maximum temperature. The decrease in performance that will occur when conditions are worse than design should be recognized.

Mechanical-draft cooling towers provide positive circulation regardless of weather. The use of fans also makes possible the use of higher velocities and a corresponding reduction in tower size. The optimum combination of fan and tower characteristics is a matter of economic evaluation.

The performance of a cooling tower cannot be predicted from theoretical considerations alone. The capabilities of a specific design can only be determined by testing. Fortunately, it is not necessary to test every size, nor is it necessary to test under all conditions of operation. Theoretical relationships can be used to convert from one set of conditions to another. Experimental data for certain typical designs are tabulated below. This data may be extrapolated for use with other similar designs. However, confirming tests should be performed.

The following analysis is for a counter-flow cooling tower arrangement, which allows the closest approach of the leaving water temperature to the entering wet-bulb temperature. The cooling range, or temperature difference between entering and leaving water ($WT_1 - WT_2$), in °F can be calculated from the cooling load (TH) in Btu/hr and the water quantity (GPM) in gpm using:

$$WT_1 - WT_2 = TH/(500 \times GPM). \qquad (453)$$

In practical applications, the wet-bulb, range, and approach are specified, and a tower with sufficient contact area must be found.

From cooling tower theory as presented by Lichtenstein*, the thermodynamic requirements are related to the dimensionless number KSV/L by:

$$\frac{KSV}{L} = \int_{WT_1}^{WT_2} \frac{dWT}{i_w - i}. \qquad (454)$$

*J. Lichtenstein, Performance and Selection of Mechanical-Draft Cooling Towers, *Trans. ASME*, vol. 65, pp. 779-787, 1943.

TABLE 113—COUNTERFLOW COOLING TOWER CONSTANTS

DECK CHARACTERISTICS	C_1	C_2	C_3	C_4	C_5
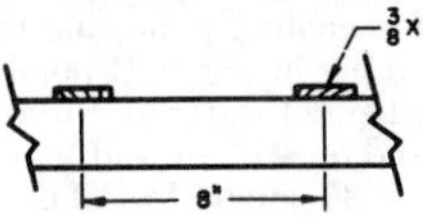 $\frac{3}{8}$ x 2"; 8"; 9" VERTICAL SPACING	.07 GRAVITY DISTRIBUTION .25 6 PSIG SPRAY DISTRIBUTION	.063	−.63	.00325	.0020
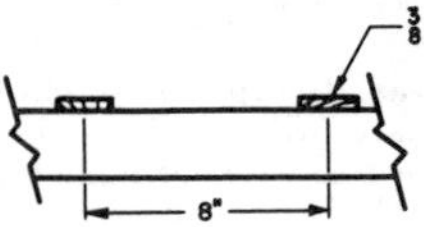 $\frac{3}{8}$ x 2"; 8"; 12" VERTICAL SPACING	.07 GRAVITY DISTRIBUTION .25 6 PSIG SPRAY DISTRIBUTION	.072	−.62	.00315	.0029
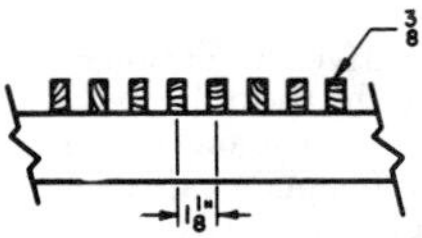 $\frac{3}{8}$ x $\frac{7}{8}$"; $1\frac{1}{8}$"; 15" VERTICAL SPACING	.07 GRAVITY DISTRIBUTION .25 6 PSIG SPRAY DISTRIBUTION	.094	−.59	.00370	.0034
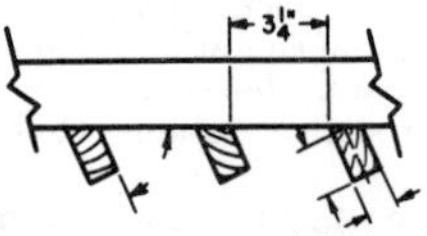 $3\frac{1}{4}$"; 24" VERTICAL SPACING	.07 GRAVITY DISTRIBUTION .25 6 PSIG SPRAY DISTRIBUTION	.112	−.45	.00560	.0051
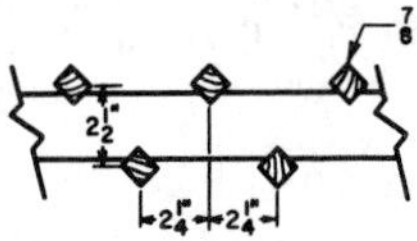 $\frac{7}{8}$ x $\frac{7}{8}$"; $2\frac{1}{2}$"; $2\frac{1}{4}$"; $2\frac{1}{4}$"; 24" VERTICAL SPACING	.07 GRAVITY DISTRIBUTION .25 6 PSIG SPRAY DISTRIBUTION	.129	−.47	.00690	.0060
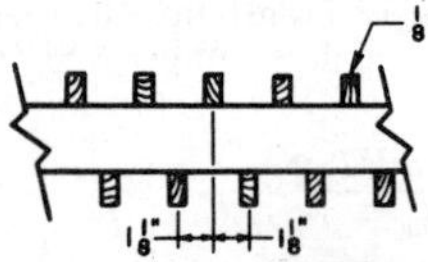 $\frac{1}{8}$ x 1"; $1\frac{1}{8}$"; $1\frac{1}{8}$"; 24" VERTICAL SPACING	.07 GRAVITY DISTRIBUTION .25 6 PSIG SPRAY DISTRIBUTION	.142	−.61	.00480	.0048

Adapted from the data of "Counterflow Cooling Tower Performance," Pritchard—EC Inc., 1957

n experimental analysis of any particular design yields:

$$\frac{KSV}{L} = C_1 + C_2\, N \left(\frac{L}{G}\right)^{C_3}. \qquad (455)$$

Equation 454 may be restated giving KSV/L as a function of various arameters:

$$\frac{KSV}{L} = f\,(t'), (WT_2 - t'), (WT_1 - WT_2), \left(\frac{L}{G}\right). \qquad (456)$$

For a particular wet-bulb (t') and range ($WT_1 - WT_2$), the various pproaches ($WT_2 - t'$) may be plotted as curves of KSV/L versus L/G. Similarly, from the experimental data, the various numbers of decks V) may also be represented as curves of KSV/L versus L/G. In Equation 55 the two terms represent the contribution of the distribution system nd the fill respectively.

The intersection of a curve for a particular number of decks with any articular approach curve defines the appropriate L/G. In this way the pecific determination of the coefficient of diffusion (K) or the interfacial urface (S) becomes unnecessary. The active tower volume (V) is a funcion of the number of decks (N) and the plan area (A) for any specific esign.

The water mass velocity (L) equals the weight rate of water flow (w_w) ivided by the area (A). The air mass velocity (G) equals the weight rate f air flow (w_a) divided by the area (A). Therefore, $L/G = w_w/w_a$ and independent of A.

The selection of a specific plan area should be made to give the most conomical results. Usually the most economical air mass velocity (G) ill range from 1400 with tall (40 ft towers) to 2100 lb per hr per sq ft ith short towers. The water mass velocity should be checked to see that falls between 500 and 3000 lb per hr per sq ft. The smaller the approach r the larger the range, the taller must be the tower height for economial results.

Figure 169 shows a typical family of approach curves drawn on log g paper for a 70° wet-bulb and 20° range at sea level. Similar curves can e drawn for other ranges and wet-bulbs. Fifty such curves are published the reference listed in the footnote. Some manufacturers have prepared s many as 450 such curves. Figure 170 may be used in lieu of a complete et of charts to approximate the "equivalent" approach for any wet-bulb, ange, and barometer to use with this 70-20-SL chart.

To select a tower, Figure 170 is used in the manner indicated thereon to rrive at an equivalent approach. A suitable tower height is estimated nd the number of decks which will satisfy this height is calculated. Equaon 455 can then be solved for any design, using experimental data milar to that of Table 113. Two points will define this solution if lotted as a straight line on the log log plot in Figure 169. The intersecon of such a line with the appropriate equivalent approach determines he L/G. If G is then selected in accordance with the height, L will be xed by $L = G \times L/G$. The area can be calculated from $A = L/w_w$. Such procedure clearly defines the construction of the active portion of the ower. Several trial values of trial height and G may be investigated to sure an economical selection.

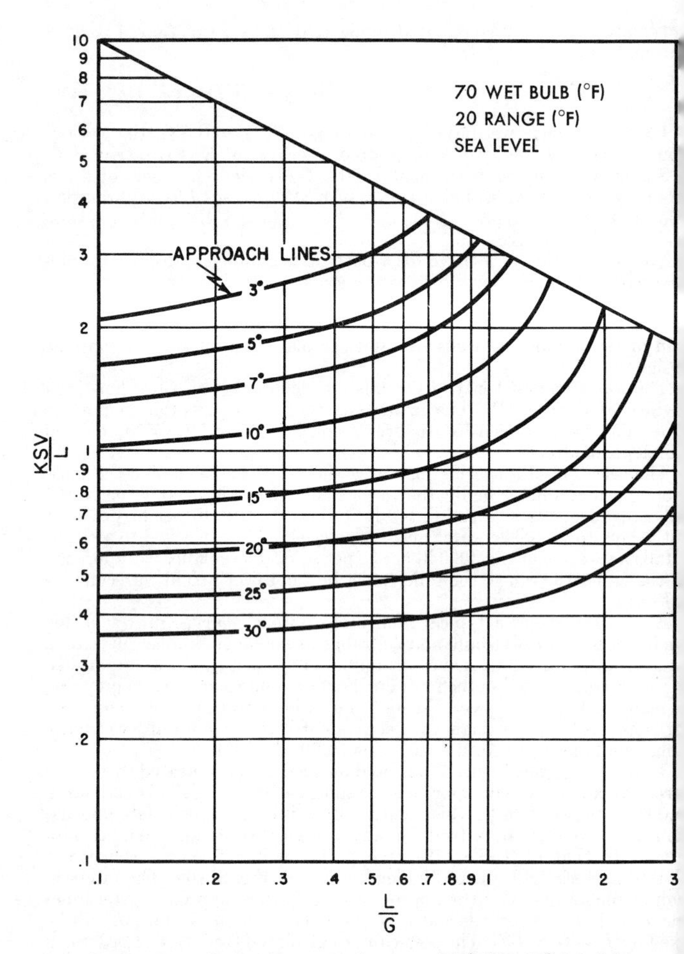

Figure 169—Cooling Tower Performance (70° WB, 20° R & S.L.)

Adapted from the data of "Counterflow Cooling Tower Performance," Pritchard—ECO Inc., 1957.

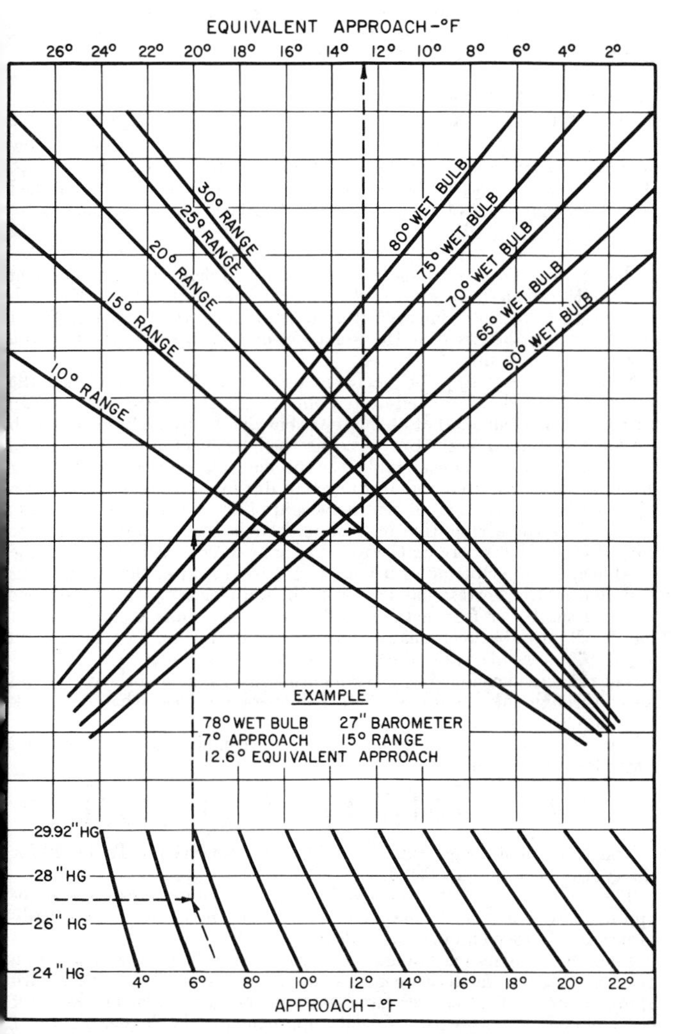

Figure 170—Equivalent Approach Chart

The economic evaluation of two or more tower selections principally revolves around the power and equipment costs. Other factors may influence a selection, too, but the mutual effect of fan and tower always bears investigation.

Cooling-Tower Fans and Pumps

During the course of determining the tower plan area, a value of G was assumed in the procedure outlined above. The weight rate of air flow required may therefore be calculated from $w_a = G/A$ or $w_a = w_w \div L/G$. The volume of air (q_a) to be handled by the fan can then be determined from the weight rate of air flow and the density at the fan according to:

$$q_a = w_a \div \delta. \tag{457}$$

The density (δ) of air handled by the fan will depend on the ambient conditions and on the position of the fan relative to the tower. Both forced- and induced-draft positions are utilized, predominantly the latter. Tower selections must be based on the worst wet-bulb conditions for which full performance is desired.

Fan capacities must also be based on the conditions for which the tower is selected. On forced-draft applications the density at the fan entrance nearly equals that at the tower entrance. Although the dry-bulb is immaterial so far as the tower is concerned, its effect on fan capacity in this instance may be considerable (the specific volume of 70° wet-bulb air is 13.67 when saturated and 14.29 at 100° dry-bulb, which amounts to a 4% difference in volume for a given weight of dry air). On induced-draft applications the assumption of saturated air is usually warranted. The condition of the air leaving the tower may be determined by adding the total heat gain per pound of dry air to the total heat of the entering air and noting the corresponding wet-bulb and density. The conditions entering the tower may actually differ from the ambient conditions, if moist exit gases are recirculated due to downdrafts, etc. Exit gases from adjacent towers may also affect the entering conditions.

The pressure developed by the fan must equal the sum of the individual losses through the filling, eliminators, louvers, etc., less whatever stack or wind effect exists.

The pressure drop across filling varies with both air velocity and water loading according to:

$$\Delta\, SP_{fill} = N\left[C_4\left(\frac{G}{1000}\right)^2 + C_5\left(\frac{G}{1000}\right)^{2/3}\left(\frac{L}{1000}\right)\right]. \tag{458}$$

The experimental constants, C_4 and C_5, are also given in Table 113 for the typical deck designs listed.

The use of herringbone wooden eliminators having a pressure drop of approximately 5 velocity heads based on the gross area will usually insure satisfactory elimination of drift.

Inlet louver losses may range from two to five velocity heads based on gross area. Some modern open designs incorporating 30° louvers with approximately 80% free area have losses as low as 2 heads. The losses of older closed designs with 45° slats approximate the higher figure of 5 heads.

The pressure losses occasioned by the various changes in direction at the bottom and top of the tower can be minimized by the use of suitable plenums. These losses and the compensating stack effect are frequently ignored.

The pressure required of the fan increases with tower height, assuming a constant air quantity. The amount of air required for any specific water-cooling job decreases with tower height. Since the power required varies as the product of quantity and pressure and since the pressure is an exponential function of the capacity, the required fan power decreases with tower height up to a point, after which a further increase in height produces an increase in required fan power. The total power required for a tower is the sum of fan and pump requirements. Since for a given water quantity the required pump power increases directly with head, the height for minimum or optimum tower power is shifted downward. The optimum height of tower will vary with the type of filling as well as with the thermodynamic aspects of the cooling problem.

Air Washers

The procedure given in Chapter 15 for selecting an air washer with heated sprays, although aimed at air-conditioning applications, can be used for water-cooling problems.

It is interesting that the economical velocities of air washers and cooling towers are similar. The economic ranges of air velocity and water loading center around 500 fpm face velocity and 3 gpm per bank per square foot water loading. Based on standard density 500 *FV* corresponds to an air mass velocity of 2250 lb per hr per sq ft and 3 gpm *WL* corresponds to 1500 lb per hr per sq ft water mass velocity for one bank and 3000 lb per hr per sq ft for two banks. All values are quite consistent with those listed for cooling towers. True counter flow cannot be achieved in a horizontal air flow air washer, but a close approximation can be obtained by staging two or more washers. Staging accomplishes the same result for an air washer as increasing the height does for a cooling tower, i.e., makes possible closer approaches and larger ranges.

Figure 171, drawn for a 70° wet-bulb, shows the relations of performance factor to approach, range, and L/G ratio. Therefore, this chart can be used to determine the amount of air required to perform any given cooling job with any washer for which the performance factor is known.

Single-stage washers are almost always built with a performance factor of 1.0, if intended for water-cooling duty. Each stage of a multi-stage washer is also built with a performance factor equal to unity. The over-all performance factor for such a condition has been calculated for two-, three-, and four-stage washers and is indicated on the chart. The amount of air required for any job using a single- or multi-stage washer can therefore be determined by noting the L/G ratio at the proper approach, for the proper range and wet-bulb. Similar charts for other wet-bulb conditions are available; however, approximate results can be obtained by using the equivalent approach concept, as discussed under "Cooling Towers." The weight rate of air flow (w_a) can be calculated from the weight rate of water flow (w_w) and the L/G ratio just as in a tower:

$$w_a = w_w \div L/G. \qquad (459)$$

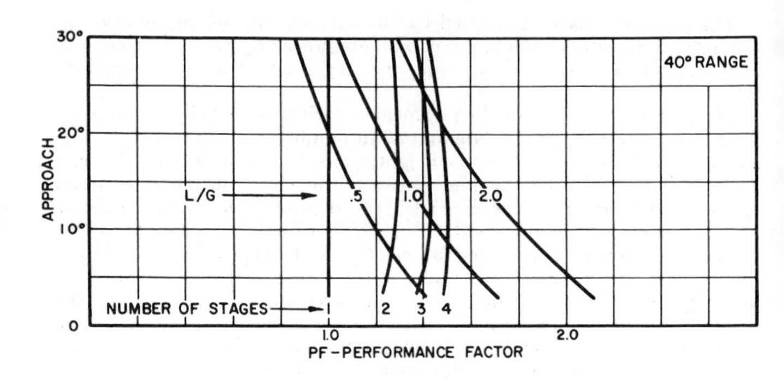

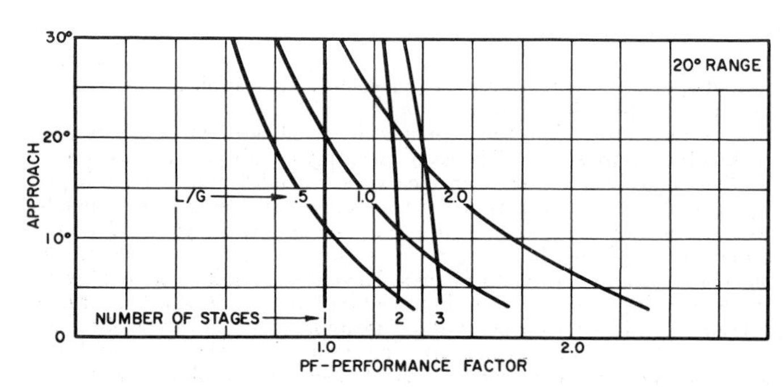

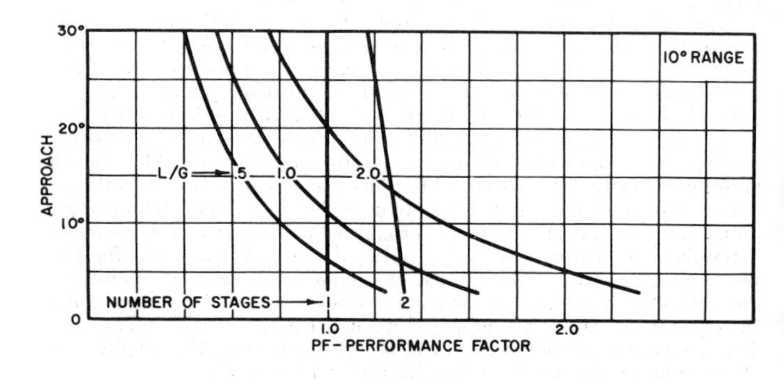

Figure 171—Air Washer Performance (70° WB & S.L.)

A washer size can be selected by choosing an economical face velocity (FV) in fpm and calculating the required face area (FA) in ft² from the equivalent volume rate of flow ($ECFM$) in cfm of standard air with

$$FA = ECFM \div FV, \text{ and} \tag{460}$$

$$ECFM = w_a \div .075. \tag{461}$$

The major distinction between air washers and cooling towers is that one is built horizontally and the other vertically. This becomes important on close approach or large range jobs, where tower heights or washer lengths of up to 40 feet may be required. Considerable value may be placed on either a low silhouette or a small plan area depending on the individual circumstances.

Air-Washer Fans and Pumps

Normal spray pressures are quite high, and the water must be re-pumped through each stage. However, air friction losses, etc., are quite low, and a complete evaluation will frequently indicate that an air washer is a better choice than a cooling tower. Spray pressures can be reduced considerably by packing the washer with fiber pads. The purpose of such a packing is to supply interfacial area by increasing the surface for film formation.

The volume of air to be handled by the fan can be calculated from the weight rate of air flow and the actual density at the fan. Fans are generally located to draw air through the air washer so that the density at the fan will be that leaving the washer. The air friction of a single-stage low velocity washer will be of the order of ¼″ water gage.

Dry-Air Coolers

The preceding discussions on ponds, towers, and washers dealt with the problem of cooling water in direct contact with air. A dry-air cooler is a fan-coil combination usually arranged so that cooling air is drawn or forced over the outside, and the warm fluid is pumped through the inside of a series of tubes, thus forming two separate circuits. The descriptions of available circuits, materials, etc., given in Chapter 15, are applicable here. The fluids which can be conditioned in such apparatus are numberless. The designers' problems include the determination of an over-all coefficient (U) and the mean effective temperature difference (Δt_m), so that the amount of surface required (S) for a given heat load (TH) may be determined from:

$$S = \frac{TH}{U \, \Delta t_m}. \tag{462}$$

Unless the number of tube passes is limited to one or two as shown in the sketches of Figure 172, the mean temperature difference should be calculated directly from:

$$\Delta t_{m \rightleftarrows} = \frac{(t_1 - WT_2) - (t_2 - WT_1)}{ln \dfrac{(t_1 - WT_2)}{(t_2 - WT_1)}} \text{ for counter flow, or from:} \tag{463}$$

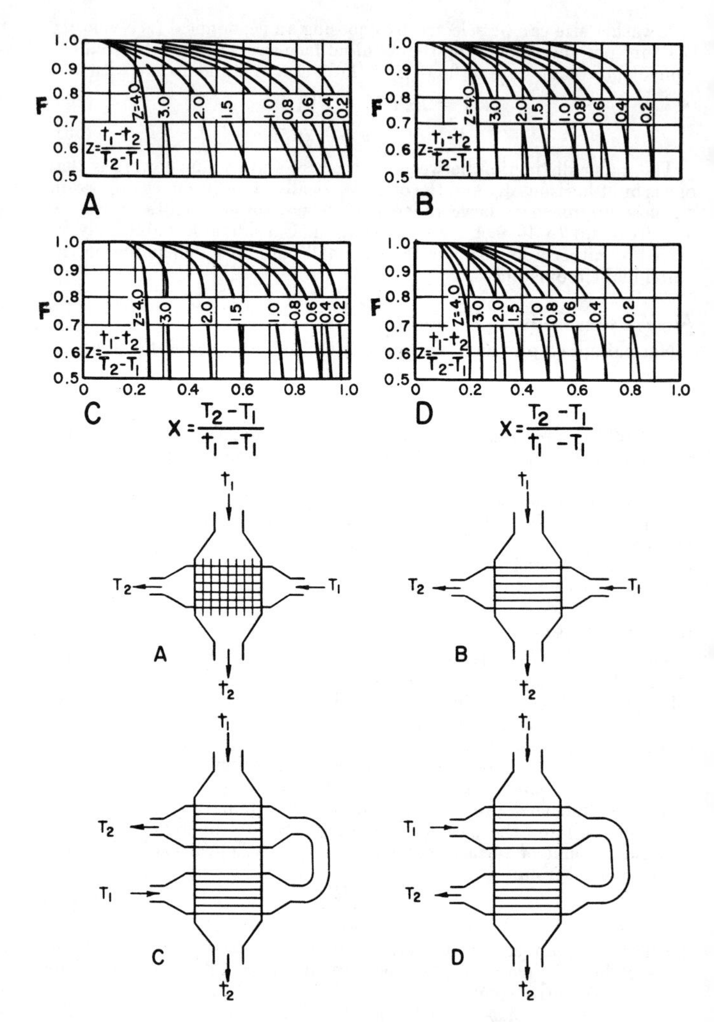

Figure 172 — MED Corrections for Crossflow

Adapted from the data of R. A. Bowman, A. C. Mueller, and W. M. Nagle, *Trans. ASME*, vol. 62, pp. 283-294, 1940.

$$\Delta t_{m\rightrightarrows} = \frac{(t_1 - WT_1) - (t_2 - WT_2)}{ln \dfrac{(t_1 - WT_1)}{(t_2 - WT_2)}} \textit{ for parallel flow.} \quad (464)$$

However, if the number of tube passes is limited, thus producing a crossflow arrangement, correction factors must be obtained from Figure 172 and applied to the log mean temperature difference calculated for counter flow:

$$\Delta t_{m+} = F \, \Delta t_{m\rightleftarrows} \quad (465)$$

Four terminal temperatures are involved in the formulas for mean effective temperature difference. In an air-cooled heat exchanger, these are the entering and leaving air temperatures (t_1 and t_2) and the entering and leaving water (or other fluid) temperatures (WT_1 and WT_2). The entering air temperature is a matter of design. One of the fluid temperatures must be assumed if neither is specified.

The cooling range ($WT_2 - WT_1$) for water is related to the cooling load (TH) and the flow rate (GPM) according to Equation 453.

The fluid being cooled is designated as the inside fluid since this is almost always the most economical arrangement. The cooling range ($WT_2 - WT_1$) for any fluid is related to the cooling load (TH), the specific heat (c_p) of the fluid, and its mass flow rate (w_i):

$$WT_2 - WT_1 = \frac{TH}{c_p \, w_i}. \quad (466)$$

In order to determine the leaving air temperature, it is necessary to assume a trial air flow rate (w_a). The air temperature rise ($t_2 - t_1$) is related to this and the cooling load (TH) according to:

$$t_2 - t_1 = \frac{TH}{0.24 \, w_a}. \quad (467)$$

Therefore, all four terminal temperatures can be determined and the MED calculated for a trial solution.

The over-all coefficient of heat transmission (U) in Btu per hr per °F per sq ft outside surface may be determined from:

$$U = \frac{1}{\dfrac{1}{h_o} + r_o + r_w + r_i \left(\dfrac{S_o}{S_i}\right) + \dfrac{1}{h_i}\left(\dfrac{S_o}{S_i}\right)}. \quad (468)$$

Typical fouling factors (r_i and r_o) may be determined from Table 114. The ratio of outside to inside surface (S_o/S_i) and the resistance of the tube wall (r_w) are defined by the dimensions and material of the tubes. The inside and outside film coefficients (h_i and h_o) are a function of: (1) the physical properties of the fluids, (2) their temperatures and mass flow rates, and (3) the circuit geometry.

For water cooling with Aerofin surface, Figure 173 may be used to determine both inside and outside film coefficients. The water side data is presented for 50°F water. A correction must be applied for other water temperatures. The air side data is based on standard air so that an equivalent face velocity must be utilized if the air density differs from .075 lb per cu ft. If the average air density across the coil is not .075 lb per cu

TABLE 114—FOULING FACTORS

FOULING FACTORS FOR WATER

Temperature of Heating Medium	Up to 240°F		240°-400°F	
Temperature of Water	125°F or Less		Over 125°F	
Types of Water	Water Velocity Ft/Sec		Water Velocity Ft/Sec	
	3 and Less	Over 3	3 and Less	Over 3
Sea Water	.0005	.0005	.001	.001
Brackish Water	.002	.001	.003	.002
Cooling Tower and Artificial Spray Pond:				
Treated Makeup	.001	.001	.002	.002
Untreated	.003	.003	.005	.004
City or Well Water (Such as Great Lakes)	.001	.001	.002	.002
Great Lakes	.001	.001	.002	.002
River Water:				
Minimum	.002	.001	.003	.002
Mississippi	.003	.002	.004	.003
Delaware, Schuylkill	.003	.002	.004	.003
East River and New York Bay	.003	.002	.004	.003
Chicago Sanitary Canal	.008	.006	.010	.008
Muddy or Silty	.003	.002	.004	.003
Hard (Over 15 grains/gal.)	.003	.003	.005	.005
Engine Jacket	.001	.001	.001	.001
Distilled	.0005	.0005	.0005	.0005
Treated Boiler Feedwater	.001	.0005	.001	.001
Boiler Blowdown	.002	.002	.002	.002

FOULING FACTORS FOR INDUSTRIAL OILS

Fuel Oil	.005
Machinery and Transformer Oils	.001
Quenching Oil	.004
Vegetable Oils	.003

FOULING FACTORS FOR INDUSTRIAL GASES AND VAPORS

Coke Oven Gas and Other Manufactured Gas	.01
Diesel Engine Exhaust Gas	.01
Organic Vapors	.0005
Steam (Non-Oil Bearing)	.0005
Alcohol Vapors	.0005
Steam, Exhaust (Oil-Bearing from Reciprocating Engines)	.001
Refrigerating Vapors (Condensing from Reciprocating Compressors)	.002
Air	.002

FOULING FACTORS FOR INDUSTRIAL LIQUIDS

Organic	.001
Refrigerating Liquids, Heating, Cooling or Evaporating	.001
Brine (Cooling)	.001

Adapted from the data of "Standards of the Tubular Exchanger Manufacturers Association," TEMA, 1959, pp. 60-61.

O.D.	FINS	S_o/FA/ROW	S_o/S_i				
			23	20	18	16	14
5/8	SERIES 140	27.8	21.45	22.22	23.40	24.94	—
5/8	SERIES 100	20.3	15.60	16.20	17.10	18.10	—
5/8	SERIES 30	9.0	6.84	7.09	7.46	7.95	—
1	8 PER INCH	20.4	—	14.05	14.50	15.03	15.68
1	10 PER INCH	25.2	—	17.26	17.80	18.47	19.26
1	12 PER INCH	30.0	—	20.45	21.10	21.90	22.83
1	13.6 PER INCH	34.0	—	23.18	23.90	24.80	25.85

A / TUBE — FT^2		
BWG	5/8" O.D.	1" O.D.
23	.00180	.00491
20	.00168	.00472
18	.00152	.00443
16	.00134	.00413
14	.00115	.00380

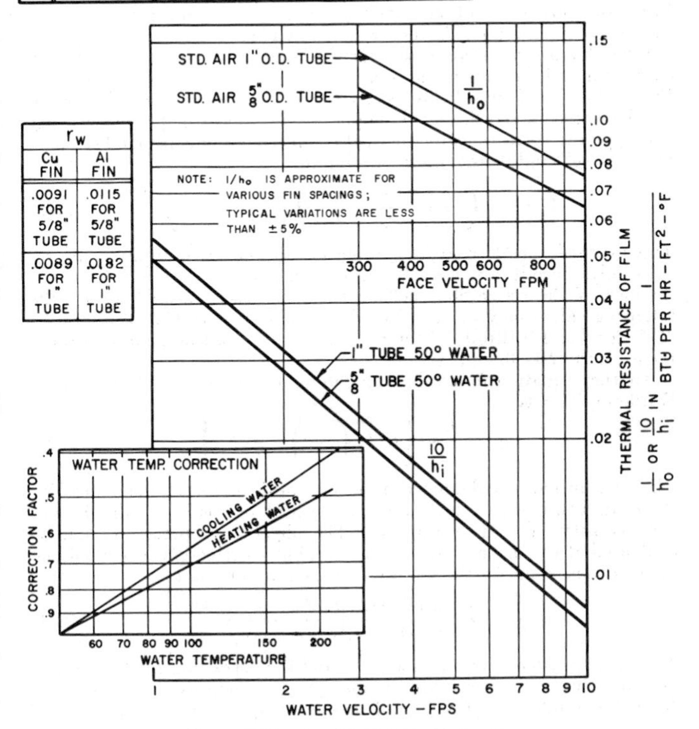

Figure 173 — Aerofin Coil Performance

Adapted from the data of Heavy Duty Coils, Aerofin Corporation, Bul. O-58, 1958.

ft due to temperature or altitude effects, an equivalent face velocity must be calculated based on the hypothetical volume that would exist for the actual weight rate of flow at standard conditions.

The effect of wall thickness on the thermal resistance of the tube metal is negligible, particularly for finned copper tubes; hence only one value is given for each fin material.

The ranges of air and water velocities shown in Figure 173 are the economical ranges. The trial face area should be chosen to yield an economical face velocity for the trial air mass flow rate selected for the purpose of determining the mean effective temperature difference. Various circuiting arrangements may be employed, as described in Chapter 15, in order to obtain an economical water velocity.

The tube wall resistance and pertinent physical data on extended-surface coils of the Aerofin design are also given in Figure 173. Solution of Equation 468 can be obtained for any water-cooling job using the data of Figure 173 with fouling factors from Table 114.

When fluids other than water must be cooled with air, the air side film coefficient and the tube metal resistance can be determined directly from Figure 173. The fluid side film coefficient (h_i) can be determined by reading the water film coefficient (h_w) opposite the approximate fluid velocity and applying corrections for thermal conductivity (k), specific heat (c_p), viscosity (μ), and density (δ) according to:

$$h_i = h_w \left(\frac{k_i}{k_w}\right)^{0.6} \left(\frac{c_{pi}}{c_{pw}}\right)^{0.4} \left(\frac{\mu_w}{\mu_i}\right)^{0.4} \left(\frac{\delta_i}{\delta_w}\right)^{0.8}. \qquad (469)$$

This expression is derived from Equation 49 and gives approximate results only, since it does not take into account any variation in Reynolds number. If the water film coefficient (h_w) is based on 50°F water, the following values may be substituted in Equation 469: 0.35 Btu/hr-sq ft-°F/ft for k_w, 1.0 Btu/lb-°F for c_{pw}, 1.30 centipoises or .00087 lb/ft-sec for μ_w, and 62.41 lb/cu ft for δ_w.

Another equation for evaluating the fluid side film coefficient (h_i) in Btu/hr-sq ft-°F is:

$$h_i = \frac{16.1}{d_i} \left[B_i \, k_i \left(\frac{c_p \mu}{k}\right)_i^{1/3} \phi_i \, K_L\right], \qquad (470)$$

where the inside tube diameter (d_i) is in inches, the thermal conductivity (k) is in Btu/hr-sq ft-°F/ft, the specific heat (c_p) is in Btu/lb-°F, and the viscosity (μ) is in centipoises. The physical properties should be evaluated at the mean fluid temperature, but a correction (ϕ_i) should be applied to account for the viscosity gradient according to:

$$\phi_i = \left(\frac{\mu \text{ @ mean fluid temp}}{\mu \text{ @ mean tube wall temp}}\right)^{0.14}. \qquad (471)$$

The heat transfer group number (B_i) and the correction for length (K_L) are functions of the Reynolds Number (N_{Re}) as indicated in Figure 174. Reynolds number is a function of mass velocity (G_i) as indicated by:

$$N_{Re} = \frac{0.0344 \, d_i \, G_i}{\mu_i}. \qquad (472)$$

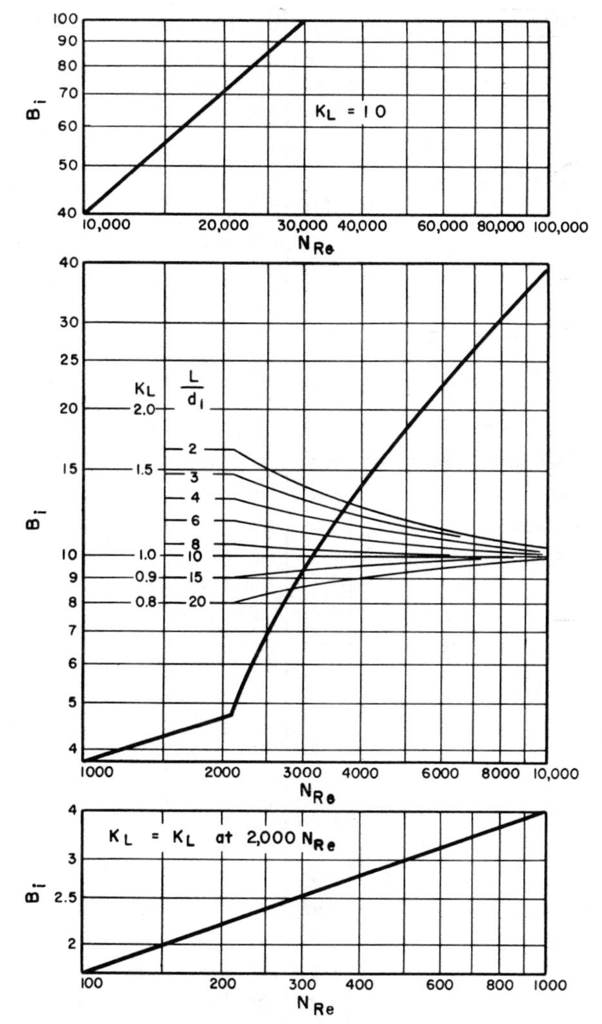

Figure 174—Heat Transfer Characteristics—Flow Through Tubes

Adapted from the data of Standards of the Tubular Exchanger Manufacturers Association, TEMA, 1952, p. 99.

TABLE 115—VALUES OF $k\ (c_p\ \mu/k)^{1/3}$ FOR VARIOUS LIQUIDS

k in Btu-ft per hr-sq ft-°F, c_p in Btu per lb-°F, μ in centipoises

Liquid	SG @ °C	$k\ (c_p\ \mu/k)^{1/3}$ @ 14.7 psia (or as noted) and					
		@ 0°F	@ 50°F	@ 100°F	@ 150°F	@ 200°F	@ 250°F
Acetic Acid—100%	1.050 @ $\frac{20}{4}$	—	—	.134	.103	.074	—
Acetone—100%	0.792 @ $\frac{20}{4}$	.142	.126	.114	—	—	—
Ammonia	0.595 @ $\frac{30}{4}$	.263 @ 16 psig	.232 @ 70 psig	.207 @ 200 psig	—	—	—
Benzene	0.879 @ $\frac{20}{4}$	—	.147	.120	.098	—	—
Butane	0.600 @ $\frac{0}{4}$	.090	.087 @ 7 psig	.081 @ 38 psig	.077 @ 90 psig	.073 @ 175 psig	.070 @ 310 psig
Brine—25% Ca Cl_2	1.228 @ $\frac{20}{4}$	.751	.601	.488	.406	.344	—
Brine—25% Na Cl	1.189 @ $\frac{20}{4}$	.582	.492	.473	.432	.396	—
Carbon Tetrachloride	1.595 @ $\frac{20}{4}$	.123	.103	.088	.073	—	—
Dowtherm "A"		.140 @ 500°F	.140 @ 560°F	.137 @ 620°F	.136 @ 680°F	.128 @ 740°F	—
Ethyl Alcohol—100%	0.789 @ $\frac{20}{4}$	.234	.204	.180	.160	—	—
Ethyl Alcohol—40%	0.935 @ $\frac{20}{4}$	.435	.393	.354	.322	—	—
Ethyl Ether	0.714 @ $\frac{20}{4}$	.106	.096	.088	—	—	—
Ethylene Glycol—100%	1.115 @ $\frac{20}{20}$	—	.814	.524	.396	.142	—
Ethylene Glycol—50%	1.067 @ $\frac{20}{20}$	.925	.542	.454	.372	.320	—
Freon 11	1.463 @ $\frac{30}{4}$	.091 @ 2.5 psia	.078 @ 8.8 psia	.067 @ 9 psig	.058 @ 37 psig	—	—
Freon 12	1.421 @ $\frac{30}{4}$	.066 @ 9 psig	.059 @ 47 psig	.054 @ 117 psig	.048 @ 235 psig	.042 @ 415 psig	—
Freon 22	1.173 @ $\frac{30}{4}$	.076 @ 24 psig	.068 @ 85 psig	.060 @ 198 psig	.052 @ 384 psig	—	—
Glycerol—100%	1.260 @ $\frac{20}{4}$	—	—	—	1.197	.793	.556
Heptane	0.684 @ $\frac{20}{4}$	.126	.115	.105	.097	.091	—
Hexane	0.660 @ $\frac{20}{4}$	.118	.107	.098	.090	—	—
Kerosene	0.820 @ $\frac{20}{4}$	.280	.224	.182	.149	.123	.104
Methyl Chloride	0.900 @ $\frac{30}{4}$	.105 @ 4 psig	.088 @ 37 psig	.073 @ 102 psig	—	—	—
Octane	0.707 @ $\frac{17}{4}$	.145	.129	.117	.106	.097	.089
Pentane	0.631 @ $\frac{20}{4}$	.105	.094	.085	—	—	—
SAE 10 Oil	0.907 @ $\frac{40}{4}$	1.900	.810	.470	.333	.249	.219
SAE 20 Oil	0.916 @ $\frac{40}{4}$	2.550	.996	.549	.388	.315	.236
SAE 30 Oil	0.922 @ $\frac{40}{4}$	3.400	1.190	.639	.414	.309	.256
Toluene	0.867 @ $\frac{20}{4}$	.148	.132	.118	.107	.096	—
Water	1.000 @ 4°C	.594	.520	.461	.379	.378	—

Calculated from the data of Aeronautical Information Report No. 24, SAE, 1952.

The mass velocity is equal to the mass flow rate (w_i) in lb/hr divided by the total cross sectional area (ΣA_i) in sq ft per pass:

$$G_i = \frac{w_i}{\Sigma A_i} = \frac{w_i}{A_i (n_t/n_p)}, \tag{473}$$

where (n_t) is the total number of tubes, (n_p) is the number of tube passes, and (A_i) is the cross sectional area of one tube. The ratio (n_t/n_p) is equal to the tube face of a single-circuit Aerofin type coil.

Values of $k\ (c_p\ \mu/k)^{1/3}$ are listed for various fluids in Table **115**.

Gilmore* suggests that a first approximation for the number of tubes per pass (n_t/n_p) can be obtained from:

$$\frac{n_t}{n_p} \approx \frac{w_i/1000}{2\ d_i\ \mu_i}, \tag{474}$$

where the mass flow rate (w_i) is in lb/hr, the inside diameter (d_i) is in inches, and the viscosity (μ_i) is in centipoises. The smallest practical tube diameters should generally be used for best economy. Established practice indicates ⅝″ OD for comparatively non-fouling conditions. One-inch or larger tubes should be specified when fouling conditions are expected.

Standard encased coils are available in various combinations of tube length, tubes in the face, circuit arrangements, and rows of tubes in depth. The trial values of air flow rate, tubes per pass, tube size, etc., should be selected with these standards in mind. The exact coil configuration will depend on the amount of surface required according to Equation **462** for alternative trial selections and the power requirements for both the fan and pump.

Dry-Air-Cooler Fans and Pumps

In the design of a dry-air cooler, the flow rates of both the hot fluid and the cooling air should be manipulated until the best design is obtained. Alternative coil selections may have varying amounts of heat transfer surface. The smaller units will generally have higher fan or pump horsepower requirements, or both.

The fan capacity in cfm should be based on the required weight rate of flow through the coil and the density of the air at the fan inlet location.

The fan pressure must be sufficient to overcome the losses occasioned by the coils and any other equipment or duct elements through which the air must pass.

Typical air friction curves for coils are presented in Figure **175**. The data are plotted for standard air. The friction and entrance losses as read opposite the hypothetical face velocity for standard air should be totaled and multiplied by the appropriate altitude and temperature factors.

The pump must have a capacity equal to the flow rate through the cooler or through the equipment which heats the fluid, whichever is higher. If more fluid is pumped than can be utilized efficiently in the cooler, the excess can be by passed.

The pump pressure must be sufficient to overcome the losses occasioned

*C. H. Gilmore, Shortcut to Heat Exchanger Design, *Chemical Engineering*, pp. 144-148, October, 1952.

AIR FRICTION PRESSURE DROP FOR WETTED COIL SURFACE IS GENERALLY 1.5 TIMES THE FRICTION DROP.

ALTITUDE IN FEET	ALTITUDE FACTOR	TEMP. AV. °F	TEMP. FACTOR
1000	1.04	0	0.87
2000	1.08	50	0.96
3000	1.12	100	1.06
4000	1.16	150	1.15
5000	1.20	200	1.25
6000	1.25	250	1.34
7000	1.29	300	1.44
8000	1.35	400	1.62

AIR FRICTION PRESSURE DROP CORRECTION FACTORS

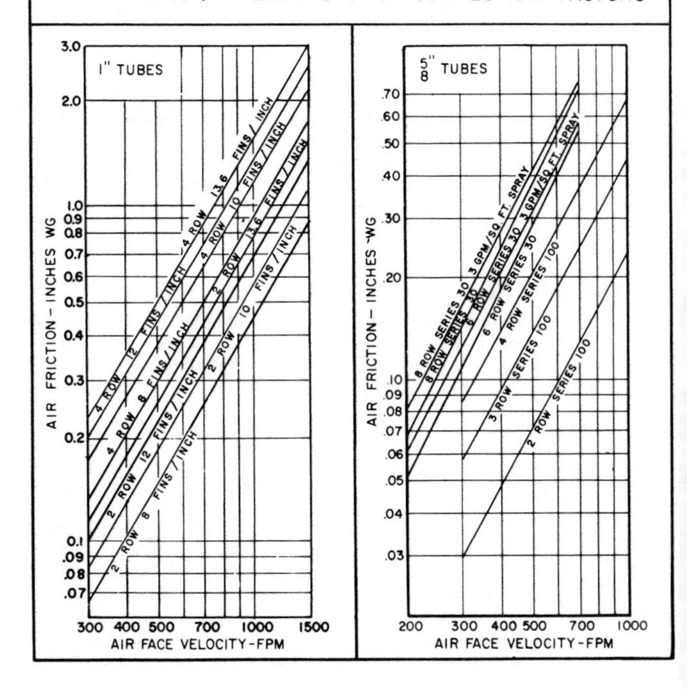

Figure 175—Aerofin Coil Air Friction

Adapted from the data of Heavy Duty Coils, Aerofin Corporation, Bul. O-58, 1958.

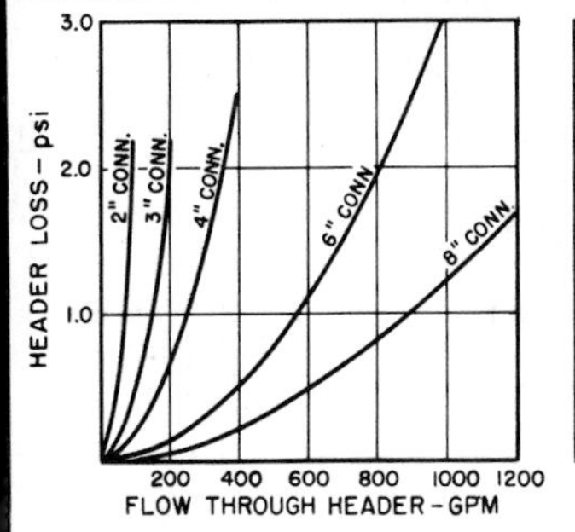

TUBE WALL FACTOR		
O.D.	THICK	FACTOR
1	14 BWG	1.17
1	16 BWG	1.07
1	18 BWG	1.00
1	20 BWG	0.94
5/8	16 BWG	1.13
5/8	18 BWG	1.00
5/8	20 BWG	.90
5/8	23 BWG	.84

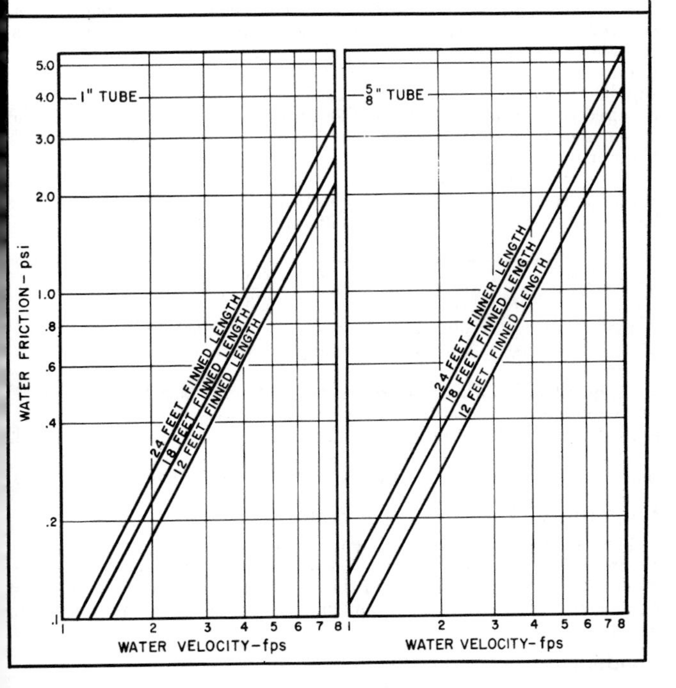

Figure 176—Aerofin Coil Water Friction

Adapted from the data of Heavy Duty Coils, Aerofin Corporation, Bul. O-58, 1958.

by the coils, piping, and any other equipment through which the fluid must pass.

Typical pressure loss curves are presented for water coils in Figure **176**. The pressure loss for any fluid ($\Delta\ p_i$) may be determined approximately from the pressure loss for water ($\Delta\ p_w$) and the ratios of density (δ) and viscosity (μ) according to:

$$\Delta\ p_i \approx \Delta\ p_w \left(\frac{\delta_i}{\delta_w}\right)^{.84} \left(\frac{\mu_i}{\mu_w}\right)^{.16}. \tag{475}$$

If the pressure loss for water is obtained from Figure 176 which is drawn for 150° water, the following values may be substituted in Equation **475**: 61.1 lb/cu ft for δ_w and 0.43 centipoises or .00029 lb /ft-sec for μ_w.

Evaporative Coolers

In evaporative coolers, the advantages (and disadvantages) of indirect-contact and evaporative apparatus are combined. The evaporation of sprayed water on the air side reduces the surface requirements as well as the amount of air necessary for any cooling job. In addition to that required for pumping the working fluid and the air, energy must be supplied to spray the water over the coils. Water treatment is frequently required to prevent excessive fouling on the air side. Even so, wide fin spacings or bare tubes are usually specified in the interests of reduced maintenance.

When evaporation takes place on a surface, only sensible heat (SH) is transmitted through the air film and the over-all coefficient should be based on the following modification of Equation 468:

$$U = \frac{1}{\frac{1}{h_o}\left(\frac{SH}{TH}\right) + r_o + r_w + r_i\left(\frac{S_o}{S_i}\right) + \frac{1}{h_i}\left(\frac{S_o}{S_i}\right)}. \tag{476}$$

Actually, the water film presents a slight additional resistance to the total heat transfer, but for the usual spray quantities this effect can be ignored.

As in all evaporative apparatus, the design is based on the worst justifiable wet-bulb conditions. The air is usually assumed to be saturated both entering and leaving the coil. The spray water is recirculated and assumes an equilibrium temperature so that the total heat surrendered by the hot fluid is transferred to the air, increasing its enthalpy accordingly.

Evaporative-Cooler Fans and Pumps

The use of sprays increases the air friction of the coil as indicated in Figure 175. Economic air velocities are accordingly somewhat lower. Aside from this, the economics of the situation determine the best selection of alternative sizes and configurations of coils, just as in dry-air coolers.

Condensers

Condensers are indirect heat exchangers in which the tube side fluid enters as a vapor and leaves as a liquid. Apparatus may be of the dry-coil or evaporative type. The fluid which is condensed may be a refrigerant, a

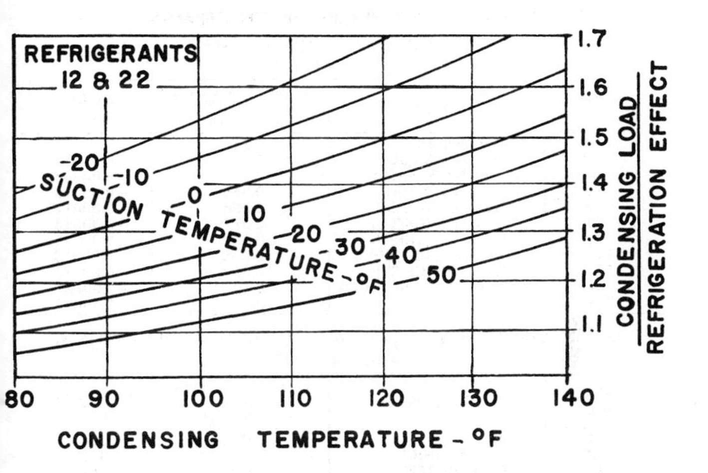

Figure 177—Condenser Load vs Refrigeration Effect

solvent, or any other vapor, including steam. The latent heat load (LH) can be established from the condensing rate (w_i) and latent heat of condensation (λ):

$$LH = w_i \lambda. \tag{477}$$

In the case of refrigerants, the amount of heat rejected in the condenser will have to exceed the refrigeration effect by an amount equal to the heat of compression plus any motor cooling less any radiation losses, etc. Figure 177 may be used to determine the ratio of condenser load to refrigeration effect for various refrigerants, suction temperatures, and condensing temperatures. The values shown are based on saturated vapor at the compressor inlet, adiabatic compression, and no motor cooling by the refrigerant. If the compressor motor is refrigerant-cooled an increase of up to 15% may be in order.

Equation 463 which gives Δt_m for counter flow should be used for condensers without any correction regardless of the number of tube passes.

The tube side film coefficient (h_i) for horizontal tube condensers may be calculated from:

$$h_i = 0.76\, k_f \left(\frac{\delta_f^2\, g_c}{\mu_f\, \Gamma} \right)^{1/3}. \tag{478}$$

Any consistent set of units may be employed in Equation 478, such as Btu/hr-sq ft-°F/ft for the thermal conductivity (k_f) of the condensate, lb/cu ft for the density (δ_f) of the condensate, lbm/ft-hr for the viscosity (μ_f) of the condensate, ft-lbm/lb-hr^2 for the conversion factor (g_c), and

TABLE 116—PROPERTIES OF REFRIGERANTS

THERMAL CONDUCTIVITIES OF LIQUIDS

$k = k_{32} + a(t - 32)$

Refrig. No.	Liquid	Thermal Conductivity k_{32} at 32°F Btu-ft/hr-ft²-°F	Temp. Coef. a
717	Ammonia (NH_3)	0.34	—
—	Brine (25% $CaCl_2$)	0.29	0.00052
—	Brine (25% $NaCl_2$)	0.25	0.00053
11	Freon, Etc. ($CFCl_3$)	0.068	−0.00013
12	Freon, Etc. (CF_2Cl_2)	0.056	−0.00012
21	Freon, Etc. ($CHFCl_2$)	0.077	−0.00013
22	Freon, Etc. (CHF_2Cl)	0.070	−0.00020
113	Freon, Etc. ($C_2F_3Cl_3$)	0.058	−0.00010
114	Freon, Etc. (CF_4Cl_2)	0.052	−0.00013
40	Methyl Chloride (CH_3Cl)	0.10	−0.00030
718	Water	0.32	0.00053

THERMAL CONDUCTIVITIES OF GASES AND VAPORS AT MODERATE PRESSURE

$k = k_{32} + a(t - 32)$

Refrig. No.	Gas or Vapor	Thermal Conductivity k_{32} at 32°F Btu-ft/hr-ft²-°F	Temp. Coef. $a \times 10^{-7}$
729	Air	0.0140	230
717	Ammonia (NH_3)	0.0128	320
11	Freon, Etc. ($CFCl_3$)	0.0045	67
12	Freon, Etc. (CF_2Cl_2)	0.0048	134
21	Freon, Etc. ($CHFCl_2$)	0.0054	56
22	Freon, Etc. (CHF_2Cl)	0.0062	112
113	Freon, Etc. ($C_2F_3Cl_3$)	0.0038	125
114	Freon, Etc. (CF_4Cl_2)	0.0066	152
40	Methyl Chloride (CH_3Cl)	0.0053	227
718	Steam	0.010	280

ABSOLUTE VISCOSITY OF LIQUIDS, lbm/hr-ft

Refrig. No.	Liquid	Temperature, °F							
		0	20	40	60	80	100	120	140
717	Ammonia (NH_3)	0.60	0.58	0.56	0.54	0.52	0.49	—	—
11	Freon, Etc. ($CFCl_3$)	1.64	1.42	1.25	1.11	1.00	0.91	0.84	0.79
12	Freon, Etc. (CF_2Cl_2)	0.81	0.74	0.69	0.65	0.61	0.59	0.56	0.53
21	Freon, Etc. ($CHFCl_2$)	1.17	1.05	0.96	0.88	0.82	0.76	0.72	0.67
22	Freon, Etc. (CHF_2Cl)	0.71	0.66	0.62	0.59	0.56	0.54	0.52	0.50
113	Freon, Etc. ($C_2F_3Cl_3$)	3.06	2.52	2.12	1.80	1.56	1.37	1.20	1.07
114	Freon, Etc. (CF_4Cl_2)	1.45	1.25	1.10	0.98	0.89	0.81	0.74	0.69
40	Methyl Chloride (CH_3Cl)	0.72	0.67	0.63	0.60	0.57	0.54	0.52	0.50
718	Water	—	—	3.75	2.71	2.08	1.66	1.36	1.14

ABSOLUTE VISCOSITY OF SATURATED VAPORS

$\mu = \mu_{32} + a(t - 32)$

Refrig. No.	Vapor	Absolute Viscosity, μ_{32}, at 32°F lbm per hr-ft	Temp. Coef. $a \times 10^{-6}$
717	Ammonia (NH_3)	0.022	51
11	Freon, Etc. ($CFCl_3$)	0.024	43
12	Freon, Etc. (CF_2Cl_2)	0.029	38
21	Freon, Etc. ($CHFCl_2$)	0.025	39
22	Freon, Etc. (CHF_2Cl)	0.029	48
113	Freon, Etc. ($C_2F_3Cl_3$)	0.023	31
114	Freon, Etc. (CF_4Cl_2)	0.026	41
40	Methyl Chloride (CH_3Cl)	0.024	37

TABLE 116—PROPERTIES OF REFRIGERANTS, Cont'd

AVERAGE SPECIFIC HEAT OF VARIOUS LIQUIDS

Refrig. No.	Liquid	Temperature Range, °F	c_p Btu per lb-°F
717	Ammonia (NH_3)	−60 to 100	1.08
11	Freon, Etc. ($CFCl_3$)	−10 to 150	0.22
12	Freon, Etc. (CF_2Cl_2)	−40 to 100	0.26
21	Freon, Etc. ($CHFCl_2$)	−10 to 150	0.26
22	Freon, Etc. (CHF_2Cl)	−40 to 120	0.30
113	Freon, Etc. ($C_2F_3Cl_3$)	−10 to 150	0.31
114	Freon, Etc. (CF_4Cl_2)	−40 to 140	0.24
40	Methyl Chloride (CH_3Cl)	−40 to 100	0.36
718	Water	35 to 200	1.00

SPECIFIC HEAT OF FREON VAPORS AT ONE ATMOSPHERE

$$c_p = c_{32} + a(t - 32)$$

Refrig. No.	Vapor	Temp. Range °F	Constant Pressure Specific Heat, c_{32}, at 32°F, Btu/lb-°F	Temp. Coef. $a \times 10^{-6}$
11	Freon, Etc. ($CFCl_3$)	0 to 200	0.130	97
12	Freon, Etc. (CF_2Cl_2)	0 to 200	0.140	135
21	Freon, Etc. ($CHFCl_2$)	0 to 200	0.133	134
22	Freon, Etc. (CHF_2Cl)	−40 to 120	0.145	140
113	Freon, Etc. ($C_2F_3Cl_3$)	0 to 200	0.148	111
114	Freon, Etc. (CF_4Cl_2)	−40 to 200	0.152	134

---

lb/hr-ft for the tube loading (Γ) when the inside coefficient (h_i) is in Btu/hr-sq ft-°F. Refer to Table 116 for values.

The physical properties of the condensate should be evaluated at a special film temperature (t_f), which may be calculated from the saturation temperature of the vapor (t_{sat}) and the mean difference between the saturated vapor and wall temperatures $(t_{sat} - t_w)_m$, according to:

$$t_f = t_{sat} - 0.75\,(t_{sat} - t_w)_m. \qquad (479)$$

The tube loading term (Γ) in lb/hr-ft may be calculated from the condensing rate (w_i) in lb/hr, the series length (L) of the circuit in ft, and the number of tubes per pass (n_t/n_p) using:

$$\Gamma = \frac{w_i}{2\,L\,(n_t/n_p)}. \qquad (480)$$

The denominator of Equation 480 is equal to two times the length of a single tube multiplied by the total number of tubes when all tubes are headered for parallel flow.

The economic range of Γ is not well defined, but for a first approximation, a value of 3.0 or 4.0 may be used. For most organic fluids, the condensing coefficient at atmospheric pressure will be between 200 and 400. The value for ammonia is approximately 1000. For steam, coefficients of 1000 to 3000 have been observed for film-type condensation, whereas for dropwise condensation values of 7000 to 70,000 have been obtained but are very difficult to maintain.

In the usual diameters and tube lengths, the value of h_i for horizontal arrangements is twice or more that for vertical arrangements. The effect of vapor velocity as it may decrease condensate film thickness is to produce higher values of h_i than Equation 478 predicts.

Appropriate fouling factors and other items should be determined and inserted into the appropriate expression for U. Equation 468 or 476 should be used depending on whether dry-air or evaporative cooling is to be used.

If the vapor feed is superheated and the temperature of the wall is above the saturation temperature at the prevailing pressure, desuperheating without condensation will occur and the surface requirements will be increased accordingly. The desuperheating and condensing surface may both be part of the same coil. If sub-cooling of the condensate is desired, a separate liquid-cooling coil must be figured. This is usually located on the cold air side of the condensing coil.

The air friction is figured in the manner outlined for dry or sprayed coils. The tube side pressure drop is a function of the vapor velocity which decreases as condensation progresses. For an accurate determination, the mean velocity should be calculated for each element along the series path and the corresponding loss figured. Since in most condenser applications the purpose in calculating pressure drop is simply to prevent an unreasonable design, the calculated value based on entering velocity is frequently halved for approximate results. When the pressure drop cannot be neglected, the nature of the flow, whether counter, parallel, or cross current, and the condensed fluid temperature difference must be accounted for in the mean temperature difference.

Receivers may be required to even out the variations in the supply and demand for liquid refrigerant resulting from load fluctuations or to avoid air accumulation of liquid refrigerant in the condenser which will lower condensing capacity.

CHAPTER 20

DRYING AND RELATED PROCESSES

The purpose of a drying system is to remove the moisture from a material to: (1) improve the material, (2) make the process more efficient in some way, or (3) recover the moisture. The material if properly dried may be more valuable or in better condition for further processing. The cost of drying may also be justified by (1) the increase in future value if preservation is thereby insured, (2) the reduction in freight or other handling charges, (3) the recovery of valuable solvent, or (4) the excess value of fuel over the cost of evaporating the moisture.

Drying is the term applied to thermal processes for removing moisture from a solid or nearly solid material. Evaporation implies vaporization of a relatively large amount of moisture, from either a liquid or solid, resulting in a concentrated but not necessarily dry residue. Dewatering is the mechanical removal of moisture by such processes as draining, pressing, filtering, centrifuging, etc. Dehumidification is the direct condensation of a vapor from a gas. Distillation involves the vaporization, separation, and recondensation of a liquid from either a liquid or a solid.

In most instances dryers utilize air to carry the vaporized moisture away from the product. The air may also be used to deliver the necessary heat for vaporization. A more inert gas such as flue products or superheated steam may be substituted for the air.

The principles of drying in air and in vacuum will be discussed. The actual sizing of a dryer should be based on test data both as regards the performance of the machine and the behavior of the material. Certain fundamentals which govern the drying of all materials will be outlined here.

Fans are used in many dryers. Therefore, many types of dryers are described in considerable detail.

Design Principles

Basically, the designer must evaluate various dryer designs to determine their technical and economic feasibility. Whenever large quantities of free liquid are associated with the material, dewatering of the feed should be considered since mechanical systems are usually cheaper than thermal systems.

The choice between batch and continuous processes primarily rests on economics. Generally, a continuous dryer will require less labor, fuel, and floor space and will discharge a more uniform product whereas a batch dryer will be lower in first cost, easier to maintain and operate, and more versatile in its possible applications.

Consideration of the various advantages and disadvantages can limit the choice of dryer to a convection, conduction, or radiation type. Convection dryers are generally lower in first cost than other types. These dryers heat the material directly with the products of combustion or with heated air. The temperature of the material is limited to the temperature of the surrounding air, which is easily controlled. Thermal efficiency may be poor, and solvents difficult to recover. Dusting, contamination, and chemical reactions with the drying atmosphere may cause serious problems. These disadvantages can be eliminated in most cases by using special techniques or equipment, but then the first cost advantages are compromised.

Conduction dryers are usually higher in first cost than convection dryers, but provide good thermal efficiency and solvent recovery with minimum dusting and contamination. In this type of dryer, also known as a contact dryer, the heat is transmitted indirectly from the medium through a wall or pan, etc. Temperatures range upward from the boiling point of the liquid, and temperature control can become complicated. Vacuum dryers are included in this classification. Vacuum dryers are considerably more expensive than atmospheric dryers, but may be selected for heat sensitive, easily oxidized materials, or where solvent is to be recovered.

Radiation dryers are particularly suitable for drying thin sheets or films which contain only small quantities of liquid to be evaporated. Operating costs are generally high except where the radiation can be directed to a particular spot, thus obviating the necessity of heating the whole object.

Combinations of the three heat transfer mechanisms are utilized in various dryers.

Dryers are often classified as stationary, conveyor, drum, rotary, web, or suspended-particle dryers. Subclassifications are often made according to the specific mechanical or constructional features, as well as the method of heat transmission.

The condition of the material itself or the process requirements may limit the types of dryers that can be used. For instance, drum dryers are not particularly suitable for materials that cannot be pumped. Web dryers are limited to sheet or bulky objects. Rotary dryers are only suitable for granular materials. Suspended-particle dryers, as implied by the name, are designed for small particles.

Moisture Content of Materials

The moisture content of a material may be stated in lb per lb of either wet or dry material. The dry weight basis is more satisfactory for computing moisture changes since a simple difference (subtraction) may be employed. The two bases are convertible according to:

$$F_{wet} = \frac{F_{dry}}{1 + F_{dry}}, \text{ and} \tag{481}$$

$$F_{dry} = \frac{F_{wet}}{1 - F_{wet}}, \tag{482}$$

where the fraction (F_{wet}) is equal to the weight of moisture divided by

TABLE 117—VALUES OF REGAIN FOR HYGROSCOPIC MATERIALS

Moisture Content Expressed in Per Cent of Dry Weight of the Substance—Temp 75° F

Material	Relative Humidity—Per Cent								
	10	20	30	40	50	60	70	80	90
Natural Textile Fibres									
Cotton, roving	2.5	3.7	4.6	5.5	6.6	7.9	9.5	11.5	14.1
Cotton, cloth	2.6	3.7	4.4	5.2	5.9	6.8	8.1	10.0	14.3
Cotton, absorbent	4.8	9.0	12.5	15.7	18.5	20.8	22.8	24.3	25.8
Wool, skein	4.7	7.0	8.9	10.8	12.8	14.9	17.2	19.9	23.4
Silk, skein	3.2	5.5	6.9	8.0	8.9	10.2	11.9	14.3	18.8
Linen, cloth	1.9	2.9	3.6	4.3	5.1	6.1	7.0	8.4	10.2
Linen, yarn	3.6	5.4	6.5	7.3	8.1	8.9	9.8	11.2	13.8
Jute, average	3.1	5.2	6.9	8.5	10.2	12.2	14.4	17.1	20.2
Hemp, rope	2.7	4.7	6.0	7.2	8.5	9.9	11.6	13.6	15.7
Rayons									
Viscose Nitrocellulose, skein	4.0	5.7	6.8	7.9	9.2	10.8	12.4	14.2	16.0
Cellulose Acetate, fibre	0.8	1.1	1.4	1.9	2.4	3.0	3.6	4.3	5.3
Paper									
M. F. Newsprint	2.1	3.2	4.0	4.7	5.3	6.1	7.2	8.7	10.6
H. M. F. Writing	3.0	4.2	5.2	6.2	7.2	8.3	9.9	11.9	14.2
White Bond	2.4	3.7	4.7	5.5	6.5	7.5	8.8	10.8	13.2
Com. Ledger	3.2	4.2	5.0	5.6	6.2	6.9	8.1	10.3	13.9
Kraft Wrapping	3.2	4.6	5.7	6.6	7.6	8.9	10.5	12.6	14.9
Misc. Organic Materials									
Leather, tanned	5.0	8.5	11.2	13.6	16.0	18.3	20.6	24.0	29.2
Catgut, strings	4.6	7.2	8.6	10.2	12.0	14.3	17.3	19.8	21.7
Glue, hide	3.4	4.8	5.8	6.6	7.6	9.0	10.7	11.8	12.5
Rubber, tire	0.11	0.21	0.32	0.44	0.54	0.66	0.76	0.88	0.99
Wood, average	3.0	4.4	5.9	7.6	9.3	11.3	14.0	17.5	22.0
Soap, white	1.9	3.8	5.7	7.6	10.0	12.9	16.1	19.8	23.8
Tobacco, cigarette	5.4	8.6	11.0	13.3	16.0	19.5	25.0	33.5	50.0
Foodstuffs									
White Bread	0.5	1.7	3.1	4.5	6.2	8.5	11.1	14.5	19.0
Crackers	2.1	2.8	3.3	3.9	5.0	6.5	8.3	10.9	14.9
Macaroni	5.1	7.4	8.8	10.2	11.7	13.7	16.2	19.0	22.1
Flour	2.6	4.1	5.3	6.5	8.0	9.9	12.4	15.4	19.1
Starch	2.2	3.8	5.2	6.4	7.4	8.3	9.2	10.6	12.7
Gelatin	0.7	1.6	2.8	3.8	4.9	6.1	7.6	9.3	11.4
Misc. Inorganic Materials									
Asbestos Fibre	0.16	0.24	0.26	0.32	0.41	0.51	0.62	0.73	0.84
Silica Gel	5.7	9.8	12.7	15.2	17.2	18.8	20.2	21.5	22.6
Domestic Coke	0.20	0.40	0.61	0.81	1.03	1.24	1.46	1.67	1.89
Activated Charcoal	7.1	14.3	22.8	26.2	28.3	29.2	30.0	31.1	32.7
Sulphuric Acid	33.0	41.0	47.5	52.5	57.0	61.5	67.0	73.5	82.5

Adapted from the data of ASHRAE Guide and Data Book, Applications, p. 93.

TABLE 118—APPROXIMATE CRITICAL MOISTURE CONTENTS

Material		Critical Moisture, % Water, Dry Basis
Name	Thick., In.	
Barium nitrate crystals, on trays	1.0	7
Beaverboard	0.17	Above 120
Brick clay	.62	14
Carbon pigment	1	40
Celotex	0.44	160
Chrome leather	.04	125
Copper carbonate (on trays)	1-1.5	60
English china clay	1	16
Flint clay refractory brick mix	2.0	13
Gelatin, initially 400% water	0.1-0.2 (wet)	300
Iron blue pigment (on trays)	0.25-0.75	110
Kaolin	—	14
Lithol red	1	50
Lithopone press cake (in trays)	0.25	6.4
	.50	8.0
	.75	12.0
	1.0	16.0
Niter cake fines, on trays	—	Above 16
Paper, white eggshell	0.0075	41
Fine book	.005	33
Coated	.004	34
Newsprint	—	60-70
Plastic clay brick mix	2.0	19
Poplar wood	0.165	120
Prussian blue	—	40
Pulp lead, initially 140% water	—	Below 15
Rock salt (in trays)	1.0	7
Sand, 50-150 mesh	2.0	5
Sand, 200-325 mesh	2.0	10
Sand, through 325 mesh	2.0	21
Sea sand (on trays)	0.25	3
	.5	4.7
	.75	5.5
	1.0	5.9
	2.0	6.0
Silica, brick mix	2.0	8
Sole leather	0.25	Above 90
Stannic tetrachloride sludge	1	180
Subsoil, clay fraction 55.4%	—	21
Subsoil, much higher clay content	—	35
Sulfite pulp	0.25-0.75	60-80
Sulfite pump (pulp lap)	0.039	110
White lead	—	11
Whiting	0.25-1.5	6-9
Wool fabric, worsted	—	31
Wool, undyed serge	—	8

Adapted from the data of R. H. Perry, C. H. Chilton, and S. D. Kirkpatrick, "Chemical Engineers Handbook," McGraw Hill Book Co., Inc., New York, 1963, p. *15*-40.

the weight of wet product, and the fraction (F_{dry}) is equal to the weight of moisture divided by the weight of dry product. When percentages are used instead of fractions, 100 should be substituted for the 1 in each equation.

Materials may be hygroscopic or not. Hygroscopic materials contain bound moisture, i.e., moisture which exerts a vapor pressure less than that of the pure liquid at the same temperature. Internal moisture is bound physically by capillary action, etc. Combined moisture is chemically bound as water of crystallization, etc.

Both hygroscopic and non-hygroscopic materials may contain unbound moisture. Surface moisture is unbound and exerts a vapor pressure very close to that of the pure liquid at the same temperature.

The equilibrium moisture content, often referred to as the percentage regain, is the ratio of the weight of moisture to the weight of dry material that a hygroscopic material contains in equilibrium with any ambient atmosphere. For many materials, the percent regain is constant for any relative humidity regardless of temperature (at least in the usual temperature range). Since any such material will "regain" sufficient moisture to produce equilibrium, it would be poor economics to dry a material below this equilibrium moisture content.

The free moisture content, or excess over the regain, may include bound or unbound liquid or both.

A critical moisture content of a drying material is reached when the surface of the material changes from completely wet to partially wet.

Drying Rate

The rate at which any material may be dried will vary with its moisture content. Most materials exhibit several distinct drying rate periods as indicated in Figure 178. In most cases the initial drying is accompanied by a warming of the material. The moisture content during this warming-up period drops from the initial value at point A to the value at point B. This period is followed by a constant rate period of drying for as long as the surface of the material remains entirely wet. The rate of drying falls off gradually below the critical moisture content at point C until the surface becomes dry at point D. The rate continues to fall even after point D until equilibrium with the surrounding atmosphere is obtained at point E.

The temperature of the material and its moisture will rise in the warming-up period. During the constant rate period the surface moisture remains at constant temperature, just like a wet-bulb thermometer, so long as the temperature and humidity and velocity of the air over the surface are constant. During the falling rate period the excess heat serves to warm the material until equilibrium is established.

Convection drying can proceed only so long as the vapor pressure (e_w) exerted by the surface water exceeds the partial pressure (e_a) of the vapor in the surrounding air. The rate of drying (w_v) will be proportional to the vapor pressure difference ($e_w - e_a$), the evaporating surface (A), and the coefficient of mass transfer (k_g) referred to the partial pressure difference:

$$w_v = k_g\, A\, (e_w - e_a). \qquad (483)$$

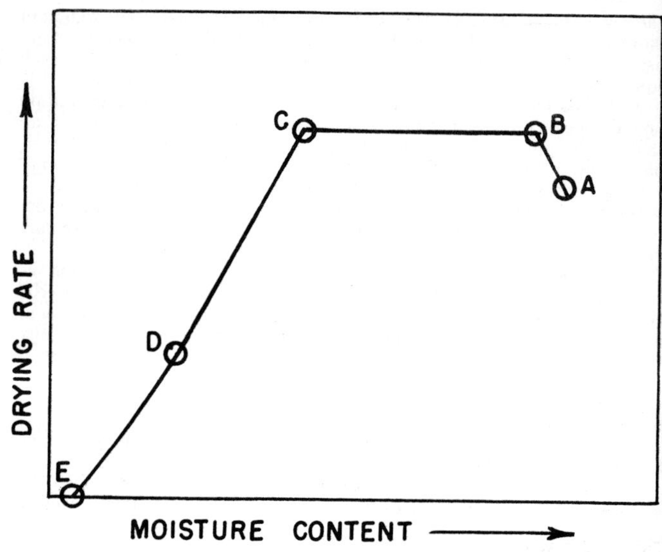

Figure 178—Drying Rate vs Moisture Content

Adapted from the data of R. H. Perry, C. H. Chilton, and S. D. Kirkpatrick, "Chemical Engineers' Handbook," McGraw-Hill Book Co., Inc., New York, 1963, p. *15*-35.

The coefficient of mass transfer is analogous to the more familiar heat transfer coefficient and varies with velocity in substantially the same way. Both are measures of resistance per unit area; one of resistance to the flow of mass and the other to the flow of heat through the thin stagnant film at the surface. Therefore, during the constant rate period, the average velocity determines the rate of evaporation, since the transfer of heat to the surface and of mass from the surface depend on velocity. The temperature of the surface remains constant because only enough heat is transmitted to evaporate the moisture. The area remains constant as long as the surface is completely wet.

During the first part of the falling rate period, the area gradually diminishes so the rate must also decrease. During the second phase of the falling rate period, the effective coefficient gradually decreases since the moisture meets additional resistance in its passage from the internal portions of the material.

The mechanisms which apparently control the migration of internal moisture to the surface are diffusion, capillarity, and pressure gradients due to shrinkage. The laws governing flows of these types will not be presented, although the general principles are embodied in the approximate formulas listed in Table 119.

Drying rates and temperatures are important as regards the physical ffect on the material. Combined moisture can only be released by raising he temperature above the decomposition level. Slow drying rates must be sed for many materials to avoid shrinkage cracks and distortion. Too apid drying in the early stages may case harden the material, retarding he subsequent flow of moisture and actually increasing the total dry-ng time.

sychrometric Aspects of Drying with Air

Several important psychrometric aspects of drying are illustrated in he skeleton psychrometric charts of Figure 179.

The arrows in Figure 179A roughly indicate the psychrometric paths vhich the air might follow in various dryers. All five dryers have the same ntering dry-bulb temperature, entering absolute humidity, and leaving bsolute humidity. The leaving dry-bulb temperatures and relative umidities vary considerably.

Either of the paths, 0-1 or 0-2, might be obtained in a convection dryer. ll of the heat required for evaporation must be supplied directly by the ir. The path, 0-1, is drawn along an adiabatic saturation line which, for ir-water vapor mixtures, is a constant wet-bulb line. Such a path can nly be obtained if the total heat of the air remains constant, i.e., the ncrease in latent heat must be exactly offset by a decrease in sensible eat. If there is any heat lost by radiation, convection, or conduction, the rocess will not be adiabatic and the leaving dry-bulb temperature will be omewhat lower, as at 2.

Any of the paths, 0-3, 0-4, or 0-5, might be obtained in a conduction or adiation dryer. Only a portion of the heat required for evaporation, if any, nay be supplied directly by the air. The path, 0-3, is drawn along a con-tant dry-bulb line. Such a path can only be obtained if the heat sup-lied by indirect means exactly matches the requirements for vaporiza-ion. Any deficit heat must be supplied by the air, in which case the eaving dry-bulb temperature will be somewhere between 1 and 3 as at 4. ny surplus heat will result in a somewhat higher dry-bulb temperature, s at 5.

The arrows in Figure 179B roughly indicate the psychrometric paths hich the air might follow in an adiabatic dryer with three combinations f preheat and reheat. All three paths start at the same absolute humidity nd finish at the same absolute humidity. The dry-bulb temperatures and elative humidities at entrance or exit vary considerably.

The path, *abc*, is the same as the 0-1 path in Figure 179A. To obtain his path the air must be preheated to a relatively high dry-bulb tempera-ure and allowed to pass completely through the dryer without any ntermediate reheating. The relative humidity at exit will be compara-ively high.

If the dry-bulb temperature at the point *a* is considered too high for ny reason, the same increase in absolute humidity can be obtained by reheating the air only to the point *a′*, passing it partially through the ryer to the point *b′*, reheating it to the point *b*, and passing it through he remainder of the dryer to point *c*.

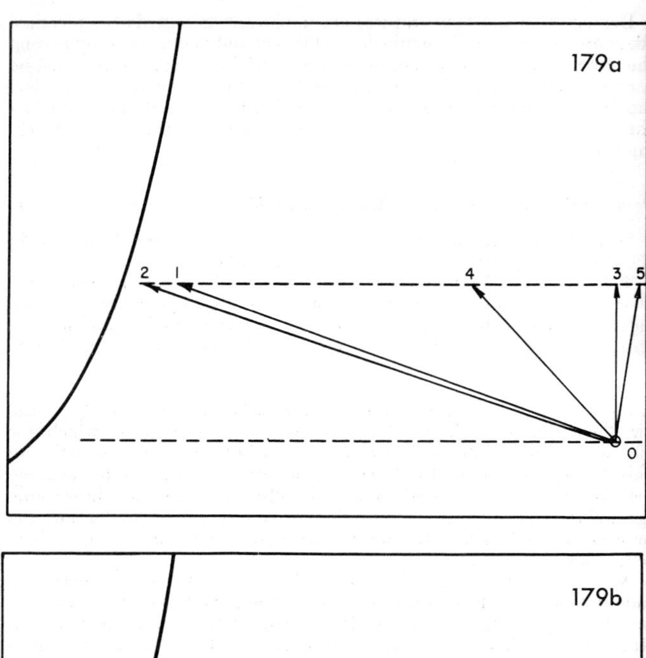

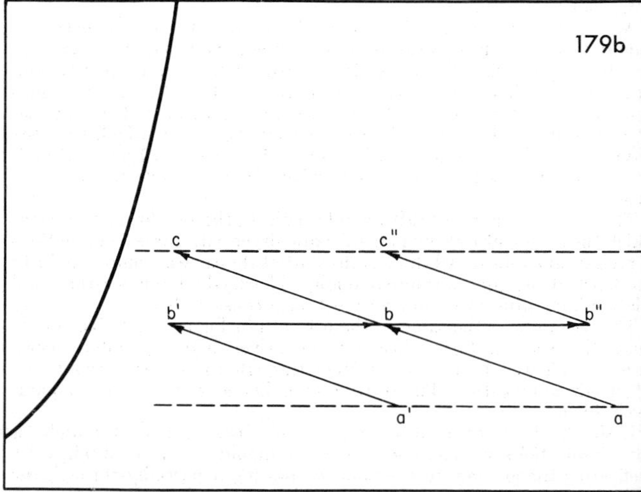

Figure 179—Psychrometric Aspects of Drying

If the relative humidity at point c is considered too high for any reason, ıe same increase in absolute humidity can be obtained by preheating ıe air to the point a, passing it partially through the dryer to the point reheating it to the point b'', and passing it through the remainder of ıe dryer to the point c''.

High temperatures may be objectionable if the product is made harder dry or otherwise damaged thereby. The highest inlet air temperature, hich will not be objectionable, should be used in the interest of efficiency will be explained below.

High relative humidities limit the drying rate and therefore should sually be avoided. In some cases, when the drying rate must be closely ntrolled, a portion of the exhaust gases may be recirculated, raising the lative humidity throughout the dryer, and thereby limiting the drying ıte to a safe value.

eat Required for Drying

The rate at which heat is required for evaporation alone (LH), may be etermined from the entering and leaving moisture contents (dry basis) of ıe material (F_1) and (F_2), the rate at which dry product or material is quired (w_P) and the latent heat of vaporization (λ) using:

$$LH = \lambda \, w_P \, (F_1 - F_2). \tag{484}$$

In addition, heat may be required to offset radiation losses to the sur- undings (SH_r). Similarly, heat may be required to raise the tempera- ıre of the product, its moisture (liquid and vapor), and the air.

The sensible heat required to superheat the vapor (SH_v) may be termined from its specific heat $(c_p)_v$, its temperature rise $(t_{v2} - t_{v1})$, ıd its mass flow rate according to:

$$SH_v = (c_p)_v \, w_P \, (F_1 - F_2) \, (t_{v2} - t_{v1}). \tag{485}$$

The sensible heat required to raise the temperature of the product and s final moisture content (SH_{P+L}) can be calculated from the specific eats of the dry product $(c_p)_P$ and liquid $(c_p)_L$, the temperature rise $_{P2} - t_{P1}$), and the flow rate (w_P) using:

$$SH_{P+L} = [(c_p)_P + (c_p)_L \, F_2] \, w_P \, (t_{P2} - t_{P1}). \tag{486}$$

The sensible heat required to raise the temperature of the air and its itial moisture content (SH_{a+H}) can be calculated from the specific eats of the dry air (0.24) and water vapor (0.45), the temperature rise $_{a2} - t_{a0}$), and the flow rate (w_a) using:

$$SH_{a+H} = [0.24 + 0.45 \, H_0] \, w_a \, (t_{a2} - t_{a0}). \tag{487}$$

he subscript zero (0) is used to designate the entering air temperature and humidity (H) instead of one (*1*), because the air may be preheated efore entering the dryer.

The total heat required (TH) may be supplied entirely by an air eater, or it may be supplied indirectly (by conduction or radiation), or oth. In any case:

$$TH = LH + SH_r + SH_v + SH_{P+L} + SH_{a+H}. \tag{488}$$

Of the total heat utilized, only the portion for latent heat is useful for ying. The sensible heat losses should be minimized by careful design

except for the obvious case where a warm product may be desired f
further processing. Ordinarily the temperature of the drying air should b
as high as possible when relatively large amounts of moisture are to b
removed. When the mass of material is large compared to the amount
moisture, it is usually better to use moderate temperatures so that th
percentage of total heat used to heat the material itself is minimize
Higher velocities may be employed to increase the drying rate in such case

Air Required for Direct Drying

A moisture balance requires that the loss by the material equal th
gain by the air or:

$$w_P (F_1 - F_2) = w_a (H_2 - H_1). \quad (48$$

The weight rate of air flow required (w_a) is seen to be a function of th
feed rate (w_P), the difference in moisture content of feed and produc
($F_1 - F_2$), and the difference in humidity ($H_2 - H_1$) of entering an
leaving air.

The entering humidity may be fixed at the ambient level or at som
higher level if moist air is to be employed. The theoretical maximu
leaving humidity depends on the nature and efficiency of the humidifica
tion process. For adiabatic saturation, the humidification efficienc
seldom exceeds 75%. Known efficiencies should be used wherever pos
sible. Since the drying rate for convection drying depends on a vapo
pressure difference, the leaving relative humidity may often be limite
to 75% or even 50% to insure rapid drying.

The rate of air flow for any specific drying problem can then be estab
lished with respect to the drying rate (w_v):

$$w_a = \frac{w_P (F_1 - F_2)}{H_2 - H_1} = \frac{w_v}{H_2 - H_1}. \quad (490$$

For the case without reheating, the air must be preheated from th
ambient temperature (t_0) to the temperature (t_1) indicated by:

$$t_1 = t_0 + \frac{TH}{(0.24 + 0.45 H_0) w_a}, \quad (491$$

where TH is the total heat requirement according to Equation 488. I
less preheat is used, the remainder must be furnished by one or mor
stages of reheat in a direct dryer.

$$TH = TH_{preheat} + TH_{reheat}. \quad (492$$

The temperature of air leaving the reheater (t_4) may be determined fror
the entering conditions (t_3) and (H_3) according to:

$$t_4 = t_3 + \frac{TH_{reheat}}{(0.24 + 0.45 H_3) w_a}. \quad (493$$

Direct Drying with Steam

Paradoxical as it may seem at first, steam may be used directly to dr
many materials. The only limitation is temperature. Superheated stea
exerts less pressure than the vapor pressure of water at the same tempera
ture. If steam is sufficiently superheated, the sensible heating require

ents can be accomplished with a considerably lower weight rate of ›w (w) than if air were used:

$$\frac{w_{steam}}{w_{air}} = \frac{(c_p \Delta t)_{air}}{(c_p \Delta t)_{steam}} = \frac{0.24}{0.45} = 0.53. \qquad (494)$$

he volume rate of steam flow $(q)_{steam}$ compared with that of air flow $)_{air}$ will depend on the absolute temperatures of the two and their olecular weights as well as on the weight ratio:

$$\frac{q_{steam}}{q_{air}} = 0.53 \times \frac{28.97}{18.0} \times \frac{T_{steam}}{T_{air}} = 0.86 \frac{T_{steam}}{T_{air}}. \qquad (495)$$

Therefore, steam can be used to advantage in many cases where the aterial will withstand the temperatures necessary for any particular rying rate. Fans may be used to provide internal circulation and re- rculation. However, for through circulation, the steam is usually ex- anded and subsequently condensed (together with the removed moisture).

ndirect Drying

In the previous discussions on direct drying, air (or steam) was used to upply the heat necessary to evaporate the moisture and also served to emove that moisture from the immediate vicinity of the material being ried.

When the heat for evaporation is supplied indirectly, either by con- uction or radiation, the material and its moisture will assume a tempera- ıre at which the vapor pressure exceeds the ambient total pressure. If he surface of the material is completely wetted, this temperature will be pproximately the same as the boiling point of the pure liquid at the ressure prevailing.

As in any boiling process the ambient pressure will increase unless the apor generated is allowed to escape sufficiently fast. Atmospheric dryers ıust be properly vented. In vacuum dryers the moisture may be pumped way. In either case, condensers or desiccants may be employed.

The use of vacuum to lower the boiling point and therefore the tem- erature provides attractive possibilities for heat sensitive materials. 'requently the moisture will be in a frozen state, and drying will occur by ublimation. This process produces additional desirable characteristics.

Due to the complexities involved, the performance of an indirect dryer s usually defined as a heat rate (TH) per unit drying surface (A) ac- ording to:

$$\frac{TH}{A} = U \Delta t, \qquad (496)$$

where the over-all heat transfer coefficient (U) is an average based on xperience and the temperature difference (Δt) is an average over all or art of the drying period. The use of fans on indirect drying applications s limited, and may in fact be prohibited to prevent dusting, contamina- ion, etc.

vaporators—Single- and Multiple-Effect

Evaporators are indirect dryers used for removing large quantities of noisture. The result may be a concentrated liquid or a dry residue. The same principles apply as for any indirect dryer. The vast majority evaporators are vacuum operated, although it is not necessarily a pr requisite for either single- or multiple-effect evaporators.

Multiple effects are often used to decrease operating costs, but onl with increased apparatus cost. In operation, for each pound of steam co densed in the first effect, approximately one pound of vapor is evaporate If this vapor is condensed in the second effect another pound of vapor wi be evaporated, and so on for additional effects.

Sizing of Convection Dryers

Although the dryer size must be based on experimentally determine factors, an approximation can sometimes be made on the basis of t required exposed drying surface.

Based on the principles previously outlined, the approximate surfa areas are formulated in terms of known or desired conditions for certai dryer types in Table 119. Once this is determined, the dryer size whic can match these requirements of exposed surface for the material i question can be determined by geometrical analysis.

Equipment

Stationary dryers include both direct- and indirect-types. The equi ment used may be nothing more than a loft or room with direct radiatio and natural convection circulation. Hay lofts and the like may even b unheated. Kilns for drying lumber usually employ circulating fans, coil and humidifiers. Cabinet dryers are heated enclosures which use fans t circulate air over or through the material being dried. The home cloth dryer falls in this category. Depending on construction, cabinet drye are called tray, shelf, compartment, or truck dryers. Through circulatio drying is usually obtained by blowing warm air from the bottom to the to of a fixed bed of material. Often, the reverse flow pattern should b investigated, particularly if recondensed moisture can be passed to th bottom of the bed without re-evaporation. All of the above are direct-typ batch-operated dryers.

The indirect stationary types are also differentiated according to co struction. The contact surfaces may be jacketed shelves, pans, or kettle All are batch dryers and may be constructed for atmospheric or vacuu operation. The heating mediums which flow through the jacketed space may be steam or any other suitable fluid. Almost any material conditio can be accommodated in stationary dryers and mechanisms can b provided for stirring or otherwise agitating.

Conveyor dryers may also be of the direct- or indirect-type. Trucks c other carriers may be utilized to pass material through a tunnel. Th lowest moisture contents of the product are obtained by using counte flow of air and material. However, drying rates may be limited if th dried product is heat sensitive. Higher temperatures can be utilized wit parallel flow of air and material since the hottest air contacts the we feed. Center-exhaust tunnels have been developed to utilize the adva tages of both. The net result is a parallel-flow tunnel on the wet end an counter-flow on the dried end. Control can be effected by controlling th

TABLE 119—EQUATIONS FOR EXPOSED DRYING SURFACE

onstant Drying Conditions—Batch Dryer

$$A_{B-C} = \frac{\lambda W_P (F_1 - F_2)}{\theta_{1-2}\, h\,(t_a - t_s)} \tag{497}$$

$$A_{C-E} = \frac{\lambda W_P F_C}{\theta_{1-2}\, h\,(t_a - t_s)}\ ln \left(\frac{F_1}{F_2}\right) \tag{498}$$

ariable Drying Conditions—Continuous Dryers
Counter Flow Type—Adiabatic—$(h/k'_g\, c_p) = 1$

$$A_{B-C} = w_a \left(\frac{c_p}{h}\right) ln \left[\frac{1 - \dfrac{w_P (F_C - F_2)}{w_a (t_a - t_s)}\left(\dfrac{\lambda}{c_p}\right)}{1 - \dfrac{w_P (F_1 - F_2)}{w_a (t_a - t_s)}\left(\dfrac{\lambda}{c_p}\right)}\right] \tag{499}$$

$$A_{C-E} = w_a \left(\frac{c_p}{h}\right) \left[\frac{1}{\dfrac{F_2}{F_C} + \dfrac{w_a (t_a - t_s)}{w_P (F_C)}\left(\dfrac{c_p}{\lambda}\right)}\right] ln \left(\frac{F_C}{F_2}\right) \left[\frac{1}{1 - \dfrac{w_P (F_C - F_2)}{w_a (t_a - t_s)}\left(\dfrac{\lambda}{c_p}\right)}\right] \tag{500}$$

Parallel Flow Type—Adiabatic—$(h/k'_g c_p) = 1$

$$A_{B-C} = w_a \left(\frac{c_p}{h}\right) ln \left[\frac{1}{1 - \dfrac{w_P (F_1 - F_C)}{w_a (t_a - t_s)}\left(\dfrac{\lambda}{c_p}\right)}\right] \tag{501}$$

$$A_{C-E} = w_a \left(\frac{c_p}{h}\right) \left[\frac{1}{\dfrac{F_1}{F_C} - \dfrac{w_a (t_a - t_s)}{w_P (F_C)}\left(\dfrac{c_p}{\lambda}\right)}\right] ln \left(\frac{F_2}{F_C}\right) \left[\frac{1 - \dfrac{w_P (F_1 - F_C)}{w_a (t_a - t_s)}\left(\dfrac{\lambda}{c_p}\right)}{1 - \dfrac{w_P (F_1 - F_2)}{w_a (t_a - t_s)}\left(\dfrac{\lambda}{c_p}\right)}\right] \tag{502}$$

SYMBOLS

A_{B-C}—exposed drying area during constant rate period .... sq ft
A_{C-E}—exposed drying area during falling rate period .... sq ft
w_P —product flow rate—dry basis (W_P—product weight)............ lb/hr (lb)
w_a —air flow rate—dry basis.. lb/hr
F_C —critical moisture content—dry basis.............................. lb/lb
F_1 —initial moisture content—dry basis................................ lb/lb
F_2 —final moisture content—dry basis.................................. lb/lb
θ_{1-2} —drying time .... hr
t_a —entering air dry-bulb temperature.................................. °F
t_s —wet surface temperature... °F
λ —latent heat of evaporation.. Btu/lb
h —local heat transfer coefficient.. Btu/hr-ft²-°F
c_p —specific heat of air—water vapor mixture.......................... Btu/lb-°F
k'_g —local mass transfer coefficient...................................... lb/hr-ft²-Δ H
ΔH —absolute humidity difference.................................. lb vapor/lb air

dapted from the data of W. C. Lapple, W. E. Clark, and E. C. Dybdal, Drying Design
z Costs, *Chemical Engineering*, pp. 177-200, November, 1955.

air temperature for each stage. Crossflow tunnels can be controlled a intermediate points along the path if individual fans and coils are pr vided. All tunnels can be equipped with recirculating dampers and co trols to provide higher heat efficiencies. Through-flow dryers can b achieved with many materials if a screen or similar conveyor is used i the tunnel. Towers are vertical tunnels which drop the material throug a rising air stream.

Another direct-acting conveyor dryer is known as the turbo-typ Turbo dryers utilize a series of fan wheels arranged on a vertical shaft t circulate air across a series of rotating annular shelves. The material i wiped down and leveled one shelf at a time, producing mixing, exposur changes, and conveying action. Normally, the stack effect is utilized t provide the necessary ventilation and the fans provide recirculatio only. Heat exchangers are usually located in the peripheral space betwee the shelves and enclosure. External heating may be applied with a force draft fan and radiation may also be used.

Forced feed may be achieved in indirect dryers by means of screw, plows, paddles, or similar devices when either the device or its enclosur or both are jacketed. Gravity feed may be assisted by vibration, et Some of these designs may be adapted for direct drying if air can b circulated through the bed of material.

Rotary dryers may be of the direct- or indirect-type, or a combination c the two. Mixing and exposure changes are produced by lifting the materia up the side of the rotating cylinder and spilling it back on itself or shower ing it down through the air stream. Continuous operation is achieved b inclining the cylinder slightly from the horizontal to produce gravity flo of the material. Direct types may be operated with parallel or counte flow of air and material. A special form of the direct type known as th louver dryer employs a series of overlapping shelves in the cylinder t support the material bed for through flow of air. The indirect type c rotary may employ a jacketed cylinder, jacketed flights, or interna tubes through which the products of combustion are passed. A specia form is known as the steam-tube dryer. The direct-indirect type utilize the hot combustion products in the jacket first and subsequently employ them directly.

Two forms of vacuum rotaries are available, both of the indirect-typ for batch operation. In one the horizontal jacketed cylindrical shell i stationary and the material is stirred internally by a rotating agitator. I the other the shell rotates.

Drum dryers consist of one or more heated horizontal drums. The top of double-drum units rotate toward each other and material is fed fro the trough between the two. Twin-drum units rotate away from eac other and may have dip or splash feed. Dried material may be stripped off the drum onto a conveyor. Units may be atmospheric or vacuu operated.

Sheeting dryers may utilize heated cylinders or platens over which th material is passed for indirect drying. Convection types are known a festoon dryers if the sheeting is draped in loops over parallel rods con veying it through, or as tenter dryers if the sheeting is stretched betwee two endless conveyors. Air may be directed against one or both sides o the sheeting with the aid of suitable nozzles. In some cases the air stream may penetrate the material and in others even support it against the conveyor.

In suspended-particle dryers the material must be rather finely divided so that it may be suitably dispersed. In spray-types liquid material is atomized in a suitable chamber so that it dries in a matter of seconds. The dried material may be collected in the bottom of the chamber or carried out with the exhaust gases and separated in cyclones, etc. Flow of air and material may be parallel, counter, or a combination of the two. In flash-type dryers solid particles are fed into a pneumatic conveyor for drying in transit. The material may be picked up directly from a pulverizer or disintegrator and ultimately separated in cyclones, etc., after drying. Material-to-air ratios are usually limited to 1.0 or under. Higher loadings are utilized in fluidized bed applications which are also more suitable for materials with high internal moisture. Although the fines may be lifted out of the bed and recovered separately, the main body of material may move by gravity down an incline, or a column may be continuously fed and tapped. Rapid drying results from the intimate contact and the thorough mixing produces uniform temperatures throughout.

Fans are used on dryer applications to supply the energy to produce through flow or recirculation of the air or gas and to supply the energy to suspend, convey, or even mix the material. The method of figuring the amount of air required for convection drying has been outlined on page 532. The pressure required of the fan depends on the losses due to friction, etc., and the energy required to transport and separate the material.

CHAPTER 21

AIR-BLAST AND OTHER PNEUMATIC DEVICES

The fan applications discussed in Chapters 14 through 20 exploit the ability of air to transport heat or materials. Additional similar applications are discussed in this chapter together with others which utilize the ability of air to absorb mechanical energy or produce forces. The specific applications, which follow, include: (1) air-blast cooling, (2) air-blast drying, (3) air-blast and vacuum cleaning, (4) air-blast and sharp freezing (and cold storage), (5) air brakes, (6) air curtains, and (7) air support. These items by no means complete the list of possible air uses or fan applications.

Air-Blast Cooling

The cooling (or heating) of objects with a blast of air may be distinguished in many ways from the heat exchanger applications discussed in Chapter 19. To begin with, unsteady state or transient conduction is frequently involved. That is, the temperature at a given point varies with time. In addition, blast cooling is normally employed on many objects whose temperatures are quite elevated, and the loss of heat by radiation may equal or exceed that lost by convection.

Numerous methods and charts have been devised for various shapes such as slabs, bricks, cylinders, and spheres. Only thin slabs will be discussed here. For other shapes the reader is referred to the standard works on heat transmission.

Insofar as the fan is concerned, the principal unknowns are the amount and velocity of air required. However, the basic problem is to cool the material in a reasonable time. The time required (θ) to cool from the initial temperature (t_A) to the final temperature (t_B) may be divided into an unknown number (n) of equal increments ($\Delta\,\theta$):

$$\theta = n\,\Delta\,\theta. \tag{503}$$

The material may be considered to be two layers of equal thickness (x). For a material of specific heat (c), density (δ), and thermal conductivity (k):

$$\Delta\,\theta = \frac{x^2}{2}\left(\frac{c\,\delta}{k}\right). \tag{504}$$

The surface temperature (t_o) at any instant depends on the temperature of the air (t_a) contacting the surface and the interior temperature (t_i) according to:

$$t_o = \frac{h_T\,x\,t_a + kt_i}{h_T\,x + k}. \tag{505}$$

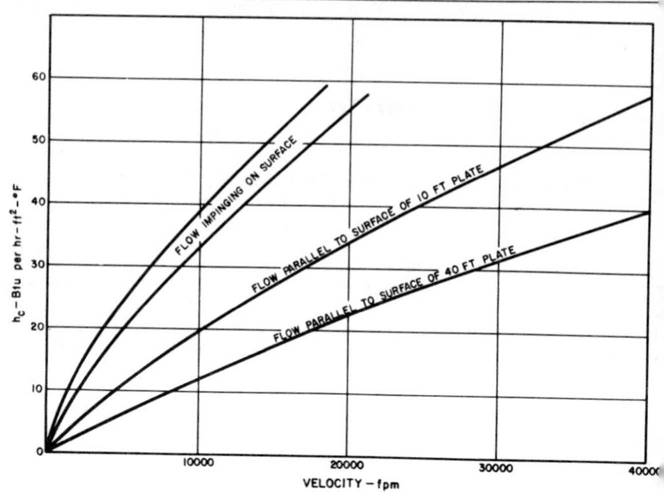

Figure 180—Film Coefficients for Air on Flat Plates

Adapted from the data of W. L. Torgeson, H. C. Johnson, and N. B. Wright, Jr., Engineering Study of Air Conditioning Load Requirements for Aircraft Compartments, Wright Air And Development Center, WADC TR 55-254, 1955, p. 8.

The combined radiation and convection coefficient of heat transfer (h_T) may be determined from:

$$h_T = h_C + h_R F_\epsilon. \tag{506}$$

The convection coefficient (h_C) may be obtained from Figure 180 for any trial air velocity.

The equivalent radiation coefficient (h_R) may be determined from the absolute temperatures of the material (T) and the surrounding surfaces (T_a) using:

$$h_R = \frac{0.1713 \left[\left(\frac{T}{100}\right)^4 - \left(\frac{T_a}{100}\right)^4\right]}{(T - T_a)}. \tag{507}$$

The temperature of the surrounding surfaces will generally equal the ambient air temperature. The temperature of the material will vary from T_A to T_B as it is cooled.

The emissivity factor (F_ϵ) may be determined from Tables 19 and 20.

For the case in which air is blown across both surfaces of a thin sheet, the interior temperature (t_i) at the end of an increment of time ($\Delta\, \theta$) may be considered equal to the surface temperature (t_o) at the beginning of that interval. (For the more general case of a thicker slab divided into more than two equal thickness layers, the temperature of any interface at the end of a particular $\Delta\, \theta$ may be assumed equal to the average of the temperatures at the two adjacent interfaces at the beginning of that particular $\Delta\ \theta$.) So:

$$(t_i)_{\Delta\theta_n} = (t_o)_{\Delta\theta_{n-1}}. \tag{508}$$

The incremental temperature difference ($\Delta\ t_i$) varies with time:

$$\Delta\ t_i = (t_i)_{\Delta\theta_n} - (t_i)_{\Delta\theta_{n+1}}. \tag{509}$$

Several incremental temperature differences should be calculated for various temperatures between T_A and T_B. These may be averaged to give the mean cooling rate ($\Delta\ t_i/\Delta\ \theta$):

$$\frac{\Delta\ t_i}{\Delta\ \theta} = \frac{(\Delta\ t_i)_1 + (\Delta\ t_i)_2 + \ldots + (\Delta\ t_i)_m}{m}. \tag{510}$$

The total cooling time (θ) may then be calculated:

$$\theta = \frac{T_A - T_B}{\Delta\ t_i/\Delta\ \theta}. \tag{511}$$

If the total time so calculated is not satisfactory, a different velocity may be assumed and the calculations repeated.

The amount of air should be sufficient to absorb the heat released by the material without an excessive temperature rise.

The weight rate of air flow (w_a) and the air temperature rise ($\Delta\ t_a$) are related to the weight of material (W), its specific heat (c), the cooling range ($t_A - t_B$), and the cooling time (θ) by a heat balance:

$$0.24\ w_a\ (\Delta\ t_a) = c\ \frac{W}{\theta}\ (t_A - t_B). \tag{512}$$

Air-cooled motors, engines, and electronic equipment may be considered air-blast cooling applications. They differ from the previous sheet cooling case in that steady state conduction is approached. Actually, the principal concern in cooling equipment of this sort is to prevent dangerous "hot spots" rather than to remove a given amount of heat or produce a specific temperature reduction in a certain time interval. The designer's problem is all the more difficult for this reason, and usually the only proof of any design is the actual measurement of hot spot temperatures by test. Radiation losses are frequently ignored, and the Nusselt equation, in modified form, is used for design purposes. In the usual case, the heat release rate varies along the air path. The flow pattern must be accurately visualized and the temperature gradient estimated. The amount of heat (TH) given off by any particular surface area (A) will depend on the temperature head or difference between the surface temperature (t_o) and air temperature (t_a) and the coefficient (h_C):

$$TH = h_C\ A\ (t_o - t_a). \tag{513}$$

The heat transfer coefficient (h_C) in Btu/hr-sq ft-°F may be determined from Figure 180 for air-cooled flat plates, or from:

$$h_C = .072\ \frac{G^{0.6}}{d^{0.4}}, \tag{514}$$

for an air-cooled cylinder. This expression is derived from Equation 54. The air mass velocity (G) is in lb/hr – sq ft of cross section occupied by the air and the diameter of the cylinder (d) is in inches.

Air-blast motor-cooling systems frequently employ evaporative cooling to reduce the entering dry-bulb temperature.

Man coolers are frequently used in hot spots. Velocities ranging from 300 to 1000 feet per minute have proved successful. However, the worker must be free to control the blast or to remove himself from it if he so desires. Evaporative cooling of such air blasts may be resorted to only when the resultant humidification can be tolerated.

Air-Blast Drying

Air blasts are frequently used to dry automobiles, bottles, and other smooth-surface objects after they have been washed. Most of these devices utilize the wiping action of the blast rather than any evaporative effect. The velocity requirements vary with the nature of the surface; however, twenty-four-thousand feet per minute is generally sufficient on smooth surfaces.

The amount of air to be used depends on the effectiveness of the nozzle arrangement and the extent of the wetted surface which must be wiped dry.

Air-Blast and Vacuum Cleaning

A vacuum cleaner is simply a portable, local exhaust system. A stream of air is caused to move past the material in such a way as to propel the material into a hood opening. With any such vacuum device, the velocity of the air decreases rapidly with distance from the hood face. The air by virtue of its velocity not only propels the dirt or refuse along, but dislodges and accelerates it as well. An air blast is considerably more effective at a distance than an equal volume of air under suction. That is to say, the velocity at any distance from the opening is considerably higher for a stream issuing from an opening than for a stream entering that opening.

If the dirt or refuse is to be collected, an air blast cannot be used alone. However, it is not necessary that separate fans be used for the vacuum and blast. The usual arrangement is to draw air through the hood and separator and then to blow through the blast nozzles. The velocity required to pick up any material depends on the size and weight of that material. Based on a drag coefficient of unity and a material weighing 400 pounds per cubic foot, a velocity in excess of 5000 feet per minute is required just to float a ½″ cube. Even higher velocities are required for rounded particles. Dislodgement is more complex than lifting, and some form of mechanical agitation is usually employed to reduce the air energy required.

Air-Blast and Sharp Freezing (and Cold Storage)

Blast freezing is one of several methods of "quick freezing." The others involve direct immersion in, or indirect contact with, the refrigerant. The advantages of quick freezing over sharp freezing include better prevention of: (1) water separation in the form of ice, (2) formation of large ice crystals, and (3) decomposition during freezing. The principal disadvantages of air-blast freezing are the dehydration of the product and the increased need for defrosting the equipment as compared to other quick methods. The types and designs of freezers are as numerous as dryers, and in fact many are quite similar to dryers.

Sharp freezing is "slow freezing." It consists of loading the food in a cold room and generally providing only natural circulation to promote heat transfer. The more forced circulation is utilized, the closer the approach to "quick freezing." Economical quick-freezing velocities depend on the product and temperature, but range around 1000 feet per minute. Too high a velocity produces excessive dehydration, and too low velocities require longer freezing times.

Cold storage is used to extend the life of perishable products. Some typical products are listed in Table 120, together with important storage information. The design of a cold-storage system is similar to that of an air-conditioning system. Since lower temperatures are generally involved, considerably more insulation can be justified to prevent excessive transmission losses. Good practice indicates over-all coefficients of .035 to .05 for freezers and .05 to .075 for coolers. Insulation should be well protected by vapor barriers and waterproof construction. Sun effect should be minimized by eliminating windows and by utilizing roof sprays or other means of reducing roof loads. For some products ventilation may be required. In most cases, infiltration can be ignored except for that through doors opened for entry. The internal load for live storage should include an allowance for lights, motors, and workers. This may be omitted on dead-storage applications. The product load includes the heat removal required to bring the product to storage temperature and an additional amount known as the "heat of evolution." The specific heat (c) in Btu per pound per °F of a food is largely determined by its water content (F_w) in pounds per pound of moist product and is usually calculated from:

$$c = 0.8\,F_w + 0.2. \tag{515}$$

The cooling period will range from twelve to twenty-four hours in most cases. As in any transient conduction, cooling proceeds most rapidly at first and gradually the rate diminishes until storage temperature is achieved.

The heats of evolution or heats of respiration for certain fruits and vegetables are listed in Table 121. The rate at which this chemical activity proceeds depends on the temperature, as indicated.

Fan-coil units, known as unit coolers, are frequently employed for cold-storage duty. The alternative is to use banks of pipe coils and natural circulation. Unlike air-conditioning units, subfreezing coil temperatures are used and frosting of the surface must be expected. The additional frictional and thermal resistance reduce air and heat capacity as shown in Figure 181 for a typical coil. Numerous methods are employed for defrosting. The necessary heat may be supplied by recirculating cold room air if it is above 34°. The time required for such a method is indicated in Figure 182 for a typical coil. Other methods include circulating warm outside air, or spraying brine over the outside of the coils, and circulating hot refrigerant gas, or warm brine, through the coils.

TABLE 120
STORAGE CONDITIONS AND PROPERTIES OF PERISHABLE PRODUCTS

Commodity	Storage Temp. °F	Relative Humid. %	Approx. Storage Life	Water Content %	Average Freez. Pt. °F	Sp. Heat Above Freez.	Sp. Heat Below Freez.
MEATS							
Bacon—frozen	−10-0	90-95	4-6 mos.	—	—	—	.24-.29
cured	34-40	85	2-6 wks.	13-29	—	.30-.43	—
Beef—frozen	−10-0	90-95	9-12 mos.	—	—	—	.38-.43
fresh	32-34	88-92	1-6 wks.	62-77	28-29	.70-.84	—
dried	36-40	65	6 mos.	5-15	—	.22-.34	.19-.26
Hams & shoulders							
frozen	−10-0	90-95	6-8 mos.	—	—	—	.34-.36
fresh	32-34	85-90	7-12 das.	47-54	28-29	.58-.63	—
cured	60-65	50-60	0-3 yrs.	40-45	—	.52-.56	.32-.33
Lamb—frozen	−10-0	90-95	8-10 mos.	—	—	—	.38-.51
fresh	32-34	85-90	5-12 das.	60-70	28-29	.68-.76	—
Livers—frozen	−10-0	90-95	3-4 mos.	70	—	—	—
Pork—frozen	−10-0	90-95	4-6 mos.	—	—	—	.30-.32
fresh	32-34	85-90	3-7 das.	35-42	28-29	.48-.54	—
Rabbit—frozen	−10-0	90-95	0-6 mos.	—	—	—	—
fresh	32-34	90-95	1-5 das.	—	—	—	—
Smoked Sausage	40-45	85-90	6 mos.	60	25	.86	.56
Sausage Casings	40-45	85-90	4 mos.	—	—	.60	—
Sausage—fresh	21-27	85	15 das.	65	26	.89	.56
Veal	32-34	90-95	5-10 das.	70-80	28-29	.76-.84	.42-.51
FISH							
Brine salted fish	40-50	90-95	10-12 mos.	—	—	.76	.41
Fresh fish	33-40	90-95	5-20 das.	—	26	.80	—
Frozen fish	−10-0	90-95	8-10 mos.	62-85	—	—	.40
Mild cured fish	28-35	75-90	4-8 mos.	—	—	.76	.41
Smoked fish	40-50	50-60	6-8 mos.	—	—	.70	.39
FRUITS							
Apples	30-32	85-90	2-7 mos.	84.1	28.2	.87	.45
Apricots	31-32	85-90	1-2 wks.	85.4	29.6	.88	.46
Bananas	56	85-95	10 das.	74.8	29.6	.80	.42
Blackberries	31-32	85-90	7 days	84.8	29.4	.88	.46
Blueberries	31-32	85-90	3-6 wks.	82.3	28.6	.86	.45
Cherries	31-32	85-90	10-14 das.	83.0	27.7	.87	.45
Cranberries	36-40	85-90	1-3 mos.	87.4	30.0	.90	.46
Currants	32	80-85	10-14 das.	84.7	30.2	.88	.45
Dates—hard	0	70-75	1 year	20.0	−4.2	.36	.26
soft	0-10	—	9-12 mos.	20.0	−4.2	—	—
Dewberries	31-32	85-90	7-10 das.	—	29.2	—	—
Dried Fruits	32	50-60	9-12 mos.	—	—	.30-.32	—
Figs—dried	32-40	50-60	9-12 mos.	24	—	.39	.27
fresh	28-32	85-90	5-7 das.	78	27.1	.82	.43
Fruits—frozen pk.	−10-0	—	6-12 mos.	—	—	—	—
Gooseberries	31-32	80-85	3-4 wks.	88.9	30.0	.90	.46
Grapefruit	32-50	85-90	4-8 wks.	88.8	28.6	.91	.46
Grapes							
American type	31-32	85-90	3-8 wks.	81.9	29.4	.86	.44
European type	30-31	85-90	3-6 mos.	81.6	27.1	.86	.44
Lemons	32, 55-88	85-90	1-4 mos.	89.3	29.0	.92	.46
Limes	48-50	85-90	6-8 wks.	86.0	28.2	.89	.46
Loganberries	31-32	85-90	7 days	82.9	29.5	.86	.45
Mangoes	50	85-90	2-3 wks.	81.4	29.4	.85	.44
Melons							
Cantal. & Persian	45-50	85-90	1-2 wks.	92.7	29.9	.94	.48
Honeyd. & Honeyb.	45-50	85-90	2-4 wks.	92.6	29.8	.94	.48

TABLE 120 (Cont.)

STORAGE CONDITIONS AND PROPERTIES OF PERISHABLE PRODUCTS

Commodity	Storage Temp. °F	Relative Humid. %	Approx. Storage Life	Water Content %	Average Freez. Pt. °F	Sp. Heat Above Freez.	Sp. Heat Below Freez.
FRUITS (Cont.)							
Casaba	45-50	85-90	4-6 wks.	92.7	29.9	.94	.48
Watermelons	36-40	85-90	2-3 wks.	92.1	30.6	.97	.48
Olives, fresh	45-50	85-90	4-6 wks.	75.2	28.5	.80	.42
Oranges	32-34	85-90	8-12 wks.	87.2	28.0	.90	.46
Papayas	45	85-90	2-3 wks.	90.8	30.1	.82	.47
Peaches	31-32	85-90	2-4 wks.	86.9	29.6	.90	.46
Pears	29-31	85-90	—	82.7	27.7	.86	.45
Persimmons	30	85-90	2 mos.	78.2	27.5	.84	.43
Pineapples							
Mature	50-60	85-90	3-4 wks.	—	29.1	—	—
Ripe	40-45	85-90	2-4 wks.	85.3	29.7	.88	.45
Plums & fresh prunes	31-32	80-85	3-4 wks.	85.7	28.7	.88	.45
Pomegranates	34-35	85-90	2-4 mos.	—	26.5	—	—
Quinces	31-32	85-90	2-3 mos.	85.3	28.1	.88	.45
Raspberries							
black	31-32	85-90	7 days	80.6	29.4	.84	.44
red	31-32	85-90	7 days	84.1	30.3	.87	.45
frozen	−10-0	—	1 year	—	—	—	—
Strawberries—fresh	31-32	85-90	7-10 das.	89.9	30.2	.92	—
frozen	−10-0	—	1 year	72.0	—	—	.42
Tangerines	31-38	90-95	3-4 wks.	87.3	29.5	.90	.46
VEGETABLES							
Artichokes (Globe)	31-32	90-95	1-2 wks.	83.7	29.6	.87	.45
Jerusalem	31-32	90-95	2-5 mos.	79.5	27.5	.83	.44
Asparagus	32	90-95	3-4 wks.	93.0	30.4	.94	.48
Avocados	45-55	85-90	4 wks.	65.4	30.0	.72	.40
Beans—green snap	45	85-90	8-10 das.	88.9	30.2	.91	.47
Lima	32-40	85-90	10-15 das.	66.5	30.8	.73	.40
Beets—bunch	32	90-95	10-14 das.	—	—	—	—
topped	32	90-95	1-3 mos.	87.6	29.2	.90	.46
Broccoli—sprouting	32	90-95	7-10 das.	89.9	30.3	.92	.47
Brussels sprouts	32	90-95	3-4 wks.	84.9	30.2	.88	.46
Cabbage—late	32	90-95	3-4 mos.	92.4	30.5	.94	.47
Carrots							
bunch	32	90-95	10-14 das.	—	—	—	—
prepackaged	32	80-90	3-4 wks.	—	—	—	—
topped	32	90-95	4-5 mos.	88.2	28.8	.90	.46
Cauliflower	32	85-90	2-3 wks.	91.7	30.2	.93	.47
Celeriac	32	90-95	3-4 mos.	88.3	30.2	.91	.46
Celery	31-32	90-95	2-4 mos.	93.7	30.9	.95	.48
Corn—sweet	31-32	85-90	4-8 das.	73.9	30.8	.79	.42
Cucumbers	45-50	90-95	10-14 das.	96.1	30.5	.97	.49
Eggplant	45-50	85-90	10 das.	92.7	30.4	.94	.48
Endive	32	90-95	2-3 wks.	93.3	31.1	.94	.48
Frozen Pk. Veg.	−10-0	—	6-12 mos.	—	—	—	—
Garlic—Dry	32	70-75	6-8 mos.	74.2	28.0	.79	.42
Horseradish	32	90-95	10-12 mos.	73.4	26.4	.78	.42
Kale	32	90-95	3-4 wks.	86.6	30.7	.89	.46
Kohlrabi	32	90-95	2-4 wks.	90.1	30.0	.92	.47
Leeks—green	32	90-95	1-3 mos.	88.2	30.4	.90	.46
Lettuce	32	90-95	3-4 wks.	94.8	31.2	.96	.48
Mushrooms	32-35	85-90	3-5 das.	91.1	30.0	.93	.47
Okra	50	85-95	7-10 das.	89.8	28.6	.92	.46
Onions & Onion Sets	32	70-75	6-8 mos.	87.5	30.1	.90	.46

TABLE 120 (Cont.)
STORAGE CONDITIONS AND PROPERTIES OF PERISHABLE PRODUCTS

Commodity	Storage Temp. °F	Relative Humid. %	Approx. Storage Life	Water Content %	Average Freez. Pt. °F	Sp. Heat Above Freez.	Sp. Heat Below Freez.
VEGETABLES (Cont.)							
Parsnips	32	90-95	2-6 mos.	78.6	29.8	.84	.46
Peas, green	32	85-90	1-2 wks.	74.3	30.1	.79	.42
Peppers, sweet	45-50	85-90	8-10 das.	92.4	30.5	.94	.47
Peppers, Chili, dry	32-40	65-75	6-9 mos.	12.0	30.9	.30	.24
Potatoes—early	50-55	85-90	—	—	30.0	—	—
late	38-50	85-90	—	77.8	29.8	.82	.43
Pumpkins	50-55	70-75	2-6 mos.	90.5	29.9	.92	.47
Radishes—spring	32	90-95	10 days	93.6	30.1	.95	.48
winter	32	90-95	2-4 mos.	93.6	—	.95	.48
Rutabagas	32	90-95	2-4 mos.	89.1	29.7	.91	.47
Salsify	32	90-95	2-4 mos.	79.1	29.6	.83	.44
Spinach	32	90-95	10-14 das.	92.7	31.3	.94	.48
Squash—acorn	45-50	75-85	4-5 wks.	—	30.0	—	—
summer	32-40	85-95	10-14 das.	95.0	30.4	.96	—
winter	50-55	70-75	4-6 mos.	88.6	29.8	.91	—
Sugar—gran.	50-100	below 60	1-3 yrs.	.5	—	.20	.20
Sweet Potatoes	55-60	90-95	4-6 mos.	68.5	29.2	.75	.40
Tomatoes—Green	55-70	85-90	2-5 wks.	94.7	30.4	.95	.48
Ripe	32	85-90	7 das.	94.1	30.4	.95	.48
Turnips, roots	32	90-95	4-5 mos.	90.9	29.8	.93	.47
Vegetable seed	32-50	50-65	—	—	—	—	—
DAIRY PRODUCTS							
Cheese							
curing	50-60	75-90	—	—	—	—	—
American	32-34	80	15 mos.	55	17	.64	.36
Camembert	30-34	85	90 das.	60	18	.70	.40
Limburger	30-34	85	60 das.	60	19	.70	.40
Roquefort	30-34	80	60 das.	55	3	.65	.32
Swiss	30-34	80	60 das.	55	15	.64	.36
Butter	32-36	80-85	2 mos.	15.5-16.5	—	.33	—
Butter, frozen	−10-−20	80-85	1 yr.	15.5-16.5	—	—	.25
Cream, swtd.	−15	—	a few mos.	—	—	—	—
Eggs							
shell	29-31	85-90	8-9 mos.	67	28	.74	.40
shell, farm cooler	40-55	75	—	67	28	.74	.40
frozen	−10-0	—	1 yr. plus	73	28	—	.42
dried, whole	35	low/pos.	6 mos.-yr.	5	—	.25	.21
dried, yolk	35	low/pos.	6 mos.-yr.	3	—	.22	.21
dried sp. albumen	35	low/pos.	6 mos.	up to 6	—	.25	—
fermented alb.	room temp.	low/pos.	1 yr. plus	3-15	—	.22-.32	—
Ice Cream	−15	—	a few mos.	—	—	—	—
Skim milk							
dried	40	—	a few mos.	3.5	—	.23	—
unsweetened	−15	—	short time	—	—	—	—
sweetened	35	—	a few mos.	—	—	—	—
FLOWERS							
Calla Lily	40	80-85	1 wk.	—	—	—	—
Camellia	45	80-85	3-6 das.	—	30.4	—	—
Carnation	33	80-85	1 wk.	—	30.6	—	—
Chrysanthemum	35	80-85	2 wks.	—	28.4	—	—
Gardenia	45	80-85	3-6 das.	—	30.8	—	—
Gladiolus	35	80-85	1 wk.	—	31.3	—	—

TABLE 120 (Cont.)
STORAGE CONDITIONS AND PROPERTIES OF PERISHABLE PRODUCTS

Commodity	Storage Temp. °F	Relative Humid. %	Approx. Storage Life	Water Content %	Average Freez. Pt. °F	Sp. Heat Above Freez.	Sp. Heat Below Freez.
FLOWERS (Cont.)							
Lily, Easter	35	80-85	2 wks.	—	31.0	—	—
Lily-of-the-Valley	35	80-85	1 wk.	—	—	—	—
Orchid	55	80-85	2-3 das.	—	31.1	—	—
Peony—tight bud	35	80-85	6 wks.	—	29.9	—	—
loose bud	35	80-85	3-4 wks.	—	29.9	—	—
Rose—tight bud	40	80-85	3-4 das.	—	30.6	—	—
loose buds	40	80-85	2-3 das.	—	30.6	—	—
GREENS							
Fern, dagger, wd. fern	30-32	85-90	4-5 mos.	—	28.6	—	—
Holly bran. & wrea.	32	85-90	1-4 wks.	—	26.3	—	—
Huckleberry	32	85-90	1-4 wks.	—	26.5	—	—
Laurel	32	85-90	1-4 wks.	—	27.4	—	—
Salal	32	85-90	1-4 wks.	—	26.5	—	—
BULBS							
Amaryllis	40-45	75-80	5 mos.	—	30.8	—	—
Dahlia	40-45	75-80	5 mos.	—	28.3	—	—
Gladiolus	40-50	75-80	8 mos.	—	28.0	—	—
Iris, Dutch, Spanish	35	75-80	4 mos.	—	—	—	—
Lily							
Candidum	32	75-80	3 mos.	—	—	—	—
Croft	32	75-80	2 mos.	—	—	—	—
Longiflorum	32	75-80	3 mos.	—	28.7	—	—
Speciosum	32	75-80	3 mos.	—	—	—	—
Peony	40-45	75-80	5 mos.	—	—	—	—
Tuberose	40-45	75-80	4 mos.	—	—	—	—
Tulip	50-55	75-80	1 mo.	—	27.3	—	—
NURSERY STOCK							
Trees and Shrubs	32-35	80-85	4-5 mos.	—	—	—	—
Roses	32-35	80-85	4-5 mos.	—	—	—	—
Strawberry Plants	30-32	80-85	4-10 mos.	—	29.6	—	—
MISCELLANEOUS							
Alfalfa Meal	30-40	70-75	—	—	—	—	—
Beer, barrelled	35-40	—	3-6 wks.	90.2	28.0	.92	—
Caviar (tub)	34-36	85	15 das.	—	20	—	—
Coffee (green)	35-37	80-85	2-4 mos.	10-15	—	—	—
Furs & Woolens	15-50	50	Apr.-Oct.	—	—	.40	—
Honey	31-33	70	1 yr.	18	—	.35	.26
Hops	29-32	50-60	May-Oct.	—	—	—	—
Lard							
without antioxidant	45	90-95	4-8 mos.	0	—	—	—
without antioxidant	0	90-95	12-14 mos.	0	—	—	—
Malt	48-52	80	May-Oct.	—	—	—	—
Maple sugar	31-32	70	May-Oct.	5	—	.24	.21
Maple syrup	31-32	70	May-Oct.	36	—	.49	.31
Nuts	32-50	65-75	8-12 mos.	3-6	—	.22-.25	.21-.22
Oil, veg. salad	35	—	1 yr.	0	—	—	—
Oleomargarine	35	60-70	1 yr.	15.5	—	.32	.25
Popcorn, unpopped	32-40	85	—	13.5	—	.31	.24
Vaccine Serum	43-55	70	4 mos.	—	—	—	—
Yeast, comp. baker's	31-32	—	—	70.9	—	.77	.41

Adapted from the data of "Refrigeration Applications," ASRE Data Book, 1959, pp. 23-02 to 23-05 and 23-09.

TABLE 121—HEATS OF EVOLUTION OF FRUITS AND VEGETABLES

In Btu per Ton per 24 hr

Commodity	32°F	40°F	60°F
Apples	300- 1,500	590- 2,660	2,270- 7,880
Bananas[1]	—	—	—
Beans			
Green or snap	5,500- 6,160	9,160-11,390	32,090-44,130
Lima	2,330- 3,160	4,300- 6,100	21,990-27,410
Beets, topped	2,650	4,060	7,240
Broccoli, sprouting	7,450	11,000-17,600	33,800-50,000
Cabbage	1,200	1,670	4,080
Carrots, topped	2,130	3,470	8,080
Celery	1,620	2,420	8,220
Cherries	1,320- 1,760	—	11,000-13,200
Corn, sweet	6,560	9,390	38,410
Cranberries[2]	600- 720	870- 970	—
Cucumbers	1,690	2,550	10,460
Grapefruit	370- 950	725- 1,300	2,200- 3,980
Grapes			
American type	602	1,170	3,487
European type	300- 430	—	2,200- 2,640
Lemons	480- 900	620- 1,890	2,310- 4,950
Lettuce	11,320	15,990	45,980
Melons, Cantaloupes	1,320	1,960	8,500
Mushrooms[3]	6,160	—	—
Onions and onion sets[4]	660- 1,100	—	—
Oranges	420- 1,030	1,300- 1,560	3,650- 5,170
Peaches	850- 1,370	1,440- 2,030	7,260- 9,310
Pears	660- 880	—	8,800-13,200
Peas, green	8,160- 8,360	13,220-16,020	39,250-44,510
Peppers, sweet	2,720	4,700	8,470
Potatoes[5]	440- 880	1,100- 1,760	—
Raspberries	3,850- 5,502	6,750- 8,470	18,080-22,250
Spinach	4,240- 4,860	7,850-11,210	36,920-38,000
Strawberries	2,730- 3,800	3,610- 6,750	15,640-20,280
Sweet Potatoes	1,190- 2,440	1,710- 3,350	4,280- 6,300
Tomatoes			
Mature green	580	1,070	6,230
Ripe	1,020	1,260	5,640
Turnips	1,940	2,150	5,280

1. Bananas at 68°F, 8,360-9,240.
2. Cranberries at 50°F, 1,650-1,800.
3. Mushrooms at 50°F, 22,000; at 70°F, 58,000.
4. Onions at 50°F, 1,760-1,980.
5. Potatoes at 70°F, 2,200-3,520.

Adapted from the data of "Refrigeration Applications," ASRE Data Book, 1959, p. 23-06.

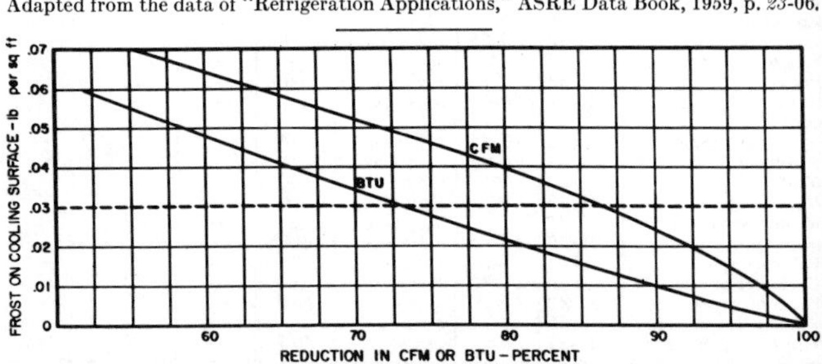

Figure 181—Effects of Frost on Coils

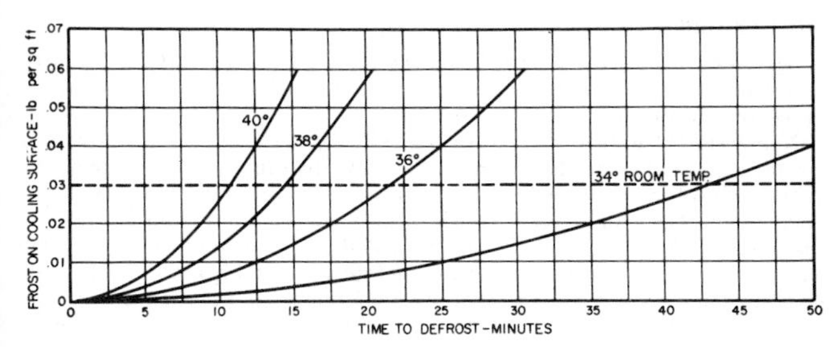

Figure 182—Defrost Time

Air Brakes

Fans may be used to advantage on many power absorbing applications. Because the torque varies as the square of the speed, fan loads are very speed sensitive. The energy is dissipated directly into the air rather than through sliding friction. Fans are employed to provide the load on dynamometer applications whenever these characteristics are desirable. Fans are also used, in conjunction with some form of friction brake, to control the fall on many hoisting applications. The actual efficiency of the fan, as a fan, is usually of very little concern in these applications. Rather, the highest power consumption for any size and speed is preferred. A backward curved blade fan operating in the wrong direction of rotation produces a rather inefficient forward curved characteristic. Tests on a Buffalo backward curved blade fan indicate that the free delivery power requirement is highest for a rotation, which is correct with respect to the housing and vanes, but incorrect with respect to the wheel. However, on hoist type applications where the fan must be driven in opposite directions on raising and lowering, the advantage lies with the combination of rotation on lowering of the hoist, which is correct with respect to the housing, but incorrect with respect to the wheel and vanes. The data of Table 122 describe these situations.

TABLE 122

WRONG ROTATION DATA—TYPICAL BACKWARD CURVED BLADE FAN

Rotation	Housing	Wheel	Vanes	Relative Horsepower	Ratio
c	c	c	c	1.00	2.25
cc	c	c	c	2.25	
c	c	c	cc	2.58	0.86
cc	c	c	cc	2.22	
cc	c	cc	c	2.32	4.07
c	c	cc	c	9.45	
cc	c	cc	cc	1.49	5.12
c	c	cc	cc	7.63	

c—clockwise
cc—counterclockwise
Relative horsepower based on horsepower at free delivery capacity

Air Curtains

Air-jet curtains can be used to form effective barriers against the entry of unconditioned air, dirt, rain, and insects, while allowing traffic to proceed unhindered through a doorway.

Neglecting wind forces, the residual velocity of the jet and its entrained air must be sufficient to sweep aside any invading insect or particle. Where wind forces are involved, the jet must be directed into the wind, higher velocities employed, or both to prevent the wind from infiltrating the opening. A hypothetically self-propelled air particle traveling at 3000 feet per minute would be displaced one foot by a 500 fpm (6 mph) cross-wind by the time it traversed a six foot opening. In other words the crosswind would infiltrate a distance of one foot. Due to entrainment, etc., a projected particle of air in a real jet would be displaced even further by the same crosswind.

Effective fly screens have been produced by using ½″ slots with 3000 fpm average initial velocities. Some designers prefer wider slots and somewhat lower velocities. The data on flow from slots (page 162) can be extrapolated to show that a 1½″ slot with 2000 fpm average initial velocity will produce on normal applications about the same residual velocity as the slots described above. Adjustable slots are usually provided.

Such high velocities can only be tolerated on industrial applications. For commercial establishments, lower velocities probably not exceeding 1200 fpm must be used. To further prevent any disagreeable blast effects, the jets must also be heated. This has led to the development of systems using recirculated air. Nozzles are arranged to blow a wide, low-velocity stream downward toward a floor grating. The stream may be directed outward to counteract crosswind effects. Controls can be arranged to produce higher velocities when higher crosswinds prevail. Materials that partially penetrate the curtain may be filtered out of the recirculated air. The highest wind that can be prevented from gaining entry depends not only on the depth, velocity, and direction of the blast, but on the wind pattern as well.

Air Support

Differential air pressure can be used to produce forces capable of supporting objects and structures of various kinds. Rigid structures can be supported or lifted, and flexible materials can be inflated to produce more rigid structures. Fan applications include: radome and rigid-roof support, inflation of various products such as nylon stockings for inspection, lifting of sheets and even loaded cartons, and ducted-fan vehicles.

The time required to inflate a structure is a function of the pressure-capacity characteristic of the fan or compressor being used. The structure need not be airtight so long as the fan is able to maintain pressure at the flow required to offset leakage. An approximate time can be calculated from the volume of the structure and the required pressure if a fan characteristic is assumed.

A step by step procedure is involved. The pressure developed by the fan should be divided into numerous increments from free delivery to the design pressure. The total weight of air (W) required within the volume of the structure (Q) to produce any given pressure (P) can be determined from the equation of state which involves the gas constant (R) and absolute temperature (T):

$$W = PQ/RT. \tag{516}$$

The incremental weight increase (ΔW) for any two pressures can be obtained by subtraction:

$$\Delta W_{1-2} = W_1 - W_2. \tag{517}$$

The average flow rate (CFM) by the fan between the two pressures in question may be used with the gas density (δ) to determine the interval ($\Delta \theta$) required to supply the needed weight:

$$\Delta \theta_{1-2} = \frac{\Delta W_{1-2}}{\left(\frac{CFM_1 + CFM_2}{2}\right) \delta}. \tag{518}$$

If there is continuous leakage during inflation, the average rate should be estimated for each incremental period and deducted from the average supply rate $(CFM_1 + CFM_2)/2$. This will increase the time interval in Equation 518.

The total time required will be the sum of the time intervals for the various pressure intervals, up to the desired pressure. Several fans might be used to reduce inflation time and only one to maintain the pressure after inflation.

The weight (W) that can be supported by a differential pressure (ΔP) acting on a given area (A) may be calculated from:

$$W = A \Delta P. \tag{519}$$

However when any weight (W) is lifted, the inertia effect must be accounted for and the effective weight (W_{eff}) will depend on the rate of acceleration (a) according to:

$$W_{eff} = W (a/g + 1). \tag{520}$$

The acceleration, if uniform, can be determined from:

$$a = \frac{2s}{\theta^2}, \tag{521}$$

where θ is the time to lift a distance (s), so that if it is desired to lift ten feet in two seconds, the value of (a) would be 5 feet per second per second and the equivalent weight would be 1.15 times the actual weight. This ratio between actual and equivalent weight increases rapidly for shorter lifting times.

CHAPTER 22

HANDLING HOT AND CORROSIVE GAS

Fans may be used to pump hot gases or corrosive fumes: (1) directly, (2) after reducing temperature or corrosiveness, or (3) indirectly.

The alternatives in the case of hot gases are: (1) to build the fan of heat-resistant materials, using cooling and insulation of various members as required, (2) to cool the gases with sprays or by dilution (assuming heat-recovery apparatus cannot be justified), or (3) to employ the fan in a jet pump.

Similarly, in the case of corrosive gases, the alternatives are: (1) to build the fan of corrosion-resistant materials, using seals and gaskets as required, (2) to absorb the corrosive portion of the gases with a liquid, or (3) to use a jet pump.

The following discussions generally cover the fundamentals of: (1) spray cooling, (2) dilution cooling, (3) heat-resistant materials, (4) corrosion-resistant materials, (5) erosion-resistant construction, (6) spark-resistant construction, and (7) jet pumps.

The proper choice for any specific application is a matter of economics. In general, the cost and frequency of replacement and the cost of power must be evaluated.

Gas Absorption

The process of gas absorption is treated briefly in Chapter 23. If the exit gas can be rendered harmless, the need for special fans is removed. Various scrubbers may be employed to dissolve components of a gas stream in liquid. The exit gas will generally be saturated with the solvent, and a fraction of the solute will also be present. In many cases where the concentration of corrosive agent in the exit gases is low enough to allow dispersion in the atmosphere, protection is still required for the fan.

Spray Cooling

For purposes of a heat balance, the cooling obtained by injecting water into a gas stream may be considered to take place along a constant wet-bulb line. If the entering water temperature (t_{w1}) is less than the wet-bulb temperature (t') and if complete evaporation occurs together with a net superheating effect, the heat balance may be written:

$$w_g (c_p)_g (t_{g1} - t_{g2}) = w_w [(c_p)_w (t' - t_{w1}) + \lambda' + (c_p)_v (t_{g2} - t')]. \quad (522)$$

The wet-bulb temperature will usually be lowered due to the sensible cooling that occurs in the area of original contact. However, the effect of assuming a constant wet-bulb on the calculated weight rate of flow of water (w_w) is negligible. The gas flow rate (w_g) and the original dry-bulb temperature (t_{g1}) are usually specified. The leaving dry-bulb temperature (t_{g2}) that can be achieved depends on the bypass factor of the apparatus used. The data on air washers in Chapter 15 may be used to estimate the effect on humidifying efficiency of any of the important variables. A conservative designer might consider a dry-bulb reduction equal to 75% of the wet-bulb depression as feasible, when spraying water with air-washer nozzles at three times the evaporation rate.

The entering wet-bulb can be determined from the very high temperature psychrometric chart (Figure 8) if the amount of water vapor per pound of dry air is known. This entering humidity can be calculated from the data of Chapter 16 for flue products or from a knowledge of the process if other than combustion.

The droplet size distribution from any nozzle covers an appreciable range. The length of the spray chamber (L) to produce complete evaporation of the largest droplets can be estimated from:

$$L = V\,\theta. \tag{523}$$

The velocity (V) of the drop can be determined from the gas velocity (V_g) and the relative velocity (V_r):

$$V = V_g - V_r. \tag{524}$$

The relative velocity equals the floating velocity (V_f) on vertical runs:

$$V_f = \sqrt{\frac{4}{3}\frac{g}{f_D}\frac{\delta_w}{\delta_g}d} = V_r \textit{ for vertical,} \tag{525}$$

but a correction must be applied on horizontal runs:

$$V_f\,(0.18 + 0.65 \times 10^{-4}\,V_g) = V_r \textit{ for horizontal.} \tag{526}$$

The time (θ), in minutes, required to evaporate spherical droplets from one diameter (d_1) to another (d_2), both in ft, may be determined from the density (δ_w) of the evaporating liquid, in lb per cu ft, the latent heat of evaporation (λ), in Btu per lb, the thermal conductivity (k) of the air film, in Btu-ft per hr-sq ft-°F, and the difference between the gas and droplet temperatures ($t_g - t'$) in °F:

$$\theta = 60\,\frac{\lambda\,\delta_w\,(d_1^2 - d_2^2)}{8\,k\,(t_g - t')}. \tag{527}$$

The velocity and evaporation time both vary with droplet diameter and air temperature. Therefore, incremental chamber lengths should be calculated by utilizing the times for partial evaporation and the average velocity for those periods. The total length can then be obtained by summation.

The use of spray cooling increases the weight of products to be handled by a fan, but the volume may be considerably reduced. The increase in humidity per pound of dry air may be determined from the psychrometric chart or the evaporation rate may be determined from the heat balance. The equation of state may be employed to calculate the volume flow rates of dry gases and water vapor based on the conditions leaving the spray cooler. Fan capacity (q) equals the sum of the two:

$$q = \frac{1545\,T}{P}\left(\frac{w_{dg}}{(MW)_{dg}} + \frac{w_{wv}}{18}\right), \tag{528}$$

where q is in cfm, T is in °R, P is in lb/ft^2 and w is in lb/min.

Refer to Chapter 1, e.g. Equation 17, for other forms of this equation.

Dilution Cooling

Cold air may be bled into a hot gas stream to produce a mixture at some intermediate temperature. The final temperature (t_{mix}) may be obtained from the weight rates of flow (w_g and w_a) and temperatures (t_g and t_a) of the air and gas, respectively, using:

$$t_{mix} = \frac{w_g\, t_g + w_a\, t_a}{w_g + w_a}. \tag{529}$$

This equation is based on equal specific heats for the air and gas. Refer to Equation 42 for a more general case. The volume rate of flow (q) of the mixture may be calculated from the temperature and pressure, using the characteristic equation for gases:

$$q = \frac{1545\; T_{mix}}{P}\left(\frac{w_g}{(MW)_g} + \frac{w_a}{28.97}\right). \tag{530}$$

where q is in cfm, T is in °R, P is in lb/ft², and w is in lb/min. A comparison of spray and dilution cooling will generally indicate that the use of sprays is superior. However, dilution is frequently employed where only a moderate amount of cooling is required.

Heat-Resistant Materials

Protecting fans in high-temperature gas streams involves both corrosive and structural considerations. Certain reactions may proceed at elevated temperatures that do not occur otherwise. The strength of a material drops with increasing temperature. Ultimate strengths of steels may improve slightly at moderate temperatures, but eventually decrease rapidly. Yield strengths decrease with temperature even when the ultimates are apparently unaffected. The design criterion may be the ultimate strength, the yield strength, the creep strength, or the rupture strength, depending on the temperature, the nature of the stressed part, and the service requirements.

Mild steel scales rapidly at temperatures above 900°F in normal atmospheres. A process involving a metal spray and heat treatment to form a steel-aluminum alloy at the surface may extend this operating range. Heat-resistant paints may provide protection against mildly corrosive gases, but usually the temperatures are limited by the binder used. Various low-alloy steels, stainless steels, and high-nickel alloys provide suitable strength and corrosion resistance in air.

Problems due to expansion and problems of cooling bearings also face the designer of high-temperature fans. In general bearings should be kept out of the air stream on all but room-temperature applications. Grease lubrication is satisfactory up to 200°F on many types of antifriction bearings. Oil lubrication is required for higher gas temperatures. Above 350°F some sort of heat slinger or cooling disk is usually required on the shaft between the fan and bearing. Above 700°F the bearing sub-base should be physically separated from the fan housing to prevent the direct conduction of heat. Fans and ductwork should be insulated.

When the fan bearings are mounted independently, the fan housing expansion will cause the inlet bell to move relative to the impeller inlet. The clearances and fits must be designed to accommodate the movement. Some efficiency may have to be sacrificed. Special high-temperature designs* are also required for shaft seals that must accommodate vertical, horizontal, and tilting movement of the supporting fan side. Alternatively, the fan housing may be center-line supported. Foundations and foundation bolts must be designed to withstand the forces generated by a restrained high-temperature fan casing. Special designs which permit the base of the fan to expand freely have been employed.

Turning gear may be required if a fan is expected to be exposed to high temperatures while it is not operating. Otherwise, the fan shaft might take a permanent set and vibrate badly when put into service. The temperature at which this might occur will vary with shaft material, bearing arrangement, and shaft loads, however, turning gear should be considered whenever a large fan is to be exposed to 500°F or higher.

The rate of temperature change is also an important criterion in fan design. Fast temperature increases may cause the impeller to become loose on the shaft. This can be prevented by incorporating a sufficient shrink fit. However, high cooling rates have resulted in cracking or breakage of the impeller hub. A rule-of-thumb limit for three foot or larger impellers with taper bores is 15°F/min. Special designs* for connecting the hub to the impeller and for suspending the hub on the shaft have been developed which are suitable for 100°F/min. Integral shafts and hubs also have been employed.

Corrosion-Resistant Materials

The choice of a particular material or coating to protect a fan from attack by a corrosive gas is an economic matter. Ordinarily a fan is constructed of the materials which provide the necessary strengths and contours most economically. If the life of such a fan handling a corrosive gas is limited, the extra first cost of a special material or coating may be justified by the increase in life obtained therewith.

Such an evaluation is easily accomplished for any two materials if actual operating experience is available. Lacking such experience, attempts to predict performance should be based on laboratory corrosion tests. Uhlig† has compiled a list of corrosive agents and materials with various degrees of resistance thereto. The accuracy of any such prediction is limited. The effect of temperature, local concentration, velocity, impurities, and fabrication must be considered when translating test results into terms of actual performance.

Where corrosion takes place, either of two types of attack may be involved. Direct chemical attack is generally limited to high temperatures or highly corrosive environments, or both. The rapid scaling of steel at temperatures above 900°F and the effect of concentrated acids or

*Buffalo Forge Company has patents pending and or granted.

†H. H. Uhlig, "Corrosion Handbook," John Wiley & Sons, Inc., New York, 1948, pp. 747-799.

TABLE 123—PROTECTIVE COATINGS

CONVENTIONAL THICKNESSES AND LIMITATIONS

Lead Linings	⅛"-¼"	12000 fpm @ 200°F 9000 fpm @ 400°F
Hard Rubber Coverings	⅛"-3/16"	6×10^6 RN^2, 150°F Max.
Soft Rubber Coverings	⅛"-3/16"	3×10^6 RN^2, 150°F Max.
Epoxy Coatings	5-10 mils	200°F Max.
Phenolic Coatings	5-10 mils	350°F Max.
PVC Lacquers	5-10 mils	180°F Max.
PVC Plastisols	30-100 mils	160°F Max.

RN^2 = radius in ft $\times$ (rpm)^2.

alkalies are examples. Such reactions may be prevented by controlling the temperature or the concentration of the corrosive substance or both, or by application of inert protective coatings.

Electrochemical attack is much more common. The requirements for such a reaction are that there be discrete, anodic and cathodic regions connected by solid material submerged in an electrolyte. Such cells are not only produced by coupling two materials, but arise from minor variations in stress, surface composition, deposits of dissimilar metals, and condensation of an electrolyte.

Each of these items suggests a preventive measure. For instance, frequent cleaning will remove deposits and thereby promote better life for any material. The composition of weld deposits and the heat affected zones in welding as well as stress relief and surface treatment should all be considered for their effect on corrosion resistance.

The formation of corrosion products may serve to retard or accelerate the reaction. Rust on mild steel tends to promote corrosion, while the rust that forms on low-alloy steels may protect the metal from further corrosion. The film that forms on the surface of stainless steel is protective in many corrosive materials, as is that which forms on aluminum.

The protection afforded by many metallic coatings is due to their sacrificial action. Zinc on galvanized products and the anodic covering on aluminum-clad and cadmium-plated materials protects scratches and even sheared edges by this means. However, to avoid undesirable sacrificial action, the formation of galvanic couples by joining together dissimilar metals should be avoided.

The protection provided by other coatings such as lead, rubber, plastics, etc., is due primarily to their inertness to corrosive media. Both the cost and effectiveness (as determined by permeability) are functions of thickness. The optimum thickness varies with corrosive media, but the values in Table 123 are generally suitable. Temperature and tip-speed limits are also shown.

Lead linings may be "burned" on or mechanically attached to the surfaces of fan wheels or housings made of steel. Costs limit use to applications where other means of protection are not particularly suitable.

Rubber coverings, in the Table thicknesses, are sheets adhered to exposed steel surfaces and vulcanized in place. Rubber-coated parts may also be sprayed or dipped. Various natural and synthetic elastomers may be used including Neoprene, Saran, and silicone rubber for increased temperature.

The various plastic coatings are generally sprayed on. To obtain the optimum thickness, multiple layers are required. Phenolics and plastisols require baking at moderate temperatures (375°-450°F), but vinyl lacquers and epoxies may be air dried. Only the more flexible types of plastics may be used on fan wheels. Even so, standard fan construction must often be modified to eliminate all gaps and voids. Continuous welds and rounded edges, as well as clean surfaces are required. Similar provisions must be made for ceramic and metal sprays. The interval between cleaning and spraying should be minimized, since newly cleaned surfaces rapidly oxidize.

Fiberglass reinforced plastics (*FRP*), both polyesters and epoxies, are used for fan housings and impellers. The portion of the shaft which will be exposed to the gas is encapsulated. Both hand-layup and pressure-molding techniques are employed. The fiberglass should be covered by a sufficient thickness of resin to protect it where the gas might attack glass as in the case of HF. Rigid polyvinyl chloride is also used to fabricate impellers and housings. It is generally limited to a fraction of the speeds for FRP equipment.

Various metals and alloys have been used to fabricate corrosion-resistant fans.

Aluminum-base alloys are not affected by most gases in the absence of water at or near room temperature. Acid gases and SO_2 in the presence of water have some action. All alkalies will attack aluminum. Many industrial fumes and vapors attack aluminum surfaces.

Copper at or near room temperature is not affected by dry halogen gases, but absolutely no moisture may be present, even with halogenated refrigerants. Normal and industrial atmospheres do not usually cause corrosion beyond the formation of a protective oxide film.

Copper-zinc, copper-nickel, copper-tin, copper-silicon alloys, although they show some individual variations, are unaffected by most dry gases at ordinary temperatures. The presence of moisture increases the corrosiveness of the halogens, SO_2, and CO_2 considerably. H_2S generally reacts even at low humidity.

Chromium-iron alloys show improved resistance to atmospheric corrosion with increasingly higher chromium content.

The austenitic stainless steels resist most dry gases except HCl and HF. Higher alloy content generally improves resistance to moist SO_2. Optimum corrosion resistance is obtained when the steel is fully annealed. Low carbon contents reduce the danger of intergranular corrosion.

Nickel is affected by the halogens, SO_2, and NH_3, only when they contain condensed moisture. Nickel-copper alloys resist wet H_2S moderately, and nickel-chrome alloys resist even wet NH_3 as well as H_2S.

Nickel-molybdenum-iron alloys are highly resistant to wet gases.

Silver is immune to most moist and dry gases. Tantalum, titanium, and zirconium also resist many substances.

Lead resists the action of chlorine, SO_2, and SO_3, wet or dry.

Rubber and plastic are generally inert to corrosive gases. Vinyls may show poor solvent resistance, phenolics poor alkali resistance, and rubbers poor resistance to certain acid fumes.

As previously noted, the choice of material or coating should be based on experience wherever possible. However, extrapolating may be dangerous for various reasons. The difference between handling wet and dry gases may be tremendous. The presence of water vapor may make some gases more corrosive; in others condensation must take place before this action occurs. The presence of a gas may raise the dew point, causing condensation at temperatures higher than expected. In some instances, the vapors arising from liquors are more corrosive than is the liquid phase.

The temperatures of gas and material are important insofar as they may make possible direct chemical reaction, as well as condensation. Certain materials may be used provided they are washed down periodically. The effect of operating stress on the material should be considered, as should the effects of coating materials on balance and on other operating characteristics.

In most instances when corrosive gases are handled, only the interior portions of the fan need be resistant. The bearings should be located outside the gas stream, either by using an overhung-wheel arrangement or inlet boxes. Some corrosion can be tolerated on fan housings and even on some wheels. The stresses in radial blade wheels are unaffected by uniform corrosion. However, curved blades will collapse and even radial blades will be unable to resist the forces produced during startup if corrosion is not checked in time.

The specification of corrosion-resistant materials is rightfully the responsibility of the user, since only he has control of operating conditions. Fan manufacturers can frequently contribute valuable suggestions if given complete information on the corrosive media, its temperature, humidity, etc.

Standard fans are usually built of steel and protected by enamel over a primer. Red lead, zinc chromate, and phosphate coatings are all good primers. The various enamels, varnishes, and lacquers cannot be evaluated on the basis of composition alone. The skill of application and the control of conditions under which they are applied are equally important.

Zinc and cadmium coatings are almost invariably specified for shipboard fans. Such galvanizing or electro-deposits are coated with phenolic varnish internally and with paint externally, both over zinc chromate primer. There is strong evidence that sprayed aluminum coatings are superior to zinc and cadmium.

Erosion-Resistant Construction

Erosion may occur on both the stationary and rotating parts of a fan. The rate of erosion will depend on the abrasiveness of the material in the airstream, the energy in the abrasive material, and the resistance of the materials of construction in the fan parts to erosion. Some of the most abrasive materials are sand, flyash, and cement clinker but even water will cause erosion. The energy in the abrasive material is a function of its mass and velocity relative to the wearing part. Small high-speed fans have high rates of erosion. Larger slow-speed fans generally have longer lives. Even though the tip speeds may be the same, the air velocity and hence the material velocity will be lower. The erosion resistance of the fan parts will depend on the nature and hardness of the surface. Most steels exhibit about the same resistance even though there may be measurable differences in hardness. Significant differences in resistance result when significantly softer, e.g., aluminum, or harder, e.g., tungsten carbide, materials are used.

Erosion can only take place when the abrasive material contacts the fan part. Most abrasion takes place in localized areas. In a centrifugal fan the particles are generally thrown to the backplate side of the impeller as the air turns radially. This portion of the leading face of the blade is frequently covered with an extra thickness of material which can be replaced if it wears through. Wear strips can also be attached at other strategic locations if wear is expected. Frequently, wear strips will be made of floor plate which has raised beads over its surface. If a particle strikes a bead and bounces into the air stream it cannot cause abrasion until it strikes the surface again. Scroll liners may also be used as replacement wear surfaces in the fan casing.

Various hard facing materials have been tried on severe wear applications. No generalized rules can be stated regarding the increase in life due to such facings. Those which are applied to the steel parts by fusion welding generally will crack and craze upon solidifying. This does not necessarily affect their utility. Perhaps the most expensive and most successful hard facing is tungsten carbide which must be attached by cementing or some other intermediate material. Naturally, the intermediate material must be fully protected from erosion or anything else that would cause it to deteriorate.

Spark-Resistant Construction

The Air Moving and Conditioning Association, in their Standard, AS 401, outlines three types of spark-resistant construction.

Type A Construction requires that all parts of the fan in contact with the air or gas being handled be made of non-ferrous material.

Type B Construction requires that the fan shall have an entirely non-ferrous wheel and a non-ferrous ring about the opening through which the shaft passes.

Type C Construction specifies that the fan shall be so constructed that a shift of the wheel or shaft will not permit two ferrous parts of the fan to rub or strike.

In all three types, bearings shall not be placed in the air or gas stream, and the user shall electrically ground all fan parts.

Bronze and aluminum are commonly used where non-ferrous parts are specified. Stainless steels have been allowed in certain instances, even though they are ferrous materials.

Jet Pump

A typical jet pump is illustrated in Figure 183. The object of this device is to transfer fluid from the suction side (s) to the discharge side (d) against a pressure head ($TP_d - TP_s$). A fan is used to produce a flow of primary air (w_j). This jet of air induces a flow of secondary air (w_s) and the two streams continue to mix in the throat section (t). Velocity pressure is converted into static pressure in the diffuser section. The resistance of the system may be on either side.

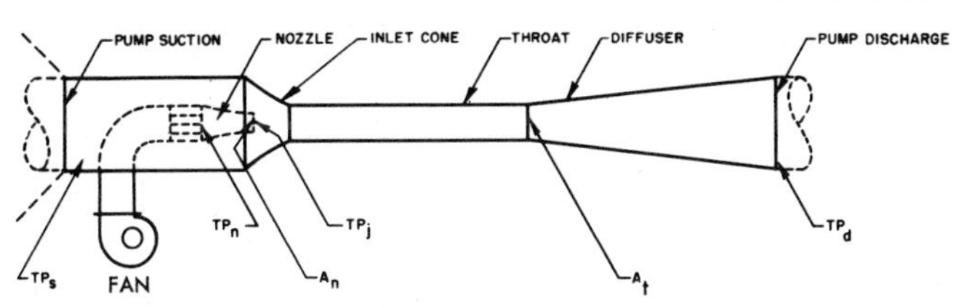

Figure 183—Jet Pump

The efficiency (η) of a jet pump may be defined as the ratio of the energy available from the secondary fluid to the energy expended by the primary fluid:

$$\eta = \frac{w_s\,(TP_d - TP_s)}{w_j\,(TP_j - TP_d)}. \tag{531}$$

Efficiencies are inherently low, since a considerable portion of the jet energy (TP_j) is expended in overcoming friction. Particular care must be exercised in design to insure satisfactory results.

If we identify capacity and pressure ratios as:

$$R_Q = w_s/w_j, \textit{ and} \tag{532}$$

$$R_P = (TP_d - TP_s)/(TP_j - TP_d), \tag{533}$$

then the expression for efficiency may be written:

$$\eta = R_Q\, R_P. \tag{534}$$

As indicated in Figure 184 (and verified by Buffalo Forge Company tests), all three terms are functions of the ratio of jet area (A_j) to throat area (A_t):

$$R_A = A_j/A_t. \tag{535}$$

The pressure-capacity curve for a jet pump is substantially a straight line which may be defined by two points, the shutoff pressure (SND) and the free delivery capacity (FD). The maximum efficiency (η_{max}) occurs at 50% of free delivery capacity, and therefore 50% of shutoff pressure. The efficiency (η) at any other point may be calculated from the relative capacity ($\%FD/50$), and the relative pressure ($\%SND/50$) and the maximum efficiency from:

$$\eta = \eta_{max}\,(\%FD/50)\,(\%SND/50). \tag{536}$$

The various jet-pump design ratios are related as shown in Figure 184. A range of data, for conditions ranging from theoretically minimum friction to high friction, is shown. It is recommended that the curves for average friction be used for any ejectors designed according to the following procedure.

The requirements of the jet pump; w_s, TP_d, and TP_s can be calculated from a knowledge of the problem and data in the preceding chapters. A value of R_A may be assumed. Although maximum efficiency occurs at a value of 0.25, values as low as 0.15 may be used to obtain smaller pumps without sacrificing too much efficiency.

$$\textit{Assume } 0.15 \leqq R_A \leqq 0.25. \tag{537}$$

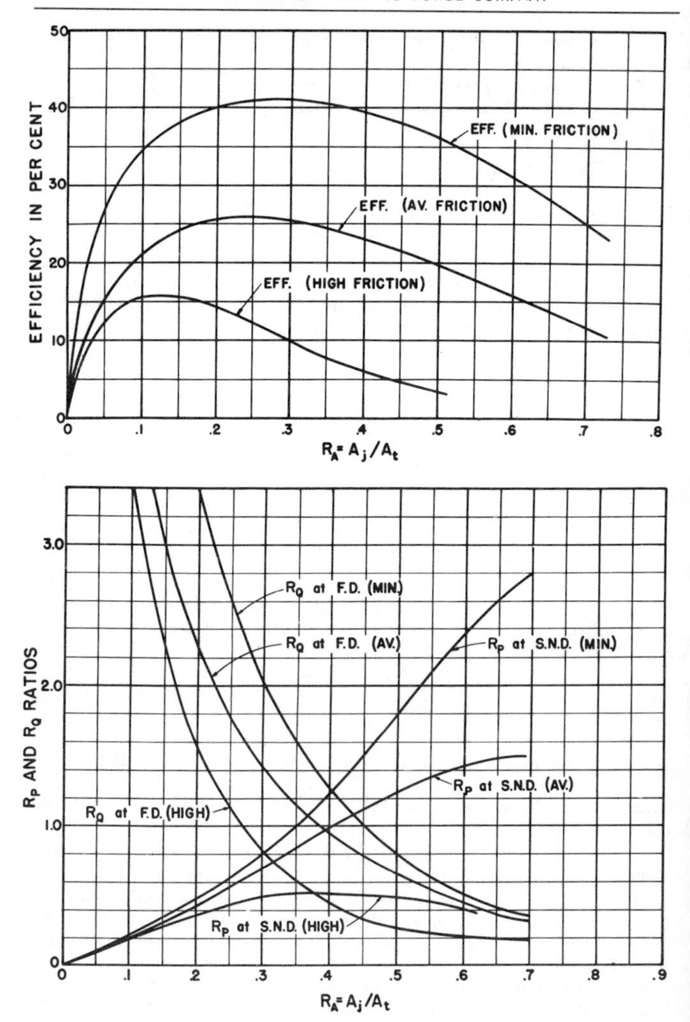

Figure 184—Jet Pump Design Ratios

Adapted from the data of J. E. Gosline and M. P. O'Brien, The Water Jet Pump, University of California Press, Berkeley, 1934, p. 180.

A dimensionless performance curve may then be established from the data of Figure 184. If operation is assumed at maximum efficiency or the midpoint, operating values for R_Q and R_P can be determined from:

$$R_Q = \frac{R_Q \ at \ FD}{2}, \ and \tag{538}$$

$$R_P = \frac{R_P \ at \ SND}{2}. \tag{539}$$

The primary flow is thereby fixed according to:

$$w_j = w_s/R_Q. \tag{540}$$

The total pressure of the jet (TP_j) may be determined from:

$$TP_j = (TP_d - TP_s)/R_P + TP_d. \tag{541}$$

The total pressure ahead of the nozzle (TP_n) depends on the coefficient of discharge (C_D):

$$TP_n = TP_j/C_D{}^2. \tag{542}$$

The area of the jet (A_j) may be calculated from:

$$A_j = \frac{1}{1096.7 \ C_D} \frac{w_j}{\delta_j} \sqrt{\frac{\delta_j}{TP_j}}, \tag{543}$$

where w_j is in lb/min, δ_j is in lb/cu ft, TP_j is in "WG, and A_j is in sq ft.

For the usual flow nozzle:

$$A_n \approx A_j. \tag{544}$$

The area of the throat is fixed by the relation:

$$A_t = A_j/R_A. \tag{545}$$

The above equations have been developed for the case where the pressure in the throat is atmospheric. This makes $TP_j = VP_j$ since $SP_j = 0$. For the general case Equation 542 should be written:

$$TP_n = VP_j/C_D{}^2 + SP_j. \tag{546}$$

The nozzle should be well centered and its position relative to the throat entry should be approximately one throat diameter upstream. If possible the nozzle location should be made adjustable.

The diameter of the suction chamber should be made two to two-and-one-half times the throat diameter to insure average friction.

The shape of the inlet cone should at least approximate a bell-mouthed entry.

The optimum length of the mixing tube is frequently given as six or seven throat diameters. Performance within 5% results with lengths between four and ten diameters.

The total included angle of the diffuser should be between four and six degrees. Angles of ten degrees or over have been used, but with a loss in efficiency.

The diffuser outlet should be no larger than the connected ductwork. The diffuser itself may be omitted in order to utilize the kinetic energy of the issuing stream directly.

The fan must be selected to deliver the primary flow (w_j) against a

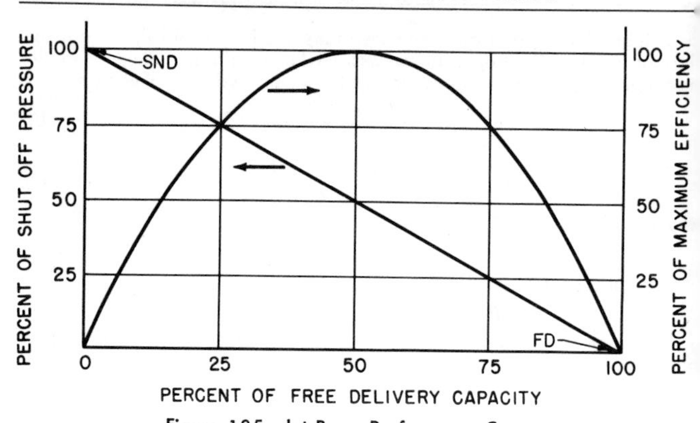

Figure 185—Jet Pump Performance Curve

Adapted from the data of J. E. Gosline and M. P. O'Brien, The Water Jet Pump, University of California Press, Berkeley, 1934, p. 179.

---

pressure equal to nozzle pressure (TP_n), plus the pressure losses of the straightener, elbow, and any other duct elements in the primary line. If the rating so obtained is not particularly suitable for the available fans, the total horsepower requirements may sometimes be reduced by sacrificing some of the possible jet-pump efficiency. Operation at 40% or 60% of the jet-pump free delivery capacity reduces jet-pump efficiency four per cent (not four points) below the maximum otherwise attainable. A sixteen per cent drop results with operation at 30% or 70% of free delivery as shown on Figure 185. Operation to the right of the midpoint increases the fan pressure requirement and decreases the fan capacity requirement. Inverse relations are produced by operation to the left for any specific R_A.

Both the jet pump and its fan will obey the fan laws so long as the system is not altered. Any increase in fan speed should produce a proportional increase in volumetric flow. A change in density, provided both primary and secondary streams remain similar, changes the pressure requirements and the capabilities an identical amount so that constant volume flow results regardless of density. The procedure outlined above may therefore be used when both primary and secondary fluids are at the same elevated temperature.

When the primary and secondary fluids are dissimilar, an approximate solution may be obtained by using the full value of R_P but reducing the value of R_Q by the ratio of secondary to primary density. Complete mixing may be assumed for purposes of calculating the exit density, pressure, and velocity. Kroll* presents a design method, based on the work of various investigations with high pressure steam-jet and air-jet air pumps.

---

*A. E. Kroll, The Design of Jet Pumps, *Chemical Engineering Progress*, pp. 21-24, February, 1947.

CHAPTER 23

AIR CLEANING

Many fan systems require provisions for air cleaning, i.e., the removal of a dispersed material from the air or gas stream. Removal is usually required in order to prevent undesirable effects on persons or property exposed to the stream. Occasionally the value of the collected material will exceed the cost of removal but in most cases the material value is practically nil and additional expense may be entailed in its ultimate disposal.

The material may be in the form of solid particles, liquid droplets, or gas molecules. In any case, to achieve significant air cleaning the dispersed material must in some way be forced across streamlines of the carrier gas to a boundary surface or boundary layer and thereafter be prevented from re-entering the stream. The various forces which can be employed, alone or in various combinations, to achieve these results are discussed in the early portions of this chapter.

Stable dispersions of fine solid or liquid particles in air or some other gas are called aerosols. Dispersions of gas or vapor molecules in air or some other gas will be referred to as gas mixtures. Although there are some striking similarities, the methods of treating aerosols and gas mixtures are usually quite different and the subject matter is divided accordingly.

Subsequent descriptions of air and gas cleaning equipment are divided into two main groups even though there are devices which fall in one group for one reason and in the other group for another reason. These two groups are called atmospheric air cleaners and stack gas cleaners. The first group is designed for comparatively low material loadings and is generally used for supply air applications. The second group comprises equipment designed for comparatively high material loadings and is generally used for industrial process or exhaust applications.

Finally, the various factors which affect the selection of equipment for a specific application will be discussed.

AEROSOLS

The behavior of the dispersed phase of an aerosol, in any force field, will depend more on the size distribution and density of the material than on whether it consists of solid particles or liquid droplets. The size of a particle is usually described by its diameter, if spherical, or one of many equivalent diameters, if of irregular shape. For instance, Stokes equivalent diameter is the diameter of a hypothetical sphere having unit density and the same terminal settling velocity as the particle in question. The customary unit of measurement is the micron, i.e., 1/1000 of a millimeter or 1/25400 of an inch. Liquid particles tend to be spherical but solid particles are of various shapes depending on the nature of the material and the method by which the particles are formed. Most aerosols contain particles covering a wide range of sizes. In many cases the cumulative particle-size-distribution can be represented by a straight line on logarithmic probability paper. Particle size distribution and particle shape information can be determined with the aid of a microscope from a representative sample of solid particles or the impressions produced on a recording surface (provided for just that purpose) by a representative sample of liquid particles. Size-distribution data for solid particles can also be obtained by elutriation or sedimentation methods. These methods utilize the differences in behavior exhibited by particles of different size, shape, and density in a gas or liquid when subjected to a gravitational or centrifugal force field. The methods of determining particle size distribution are discussed in detail by Orr and Dallevalle,* Drinker and Hatch,** and Dallevalle.***

The behavior of single particles will now be discussed although in the design of practical air cleaning equipment the added effects of particles acting on each other can not be neglected.

Particle Dynamics

Small particles (those <100 microns in size) which are dispersed in a stream of gas are generally assumed to travel along streamlines with a velocity equal to the local gas velocity. If for any reason a particle acquires a velocity different in magnitude or direction from that of the gas, drag forces will be developed resisting any such relative movement. The equation for the drag force (F_D) on a small particle,

$$F_D = \frac{f_D A_D \rho_g V^2}{K_m 2g_c}, \tag{547}$$

shows that it depends on the velocity (V) of the gas relative to that of the particle, the projected frontal area of the particle (A_D) and the mass density of the gas (ρ_g). The two factors (f_D) and (K_m) known as the coefficient of drag and the Stokes-Cunningham correction factor, respectively, will be discussed shortly. Substituting $\pi d_p^2/4$ for A_D in Equation 547 gives the drag force on a spherical particle in terms of the particle diameter (d_p); i.e.,

$$F_D = \frac{f_D \pi d_p^2 \rho_g V^2}{K_m 8 g_c}. \tag{548}$$

The velocity of the particle relative to that of the gas, will be zero unless a force is applied to the particle. If such a force (F_A) is applied it will accelerate the particle at a rate (a) which will depend on the mass (M) of the particle according to Newton's second law; i.e.,

---

*C. Orr, Jr., and J. M. Dallevalle, "Fine Particle Measurement," The Macmillan Company, New York, 1959.

**P. Drinker and T. Hatch, "Industrial Dust," McGraw-Hill Book Company, Inc., New York, 1954.

***J. M. Dallevalle, "Micromeretics," Pitman Publishing Corporation, New York, 1948.

$$F_A = \frac{Ma}{g_c}. \tag{549}$$

Substituting $\pi\ d_p{}^3\rho_p/6$ for M in Equation 549 gives the applied force on a spherical particle in terms of the particle diameter (d_p), density (ρ_g) and acceleration (a), i.e.,

$$F_A = \frac{\pi\ d_p{}^3\ \rho_p\ a}{6\ g_c}. \tag{550}$$

The particle will accelerate, i.e., the relative velocity will increase, until the drag force balances the applied force. Thereafter the particle will move at a constant velocity called its terminal velocity. In most cases where particles are smaller than 50 microns in diameter the acclera-tion period is negligibly brief compared to the terminal velocity period. The terminal velocity of an aerosol particle in any force field can be determined by equating the applied force to the drag force, i.e., $F_A = F_D$ or from Equations 550 and 548 for a spherical particle of diameter (d_p):

$$V = \sqrt{\frac{4}{3}\ \frac{K_m}{f_D}\ \frac{\rho_p}{\rho_g}\ d_p\ a}. \tag{551}$$

The coefficient of drag (f_D) is a function of Reynolds number (N_{Re}) as indicated in Figure 186 for several particle shapes. Reynolds number is a function of a characteristic dimension (d_p) of the particle (the diameter for spheres), the relative velocity (V) of the particle and gas, and the gas density (ρ_g) and viscosity (μ). Figure 186 is drawn for smooth particles and is therefore only an approximation for particles with rough surfaces.

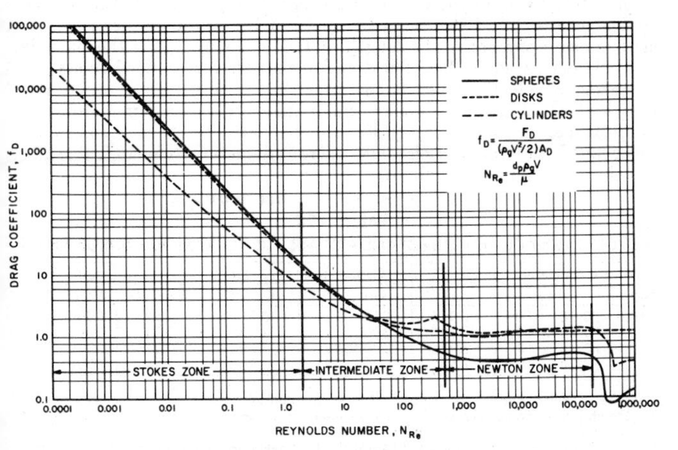

Figure 186—Drag Coefficients for Particles

Adapted from the data of R. H. Perry, C. H. Chilton, and S. D. Kirkpatrick, "Chemical Engineers' Handbook," McGraw-Hill Book Co., Inc., New York, 1963. p. 5-60.

Of the three zones marked on Figure 186, the one called the Newton zone, for which the Reynolds number range is 500 to 200000, is of least importance in air cleaning. This is so because particles with Reynolds numbers in this range usually settle so rapidly that more attention must be given to preventing premature settling or drifting in ducts than to providing for subsequent removal in air cleaners. The fact that the drag coefficients for each of the various particle shapes is very nearly constant in this zone was noted and an adaptation of Equation 551 was utilized in Chapter 18 "Conveying."

In air cleaning, the Stokes zone, which covers a range of Reynolds numbers from 0.001 to 2.0, is the most important. The drag coefficients for particles in this zone vary inversely with the Reynolds number, e.g., for spherical particles

$$f_D = \frac{24}{N_{Re}} = \frac{24\ \mu}{d_p\ V\ \rho_g}. \tag{552}$$

Substituting this relationship in Equation 551 yields Stokes' law of particle motion:

$$V = \frac{K_m\ d_p^2\ \rho_p\ a}{18\ \mu}. \tag{553}$$

Any consistent units of measurement, such as velocity (V) in ft/sec, diameter (d_p) in ft, density (ρ_g) in lbm/ft^3, viscosity (μ) in lbm/ft-sec, and acceleration (a) in ft/sec^2, may be employed. In liquid dispersions, the buoyant force of the fluid on the particle must also be considered but in air dispersions, buoyant effects can be ignored.

The Stokes-Cunningham correction factor (K_m) is a function of the particle size (d_p) and the mean free path of the gas molecules (λ_m). As particle size approaches the length of the mean free path the particle slips between gas molecules. The drag force is therefore somewhat less and the terminal velocity somewhat greater than if this did not occur. For particles larger than about 3.0 micron diameter the correction factor may safely be assumed equal to 1.0. For smaller particles the factor becomes larger and is 22.6 for particles 0.01 micron diameter. Refer to Table 124 for other representative values.

TABLE 124
PARTICLE DISPLACEMENTS IN STANDARD AIR DUE TO VARIOUS FORCE FIELDS

Particle Diameter		K_m (1)	Displacements in 1 sec for Force Field Listed—ft			
Microns	Feet		Grav. (2)	Cent. (3)	Elect. (4)	Brown. (5)
10.0	3.28×10^{-5}	1.016	.024	20.5	0.98	.0000057
1.0	3.28×10^{-6}	1.165	.00027	.235	0.11	.0000194
0.1	3.28×10^{-7}	2.93	.0000069	.0059	0.27	.0000972
0.01	3.28×10^{-8}	22.6	.00000053	.00046	2.12	.0008540

(1) Stokes-Cunningham slip correction factor—dimensionless.
(2) Gravitational Force Field—downward linear displacements based on 32.2 ft/sec^2 acceleration.
(3) Centrifugal Force Field—outward radial displacements based on 862 g's acceleration.
(4) Electrostatic Force Field—normal linear displacements based on 7500 volts/in. field strength and a saturation charge on the particles.
(5) Brownian Movement—random linear displacements based on average values.
(6) All data based on 150 lb per cu ft particle density.

Stokes' law may be employed to determine the terminal velocity of a spherical particle in gravitational, centrifugal, or electrostatic force fields.

To determine the terminal velocity (V_S) in the earth's gravitational field, the local acceleration due to gravity (g) may be substituted for (a) in Equation 553. Then V will equal V_S. For instance, a 10 micron sphere of glass will fall at a terminal velocity of 1.5 fpm. An irregularly shaped particle of the same mass and density, such as a grain of silica, will fall at approximately 1.0 fpm.

To determine the terminal radial velocity (V_R) in a centrifugal force field, the radial acceleration, which is equal to the square of the tangential velocity ($V_{tang}{}^2$) divided by the radius of curvature (R_C) of the path, may be substituted in Equation 553 for (a), i.e.,

$$a = \frac{V_{tang}{}^2}{R_C}. \tag{554}$$

Then V will equal V_R.

To determine the terminal migration velocity (V_M) of a particle along the line of force in an electrostatic field, the acceleration may be computed as the product of the strength of the field (Ξ) and the charge on the particle (ξ) divided by its mass (M), i.e.,

$$a = \frac{\Xi\ \xi}{M}. \tag{555}$$

Then V will equal V_M.

The distance (X) across streamlines which a particle will travel during a time interval (θ) while moving at a constant terminal velocity (V) is

$$X = \theta\ V = \frac{l\ V}{V_g}. \tag{556}$$

The time (θ) which is available is determined by the length of the gas path (l) and the average gas velocity (V_g) (both parallel to a boundary), as indicated in the second equality, assuming, of course, that the velocity component of the particle parallel to the boundary is equal to the gas velocity. The terminal velocity (V) is constant in a gravitational field. The field strength and therefore the terminal velocity varies along the particle path in a centrifugal force field.

The effects of particle size and gas velocity on the dimensions of apparatus designed to utilize the various force fields may be estimated using the above relationships and an average terminal velocity. In each of the following numerical examples the carrier gas will be assumed to be air with a viscosity of 1.225×10^{-5} lbm/ft-sec, the particle will be assumed to be spherical and have a density of 150 lbm/cu ft, and the Stokes-Cunningham slip correction factor will be assumed equal to 1 unless otherwise specified.

In a gravitational field the local acceleration (g) may be assumed equal to 32.2 ft/sec^2. The terminal settling velocity (V) according to Equation 553 for a 25 micron diameter particle is

$$V = \frac{\left(\frac{25}{25400 \times 12}\right)^2 (150)}{(18)\ (1.225 \times 10^{-5})}\ (32.2) = 0.147\ ft/sec.$$

Assuming a horizontal gas velocity (V_g) of 10 ft/sec and a 10 foot long gas path, the distance (X) that a 25 micron particle will settle may be determined from Equation 556, i.e.,

$$X = \frac{(10)\,(0.147)}{10} = 0.147\ ft.$$

The settling distance can be increased either by increasing the length of the gas path or by reducing the gas velocity. As a practical matter gravitational settling is not employed in air cleaning for particles much below 50 microns in size.

In a centrifugal force field the radial acceleration may be as high as 80000 ft/sec² which is about 2500 g's. The radial acceleration for a tangential gas velocity ($V_{tang} = V_g$) of 5000 ft/min and a radius of curvature of 3 inches according to Equation 554 is,

$$a = \frac{(5000/60)^2}{(3/12)} = 27800\ ft/sec^2.$$

For a 5 micron particle in such a force field the terminal radial velocity according to Equation 553 is,

$$V = \frac{\left(\frac{5}{25400 \times 12}\right)^2 (150)}{(18)\,(1.225 \times 10^{-5})} (27800) = 5.06\ ft/sec.$$

Assuming a 1.0 ft long gas path, the distance (X) that a 5 micron particle will travel radially may be approximated by using Equation 556, i.e.,

$$X = \frac{(1.0)\,(5.06)}{(5000/60)} = 0.061\ ft.$$

This value is only approximate since it is based on a constant value of R_C whereas R_C increases as the particle migrates radially. A more exact value can be obtained by dividing the path into short incremental lengths, solving for X, adding this to R_C, and repeating the process over the entire path. The total X can then be obtained by summation. This radial distance can be increased by increasing the length of the gas path, by decreasing the radius of curvature, or by increasing the gas velocity. As a practical matter centrifugal separation is not employed in air cleaning for particles much below 5 microns in size.

In an electrostatic force field migration velocities of the order of 0.1 ft/sec for 1.0 micron particles are usually produced. Corresponding velocities for both larger and smaller particles are somewhat higher. Substituting $\pi\, d_p^3 \rho_p/6$ for the mass M in Equation 555 and substituting the result in Equation 553 yields

$$V = \frac{K_m\, d_p^2\, \rho_p}{18\, \mu} \left(\frac{6\, \Xi\, \xi}{\pi\, d_p^3\, \rho_p}\right) = \frac{K_m\, \Xi\, \xi}{3\pi\, \mu\, d_p}. \qquad (557)$$

Thus for particles larger than 1 micron, which can receive a saturation charge (ξ) proportional to their surface, i.e., proportional to the square of the diameter (d_p^2), the migration velocity increases directly with particle size. However, for particles smaller than 1 micron diameter the saturation charge (ξ) which can be imposed is proportional to the first power of the diameter. Thus it would appear that the migration velocity for particles below 1 micron size should be independent of particle size but because the Stokes-Cunningham slip correction factor increases for smaller particles there is an actual increase in velocity with a decrease in size. Assuming a 1 micron particle with a migration velocity (V) of 0.1 ft/sec, the migration distance through air traveling at 300 feet per minute along a 2 foot boundary may be determined from Equation 556, i.e.,

$$X = \frac{(2.0)\ (0.1)}{(300/60)} = 0.04\ ft.$$

This migration distance can be increased by increasing the length of the gas path, by increasing the field strength, or by decreasing the gas velocity. As a practical matter electrostatic precipitation is not employed in air cleaning unless high efficiencies are required for particles smaller than 1 micron size. Larger particles which may be present will be collected also.

Diffusion may be utilized to remove small particles from aerosols. Aerosol particles smaller than 0.1 micron diameter exhibit a significant random motion called Brownian movement due to collisions with individual gas molecules. The average linear displacement (ΔX) in ft of such a particle in a time interval (θ) in sec is a function of the particle size (d_p) in ft and various gas properties as indicated by:

$$\Delta X = \sqrt{\frac{4\ g_c\ R'\ T\ K_m\ \theta}{3\pi\ \mu\ N\ d_p}}, \tag{558}$$

in which the universal gas constant (R') is approximately 1545 ft-lb/(lb)mol$-$°F, the gas temperature (T) is in degrees Rankin, the viscosity (μ) is in lbm/ft-sec, and Avogadro's number (N) is 2.76×10^{26}/(lb)mol. The factor (K_m) is the Stokes-Cunningham slip correction factor previously discussed.

Brownian movement will lead to diffusion, i.e., a net streaming of particles through the carrier gas in a particular direction, when a concentration gradient exists. Concentration gradients are produced when the streaming particles are continuously removed from the gas at a boundary as discussed below under "Separation." Diffusion will be discussed in greater detail under the heading "Gas Mixtures."

Values of ΔX for various particle sizes for standard air as determined from Equation 558 for a one second interval are listed in Table 124. The distances traversed by the same size particles in gravitational, centrifugal, and electrostatic fields for a one second interval are also shown. The greatest movements in any given time interval are produced by centrifugal force for 10 micron particles and by electrostatic force for 0.01 micron particles. It should also be noticed that the mean Brownian movement greatly exceeds the gravitational displacement for 0.1 and 0.01 micron size particles.

Separation

Separation of an aerosol particle from its carrier gas can be accomplished in either of two ways. In one, it is necessary that the particle be forced into contact with a boundary surface so that its motion can be completely arrested by the surface forces which must be greater than the re-entraining forces. In the other, it is only necessary that the resultant of all forces acting on the particle cause the particle to move to a receptacle where it will be beyond the influence of the gas stream.

The physico-chemical forces of attraction which cause a particle to adhere to a surface are not completely understood. However, it would appear that most small particles once deposited on a surface, can be retained. Larger particles may project far enough into a high-velocity stream so that the re-entraining forces exceed the adhesive forces. Similarly, small particles may pile up, one on top of another, to the point where the resuspension forces exceed the retaining forces and some of the material is blown off.

The ability of a surface to hold large particles or accumulations of particles can be increased by coating that surface with a static film of a viscous liquid. Larger particles become embedded thereby exposing a greater area to the adhesive forces. Dynamic films of less viscous liquids like water may be used with the same result and the added benefit of continuous cleaning. The use of viscous or non-viscous liquids may be impractical in those applications where such coatings might contaminate or render the material more difficult to dispose of or recover.

The over-all shape of a surface, except as it affects the amount of surface in contact with a particle, has very little influence on the strength of the adhesive forces. The microscopic nature of the surface, not whether the surface is part of a flat plate, round tube, or even a small fiber, determines the adhesive forces.

In addition to the stabile surfaces listed above, mobile surfaces in the form of air entrained liquid drops are utilized to provide contact surface in some types of equipment. This is discussed more fully in the next section on particle conditioning. The most commonly used dust catcher, the cyclone, does not have a permanent dust retention surface; rather, the material is concentrated at the wall and conveyed to a receptacle connecting with the bottom.

Particle Conditioning

Any process that increases particle size, increases the effectiveness of gravitational or centrifugal force in producing particle movement across streamlines, and is classified as particle conditioning. In addition, the charging of particles so that electrostatic force may be used to promote movement across streamlines is often called particle conditioning.

Particle conditioning may be spontaneous or induced. Natural flocculation is an example of the former. Deposition of particles on droplets and condensation of vapor around particles are examples of the latter. Small particles act as condensation nuclei for humid gases that are cooled below their dew point. The cooling may result from spraying comparatively cold water into the aerosol or it may result from an expansion of the gases. In either case the effective mass and size of the particles on which condensation takes place is increased.

Small particles, which exhibit significant Brownian movement, will collide with each other spontaneously. Inelastic collisions of solid particles produce aggregates of various shapes ranging from near spheres to long chains. The bulk density for such a floc is generally only a fraction of the true density of the material due to comparatively large percentages of void. Liquid particles which collide usually coalesce to a single drop. The flocculation rate ($-dY/d\theta$) for a homogenous aerosol composed of spherical particles in still gas is expressed:

$$- \frac{dY}{d\theta} = \frac{4\ R\ T}{3\ \mu\ N} K_m\ Y^2. \qquad (559)$$

It will be observed that the change in concentration per unit volume per unit time ($dY/d\theta$) is a function of the gas constant (R), gas viscosity (μ), Avogadro's number (N), the Stokes-Cunningham slip correction factor (K_m), the absolute temperature (T), and the concentration of particles per unit volume (Y). The rate of flocculation decreases as flocculation proceeds due to reductions in the Stokes-Cunningham slip correction factor and concentration. Somewhat higher rates can be obtained by using elevated temperatures.

Particles of any size may be made to collide with and adhere to water droplets which are injected into the gas stream for that purpose. The rate at which such deposition will take place depends on the size and number of particles, the size and number of droplets, and the manner in which particles and droplets are brought together. Two mechanisms, deposition by impaction and deposition by diffusion, are involved.

Deposition of a particle on a droplet by impaction results whenever the two are on a collision path and the relative velocity of the droplet and the gas stream is high enough that the inertia of the particle prevents it from following the streamlines of the gas around the droplets. A relative velocity between the gas and the droplets can be produced in various ways. It would make no difference whether the droplets were stationary and the gas simply moved past them, the gas was still and the droplets moved through it, or both processes occur simultaneously.

In one type of air cleaning device (i.e., the jet scrubber) the drops are propelled through the gas with such force that the gas is swept along by the water and appreciable pressure differentials are developed by the transfer of momentum from the water to the gas. In other types of devices (i.e., the Venturi and submerged nozzle scrubbers) a transfer of momentum from the gas to the water is utilized to atomize the water and to convey it as well. In still other types of devices the water is atomized by hydraulic spraying and propelled through the gas by centrifugal force which may be developed entirely by gas action (e.g., in cyclone and fog scrubbers) or rotor action (e.g., in dynamic and multi-dynamic scrubbers).

Figure 187 shows the relationship between impaction parameter and target efficiency for various target shapes. Impaction parameter (N_I) is a dimensionless group which embodies Stokes' law for an inertial field:

$$N_I = d_p^2\ \rho_p\ V_I\ /\ 18\ \mu\ d_t \qquad (560)$$

where the characteristic dimension of the target (d_t) is as shown on Figure 187 and the impaction velocity (V_I) is the relative velocity between particle and target. Target efficiency is the number of particles of a

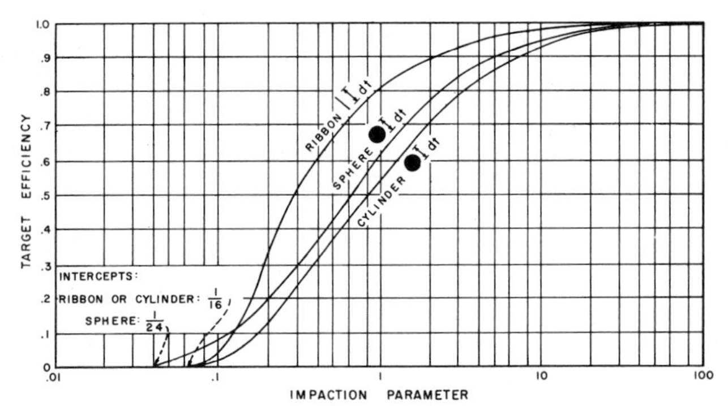

Figure 187—Target Efficiency vs Impaction Parameter

Adapted from the data of R. H. Perry, C. H. Chilton, and S. D. Kirkpatrick, Chemical Engineers' Handbook, McGraw-Hill Book Company, Inc., New York, 1963, p. *20* - 68.

---

given size which strike the target compared to the number of particles contained in the volume swept out by the target.

There is a minimum size of particle that can be deposited by impaction on any specific size of droplet for any particular relative velocity of gas and droplet. Increasing the relative velocity or decreasing the droplet size reduces the minimum size of impactible particle. That there is a minimum particle size is due to the existence of the boundary layer of air which is anchored to the droplet. Small particles of limited velocity simply do not possess enough inertia to penetrate the boundary layer. That the minimum particle size should be decreased by reducing the droplet size is due to the decrease in the radius of curvature of the streamlines of the gas as they bend around the droplet. Consequently the particles more closely approach the droplets before starting to cross streamlines and therefore have a better chance of penetrating to the droplet. The motion of the particle in crossing streamlines is actually developed by the application of centrifugal force which is generated by the gas bending around the droplets but it is just as convenient, if not more so, to speak of the inertia of the particle carrying it across streamlines.

The above analysis indicates that impaction is more successful with small target drops than with large drops all other conditions being equal. However, it is not always possible to maintain the equality of other conditions when the droplet size is changed. In particular, in those cases where centrifugal force is used to produce the relative motion of gas and droplets, there is a theoretical, optimum droplet size of approximately 100 micron diameter. This is so because below that size the reduction in relative velocity due to the decrease in droplet mass has a greater effect on impactibility than the decrease in the radius of curvature of the streamlines as they bend around the droplet.

Deposition of a particle on a droplet by Brownian motion results whenever the particle has sufficient time to migrate to the droplet. Diffusion is favored by the use of the smallest possible target droplets because they most rapidly assume the velocity of the gas and the relative velocity is minimized thereby. The use of the smallest target droplets also produces the largest amount of surface and the greatest number of droplets possible with a given amount of water, both of which also favor collision by Brownian movement. Increasing amounts of energy are required to produce decreasing droplet sizes. Some of the devices (e.g., the high-pressure spray nozzles of a fog scrubber) which produce the highest relative velocities of droplets and gas also produce the smallest droplets. As the droplets gradually assume the velocity of the air stream, Brownian motion gradually replaces impaction as the removal mechanism. It is also theorized that some particles are entrained in the trailing eddy and thereby deposited on the trailing portions of high-velocity droplets. This would account for the increase in deposition rate over the theoretical combined rate for diffusion and impaction which frequently occurs.

While the process of applying an electrostatic charge is a vital part of electrostatic precipitation it is classified as particle conditioning. There are various spontaneous and induced processes by which a particle can be charged including the formation and dispersion processes if they are violent enough (i.e., explosions, atomizations, and even air blasts) and adsorption of gas ions. In commercial electrostatic precipitation the gas is ionized by locally exceeding its electrical breakdown strength and producing what is known as corona discharge of either positive or negative polarity. Ozone formation is greater with negative discharge than with positive discharge. Higher voltages can be applied with negative discharge without detrimental sparking. Since excessive ozone is objectionable in supply air, atmospheric air cleaners employ positive discharge. Since higher voltages produce higher migration velocities, stack gas cleaners utilize negative discharge.

Another form of particle conditioning for electrostatic precipitation involves humidifying or otherwise treating the aerosol so that the deposited particles will have a higher electrical conductivity (or lower resistance) and consequently the strength of the field in the air gap between electrodes will be less affected by the deposit.

Particle conditioning may precede the separation of particles and gas or the two processes may be simultaneous. Various examples of each will be discussed in the sections describing equipment. Particle conditioning equipment makes it possible to utilize less expensive separating equipment or stated another way makes it possible to extend the range of application of certain separators. However, unless the cost of the conditioning equipment is less than the savings in cost in separation equipment, particle conditioning may not be justifiable.

GAS MIXTURES

Gas mixtures behave differently from aerosols. For one thing, the size of the dispersed material is essentially the same as that of the carrier gas, eliminating any differences in velocity toward a collecting surface due to differences in size which can result from the application of mechanical or electrostatic force. For another thing, some sort of phase change must be produced or the gas molecules will be free to re-disperse even if moved to a collecting surface. Of the four mechanisms which may be utilized to produce movement of aerosol particles across streamlines only diffusion can be used to practical advantage to force dispersed gas molecules through the carrier gas molecules. Gravitational force cannot be utilized to advantage because, for even the heaviest dispersed molecules, displacements are insignificant compared to those produced by diffusion. Table 124 shows that this is the case for small solid or liquid particles as well. Recognizing that the diameter of a large molecule of vapor will probably not exceed 0.0003 microns it becomes evident that even the strongest centrifugal force field will not be as effective as diffusion. Although electrostatic force is extremely effective in producing cross stream movement of relatively small particles there is no practical method of applying it differentially to the dispersed and carrier materials when both are gas molecules. Diffusion is, therefore, the only practical mechanism for forcing the dispersed gas molecules to a collecting surface.

Other mechanisms must be employed to effect permanent separation of the gas components. The two principal ones, adsorption and absorption, utilize the same kind of physico-chemical forces which lead to the adhesion of solid or liquid particles on a boundary. Separate sections will be devoted to these two processes and to the theoretical aspects of diffusion upon which both are dependent. Other processes which lead to gas separations are discussed briefly in the following paragraphs.

If the dispersed gas has a sufficiently higher dew point than the carrier gas it can be condensed on a surface maintained at the proper temperature. This process is widely used in the dehumidification of air-water vapor mixtures for air conditioning. It finds only limited application in separating components of other gas mixtures for gas cleaning.

Condensation or chemical reaction within the body of the carrier gas are processes somewhat akin to particle conditioning. They are usually spontaneous, but may be induced for the sole purpose of transforming a gas mixture into an aerosol. Fine solid particles which result from the sublimation of or chemical reaction in the vapor phase are called fumes. Fine liquid particles which are produced by condensation or reaction in the vapor phase are called mists. Condensation may be induced by spraying a cool liquid into the gas mixture. Unless the condensed liquid remains on the surface of the drop the process is best described as gas absorption rather than condensation. In any case the condensed material must be removed using the methods described under "Aerosols."

All the processes for treating gas mixtures involve mass transfer, that is, a change of material from one phase to another. There is also a transfer of heat, either the latent heat of condensation, the heat of adsorption, the heat of chemical reaction, or the heat of solution. The amount of heat released per unit of mass undergoing phase change is an indication of the strength of the forces holding the "condensed" material to the collecting surfaces.

Regardless of the process employed, the maximum degree to which the components of a gas mixture can be separated is determined by equilibrium conditions. The rate at which equilibrium is approached is of extreme importance in equipment design as will become evident in the following discussions.

Diffusion and Mass Transfer

If a material consists of two or more molecular components there will be a strong tendency for each component to become uniformly distributed throughout the others due to molecular activity. That is, if for any reason there is an excessive concentration of one component at some region in a gas mixture there will be a greater tendency for molecules to leave than to enter that region. Molecular diffusion such as this takes place not only in gas mixtures but in liquid mixtures and in small particle aerosols. A more rapid transfer of material due to convection, called eddy diffusion, frequently takes place in fluids which are in turbulent motion but only molecular diffusion takes place when flow is laminar. There is almost always a laminar layer at the boundary walls and surrounding any target droplets.

Molecular and eddy diffusion are both very important processes in the treatment of gas mixtures for air cleaning purposes. In every practical application a number of diffusional steps are involved. In gas absorption for instance the steps are eddy diffusion in the gas phase from the main stream to the boundary layer (see chapter 3 for boundary layer theory), molecular diffusion in the gas phase through the boundary layer, molecular diffusion through the liquid boundary layer, and finally eddy diffusion in the liquid. Only the first two steps are involved in condensation on a surface. Adsorption involves only gas side diffusion and migration into the pores of the adsorbent.

The rate of diffusion in each of the steps enumerated above affects the over-all rate of mass transfer. The situation is analogous to that for heat transfer. The over-all rate of mass transfer between phases (m) is proportional to the effective interfacial area (A) and the driving force which may be expressed as the average partial pressure gradient (Δp_m) or the average concentration gradient (ΔY_m) between the liquid and gaseous phases as indicated by

$$m = K_p A \Delta p_m = K_Y A \Delta Y_m. \tag{561}$$

The mass transfer coefficient (K) is quite similar to the over-all coefficient of heat transfer (U). Its units must correspond to those for the driving force as indicated by the subscript. Its reciprocal, the resistance to mass transfer ($1/K$), is equal to the sum of the individual resistances in each of the diffusional steps which may be involved. Accordingly,

$$\frac{1}{K} = \frac{1}{k_G'} + \frac{1}{k_G''} + \frac{1}{k_L''} + \frac{1}{k_L'}, \tag{562}$$

where the individual resistances ($1/k_G'$, $1/k_G''$, $1/k_L''$ and $1/k_L'$) are for diffusion in the bulk gas, gas film, liquid film, and bulk liquid, respectively. These coefficients vary with the temperature and pressure of the system as well as the natures of the diffusing substance and of the gas or liquid through which diffusion must take place. Various empirical and theoretical expressions, details of which are beyond the scope of this chapter, have been developed to give the relationships between these basic properties and the individual resistances. Because of the difficulties of obtaining accurate individual resistances most published data pertain to the over-all coefficient of mass transfer (K) for a given system. As a matter of fact, most experimental data are given in terms of the product of the over-all coefficient (K) and the amount of effective interfacial surface (A) because the latter is also a difficult quantity to measure accurately.

It should be pointed out that one or another of the resistances in Equation 562 may be controlling, i.e., so large as to make the others insignificant. The resistance to mass transfer through a unit thickness of liquid is much higher than that through a unit thickness of gas due to the closer molecular spacing of the former. However, the average lengths of the diffusion path on the liquid side may be reduced to very small distances in some practical applications, e.g., those involving adsorption or condensation on a surface where there is no liquid side or those involving very fast chemical reactions of the diffusing substance and the liquid where there is a liquid side but the reaction may be considered to take place on the surface. The resistance on the liquid side otherwise decreases with increased solubility of the diffusing substance and may or may not be significant compared to the gas side resistance.

Equilibrium and the Height of a Transfer Unit

In condensation, adsorption, or absorption a mass balance requires that the amount of dispersed gas removed from a gas mixture must equal the amount condensed on the surface, the amount adsorbed on the surface, or the amount dissolved in the liquid solvent, respectively. In any case, the amount removed per unit time (m) may be expressed as the product of the carrier gas mass velocity, i.e., mass flow rate per unit face area (G), the superficial face area (FA), and the difference between the concentration in the entering gas (Y_1) and that in the leaving gas (Y_2), both expressed as weight fractions relative to the weight of the carrier gas. In the cases of adsorption or condensation on a surface, the rate at which material is condensed is given by

$$m = G\,(FA)\,(Y_1 - Y_2). \tag{563}$$

In the case of absorption in a liquid the amount of dispersed gas dissolved in the liquid per unit time (m) may be expressed as above and also as the product of the liquid solvent mass velocity, i.e., mass flow rate per unit face area (L), the superficial face area (FA), and the difference between the concentration in the liquid at the entering gas location (X_1) and that in the liquid at the leaving gas location (X_2), both expressed as weight fractions relative to the weight of the liquid solvent, or

$$m = L\,(FA)\,(X_1 - X_2). \qquad (564)$$

In most air cleaning applications the entering concentration (Y_1) is fixed at a predetermined value by the amount of contaminant released and the ventilation rate. The value of the leaving concentration (Y_2) can only be established in relation to the proposed method of treatment and associated equilibrium conditions. In the case of adsorption, values of Y_2 close to zero are possible. In the case of condensation, the lower limit of Y_2 is determined by dew point considerations. In the case of absorption, Y_2 must be established in relation to X_2 on the basis of solubility and chemical reactions. For more specific details refer to the sections on adsorption and absorption which follow or to the section on dew-point temperature in Chapter 1.

Combining Equations 561 and 563 yields

$$(FA)\,G\,(Y_1 - Y_2) = K_p\,A\,\Delta\,p_m = K_Y\,A\,\Delta\,Y_m. \qquad (565)$$

If the effective interfacial area (A) is factored giving the superficial face area (FA), the packed height of the apparatus (Z) and the amount of interfacial area per unit volume (S), Equation 565 may be rewritten as

$$Z = \left(\frac{G}{KS}\right)_p \left(\frac{Y_1 - Y_2}{\Delta\,p_m}\right) = \left(\frac{G}{KS}\right)_Y \left(\frac{Y_1 - Y_2}{\Delta\,Y_m}\right). \qquad (566)$$

The $(G/KS)_Y$ term is frequently referred to as the height of one transfer unit (HTU). The $(Y_1 - Y_2)/\Delta Y_m$ term is the number of transfer units required for any specific application. The $(G/KS)_p$ and $(Y_1 - Y_2)/\Delta p_m$ terms correspond exactly to the height of a transfer unit and the number of transfer units but are based on driving forces expressed in terms of partial pressure differences rather than concentration differences. When the driving force is expressed in concentration units the height of a transfer unit may be expressed simply as a length and the number of transfer units as a dimensionless number. When the driving force is expressed in partial pressure units the height of a transfer unit must be expressed as a length per unit of concentration difference divided by driving force, and the number of transfer units expressed as the number of units of concentration difference divided by the driving force.

The transfer unit may also be defined for counterflow apparatus as a change in gas concentration equal to the average driving force. The depth of apparatus required to produce this change is called the height of one transfer unit. Table 125 illustrates the effect of increasing the depth of

TABLE 125

Number of Transfer Units	Per Cent Solute Absorbed
1	63.2
2	86.5
3	95.0
4	98.2
5	99.3

apparatus for the special case where there is no back pressure, i.e., no vapor pressure of the solute over the liquid as would occur if the solute were completely neutralized.

The height of a transfer unit must be determined experimentally for the solute-solvent, adsorbate-adsorbent, or other system in question, and for the particular type of apparatus which it is desired to use. The effects of different gas and liquid loadings, i.e., different values of (G) and (L), must also be determined so that the most economical selection can be made. This is discussed further in the next section.

The simple appearance of the term for the number of transfer units required in any particular situation is misleading since this quantity varies in a complicated way throughout the apparatus. That is, the driving force is not a constant but is a variable. However, the average driving force, upon which both the height and number of transfer units are based, can be determined for a number of situations. This too is discussed in the next section.

Gas Absorption

Gas absorption is a mass transfer process wherein the soluble components of a gas mixture are dissolved in a liquid. In air cleaning applications (as contrasted to chemical manufacturing) the initial concentration of absorbate or solute in the carrier gas is generally only a small fractional value. The final concentration will depend on equilibrium conditions. There is usually no need to produce concentrated solutions in air cleaning applications so that the final solute concentration in the solvent will be only a small fractional value in most cases. Initial concentrations in the solvent depend on whether there is recirculation of the liquid and if so whether there is chemical reaction.

If the solution is sufficiently dilute, i.e., the concentration of solute in solvent is low, the number of transfer units required to reduce the solute concentration in the carrier gas from Y_1 to Y_2 can be determined from relatively simple analytical expressions when equilibrium data are available, provided there are no complicating heat transfer effects. The average driving force may be taken as the logarithmic mean of the terminal potentials in most air cleaning applications involving only dilute solutions and low gas concentrations. The terminal potentials may be based on the weight fraction of solute in the gas (Y) and the weight fraction of solute in the gas at equilibrium with the bulk liquid concentration (Y_e). Using the subscripts (1) and (2) to denote the two terminals

$$\Delta Y_m = \frac{(Y - Y_e)_1 - (Y - Y_e)_2}{ln\,[(Y - Y_e)_1/(Y - Y_e)_2]}. \qquad (567)$$

This expression is theoretically correct when both the equilibrium curve and the operating line can be assumed to be linear as shown in Figure 188. The operating lines are the lines 1-2, 2-3, and 3-4. The equilibrium curves are labeled and may be established by reference to data such as that given in Table 126 using the equation of state and Dalton's law of partial pressures.

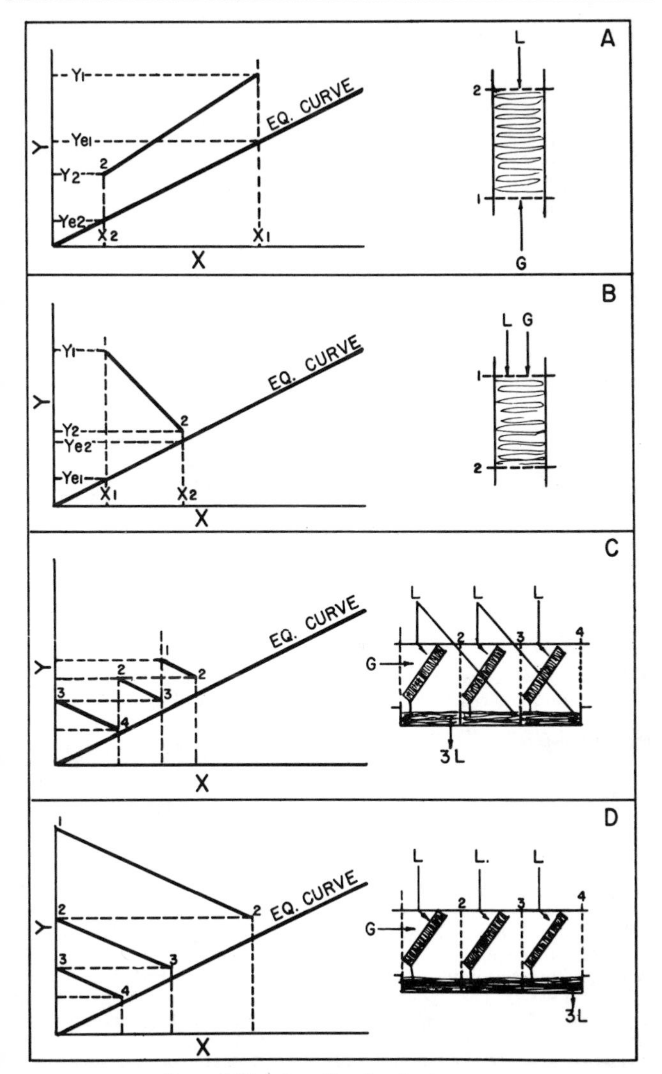

Figure 188—Gas Absorber Performance

TABLE 126
EQUILIBRIUM DATA FOR AMMONIA IN WATER

Wt. Conc. %	Partial Pressure of NH_3—mm Hg							
	0°C	10°C	20°C	25°C	30°C	40°C	50°C	60°C
100	947							
90	785							
80	636	987	1450			3300		
70	500	780	1170			2760		
60	380	600	945			2130		
50	275	439	686			1520		
40	190	301	470		719	1065		
30	119	190	298		454	692		
25	89.5	144	227		352	534	825	
20	64	103.5	166		260	395	596	834
15	42.7	70.1	114		179	273	405	583
10	25.1	41.8	69.6		110	167	247	361
7.5	17.7	29.9	50.0		79.7	120	179	261
5	11.2	19.1	31.7		51.0	76.5	115	165
4		16.1	24.9		40.1	60.8	91.1	129.2
3		11.3	18.2	23.5	29.6	45	67.1	94.3
2.5			15.0	19.4	24.4	(37.6)*	(55.7)	77.0
2			12.0	15.3	19.3	(30.0)	(44.5)	61.0
1.6				12.0	15.3	(24.1)	(35.5)	48.7
1.2				9.1	11.5	(18.3)	(26.7)	36.3
1.0				7.4		(15.4)	(22.2)	30.2
0.5				3.4				

***Extrapolated values.**

Adapted from the data of R. H. Perry, C. H. Chilton, and S. D. Kirkpatrick, "Chemical Engineers' Handbook," McGraw-Hill Book Company, Inc., New York, 1963, p. *14*-4.

Substituting Equation 567 in Equation 566 yields

$$Z = \left(\frac{G}{K\,S}\right)_Y \frac{(Y_1 - Y_2)}{(Y - Y_e)_1 - (Y - Y_e)_2}\, ln\, \frac{(Y - Y_e)_1}{(Y - Y_e)_2}. \qquad (568)$$

This expression may be used to determine the packed height (Z) for either a countercurrent stage or a co-current stage. Figure 188-A illustrates the concentration relationships for a countercurrent absorber while Figure 188-B is for a co-current absorber. The slope of the operating line depends on the ratio of liquid flow to gas flow (L/G). It can be observed that the operating line approaches, but theoretically never reaches, the equilibrium curve according to Equation 568 because an infinite packed height would be required if Y_2 were to equal Y_{e2}.

As a practical matter, the concentration in the leaving gas stream may be so close to the equilibrium concentration that equilibrium can be said to exist. If this condition prevails for a co-current stage, it can be said that the stage produces an equilibrium step.

As in heat transfer, a countercurrent stage is much more effective than a co-current stage. It is possible to approximate countercurrent performance by using multiple co-current stages as illustrated in Figures 188-C and 188-D. The former is for a 3-stage unit wherein the fresh liquid is pumped to the final gas treating stage and the resulting liquid with its increased concentration of absorbate is pumped to the second last stage and so on. The bottom diagram is also for a 3-stage unit, but fresh liquid is pumped to each stage.

The diagrams are scaled to illustrate that more absorbate can be absorbed if all fresh absorbent is used rather than recirculated absorbent.

Whenever the solute is completely neutralized in the liquid, the equilibrium value (Y_e) becomes zero and Equation 568 reduces to

$$Z = \left(\frac{G}{K\ S}\right)_Y ln\ \frac{Y_1}{Y_2}. \tag{569}$$

For this situation, the equilibrium curves in Figure 188 would all become horizontal lines through $Y = 0$, the driving forces would increase, and the operating lines would all become longer.

Table 125 was obtained from Equation 569 by setting Z equal to various multiples of $(G/KS)_Y$ and solving for (Y_2/Y_1).

As indicated by Equations 566 and 568, large values of contact surface per unit volumes are desirable. This may be achieved either by breaking the liquid up into a fine spray in the gas or by spreading it over a finely divided material through which the gas is passed. Numerous types of packing material are available commercially. Ideally the height of a transfer unit $(G/KS)_Y$ should be determined for the proposed packing material and for the gas-liquid system in question. Such data are available but only for a limited number of systems. Test results are usually plotted as $(G/KS)_Y$ vs G with L as parameter or $(G/KS)_Y$ vs L with G as parameter as illustrated in Figure 189. Many more such tests are needed.

In the absence of a test on the proposed gas-liquid system a reasonably close approximation can sometimes be obtained from other test data by comparing the Schmidt numbers for the proposed and tested systems.

The Schmidt number (N_{Sc}) is a dimensionless ratio relating the viscosity (μ) and density (ρ) of the gas mixture and the diffusivity (∂) of the diffusing gas in the gas mixture as follows:

$$N_{Sc} = \mu/\rho\partial. \tag{570}$$

The Schmidt numbers for various gases and vapors, based on diffusivity in air, are given in Table 127.

The height of a transfer unit is approximately proportional to the square root of the Schmidt number, i.e., $H\ T\ U \propto N_{Sc}{}^{1/2}$ or,

$$\left[\left(\frac{G}{K_G\ S}\right)_Y\right]_A = \left[\left(\frac{G}{K_G\ S}\right)_Y\right]_B \times \left[\frac{(N_{Sc})_A}{(N_{Sc})_B}\right]^{0.5}. \tag{571}$$

If the height of a transfer unit for gas "B" is known, the corresponding value for gas "A" may be calculated using the appropriate values for the Schmidt number in Equation 571. The data of Figure 189 are drawn for the absorption of ammonia in water from air. The chart values can be used for acetic acid by increasing them 22%, i.e., $[(1.16/0.78)^{0.5} = 1.22$ based on data for 77°F].

There are many limitations on the applicability of the preceding relationships. In both forms of Equation 561, for instance, the average driving force and the mass transfer coefficients are given in terms of overall conditions, but in evaluating these quantities in Equations 567, 568, and 569 only the equivalent gas side conditions were considered. No appreciable error results provided the liquid side resistance is negligible. In most air cleaning applications this is the case. Either the dispersed gas

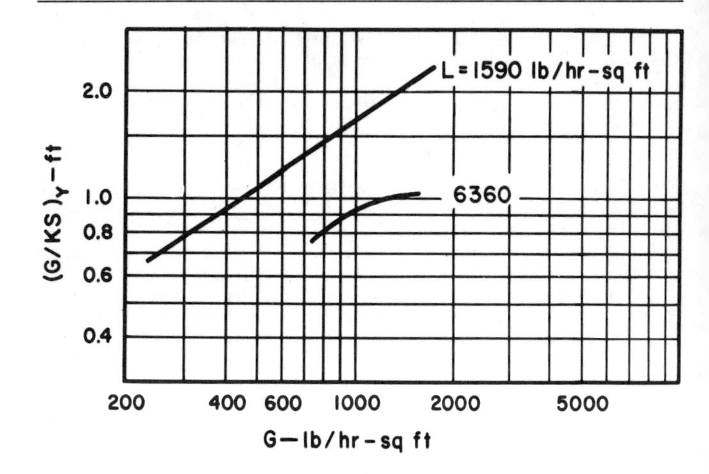

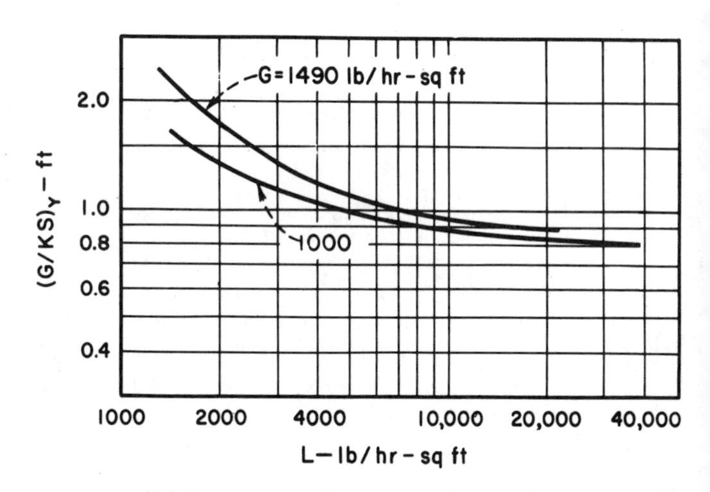

Figure 189—HTU's for Absorption of NH_3 in Water from Air using 4.7 lb/cu ft Fiberglass Pads (Fibers Vertical)

Adapted from the data of R. H. Perry, C. H. Chilton, and S. D. Kirkpatrick, "Chemical Engineers' Handbook," McGraw-Hill Book Co., Inc., New York, 1963, p. *18*-43.

TABLE 127—SCHMIDT NUMBERS FOR VARIOUS GASES AND VAPORS

based on diffusivities in air at 77°F and 29.92″ Hg

Substance	$\mu/\rho\,\partial$
Acetic acid	1.16
Ammonia	0.78
Amyl alcohol	2.21
Aniline	2.14
Benzene	1.76
i-Butyric acid	1.91
Butyl alcohol	1.72
Butyl amine	1.53
i-Caproic acid	2.58
Carbon dioxide	0.94
Carbon disulfide	1.45
Chloro benzene	2.12
Chloro toluene	2.38
Diethyl amine	1.47
Diphenyl	2.28
Ethyl alcohol	1.30
Ethyl benzene	2.01
Ethyl ether	1.66
Formic acid	0.97
Hexyl alcohol	2.60
Hydrogen	0.22
Methanol	0.97
Mesitylene	2.31
n-Octane	2.58
Oxygen	0.75
Propionic acid	1.56
Propyl alcohol	1.55
Propyl benzene	2.62
Propyl bromide	1.47
Propyl iodide	1.61
Toluene	1.84
Valeric acid	2.31
Water	0.60
Xylene	2.18

Adapted from the data of J. H. Perry, "Chemical Engineers' Handbook," Third Edition, McGraw-Hill Book Co., Inc., New York, 1950, p. 539.

---

or vapor is very soluble in the liquid used or back pressure is completely eliminated by the use of a neutralizing solution. When the dispersed material is comparatively insoluble more sophisticated methods, such as those found in Sherwood and Pigford* and other reference works, are required for reasonable accuracy. Also, the Schmidt number relationships given in Equation 571 should not be used unless molecular diffusion predominates over eddy diffusion. This will not be the case at high Reynolds numbers.

Another factor which is implicit throughout all these discussions is that the carrier gas be relatively insoluble in the liquid. This, as well as the condition of very low initial concentration of solute in the carrier gas, is necessary to insure comparatively constant gas flow and therefore constant gas velocities and constant diffusion per unit of driving force.

*T.K. Sherwood and R. L. Pigford, "Absorption and Extraction," McGraw-Hill Book Co., Inc., New York, 1952, pp. 137-144.

The temperature and pressure should also be comparatively constant for the same reason. If these conditions are not satisfied, the effect of variable diffusivity must be determined by a complicated integration.

Adsorption

Adsorption is a mass transfer process wherein certain components of a fluid are deposited on the surfaces of a solid as a result of surface forces. Air cleaning applications of adsorption are concerned with the removal of dispersed gases and vapors (including malodorous substances) from gas mixtures.

The initial concentration of adsorbate is usually only a small fraction of the inert or carrier gas. The final concentration may be close to zero if the adsorbent is replaced or regenerated before it becomes saturated (more specifically, before the "break point" is reached). This is the method of operation in most air cleaning applications.

The height of a transfer unit concept may be employed in adsorber design. The principal difficulty in doing so is that the height of a transfer unit varies with time as well as location through the adsorber. The effective surface area gradually diminishes as adsorbate is deposited. Considerably more adsorbent must be provided than the minimum amount required at startup. An adsorption system should therefore be designed with a depth of adsorbent which will remove the adsorbate at the desired efficiency over a reasonable operating span. Most rating data are given in terms of the weight of adsorbate that a unit weight of adsorbent will adsorb under specified conditions of temperature, pressure, flow rate, etc, rather than in terms of heights of a transfer unit.

Adsorbents are characterized by their extremely porous structures which provide internal surface areas that are many times larger than the external surface. Many adsorbent materials have been developed, each with a special affinity for certain vapors. These vapors diffuse into the pores and are there bound to the surface in various ways. (In most air cleaning applications the collected material may be "boiled" off unchanged if the temperature is raised.) To promote rapid diffusion, the gas mixture is passed through a bed of granular adsorbent material. Just before the adsorbent becomes incapable of removing the dispersed material at the required rate, it is either replaced or regenerated for further use.

Commercial adsorbent materials include activated carbon, activated aluminum, silica gel, and activated bauxite. The last three are primarily dessicants, i.e., they exhibit a decided preference for water vapor at normal temperatures, whereas activated carbon shows a decided preference for organic vapors and gases, including many odorous ones. The application of silica gel, etc., in dehumidification is discussed briefly in Chapter 15. The application of activated carbon in air cleaning is discussed further in the equipment sections of this chapter.

ATMOSPHERIC AIR CLEANERS

Atmospheric air cleaners which are used to purify air used for ventilation, comprise four general classes of devices: odor adsorbers, air washers, electrostatic precipitators, and air filters. The important characteristics of these devices are summarized in Table 128 and Figure 190 and are elaborated on in the following sections. Absolute filters which may be used for ventilation or industrial service are discussed also.

Odor Adsorbers

An odor adsorber consists of a relatively shallow bed of activated charcoal. All of the supply air may be passed through the bed or a portion may be bypassed around the unit. For this purpose the bed may be discontinuous.

Continuous beds are fabricated into pleated or flat cells or into hollow cylindrical canisters. Porous materials are required to support the granular bed yet allow the air to pass through. Superficial face velocities (based on frame dimensions) are usually limited to 250 fpm for pleated cells and "V" arrangements of cells are indicated where it is necessary to reduce space requirements. Flat cells are limited to approximately 80 fpm face velocity. Canisters are mounted on manifold plates in multiples to suit capacity. The use of pleated cells far surpasses that of the other two types combined.

Discontinuous beds incorporate porous tubes filled with charcoal granules or flat strips upon which granules have been glued. The tubes or strips may be spaced to vary the fraction of air that passes through the bed. These cells may be used at face velocities up to 700 or 800 fpm. Efficiency will be proportional to the percentage of gas contacting the granules which is generally low. The capacity of these units is very limited because of the small amount of charcoal utilized.

Charcoals derived from different raw materials and "activated" by different processes, exhibit different adsorption characteristics. "Activated charcoal" is produced by subjecting the char of coal or nutshells to a high-temperature roasting process under an inert atmosphere to prevent combustion. Vast numbers of sub-microscopic interconnecting pores are formed providing literally millions of square feet of adsorption surface per pound of granules. Also, high boiling point organic substances are destroyed.

In most air conditioning applications, a continuous bed thickness of 1″ will provide sufficient contact time for the dispersed molecules to be adsorbed even in partially spent charcoal at the rather high face velocity of 120 fpm through the bed. This amounts to 1/24 of a second total contact time (and even less time on the basis of partially spent adsorbent) which indicates the rapidity of the adsorption process. The same contact time can be provided with a thinner bed by using a lower velocity, entailing lower air resistance but larger equipment.

The effectiveness of activated charcoal depends on the nature of the adsorbate as well as the nature of the adsorbent. Most malodors encountered in air conditioning can be removed completely during a single pass through a continuous bed of activated charcoal. Something less than complete removal may give satisfactory results when odors are not generated continuously as may be the case in conference rooms. If a portion of the air is recirculated, as is usually the case, successive passes through a discontinuous bed adsorber may eventually reduce odors to an acceptable level during a period of non-occupancy.

The amount of charcoal to be used in a system should be determined from an economic evaluation. That is, the depth of bed should be sufficient to provide a reasonable service life relative to first cost. Most air conditioning applications require from 5 to 50 lb. of good quality activated charcoal per 1000 cfm of air capacity. The lower figure may be used when initial odor concentrations are low (about 0.0001 gr/ft^3). The higher figure should be used when initial odor concentrations are high (0.001 gr/ft^3) or when very long service life is required. Assuming that replacement or reactivation is necessary when the adsorbate amounts to 25% of the weight of the absorbent, the service life for a unit containing 50 lb of adsorbent per 1000 cfm of air handled will be the equivalent of about 180 eight-hour days if the initial concentration of odors is 0.001 gr/ft^3. Service life is usually much longer in practice as spontaneous chemical changes of adsorbed materials free the adsorption sites for additional service.

Air Washers

An air washer may be of the spray chamber or wetted-fiber cell type. Both types are usually arranged for horizontal air flow and both usually have bent plate droplet eliminators on the discharge end. The spray chamber type often contains multiple banks of spray nozzles directed against and with the air stream. Since air flow is horizontal, the spray droplets fall through the air in a cross flow pattern. The wet cell type generally contains one or two banks of coarse fiber cells wetted by low pressure spray nozzles. The water and air flow through the packing cocurrently. Either type, with modifications, may function as a humidifier, dehumidified, scrubber, or gas absorber.

The spray type air washer utilizes nozzles that produce coarse droplets with little capacity for capturing small particles. Particle removal is largely accomplished in the eliminator section which, in the usual case, is quite effective for particles larger than 20 microns in diameter. Dust collection efficiencies based on weight removal are quite low for aerosols containing particles that are mostly less than one micron in size. (Atmospheric air is normally in this category.) Since removal is effected in the eliminators, which are inertial devices, the use of higher velocities results in improved efficiency up to the point of carryover. However, the choice of air velocities is limited by air resistance considerations and by the fact that most air washers are also used for humidification or dehumidification, both of which are mass transfer processes which are favored by low velocities insofar as velocity affects contact time. Humidification, dehumidification, odor removal and gas absorption efficiencies, all other conditions being equal, are improved by lowering air velocity. However, the unfavorable effects of high velocity on mass transfer processes can be overcome by increasing the water rate and the contact surface. Only those odors or gases which are very water soluble can be removed effectively with a spray type air washer.

The wet cell air washer usually utilizes such coarse fibers (over 100 micron diameter) that only 5 micron diameter particles or larger can be removed effectively. This is a considerable improvement over spray types. Wetted fiber filled cells are basically impaction devices so that efficiency improves with increased velocity. Like spray types, wet cell washers are also used for humidification or dehumidification so that air velocities may be limited by mass transfer considerations as well as by air resistance. Similarly, only odors and gases which are water soluble can be removed effectively with a wet cell washer.

Low-voltage Two-Stage Electrostatic Precipitators

A two-stage electrostatic precipitator consists of an initial bank of positively charged ionizing wires between co-planar grounded electrodes followed by a bank of grounded collection plates. Between each pair of collection plates is a positively charged repulsion plate. The use of relatively low voltages and currents of positive polarity reduces ozone formation to permissible levels.

Two-stage units operate with approximately 12,000 volts in the ionizing stage and 6,000 volts in the collecting stage. (This is considered low voltage compared to the higher voltages used in single-stage industrial units.) The first-stage potential must be sufficient to produce corona discharge so that the aerosol particles will become charged by air ions. The potential in the second stage must be sufficient to drive the previously charged particles across the gap between plates. Plate spacings are between ¼″ and ½″ in most designs. Since there is no corona discharge in the second stage there can be no recharging of particles should they lose their charge. Most if not all the charge is lost once a particle contacts a grounded collecting plate. Therefore, it is imperative that re-entrainment of collected particles be prevented. The usual practice is to apply a viscous coating to the plates. Periodic cleaning and reoiling is required to insure good efficiency. Units may be equipped with automatic cleaning and reoiling apparatus. Rated efficiency for atmospheric dust increases with decreasing air velocity, ranging from 85% at 550 fpm to 95% at 400 fpm*. Because of their low air resistance most units incorporate a perforated inlet plate or prefilters to insure good air distribution. Power consumption for particle charging and collecting is quite low, averaging about 15 watts per 1000 cfm for both stages.

A two-stage electrostatic precipitator consisting of a conventional first-stage bank of positively charged ionizing wires and co-planar grounded electrodes followed by a bank of charged and grounded filters instead of plates is also available. A potential of around 9,000 volts is applied across different portions of the filter media. Higher efficiency is claimed for the charged filter than for the same filter uncharged but the increase is small for atmospheric dust.

Air Filters

Air filters may be of the viscous-coated or dry fiber type. Neither type depends to any appreciable extent on sieving action. Instead centrifugal, electrostatic, and diffusional forces are employed in various degrees and combinations.

*Efficiencies based on U. S. Bureau of Standards Discoloration Test Method.

Viscous-coated filters consist of one to six inch deep beds of comparatively coarse fibers, wires, or ribbons (of various materials) through which supply air is passed. Frequently, the bed is arranged so that there will be a gradual decrease in fiber and pore size from the entering face to the leaving air side, thereby providing a longer useful life. As dust builds up, resistance increases at a slower rate in the graduated media types than in the others. Efficiency generally improves as dust builds up (to the point where "blow off" begins) and increases with increased velocity since desposition is largely by impaction. Efficiency may be around 85% for particles 10 microns and larger but considerably lower for atmospheric dust which contains a large percentage of particles one micron in size and smaller.*

Both cleanable and throwaway types of viscous filters give about the same performance and service life between cleanings and replacements, respectively. Glass and synthetic fiber viscous-coated filters are usually single service units whereas metal wire or ribbon filled units are washed and reoiled periodically over a period of 10 to 20 years.

A dry fiber filter consists of a porous mat or bed of relatively fine bonded fibers of glass or synthetic materials through which supply air is passed. Efficiency increases with decreased fiber size and with decreased velocity since deposition of small particles is mainly by diffusion. Because very low velocities are used with the most efficient filters, the medium is usually formed into cells by pleating or rolling into tubes. Service life is somewhat less than for viscous-coated types, even with the somewhat lower dust loadings usually recommended, since dust pickup is so much greater.

The media for either the viscous-coated or dry filter types of air filters may be fabricated into cells of a size suitable for manual servicing, into rolls for automatic renewal, or into endless chain arrangements (only viscous-coated type) for automatic cleaning. A "V" arrangement of cells is frequently employed to save space.

Absolute Filters

An absolute filter is a dry fiber filter made from a porous paper containing a high percentage of ultra fine glass or asbestos fibers (less than 1 micron diameter) pleated into a cell. Efficiency is generally guaranteed to be 99.97% or better for 0.3 micron particles by the DOP (dioctyl phthalate) test. Somewhat lower efficiencies are obtained with filters designed for extremely hot gases (i.e., greater than 1000°F) due to the minimum fiber diameter limitations (about 2 microns for some ceramic fibers according to First and Graham†).

Prefilters are recommended for use with absolute filters in order to decrease dust deposits on the absolute filter and thereby extend its useful service life. For pleated cells, 12 inches deep initial resistance at rated airflow of 250 fpm, face velocity is 1″ WG.

Absolute filters are sometimes called HEPA filters. HEPA stands for high-efficiency particulate air (or aerosol).

---

*Efficiencies based on U.S. Bureau of Standards Discoloration Test Method.

†M. W. First and J. B. Graham, Ceramic Filters for High Temperature Gas Filtration, *Industrial and Engineering Chemistry*, pp. 63A and 64A, June, 1958.

STACK GAS CLEANERS

Stack gas cleaners comprise seven general classes of devices: cleanable cloth industrial filters, electrostatic precipitators, dry inertial collectors, wet particle collectors or scrubbers, gas incinerators, gas absorbers, and gas adsorbers. The important characteristics of the various types of devices included in each of these classifications are summarized in Table 128 and Figure 190 and elaborated on in the following sections.

Cloth Type Industrial Filters

Cleanable cloth collectors which are built for industrial service may be classified as shaking, reverse-flow, reverse-jet, or pulse-jet types depending on the method used to dislodge the collected material. All utilize fabrics made from natural or synthetic fibers sewn into bags, tubes, or envelopes. Lateral support may be needed depending on the shape of the filter element, the fabric strength, and the direction of air flow. Multiple filter elements are mounted over a hopper into which the collected material falls when dislodged.

Shaking type filters generally utilize woven fabrics because they can withstand the vigorous shaking forces. When bags are used for the filter elements, they are hung vertically with the closed ends at the top and the open bottoms attached to a tube sheet. The dirty gas enters the unit at the side through a knock-out chamber which may be in or above the dust hopper. The dirty gas then enters the bags through the bottom openings, passes through the fabric from inside to outside, and deposits the dust on the inside surface. When envelopes are used for the filter elements, they are mounted over screens or other lateral supports with the open ends attached to a tube sheet at one side of the unit. The dirty gas enters the unit at the opposite side, passes through the cloth from outside to inside, and deposits the dust on the outside surface.

Shaking mechanisms may be manual or power-operated, but in either case air flow must be cut off so that the dislodged dust will fall to the hopper. For continuous full-capacity operation, multiple compartment units must be employed and enough excess capacity must be provided so one compartment at a time can be shut down.

Reverse flow is sometimes used in combination with shaking to clean the fabric. More often, reverse flow is used as the sole cleaning mechanism when delicate fabrics such as glass cloth are used for their special chemical or heat resisting properties. A system of air regulating dampers is required to shut off the normal flow and direct outside air or cleaned air through the filter elements in a reverse direction.

Reverse-jet filters generally utilize felted fabrics sewn into tubular elements. In the Hersey type unit, tubes are mounted vertically between two tube sheets. Dirty gas enters at the top and passes from inside to outside through laterally unsupported fabric. Dust is deposited on the inside surface and is dislodged by travelling blow rings. Auxiliary air is fed to the blow rings and emerges through a peripheral inside slot directed at the cloth. As the main airflow need not be cut off during cleaning, no compartmentation or excess capacity is necessary for full capacity operation.

The pulse-jet type of fabric collector also may be used continuously without compartmentation. Main air flow is from outside to inside through laterally supported bags. Dust is deposited on the outside and clean gas emerges from the top openings which are attached to a tube sheet. The filter elements are cleaned sequentially by a pulse of compressed air which snaps the fabric away from its supports and dislodges the dust cake. Some cleaning action is also due to the back flow of cleaned air which is induced by the jet into the bag and forced through the fabric even though the main air flow is not cut off.

All types of cloth collectors can be equipped with automatic controls to activate the cleaning mechanism in response to a rise in pressure drop across the collector beyond the set point. For steady state processes cleaning may be done on a timed cycle. Isolation valves and dampers must be controlled as well on many types of self-cleaning compartmented units. Economical pressure drops range from 2 to 6″ WG. Air-to-cloth ratios range from 1 to 6 cfm per sq ft for shaking and reverse flow type units and from 5 to 30 cfm per sq ft for reverse-jet and pulse-jet type units.

Efficiencies are exceptionally high for cloth collectors in good condition after they have acquired a filter cake of the collected material. Conditioning of the fabric with dust usually takes only a few hours for industrial dusts. Industrial filters can be used for high-efficiency atmospheric air cleaning after they have been precoated artificially with filter aids such as asbestos floats.

High-Voltage Single-Stage Electrostatic Precipitators

A single-stage electrostatic precipitator may be of the pipe or plate type. Both utilize simultaneous ionization and collection with potentials ranging from 30,000 to 100,000 volts. Negative polarity ionization is generally utilized as this makes it possible to use high voltages without sparking. Since the effluent gas is not used for supply, ozone formation is not a factor. The exact voltage utilized depends on the efficiency required, the spacing between the ionization and collecting electrodes, the length of the electrodes along the air path, and the gas velocity.

A plate type electrostatic precipitator consists of alternate parallel banks of ionizing wires and collecting plates. Plate spacings may range from 6″ to 15″ and lengths from 10′ to 18′ along the gas path, which is usually horizontal.

A pipe type electrostatic precipitator consists of a group of vertical collecting pipes each with an individual concentric ionizing wire. Pipe diameters may range from 6″ to 15″ and lengths from 6′ to 15′. Gas flow is upward.

Both types are mounted over hoppers into which the dust may fall. Dislodgment of the dust by rapping or scraping may be continuous or intermittent. Some collecting electrodes are made with pockets or guides to direct falling dust to the hopper and thereby minimize re-entrainment during continuous dislodgment.

Pipe types are usually used to collect mists and plate types for dusts. Both are used for various fumes. Mist collection is usually more efficient than dust collection because the collected material presents less of a problem with respect to re-entrainment and resistivity. Liquids run down the electrode whereas any dust must be dislodged mechanically. The conductivity of dust is frequently increased by introducing water vapor or certain gases, such as ammonia, into the stream. The effectiveness of electrostatic precipitation for pulverized-coal fly ash is greatly influenced by the presence of sulphur in the coal. When low-sulphur coals are used dust collecting efficiency will decrease markedly because of reduced electrical conductivity through the deposited dust.

Efficiency improves with decreasing gas velocity due to the resultant increase in treatment time and decrease in mechanical re-entrainment.

Power consumption for charging is considerably higher than for two-stage units as indicated in Table 128. Air resistance is largely due to inlet distribution plates and entrance-exit flow conditions.

Dry Inertial Collectors

A dry inertial collector may be of the settling chamber, baffle chamber, skimming chamber, cyclone, multiple cyclone, impingement, or dynamic type. All types utilize the greater mass or inertia of the dispersed particles relative to that of the carrier gas molecules to effect movement across streamlines. Each type is built over a hopper into which the collected material eventually finds its way. The migration velocity of the particles toward the collecting surface is increased by the application of centrifugal force in all except the settling chamber type. In the more elaborate types of equipment the dispersed material is concentrated in a portion or layer of the gas from which it is ultimately removed by settling action. Dry inertial collectors are used principally for collecting dry dusts or fumes but they may also be used to collect mists or sprays. The term "dry" is used to distinguish these devices from scrubbers.

A settling chamber may be no more than a long straight bottomless horizontal duct over a hopper or it may consist of a group of horizontal passages formed by shelves in a chamber. The former is suitable for removing large particles (greater than 50 microns) and those which flocculate rapidly. The shelf arrangement is suitable for droplets as small as 10 microns depending on spacing, etc. but its use for dusts is limited due to the difficulties of cleaning closely spaced shelves without creating a new dust problem.

A baffled chamber may be simply a box with horizontal entry and exit and one or more vertical baffles to induce curved air flow around them and permit entrained particles to strike them by inertia and fall to the hopper below.

A skimming chamber may consist of a slotted scroll-shaped chamber patterned after a centrifugal fan housing but with inlet and outlet reversed. The gas enters tangentially, whirling around the periphery to concentrate the dust in the outer layers which are skimmed off by the peripheral slots while the inner layers spiral inwardly to the outlet located in the side. The concentrated dust must be separated before the skimmed gas is returned to the main stream.

A cyclone collector is a cylindrical chamber with a means of producing spiral flow at the top and a dust bin below. Vortical flow may be induced by one or more rectangular tangential air inlets or by airfoil-shaped vanes arranged to impart spin to axial flow. In most cases the gas inlet and outlet are located at the same end of the tube. The gas spirals down the inner wall of the tube and back up the axis of the tube. When water sprays are used in cyclones, the inlet and outlet are often on opposite ends. Most cyclones incorporate a conical tailpiece to turn the downward moving outer spiral of air into the rising inner spiral, smoothly so as not to re-entrain the dust sliding along the cyclone walls to the dust bin.

Cyclones are usually designed for an inlet velocity of about 3000 feet per minute. The tangential velocity in the main spiral may be several times that value. Small diameter cyclones have small radii of curvature and therefore produce greater radial accelerations for the same tangential velocity than larger cyclones. This fact, together with a shorter radial distance through which the dust must travel to reach the wall, makes small cyclones more efficient for the collection of small particles than large diameter cyclones. Where moderate efficiency is acceptable, cyclone size is chosen to match capacity with a reasonable pressure drop. Where best efficiency is required, numerous small cyclones are used in a parallel flow arrangement and somewhat higher pressure drops result.

Efficiency may be higher with higher inlet dust concentration due to greater particle conditioning by agglomeration. Increasing velocity improves efficiency by producing higher radial accelerations but if carried to an extreme may reduce efficiency by inducing re-entrainment, preventing flocculation, or producing deflocculation.

An impingement collector may consist of a number of nozzles or orifices discharging against a baffle so that the gas must make a sharp turn after accelerating. The number of nozzles in parallel is based on total capacity requirements. Efficiency is related to the number of nozzles in series (as discussed in the last section of this chapter). Many impingement type dust collectors are designed so that the material is thrown out of the gas stream into a quiescent region where it may settle into a hopper located below. A perforated baffle between the nozzle and the solid baffle will provide such a region since only a limited amount of the gas will flow through the perforations and back again in comparison to the amount that will proceed directly to the next nozzle. Some of the dust will penetrate the perforations and some of it will impinge on the solid surfaces. (See Figure 190). Rappers may be provided to dislodge the collected material when it is a dry dust but liquid droplets simply run down the baffle plates.

A dynamic collector consists of a power driven centrifugal fan with slots in the housing for skimming off the outer layer of gas in which the dust has been concentrated. The fan accelerates the material causing migration to the skimmer and pressure for overcoming the losses through the collector as well as the attached system.

Conventional fans equipped with slotted scrolls are of limited effectiveness because some of the material may be thrown directly through the outlet before it reaches the slots. Efficiency can be improved by baffling the outlet (or complete scroll) so that, on leaving the wheel, the air must turn to the axial direction and then back to the radial direction before leaving the housing.

All of the various types of dry inertial collectors can be built of special materials to combat the effects of corrosion, erosion, or temperature.

Scrubbers (Wet Particle Collectors)

A scrubber may be of the cyclone, impingement, dynamic, fog-tower, pebble-bed, multi-dynamic, Venturi, submerged nozzle, or jet type. All types utilize water or other scrubbing liquid to condition small dispersed particles, to prevent particle re-entrainment, to assist in particle disposal, to cool the gases, or all four. It is difficult to distinguish among these mechanisms in some cases. Six scrubber types have their counterparts among dry inertial collectors. The relationship is obvious for cyclone, impingement, and dynamic scrubbers and dry collectors of the same description. Fog towers, pebble beds, and multi-dynamic scrubbers are more sophisticated wet versions of the cyclone, impingement, and dynamic dry types, respectively. The Venturi, submerged nozzle, and jet scrubber types have no real counterpart in the dry group. All, in fact, require an additional downstream collector section since their principal function is particle conditioning. The dynamic, multi-dynamic, and jet types may provide, in addition, sufficient draft to overcome some external system losses.

A cyclone scrubber is a cyclone collector with centrally located coarse sprays, usually directed radially outward. Very little particle conditioning is accomplished by these spray droplets. The main purpose of the water is for gas cooling and to prevent re-entrainment. This is accomplished by slurrying and carrying away the material which is deposited on the wall by centrifugal force.

An impingement scrubber is an impingement collector with provisions for wetting the baffles. The purpose of the water (as in the cyclone scrubber) is to prevent re-entrainment.

A dynamic scrubber is a dynamic collector with coarse sprays preceding the fan elements. There may be some particle conditioning by deposition on droplets depending on the size and number of spray droplets produced. The main function of the water, however, is to wet the housing walls and impeller blades to prevent particle deposition and retention on the blades and re-entrainment. The impingement of dispersed particles onto wetted blades is a sort of particle conditioning insofar as the water is subsequently thrown from the blades onto the scroll of the housing and then collected.

A fog scrubber is a cyclone collector with high-pressure hydraulic spray nozzles to produce very fine sprays. The main purpose of the fog is to condition particles by promoting their deposition on spray droplets. There is usually an integral collector section, i.e., the cyclone body is extended beyond that necessary for conditioning alone so that conditioned particles and excess droplets may be collected by cyclonic action, but a second cyclone may be provided for collection.

A pebble bed scrubber consists of a tower filled with coarse wetted packing. The purpose of the water is to prevent plugging or re-entrainment by slurrying and carrying away the material which impinges on the film on the packing.

A multi-dynamic scrubber consists of a series of power driven rotors and coarse sprays arranged so that the gas flows through the first rotor from the inside out and through the second rotor from the outside in, and so on. The water serves to condition the particles and prevent re-entrainment or fouling of the blades. The dynamic action of the rotors not only promotes deposition on the wetted blades and housing but breaks up the coarse spray droplets as well.

A Venturi scrubber consists of a Venturi-shaped air passage with water introduced just ahead of or in the high-velocity throat. The water may be introduced by means of an overflow or through nozzles or slots and is broken up into fine droplets by the action of the high-velocity gas stream. Particle conditioning takes place in the throat and as the gas decelerates in the diffuser section. That is, the dispersed material in the dirty gas is deposited on the droplets by impaction, diffusion, and condensation. Subsequently, the droplets coalesce so that a comparatively simple device such as a cyclone scrubber may then be used for collection.

A submerged nozzle scrubber consists of a nozzle partially submerged in water. Some particles are impacted on the surface of the water which collects them and prevents re-entrainment. The gas on passing through the nozzle picks up a considerable amount of water which breaks up and promotes particle conditioning. Although some conditioned particles may be deposited in the pool of water due to turbulent action, others require the use of a separate or attached collecting section.

A jet scrubber consists of a water activated jet pump. The downward flow gas passage is Venturi-shaped. The water nozzle is centered just ahead of the throat. The water breaks up and creates a draft by transfer of momentum while simultaneously conditioning dispersed particles. Much of the water drops directly into a tank but the finer droplets which are most effective in conditioning must be separated by more elaborate means.

Although scrubbers are designed primarily for aerosol treatment they may be used for treating gas mixtures. Those which produce large numbers of well dispersed fine droplets are most suitable for promoting mass transfer. Nevertheless, they are not as effective in providing interfacial area as the gas absorbers specifically designed for this purpose. Most scrubbers utilize centrifugal force in one way or another, to move the particles through the gas or to move water through the gas. Those in which centrifugal force is limited utilize momentum transfer, also an inertia effect, to disperse water.

Gas Incinerators

A gas incinerator qualifies as a gas cleaning device when it renders airborne material innocuous by altering its chemical composition, converting it into simple compounds. Complete combustion of hydrocarbons yields H_2O and CO_2, which are non-odorous, non-toxic, non-reactive gases. Incomplete combustion may yield products that are more offensive than the original materials. Organic sulphur compounds, when burned, yield SO_2 which is usually less offensive than the original substances (but may require further treatment). Nitrogen containing compounds may produce free nitrogen or its oxides depending on the conditions of operation.

Incineration may take place in high temperature flames or by catalytic (low temperature) combustion. Direct combustion may be used for either aerosols or gas mixtures. The carrier gas and dispersed material are heated by direct firing of additional fuel to reach the required temperature for destruction of the offensive material. Combustion is not usually self sustaining for the concentration of combustibles found in most stack gases. Retention time at incineration temperature must be sufficient for the reaction to proceed to completion. Additional heat is usually generated by the reaction.

Catalytic incineration is more effective for gas mixtures than for aerosols. Preheating is required to initiate the catalytic type of combustion but fuel requirements are less than for the direct type. Combustion may become self sustaining when there is enough fuel value in the material consumed. Catalysis is a surface phenomenon which promotes or accelerates chemical reactions. Catalytic combustion, i.e., the oxidation of certain materials in the presence of a catalyst, can be accomplished at considerably lower temperatures than are required for direct combustion.

Catalytic agents include various noble metals, notably platinum. They are usually applied as a thin coating on metal ribbons, ceramic pellets, and other shapes, since their effectiveness is related to the total contact surface provided. For many gases and vapor, the depth of bed needed is not great and the catalytic agent is employed in shallow cells.

Gas Absorbers

A gas absorber may be a spray tower, packed column, or fiber cell unit. All are liquid-gas contacting devices which utilize both eddy and molecular diffusion to effect movement of dispersed molecules across stream lines and solution to effect the necessary phase change to prevent redispersion. All are suitable for promoting the transfer of the soluble components of a gas mixture from the gaseous to the liquid phase. The liquid used may be water, another solvent, or a neutralizing or reacting solution. An important difference among equipment types is the method of dividing the liquid to produce the necessary interfacial area between the liquid and gas so that mass transfer will proceed at a reasonable rate.

In a spray tower the liquid is broken up into droplets by a spray nozzle or perforated plate and allowed to fall the height of the tower. The gas is usually passed upward through the falling drops. A large number of spray drops quickly find their way to the walls. The height of a transfer unit is comparatively large so that spray towers are generally limited to applications which require only a few transfer units. The principal advantages of spray towers over other types of gas absorbers are low resistance, simplicity of construction and operation, non-clogging, and non-flooding features.

In a packed column the liquid is broken up into thin films by distributing it over the top of deep beds of extended surface packing and allowing it to trickle downward while the gas passes up from the bottom, thereby producing counterflow of liquid and gas. The height of a transfer unit in a packed tower is considerably less than for a spray tower for most types of packings. Packings range from crushed rock to special fabricated shapes known as Rashig rings, Berl saddles, etc., which may be stacked or dumped in the tower. Air flow resistance is higher than for other types of gas absorbers. There may be a danger of clogging when the gas has an appreciable quantity of entrained solids. Liquid holdup due to the rising gas action, known as flooding, may occur if either the gas or liquid rate is too great. Channeling, i.e., uneven distribution of the liquid or gas, can occur in high columns, thereby rendering a portion of the packing surface useless for absorption purposes.

In the fiber cell type of gas absorber, which is a variation of the packed tower, the liquid is distributed over the face of the cell by sprays and allowed to pass through co-currently with the gas flow. The large surface area of the fibers and their good wetting properties make the height of a transfer unit considerably smaller than for other types. Cell depth is usually limited to prevent channeling of the liquid. Several stages of cells are frequently required to obtain the necessary mass transfer because a co-current stage can produce only one equilibrium step, except when neutralizing or reacting solutions are used. When multiple cells are used in series, performance can be improved by using fresh liquid on each cell as illustrated in Figure 188.

Fibrous packings provide more surface per unit volume, require less weight of material, and have greater porosity than conventional tower packings. This results in first cost savings due to the reduction in the weight of material required and savings in operating cost due to the reduction in air resistance which is a result of greater porosity. The compactness of fibrous packings is offset in part by the need for space between nozzle and cell to develop the spray pattern. Horizontal arrangements of stages lead to lower pumping heads although the necessary redistribution of liquid in each stage increases pumping capacity.

All types of gas absorbers may be built to give any desired degree of absorption. Theoretically, removal efficiency is limited only by equilibrium considerations. Practically, degree of cleaning is limited by economic considerations. The number of transfer units required increase rapidly when high efficiencies are required so that cleaning efficiency must be balanced against cost in many applications. For a given percentage removal, the number of transfer units required increases as the solubility of solute in solvent decreases. Solubility decreases when the concentration of solute in solvent rises. The remedy for this is to use fresh solvent instead of recirculated solvent or to incorporate a neutralizing agent in the solvent which will reduce back pressure, i.e., reduce the tendency of the solute to rediffuse into the gas stream. The number of transfer units required is fewer for counterflow of gas and liquid than for any other arrangement. Frequently this number must be adjusted to account for channeling or flooding. When a very low concentration of an offensive material is required in the effluent gases it may be more practical to provide an adsorber for the final cleanup than to attempt the complete removal by absorption alone.

Absorption devices are seldom used for atmospheric air cleaning because the low concentration of any dispersed gas or vapor makes shallow bed adsorbers more economical wherever high removal efficiencies are required. Gas absorbers are unsuitable for removing small insoluable particles. A special aerosol scrubber may be required upstream to prevent plugging and fouling of the packings when large quantities of coarse, sticky particles are present.

All types of absorbers may be built from special materials to combat corrosion. Gas and water temperatures should be kept low since gas solubility generally increases with decreasing temperature more than enough to offset the usual decrease in diffusivity. The danger of freezing sets a lower limit on temperature.

Gas Adsorbers

A gas adsorber consists of a comparatively deep bed of activated charcoal through which a gas mixture is passed so that one or more components can be removed selectively. An industrial gas adsorber may be further distinguished from an atmospheric odor adsorber by the fact that equipment for in place recovery of the adsorbed material and regeneration of the bed is provided. Ventilation air odor adsorbers may incorporate discontinuous beds, industrial gas adsorbers do not.

Regeneration in place is accomplished by passing low pressure steam through the bed, usually in the direction opposite to normal gas flow (which is discontinued during regeneration). As the bed becomes heated, the previously adsorbed gas is released. When recovery of the desorbed material is required, condensing equipment must be located downstream together with whatever other equipment may be required to separate the condensed gas from the condensed steam. Alternatively, vapors released on regeneration may be discharged to atmosphere after passing through a gas incinerator.

A single industrial unit may be used on batch processes that allow sufficient time for desorption and cooling between batches. Multiple units are required for continuous processes. Twin units may be sized so that one unit has sufficient capacity to allow the other to be regenerated and cooled. Such units must be designed for something less than full utilization of the carbon in order to maintain highest efficiency. Triplet units may be sized so that each unit can be used in turn to its full capacity. This is accomplished by utilizing the most recently generated unit as a second stage downstream of the unit previously regenerated. Quadruplet units may be sized so that any two units in parallel provide the required capacity. The cycle is usually arranged so that any two units can be used in parallel. The discharge from the most recently regenerated unit of the two in use is passed directly to atmosphere. The discharge from the other unit is first passed through a third unit and then to the atmosphere. This third unit which is the most recently regenerated one removes any previously unadsorbed material and is itself cooled by the stream. The fourth unit is free for regeneration. With four units, two can be on line, one can be undergoing regeneration and the other can be taken out of service completely if need be. The two on line can be used in series at reduced capacity or in parallel at reduced efficiency. Two fans are required for normal operation, one to force the gas through the main system including the two parallel units, and the other to force recirculating gas through the unit being cooled. With proper sizing and inter-connections, the second fan can be used on the main stream if the main fan has to be taken out of service for any reason.

The face area and thickness of the charcoal bed must be selected not only to provide the required weight of charcoal for the desired operating cycle but also to provide the best combination of equipment size and pressure drop. This is a problem in economic evaluations.

SELECTION OF EQUIPMENT

Previous discussions have indicated that there are numerous factors which must be considered before the advisability of selecting one or another type of air or gas cleaning equipment can be determined. These factors include: the general nature of the problem, i.e., whether atmospheric air or stack gas is to be cleaned; the general nature of the contaminant to be removed, i.e., whether gas, solid or liquid; the specific properties of the contaminated stream. i.e., flow rate, temperature, size, distribution, and initial concentration of contaminant, etc.; the degree of cleaning required; and any limitations on the state of the collected material.

The information given in Table 128 may be of help to narrow the selection once the above factors have been defined. Final selection should be based on complete evaluation of all pertinent factors, both functional and economic.

In the following sections, methods of estimating the required degree of cleaning are reviewed, the influence of the condition of the collected material on equipment selection is examined, and finally the application of multiple air cleaners in series is discussed.

Degree of Cleaning Required

In cases where the loss of valuable product is the only concern, the percentage of material to be removed should be that which gives the maximum return on the equipment investment. In most air or gas cleaning applications, however, the dispersed material has little or no value but a high cleaning efficiency may be required to prevent undesirable effects on persons or property which may be exposed to the air or gas stream.

When the purified air stream is used directly for ventilation purposes, the degree of cleaning selected should be that which gives the required purity as determined by health or comfort requirements or by an evaluation of equipment cost versus housekeeping expense, whichever leads to the most stringent requirement. When the cleaned air or gas stream is discharged directly to atmosphere the cleaning efficiency should be that which gives the required purity as determined by air pollution considerations and regulations.

For most air cleaning applications the major objective will be to reduce housekeeping expenses, etc., by removing as much soiling dirt and dust as possible consistent with the original and expected operating costs of the equipment. Such an evaluation usually requires judgment based on experience. Reductions in soiling power of the cleaned air provide an ideal method of rating air cleaning devices for this service. Although results of discoloration tests are seldom available for the particular atmosphere under study and are often difficult to reproduce, most atmospheric air cleaners are rated on discoloration efficiency and these results may be used as an indication of usefulness in reducing housekeeping expenses, etc.

The major objective of some supply air cleaning applications is to protect against discomfort or a health hazard by removing sufficient contaminant to maintain room conditions below maximum allowable concentrations. These applications range from civil defense shelters which require protection against nuclear or any chemical warfare contaminants to residences needing protection against airborne allergy-producing contaminants. If a contaminant is not generated within the room, but comes in with the ventilation air, the room concentration will very nearly equal the air cleaner exit concentration if the air cleaner discharges into the room continuously. Efficiencies based on the reduction in weight or particle count, e.g., pollens, may be used to estimate exit concentration for any inlet concentration. Results of weight or count tests are seldom available for every contaminant but reliable estimates can be made when size distributions are known.

The mass rate of emission of a contaminant is far more important than the exit or stack concentration when estimating ground level concentrations resulting from exhaust air cleaning applications. The two are, of course, related through the total gas flow rate. Nevertheless, many air pollution control regulations limit emission rates on a concentration basis. Other factors which must be considered when evaluating ground level concentrations are gas temperature, height of the stack, topography, and meteorological conditions.

The maximum downwind ground level concentration theoretically varies inversely with wind velocity and inversely with the square of the stack height as well as directly with the total emission rate. The downwind distance to the point of maximum ground concentration is only slightly greater than that to the point where the diffusing stream first meets the ground and is of the order of ten stack heights for the most unfavorable meteorological conditions. The center line concentration decreases slowly thereafter until at distances of the order of fifty stack heights or greater the concentration becomes inversely proportional to the square of the distance. High stack gas temperatures increase the effective height of the stack. The stability of the atmosphere also has an important effect. Temperature inversion may produce increased or reduced ground concentrations depending on inversion height relative to stack height. Downdrafts produce looping streams which may even touch the ground within one stack height (in which case stack concentration may be more important than total emission rate). In a neutral atmosphere the stream will be conical over flat terrain. Hills and buildings produce effects which cannot be predicted accurately except by model tests.

Methods of Handling Collected Material

The preferred method of handling and disposing of the collected material may influence the choice of air or gas cleaning equipment. Table 128 lists the condition of the collected material for each type of device. Solid materials may be collected as dry dusts, as slurries in water or oil, or they may be inseparably combined with the collecting filter (in which case the filter must be disposable). Liquid and soluble materials may be collected as concentrated liquids or as dilute solutions in water. Gaseous materials may be collected on adsorbents, as dilute solutions in water or other solvent, or the chemical state may be completely changed by reaction with another material.

In supply air cleaning applications the final state of the collected matter makes no difference so long as it may be disposed of easily, i.e., without undue cost and without creating a new hazard. The same thing is true in many air pollution control applications. However, when product recovery is a consideration, the required final state of the collected material will influence the choice of equipment. It may prove more economical to purchase a collector which permits easy recovery rather than a less expensive one which does not.

As the problems of disposal and recovery are beyond the scope of this handbook, the many ways in which the physical and chemical state of the collected material may enter into selection of air cleaning equipment cannot be explored fully. A few ways in which the characteristics of the collected material affect equipment selection are listed below.

Dry dusts may be recovered and used directly in many cases whereas slurries may require mechanical dewatering or even thermal drying before reuse. Sludges are less subject to dispersion by wind and other forces than are dry dusts. Solutions and sludges are lesser fire and explosion hazards than dry materials but the latter are generally less corrosive. High gas temperatures are reduced in wet collection leading to smaller gas volumes than in dry collection. These examples will indicate that each case must be evaluated separately.

Multiple Air Cleaners in Series

Many air or gas cleaning problems can be solved with a single air cleaner. When the air flow capacity of a single unit is inadequate, multiple units in parallel may be used. Efficiency should be the same for multiple units as for a single unit, all other conditions being equal. The use of units in series has advantages but may or may not lead to improved efficiency.

Theoretically, if the dispersed material is perfectly homogeneous and remains so, each of two or more identical devices arranged in series should remove substantially the same percentage of the material which reaches it, (i.e., penetrates the previous stage) thereby increasing over-all efficiency. For example, if three units each with 80% efficiency are arranged in series the first will remove 80% of the total material, the second will remove 80% of the remainder or 16% of the total ($.80 \times .20 = .16$) and the third will remove 80% of the new remainder or 3.2% of the total ($.80 \times .04 = .032$) so that the over-all efficiency will be 99.2% ($.80 + .16 + .032 = .992$).

The limitation of the above rule to cases where the dispersed material is perfectly homogeneous cannot be over-emphasized because air cleaners handling a heterogeneous dispersed material generally remove the coarsest material at close to 100% efficiency and the finest materials at close to 0% efficiency. Consequently, most, if not all, of the material which penetrates the first stage of a series of identical stages will penetrate all succeeding stages unless agglomeration occurs between stages. Identical stages in series, employed in some impingement collectors, impingement scrubbers, and multi-dynamic scrubbers, give increased efficiency because of particle conditioning, either agglomeration or deposition on droplets, that takes place in the early stages.

As the dispersed material may be considered homogeneous in the case of gas mixtures, additional stages are used to improve efficiency in the case of gas removal although this rule can only be applied with accuracy when the driving force is the same for all stages. This condition is satisfied when neutralizing solutions are employed or when each stage of a gas absorber is supplied with fresh water and loadings are light. Gas absorber stages may be in a single casing or multiple units may be piped in series.

Gas adsorbers can be staged to extend the period of operation between regenerations by providing additional depth of bed in a single unit or by using multiple units in series.

Dissimilar stages are used frequently in both gas and particle removal applications. It is often more economical to use a gas adsorber following a gas absorber rather than add extra gas absorber stages. Gas absorbers may incorporate a mist eliminator stage downstream of the absorber stages. Both gas absorbers and gas adsorbers may require a particle removal stage upstream to prevent plugging.

Particle conditioning devices such as fog, Venturi, submerged nozzle, and jet scrubbers, require downstream stages for collection. The conditioning and collection stages may be separate devices or integral parts of one device as previously mentioned.

Low efficiency devices are frequently used upstream of more efficient devices to increase the service life of the latter. Prefilters which remove the bulk of the coarse particles, are frequently used upstream of absolute filters to reserve the dust holding capacity of the latter for fine particles exclusively. Low efficiency filters are often used as prefilters for two-stage electrostatic precipitators to capture lint or other material which might cause arcing or necessitate too frequent washing of the collecting plates. Multiple-cyclone collectors are used upstream of single-stage electrostatic precipitators for fly ash collection in steam power stations to decrease the dust load on the precipitators and thereby reduce maintenance and operating costs.

For hot gases a scrubber can be used as a first-stage to take out coarse material and reduce the gas temperature as well. It may be necessary to reheat the gas slightly to eliminate water droplets and prevent condensation in subsequent stages. The final stage may be a filter, or a combination of filters which could not be used for the hot gases without precooling.

After-filters may be required to collect material which becomes dislodged from a two-stage electrostatic precipitator or to eliminate mists from spray washers.

PART IV

APPENDICES

APPENDIX I

UNITS, DIMENSIONS, AND DIMENSIONLESS NUMBERS

Units (such as the foot) are the names assigned to describe the magnitudes of substantial physical variables. Dimensions (such as length) are generalized units. Dimensionless groups (such as length/length) are used to describe natural physical variables. Both the number of units and dimensionless numbers represent the precise magnitudes of physical variables. The difference is that artificial standards such as the foot, the second, or the pound are required for the measurement of substantial variables whereas no artificial standards are required for the measurement of natural variables. The classification of physical variables as either substantial or natural is taken from Ipsen* who examines the nature of units and dimensions in great detail.

Units

The system of units employed in this Handbook is based on the U. S. system of weights and measures and generally reflects the conventions of the fan industry. Eventually, some form of the metric system probably will be adopted universally. An International System of Units (SI) has already been adopted by the International Organization for Standardization (ISO). Details are published by the National Bureau of Standards.† Conversion factors and equivalents are given in Appendix 3 based on these N.B.S. data.

The system of units used may be further described as the two-pound system with gravitational exceptions. In the two-pound system both force and mass are measured in pounds. The alternatives of using either the poundal for force or the slug for mass have not been widely adopted in fan engineering practice.

The pound force is designated, lb, and the pound mass is designated, lbm. In any equations involving mass, a conversion factor, g_c, is used in order to make the units consistant with the use of lbm. The numerical value of g_c is equal to the value of the standard gravitational acceleration for the units used. Thus, Newton's second law of motion would be written,

$$F = Ma/g_c$$

which for the ft-lbm-sec system results in force(F) in lb if mass(M) is in lbm, acceleration (a) is in fps, and g_c is 32.174 ft-lbm/lb-sec^2. Other commonly used values for g_c include 386.09 in.-lbm/lb-sec^2 for the in.-lbm-sec system, 980.67 cm-g/gf-sec^2 for the cm-g-sec system, and 1.0 m-kg/N-sec^2 for the m-kg-sec or International System.

In keeping with certain conventions, some equations are written in

*D. C. Ipsen, "Units, Dimensions, and Dimensionless Numbers," McGraw-Hill Book Co., Inc., New York, 1960.

†National Bureau of Standards Handbook 102, The Superintendent of Documents, U. S. Government Printing Office, Washington, D. C., 1967.

terms of weight divided by the acceleration of gravity instead of mass. This use of gravitational notation can be misleading unless the engineer recognizes that mass is the significant variable, not the acceleration of gravity. A case in point is Equation 331 where the energy stored in a rotating body is given with respect to its weight times its radius of gyration squared (WK^2). This is obviously misleading since even in weightless space the energy would be the same as on earth.

Another interesting case is the Bernoulli equation which is conventionally written,

$$P/\delta + V^2/2g + Z = Constant.$$

The pressure head (P/δ) appears to be dependent upon gravity by virtue of the use of weight density (δ). The velocity head ($V^2/2g$) appears dependent upon g and the elevation head (Z) independent of g. These appearances are misleading particularly in space applications. Another form of the Bernoulli equation is more informative with respect to the influence of gravity,

$$P/\rho g_c + V^2/2g_c + gZ/g_c = Constant.$$

All of the g_c's could be omitted if mass density (ρ) were in slugs/ft^3, but in the two-pound system it is in lbm/ft^3. This expression properly links g to Z indicating that g is only important if there is a difference in elevation (Z) and, conversely, that if g = 0 elevation head (gZ/g_c) is also zero.

The equation of state and all of the tables and charts of Chapter 1 are written in terms of the weight (W) or weight density (δ) of the gas. Once again, few, if any, problems arise because of this convention when dealing with terrestrial applications. In a standard gravitational field, the mass of a substance in lbm and its weight in lb are equal numerically. Similarly, various other quantities such as density, gas constant, specific heat, and enthalpy can be referenced to either mass or weight and will have the same numerical value in either case in a standard gravitational field.

Dimensions

The system of dimensions employed here is the force (F) – mass (M) – length (L) – time (θ) – temperature (T) – heat (H) system. The use of the symbol θ for time and the symbol T for temperature may be considered unusual, but it is consistant with the text wherein temperature appears much more frequently than time. The treatment of both temperature and heat as fundamental dimensions reflects the choice of units in the text and is generally consistant with fan engineering practice. The conversion factor (J_c) facilitates the writing of equations involving both work and heat terms.

The dimensions of the various quantities referred to in the text are given with the nomenclature listed in Appendix 2. Dimensions are also listed for the various conversion factor tables of Appendix 3. In some cases two sets of dimensions are shown. This reflects either the equivalency of heat and work or the relationship of force and mass. For example, in Table 130, power and heat flow rate units are listed in a single table with the dimensions of LF/θ and H/θ. Also in Table 130, absolute viscosity units are listed with the dimensions of either $M/L\theta$ or $F\theta/L^2$. In this case $F\theta/L^2$ better reflects the physical meaning of viscosity as the ratio of stress (F/L^2) to velocity gradient $(L/\theta/L)$, but $M/L\theta$ eliminates the need for a conversion factor in the Reynolds number formula.

Dimensionless numbers

In many of the problems of fan engineering, it is convenient to utilize various dimensionless numbers based on the pertinent operating variables. Organizing experimental data by dimensional analysis frequently leads to a simplified representation of results as well as easier and more general interpretation. The correlation of friction factor, relative roughness, and Reynolds number in fluid flow is a case in point. The advantage of using dimensionless numbers is that the number of dimensionless ratios or groups necessary to express a relationship is always fewer than the number of dimensional variables involved. Dimensionless equations involving two or more dimensionless groups are frequently used. Dimensional analysis provides a method of grouping the variables involved in a problem, provided all the necessary factors are known (or assumed). There are several mathematical method of arriving at the desired dimensionless parameters, but the functional relationship between them must be determined experimentally.

Table 129 lists several dimensionless groups frequently employed in fan engineering. A much more comprehensive list has been tabulated by Boucher and Alves*.

*D. F. Boucher and G. E. Alves, Dimensionless Numbers, Chemical Engineering Progress, vol. 55, no. 9, pp. 55-64, 1959; vol 59, no. 8, pp. 75-83, 1963.

TABLE 129—DIMENSIONLESS NUMBERS

Name	Symbol	Group	Where Used	Force Ratio
Archimedes number	Ar	$D^3 \Delta\rho g \rho/\mu^2$	Fluidization	IG/V²
Bond number	Bo	$D^2 \Delta\rho g/g_c \sigma$	Atomization	G/S
Cauchy number	Ca	$\rho V^2/g_c e$	Compressible flow	I/C
Cavitation number	—	$2 \Delta p' g_c/\rho V^2$	Cavitation	—
Darcy friction factor	f	$(2 \Delta p g_c/\rho V^2)(D/L)$	Flow in conduits	P/I
Drag coefficient	f_D	$D \Delta\rho g/\rho V^2$	Settling of particles	G/I
Euler number	Eu	$D(-dp/dL) g_c/\rho V^2$	Flow in conduits	P/I
Fanning friction factor	f'	$(2 \Delta p g_c/\rho V^2)(D/4L)$	Flow in conduits	P/I
Froude number	Fr	$V^2/g L$	Surface effects	I/G
Grashof number	Gr	$L^3 \rho^2 g \beta \Delta t/\mu^2$	Free convection	IB/V²
Knudsen number	Kn	λ_m/L	Rarefied flow	—
Mach number	Ma	V/c	Compressible flow	$(I/C)^{1/2}$
Merkel number	Me	$K' S' V'/L'$	Liquid-gas contacting	—
Number of diameters	—	L/D	Flow in conduits	—
No. of dia. per vel. hd.	N	$(L/D)(\rho V^2/2 \Delta p g_c)$	Flow in conduits	I/P
Number of velocity heads	—	$2 \Delta p g_c/\rho V^2$	Flow in conduits	P/I
Nusselt number	Nu	$h D/k$	Forced convection	—
Pecklet number	Pe	$D V \rho c_p/k$	Forced convection	—
Prandtl number	Pr	$c_p \mu/k$	Convection	—
Ratio of specific heats	γ	c_p/c_v	Compressible flow	—
Reynolds number	Re	$D V \rho/\mu$	Fluid flow	I/V
Rossby number	Ro	$V/2 \omega D \sin \alpha$	Coriolis effects	I/E
Roughness ratio	—	ϵ/D	Fluid flow	—
Schmidt number	Sc	$\mu/\rho \partial$	Diffusion	—
Size & Speed ratios	—	$D_1/D_2, N_1/N_2$	Fan laws	—
Sherwood number	Sh	$k' L/\partial$	Diffusion	—
Sommerfeld number	So	$(\mu N/g_c p)(D/C)^2$	Journal bearings	V/L
Stanton number	St	$h/c_p \rho V$	Forced convection	—
Stokes number	—	$\mu/\rho D^2 f_o$	Particle dynamics	—
Strouhal number	Sl	$f_o D/V$	Vortex streets	—
Weber number	We	$D V^2 \rho/g_c \sigma$	Droplets and bubbles	I/S

NOMENCLATURE

C	clearance
c	sonic velocity
c_p	specific heat at constant pressure
c_v	specific heat at constant volume
D	diameter or dimension
d	differential
e	bulk modulus of elasticity
f_o	frequency
g	acceleration of gravity
g_c	conversion factor
h	coefficient of heat transfer
K'	over-all coefficient of mass transfer
k	thermal conductivity
k'	coefficient of mass transfer
L	length or dimension
L'	liquid mass flow rate
N	rotative speed
p	pressure
S'	surface per unit volume
t	temperature
V	velocity
V'	total volume
α	angle re earth's rotation
β	coefficient of thermal expansion
Δ	difference
Δp	pressure drop
$\Delta p'$	static pressure — vapor pressure
Δt	temperature drop across film
$\Delta\rho$	particle density — fluid density
∂	diffusivity
ϵ	absolute roughness
λ_m	mean free path
μ	absolute viscosity
ρ	mass density of fluid
σ	surface tension
ω	angular velocity

FORCE RATIO NOMENCLATURE

B	Bouyancy force	$\propto$	$D^3 \rho g \beta \Delta t/g_c$
C	Compressibility force	$\propto$	$D^2 e$
E	Coriolis force	$\propto$	$D^3 \rho V 2 \omega \sin \alpha/g_c$
G	Gravitational force	$\propto$	$D^3 \Delta\rho g/g_c$
I	Inertia force	$\propto$	$D^2 \rho V^2/g_c$
L	Load force	$\propto$	$D^2 p$
P	Pressure force	$\propto$	$D^2 \Delta p$
S	Surface tension force	$\propto$	$D \sigma$
V	Viscous force	$\propto$	$D \mu V/g_c$

APPENDIX 2

NOMENCLATURE

All of the basic symbols which are used in the text, their definitions, and their dimensions are listed below. The system of dimensions which is used is the force (F)—mass (M)—length (L)—time (θ)—temperature (T)—heat (H) system. (See Appendix 1). Any consistent system of units of measurement may be employed in most of the equations. However, there are several symbols which imply a particular set of units. Such units are given parenthetically after the definitions.

BASIC SYMBOLS AS USED IN TEXT

Symbol	Definitions	Dimensions
A	area	L^2
ADP	apparatus dew point	T
AHP	air horsepower (hp)	LF/θ
AR	aspect ratio	none
a	acceleration	L/θ^2
B	coefficient	none
BHP	brake horsepower (hp)	LF/θ
BP	barometric pressure ("WG)	F/L^2
BPF	bypass factor	none
BPL	band pressure level(dB)	none
b	barometric pressure ("Hg)	F/L^2
C	coefficient	none
CF	centrifugal force	F
CFM	capacity or volume flow rate (cfm)	L^3/θ
CGR	contaminant generation rate	M/θ
CR	curve ratio	none
C_C	coefficient of contraction	none
C_D	coefficient of discharge	none
C_p	coefficient of pressure recovery	none
C_R	coefficient of resistance	none
C_V	coefficient of velocity	none
c	sonic velocity	L/θ
c_p	specific heat at constant pressure	H/MT
c_v	specific heat at constant volume	H/MT
D	diameter or other dimension	L
D_s	specific size	L
d	diameter or other dimension	L
E	energy	LF
E	modulus of elasticity	F/L^2
$ECFM$	equivalent capacity (cfm)	L^3/θ
ESP	equivalent static pressure ("WG)	F/L^2
ET	effective temperature	T
ETD	equivalent temperature difference	T
ETP	equivalent total pressure ("WG)	F/L^2

BASIC SYMBOLS (Cont.)

Symbol	Definitions	Dimensions
e_a	actual vapor pressure ("Hg)	F/L^2
e_w	vapor pressure of pure water ("Hg)	F/L^2
F	fractional content	none
F	force	F
FA	face area	L^2
FD	free delivery capacity (cfm)	L^3/θ
FHP	fan horsepower (hp)	LF/θ
FSP	fan static pressure ("WG)	F/L^2
FTP	fan total pressure ("WG)	F/L^2
FV	face velocity	L/θ
FVP	fan velocity pressure ("WG)	F/L^2
f	frequency	$1/\theta$
f	Darcy friction factor	none
f'	Fanning friction factor	none
f_D	coefficient of drag	none
G	gas mass velocity	$M/\theta L^2$
G	modulus of rigidity	F/L^2
GPM	capacity or volume flow rate (gpm)	L^3/θ
g	gravitational acceleration	L/θ^2
g_c	conversion factor	$ML/F\theta^2$
H	head	LF/M (or L)
H	absolute humidity	none
HHV	higher heating value	H/M
HP	horsepower (hp)	LF/θ
HTU	height of one transfer unit	L
h	coefficient of heat transfer	$H/\theta L^2T$
h	relative humidity	none
I	second moment of area	L^4
I_m	mass moment of inertia	ML^2 (or $FL\theta^2$)
IL	intensity level (dB)	none
i	interest rate	none
i	enthalpy	H/M
J	polar moment of inertia	L^4
J_c	conversion factor	LF/H
K	over-all coefficient of mass transfer	$M/\theta F$
K	proportionality factor	none
K	radius of gyration	L
K_p	compressibility factor	none
k	coefficient of mass transfer	$M/\theta F$

BASIC SYMBOLS (Cont.)

;ymbol	Definitions	Dimensions
;	thermal conductivity	$H/\theta LT$
L	liquid mass velocity	$M/\theta L^2$
L	length	L
"*L*"	factor	M/L^3
LEL	lower explosive limit	none
LH	latent heat rate	H/θ
LHV	lower heating value	H/M
;	length	L
'*n*	logarithm to the base e	—
og	logarithm to the base 10	—
M	mean hydraulic radius	L
M	bending moment	FL
M	mass	M
"*M*"	factor	$H/\theta L^2T$
MAC	maximum allowable concentration	none
MV	molal volume (ft^3/(lb)mol)	L^3/M
MW	molecular weight (lb/(lb)mol)	none
m	mass flow rate	M/θ
m	number or exponent	none
N	number or dimensionless group	none
N	rotational speed	$1/\theta$
N_s	specific speed	$1/\theta$
n	number or exponent	none
P	perimeter	L
P	pressure	F/L^2
PF	performance factor	none
Pf	power factor	none
PRCFM	point of rating capacity (cfm)	L^3/θ
PRSP	point of rating static pressure ("WG)	F/L^2
PW	power	LF/θ
PWL	sound power level (dB)	none
PWL_s	specific sound power level (dB)	none
p	pressure or partial pressure	F/L^2
Q	directivity factor	none
Q	volume	L^3
q	volume flow rate	L^3/θ
$\mathcal{R}$	room constant	L^2
R	radius	L

BASIC SYMBOLS (Cont.)

Symbol	Definitions	Dimensions
R	ratio	none
R	resistance (electrical)	θ/L
R	gas constant	L/T (or LF/MT)
R′	universal gas constant	L/T (or LF/MT)
RPM	fan speed (rpm)	1/θ
RR	radius ratio	none
r	resistance (thermal)	$\theta L^2 T/H$
r	radius	L
S	surface area	L^2
SG	specific gravity	none
SH	sensible heat rate	H/θ
SND	static no delivery pressure (″WG)	F/L^2
SP	static pressure (″WG)	F/L^2
SPL	sound pressure level (dB)	none
s	relative density of steam	none
s	stress	F/L^2
T	absolute temperature	T
TH	total heat rate	H/θ
TL	transmission loss (dB)	none
TP	total pressure (″WG)	F/L^2
TR	transmissibility	none
t	dry-bulb temperature	T
t′	wet-bulb temperature	T
t″	dew-point temperature	T
t‴	temperature of adiabatic saturation	T
U	linear rotor velocity	L/θ
U	over-all coefficient of heat transfer	$H/\theta L^2 T$
V	vertical or direct shearing force	F
V	volume	L^3
V	velocity	L/θ
VP	velocity pressure (″WG)	F/L^2
W	width	L
W	weight	F
WK^2	weight moment of inertia—fly wheel effect	FL^2
WL	water loading	$M/\theta L^2$
WP	water pressure	F/L^2
WT	water temperature	T
w	weight flow rate	F/θ
X	concentration in liquid	none
X	distance or dimension	L

BASIC SYMBOLS (Cont.)

Symbol	Definitions	Dimensions
x	distance or dimension	L
Y	concentration in gas	none
Y	distance or dimension	L
y	distance or dimension	L
Z	distance or dimension	L
α	fluid angle (deg)	none
$\bar{\alpha}$	average sound absorption coefficient	none
β	blade angle (deg)	none
Γ	condenser tube loading	$M/\theta L$
γ	stagger or blade setting angle (deg)	none
γ	ratio of specific heats	none
Δ	prefix designating difference	—
Δ	impedance correction (dB)	none
δ	density based on weight	F/L^3
∂	diffusivity	L^2/θ
ϵ	emissivity	none
ϵ	absolute roughness	L
ϵ/D	relative roughness	none
ζ	sound energy attenuation constant	1/L
η	efficiency or effectiveness	none
θ	time	θ
θ	angle	none
Λ	wave length	L
λ	latent heat of vaporization	H/M
λ_m	mean free path of gas molecules	L
μ	absolute viscosity	$M/L\theta$ (or $F\theta/L^2$)
ν	Poisson's ratio	none
ν	kinematic viscosity	L^2/θ
Ξ	field strength	$F^{1/2}/L$
ξ	electrostatic charge	$F^{1/2}L$

BASIC SYMBOLS (Cont.)

Symbol	Definitions	Dimensions
π	3.1416	none
ρ	mass density	M/L^3
ρc	characteristic impedance	$M/\theta L^2$
Σ	prefix indicating summation	—
Σ	sigma function	H/M
σ	surface tension	F/L
τ	torque	LF
Φ	capacity coefficient	none
ϕ	velocity of approach factor	none
φ	coefficient	none
Ψ	head coefficient	none
ψ	expansion or compression factor	none
Ω	permeance	$M/\theta F$
ω	angular velocity	$1/\theta$

UNITS OF MEASUREMENT

Abbrev.	Definitions	Dimensions
Å	angstrom units	L
A	amperes	$F^{1/2}L/\theta$
atm	atmospheres	F/L^2
Btu	British thermal units	H
bar	bars	F/L^2
bbl	barrels	L^3
bu	bushels	L^3
C	coulombs (charge)	$F^{1/2}L$
cal	gram or small calories	H
cfm	cubic feet per minute	L^3/θ
cm	centimeters	L
cP	centipoises	$M/L\theta$
cps	cycles per second	$1/\theta$
cSt	centistokes	L^2/θ
cu cm	cubic centimeters	L^3
cu ft	cubic feet	L^3
cu in.	cubic inches	L^3

UNITS OF MEASUREMENT (Cont.)

Abbrev.	Definitions	Dimensions
da	days	θ
dB	decibels	none
deg	degrees of angle	none
dr	drams	F
dy	dynes	F
erg	ergs	LF
F	farads (capacitance)	L
fpm	feet per minute	L/θ
fps	feet per second	L/θ
ft	feet	L
gf	grams force	F
g	grams mass	M
gal	gallons	L^3
gi	gills	L^3
gpm	gallons per minute	L^3/θ
gr	grains force	F
H	henrys (inductance)	θ^2/L
Hz	hertz (cycles per second)	1/θ
hp	horsepower	LF/θ
hr	hours	θ
in.	inches	L
J	joules	H
kcal	kilogram or large calories	H
kg	kilograms mass	M
kgf	kilograms force	F
(kg)mol	kilogram mole	M
kl	kiloliters	L^3
km	kilometers	L
kW	kilowatts	LF/θ
l	liters	L^3
lb	pounds force	F
lbm	pounds mass	M
(lb)mol	pound mole	F
lyr	leap years	θ
m	meters	L
mg	milligrams	M
mi	miles	L
ml	milliliters	L^3
mm	millimeters	L
mo	months	θ
min	minutes	θ
mph	miles per hour	L/θ

UNITS OF MEASUREMENT (Cont.)

Abbrev.	Definitions	Dimensions
N	newtons	F
oz	ounces force	F
ozm	ounces mass	M
oz (vol)	ounces volume	L^3
pdl	poundals	ML/θ^2
pH	scale of hydrogen ion concentration	none
pk	pecks	L^3
ppm	parts per million	none
psi	pounds per square inch	F/L^2
pt	pints	L^3
qt	quarts	L^3
rad	radians	none
rev	revolutions	none
rpm	revolutions per minute	$1/\theta$
s	scruples	F
sec	seconds	θ
slug	slugs mass	M
sq ft	square feet	L^2
V	volts	$F^{1/2}$
W	watts	LF/θ
wk	weeks	θ
yd	yards	L
yr	years	θ
μ	microns	L
Ω	ohms (resistance)	θ/L
°*C*	degrees Celcius (formerly centigrade)	T
°*F*	degrees Fahrenheit	T
°*K*	degrees Kelvin	T
°*R*	degrees Rankine	T
"Hg	inches mercury column	F/L^2
"WG	inches water gage	F/L^2
$	dollars	—
%	percent	none
"	seconds of angle	none
'	minutes of angle	none
°	degrees of angle	none

APPENDIX 3

CONVERSION FACTORS & EQUIVALENTS

TABLE 130—CONVERSION FACTORS

θ Time Units θ

Mean Solar				Mean Calendar			
sec*	min	hr	da	wk	mo	yr	l yr
1	.01667	.$_{3}$2778	.$_{4}$1157	.$_{5}$1653	.$_{6}$3805	.$_{7}$3171	.$_{7}$3163
60	1	.01667	.$_{3}$6944	.$_{4}$9921	.$_{4}$2283	.$_{5}$1903	.$_{5}$1898
3600	60	1	.04167	.$_{2}$5952	.$_{2}$1370	.$_{3}$1142	.$_{3}$1138
86400	1440	24	1	.14286	.03288	.$_{2}$2740	.$_{2}$2732
6048$_{2}$.	10080	168	7	1	.23013	.01918	.01913
2628$_{3}$.	43800	730	30.417	4.3453	1	.08333	.08333
3154$_{4}$.	5256$_{2}$.	8760	365	52.143	12	1	—
3162$_{4}$.	5270$_{2}$.	8784	366	52.286	12	—	1

1 sidereal second = .99727 mean solar sec
1 sidereal day = 86164 mean solar sec
1 lunar month = 29.532 mean solar da
1 sidereal year = 365.256 mean solar da

L Length Units L

U.S. System					Metric System				
mil	in.	ft	yd	mi	Å	μ	mm	m*	km
1	.001	.$_{4}$8333	.$_{4}$2778	.$_{7}$1578	2540$_{2}$.	25.400	.02540	.$_{4}$2540	.$_{7}$2540
1000	1	.08333	.02778	.$_{4}$1578	2540$_{5}$.	25400	25.400	.02540	.$_{4}$2540
12000	12	1	.33333	.$_{3}$1894	3048$_{6}$.	3048$_{2}$.	304.80	.30480	.$_{3}$3048
36000	36	3	1	.$_{3}$5682	9144$_{6}$.	9144$_{2}$.	914.40	.91440	.$_{3}$9144
6336$_{4}$.	63360	5280	1760	1	1609$_{10}$.	1609$_{6}$.	1609$_{3}$.	1609.3	1.6093
.$_{5}$3937	.$_{8}$3937	.$_{9}$3281	.$_{9}$1094	.$_{13}$621	1	.0001	10^{-7}	10^{-10}	10^{-13}
.03937	.$_{4}$3937	.$_{5}$3281	.$_{5}$1094	.$_{9}$6214	10000	1	.001	10^{-6}	10^{-9}
39.370	.03937	.$_{2}$3281	.$_{2}$1094	.$_{6}$6214	10^{7}	1000	1	.001	10^{-6}
39370	39.370	3.2808	1.0936	.$_{3}$6214	10^{10}	10^{6}	1000	1	.001
3937$_{4}$.	39370	3280.8	1093.6	.62137	10^{13}	10^{9}	10^{6}	1000	1

1 hand = 4 in. = 10.160 cm
1 fathom = 6 ft = 1.8288 m
1 rod = 5.5 yd = 5.0292 m
1 furlong = 220 yd = 201.17 m
1 naut. mile = 1.1508 mi = 1.8520 km
1 league = 3 mi = 4.8280 km
1 light year = 5.8785 x 10^{12} mi = 9.4606 x 10^{12} km

F Force Units F

U.S.		Metric	
lb	pdl	dy	N†
1	32.174	4448$_{2}$.	4.4482
.03108	1	13826.	.13826
.$_{5}$2248	.$_{4}$7233	1	10^{-5}
.22481	7.2330	10^{5}	1

M Mass Units M

U.S.		Metric	
lbm	slugs	g	kg*
1	.03108	453.59	.45359
32.174	1	14594	14.594
.$_{2}$2205	.$_{4}$6852	1	.001
2.2046	.06852	1000	1

T Temp. Units T

U.S.		Metric	
°F	°R	°C	°K*
1	1	5/9	5/9
1.8	1.8	1	1
32	491.67	0	273.15
−459.67	0	−273.15	0

H Heat Units H

U.S.	Metric		
Btu©	Joule†	cal©	kcal©
1	1055.1	252.00	.25200
.$_{3}$9478	1	23885	.$_{3}$2389
.$_{2}$3968	4.1868	1	.001
3.9683	.$_{2}$4187	1000	1

Inferior numerals indicate number of zeros (e.g., .$_{4}$8333 = .00008333)
*Base unit in SI system. †Derived unit in SI system.
©Btu, cal, and kcal based on International Steam Table.

TABLE 130 (Cont.)—CONVERSION FACTORS

F Weight and Mass Units⊙ M

U.S. Avoirdupois System						Metric System			
gr	dr	oz	lb	Ton	L. Ton	mg	g	kg*	M. Ton
1	.03657	$._{2}2286$	$._{3}1429$	$._{7}7143$	$._{7}6378$	64.799	.06480	$._{4}6480$	$._{7}6480$
27.344	1	.06250	$._{2}3906$	$._{5}1953$	$._{5}1744$	1771.8	1.7718	$._{2}1772$	$._{5}1772$
437.5	16	1	.0625	$._{4}3125$	$._{4}2790$	28350	28.350	.02835	$._{4}2835$
7000	256	16	1	$._{3}5000$	$._{3}4464$	$4536_{2}.$	453.59	.45359	$._{3}4536$
$1400_{4}.$	$5120_{2}.$	32000	2000	1	.89286	$9072_{5}.$	$9072_{2}.$	907.18	.90718
$1568_{4}.$	$5734_{2}.$	35840	2240	1.1200	1	$1016_{6}.$	$1016_{3}.$	1016.0	1.0160
.01543	$._{3}5644$	$._{4}3527$	$._{5}2205$	$._{8}1102$	$._{9}9842$	1	.001	10^{-6}	10^{-9}
15.432	.56438	.03527	$._{2}2205$	$._{5}1102$	$._{6}9842$	1000	1	.001	10^{-6}
15432	564.38	35.274	2.2046	$._{2}1102$	$._{3}9842$	10^{6}	1000	1	.001
$1543_{4}.$	$5644_{2}.$	35274	2204.6	1.1023	.98421	10^{9}	10^{6}	1000	1

Avoirdupois weight used for ordinary materials.

Troy weight used for jewels and precious metals.

1 grain (troy) = 1 gr (avoir.) = 64.799 mg
1 carat (troy) = 3.086 gr = 200 mg
1 pennywt (troy) = 24 gr = 1.555 g
1 ounce (troy) = 20 pennywt = 31.1035 g
1 pound (troy) = 12 oz (troy) = 373.24 g

Apothecaries' weight used for drugs, etc.

1 grain (ap.) = 1 gr (avoir.) = 64.799 mg
1 scruple (ap.) = 20 gr = 1.296 g
1 dram (ap.) = 3 s (ap.) = 3.8879 g
1 ounce (ap.) = 8 dr (ap.) = 31.1035 g
1 pound (ap.) = 12 oz. (ap.) = 373.24 g

Angular Measure

U.S. and Metric

″	′	°	rad*	rev
1	.01667	$._{3}2778$	$._{5}4848$	$._{6}7716$
60	1	.01667	$._{3}2909$	$._{4}4630$
3600	60	1	.01745	$._{2}2778$
$2063_{2}.$	3437.8	57.296	1	.15916
$6480_{2}.$	10800	180	π	.5
$1296_{3}.$	21600	360	2π	1

L^2 Area Units L^2

U.S. System					Metric System				
sq in.	sq ft	sq yd	acres	sq mi	sq μ	sq mm	sq m †	ares	sq km
1	$._{2}6944$	$._{3}7716$	$._{6}1594$	$._{9}2491$	$6451_{5}.$	645.16	$._{3}6452$	$._{5}6452$	$._{9}6452$
144	1	.11111	$._{4}2296$	$._{7}3587$	$9290_{7}.$	92903	.09290	$._{3}9290$	$._{7}9290$
1296	9	1	$._{3}2066$	$._{6}3228$	$8361_{8}.$	$8361_{2}.$	.83613	$._{2}8361$	$._{6}8361$
$6273_{3}.$	43560	4840	1	$._{2}1563$	$405_{12}.$	$4047_{6}.$	4046.9	40.469	$._{2}4047$
$4014_{6}.$	$2788_{4}.$	$3098_{3}.$	640	1	$259_{16}.$	$2590_{9}.$	$2590_{3}.$	25900	2.5900
$._{8}1550$	$._{10}108$	$._{11}120$	$._{15}247$	$._{18}386$	1	10^{-6}	10^{-12}	10^{-14}	10^{-18}
$._{2}1550$	$._{4}1076$	$._{5}1196$	$._{9}2471$	$._{12}386$	10^{6}	1	10^{-6}	10^{-8}	10^{-12}
1550	10.764	1.1960	$._{3}2471$	$._{6}3861$	10^{12}	10^{6}	1	.01	10^{-6}
$1550_{2}.$	1076.4	119.60	.02471	$._{4}3861$	10^{14}	10^{8}	100	1	.0001
$1550_{6}.$	$1076_{4}.$	$1196_{3}.$	247.10	.38610	10^{18}	10^{12}	10^{6}	10000	1

1 square mil = 10^{-6} sq in. = 645.162 sq μ
1 circular mil = 0.78540 sq mil = 506.71 sq μ
1 square rod = 30.25 sq yd = 25.293 sq m

⊙See Appendix 1 for discussion of weight and mass.
*Base unit in SI system. † Derived unit in SI system.

TABLE 130 (Cont.)—CONVERSION FACTORS

L^3 **Volume Units** L^3

U.S.			Metric System				
cu in.	cu ft	cu yd	cu cm	cu m†	ml	l	kl
1	.$_3$5787	.$_4$2143	16.387	.$_4$1639	16.387 —	.01639 —	.$_4$1639 —
1728	1	.03704	28317	.02832	28317 —	28.317 —	.02832 —
46656	27	1	7646$_2$.	.76456	7645$_2$. —	764.56 —	.76456 —
.06102	.$_4$3532	.$_5$1308	1	10^{-6}	1 —	.001 —	10^{-6} —
61024	35.315	1.3080	10^6	1	10^6 —	1000 —	1 —
.06102+	.$_4$3531+	.$_5$1308+	1+	10^{-6}+	1*	.001	10^{-6}
61.024+	.03531+	.$_2$1308+	1000+	.001+	1000	1*	.001
61024.+	35.315+	1.3080+	10^6+	1+	10^6	1000	1*

L^3 **Dry Measure (by volume)** L^3

U.S. System							Metric		
pt	qt	pk	bu	bbl	cu in.	cu ft	cu cm	l	cu m†
1	.5	.0625	.01563	.$_2$4762	33.600	.01944	550.61	.55060	.$_3$5506
2	1	.125	.03125	.$_2$9524	67.201	.03889	1101.2	1.1012	.$_2$1101
16	8	1	.25	.07619	537.61	.3111	8809.8	8.8098	.$_2$8810
64	32	4	1	.30479	2150.4	1.2444	35239	35.238	.03524
210	105	13.125	3.281	1	7056	4.0833	1156$_2$.	115.62	.11562
.02976	.01488	.$_2$1860	.$_3$4650	.$_3$1417	1	.$_3$5787	16.387	.01639	.$_4$1639
51.428	25.714	3.214	.80357	.$_2$4492	1728	1	28317	28.316	.02832
.$_2$1816	.$_3$9081	.$_3$1135	.$_4$2838	.$_6$8649	.06102	.$_4$3531	1	.001 —	10^{-6}
1.8162	.90811	.11351	.02838	.$_3$8649	61.025	.03532	1000+	1*	.001+
1816.2	908.08	113.51	28.378	.86492	61024	35.315	10^6	1000 —	1

1 board foot = 144 cu in. = 2359.7 cu cm
1 acre foot = 43560 cu ft = 1233.5 cu m

L^3 **Liquid Measure (by volume)** L^3

U.S. System							Metric		
oz	gi	pt	qt	gal	cu in.	cu ft	cu cm	l	cu m†
1	.25	.0625	.03125	.$_2$7813	1.8047	.$_2$1044	29.574	.02957	.$_4$2957
4	1	.25	.125	.03125	7.2188	.$_2$4177	118.29	.11829	.$_3$1183
16	4	1	.5	.125	28.875	.01671	473.18	.47318	.$_3$4732
32	8	2	1	.25	57.75	.03342	946.35	.94635	.$_3$9463
128	32	8	4	1	231	.13368	3785.4	3.7854	.$_2$3785
.55411	.13853	.03463	.01732	.$_2$4329	1	.$_3$5787	16.387	.01639	.$_4$1639
957.50	239.38	59.844	29.922	7.4805	1728	1	28317	28.317	.02832
.03381	.$_2$8454	.$_2$2113	.$_2$1057	.$_3$2642	.06103	.$_4$3532	1	.001 —	10^{-6}
33.814	8.4537	2.1134	1.0567	.26417	61.024	.03532	1000+	1*	.001+
33814	8453.7	2113.4	1056.7	264.17	61024	35.315	10^6	1000 —	1

1 gallon (Imp.) = 1.20094 gal (U.S.) = 4.5461 l
1 barrel (U.S.) = 31.5 gal (U.S.) = 119.24 l
1 barrel (oil) = 42 gal (U.S.) = 158.99 l
1 hogshead = 63 gal (U.S.) = 238.48 l
1 acre foot = 325,851 gal (U.S.) = 1,233,482 l

Apothecaries' fluid measure for drugs, etc.

1 minim = 1 drop = .06161 ml
1 dram = 60 minims = 3.6966 ml
1 ounce = 8 drams = .02957 l

*1 liter = vol. of 1 kg H_2O @ 4°C = 1000.028 cu cm, 1 new liter = 1000 cu cm
1 cu ft = vol. of 62.427 lb H_2O @ 4°C
+ or — signifies plus or minus 28 parts per million, ignore for new liters
†Derived unit in SI system.

TABLE 130 (Cont.)—CONVERSION FACTORS

L^3/θ Volume Flow Rate Units L^3/θ

U.S. System					Metric System				
cfs	cfm	cfh	gps	gpm	cc/sec	l/sec	m³/sec†	m³/min	m³/hr
1	60	3600	7.4805	448.83	28317	28.317	.02832	1.6990	101.94
.01667	1	60	.12468	7.4805	471.95	.47195	.$_3$4720	.02832	1.6990
.$_3$2778	.01667	1	.$_2$2078	.12468	7.8658	.$_2$7866	.$_5$7866	.$_3$4720	.02832
.13368	8.0208	481.25	1	60	3785.4	3.7854	.$_2$3785	.22712	13.627
.$_2$2228	.13368	8.0208	.01667	1	63.091	.06309	.$_4$6309	.$_2$3785	.22712
.$_4$3532	.$_2$2119	.12713	.$_3$2642	.01585	1	.001 −	10^{-6}	.00006	.0036
.03532	2.1189	127.13	.26419	15.850	1000 +	1	.001 +	.06 +	3.6 +
35.315	2118.9	1271$_2$	264.19	15850	10^6	1000 −	1	60	3600
.58861	35.314	2119.0	4.403	264.19	16667	16.666	.01667	1	60
.$_2$9810	.58861	35.314	.07338	4.4029	277.78	.27778	.$_3$2778	.01667	1

L/θ Velocity Units L/θ

U.S. System					Metric System				N_{Ma}
in./sec	fps	fpm	mph	knots	cm/sec	m/sec†	m/min	km/hr	—
1	.08333	5	.05682	.04938	2.5400	.02540	1.5240	.09144	.$_4$7461
12	1	60	.68182	.5949	30.480	.30480	18.288	1.0973	.$_3$8953
.2	.01667	1	.01136	.$_2$9875	.50800	.$_2$5080	.30480	.01829	.$_4$1492
17.599	1.4667	88	1	.86896	44.704	.44704	26.822	1.6093	.$_2$1313
20.252	1.6878	101.27	1.1508	1	51.444	.51444	30.867	1.8520	.$_2$1511
.39370	.03281	1.9685	.02237	.01944	1	.01	.6	.036	.$_4$2937
39.370	3.2808	196.85	2.2369	1.9438	100	1	60	3.6	.$_2$2937
.65616	.05468	3.2808	.03728	.03240	1.6667	.01667	1	.06	.$_4$4896
10.936	.91134	54.681	.62137	.53996	27.778	.27778	16.667	1	.$_3$8159
13403.	1116.9	67013.	761.52	661.81	34043	340.43	20426.	1225.6	1

L/θ^2 Acceleration Units L/θ^2

U.S. System				Metric System				Gravity
in./sec²	ft/sec²	ft/min²	mph/sec	cm/sec²	m/sec²†	m/min²	kmph/sec	g's
1	.08333	300	.05682	2.5400	.02540	91.44	.09144	.$_2$2590
12	1	3600	.68182	30.480	.30480	1097.3	1.0973	.03106
.$_2$3333	.$_3$2778	1	.$_3$1894	.$_2$8467	.$_4$8467	.30480	.$_3$3048	.$_5$8636
17.599	1.4667	5280.0	1	44.704	.44704	1609	1.609	.04559
.39370	.03281	118.11	.02237	1	.01	36	.036	.$_2$1020
39.370	3.2808	11811.	2.2369	100	1	3600	3.6	.10197
.01094	.$_3$9113	3.2808	.$_3$6214	.02778	.$_3$2778	1	.001	.$_4$2832
10.936	.91134	3280.8	.62137	27.778	.27778	1000	1	.02832
386.09	32.174	1158$_2$.	21.937	980.67	9.8067	35305	35.305	1

g_c Conversion Factor Values $ML/F\theta^2$

U.S. ENGINEERING SYSTEM
32.174 ft-lbm/lb-sec²
386.09 in.-lbm/lb-sec²
41697$_4$.0 ft-lbm/lb-hr²

U.S. PHYSICAL SYSTEM
1.0 ft-lbm/pdl-sec²

METRIC ENGINEERING SYSTEM
980.665 cm-g/gf-sec²

METRIC PHYSICAL SYSTEM
1.0 cm-g/dy-sec²

SYSTÈME INTERNATIONAL D'UNITÉS (SI)
1.0m-kg/N-sec²

†Derived unit in SI system.

TABLE 130 (Cont.)—CONVERSION FACTORS

LF — Work, Energy and Heat Units — H

U.S. System				Metric System					
ft-lb	ft-pdl	Btu*	hp-hr	joule†	dy-cm	gf-cm	cal*	kcal*	kW-hr
1	32.174	$.{}_{2}1285$	$.{}_{6}5050$	1.3558	$1356_{4}.$	13825	.32383	$.{}_{3}3238$	$.{}_{6}3766$
.03108	1	$.{}_{4}3994$	$.{}_{7}1570$	.04214	$4214_{2}.$	429.70	.01006	$.{}_{4}1006$	$.{}_{7}1171$
778.17	25037	1	$.{}_{3}3930$	1055.1	$1055_{7}.$	$1076_{4}.$	252.00	.25200	$.{}_{3}2931$
$1980_{3}.$	$6370_{4}.$	2544.5	1	$2685_{3}.$	$269_{11}.$	$2738_{7}.$	$6412_{2}.$	641.19	.7457
.73756	23.730	$.{}_{3}9478$	$.{}_{6}3725$	1	10^{7}	10197	.23885	$.{}_{3}2389$	$.{}_{6}2778$
$.{}_{7}7376$	$.{}_{5}2373$	$.{}_{10}948$	$.{}_{13}373$	10^{-7}	1	$.{}_{2}1020$	$.{}_{7}2389$	$.{}_{10}2389$	$.{}_{13}278$
$.{}_{4}7233$	$.{}_{2}2327$	$.{}_{7}9295$	$.{}_{10}366$	$.{}_{4}9807$	980.67	1	$.{}_{4}2342$	$.{}_{7}2342$	$.{}_{10}273$
3.0880	99.354	$.{}_{2}3968$	$.{}_{5}1560$	4.1868	$4187_{4}.$	42693	1	.001	$.{}_{5}1163$
3088.0	99354	3.9683	$.{}_{2}1560$	4186.8	$4187_{7}.$	$4269_{4}.$	1000	1	$.{}_{2}1163$
$2655_{3}.$	$8542_{4}.$	3412.2	1.3410	$3600_{3}.$	$360_{11}.$	$3671_{7}.$	$8598_{2}.$	859.85	1

1 joule = 1 watt-sec = 1 newton-m
1 erg = 1 dyne-cm = 10^{-7} joules

LF/θ — Power and Heat Flow Rate Units — H/θ

U.S. System					Metric System				
ft-lb/sec	ft-lb/min	Btu/min*	Btu/hr*	hp	erg/sec	kcal/sec*	kcal/min*	W†	kW
1	60	.07710	4.6262	$.{}_{2}1818$	$1356_{4}.$	$.{}_{3}3238$	.01943	1.3558	$.{}_{2}1356$
.01667	1	$.{}_{2}1285$	.07710	$.{}_{4}3030$	$2260_{2}.$	$.{}_{5}5397$	$.{}_{3}3238$	.02260	$.{}_{4}2260$
12.970	778.17	1	60	.02358	$1758_{5}.$	$.{}_{2}4200$	.25200	17.584	.01758
.21616	12.970	.01667	1	$.{}_{3}3930$	$2930_{3}.$	$.{}_{4}7000$	$.{}_{2}4200$	.29307	$.{}_{3}2931$
550	33000	42.408	2544.5	1	$7457_{6}.$	.17811	10.687	745.70	.74570
$.{}_{7}7376$	$.{}_{5}4425$	$.{}_{8}5687$	$.{}_{6}3412$	$.{}_{9}1341$	1	$.{}_{10}2389$	$.{}_{8}1433$	10^{-7}	10^{-10}
3088.0	$1853_{2}.$	238.10	14286	5.6144	$4187_{7}.$	1	60	4186.8	4.1868
51.467	3088.0	3.9683	238.10	.09357	$6978_{5}.$	.01667	1	69.78	.06978
.73756	44.254	.05687	3.1422	.00134	10^{7}	$.{}_{3}2389$	.01433	1	.001
737.56	44254	56.870	3412.2	1.3410	10^{10}	.23885	14.331	1000	1

1 ton refrigeration = 12000 Btu/hr
1 metric hp = 75 kg-m/sec = .98632 U.S. hp
1 boiler hp = 33479 Btu/hr = 9.803 kW

L^2/θ — Kinematic Viscosity and Diffusivity Units — $L^3/L\theta$

U.S. System		Metric System		
ft^2/sec	ft^2/hr	centistokes	m^2/sec†	m^2/hr
1	3600	92903	929.03	334.45
$.{}_{3}27778$	1	25.806	.25806	.09290
$.{}_{4}10764$	.038751	1	.01	.00360
$.{}_{2}10764$	3.8751	100	1	3600
$.{}_{2}29900$	10.764	277.78	$.{}_{3}27778$	1

1 stoke = 1 cm^2/sec = 1 poise-cm^3/g
1 centistoke = cP/ρ (in g/cm^3)
1 centistoke = cP/(SG referred to water)

M/Lθ — Absolute Viscosity Units — $F\theta/L^2$

U.S. System			Metric System	
lbm/ft-sec	lbm/ft-hr	lb-sec/ft^2	centipoises	N-sec/m^2†
1	3600	.031081	1488.2	1.4882
$.{}_{3}27778$	1	$.{}_{5}8634$	.41338	$.{}_{3}4134$
32.174	115877	1	47880	47.880
$.{}_{3}67197$	2.4191	$.{}_{4}20885$	1	.001
.67197	2419.1	.020885	1000	9.8067

1 poise = 100 centipoise = 1 g/cm-sec = 1 dy-sec/cm^2

*Btu, cal and kcal based on International Steam Table.
†Derived unit in SI system.

TABLE 130 (Cont.)—CONVERSION FACTORS

F/L³ Weight and Mass Density Units M/L³

U.S. System				Metric System					
gr/ft³	lb/in.³	lb/ft³	slug/ft³	g/cm³	g/ml	g/l	g/m³	kg/l	kg/m³†
1	.$_7$8267	.$_3$1429	.$_5$4440	.$_5$2288	.$_5$2288	.$_2$2288	2.2883	.$_5$2288	.$_2$2288
1210$_4$.	1	1728	53.708	27.681	27.681	27681	2768$_4$.	27.681	27680
7000	.$_3$5787	1	.03108	.01602	.01602	16.019	16018	.01602	16.018
2252$_2$.	.01862	32.174	1	.51538	.51539	515.39	5154$_2$.	.51539	515.38
4370$_2$.	.03613	62.428	1.9403	1	1+	1000+	10^6	1+	1000
4370$_2$.	.03613	62.427	1.9403	1−	1	1000	10^6−	1	1000−
436.99	.$_4$3613	.06243	.$_2$1940	.001−	.001	1	1000−	.001	1−
.43700	.$_7$3613	.$_4$6243	.$_5$1940	10^{-6}	10^{-6}+	.001+	1	10^{-6}+	.001
4370$_2$.	.03613	62.427	1.9403	1−	1	1000	10^6−	1	1−
437.00	.$_4$3613	.06243	.$_2$1940	.001	.001+	1+	1000	.001+	1

F/L² Pressure and Equivalent Head Units F/L²

U.S. System					Metric System				
psi	psf	"WG	ft WG	"Hg	dy/cm²	N/m²†	mm WG	mm Hg	atm
1	144	27.736	2.3113	2.0360	68947	6894.7	704.49	51.714	.06805
.$_2$6944	1	.19261	.01605	.01414	478.80	47.880	4.8923	.35913	.$_3$4726
.03605	5.1918	1	.08333	.07341	2485.8	248.58	25.400	1.8627	.$_2$2453
.43265	62.302	12	1	.88089	29830	2983.0	304.80	22.374	.02944
.49116	70.727	13.623	1.1350	1	33864	3386.4	346.02	25.400	.03342
.$_4$1450	.$_2$2089	.$_3$4023	.$_4$3352	.$_4$2953	1	.1	.01022	.$_3$7501	.$_6$9869
.$_3$1450	.02089	.$_2$4023	.$_3$3352	.$_3$2953	10	1	.10219	.$_2$7501	.$_5$9869
.$_2$1420	.20440	.03937	.$_2$3281	.$_2$2890	97.863	9.7863	1	.07341	.$_4$9661
.01934	2.7845	.53632	.04469	.03937	1333.2	133.32	13.623	1	.$_2$1316
14.696	2116.3	407.61	33.968	29.921	1013$_3$.	1013.$_2$	10353	760	1

WG @ 70°F

1 bar = 10^6 dy/cm²
1 pascal = 1 N/m²
1 torr = 1 mm Hg

Hg @ 32°F or 0°C

F/L Surface Tension Units M/θ²

U.S. System			Metric System	
lb/in.	ft-lb/ft²	mg/in.	dy/cm	erg/cm²
1	12	453600	175130	175130
.083333	1	37800	14594	14594
.$_5$22046	.$_4$26455	1	.38609	.38609
.$_5$57101	.$_4$68522	2.5901	1	1

L⁴ Second Moment of Area L⁴

U.S. System		Metric System	
in.⁴	ft⁴	cm⁴	m⁴†
1	.$_4$4823	41.622	.$_6$4162
20740	1	86312.	.$_2$8631
.02403	.$_5$1159	1	10^{-8}
2403$_3$.	115.87	10^8	1

ML² Mass Moment of Inertia FLθ²

U.S. System		Metric System	
lbm-in.²	lbm-ft²	g-cm²	kg-cm²
1	.006945	2926.4	2.9264
144	1	421400	421.40
.$_3$34172	.$_5$23730	1	.001
.34172	.002373	1000	1

†Derived units in SI system.

TABLE 130 (Cont.)—CONVERSION FACTORS

$M/\theta L^2$ Mass Velocity Units $M/\theta L^2$

U.S. System		Metric System		
lbm/hr-ft^2	lbm/sec-ft^2	g/sec-cm^2	kg/hr-cm^2	kg/hr-m^2
1	$._{3}27778$	$._{3}13562$	$._{3}48824$	4.8824
3600	1	.48824	1.7576	17576
7373.5	2.0482	1	3.6	36000
2048.2	.56893	.27778	1	10000
.20482	$._{4}56893$	$._{4}27778$	.0001	1

$M/\theta F$ Permeance Units $M/\theta L^2(F/L^2)$

U.S. System		Metric System	
lbm/hr-ft^2-"Hg	grm/hr-ft^2-"Hg	g/sec-cm^2-mmHg	g/sec-cm^2-dy/cm^2
1	7000	$._{5}53395$	$._{8}40049$
$._{3}14286$	1	$._{9}76279$	$._{12}57213$
187285	$13110_{5}.$	1	$._{3}75006$
$24969_{4}.$	$17479_{8}.$	1333.2	1

1 perm = 1 grm/hr-ft^2-"Hg vapor pressure diff.

H/MT Specific Heat Units H/MT

U.S. System	Metric System	
Btu/lbm-°F	joule/g-°C	cal/g-°C
1	4.1868	1
.23885	1	.23885

H/M Enthalpy Units H/M

U.S. System	Metric System	
Btu/lbm	joule/g	cal/g
1	2.3260	.55556
.42992	1	.23885
1.8	4.1868	1

$H/\theta LT$ Thermal Conductivity $HL/\theta L^2T$

U.S. System		Metric System	
Btu/hr-ft^2-°F/in.	Btu/hr-ft^2-°F/ft	joule/sec-cm^2-°C/cm	cal/sec-cm^2-°C/cm
1	.08333	.001442	$._{3}34448$
12	1	.017307	$._{2}41338$
693.35	57.779	1	.23885
2902.9	241.91	4.1868	1*

1 watt/cm^2-°C/cm = 1 joule/sec-cm^2-°C/cm

$H/\theta L^2T$ Thermal Conductance $H/\theta L^2T$

U.S. System	Metric System	
Btu/hr-ft^2-°F	joule/sec-cm^2-°C	cal/sec-cm^2-°C
1	$._{3}56781$	$._{3}13562$
1761.1	1	.23885
7373.5	4.1868	1

*cal based on 15°C water.

TABLE 131—FAHRENHEIT—CELCIUS EQUIVALENTS

Fahrenheit Equivalents for Every 10° Celcius

°C	0	−10	−20	−30	−40	−50	−60	−70	−80	−90
−200	−328	−346	−364	−382	−400	−418	−436	−454	—	—
−100	−148	−166	−184	−202	−220	−238	−256	−274	−292	−310
0	+32	+14	−4	−22	−40	−58	−76	−94	−112	−130

°C	0	+10	+20	+30	+40	+50	+60	+70	+80	+90
0	32	50	68	86	104	122	140	158	176	194
100	212	230	248	266	284	302	320	338	356	374
200	392	410	428	446	464	482	500	518	536	554
300	570	590	608	626	644	662	680	698	716	734
400	752	770	788	806	824	842	860	878	896	914
500	932	950	968	986	1004	1022	1040	1058	1076	1094
600	1112	1130	1148	1166	1184	1202	1220	1238	1256	1274
700	1292	1310	1328	1346	1364	1382	1400	1418	1436	1454
800	1472	1490	1508	1526	1544	1562	1580	1598	1616	1634
900	1652	1670	1688	1706	1724	1742	1760	1778	1796	1814
1000	1832	1850	1868	1886	1904	1922	1940	1958	1976	1994
1100	2012	2030	2048	2066	2084	2102	2120	2138	2156	2174
1200	2192	2210	2228	2246	2264	2282	2300	2318	2336	2354
1300	2372	2390	2408	2426	2444	2462	2480	2498	2516	2534
1400	2552	2570	2588	2606	2624	2642	2660	2678	2696	2714
1500	2732	2750	2768	2786	2804	2822	2840	2858	2876	2894

Fahrenheit Equivalents for Each Degree Celcius

°C	1	2	3	4	5	6	7	8	9	10
°F	1.8	3.6	5.4	7.2	9.0	10.8	12.6	14.4	16.2	18.0

Celcius Equivalents for Each Degree Fahrenheit

°F	1	2	3	4	5	6	7	8	9
°C	0.56	1.11	1.67	2.22	2.78	3.33	3.89	4.44	5.00
°F	10	11	12	13	14	15	16	17	18
°C	5.56	6.11	6.67	7.22	7.78	8.33	8.89	9.44	10.00

EXAMPLES:

−75°C to °F

read −94°F opposite −70°C
read 9°F opposite 5°C
∴ −103°F = −75°C

+900°F to °C

read 480°C opposite 896°F
read 2.22°C opposite 4°F
∴ 482.22°C = 900°F

FORMULAS:

$$°F = \left(\frac{9}{5}\,°C + 32°\right)$$

$$°C = \frac{5}{9}\,(°F - 32°)$$

TABLE 132—DECIMAL EQUIVALENTS

Angular				Linear				
min	deg	sec	deg	inches			inches	mm
						1/64	.015625	.397
0′	.0000	0″	.0000		1/32		.03125	.794
1′	.0167	1″	.0003			3/64	.046875	1.191
2′	.0333	2″	.0006	1/16			.0625	1.588
3′	.05	3″	.0008			5/64	.078125	1.984
4′	.0667	4″	.0011		3/32		.09375	2.381
5′	.0833	5″	.0014			7/64	.109375	2.778
6′	.10	6″	.0017	1/8			.125	3.175
7′	.1167	7″	.0019			9/64	.140625	3.572
8′	.1333	8″	.0022		5/32		.15625	3.969
9′	.15	9″	.0025			11/64	.171875	4.366
10′	.1667	10″	.0028	3/16			.1875	4.763
11′	.1833	11″	.0031			13/64	.203125	5.159
12′	.2	12″	.0033		7/32		.21875	5.556
13′	.2167	13″	.0036			15/64	.234375	5.953
14′	.2333	14″	.0039	1/4			.25	6.350
15′	.25	15″	.0042			17/64	.265625	6.747
16′	.2667	16″	.0044		9/32		.28125	7.144
17′	.2833	17″	.0047			19/64	.296875	7.541
18′	.3	18″	.005	5/16			.3125	7.938
19′	.3167	19″	.0053			21/64	.328125	8.334
20′	.3333	20″	.0056		11/32		.34375	8.731
21′	.35	21″	.0058			23/64	.359375	9.128
22′	.3667	22″	.0061	3/8			.375	9.525
23′	.3833	23″	.0064			25/64	.390625	9.922
24′	.4	24″	.0067		13/32		.40625	10.319
25′	.4167	25″	.0069			27/64	.421875	10.716
26′	.4333	26″	.0072	7/16			.4375	11.113
27′	.45	27″	.0075			29/64	.453125	11.509
28′	.4667	28″	.0078		15/32		.46875	11.906
29′	.4833	29″	.0081			31/64	.484375	12.303
30′	.5	30″	.0083	1/2			.5	12.700
						33/64	.515625	13.097
31′	.5167	31″	.0086		17/32		.53125	13.494
32′	.5333	32″	.0089			35/64	.546875	13.891
33′	.55	33″	.0092	9/16			.5625	14.288
34′	.5667	34″	.0094			37/64	.578125	14.684
35′	.5833	35″	.0097		19/32		.59375	15.081
36′	.6	36″	.01			39/64	.609375	15.478
37′	.6167	37″	.0103	5/8			.625	15.875
38′	.6333	38″	.0106			41/64	.640625	16.272
39′	.65	39″	.0108		21/32		.65625	16.669
40′	.6667	40″	.0111			43/64	.671875	17.066
41′	.6833	41″	.0114	11/16			.6875	17.463
42′	.7	42″	.0117			45/64	.703125	17.859
43′	.7167	43″	.0119		23/32		.71875	18.256
44′	.7333	44″	.0122			47/64	.734375	18.653
45′	.75	45″	.0125	3/4			.75	19.050
46′	.7667	46″	.0128			49/64	.765625	19.447
47′	.7833	47″	.0131		25/32		.78125	19.844
48′	.8	48″	.0133			51/64	.796875	20.241
49′	.8167	49″	.0136	13/16			.8125	20.638
50′	.8333	50″	.0139			53/64	.828125	21.034
51′	.85	51″	.0142		27/32		.84375	21.431
52′	.8667	52″	.0144			55/64	.859375	21.828
53′	.8833	53″	.0147	7/8			.875	22.225
54′	.9	54″	.015			57/64	.890625	22.622
55′	.9167	55″	.0153		29/32		.90625	23.019
56′	.9333	56″	.0156			59/64	.921875	23.416
57′	.95	57″	.0158	15/16			.9375	23.813
58′	.9667	58″	.0161			61/64	.953125	24.209
59′	.9833	59″	.0164		31/32		.96875	24.606
60′	1.	60″	.0167			63/64	.984375	25.003

APPENDIX 4

PROPERTIES OF MATERIALS

TABLE 133—PROPERTIES OF THE ELEMENTS

Name	No.	Sym.	At. Wt.
Actinium	89	Ac	[227]
Aluminum	13	Al	26.982
Americium	95	Am	[243]
Antimony	51	Sb	121.75
Argon	18	A	39.948
Arsenic	33	As	74.9216
Astatine	85	At	[210]
Barium	56	Ba	137.34
Berkelium	97	Bk	[247]
Beryllium	4	Be	9.012
Bismuth	83	Bi	208.9806
Boron	5	B	10.811
Bromine	35	Br	79.909
Cadmium	48	Cd	112.40
Calcium	20	Ca	40.08
Californium	98	Cf	[251]
Carbon	6	C	12.011
Cerium	58	Ce	140.12
Cesium	55	Cs	132.905
Chlorine	17	Cl	35.453
Chromium	24	Cr	51.996
Cobalt	27	Co	58.933
Copper	29	Cu	63.546
Curium	96	Cm	[247]
Dysprosium	66	Dy	162.50
Einsteinium	99	E	[254]
Erbium	68	Er	167.26
Europium	63	Eu	151.96
Fermium	100	Fm	[253]
Fluorine	9	F	18.9984
Francium	87	Fr	[223]
Gadolinium	64	Gd	157.25
Gallium	31	Ga	69.72
Germanium	32	Ge	72.59
Gold	79	Au	196.967
Hafnium	72	Hf	178.49
Helium	2	He	4.0026
Holmium	67	Ho	164.930
Hydrogen	1	H	1.00797
Indium	49	In	114.82
Iodine	53	I	126.04
Iridium	77	Ir	192.2
Iron	26	Fe	55.847
Krypton	36	Kr	83.80
Lanthanum	57	La	138.91
Lawrencium	103	Lw	[257]
Lead	82	Pb	207.19
Lithium	3	Li	6.939
Lutetium	71	Lu	174.97
Magnesium	12	Mg	24.312
Manganese	25	Mn	54.938
Mendelevium	101	Mv	[256]
Mercury	80	Hg	200.59
Molybdenum	42	Mo	95.94
Neodymium	60	Nd	144.24
Neon	10	Ne	20.183
Neptunium	93	Np	[237]
Nickel	28	Ni	58.71
Niobium	41	Nb	92.906
Nitrogen	7	N	14.0067
Nobelium	102	No	[254]
Osmium	76	Os	190.2
Oxygen	8	O	15.9994
Palladium	46	Pd	106.4
Phosphorus	15	P	30.9738
Platinum	78	Pt	195.09
Plutonium	94	Pu	[242]
Polonium	84	Po	[210]
Potassium	19	K	39.102
Praseodymium	59	Pr	140.9077
Promethium	61	Pm	[147]
Protactinium	91	Pa	[231]
Radium	88	Ra	[226]
Radon	86	Rn	[222]
Rhenium	75	Re	186.2
Rhodium	45	Rh	102.905
Rubidium	37	Rb	85.47
Ruthenium	44	Ru	101.07
Samarium	62	Sa	150.35
Scandium	21	Sc	44.956
Selenium	34	Se	78.96
Silicon	14	Si	28.086
Silver	47	Ag	107.870
Sodium	11	Na	22.9898
Strontium	38	Sr	87.62
Sulfur	16	S	32.064
Tantalum	73	Ta	180.948
Technetium	43	Tc	[99]
Tellurium	52	Te	127.60
Terbium	65	Tb	158.924
Thallium	81	Tl	204.37
Thorium	90	Th	232.038
Thulium	69	Tm	168.934
Tin	50	Sn	118.69
Titanium	22	Ti	47.90
Tungsten	74	W	183.85
Uranium	92	U	238.03
Vanadium	23	V	50.942
Xenon	54	Xe	131.30
Ytterbium	70	Yb	173.04
Yttrium	39	Y	88.905
Zinc	30	Zn	65.37
Zirconium	40	Zr	91.22
Columbium	41	Cb	See Nb

Unstable elements have mass numbers of most stable isotope listed in brackets rather than atomic weights.

TABLE 134—PROPERTIES OF SATURATED STEAM

Pressure	Temp.	Density	Spec. Vol.	Enthalpy		
				Sat. Liq.	Evap.	Sat. Vap.
psig	°F	lb/ft³	ft³/lb	Btu/lb	Btu/lb	Btu/lb
0	212.00	.03731	26.800	180.07	970.3	1150.4
1	215.33	.03967	25.210	183.43	968.2	1151.6
2	218.50	.04202	23.800	186.61	966.2	1152.8
3	221.51	.04439	22.530	189.66	964.2	1153.9
4	224.39	.04673	21.400	192.56	962.3	1154.9
5	227.14	.04907	20.380	195.32	960.6	1155.9
6	229.80	.05139	19.460	198.01	958.9	1156.9
7	232.32	.05371	18.620	200.55	957.2	1157.8
8	234.76	.05601	17.853	203.04	955.6	1158.6
9	237.11	.05828	17.148	205.41	954.1	1159.5
10	239.39	.06062	16.496	207.72	952.6	1160.3
15	249.75	.07207	13.876	218.23	945.7	1163.9
20	258.76	.08335	11.999	227.38	939.6	1166.9
25	266.78	.09456	10.576	235.55	934.0	1169.6
30	274.02	.10595	9.438	242.95	929.0	1171.9
35	280.62	.11674	8.566	249.69	924.3	1174.0
40	286.71	.12778	7.826	257.99	918.4	1176.4
45	292.37	.13871	7.210	261.73	915.7	1177.4
50	297.66	.14959	6.685	267.18	911.9	1179.1
55	302.62	.16044	6.233	272.31	908.2	1180.5
60	307.32	.17126	5.839	277.14	904.6	1181.7
65	311.77	.18265	5.475	281.75	901.2	1183.0
70	316.00	.19287	5.185	286.13	898.0	1184.1
75	320.03	.20359	4.912	290.36	894.9	1185.3
80	323.90	.21437	4.665	294.34	891.9	1186.2
85	327.59	.22498	4.445	298.18	888.9	1187.1
90	331.15	.23564	4.244	301.88	886.1	1188.0
95	334.57	.24625	4.061	305.46	883.3	1188.8
100	337.88	.25695	3.892	308.91	880.7	1189.6
110	344.15	.27818	3.595	315.49	875.6	1191.1
120	350.04	.29950	3.339	321.67	870.7	1192.3
130	355.59	.32075	3.121	327.53	865.9	1193.4
140	360.84	.34166	2.927	333.07	861.5	1194.6
150	365.85	.36272	2.757	338.38	857.1	1195.6
160	370.62	.38398	2.607	343.44	853.0	1196.4
170	375.17	.40488	2.470	348.29	848.9	1197.2
180	379.54	.42593	2.348	352.95	845.0	1198.0
190	383.74	.44685	2.238	357.45	841.0	1198.5
200	387.78	.46795	2.137	361.78	837.5	1199.3

Adapted from the data of J. H. Keenan and F. G. Keyes, "Thermodynamic Properties of Steam," John Wiley & Sons, Inc., New York, 1936. Based on a barometric pressure of 14.696 psi and enthalpy of liquid above 32°F. Refer to Table 3 for vapor pressures of ice and water in "Hg which are given for each °F from —20°F to 409°F.

TABLE 135—PROPERTIES OF GASES

Gas (at 29.92 "Hg)	Formula	Mol. Wt.	Spec. Grav.	Spec. Heat	Gas Const.	c_p/c_v	Abs. Visc.	Ther. Cond.
		MW	SG	c_p @ 59°F	R	γ @ 59°F	μ @ 59°F	k @ 32°F
		—	air = 1	Btu / lb-°F	ft / °F	—	cp	Btu / hr-ft-°F
Acetylene	C_2H_2	26.04	.906	.383	(59.35)	1.26	.009	.0106
Air	see Table 1	28.97	1.00	.240[a]	53.30	1.40	.0181[b]	.0135
Ammonia	NH_3	17.03	.597	.523	90.77	1.31	.010[c]	.0124
Argon	A	39.95	1.38	.125[a]	(38.69)	1.668	.022	.0094
Bromine	Br_2	159.8	5.87	.055	(9.671)	1.32	.015	
Butane	C_4H_{10}	58.12	(2.01)	.456	(26.59)	1.11	.008[c]	
Butylene	C_4H_8	56.11	(1.94)		(27.54)		.007	
Carbon dioxide	CO_2	44.00	1.53	.199[a]	35.13	1.304	.015[c]	.0082
Carbon disulfide	CS_2	76.14	2.63	.157	(20.30)	1.63	.010	.0039
Carbon monoxide	CO	28.01	.968	.248[a]	(55.17)	1.404	.017	.0131
Chlorine	Cl_2	70.91	2.49	.115	(21.79)	1.355	.013	.0044
Cyanogen	$(CN)_2$	52.04	1.80	.410	(29.70)	1.256	.010	
Deuterium	D_2	4.028	.139		(383.7)		.013	
Ethane	C_2H_6	30.07	1.05	.386	(51.39)	1.22	.009[c]	.0104
Ethylene	C_2H_4	28.05	.975	.359	(55.09)	1.255	.010	.0097
Fluorine	F_2	38.00	1.31	.196	40.68		.021	.0142
Formaldehyde	CH_2O	30.03	(1.04)		(51.46)			
Helium (−292°F)*	He	4.003	.137	*1.248[a]	386.3	*1.660	.020[b]	.0810
Hydrogen	H_2	2.016	.069	3.388[a]	766.5	1.410	.009[b]	.0958
Hydrogen chloride	HCl	36.46	1.27	.194	(42.39)	1.41	.014	
Hydrogen sulfide	H_2S	34.08	1.19	.253	(45.35)	1.32	.012	.0074
Krypton	Kr	83.70	2.82	(.439)[a]	(18.46)	1.68	.025	
Methane	CH_4	16.04	.554	.528	(96.35)	1.31	.011	.0174
Methyl bromide	CH_3Br	94.94	(3.28)		(16.28)	1.27	.010	.0042
Methyl chloride	CH_3Cl	50.49	1.79	.240	(30.61)	1.28	.010[c]	.0054
Neon	Ne	20.18	.674	(1.82)[a]	(76.58)	1.64	.031	.0264
Nitric oxide	NO	30.01	1.04	.233	(51.50)	1.400	.018	.0134
Nitrogen	N_2	28.01	.967	.248[a]	55.16	1.404	.017[b]	.0137
Nitrous oxide	N_2O	44.01	1.53	.200	(35.11)	1.303	.014	.0085
Oxygen	O_2	32.00	1.10	.218[a]	48.31	1.401	.020[b]	.0138
Ozone	O_3	48.00	1.66	.197	32.21			
Phosgene	$COCl_2$	98.92	(4.16)		(15.63)			
Phosphine	PH_3	34.00	1.15		(45.45)		.011	
Propane	C_3H_8	44.11	1.56	.473	(35.04)	1.13	.008	
Propylene	C_3H_6	42.08	1.50		(36.73)		.008	
Sulfur dioxide	SO_2	64.06	2.26	.152	(24.12)	1.29	.012[c]	.0047
Sulfur trioxide	SO_3	80.06	2.75		(19.30)			
Vinyl chloride	C_2H_3Cl	62.50	(2.16)		(24.73)			
Water Vapor (212°)†	H_2O	18.02	.622	†.484[a]	85.81	†1.324	†.013[b]	†.0133
Xenon	Xe	131.30	4.53	(.028)[a]	(11.77)	1.66	.022	

[a]Refer to Table 6 for additional values.
[b]Refer to Figure 22 for additional values.
[c]Refer to Figure 23 for additional values.

Adapted from the data of N. A. Lange, "Handbook of Chemistry," Handbook Publishers, Inc., Sandusky, Ohio, 1952. Data in parentheses calculated from MW.

TABLE 136—PROPERTIES OF LIQUIDS

Liquid (at 68°F & 29.92 "Hg or as noted) (100% or % in H_2O as noted)	Formula	Spec. Grav. SG $H_2O = 1$	Spec. Heat c_p Btu/lb-°F	Latent Heat λ_v Btu/lb	Vapor Press. e_{sat} "Hg	Abs. Visc. μ cp	Therm. Cond. k @ 54°F Btu/hr-ft-°F
Acetic acid	$C_2H_4O_2$	1.049	.468	174	.461	1.22	.099
Acetone	C_3H_6O	.791	.528	237	7.28	.331	.102
Ammonia	NH_3	.618	1.13	518	253	.266	.29
Amyl acetate	$C_7H_{14}O_2$	.871	.459			.806	.073
Aniline	$C_6H_5NH_2$	1.022	.495	187	.002	4.47	.099
Benzene	C_6H_6	.879	.406	188	3.01	.647	.081
Brine—25%	$CaCl_2$	1.228	.687			2.67	.318
Brine—25%	$NaCl$	1.189	.814			2.02	.265
Butane	C_4H_{10}	.579	.550	158	61.5	.187	.076
Carbon dioxide	CO_2	1.101	.92	63.1	1690	.071	
Carbon disulfide	CS_2	1.263	.240	157	11.60	.376	.083
Carbon tetrachloride	CCl_4	1.594	.201	93.8	3.58	.958	.061
Chloroform	$CHCl_3$	1.489	.234	113	6.27	.563	.070
Ethyl Acetate	$C_4H_8O_2$	.901	.459	183	2.87	.455	.084
Ethyl Alcohol	C_2H_6O	.789	.622	368	1.73	1.19	.101
Ethyl Alcohol—40%	C_2H_6O	.935	.920			1.25	.224
Ethyl Ether	$C_4H_{10}O$	.708	.503	151	17.4	.245	.073
Ethylene glycol	$C_2H_6O_2$	1.115	.57	344	.002	20.9	.167
Ethylene glycol—50%	—	1.067	.70		.40	4.1	.242
Freon 11—12.87 psia	$CFCl_3$	1.490	.214	78.9	27.3	.46	.064
Freon 12—82.28 psia	CF_2CL_2	1.331	.253	60.6	153	.27	.052
Freon 22—133 psia	CHF_2Cl	1.215	.298	81.0	279	.24	.062
Gasoline	—	.687	.70			.35	
Glycerol	$C_3H_8O_2$	1.261	.573			1069	.162
Heptane	C_7H_{16}	.684	.508	157	1.30	.416	.082
Hexane	C_6H_{14}	.659	.537	157	4.96	.326	.088
Hydrochloric acid—40%	HCl	1.198	.60	178			.254
Kerosene	—	.82	.50			1.8	.085
Methyl acetate	$C_3H_6O_2$	.933	.468	190	6.68	.388	.093
Methyl alcohol	CH_4O	.792	.610	499	3.78	.593	.120
Methyl chloride	CH_3Cl	.92	.385	172	144	.183	.089
Milk	—	1.03	.93				
Nitric acid	HNO_3	1.502		206		1.77	
Octane	C_8H_{18}	.703	.523	156	.417	.542	.091
Oil, draft gage	—	.834					
Oil, linseed	—	.941	.53			33	
Oil, lube. (med.)	—	.91	.45			200	.080
Oil, olive	—	.92	.33			84	.109
Oil, vegetable	—	.92	.434			40.6	
Pentane	C_5H_{12}	.626	.527	158		.240	.069
Phenol	C_6H_6O	1.071	.561		.001	12.7	
Propane	C_3H_8	.585	.576	150	258	.14	.075
Sulfur dioxide	SO_2	1.434	.35	151	96.5	.27	.115
Sulfuric acid—98%	H_2SO_4	1.836	.336	202		23.0	.205
Toluene	C_7H_8	.866	.407	178	.870	.590	.074
Turpentine	—	.867	.472	133	.17	1.49	.063
Water, 39.2°F (4°C)	H_2O	1.000	1.005	1069	.240	1.567	.325
Water, 59°F (15°C)	H_2O	.999	1.000	1058	.504	1.140	.339
Water, 68.7°F (20.2°C)	H_2O	.998	.998	1054	.707	1.000	.346
Water, 70°F (21.1°C)	H_2O	.998	.998	1053	.739	.978	.347
Water, 212°F (100°C)	H_2O	.958	1.006	970	29.92	.284	.393
Water, heavy	D_2O	1.108	1.018	894			
Water, sea	—	1.025	.94			1.03	.349

Adapted from the data of N. A. Lange, "Handbook of Chemistry," Handbook Publishers, Inc., Sandusky, Ohio, 1952. Refer to manufacturers' data for exact properties.

TABLE 137—PROPERTIES OF SOLIDS

Solid	Density	Specific Heat	Thermal Conductivity
	δ	c_p	k
	lb/ft³	Btu/lb-°F	Btu-in./hr-ft²-°F
Asbestos	153	.20	1.7
Asbestos—cement board	120	—	4.0
Ashes	43	.20	0.5
Asphalt	82	—	5.2
Bakelite	86	.33	—
Borax	109	.38	—
Brick, common	120	.22	5.0
Brick, face	130	.22	9.0
Calcium carbonate	177	.19	14.4
Calcium chloride	134	.16	—
Carborundum	195	.16	1.5
Celluloid	87	.36	1.4
Cellulose	94	.37	—
Cement, loose	94	.20	2.1
Cement, mortar	116	.20	5.0
Chalk	142	.21	5.8
Charcoal, hardwood	34	.20	—
Cinders, loose	43	.18	—
Clay, dry	63	.22	—
Clay, moist	110	.55	—
Coal, anth., solid	98	.31	—
Coal, bitum., solid	85	.30	—
Coke, solid	75	.20	—
Concrete, cinder	97	.18	3.5
Concrete, stone	140	.19	12.5
Cork	15	.48	0.4
Corkboard	8	—	0.3
Cotton	5	.32	0.4
Dry Ice	97	.12	—
Earth, moist	78	.44	12.0
Ebonite	72	.35	1.2
Fats	58	.46	—
Feldspar	160	.20	16.2
Flannel	—	—	0.7
Glass, crown	160	.16	5.5
Glass, flint	215	.13	4.1
Glass, pyrex	140	.20	7.5
Granite	165	.19	12.5
Graphite	99	.20	306
Gypsum, compressed	152	.26	9.0
Gypsum board	50	—	1.4
Hay, baled	20	.32	—

TABLE 137 (Cont.)—PROPERTIES OF SOLIDS

Solid	Density	Specific Heat	Thermal Conductivity
	δ	c_p	k
	lb/ft³	Btu/lb-°F	Btu-in./hr-ft²-°F
Ice	56	.50	14.5
Leather, dried	56	.36	1.2
Limestone	163	.22	12.5
Magnesia, 85%	17	.22	0.5
Marble	168	.21	14.0
Mica	183	.21	5.2
Neoprene	77	.40	0.1
Nylon	70	.55	—
Paper	58	.32	0.9
Paraffin	56	.69	1.7
Plywood	34	—	0.8
Porcelain	150	.26	7.2
Potatoes, piled	42	.80	—
Quartz	165	.21	46.0
Rubber, hard	70	.40	1.3
Rubber, soft	60	.50	0.9
Salt, granulated and piled	48	.21	—
Sand, dry	99	.20	2.7
Sandstone	144	.22	12.5
Sawdust	13	.52	.35
Slate	172	—	10.4
Snow, fresh	10	.50	—
Snow, compact	35	—	3.2
Sodium carbonate	91	.27	—
Sodium nitrate	141	.28	—
Sodium sulfate	167	.21	—
Stucco	116	—	5.0
Sucrose	100	.30	—
Sugar, bulk	55	.28	—
Sulfur	126	.17	1.9
Synthane	86	.35	2.0
Talc	170	.21	—
Vinyl	84	.24	—
Wood, hard	45	.57	1.1
Wood, soft	32	.47	0.8
Wood, parallel grain	—	—	2.4
Zinc Oxide	350	.12	4.1

Refer to the following tables for additional data: Table 16—Metals and Alloys, Table 17—Insulating Materials, Tables 80 through 87—Building Materials, Table 112—Finely Divided Materials, Table 120—Perishable Products.

TABLE 138—PROPERTIES OF METALS AND ALLOYS

Metal or Alloy	CTE 10^{-6}/°F	TS M psi	YS M psi	FS M psi	E M psi	G M psi	ν —
Aluminum Alloys							
1100—H18	13.0	24	21	8.5	10000	3850	0.33
2024—T4	12.9	68	46	18	10600	3850	0.33
3003—H18	12.9	29	25	10	10000	3850	0.33
5052—H38	13.3	41	36	19	10200	3850	0.33
5086—H34	13.4	47	37	—	10300	3850	0.33
6061—T6	13.0	45	40	13.5	10000	3850	0.33
7075—T6	13.1	82	72	22.5	10400	3850	0.33
Copper Alloys							
pure Copper	9.16	32	—	—	—	—	0.33
deoxidized Copper	9.82	32	10	11	17000	—	—
commercial Bronze	10.1	37	10	21	17000	—	—
red Brass	10.4	39	10	20	17000	—	—
Muntz Metal	11.6	54	21	—	15000	—	—
Naval Brass	11.8	55	25	15	15000	—	—
Admiralty Metal	11.2	48	18	18	15000	—	—
Silicon Bronze	10.0	56	21	16	15000	—	—
Nickel Alloys							
pure Nickel	13.3	46	8.5	—	30000	—	—
Monel	7.8	75	40	38.5	26000	9500	—
"K" Monel	7.8	90	40	38.5	26000	—	—
Inconel X750	7.0	181	124	25	31000	11000	0.29
Inconel 600	7.4	98	36.5	39	31000	11000	0.29
Hastelloy B	5.5	130	56	—	30750	—	—
Hastelloy C	6.3	120	55	—	28500	—	—
Hastelloy D	6.1	110	—	—	28850	—	—
Miscellaneous Metals							
pure Lead	—	2.51	1.32	.52	—	—	—
lead Babbitt	13.3	10	—	3.9	4200	—	—
pure Magnesium	14.4	27	14	9	6500	2400	0.35
pure Tin	12.8	2.4	—	—	6000	2400	0.33
Titanium 75A	5.0	75	60	75	15500	5300	—
rolled Zinc Alloy	19.3	28	—	6.8	—	—	—
Iron							
wrought	6.35	48	27	23	—	—	0.28
cast—gray No. 20	—	20	—	10	12000	—	0.27
pure	6.5	42	26	26	29800	11600	0.28
Steel							
AISI 1006	6.77	42	21	—	29000	—	—
AISI 1040	5.2	77	38.5	—	29000	—	—
ASTM A242	6.3	70	50	42	29000	—	—
Heat Treated (T1)	7.6	115	100	50	30000	—	—
Stainless Steel							
302	9.6	85	35	42	28000	12500	—
304	9.6	85	30	40	28000	12500	—
309	8.3	90	40	—	29000	—	—
310	8.0	95	45	—	29000	—	—
316	8.9	80	30	38	28000	—	—
317	8.9	85	40	—	28000	—	—
321, 347	9.3	90	35	39	28000	—	—
403, 410	5.5	65	35	40	29000	—	—
416	5.5	75	40	40	29000	—	—
430	5.4	75	40	40	29000	—	—
501	6.2	70	30	—	29000	—	—
502	6.2	65	25	—	29000	—	—

CTE, coefficient of thermal expansion; TS, tensile strength; YS, yield strength; FS, fatigue strength; E, modulus of elasticity; G, modulus of rigidity; ν, Poisson's ratio.
Refer to Table 16 for Thermal Properties.
Refer to Manufacturers' data for exact properties.

Adapted from the data of S. L. Hoyt, "Metals Properties," *ASME Handbook*, McGraw-Hill Book Co., Inc., New York, 1954, (hot rolled or annealed sheet or plate in most cases).

APPENDIX 5

METAL PRODUCT INFORMATION

TABLE 139—WEIGHTS OF STEEL

In Pounds per Foot of Length

Round Steel Shafts

Fraction of In.	Diameter in Inches										
	0	1	2	3	4	5	6	7	8	9	10
0	0	2.67	10.68	24.03	42.73	66.76	96.1	130.9	170.9	216.3	267.0
1/16	0.010	3.015	11.36	25.05	44.07	68.44	98.2	133.2	173.6	219.3	270.4
1/8	0.042	3.380	12.06	26.08	45.44	70.14	100.2	135.6	176.3	222.4	273.8
3/16	0.094	3.766	12.78	27.13	46.83	71.86	102.2	138.0	179.0	225.4	277.1
1/4	0.167	4.172	13.52	28.21	48.23	73.60	104.3	140.4	181.8	228.5	280.6
5/16	0.261	4.600	14.28	29.30	49.66	75.36	106.4	142.8	184.5	231.6	284.0
3/8	0.376	5.049	15.06	30.42	51.11	77.15	108.5	145.2	187.3	234.7	287.4
7/16	0.511	5.518	15.87	31.55	52.58	78.95	110.7	147.7	190.1	237.8	290.9
1/2	0.668	6.008	16.69	32.71	54.07	80.78	112.8	150.2	192.9	241.0	294.4
9/16	0.845	6.519	17.53	33.89	55.59	82.62	115.0	152.7	195.8	244.2	297.9
5/8	1.043	7.051	18.40	35.09	57.12	84.49	117.2	155.3	198.7	247.4	301.5
11/16	1.262	7.604	19.29	36.31	58.67	86.38	119.4	157.8	201.5	250.6	305.0
3/4	1.502	8.178	20.20	37.55	60.25	88.29	121.7	160.4	204.5	253.9	308.6
13/16	1.763	8.773	21.12	38.81	61.85	90.22	123.9	163.0	207.4	257.1	312.2
7/8	2.044	9.388	22.07	40.10	63.46	92.17	126.2	165.6	210.3	260.4	315.8
15/16	2.347	10.024	23.04	41.40	65.10	94.14	128.5	168.2	213.3	263.7	319.5

Steel Flats and Bars

Thickness	Width in Inches										
	1	1 1/2	2	2 1/2	3	3 1/2	4	4 1/2	5	5 1/2	6
1/4	.85	1.27	1.70	2.12	2.55	2.97	3.40	3.82	4.25	4.67	5.10
3/8	1.28	1.91	2.55	3.19	3.83	4.46	5.10	5.74	6.38	7.01	7.65
1/2	1.70	2.55	3.40	4.25	5.10	5.95	6.80	7.65	8.50	9.35	10.20
5/8	2.13	3.19	4.25	5.31	6.38	7.44	8.50	9.56	10.63	11.69	12.75
3/4	2.55	3.83	5.10	6.38	7.65	8.93	10.20	11.48	12.75	14.03	15.30
7/8	2.98	4.46	5.95	7.44	8.93	10.41	11.90	13.39	14.88	16.36	17.85
1	3.40	5.10	6.80	8.50	10.20	11.90	13.60	15.30	17.00	18.70	20.40

Standard Steel Angles

Size	Thickness of Leg in Inches									
	1/8	3/16	1/4	5/16	3/8	7/16	1/2	5/8	3/4	7/8
1 x 1	.80	1.16	1.49	—	—	—	—	—	—	—
1 1/4 x 1 1/4	1.01	1.48	1.92	—	—	—	—	—	—	—
1 1/2 x 1 1/2	1.23	1.80	2.34	—	—	—	—	—	—	—
2 x 1 1/2	1.44	2.12	2.77	—	—	—	—	—	—	—
2 x 2	1.65	2.44	3.19	3.92	4.7	—	—	—	—	—
2 1/2 x 2	—	2.75	3.62	4.5	5.3	—	—	—	—	—
2 1/2 x 2 1/2	—	3.07	4.1	5.0	5.9	—	7.7	—	—	—
3 x 2 1/2	—	—	4.5	5.6	6.6	7.6	8.5	—	—	—
3 x 3	—	3.71	4.9	6.1	7.2	8.3	9.4	—	—	—
3 1/2 x 2 1/2	—	—	4.9	6.1	7.2	8.3	9.4	—	—	—
3 1/2 x 3	—	—	5.4	6.6	7.9	9.1	10.2	—	—	—
3 1/2 x 3 1/2	—	—	5.8	7.2	8.5	9.8	11.1	—	—	—
4 x 3	—	—	5.8	7.2	8.5	9.8	11.1	13.6	—	—
4 x 4	—	—	6.6	8.2	9.8	11.3	12.8	15.7	18.5	—
5 x 3	—	—	6.6	8.2	9.8	11.3	12.8	—	—	—
5 x 5	—	—	—	10.3	12.3	14.3	16.2	20.0	23.6	27.2

TABLE 140—SHEET METAL AND WIRE GAUGES AND WEIGHTS

Gauge	Mfrs'. Std. Ga.① Plate & Sheet			Mill Std. Th.② Plate & Sheet		Brown & Sharpe (B&S) Gauges③ Non-Ferrous Plate & Sheet				
see note 7	Thick.	Steel	Galv.	Thick.	Alum.	Thick.	Alum.	Copper	Brass	Mag.
no.	in.	lb/ft²	lb/ft²	in.	lb/ft²	in.	lb/ft²	lb/ft²	lb/ft²	lb/ft²
7-0's	½	20.4	—	.500	7.06	—	—	—	—	—
6-0's	15/32	19.125	—	—	—	—	—	—	—	—
5-0's	7/16	17.85	—	—	—	—	—	—	—	—
4-0's	13/32	16.575	—	—	—	.460	6.48	21.27	20.37	—
000	⅜	15.3	—	.375	5.29	.410	5.77	18.94	18.14	—
00	11/32	14.025	—	—	—	.365	5.14	16.87	16.15	—
0	5/16	12.75	—	.313	4.42	.325	4.58	15.07	14.39	—
1	9/32	11.475	—	—	—	.289	4.08	13.40	12.81	—
2	¼	10.2	—	.250	3.53	.258	3.63	11.96	11.41	—
3	.2391	10.0	—	—	—	.229	3.23	10.61	10.16	—
4	.2242	9.375	—	—	—	.204	2.88	9.45	9.05	—
5	.2092	8.75	—	—	—	.182	2.56	8.41	8.05	—
6	.1943	8.125	—	.190	2.68	.162	2.28	7.49	7.17	—
7	.1793	7.50	—	—	—	.144	2.03	6.67	6.39	—
8	.1644	6.875	7.031	.160	2.26	.128	1.81	5.94	5.68	1.18
9	.1495	6.25	6.406	—	—	.114	1.61	5.29	5.07	—
10	.1345	5.625	5.781	—	—	.102	1.44	4.71	4.51	.940
11	.1196	5.00	5.156	.125	1.76	.091	1.28	4.20	4.02	—
12	.1046	4.375	4.531	.100	1.41	.081	1.14	3.74	3.58	.746
13	.0897	3.75	3.906	.090	1.27	.072	1.01	3.33	3.19	—
14	.0747	3.125	3.281	.080	1.13	.064	.903	2.97	2.84	.590
15	.0673	2.812	2.969	.071	1.00	.057	.804	2.64	2.53	—
16	.0598	2.50	2.656	.063	.889	.051	.716	2.35	2.25	.470
17	.0538	2.25	2.406	—	—	.045	.638	2.10	2.01	.415
18	.0478	2.00	2.156	.050	.706	.040	.568	1.86	1.78	.369
19	.0418	1.75	1.906	—	—	.036	.506	1.66	1.59	.332
20	.0359	1.5	1.656	.040	.564	.032	.450	1.48	1.42	.295
21	.0329	1.375	1.531	—	—	.0285	.401	1.32	1.26	.258
22	.0299	1.25	1.406	.032	.452	.0253	.357	1.17	1.12	.230
23	.0269	1.125	1.281	—	—	.0226	.318	1.05	1.00	.212
24	.0239	1.00	1.156	.025	.353	.0201	.283	.930	.890	.184
25	.0209	.875	1.031	—	—	.0179	.252	.828	.793	—
26	.0179	.750	.9062	.020	.282	.0159	.225	.735	.706	—
27	.0164	.6875	.8438	—	—	.0142	.200	.657	.628	—
28	.0149	.625	.7813	.016	.226	.0126	.178	.583	.560	—

①Manufacturers' Standard Gauges for Steel Products are definite thickness gauges. Weights are based on steel with a density of 489.6 lb/ft³. An additional 2.5% is included in the sheet weights to allow for thickness variation and shearing tolerance. Galvanized sheets are .0037″ thicker and 2.5 oz/ft² heavier than uncoated sheets. Thinner coatings are also available. (Commercial coating is 1.25 oz/ft².) All thicknesses ¼″ or more are plates and have no relationship to gauge numbers. Refer to Steel Products Manual of AISI and Manufacturers' data.

②Mill Standard Thicknesses for Aluminum Products have no relationship to gauge numbers. Weights are based on alloy with a density of .098 lb/in.³ or 169.4 lb/ft³. Refer to Manufacturers' data.

③Brown & Sharpe Gauges are identical to American Wire Gauges. Weights are based on aluminum, copper, brass, and magnesium alloys with densities of .098, .321, .308, and .064 lb/in.³, respectively. Refer to Manufacturers' data.

TABLE 140 (Cont.)—SHEET METAL AND WIRE GAUGES AND WEIGHTS

Gauge	Zinc Ga. Sheet & Plate		B. W. Ga.④ Plate & Sheet		U.S. Steel Wire Ga.⑤ Wire			U.S. Std. Ga.⑥ Plate & Sheet		
see note 7	Thick.	Zinc	Thick.	Copper	Diam.	Steel	Copper	Thick.	316SS	Titan
no.	in.	lb/ft²	in.	oz/ft²	in.	lb/ft	lb/ft	in.	lb/ft²	lb/ft²
7-0's	—	—	—	—	.4900	.6404	.7259	½	20.67	11.72
6-0's	—	—	—	—	.4615	.5681	.6439	15/32	19.38	10.99
5-0's	—	—	—	—	.4305	.4943	.5603	7/16	18.09	10.26
4-0's	—	—	.454	337.5	.3938	.4136	.4689	13/32	16.80	9.524
000	—	—	.425	316.0	.3625	.3505	.3973	3/8	15.50	8.791
00	—	—	.380	282.5	.3310	.2922	.3313	11/32	14.21	8.059
0	—	—	.340	252.8	.3065	.2506	.2840	5/16	12.92	7.326
1	.002	.075	.300	223.0	.2830	.2136	.2421	.281	11.63	6.593
2	.004	.150	.284	211.0	.2625	.1838	.2083	.266	10.98	6.227
3	.006	.225	.259	192.5	.2437	.1584	.1796	.250	10.34	5.861
4	.008	.300	.238	177.0	.2253	.1354	.1535	.234	9.690	5.495
5	.010	.375	.220	163.5	.2070	.1143	.1296	.219	9.044	5.128
6	.012	.450	.203	151.0	.1920	.0983	.1115	.203	8.398	4.762
7	.014	.525	.180	134.0	.1770	.0836	.0947	.188	7.752	4.396
8	.016	.600	.165	122.5	.1620	.0700	.0794	.172	7.218	4.029
9	.018	.675	.148	110.0	.1483	.0587	.0665	.156	6.563	3.663
10	.020	.750	.134	99.50	.1350	.0486	.0551	.141	5.906	3.297
11	.024	.900	.120	89.25	.1205	.0387	.0439	.125	5.250	2.930
12	.028	1.05	.109	81.00	.1055	.0297	.0337	.109	4.594	2.564
13	.032	1.20	.095	70.62	.0915	.0223	.0253	.094	3.938	2.198
14	.036	1.35	.083	61.76	.0800	.0171	.0194	.078	3.281	1.832
15	.040	1.50	.072	53.58	.0720	.0138	.0157	.070	2.953	1.648
16	.045	1.68	.065	48.30	.0625	.0104	.0118	.062	2.625	1.465
17	.050	1.87	.058	43.15	.0540	.0078	.0088	.056	2.363	1.319
18	.055	2.06	.049	36.40	.0475	.0060	.0068	.050	2.100	1.172
19	.060	2.25	.042	31.25	.0410	.0045	.0051	.0438	1.837	1.026
20	.070	2.62	.035	26.00	.0348	.0032	.0037	.0375	1.575	0.879
21	.080	3.00	.032	23.80	.0317	.0027	.0030	.0344	1.444	0.806
22	.090	3.37	.028	20.80	.0286	.0022	.0025	.0312	1.313	0.733
23	.100	3.75	.025	18.60	.0258	.0018	.0020	.0281	1.181	0.659
24	.125	4.70	.022	16.40	.0230	.0014	.0016	.0250	1.050	0.586
25	.250	9.40	.020	14.85	.0204	.0011	.0013	.0219	.9187	0.513
26	.375	14.1	.018	13.35	.0181	.0009	.0010	.0188	.7875	0.440
27	.500	18.8	.016	11.90	.0173	.0008	.0009	.0172	.7218	0.403
28	1.000	37.6	.014	10.40	.0162	.0007	.0008	.0156	.6562	—

④ Birmingham Wire Gauges are identical to Stubs' Wire Gauges. Weights are based on copper with a density of .321 lb/in.³. Refer to Manufacturers' data.

⑤ United States Steel Wire Gauges are identical to American Steel & Wire Gauges, Washburn & Moen Wire Gauges, and Roebling Wire Gauges. Weights are based on steel and copper with densities of .283 and .321 lb/in.³, respectively. Refer to Manufacturers' data.

⑥ United States Standard Gauges for Iron & Steel Products are weight gauges based on wrought iron with a density of 480 lb/ft³. Weights are based on stainless steel and titanium alloys with densities of .287 and .163 lb/in.³, respectively. All thicknesses 3/16″ or more are plates. Thicknesses 5/16″ or more have no relationship to gauge numbers. Refer to Manufacturers' data.

⑦ It is recommended that sheet and wire always be specified by decimal thickness rather than gauge number.

TABLE 141—STEEL BEAM AND CHANNEL DATA

Section		Steel Wt.	Flange		Web	Neutral Axis			
Depth	Area		Width	Thick.	Thick.	I_x	I_x/c_x	I_y	I_y/c_y
in.	in.^{2}	lb/ft	in.	in.	in.	in.^{4}	in.^{3}	in.^{4}	in.^{3}
American Standard Steel I-Beams									
24	30.98	105.9	7.875	1.102	.625	2811.5	234.3	78.9	20.0
24	23.33	79.9	7.000	.871	.500	2087.2	173.9	42.9	12.2
20	24.80	85.0	7.053	.916	.653	1501.7	150.2	47.0	13.3
20	19.08	65.4	6.250	.789	.500	1169.5	116.9	27.9	8.9
18	15.94	54.7	6.000	.691	.460	795.5	88.4	21.2	7.1
15	12.49	42.9	5.500	.622	.410	441.8	58.9	14.6	5.3
12	11.84	40.8	5.250	.659	.460	268.9	44.8	38.8	5.3
12	9.26	31.8	5.000	.544	.350	215.8	36.0	9.5	3.8
10	7.38	25.4	4.660	.491	.310	122.1	24.4	6.9	3.0
8	5.34	18.4	4.000	.425	.270	56.9	14.2	3.8	1.9
7	4.43	15.3	3.660	.392	.250	36.2	10.4	2.7	1.5
6	3.61	12.5	3.330	.359	.230	21.8	7.3	1.8	1.1
5	2.87	10.0	3.000	.326	.210	12.1	4.8	1.2	.82
4	2.21	7.7	2.660	.293	.190	6.0	3.0	.77	.58
3	1.64	5.7	2.330	.260	.170	2.5	1.7	.46	.40
American Standard Steel Channels									
18	12.48	42.7	3.950	.625	.450	549.2	61.0	15.0	4.9
15	9.90	33.9	3.400	.650	.400	312.6	41.7	8.2	3.2
12	6.03	20.7	2.940	.501	.280	128.1	21.4	3.9	1.7
10	4.47	15.3	2.600	.436	.240	66.9	13.4	2.3	1.2
9	3.89	13.4	2.430	.413	.230	47.3	10.5	1.8	.97
8	3.36	11.5	2.260	.390	.220	32.3	8.1	1.3	.79
7	2.85	9.8	2.090	.366	.210	21.1	6.0	.98	.63
6	2.39	8.2	1.920	.343	.200	13.0	4.3	.70	.50
5	1.95	6.7	1.750	.320	.190	7.4	3.0	.48	.38
4	1.56	5.4	1.580	.296	.180	3.8	1.9	.32	.29
3	1.19	4.1	1.410	.273	.170	1.6	1.1	.20	.21
Steel Wide Flange Beams									
35.88	67.73	230	16.475	1.260	.765	14988	835.5	870.9	105.7
35.84	44.16	150	11.972	.940	.625	9012	502.9	250.4	41.8
33.00	58.79	200	15.750	1.150	.715	11048	669.6	691.7	87.8
33.10	38.26	130	11.510	.855	.580	6699	404.8	201.4	35.0
29.88	50.65	172	14.985	1.065	.655	7892	528.2	550.1	73.4
29.82	31.77	108	10.484	.760	.548	4461	299.2	135.1	25.8
26.91	27.65	94	9.990	.747	.490	3267	242.8	115.1	23.0
23.91	22.37	76	8.985	.682	.440	2096	175.4	76.5	17.0
20.99	18.23	62	8.240	.615	.400	1327	126.4	53.1	12.9
18.00	14.71	50	7.500	.570	.358	800.6	89.0	37.2	9.9
15.85	10.59	36	6.992	.428	.299	446.3	56.3	22.1	6.3
13.86	8.81	30	6.733	.383	.270	289.6	41.8	17.5	5.2
11.95	7.97	27	6.500	.400	.240	204.1	34.1	16.6	5.1
9.90	6.19	21	5.75	.340	.240	106.3	21.5	9.7	3.4
8.00	5.00	17	5.25	.308	.230	56.4	14.1	6.7	2.6
Steel Car and Ship Channels									
13	9.30	31.8	4.000	.610	.375	237.5	36.5	11.6	3.9
12	10.22	35.0	3.767	.700	.467	214.9	35.8	12.9	4.8
12	9.00	30.9	3.450	.600	.450	181.8	30.3	8.9	3.5
10	6.38	21.9	3.450	.500	.325	97.6	19.5	7.0	2.8
9	6.96	23.9	3.450	.550	.400	84.3	18.7	7.5	3.1
8	5.43	18.7	2.975	.500	.350	51.9	13.0	4.4	2.1
7	5.12	17.6	3.000	.475	.375	37.3	10.7	4.2	2.0
6	4.47	15.3	3.500	.385	.340	25.3	8.4	5.1	2.1
6	3.52	12.0	2.500	.375	.313	18.6	6.2	2.0	1.1
4	4.00	13.8	2.500	.500	.500	8.8	4.4	2.2	1.4
3	2.08	7.1	1.938	.351	.312	2.7	1.8	.71	.56

Refer to AISC Manual or Manufacturers' Catalogs for data on heavier beams and other details.

TABLE 142—PIPE AND PIPE FLANGE DATA

Welded and Seamless Steel and Stainless Steel Pipe

Nom. Size	Outs. Dia.	Std., Sched. 40 or 40S				Extra Strong, Sched. 80 or 80S			
		wall	I.D.	wt.	I.A.	wall	I.D.	wt.	I.A.
in.	in.	in.	in.	lb/ft	in.^{2}	in.	in.	lb/ft	in.^{2}
⅛	0.405	.068	.269	.245	.0568	.095	.215	.315	.0363
¼	0.540	.088	.364	.425	.1041	.119	.302	.535	.0716
⅜	0.675	.091	.493	.568	.1909	.126	.423	.739	.1405
½	0.840	.109	.622	.851	.3039	.147	.546	1.088	.2341
¾	1.050	.113	.824	1.131	.5333	.154	.742	1.474	.4324
1	1.315	.133	1.049	1.679	.8643	.179	.957	2.172	.7193
1 ¼	1.660	.140	1.380	2.273	1.496	.191	1.278	2.997	1.283
1 ½	1.900	.145	1.610	2.718	2.036	.200	1.500	3.631	1.767
2	2.375	.154	2.067	3.653	3.355	.218	1.939	5.022	2.953
2 ½	2.875	.203	2.469	5.793	4.788	.276	2.323	7.661	4.238
3	3.5	.216	3.068	7.576	7.393	.300	2.900	10.25	6.605
3 ½	4.0	.226	3.548	9.109	9.886	.318	3.364	12.51	8.888
4	4.5	.237	4.026	10.79	12.73	.337	3.826	14.98	11.50
5	5.563	.258	5.047	14.62	20.01	.375	4.813	20.78	18.19
6	6.625	.280	6.065	18.97	28.89	.432	5.761	28.57	26.07
8	8.625	.322	7.981	28.55	50.03	.500	7.625	43.39	45.66
		Standard (& 40S*)				Extra Strong (& 80S*)			
10	10.75	.365*	10.02	40.48	78.85	.500*	9.75	54.74	74.66
12	12.75	.375*	12.00	49.56	113.1	.500*	11.75	65.42	108.4
14 O.D.	14.0	.375	13.25	54.57	137.9	.500	13.00	72.09	132.7
16 O.D.	16.0	.375	15.25	62.58	182.7	.500	15.00	82.77	176.7
18 O.D.	18.0	.375	17.25	70.59	233.7	.500	17.00	93.45	227.0
20 O.D.	20.0	.375	19.25	78.60	291.0	.500	19.00	104.1	283.5
24 O.D.	24.0	.375	23.25	94.62	424.6	.500	23.00	125.5	415.5
		Schedule 40 Only				Schedule 80 (& 80S*)			
10	10.75	.365	10.02	40.48	78.85	.593	9.56	64.33	71.78
12	12.75	.406	11.94	53.53	112.0	.687	11.38	88.51	101.7
14 O.D.	14.0	.438	13.12	63.37	135.2	.750	12.50	106.1	122.7
16 O.D.	16.0	.500	15.00	82.77	176.7	.843	14.31	136.5	160.8
18 O.D.	18.0	.562	16.88	104.8	223.8	.937*	16.13	170.8	204.3
20 O.D.	20.0	.593	18.81	122.9	277.9	1.031	17.94	208.9	252.8
24 O.D.	24.0	.687	22.63	171.2	402.2	1.218*	21.56	296.4	365.1

Stainless Steel Schedules indicated by Suffix S.

American Standard Cast Iron Flanges

Nom. Size	Class 125				Class 250			
	Flange		Bolt Circle		Flange		Bolt Circle	
	Diam.	Thick.	Diam.	No.—Size	Diam.	Thick.	Diam.	No.—Size
in.	in.	in.	in.	#—in.	in.	in.	in.	#—in.
1	4 ¼	7/16	3 ⅛	4— ½	4 ⅞	11/16	3 ½	4— ⅝
1 ¼	4 ⅝	½	3 ½	4— ½	5 ¼	¾	3 ⅞	4— ⅝
1 ½	5	9/16	3 ⅞	4— ½	6 ⅛	13/16	4 ½	4— ¾
2	6	⅝	4 ¾	4— ⅝	6 ½	⅞	5	8— ⅝
2 ½	7	11/16	5 ½	4— ⅝	7 ½	1	5 ⅞	8— ¾
3	7 ½	¾	6	4— ⅝	8 ¼	1 ⅛	6 ⅝	8— ¾
3 ½	8 ½	13/16	7	8— ⅝	9	1 3/16	7 ¼	8— ¾
4	9	15/16	7 ½	8— ⅝	10	1 ¼	7 ⅞	8— ¾
5	10	15/16	8 ½	8— ¾	11	1 ⅜	9 ¼	8— ¾
6	11	1	9 ½	8— ¾	12 ½	1 7/16	10 ⅝	12— ¾
8	13 ½	1 ⅛	11 ¾	8— ¾	15	1 ⅝	13	12— ⅞
10	16	1 3/16	14 ¼	12— ⅞	17 ½	1 ⅞	15 ¼	16—1
12	19	1 ¼	17	12— ⅞	20 ½	2	17 ¾	16—1 ⅛
14 O.D.	21	1 ⅜	18 ¾	12—1	23	2 ⅛	20 ¼	20—1 ⅛
16 O.D.	23 ½	1 7/16	21 ¼	16—1	25 ½	2 ¼	22 ½	20—1 ¼
18 O.D.	25	1 9/16	22 ¾	16—1 ⅛	28	2 ⅜	24 ¾	24—1 ¼
20 O.D.	27 ½	1 11/16	25	20—1 ⅛	30 ½	2 ½	27	24—1 ¼
24 O.D.	32	1 ⅞	29 ½	20—1 ¼	36	2 ¾	32	24—1 ½

Class 250 has 1/16″ raised face. Bolt holes are ⅛″ larger than bolt (3/16″ for 1 ½″).

TABLE 143—WEIGHTS OF TUBING

Seamless Steel Round Tubing

in lb per ft of length

Size	Mechanical Tubing—Wall gauge (B.W.) and Thickness (in.)								
O.D. in.	22G .028	20G .035	18G .049	16G .065	14G .083	12G .109	10G .134	3/16″ .1875	1/4″ .25
1/4	.0664	.0804	.1052	.1284	.1480	—	—	—	—
3/8	.1038	.1271	.1706	.2152	.2585	.3097	.3449	—	—
1/2	.1411	.1738	.2360	.3020	.3696	.4552	.5238	.6264	—
5/8	.1785	.2205	.3014	.3888	.4805	.6007	.7027	.8774	1.001
3/4	.2159	.2673	.3668	.4755	.5913	.7462	.8816	1.128	1.335
7/8	.2533	.3140	.4323	.5623	.7021	.8917	1.060	1.379	1.669
1	.2907	.3607	.4977	.6491	.8129	1.037	1.239	1.630	2.003
1 1/8	.3280	.4074	.5631	.7359	.9237	1.183	1.418	1.881	2.336
1 1/4	.3654	.4542	.6285	.8226	1.034	1.328	1.597	2.132	2.610
1 3/8	.4028	.5009	.6939	.9094	1.145	1.474	1.776	2.383	3.004
1 1/2	.4402	.5476	.7593	.9962	1.256	1.619	1.955	2.634	3.338
1 5/8	—	.5943	.8248	1.083	1.346	1.765	2.134	2.885	3.671
1 3/4	—	.6411	.8902	1.170	1.478	1.910	2.313	3.136	4.005
1 7/8	—	.6878	.9556	1.257	1.589	2.056	2.492	3.387	4.339
2	—	.7345	1.021	1.343	1.699	2.201	2.670	3.638	4.673

Refer to Manufacturers' Catalogs for data on other sizes, gauges, and shapes.

Heat Exchanger Tubing

O.D. in.	Wall Thickness (in.)						
	.035	.050	.065	.085	.095	.105	.120
1/2	.1738	.2403	.3020	—	—	—	—
5/8	.2205	.3071	.3888	.4902	—	—	—
3/4	—	.3738	.4755	.6037	.6646	—	—
7/8	—	.4406	.5623	.7172	.7914	—	—
1	—	.5073	.6491	.8306	.9182	—	—
1 1/4	—	.6408	.8226	1.058	1.172	1.284	—
1 1/2	—	.7743	.9962	1.285	1.426	1.564	—
1 3/4	—	—	1.170	1.512	1.679	1.845	2.089
2	—	—	1.343	1.738	1.933	2.125	2.409

Boiler Tubing

Size	Wall gauge (B.W.) and Thickness (in.)								
O.D. in.	13 .095	12 .109	11 .120	10 .134	9 .148	8 .165	7 .180	6 .203	5 .220
1	1.037	1.168	1.263	1.384	—	—	—	—	—
1 1/4	1.323	1.502	1.628	1.793	—	—	—	—	—
1 1/2	1.619	1.836	1.994	2.201	—	—	—	—	—
1 3/4	1.910	2.169	2.360	2.610	—	—	—	—	—
2	2.201	2.503	2.726	3.018	—	—	—	—	—
2 1/4	2.492	2.837	3.092	3.427	—	—	—	—	—
2 1/2	—	3.171	3.457	3.835	4.207	—	—	—	—
2 3/4	—	3.504	3.823	4.244	4.658	—	—	—	—
3	—	3.838	4.189	4.652	5.110	—	—	—	—
3 1/4	—	—	4.555	5.061	5.561	6.179	—	—	—
3 1/2	—	—	4.921	5.469	6.012	6.683	—	—	—
4	—	—	—	6.286	6.915	7.693	8.347	—	—
4 1/2	—	—	—	7.103	7.817	8.702	9.447	—	—
5	—	—	—	—	8.720	9.711	10.55	11.81	—
5 1/2	—	—	—	—	9.620	10.72	11.65	13.05	—
6	—	—	—	—	—	—	12.75	14.29	15.41

TABLE 144—WEIGHTS OF TUBING

Non-Ferrous Pipe and Tubing

in lb per ft of length

Nominal Size	Copper Water Tube						
	Outside Diameter	Type K		Type L		Type M	
		Wall	Wt.	Wall	Wt.	Wall	Wt.
in.	in.	in.	lb/ft	in.	lb/ft	in.	lb/ft
¼	⅜	.035	.145	.030	.126	.025	.106
⅜	½	.049	.269	.035	.198	.025	.144
½	⅝	.049	.344	.040	.285	.028	.203
⅝	¾	.049	.418	.042	.362	.030	.263
¾	⅞	.065	.641	.045	.455	.032	.328
1	1 ⅛	.065	.839	.050	.655	.035	.465
1 ¼	1 ⅜	.065	1.04	.055	.884	.042	.682
1 ½	1 ⅝	.072	1.36	.060	1.14	.049	.940
2	2 ⅛	.083	2.06	.070	1.75	.058	1.46
2 ½	2 ⅝	.095	2.93	.080	2.48	.065	2.03
3	3 ⅛	.109	4.00	.090	3.33	.072	2.68
3 ½	3 ⅝	.120	5.12	.100	4.29	.083	3.58
4	4 ⅛	.134	6.51	.110	5.38	.095	4.66
5	5 ⅛	.160	9.67	.125	7.61	.109	6.66
6	6 ⅛	.192	13.9	.140	10.2	.122	8.92
8	8 ⅛	.271	25.9	.200	19.3	.170	16.5
10	10 ⅛	.338	40.3	.250	30.1	.212	25.6
12	12 ⅛	.405	57.8	.280	40.4	.254	36.7

Nom. Size	Schedule 40 Pipe of Various Materials								
	O.D.	Wall	I.D.	Monel	Nickel	Incon.	PVC	Alum.	Copper*
in.	in.	in.	in.	lb/ft	lb/ft	lb/ft	lb/ft	lb/ft	lb/ft
⅛	.405	.068	.269	.276	.277	—	—	.085	.259
¼	.540	.088	.364	.478	.481	.460	—	.147	.460
⅜	.675	.091	.493	.639	.643	.615	—	.196	.644
½	.840	.109	.622	.958	.964	.922	0.16	.294	.959
¾	1.050	.113	.824	1.27	1.28	1.23	0.21	.391	1.299
1	1.315	.133	1.049	1.89	1.90	1.82	0.31	.581	1.831
1 ¼	1.660	.140	1.380	2.56	2.58	2.46	0.42	.786	2.692
1 ½	1.900	.145	1.610	3.06	3.08	2.95	0.50	.940	3.196
2	2.375	.154	2.067	4.11	4.14	3.96	0.68	1.264	4.228
2 ½	2.875	.203	2.469	6.52	6.56	6.28	—	2.004	6.136
3	3.5	.216	3.068	8.53	8.58	8.21	1.40	2.621	8.750
3 ½	4.0	.226	3.548	10.3	10.3	9.87	—	3.151	11.42
4	4.5	.237	4.026	12.1	12.2	11.7	2.00	3.733	12.94
5	5.563	.258	5.047	16.4	16.6	15.8	—	5.057	16.20
6	6.625	.280	6.065	21.4	21.5	20.6	—	6.564	19.41
8	8.625	.322	7.981	32.2	32.4	—	—	9.878	31.63
10	10.75	.365	10.02	—	—	—	—	14.00	51.94

*Copper pipe not Schedule 40 (different wall and I.D.).

APPENDIX 6

MISCELLANEOUS DATA

TABLE 145—STANDARD TWIST DRILL SIZES

Drill Size	Diam. in.	Area in.^{2}	Drill Size	Diam. in.	Area in.^{2}	Drill Size	Diam. in.	Area in.^{2}
1/2	.5000	.1964	3	.213	.03563	3/32	.0938	.00690
31/64	.4844	.1843	4	.209	.03431	42	.0935	.00687
15/32	.4688	.1726	5	.2055	.03317	43	.0890	.00622
29/64	.4531	.1613	6	.204	.03269	44	.0860	.00581
7/16	.4375	.1503	13/64	.2031	.03241	45	.0820	.00528
27/64	.4219	.1398	7	.201	.03173	46	.0810	.00515
Z	.413	.1340	8	.199	.03110	47	.0785	.00484
13/32	.4062	.1296	9	.196	.03017	5/64	.0781	.00479
Y	.404	.1282	10	.1935	.02940	48	.0760	.00454
X	.397	.1238	11	.191	.02865	49	.0730	.00419
25/64	.3906	.1198	12	.189	.02806	50	.0700	.00385
W	.386	.1170	3/16	.1875	.02761	51	.0670	.00353
V	.377	.1116	13	.185	.02688	52	.0635	.00317
3/8	.375	.1104	14	.182	.02602	1/16	.0625	.00307
U	.368	.1064	15	.1800	.02545	53	.0595	.00278
23/64	.3594	.1014	16	.1770	.02461	54	.0550	.00238
T	.358	.1007	17	.1730	.02351	55	.0520	.00212
S	.348	.09511	11/64	.1719	.02320	3/64	.0469	.00173
11/32	.3438	.09281	18	.1695	.02256	56	.0465	.001698
R	.339	.09026	19	.1660	.02164	57	.0430	.001452
Q	.332	.08657	20	.1610	.02036	58	.0420	.001385
21/64	.3281	.08456	21	.1590	.01986	59	.0410	.001320
P	.323	.08194	22	.1570	.01936	60	.0400	.001257
O	.316	.07843	5/32	.1562	.01917	61	.039	.001195
5/16	.3125	.07670	23	.1540	.01863	62	.038	.001134
N	.302	.07163	24	.1520	.01815	63	.037	.001075
19/64	.2969	.06922	25	.1495	.01755	64	.036	.001018
M	.295	.06835	26	.1470	.01697	65	.035	.00962
L	.29	.06605	27	.1440	.01629	66	.033	.000855
9/32	.2812	.06213	9/64	.1406	.01553	67	.032	.000804
K	.281	.06202	28	.1405	.01550	1/32	.0312	.000767
J	.277	.06026	29	.1360	.01453	68	.031	.000755
I	.272	.05811	30	.1285	.01296	69	.0292	.000670
H	.266	.05557	1/8	.1250	.01227	70	.028	.000616
17/64	.2656	.05542	31	.1200	.01131	71	.026	.000531
G	.261	.05350	32	.1160	.01057	72	.025	.000491
F	.257	.05187	33	.1130	.01003	73	.024	.000452
E 1/4	.2500	.04909	34	.1110	.00968	74	.0225	.000398
D	.246	.04753	35	.1100	.00950	75	.021	.000346
C	.242	.04600	7/64	.1094	.00940	76	.020	.000314
B	.238	.04449	36	.1065	.00891	77	.018	.000254
15/64	.2344	.04314	37	.1040	.00849	78	.016	.000201
A	.234	.04301	38	.1015	.00809	1/64	.0156	.000191
1	.228	.04083	39	.0995	.00778	79	.0145	.000165
2	.221	.03836	40	.0980	.00754	80	.0135	.000143
7/32	.2188	.03758	41	.0960	.00724			

Metric sizes available in the same range.

TABLE 146—AREAS AND CIRCUMFERENCES OF CIRCLES

Diam.	Area		Circum.		Diam.	Area		Circum.	
in in.	in.²	ft²	in.	ft	in in.	in.²	ft²	in.	ft
1/16	.00307	.00002	.1963	.01636	7 3/4	47.17	.3276	24.35	2.029
1/8	.01227	.00008	.3927	.03272	8	50.27	.3491	25.13	2.094
3/16	.02761	.00019	.5890	.04908	8 1/4	53.46	.3713	25.92	2.160
1/4	.04909	.00034	.7854	.06545	8 1/2	56.75	.3942	26.70	2.225
5/16	.07670	.00053	.9817	.08180	8 3/4	60.13	.4175	27.49	2.291
3/8	.1104	.00077	1.178	.09816	9	63.62	.4418	28.27	2.356
7/16	.1503	.00104	1.374	.1145	9 1/4	67.20	.4668	29.06	2.422
*1/2	.1963	.00136	1.571	.1309	9 1/2	70.88	.4923	29.85	2.488
9/16	.2485	.00173	1.767	.1472	9 3/4	74.66	.5185	30.63	2.553
5/8	.3068	.00213	1.964	.1636	10	78.54	.5454	31.42	2.618
11/16	.3712	.00258	2.160	.1800	10 1/4	82.52	.5731	32.20	2.683
3/4	.4418	.00307	2.356	.1964	10 1/2	86.59	.6010	32.99	2.750
13/16	.5185	.00360	2.553	.2128	10 3/4	90.76	.6303	33.77	2.814
7/8	.6013	.00418	2.749	.2290	11	95.03	.6600	34.56	2.880
15/16	.6903	.00479	2.945	.2454	11 1/4	99.40	.6903	35.34	2.945
1	.7854	.00545	3.142	.2618	11 1/2	103.9	.7215	36.13	3.011
1 1/8	.9940	.00690	3.534	.2945	11 3/4	108.4	.7528	36.91	3.076
1 1/4	1.227	.00852	3.927	.3273	12	113.1	.7854	37.70	3.142
1 3/8	1.485	.0103	4.320	.3600	12 1/4	117.9	.8188	38.48	3.207
1 1/2	1.767	.0123	4.712	.3927	12 1/2	122.7	.8520	39.27	3.273
1 5/8	2.074	.0144	5.105	.4254	12 3/4	127.7	.8868	40.06	3.338
1 3/4	2.405	.0167	5.498	.4582	13	132.7	.9218	40.84	3.403
1 7/8	2.761	.0192	5.890	.4908	13 1/4	137.9	.9577	41.63	3.469
2	3.142	.0218	6.283	.5236	13 1/2	143.1	.9937	42.41	3.535
2 1/8	3.547	.0246	6.676	.5563	13 3/4	148.5	1.031	43.20	3.600
2 1/4	3.976	.0276	7.069	.5891	14	153.9	1.069	43.98	3.665
2 3/8	4.430	.0308	7.461	.6217	14 1/4	159.5	1.108	44.77	3.731
2 1/2	4.909	.0341	7.854	.6546	14 1/2	165.1	1.146	45.55	3.796
2 5/8	5.412	.0376	8.247	.6872	14 3/4	170.9	1.187	46.34	2.862
2 3/4	5.939	.0412	8.639	.7200	15	176.7	1.227	47.12	3.927
2 7/8	6.492	.0451	9.032	.7527	15 1/2	188.7	1.310	48.69	4.058
3	7.069	.0491	9.425	.7854	16	201.1	1.396	50.27	4.189
3 1/4	8.296	.0576	10.21	.8510	16 1/2	213.8	1.485	51.84	4.321
3 1/2	9.621	.0668	10.99	.9160	17	226.9	1.576	53.41	4.451
3 3/4	11.04	.0767	11.78	.9818	17 1/2	240.5	1.670	54.98	4.582
4	12.57	.0873	12.57	1.047	18	254.5	1.767	56.55	4.712
4 1/4	14.19	.0986	13.35	1.113	18 1/2	268.8	1.867	58.12	4.845
4 1/2	15.90	.1104	14.14	1.178	19	283.5	1.969	59.69	4.974
4 3/4	17.72	.1231	14.92	1.243	19 1/2	298.6	2.074	61.26	5.105
5	19.64	.1364	15.71	1.309	20	314.2	2.182	62.83	5.236
5 1/4	21.65	.1504	16.49	1.374	20 1/2	330.1	2.293	64.40	5.367
5 1/2	23.76	.1650	17.28	1.440	21	346.4	2.405	65.97	5.498
5 3/4	25.97	.1840	18.06	1.505	21 1/2	361.1	2.508	67.54	5.629
6	28.27	.1964	18.85	1.571	22	380.1	2.640	69.12	5.760
6 1/4	30.68	.2131	19.64	1.637	22 1/2	397.6	2.761	70.69	5.891
6 1/2	33.18	.2304	20.42	1.702	23	415.5	2.885	72.26	6.021
6 3/4	35.79	.2486	21.21	1.768	23 1/2	433.7	3.012	73.83	6.153
7	38.49	.2673	21.99	1.833	24	452.4	3.142	75.40	6.283
7 1/4	41.28	.2867	22.78	1.899	24 1/2	471.4	3.274	76.97	6.415
7 1/2	44.18	.3068	23.56	1.964	25	490.9	3.409	78.54	6.545

*See Previous page for areas corresponding to drill sizes.

TABLE 146 (Cont.)—AREAS AND CIRCUMFERENCES OF CIRCLES

Diam.	Area		Circum.		Diam.	Area		Circum.	
in in.	in.^{2}	ft^2	in.	ft	in.	in.^{2}	ft^2	in.	ft
25½	510.7	3.547	80.11	6.676	51	2043	14.19	160.2	13.35
26	530.9	3.687	81.68	6.807	52	2124	14.75	163.4	13.61
26½	551.6	3.832	83.25	6.938	53	2206	15.32	166.5	13.88
27	572.6	3.976	84.82	7.069	54	2290	15.90	169.6	14.14
27½	593.9	4.125	86.39	7.199	55	2376	16.50	172.8	14.40
28	615.8	4.276	87.97	7.330	56	2463	17.10	175.9	14.66
28½	637.9	4.430	89.54	7.462	57	2552	17.72	179.1	14.92
29	660.5	4.587	91.11	7.592	58	2642	18.35	182.2	15.18
29½	683.5	4.747	92.63	7.725	59	2734	18.99	185.4	15.45
30	706.8	4.909	94.25	7.854	60	2827	19.63	188.5	15.71
30½	730.6	5.074	95.82	7.985	61	2922	20.29	191.6	15.97
31	754.8	5.241	97.39	8.116	62	3019	20.97	194.8	16.23
31½	779.3	5.412	98.96	8.247	63	3117	21.65	197.9	16.49
32	804.3	5.585	100.5	8.378	64	3217	22.34	201.1	16.76
32½	829.6	5.761	102.1	8.508	65	3318	23.04	204.2	17.02
33	855.3	5.940	103.7	8.639	66	3421	23.76	207.3	17.28
33½	881.4	6.121	105.2	8.767	67	3526	24.48	210.5	17.54
34	907.9	6.305	106.8	8.901	68	3632	25.22	213.6	17.80
34½	934.8	6.492	108.4	9.033	69	3739	25.97	216.8	18.06
35	962.1	6.681	109.9	9.163	70	3848	26.73	219.9	18.33
35½	989.8	6.874	111.5	9.294	71	3959	27.49	223.1	18.59
36	1018	7.069	113.1	9.425	72	4072	28.27	226.2	18.85
36½	1046	7.264	114.7	9.555	73	4185	29.07	229.3	19.11
37	1075	7.467	116.2	9.686	74	4301	29.87	232.5	19.37
37½	1104	7.667	117.8	9.817	75	4418	30.68	235.6	19.63
38	1134	7.876	119.4	9.948	76	4536	31.50	238.8	19.90
38½	1164	8.084	120.9	10.08	77	4657	32.34	241.9	20.16
39	1195	8.296	122.5	10.21	78	4778	33.18	245.0	20.42
39½	1225	8.507	124.1	10.34	79	4902	34.04	248.2	20.68
40	1256	8.727	125.6	10.47	80	5027	34.91	251.3	20.94
40½	1288	8.945	127.2	10.60	81	5153	35.78	254.5	21.21
41	1320	9.168	128.8	10.73	82	5281	36.67	257.6	21.47
41½	1353	9.396	130.4	10.86	83	5411	37.57	260.8	21.73
42	1385	9.621	131.9	10.99	84	5542	38.48	263.9	21.99
42½	1419	9.854	133.5	11.13	85	5675	39.41	267.0	22.25
43	1452	10.08	135.1	11.26	86	5809	40.34	270.2	22.51
43½	1486	10.32	136.7	11.39	87	5945	41.28	273.3	22.78
44	1521	10.56	138.2	11.52	88	6082	42.24	276.5	23.04
44½	1555	10.80	139.8	11.65	89	6221	43.20	279.6	23.30
45	1590	11.04	141.4	11.78	90	6362	44.18	282.7	23.56
45½	1626	11.29	142.9	11.91	91	6504	45.17	285.9	23.82
46	1662	11.54	144.5	12.04	92	6648	46.16	289.0	24.09
46½	1698	11.79	146.1	12.17	93	6793	47.17	292.2	24.35
47	1735	12.05	147.7	12.30	94	6940	48.19	295.3	24.61
47½	1772	12.31	149.2	12.43	95	7088	49.22	298.4	24.87
48	1810	12.57	150.8	12.57	96	7238	50.27	301.6	25.13
48½	1847	12.83	152.4	12.70	97	7390	51.32	304.7	25.39
49	1886	13.09	153.9	12.83	98	7543	52.38	307.9	25.66
49½	1924	13.36	155.5	12.96	99	7698	53.46	311.0	25.92
50	1963	13.64	157.1	13.09	100	7854	54.54	314.2	26.18

TABLE 147—MATHEMATICAL DATA

Geometry

Plane Figures

Circle	Circumference $= 2\pi r = \pi d$
	Area $= \pi r^2 = \pi d^2/4$
	Chord $= 2r \sin(\phi/2)$
Ellipse	Approx. circum. $= 2\pi\sqrt{(a_1^2 + a_2^2)/2}$
	Area $= \pi a_1 a_2$
Sector	Area $= \pi r^2\phi/360 = sr/2$
Segment	Area $= (\pi r^2\phi/360) - (r^2 \sin(\phi)/2)$
	Area $= r^2 (\theta - \sin\theta)/2$
Rhomboid	Area $= b_1 h$
Trapezoid	Area $= (b_1 + b_2)h/2$
Triangle	Area $= b_1 h/2$

Solid Figures

Cone	Volume $= \pi r^2 h/3$
	Lateral area $= 2\pi rk/2$
Cylinder	Volume $= \pi r^2 h$
	Lateral area $= 2\pi rh$
Sphere	Volume $= 4\pi r^3/3 = \pi d^3/6$
	Area $= 4\pi r^2 = \pi d^2$
Pyramid	Volume $=$ (Base Area)h/3
	Lateral area $=$ (Base Perimeter) k/2

Analytical Geometry

Circle (origin at center)	$x^2 + y^2 = r^2$
Ellipse (origin at center)	$x^2/a_1^2 + y^2/a_2^2 = 1$
Hyperbola (origin at center)	$x^2/a_1^2 - y^2/a_2^2 = 1$
Parabola (origin at vertex)	$y^2 = 4a_1 x$
Straight Line (slope form)	$y = mx + b$
Straight Line (intercept form)	$x/a + y/b = 1$
Spiral of Archimedes	$r = c\theta/2\pi$
Logarithmic Spiral	$r = ae^{m\theta}$

NOMENCLATURE

a = x intercept	e = 2.7183	x = coordinate
a_1 = semiaxis	h = height	y = coordinate
b = y intercept	k = slant height	ϕ = angle in degrees
b_1 = base length	m = slope	θ = angle in radians
c = coil spread	r = radius	π = 3.1416
d = diameter	s = length of arc	

TABLE 147 (cont.)—MATHEMATICAL DATA

Exponents

$a^x a^y = a^{x+y}$ $a^{-x} = 1/a^x$ $a^{1/x} = \sqrt[x]{a}$

$a^x/a^y = a^{x-y}$ $(a^x)^y = a^{xy}$ $a^x b^x = (ab)^x$

Logarithims

$\log_{10}(10^x) = x$ (common, denary, or Briggsian logarithm)

$\log_e(e^x) = x$ (natural or Naperian logarithm)

$\log_e(a) = 2.3026 \log_{10}(a)$ (conversion formula)

$\log(ab) = \log(a) + \log(b)$ $\log(0) = -\infty$

$\log(a/b) = \log(a) - \log(b)$ $\log(1) = 0$

$\log(a^x) = x \log(a)$ $\log(\text{base}) = 1$

$\log(1/a) = -\log(a)$ $\log(\infty) = \infty$

Trigonometric Functions

$\sin(a)$ = opposite side/hypotenuse (sine)

$\cos(a)$ = adjacent side/hypotenuse (cosine)

$\tan(a)$ = opposite side/adjacent side (tangent)

$\cot(a) = 1/\tan(a)$ (cotangent)

$\sec(a) = 1/\cos(a)$ (secant)

$\csc(a) = 1/\sin(a)$ (cosecant)

$\sin^{-1}(x)$ = angle whose sine is (x) (inverse sine)

$\cos^{-1}(x)$ = angle whose cosine is (x) (inverse cosine)

$\tan^{-1}(x)$ = angle whose tangent is (x) (inverse tangent)

$\text{arc} \sin(x) = \sin^{-1}(x)$ (arc sine, etc.)

$\text{vers}(a) = 1 - \cos(a)$ (versed sine)

$\text{covers}(a) = 1 - \sin(a)$ (coversed sine)

$\text{exsec}(a) = \sec(a) - 1$ (exterior secant)

$\sin(a + b) = \sin(a) \cos(b) + \cos(a) \sin(b)$ (sin addition)

$\cos(a + b) = \cos(a) \cos(b) - \sin(a) \sin(b)$ (cos addition)

$\sin^2(a) + \cos^2(a) = 1$ (identity)

$1 + \tan^2(a) = \sec^2(a)$ (identity)

$\sin(2a) = 2 \sin(a) \cos(a)$ (sin twice angle)

$\cos(2a) = \cos^2(a) - \sin^2(a)$ (cos twice angle)

$\tan(2a) = 2 \tan(a)/(1 - \tan^2(a))$ (tan twice angle)

Miscellaneous Algebra

$(a + b)/2, (a + b + c)/3$, etc (arithmetical mean)

$\sqrt{ab}, \sqrt[3]{abc}$, etc (geometric mean)

$x = (-b \pm \sqrt{b^2 - 4ac})/2a$ (quadratic roots)

$n! = 1 \times 2 \times 3 \times \ldots \times n$ (n factorial)

$e = 2.7183 = 1 + 1/1! + 1/2! + 1/3! + \ldots$ (base e)

$i = \sqrt{-1}$ (imaginary root)

$\sin(a) = (e^{ia} - e^{-ia})/2i$ (sine)

$\cos(a) = (e^{ia} + e^{-ia})/2$ (cosine)

$\sinh(a) = (e^a - e^{-a})/2$ (hyperbolic sine)

$\cosh(a) = (e^a + e^{-a})/2$ (hyperbolic cosine)

TABLE 148—MISCELLANEOUS EQUATIONS

Mechanics

Mass, Mass Moment of Inertia

$m = (w/g)g_c$ | $I_m = mr^2$

Force, Torque

$F = ma/g_c = wa/g$ | $\tau = I_m \alpha/g_c = Fr$

Momentum, Angular Momentum

$M = mv/g_c$ | $\mu = I_m \omega/g_c$

$M_t = M_o + Ft$ | $\mu_t = \mu_o + \tau t$

Work, Power, Energy

$W = Fs$ | $W = \tau\theta$

$P = Fv = W/t$ | $P = \tau\omega = W/t$

$E_p = wh$

$E_k = mv^2/2g_c$ | $E_k = I_m \omega^2/2g_c$

Uniform Motion

$a = o$ | $\alpha = o$

$v = \text{constant}$ | $\omega = \text{constant}$

$s_t = s_o + v_o t$ | $\theta_t = \theta_o + \omega t$

Uniformly Accelerated Motion

$a = \text{constant}$ | $\alpha = \text{constant}$

$v_t = v_o + at$ | $\omega_t = \omega_o + \alpha t$

$s_t = s_o + v_o t + at^2/2$ | $\theta_t = \theta_o + \omega_o t + \alpha t^2/2$

Simple Harmonic Vibration

$s_t = A\cos(\omega t)$ | $f = \omega/2\pi$

$v_t = -A\omega\sin(\omega t)$ | $T = 2\pi/\omega$

$a_t = -A\omega^2\cos(\omega t)$ | $\omega = 2\pi f$

Electricity

Ohm's Law

$I = E/R$ $E = IR$ $R = E/I$

Power

$P = EI$ (d-c)

$P = EI\cos\theta$ (a-c, 1 phase)

$P = \sqrt{3}\,EI\cos\theta$ (a-c, 3 phase)

NOMENCLATURE

A	= peak amplitude	R	= resistance
a	= acceleration	r	= radius of gyration
E	= emf	s	= displacement
E_k	= energy, kinetic	T	= period
E_p	= energy, potential	t	= time
F	= Force	v	= velocity
f	= frequency	W	= Work
g	= acceleration of gravity	w	= weight
g_c	= conversion factor	α	= angular acceleration
h	= height	θ	= angular displacement
I	= current	μ	= angular momentum
I_m	= mass moment of inertia	π	= 3.1416
M	= momentum	τ	= torque
m	= mass	ω	= angular velocity
P	= power	$\cos\theta$	= power factor

Subscript o = at time o   subscript t = at time t

TABLE 149—MISCELLANEOUS DATA

Greek Alphabet

Alpha	Α α	Eta	Η η	Nu	Ν ν	Tau	Τ τ
Beta	Β β	Theta	Θ θ	Xi	Ξ ξ	Upsilon	Υ υ
Gamma	Γ γ	Iota	Ι ι	Omicron	Ο o	Phi	Φ ϕ φ
Delta	Δ δ ∂	Kappa	Κ κ	Pi	Π π	Chi	Χ χ
Epsilon	Ε ϵ	Lambda	Λ λ	Rho	Ρ ρ	Psi	Ψ ψ
Zeta	Ζ ζ	Mu	Μ μ	Sigma	Σ σ	Omega	Ω ω

Chemical Prefixes

hemi	½	tri	3	hepta	7	eicosa	20
mono	1	tetra	4	octa	8	tri conta	30
sesqui	1½	penta	5	nona	9	tetra conta	40
di or bi	2	hexa	6	deca	10	penta conta	50

Metric Prefixes

atto	a	10^{-18}	micro	μ	10^{-6}	deka	da	10	mega	M	10^6
femto	f	10^{-15}	milli	m	10^{-3}	hecto	h	10^2	giga	G	10^9
pico	p	10^{-12}	centi	c	10^{-2}	kilo	k	10^3	tera	T	10^{12}
nano	n	10^{-9}	deci	d	10^{-1}						

Approximate Weight of United States Coins

1¢ piece = 3.1 grams = 50 grains   10¢ piece = 2.5 grams = 40 grains
5¢ piece = 5.0 grams = 80 grains   25¢ piece = 6.25 grams = 100 grains
50¢ piece = 12.5 grams = 200 grains

Approximate Determination of Temperature by Color

Red visible in dark	800°F
Red visible in daylight	900°F
Dull red	1000°F
Dark cherry	1200°F
Cherry red	1400°F
Bright cherry red	1600°F
Light orange	1800°F
Yellow-white	2000°F
White	2400°F

Some Approximate Dimensions

Diameter of Human Hair	50-200μ
Limit of Visibility	10-40μ
Wave Length of Red Light	0.7μ
Wave Length of Violet Light	0.4μ
Mean Free Path of Air Molecules	0.1μ
Diameter of Large Molecules	50Å

TABLE 150—FORTRAN DATA

Operation or Function	Ordinary Symbols	Fortran	Basic
Addition	A + B	A + B	A + B
Subtraction	A − B	A − B	A − B
Multiplication	A × B or AB	A*B	A*B
Division	A ÷ B or A/B	A/B	A/B
Exponentiation	A^B	A**B	A↑B
Absolute Value	|A|	ABS(A)	ABS(A)
Square Root	$\sqrt{A}$	SQRT(A)	SQR(A)
Sine	sinA	SIN(A)	SIN(A)
Cosine	cosA	COS(A)	COS(A)
Arctangent	arctanA	ATAN(A)	ATN(A)
Exponent (Base e)	e^A	EXP(A)	EXP(A)
Natural Logarithm	lnA	ALOG(A)	LOG(A)

Format	Alphameric Example	Fortran Format Statement and Meaning
Floating Decimal	+1234.12	10 FORMAT (F8.2) for 8 characters, 2 places
Exponential of 10	−1.2345678E+12	11 FORMAT (E14.7) for 14 characters, 7 places
Integer	+12	12 FORMAT (I3) for 3 characters
Hollerith	FAN ENGINEERING	13 FORMAT (15H FAN ENGINEERING)
Literal	FAN ENGINEERING	14 FORMAT ('FAN ENGINEERING')

Fortran I/O Example	Meaning of Input or Output Statement
READ(I,10)A	Read A from card (or other input per I). Format per statement 10.
WRITE(J,11)X	Punch (or other output per J) values of X. Format per statement 11.

Control Example	Meaning of Fortran Control Statement
Go to 17	Next statement to be executed is number 17.
Go to (17,25,28),L	Next statement to be executed is number 17, 25, or 28 depending upon whether last computed value of L is 1, 2, or 3.
IF(X−Y)30,40,50	Next statement to be executed is number 30, 40, or 50 depending upon whether computed value of X is less than, equal to, or greater than Y.
DO 35 I=J,K,L	Execute all statements following through 35, repeatedly. Let I=J the first time. Increase J by L each subsequent time. When I becomes greater than K go to next statement after 35.

APPENDIX 7

SELECTED BIBLIOGRAPHY

The books and other sources of information which were consulted in the preparation of this handbook are listed below. These books contain more extensive treatments of one or more of the topics considered in this text and are therefore recommended as supplementary readings. In all cases where spciefic data for a table or chart have been copied, permission to do so has been granted by the copyright owner and the source has been completely identified in a footnote or caption.

Book references are divided into four groups according to the comparative amounts of text and tabular data. Those which contain only a few pages of text and a preponderance of tabular (or graphical) data are classified as "Tables and Charts." Those which contain considerable amounts of both text and tabular (or graphical) data are classified as "Handbooks." Those which contain a preponderance of text are classified as "Reference Books" or "Textbooks." In the former group are those written primarily for practicing engineers and in the latter group are those written primarily for students.

The journals, transactions, and other publications which contain most of the technical papers that are important in fan engineering are grouped under "Technical Papers." Cumulative Indexes are available as indicated.

The publishers of most of the codes and standards that are important in fan engineering are grouped under "Codes and Standards." General subjects are as indicated. Up-to-date lists of individual titles are available from the publishers periodically.

The names and addresses of various technical societies, trade associations, and governmental agencies are listed, together with the abbreviations used in this bibliography, in the final list "Key to Abbreviations and Addresses."

HANDBOOKS

Standard Handbook for Mechanical Engineers—1967, 7th ed.
T. Baumeister, Editor
McGraw-Hill Book Co., Inc., New York, New York

American Institute of Physics Handbook—1963, 2nd ed.
D. E. Gray, Editor
McGraw-Hill Book Co., Inc., New York, New York

Handbook of Noise Control—1957
C. M. Harris, Editor
McGraw-Hill Book Co., Inc., New York, New York

HANDBOOKS, Cont.

Metals Engineering Design—(ASME Handbook)—1965, 2nd ed.
O. J. Horger, Editor
McGraw-Hill Book Co., Inc., New York, New York

Chemical Engineers' Handbook—1963, 4th ed.
R. H. Perry, C. H. Chilton and S. D. Kirkpatrick, Editors
McGraw-Hill Book Co., Inc., New York, New York

Handbook of Noise Measurement—1967, 6th ed.
A. P. G. Peterson and E. E. Gross, Jr.
General Radio Co., West Concord, Massachusetts

Gas Engineers Handbook—1966
C. G. Segeler, Editor
The Industrial Press, New York, New York

The Corrosion Handbook—1948
H. H. Uhlig, Editor
John Wiley & Sons, Inc., New York, New York

Aero-Space Applied Thermodynamics Manual—1960
Committee A-9 on Aero-Space Environmental Control Systems
Society of Automotive Engineers, New York, New York

Industrial Ventilation—1968, 10th ed.
Committee on Industrial Ventilation
American Conference of Governmental Industrial Hygienists, Lansing, Michigan

ASHRAE—Handbook of Fundamentals—1967

ASHRAE—Guide and Data Book—Applications—1968

ASHRAE—Guide and Data Book—Equipment—1969

ASHRAE—Guide and Data Book—Systems—1970
Guide and Data Book Committee
American Society of Heating, Refrigerating and Air Conditioning Engineers, New York, New York

A Guide to Current Practice—1965, 3rd ed.
Guide Committee
The Institution of Heating and Ventilating Engineers, London, England

Warm Air Heating and Air Conditioning Library—1950-1958 11 manuals and worksheets
Members and Staff
National Warm Air Heating and Air Conditioning Association, Cleveland, Ohio

Steam—1963, 37th ed.
Staff
The Babcock and Wilcox Co., New York, New York

TABLES AND CHARTS

Evaluated Weather Data for Cooling Equipment Design—1958, 1st ed.
L. W. Crow, Analyst, and W. W. Smith, Editor
Fluor Products Co., Whittier, California
Thermodynamic Charts—1944, 2nd ed.
F. O. Ellenwood and C. O. Mackey
John Wiley & Sons, Inc., New York, New York
Handbook of Chemistry and Physics—1969, 50th ed.
R. C. Weast, Editor
Chemical Rubber Publishing Co., Cleveland, Ohio
Metals Properties—(ASME Handbook)—1954, 1st ed.
S. L. Hoyt, Editor
McGraw-Hill Book Co., Inc., New York, New York
Industrial Heat Transfer—1952
F. W. Hutchinson
The Industrial Press, New York, New York
Gas Tables—1948
J. H. Keenan and J. Kaye
John Wiley & Sons, Inc., New York, New York
Handbook of Chemistry—1967, 10th ed.
N. A. Lange, Editor (assisted by G. M. Forker)
McGraw-Hill Book Co., Inc., New York, New York
Thermodynamic and Transport Properties of Steam—1967
C. A. Meyer, R. B. McClintock, G. J. Silvestri, R. C. Spencer, Jr.
American Society of Mechanical Engineers, New York, New York
Report on the Strength of Wrought Steels at Elevated Temperatures—1950
R. F. Miller and J. J. Heger—Spec. Tech. Pub. No. 100
American Society for Testing Materials, Philadelphia, Pennsylvania
International Critical Tables—1926-1933, 1st ed., 8 vols.
E. W. Washburn, Editor, National Research Council
McGraw-Hill Book Co., Inc., New York, New York
Heat Transfer—Airplane Air Conditioning Engineering Data—1952
Air Conditioning Equipment Committee—Rept. No. 24
Society of Automotive Engineers, New York, New York
Steel Construction Manual—1966, 6th ed.
Committee on Manual
American Institute of Steel Construction, New York, New York
Steel Plates—1948, Catalog 234
Staff
Bethlehem Steel Co., Bethlehem, Pennsylvania
Flow of Fluids—1957
Engineering Division—Tech. Pap. No. 410
Crane Co., Chicago, Illinois
Standard Atmosphere—Tables and Data for Altitudes to 65,800 feet—1955
National Aeronautics and Space Administration—NACA Rept. 1235
U.S. Government Printing Office, Washington 25, D. C.
Counterflow Cooling Tower Performance—1957
Staff
J. F. Pritchard Co. of California, Kansas City, Missouri

REFERENCE BOOKS

Fluid Meters—1959
American Society of Mechanical Engineers, New York, New York
Flow and Fan—1954
C. H. Berry
The Industrial Press, New York, New York
Industrial Health Engineering—1947
A. D. Brandt
John Wiley & Sons, Inc., New York, New York
Fatigue of Metals—1953
R. Cazaud (trans. by A. J. Fenner)
Philosophical Library, Inc., New York, New York
Exhaust Hoods—1945
J. M. Dallavalle
The Industrial Press, New York, New York
The Industrial Environment and Its Control—1948
J. M. Dallavalle
Pitman Publishing Corporation, New York, New York
Industrial Dust—1954, 2nd ed.
P. Drinker and T. Hatch
McGraw-Hill Book Co., Inc., New York, New York
Plant and Process Ventilation—1963, 2nd ed.
W. C. L. Hemeon
The Industrial Press, New York, New York
Adsorption—1951, 2nd ed.
C. L. Mantell
McGraw-Hill Book Co., Inc., New York, New York
Fine Particle Measurement—1959
C. Orr, Jr. and J. M. Dallavalle
The Macmillan Co., New York, New York
Formulas for Stress and Strain—1965, 4th ed.
R. J. Roark
McGraw-Hill Book Co., Inc., New York, New York
Turboblowers—1955
A. J. Stepanoff
John Wiley & Sons, Inc., New York, New York
Centrifugal and Axial Flow Pumps—1957, 2nd ed.
A. J. Stepanoff
John Wiley & Sons, Inc., New York, New York
Applied Heat Transmission—1941, 1st ed.
H. J. Stoever
McGraw-Hill Book Co., Inc., New York, New York
Fluidization and Fluid Particle Systems—1960
F. A. Zenz and D. F. Othmer
Reinhold Publishing Corp., New York, New York

TEXTBOOKS

Acoustics—1954 and Noise Reduction—1960
L. L. Beranek
McGraw-Hill Book Co., Inc., New York, New York
Centrifugal Pumps and Blowers—1944
A. H. Church
John Wiley & Sons, Inc., New York, New York
Micromeritics—1948, 2nd ed.
J. M. Dallavalle
Pitman Publishing Corp., New York, New York
Mechanical Vibrations—1948, 3rd ed.
J. P. Den Hartog
McGraw-Hill Book Co., Inc., New York, New York
Automatic Control of Heating & Air Conditioning—1953
J. E. Haines
McGraw-Hill Book Co., Inc., New York, New York
Fluid Dynamics and Heat Transfer—1958
J. G. Knudsen and D. L. Katz
McGraw-Hill Book Co., Inc., New York, New York
Air Conditioning Principles—1941, 1st ed.
C. O. Mackey
International Textbook Co., Scranton, Pennsylvania
Heat Transmission—1954, 3rd ed.
W. H. McAdams
McGraw-Hill Book Co., Inc., New York, New York
The Dynamics and Thermodynamics of Compressible Fluid Flow—1953, Vol. 1
A. H. Shapiro
The Ronald Press Co., New York, New York
Principles of Turbomachinery—1956
D. G. Shepherd
The Macmillan Co., New York, New York
Absorption and Extraction—1952, 2nd ed.
T. K. Sherwood and R. L. Pigford
McGraw-Hill Book Co., Inc., New York, New York
Air Pollution—1968, 2nd ed., 3 vol.
A. C. Stern, Editor
Academic Press, New York, New York
Mechanical Vibrations—1953, 2nd ed.
W. T. Thomson
Prentice-Hall, Inc., Englewood Cliffs, New Jersey
Strength of Materials—1955-56, 3rd ed. 2 vols.
S. Timoshenko
D. Van Nostrand Co., Inc., Princeton, New Jersey
Elementary Fluid Mechanics, 1961, 4th ed.
J. K. Vennard
John Wiley & Sons, Inc., New York, New York
Fluid Mechanics and Turbomachinery—1965, 2nd ed.
G. F. Wislicenus
Dover Publications, Inc., New York, New York

TECHNICAL PAPERS

AcSA Journal—Vol. 1 (1929)—Vol. 47 (1970)*
Author and Subject Indexes printed for Vols. 1-10 (1929-1938), Vols. 11-20 (1939-1948), Vols. 21-30 (1949-1958), Vols. 31-35 (1959-1963)

APCA Journal—Vol. 1 (1950)—Vol. 19 (1970)*

ASHAE Transactions—Vol. 61 (1955)—Vol. 64 (1958)

ASHAE Journal Section of HPAC—Vol. 27 (1955)—Vol. 30 (1958)

ASHVE Transactions—Vol. 1 (1895)—Vol. 60 (1954)
Subject and Chronological Indexes printed for Vols. 1-36 (1895-1930) in Separate Issue and for Vols. 36-56 (1930-1950) in Vol. 56

ASHVE Journal—Vol. 21 (1915)—Vol. 35 (1929)

ASHVE Journal Section of HPAC—Vol. 1 (1929)—Vol. 26 (1954)

ASHRAE Transactions—Vol. 65 (1959)

ASHRAE Journal—Vol. 1 (1959)

ASME Transactions—Vol. 1 (1880)—Vol. 81 (1959)*
Vol. 1 (1880)—Vol. 48 (1926)—consecutive page numbering.
Vol. 50 (1928)—Vol. 56 (1934)—numbering according to subject.
Vol. 57 (1935)—Vol. 69 (1947)—"A" numbers for J.A.M.
Vol. 70 (1948)—Vol. 80 (1958)—sep. nos. for Trans. and J.A.M.
Vol. 81 (1959)—Vol. 92 (1970)*—sep. nos. for Six Journals listed below.
Subject and Author Indexes printed for 77 year period (1880-1956).

ASME Journal of Engineering for Power—
Vol. 81 A (1959)—Vol. 92 A (1970)*

ASME Journal of Engineering for Industry—
Vol. 81 B (1959)—Vol. 92 B (1970)*

ASME Journal of Heat Transfer—
Vol. 81 C (1959)—Vol. 92 C (1970)*

ASME Journalof Basic Engineering—Vol. 81 D (1959)—Vol. 92 D (1970)*

ASME Journal of Applied Mechanics—Vol. 1 (1933)—Vol. 37 E (1970)*

ASME Journal of Lubrication Technology—Vol. 92 F (1970)*

ASRE Transactions—Vol. 1 (1905)—Vol. 9 (1913)

ASRE Journal—Vol. 1 (1914-15)—Vol. 8 (1921-22)

ASRE Technical Section of Refrig. Engr'g.—
Vol. 9 (1922-23)—Vol. 67 (1959)
(Title and Author Indexes printed for 30 year period (1905-1934) in Dec. 1934 Ref. Eng.)

IHVE Proceeding—Vol. 1 (1899)—Vol. 31 (1933)
Subject and Author Indexes printed for Vols. 1-31 (1899-1933) in 1965 IHVE Guide

IHVE Journal—Vol. 1 (1933)—Vol. 37 (1970)*
Subject and Author Indexes printed for Vols. 1-31 (1933-1964) in 1965 IHVE Guide

TECHNICAL PAPERS, Cont.

NACA Publications

Publications	*Designations*
Reports	Rept. 1—1392
Technical Notes	TN 1—4410
Technical Memorandums	(TM) 1—1441
Research Memorandums	RM Source code and date

Subject and Author Indexes printed for 1915-1949, 1949-1951, 1951-1953, 1953-54, 1954-55, 1955-56, 1956-57, 1957-58 and 1958-59

NASA Publications

Publications	*Designations*
Technical Report	TR R-1, etc.*
Technical Notes	TN D-1, etc.*
Technical Memorandums	TM X-1, etc.*
Technical Translations	TT F-1, etc.*

Subject and Author Indexes printed for 1959-60.*

*continuing publications

CODES AND STANDARDS

AMCA—Standards on Air Moving and Conditioning Equipment

AMCA—Test Codes on Air Moving and Conditioning Equipment

ANSI—"American National Standards" on a wide variety of subjects.

ARI—Standards on Air-Conditioning and Refrigeration Equipment

ASHRAE—Standards on Air-Conditioning and Refrigeration Equipment

ASME—Code on Boilers and Pressure Vessels

ASME—Test Codes on Instruments, Apparatus, and Power Equipment

ASRE—Standards on Air-Conditioning and Refrigeration Equipment

ASHVE—Standards on Heating and Ventilating Equipment

ASTM—Standards on Testing Materials

ASA—"American Standards" on a wide variety of subjects

HI—Standards on Hydraulics and Pumping Equipment

NBFU—Standards on Fire Protection

NEMA—Standards on Electrical Equipment

NFPA—Codes on Fire Protection

TEMA—Standards on Tubular Heat Exchangers

KEY TO ABBREVIATIONS AND ADDRESSES

AcSA—Acoustical Society of America
335 East 45th St., New York, New York 10017
ACGIH—American Conference of Governmental Industrial Hygienists
ACGIH-CIV—Committee on Industrial Ventilation
Post Office Box 453, Lansing, Michigan 48902
ACGIH-CTL—Committee on Threshold Limits
AGA—American Gas Association
605 Third Ave., New York, New York 10016
AIChE—American Institute of Chemical Engineers
345 East 47th St., New York, New York 10017
AIP—American Institute of Physics
335 East 45th St., New York, New York 10017
AISE—Association of Iron and Steel Engineers
1010 Empire Building, Pittsburgh, Pennsylvania 15222
AISI—American Iron and Steel Institute
150 East 42nd St., New York, New York 10017
AMCA—Air Moving and Conditioning Association, Inc.
30 West University Dr., Arlington Heights, Illinois 60004
ANSI—American National Standards Institute
1430 Broadway, New York, New York 10008
APCA—Air Pollution Control Association
4400 Fifth Ave., Pittsburgh, Pennsylvania 15213
ARI—Air-Conditioning and Refrigeration Institute
1815 N. Fort Meyer Dr., Arlington, Virginia 22209
ASA—American Standards Association, Inc.
(renamed USASI then ANSI)
ASHAE—American Society of Heating and Air Conditioning Engineers
(merged with ASRE in 1959 to form ASHRAE)
ASHRAE—American Society of Heating, Refrigerating & Air-Conditioning Engineers
345 East 47th St., New York, New York 10017
ASHVE—American Society of Heating and Ventilating Engineers
(renamed ASHAE in 1955)
ASME—American Society of Mechanical Engineers
345 East 47th St., New York, New York 10017
ASRE—American Society of Refrigerating Engineers
(merged with ASHAE in 1959 to form ASHRAE)
ASTM—American Society for Testing Materials
1916 Race St., Philadelphia, Pennsylvania 19103
AWS—American Welding Society
345 East 47th St., New York, New York 10017
HI—Hydraulic Institute
122 East 42nd St., New York, New York 10017
IEEE—Institute of Electrical and Electronics Engineers
345 East 47th St., New York, New York 10017
IGCI—Industrial Gas Cleaning Institute
Box 448, Rye, New York 10580

KEY TO ABBREVIATIONS AND ADDRESSES, Cont.

HVE—Institution of Heating and Ventilating Engineers
49 Cadogan Square, London, S.W.I., England

NACA—National Advisory Committee for Aeronautics
(reorganized and renamed NASA in 1959)

NACE—National Association of Corrosion Engineers
2400 West Loop St., Houston, Texas 77027

NASA—National Aeronautics and Space Administration
Washington, D.C. 20546

NBS—National Bureau of Standards
Washington, D.C. 20230

NEMA—National Electrical Manufacturers Association
155 East 44th St., New York, New York 10017

NESCA—National Environmental Systems Contractors Association
221 N. LaSalle St., Chicago, Illinois 60611

NFPA—National Fire Protection Association
60 Batterymarch St., Boston, Massachusetts 02110

NWAHACA—National Warm Air Heating & Air Conditioning Association
(dissolved 1968—now NESCA)

SAE—Society of Automotive Engineers, Inc.
2 Pennsylvania Plaza, New York, New York 10001

SMACNA—Sheet Metal & Air Conditioning Contractors' National Association, Inc.
1611 N. Kent St., Arlington, Virginia 22209

SPI—Society of The Plastics Industry, Inc.
250 Park Ave., New York, New York 10017

TEMA—Tubular Exchanger Manufacturers Association
331 Madison Ave., New York, New York 10017

APPENDIX 8

Buffalo Forge Company Air Moving & Conditioning Products

General Classification & Types	*Buffalo Trademarks*	*Page*
Air & Gas Cleaning Equipment		
Cleanable Cloth Filters	Reverse-Jet Aeroturn®	668
Cleanable Cloth Filters	Shaking-Bag Aeroturn®	669
Multiple Cyclone Collectors	Buf-clone™	670
Wetted-fiber Gas Absorbers	Designs 6, 7 & 8	671
Fog Scrubbers	Hydraulic Scrubbing Tower™	672
Multi-dynamic Scrubbers	Rotary Gas Scrubber™	673
Spray-chamber Air Washers	Types A, B, & C	674
Wetted-fiber Air Washers	Types PCGW & LGW	675
Comfort Air Conditioning Equipment		
Evaporative Coolers & Humidifiers	Types SH, DSH, & SSH	676
Sprayed-coil Dehumidifiers	Types PCLW, PCLWB, etc.	677
Draw-thru HVAC Cabinets	Types V, HV, PC, VPC, etc.	678
Blow-thru HVAC Cabinets	Types HVB, PCB, PCHB, etc.	679
Special HVAC Cabinets	Big Buffalos™	680
Make-up Air Units	Styles CG, CS, HG, AS, etc.	681
Unit Heaters	Model C Breezo-Fin™	682
Heat Exchangers		
Process-air Heaters	Types BHV & BHVM	683
Process-air Coolers	Types PCL, PCLB, PCLHB, etc.	684
Air-cooled Heat Exchangers	Types ACC & AWC	685
Evaporative Heat Exchangers	Types ECC & EWC	686
Heat Exchange Surface		
Chilled-or Hot-water Coils	Aerofin® Types C, R, CH, & RC	687
Direct-Expansion Coils	Aerofin® Type DP	688
Non-freeze Steam Coils	Aerofin® Types ANF & BNF	689
Heavy-duty Coils	Aerofin® Type PD	690
Industrial Blowers & Exhausters		
Cast-iron Low-pressure Fans	Type V Volume Fans™	691
Cast-iron Medium-pressure Fans	Types E & RE Blowers™	692
Steel-plate Medium-pressure Fans	Types AW, OW, MW, & PW	693
Steel-plate High-pressure Fans	Types CB & R	694
Rubber-lined Fans	Types V, MW, & BL	695
Fiberglass-reinforced Plastic Fans	Types FRPMW, FRPBL, etc.	696
Mechanical Draft Fans		
Airfoil Blade Fans	A Series	697
Backwardly-curved Blade Fans	L Series	698
Radial Blade Fans	H & R Series	699
Forwardly-curved Blade Fans	FC Series	700
Ventilating Fans		
Centrifugal Fans	Types BL® & BL-Aerofoil®	701
Axial Flow Fans	Type B-Vaneaxial, etc.	702
Adjustable-blade Axials	Adjustax®	703
Ventilating Sets		
Belt-drive Centrifugal Fans	Belted Vent Set™	704
Direct-drive Centrifugal Fans	Baby Vent Set™	705
Power Roof Ventilators	Style V Sky-Vents®	706
Power Roof Ventilators	Style H Sky-Vents®	707
Belt-drive Propeller Fans	Belt-air™, Breez-air™, etc.	708
Direct-drive Propeller Fans	Breezo™, Type NV, etc.	709

BUFFALO REVERSE-JET AEROTURN®

12 modules; exhaust manifold, fan, and stack each side; top intakes

TYPICAL APPLICATIONS

Cleaning exhaust gases from sanders, smelters, dryers, etc. where the contaminants are dusts or fumes and gas temperatures are not highly elevated (less than 180°F.).

DESCRIPTION AND PERFORMANCE

Baghouse with cloth tubes extending between two tubesheets. Dirty gas enters tubes at top depositing contaminant on inside of cloth. Travelling reverse-jet blow rings dislodge the deposits which fall to the hopper. Main gas flow need not be interrupted.
Efficiency generally exceeds 99%.
Pressure drop generally ranges between 4″ and 6″ WG.

STANDARD SIZES AND CAPACITIES

16 tube modules—12″ diameter, 8′ to 20′ long tubes.
Cloth velocities up to 30 fpm.

STANDARD DESIGN FEATURES

Painted steel casing and hopper (60° sides).
Choice of various felted or woven fabrics.
Self-adjusting blow rings on travelling carriage.
Carriage and counterweight chain driven.
3 RE blower for reverse-jet supply.
Control panel for motor starters, pressure sensors, disconnects, and push buttons.

SPECIAL DESIGN FEATURES AND ACCESSORIES AVAILABLE

Special metal construction.
Conveyors, air locks, etc.

REFERENCE

Bulletin AP-650A.

BUFFALO SHAKING-BAG AEROTURN®

TYPICAL APPLICATIONS

Cleaning exhaust gases from sanders, smelters, dryers, etc. where the contaminants are dusts or fumes and gas temperatures are not highly elevated (less than 400°F.).

DESCRIPTION AND PERFORMANCE

Baghouse with cloth bags hung from closed end and attached at bottom to tubesheet. Dirty gas passes through knock-out chamber and enters bags at bottom depositing contaminants on inside of cloth. By shaking bags from top, deposits are dislodged and fall to the hopper. Main gas flow must be interrupted.
Efficiency generally exceeds 99%.
Pressure drop generally ranges between 4″ and 6″ WG.

STANDARD SIZE AND CAPACITIES

60 bag modules—6″ diameter, 10′ long bags.
Cloth velocities to 5 fpm.

STANDARD DESIGN FEATURES

Painted steel casing and hopper (60° sides).
Choice of various woven fabrics.
Internal or external shaking mechanism.
Control panel for motor starters, pressure sensors, disconnects, and push buttons.

SPECIAL DESIGN FEATURES AND ACCESSORIES AVAILABLE

Special metal construction.
Conveyors, air locks, etc.
Dampers, etc. for compartmented units.

REFERENCE

Bulletin AP-950.

BUFFALO BUF-CLONE DUST COLLECTOR

14 Tube Modules.

9 Module Unit.

TYPICAL APPLICATIONS

Cleaning high dust concentration (up to 9 gr/ft³) exhaust gases from coal-fired furnaces, kilns, dryers, etc. where the contaminants include a large percentage of coarse (over 5 micron) particles.

DESCRIPTION AND PERFORMANCE

Groups of 6″ diameter tubes each with gas inlet arranged to produce cyclonic action.
From 2 to 4″ WG air resistance for 255 to 355 cfm per tube.
Efficiency ranges from 82% on 5 micron particles to over 97% on 10 micron particles.

STANDARD SIZES AND CAPACITIES

From 2 to 500 tubes (or more).
From 500 to 100000 cfm (or more).

STANDARD DESIGN FEATURES

Steel tubes, casing, and hopper.
Removable cast iron inlet flights and discharge cones.
Modular tube arrangement with knife-edge seal.

SPECIAL DESIGN FEATURES AND ACCESSORIES AVAILABLE

Stainless steel construction.
Integral exhauster.

REFERENCE

Bulletin AP-625.

BUFFALO DESIGNS 6, 7 AND 8 GAS ABSORBERS

Design 7 Unit—Fiberglass Construction.

TYPICAL APPLICATIONS

Cleaning exhaust gases from open surface tanks, chemical reactors, dryers, etc. where the contaminants are primarily gases, vapors, mists, or fumes (including malodorous substances) which are soluble in water or other scrubbing liquid.

DESCRIPTION AND PERFORMANCE

One to three wetted stages followed by a dry fine-fiber moisture elimination stage. Wetted stages may all be fine-fiber type or an impingement scrubber first stage may be used for particle removal.

Approximately 0.5″ WG air resistance per wetted-fiber stage, 0.2″ WG per dry-fiber stage and 3.2″ WG per impingement stage. Total clean resistance may range from 0.7″ to 4.4″ WG.

From 8 to 12 psi nozzle pressure required.

STANDARD SIZES AND CAPACITIES

Widths to 204″ and heights to 136″.
From 1200 to 48000 cfm.

STANDARD DESIGN FEATURES

Steel, FRP, or special metal casing, tank, etc. as required.
Bronze, plastic, or special metal nozzles as required.
Automatic make-up and quick-fill fittings.
Overflow, drain, and screened pump suction connections.
4″ deep wet stages and 2″ deep dry stages with Dynel media.
Stainless steel, Monel, or Carpenter 20 Neva-Clog screen impingement stages.

SPECIAL DESIGN FEATURES AND ACCESSORIES AVAILABLE

No. 800 Fiberglass or K-115 Curly Glass media.
Coil sections for condensing oil vapors, etc.
Automatic pH control.

REFERENCES

Bulletins AP-225 and AP-2500.

BUFFALO HYDRAULIC SCRUBBING TOWER

Two No. 11 HST

TYPICAL APPLICATIONS

Cleaning exhaust gases from chemical furnaces, open surface tanks, coke dryers, forging presses, etc. where the contaminants include a large percentage of fine (less than 2 micron) particles.

DESCRIPTION AND PERFORMANCE

Cylindrical tower with tangential gas entry and high-pressure (up to 400 psi) fog-type spray nozzles directed tangentially. Efficiency ranges from 78% on 0.5 micron particles to over 99% on 8 micron particles.

Less than 2½″ WG air resistance.

STANDARD SIZES AND CAPACITIES

From 3′ to 11′ diameters.
From 2500 to 55000 cfm.

STANDARD DESIGN FEATURES

Steel tower with flanged inlet, outlet, and drain.
Individually removable bronze nozzles with flexible hose connections.
Quick-opening cast iron nozzle latches.

SPECIAL DESIGN FEATURES AND ACCESSORIES AVAILABLE

Special metal, rubber lined, or plastic construction.
Integral pump. Integral exhauster. Storage sump.
Low pressure nozzles on central standpipe.

REFERENCE

Bulletin AP-525A.

BUFFALO ROTARY GAS SCRUBBER

Cast Iron Unit on Structural Base.

Cover Removed Showing 4-stage Rotor.

TYPICAL APPLICATIONS

Cleaning high dust concentration (up to 22 gr/ft³) exhaust gases from gas producers, electrometallurgical furnaces, etc. where the contaminants are easily wetted and include a large percentage of fine (0.5 to 1.0 micron) particles.

DESCRIPTION AND PERFORMANCE

Two or four rotating fan-like stages arranged for alternating inflow and outflow with low pressure (25 psi) sprays.
Better than 99% cleaning efficiency on one micron or larger particles.

CAPACITY RANGE

From 500 to 4000 cfm.

STANDARD DESIGN FEATURES

Cast iron housing with flanged inlet and outlet.
Stainless steel rotor. Stainless steel spray system.
Double extension shaft, Stellited at stuffing boxes.
Anti-friction bearings. C.I. pedestals. Structural base.
Bolted inspection covers. Rubber explosion ports.

SPECIAL DESIGN FEATURES AND ACCESSORIES AVAILABLE

Quick-opening access doors.
Cast steel or welded steel housing.

REFERENCES

Bulletins AP-425 and AP-4500.

BUFFALO TYPES A, B, AND C AIR WASHERS

Type B Unit—Inlet View.

TYPICAL APPLICATIONS

Cleaning together with humidifying, dehumidifying, or evaporative cooling of supply air for office buildings, public buildings, factories, motor rooms, etc.

DESCRIPTION AND PERFORMANCE

One or two low pressure (less than 50′ head) spray banks followed by bent plate eliminators.
Less than 0.4″ WG air resistance.
Up to 90% cleaning efficiency on particles over 20 micron size.
Up to 95% humidifying efficiency.

STANDARD SIZES AND CAPACITIES

Up to 12′ high x 24′ wide inlet opening.
From 1500 to 130,000 cfm.

STANDARD DESIGN FEATURES

Galvanized steel casing, eliminators, baffles, distributor plates, and spray headers.
Steel flat bottom tank.
Bronze "hollow-cone" non-clogging nozzles.
Cast iron inspection doors with windows. Marine lights.
Automatic make-up and quick-fill fittings.
Overflow, drain, and screened pump suction connections.

SPECIAL DESIGN FEATURES AND ACCESSORIES AVAILABLE

Special metal or plastic construction. Fiber cell eliminators.
Sloping bottom or hopper tanks.
Coil sections, plenums, and special access doors.
Rotary strainers, pot strainers, water heaters, and separate pump boxes.
Integral fans. Integral pumps.

REFERENCE

Bulletin AP-750.

BUFFALO TYPES PCGW AND LGW WET CELL WASHERS

Type PCGW Unit—Inlet View.

TYPICAL APPLICATIONS

Cleaning together with humidifying, dehumidifying, or evaporative cooling of supply air for office buildings, public buildings, factories, motor rooms, etc.

DESCRIPTION AND PERFORMANCE

Very low pressure (less than 35′ head) sprays over fiber cells followed by eliminators.
Less than 0.65″ WG air resistance.
Up to 90% cleaning efficiency on particles over 10 micron size.
Up to 98% humidifying efficiency.

STANDARD SIZES AND CAPACITIES

Up to 4 tiers (2 cells each) high and 10 cells wide.
From 4200 to 85000 cfm (based on 1050 cfm per cell).
Fan sections to 20000 cfm.

STANDARD DESIGN FEATURES

Galvanized steel casing, tank, cell frames, eliminators, and spray headers.
Bronze "solid-spray" non clogging nozzles.
Cast iron inspection doors with windows. Marine light.
Automatic make-up and quick-fill fittings.
Overflow, drain, and screened pump suction connections.
Replaceable glass or plastic fiber media, 3 to 8″ thick.

SPECIAL DESIGN FEATURES AND ACCESSORIES AVAILABLE

Special metal or plastic construction. Fiber cell eliminators.
Sloping bottom or hopper tanks.
Coil sections, plenums, and special access doors.
Rotary strainers, pot strainers, water heaters, and separate pump boxes.
Integral fans (Std. on PCGW). Integral pumps.

REFERENCE

Bulletin 3457C.

BUFFALO TYPES SH, DSH, AND SHH HUMIDIFIERS

Type SH Unit—Partially Assembled.

TYPICAL APPLICATIONS

Evaporative cooling and/or humidifying of supply air for office buildings, public buildings, factories, etc. Also engine intake coolers.

DESCRIPTION AND PERFORMANCE

Spray-chamber with inlet baffles, countercurrent sprays, and fiber pad eliminators. Type SH has one spray header and Type DSH has two for finer control. Both are designed to spray 0.2 GPM per 1000 cfm at 25 psi. SSH is designed for 0.8 gpm per 1000 cfm at 22 psi. Humidifying efficiencies up to 80%. Air resistance less than 0.75″ WG.

STANDARD SIZES AND CAPACITIES

Width to 44′ and heights to 12′.
From 2500 to 210000 cfm.

STANDARD DESIGN FEATURES

Galvanized steel casing, baffles, access doors, spray headers, etc.
Brass spray nozzles. Marine light.
Steel pan with bitumastic coating. Drain connection.
Replaceable Dynel or polyester media.

SPECIAL DESIGN FEATURES AND ACCESSORIES AVAILABLE

Special metal or plastic construction.
Coil sections, plenums, and special access doors.
Integral fans (see make-up air units).
Type SSH is specially designed for recirculation of water and includes tank, pump, and media flushing systems.

REFERENCE

Bulletin AP-850A.

BUFFALO SPRAYED-COIL DEHUMIDIFIERS

Type PCLW Units—Inlet View.

TYPICAL APPLICATIONS

Cooling and dehumidifying, humidifying, and/or evaporative cooling of supply air for public buildings, clean rooms, computer rooms, operating rooms, laboratories, etc.

DESCRIPTION AND PERFORMANCE

Central station air conditioning cabinet housing Aerofin cooling coils, recirculating spray system, and eliminators. Type PCLW units suitable for draw-thru applications up to 1¾″ WG suction. Types PCLWB, PCLMWB, PCLHWB suitable for blow-thru applications up to 3″, 6″, and 9″ WG positive pressure.

STANDARD SIZES AND CAPACITIES

Up to 10′ tube length and 90 tube face.
From 9500 to 52000 cfm (based on 500 fpm face velocity).

STANDARD DESIGN FEATURES

Galvanized steel casing, coil header box, eliminators, and spray headers. Steel tank.
Aerofin 4, 6, or 8 row-cooling coils.
Brass "square-pattern" spray nozzles.
Quick-opening access doors.
Automatic make-up and quick-fill fittings.
Overflow, drain, and screened pump suction connections.

SPECIAL DESIGN FEATURES AND ACCESSORIES AVAILABLE

Special metal or plastic construction.
Inlet baffles and distributor plates.
Coil sections, plenums, filter boxes, and mixing boxes.
Face and/or bypass dampers. Bypass ducts.
Integral fans. Integral pumps.

REFERENCE

Bulletin AC-321.

BUFFALO DRAW-THRU HVAC CABINETS

Model J—Type PC Unit—Inlet View.

TYPICAL APPLICATIONS

Supply conditioned air for any type of space or building. Types V, VM, and VH are suitable for ventilation applications. Types HV and HVM are suitable single zone heating and ventilating applications. Types PC, PCW, PCM, and VPC are suitable for single-zone air-conditioning applications. Types PCM, PCMW, PCH, and PCHW are suitable for conditioning primary air for induction units, etc. Types PCW, PCMW, and PCHW are particularly suitable for applications involving 100% outdoor air for hospitals, etc.

DESCRIPTION AND PERFORMANCE

Factory-assembled fan-coil units of the draw-thru type. Types V, VM, and VH have no coils. Types HV and HVM have heating coils. Types PC, PCM, PCH, and VPC have cooling coils. Types PCW, PCMW, and PCHW are sprayed coil dehumidifiers having cooling coils, recirculating spray systems and eliminators. Fans for V, HV, VPC, and PCW suitable for 2½″ WG. Fans for VM, PCM, and PCMW suitable for 5″ WG. Fans for VH, PCH, and PCHW suitable for 10″ WG.

STANDARD SIZES AND CAPACITIES

Heating and Ventilating—1000 to 62000 cfm.
Air Conditioning—1000 to 50000 cfm.

STANDARD DESIGN FEATURES

Galvanized steel casing.
Aerofin heating and/or cooling coils.
Buffalo HVA or BL fans.
Adjustable V-belt drive and motor base.
Internal fiberglass insulation, insulated pan and drain on AC Units.

SPECIAL DESIGN FEATURES AND ACCESSORIES AVAILABLE

Angle, flat, cube, and roll type filter boxes. Mixing boxes.
Face and/or bypass dampers.
Steam grid humidifiers.
Plenum and access sections. Variable inlet vanes.
Inertia bases and flexible connections between sections.
Vibration isolators and sound attenuators.

REFERENCES

Bulletins AC-125 and AC-130.

BUFFALO BLOW-THRU HVAC CABINETS

Model J—Type PCHB Unit—Inlet View

TYPICAL APPLICATIONS

Supply conditioned air for any type of space or building where individual temperature control is required for multiple zones. Types PCB and HVB are suitable for multi-zone-duct applications. Types PCHB and HVHB are suitable for high velocity dual-duct applications. Types PCMB and HVMB are suitable for either.

DESCRIPTION AND PERFORMANCE

Factory-assembled fan-coil units of the blow-thru type. Types PCB, PCMB, and PCHB have a hot-and-cold-deck coil section. Types HVB, HVMB, and HVHB have a hot-deck-and-bypass section. Zone dampers are furnished for multi-zone-duct applications but not for dual-duct applications. Fans for PCB and HVB suitable for 2½″ WG. Fans for PCMB and HVMB suitable for 5″ WG. Fans for PCHB and HVHB suitable for 10″ WG.

STANDARD SIZES AND CAPACITIES

Heating and Ventilating—1000 to 62000 cfm.
Air Conditioning—1000 to 50000 cfm.

STANDARD DESIGN FEATURES

Galvanized steel casing.
Aerofin heating and/or cooling coils.
Buffalo HVA or BL fans.
Adjustable V-belt drive and motor base.
Internal fiberglass insulation, insulated pan and drain on AC units.

SPECIAL DESIGN FEATURES AND ACCESSORIES AVAILABLE

Angle, flat, cube, and roll type filter boxes. Mixing boxes.
Face and/or bypass dampers.
Steam grid humidifiers.
Plenum and access sections. Variable inlet vanes.
Inertia bases and flexible connections between sections.
Vibration isolators and sound attenuators.

REFERENCES

Bulletins AC-125 and AC-130.

BIG BUFFALO™ HVAC CABINETS

Big Buffalo Fan and Coil Sections Under Construction.

TYPICAL APPLICATIONS

Supply conditioned air for any type of space or building.

DESCRIPTION AND PERFORMANCE

Factory-assembled sections for high-capacity fan-coil units of either the draw-thru or blow-thru types. Any of the unit types described in the previous two pages can be provided.

SIZES AND CAPACITIES

Units are custom designed for any capacity and pressure. Sections from previously designed units can frequently be employed. Most sections have been sized within shipping limitations.

DESIGN FEATURES AND ACCESSORIES

See preceding two pages.

Big Buffalo Sections ready for shipping.

BUFFALO MAKE-UP AIR UNITS

Style PG Unit—Discharge View

TYPICAL APPLICATIONS

Supply tempered fresh air to make up for exhaust in factories, garages, auditoriums, etc.

DESCRIPTION AND PERFORMANCE

Factory-assembled fan-heater units. Styles CG, CS, CE, and CW are low pressure (up to 2½″ WG) centrifugal fan units with direct-gas-fired, steam, electric, or water heater sections. Medium pressure (up to 5″ WG) centrifugal units are also available (e.g. Style CMG). Corresponding styles are available with propeller fans (e.g. Style PG), Adjustax fans (e.g. Style AG), Vaneaxial fans (e.g. Style VG), or propeller fans in a stack with mushroom hood (e.g. Style HG).

STANDARD SIZES AND CAPACITIES

Centrifugal Units—12000 cfm to 62000 cfm.
Axial Units—16000 cfm to 96000 cfm.
Propeller Units—20000 cfm to 106000 cfm.
Stack and Hood Units—2500 cfm to 40000 cfm.

STANDARD DESIGN FEATURES

Galvanized steel casing. Walk-in door.
Buffalo fans. Aerofin coils.
Maxon NP gas burner with complete control system.

SPECIAL DESIGN FEATURES AND ACCESSORIES AVAILABLE

Bird screens and inlet louvers.
Inertia bases and vibration isolation.
Flat, angle, cube, or roll filters.
Buffalo evaporative cooling and humidifying section.
Penthouse designs. Exterior protection.

REFERENCES

Bulletins AC-500 and AC-510.

BUFFALO MODEL C BREEZO-FIN UNIT HEATERS

Model C Unit—Discharge View.

TYPICAL APPLICATION

Heat and circulate air for spot duty in factories, warehouses, garages, etc. where ventilation is provided by other means.

DESCRIPTION AND PERFORMANCE

Horizontal-blow, propeller-fan, steam or hot-water coil unit.

STANDARD SIZES AND CAPACITIES

One or two row coils.
One, 8 to 24″ wheel diameter fan.
Nominally, 15000 to 500,000 Btu/hr.

STANDARD DESIGN FEATURES

Steel casing. Invisible threaded hanger connections.
Continuous tube coils suitable for steam pressures to 250 psi.
Breezo fans mounted on motor shaft.

SPECIAL DESIGN FEATURES AND ACCESSORIES AVAILABLE

Spark-resistant construction.

REFERENCE

Bulletin 3137-E.

BUFFALO PROCESS-AIR HEATERS

Model G—Type BHV Unit

TYPICAL APPLICATIONS

Heat air for use in industrial processes such as drying, curing, etc.

DESCRIPTION AND PERFORMANCE

Blow-thru type fan-coil units for connecting to a duct system. Type BHV is suitable for pressures to 2½″ WG. Type BHVM is suitable for 5″ WG.

STANDARD SIZES AND CAPACITIES

1000 to 62000 cfm.

STANDARD DESIGN FEATURES

Galvanized steel casing.
Aerofin heating coils. Buffalo fans.
Adjustable V-belt drive and motor base.

SPECIAL DESIGN FEATURES AND ACCESSORIES AVAILABLE

Vibration isolators and inertia bases.
Face and bypass dampers.
Plenum and access section.

REFERENCE

Bulletin AC-130.

BUFFALO PROCESS-AIR COOLERS

Type PCLB Unit Under Construction

TYPICAL APPLICATIONS

Cooling and dehumidifying air for equipment spaces such as motor rooms, dry-wells for nuclear plants, etc., or for use in a process.

DESCRIPTION AND PERFORMANCE

Air-Conditioning cabinet housing Aerofin cooling coils, eliminators, and drain pan. Type PCL units suitable for draw-thru applications up to 1¾″ WG suction. Types PCLB, PCLMB, and PCLHB suitable for blow-thru applications up to 3″, 6″, and 9″ WG positive pressure.

STANDARD SIZES AND CAPACITIES

1000 to 62000 cfm.

STANDARD DESIGN FEATURES

Galvanized steel casings and eliminators.
Aerofin cooling coils.
Insulated pan and drain.

SPECIAL DESIGN FEATURES AND ACCESSORIES AVAILABLE

Face and bypass dampers.
Plenum and access sections.
Separate centrifugal or axial fans.
Integral fans (see HVAC cabinet descriptions).

BUFFALO AIR-COOLED HEAT EXCHANGERS

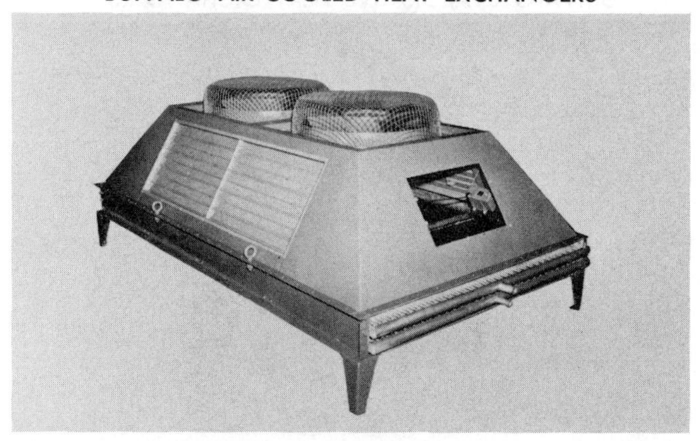

Type ACC Unit—Propeller Fan Type

TYPICAL APPLICATIONS

Cool water, oil, or other fluids for engines, quenching tanks, etc. Condense steam, refrigerant, or other vapors for power of other processes.

DESCRIPTION AND PERFORMANCE

Dry cooling tower or fin-fan units with propeller type fans. Centrifugal or axial fan units available for service with ductwork. Type AWC is for liquid cooling. Type ACC is for condensing service.

STANDARD SIZES AND CAPACITIES

Normally 200000 Btu/hr to 4000000 Btu/hr.

STANDARD DESIGN FEATURES

Galvanized steel casing, access doors, etc.
Aerofin cooling or condensing coils.
Buffalo propeller, axial or centrifugal fans.

SPECIAL DESIGN FEATURES AND ACCESSORIES AVAILABLE

Special metal casings, coils, or fans.
Bypass dampers.

BUFFALO EVAPORATIVE HEAT EXCHANGERS

Type EWC Unit with Recirculating Dampers

TYPICAL APPLICATIONS

Cool water, oil, or other fluids for engines, quenching tanks, etc. Condense steam, refrigerant, or other vapors for power or other processes.

DESCRIPTION AND PERFORMANCE

Fan-coil units with recirculating spray system. Centrifugal fan units suitable for external pressure.

STANDARD SIZES AND CAPACITIES

400000 Btu/hr to 4,500,000 Btu/hr.

STANDARD DESIGN FEATURES

Galvanized steel casing. Vertical arrangement.
Aerofin cooling or condensing coils.
Buffalo centrifugal fans.

SPECIAL DESIGN FEATURES AND ACCESSORIES AVAILABLE

Special metal casings, coils, or fans.
Recirculating dampers for control.
Buffalo axial fans.

AEROFIN TYPES C, CH, R, AND RC WATER COILS

Type C Coil. *Type R or RC Coil.*

TYPICAL APPLICATIONS

Air cooling or air heating in air-conditioning units or systems for offices, stores, factories, etc. where the refrigeration and/or heating plants are remotely located.
Cooling water or other liquids in dry or evaporative heat exchangers of the air-cooled type.

DESCRIPTION AND PERFORMANCE

Extended surface coils with fixed header and fixed return bend, continuous tubes (C), with removable headers for cleanability (R), or with a single removable header for drainability (RC).
Suitable for 220°F and 200 psig (C), 400°F and 200 psig (CH), or 160°F and 100 psig (R and RC).

STANDARD SIZES AND CAPACITIES

From 2 to 8 rows deep, 1 or 2 rows (CH only).
From 12 to 24 tube faces.
From 2 to 10′ tube lengths.

STANDARD DESIGN FEATURES

Galvanized steel casing. Steel headers.
Copper tube, ⅝″ OD. Various fin spacings.
Aluminum or copper, smooth helical fins.

SPECIAL DESIGN FEATURES AND ACCESSORIES AVAILABLE

Special metal construction. Solder coating.
Special circuit arrangements.
High pressure or high temperature construction.

REFERENCES

Bulletin C-58, R-50, RC-57, and CH-62.

AEROFIN TYPE DP DIRECT-EXPANSION COILS

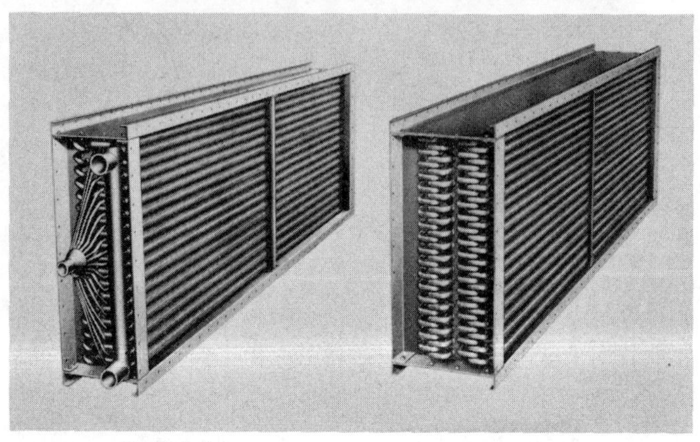

Type DP Coil. *Fixed Return Bends.*

TYPICAL APPLICATIONS

Air cooling in air-conditioning units or systems for offices, stores, factories, etc. where the refrigeration plant is closely situated or even self-contained.

DESCRIPTION AND PERFORMANCE

Extended-surface coils with fixed return bend, continuous tubes and pressure drop (orifice) type distributors to divide the refrigerant evenly between circuits.

STANDARD SIZES AND CAPACITIES

From 2 to 6 rows deep.
From 12 to 24 tube faces.
From 3 to 10′ tube lengths.

STANDARD DESIGN FEATURES

Galvanized steel casings.
Copper tubes, ⅝″ OD. Various fin spacings.
Aluminum or copper, smooth helical fins.

SPECIAL DESIGN FEATURES AND ACCESSORIES AVAILABLE

Special metal construction. Solder coating.
Centrifugal distribution headers.

REFERENCE

Bulletin DP-66.

AEROFIN TYPES ANF AND BNF STEAM COILS

Type ANF Coil. *Type BNF Coil.*

TYPICAL APPLICATIONS

Air heating in air-conditioning units or systems for offices, stores, factories, etc. where the heating plant is remotely located.
Air preheating for combustion and to prevent condensation in subsequent regenerative or recuperative units.

DESCRIPTION AND PERFORMANCE

Extended-surface coils with non-freeze construction, i.e., a steam distributing tube within each finned tube.
Suitable for 400°F and 200 psig.

STANDARD SIZES AND CAPACITIES

One row (ANF). One or two rows (BNF).
From $20\frac{9}{16}$ to $37\frac{7}{16}$ casing widths.
From 2 to 10′ tube lengths.

STANDARD DESIGN FEATURES

Galvanized steel casings. Steel headers.
Copper, 1″ OD (ANF) or ⅝″ OD (BNF) outer tube.
Copper, ⅝″ OD (ANF) or ⅜″ OD (BNF) inner tube.
Aluminum or copper, smooth helical fins.
Tubes pitched for vertical or horizontal air flow.
Various tube and/or fin spacings.

SPECIAL DESIGN FEATURES AND ACCESSORIES AVAILABLE

Special metal construction. Solder coating.
Designs other than non-freeze types include flexitube, booster, universal, and high-pressure types.

REFERENCES

Bulletins A-61 and B-58.

AEROFIN TYPE PD HEAVY DUTY COILS

Type PD Coil—Removable Plug Construction.

TYPICAL APPLICATIONS

Cooling water or other liquids in dry or evaporative heat exchangers of the air-cooled type.

DESCRIPTION AND PERFORMANCE

Extended-surface coils with removable plug or removable cover header construction. Suitable for a series of working pressures from 150 to 1500 psig at 500°F.

STANDARD SIZES AND CAPACITIES

From 2 to 6 rows deep.
Either 41 $\frac{7}{16}$ or 66⅜″ casing width.
From 12 to 24′ tube lengths.

STANDARD DESIGN FEATURES

Structural steel casing. Flanged connections.
Copper, 1″ OD or ⅝″ OD tubes. Various fin spacings.
Aluminum or copper, smooth helical fins.

SPECIAL DESIGN FEATURES AND ACCESSORIES AVAILABLE

Special metal construction. Solder coating.

REFERENCE

Bulletin O-58.

BUFFALO TYPE V VOLUME FANS

Type V Unit—Arrangement 4.

TYPICAL APPLICATIONS

Supply air for conveying systems, dryers, forges, etc.
Exhaust air from grinding and buffing machines, pickling tanks, etc.

DESCRIPTION AND PERFORMANCE

Radial blade centrifugal fans.
Best efficiency at 15000 specific speed.

STANDARD SIZES, CAPACITIES, AND PRESSURES

From 5⅛ to 16⅞″ inlet diameters.
From 100-8000 cfm at up to 12″ SP.

STANDARD ARRANGEMENTS

Single inlet. Arrangement 1, 2, 4, 8, and 10.

STANDARD DESIGN FEATURES

Cast iron housing. Either rotation—8 or 12 discharge positions.
Fabricated steel wheel. Flanged or open types.

SPECIAL DESIGN FEATURES AND ACCESSORIES AVAILABLE

Flanged inlet and/or outlet. Drains.
Special metal wheel and housing construction.
Special paints and coatings. Rubber lining.
Water-cooled bearing arm (Arr. 2).
Cast iron and extra-heavy steel wheels. Sharpened blades.

REFERENCE

Bulletin FI-211.

BUFFALO TYPES E AND RE BLOWERS

Type E Unit—Arrangement 1.

Type E Flanged Wheel.

TYPICAL APPLICATIONS

Supply air for oil burners, gas burners, over-fire air jets, cupolas, conveying systems, etc.
Exhaust air from grinding and buffing machines, pickling tanks, etc.
Boost gas pressure, inflate fabric structure, etc.

DESCRIPTION AND PERFORMANCE

Radial blade centrifugal fans. Various designs.
Best efficiency at from 5000 to 20000 specific speed.

STANDARD SIZES, CAPACITIES, AND PRESSURES

From 5½ to 16″ (E), 3 to 6″ (RE) inlet diameters.
From 50 to 10000 cfm at up to 3 psi SP (E), 50 to 1600 cfm at up to 1½ psi SP (RE).

STANDARD ARRANGEMENTS

Single inlet. Arrangements 1, 4, and 8.

STANDARD DESIGN FEATURES

Cast iron housing. Either rotation—8 discharge positions (E).
Counter-clockwise rotation—16 discharge positions (RE).
Heavy-duty anti-friction bearings (Arr. 1 and 8).
Fabricated steel wheel. Flanged or open types.
Various diameter wheels in each size housing.

SPECIAL DESIGN FEATURES AND ACCESSORIES AVAILABLE

Flanged inlet and/or outlet (except No. 2RE). Drains.
Special metal wheel and housing construction. FRP construction.
Special paints and coatings.
Shaft seals, gas-tight stuffing boxes, and heat slingers.
Extra-heavy steel wheels.

REFERENCE

Bulletin FI-411.

BUFFALO TYPES AW, MW, AND OW INDUSTRIAL EXHAUSTERS

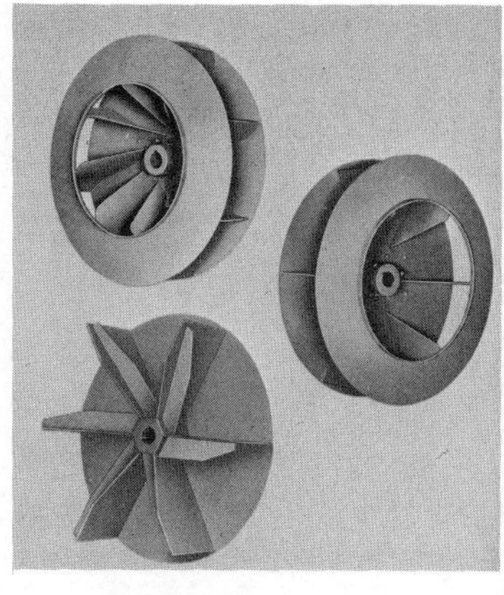

AW, MW, and OW Wheels.

Arrangement 9 Unit.

TYPICAL APPLICATIONS

Supply air for conveying systems, dryers, etc.
Exhaust air from grinding and buffing machines, pickling tanks, textile machinery, etc.

DESCRIPTION AND PERFORMANCE

Backwardly-curved (AW), flanged radial (MW), or open radial (OW) blade centrifugal fans.
Best efficiency at 18000-20000 specific speed.

STANDARD SIZES, CAPACITIES, AND PRESSURES

From 7½ to 50¾″ inlet diameter.
From 600 to 85000 cfm at up to 20″ SP.

STANDARD ARRANGEMENTS

Single inlet. Arrangements 1, 4, 8, 9, and 10.

STANDARD DESIGN FEATURES

Steel plate housing and bearing stand.
Either rotation—16 discharge positions.
Heavy-duty anti-friction bearings (Arr. 1, 8, 9, and 10).
Fabricated steel wheels. All types use same housing.

SPECIAL DESIGN FEATURES AND ACCESSORIES AVAILABLE

Flanged inlet and/or outlet. Drains. Inlet screens. Outlet dampers.
Special metal wheel and housing construction. Rubber-lined and FRP construction.
Special paints and coatings. Clean-out doors.
Shaft seals, gas-tight stuffing boxes, heat slingers, and belt guards.
Extra-heavy wheels, shafts, and bearings. Paddle wheels (PW).

REFERENCE

Bulletin FI-112A.

BUFFALO TYPES CB AND R PRESSURE BLOWERS

Type CB Unit—Arrangement 4.

Type CB Flanged Wheel.

TYPICAL APPLICATIONS

Supply air for process cooling, drying, conveying, and combustion systems.
Exhaust gases from process cooling, drying, conveying, and combustion systems.
Boost gas pressure, inflate fabric structures, etc.

DESCRIPTION AND PERFORMANCE

Radial blade centrifugal fans. Various designs.
Best efficiency at from 3000 to 20000 specific speed.

STANDARD SIZES, CAPACITIES, AND PRESSURES

From 4 to 30½″ inlet diameters (CB).
From 150 to 35000 cfm at up to 70″ SP (CB).
Capacities to 250000 cfm (R). Pressures to 4 psi (R).

STANDARD ARRANGEMENTS

Single inlet. Arrangements 1, 3, 4, and 8.
Double inlet. Arrangements 3 and 7.

STANDARD DESIGN FEATURES

Flanged inlet and outlet.
Either rotation—5 discharge positions.
Steel plate housing and bearing stand.
Heavy-duty anti-friction bearings (Arr. 1 and 8).
Fabricated steel wheel. Diameter to suit specification.

SPECIAL DESIGN FEATURES AND ACCESSORIES AVAILABLE

Extra-heavy housings. Soap bubble test. Drains.
Special metal and housing construction. FRP construction.
Special paints and coatings. Clean-out doors.
Shaft seals, gas-tight stuffing boxes, and heat slingers.
Extra-heavy wheels, shafts, and bearings. SAWC and SAAC sleeve bearings.

REFERENCE

Bulletin FI-310.

BUFFALO TYPES V, MW, AND BL RUBBER-LINED FANS

Type MW Housing-Inlet Cone Removed.

Type MW Paddle Wheel.

TYPICAL APPLICATIONS

Exhaust gases from chemical reactors, open-surface tanks, etc. where the corrosion resistance of rubber is required.

DESCRIPTION AND PERFORMANCE

Radial (V and MW) or backwardly-curved (BL) blade centrifugal fans.
Best efficiency at 15000 (V), 20000 (MW), or 40000 (BL) specific speed.

STANDARD SIZES, CAPACITIES, AND PRESSURES

From 5⅛ to 16⅞″ (V), 7½ to 50¾″ (MW), or 15¾″ to 80¼″ (BL) diameter inlet.
From 100 to 4000 cfm at up to 8″ SP (V), 600 to 70000 cfm at up to 8″ SP (MW), and 700 to 100000 cfm at up to 6¾″ SP (BL).

STANDARD ARRANGEMENTS

Single inlet. Arrangements 1, 2, 4, and 9.

STANDARD DESIGN FEATURES

Flanged inlet and outlet. Tapped drain.
Rubber-lined (vulcanized to) steel (MW or BL) or cast iron (V) housing.
Steel shaft, rubber covered to inboard bearing. Simple shaft seal.
Steel wheel, rubber covered.

SPECIAL DESIGN FEATURES AND ACCESSORIES AVAILABLE

Clean-out doors.
Various types of elastomers.

REFERENCE

Bulletin 2424-F.

BUFFALO FIBERGLASS-REINFORCED PLASTIC FANS

Type FRPMW Fan

Type FRPVA Fan—Arr. 9

TYPICAL APPLICATIONS

Exhaust gases from pickling, plating, chemical processes, etc. where the chemical resistance of FRP is required.

DESCRIPTION AND PERFORMANCE

Various types of fans are made in FRP construction. Only the Type FRPMW will be described here. This is a radial-bladed industrial exhauster. See E and RE, CB and R, and various propeller, axial, and centrifugal ventilating fans for details on these other designs.

STANDARD SIZES, CAPACITIES, AND PRESSURES

From 7 to 38″ inlet diameter.
From 270 to 43000 cfm at up to 20″ SP.

STANDARD ARRANGEMENTS

Single inlet. Arrangements 1, 9, and 10.

STANDARD DESIGN FEATURES

Flanged inlet and outlet. Drain connections.
Either rotation—15 discharge positions.
Solid FRP housing and wheel.
Hub and steel shaft encapsulated through seal.

SPECIAL DESIGN FEATURES AND ACCESSORIES AVAILABLE

Flanged drain. Stuffing box.
Weather hood. Access doors.
Various resins including most polyesters and epoxy.

REFERENCES

Bulletins FRP-501A and FRP-502.

BUFFALO AIRFOIL MECHANICAL DRAFT FANS

Forced Draft Fan with Inlet Boxes for Cyclone Fired Boiler.

TYPICAL APPLICATIONS

Supply air for combustion (forced draft including that for cyclone burner type furnaces) and for industrial uses.
Exhaust products of combustion (induced draft) and other industrial gases when non-erosive.

DESCRIPTION AND PERFORMANCE

Backwardly-curved blades of airfoil cross section for highest efficiency.
Limit-load horsepower characteristic.
Stable pressure curve throughout entire range.
Best efficiency at from 15000 to 40000 specific speed SISW.

SIZES, CAPACITIES, AND PRESSURES

From 5000 to 800,000 cfm at up to 100″ SP.
Sizes and construction to meet operating requirements.

STANDARD ARRANGEMENTS

Single inlet. Arrangements 1, 3, 4, 7, and 8.
Double inlet. Arrangements 3 and 7.

STANDARD DESIGN FEATURES

Continuously welded steel housing. Flanged split joints for rotor removal.
Flanged inlet and outlet. Access doors. Drains connections.
Airfoil blades continuously welded to flange and back or center plate.
Anti-friction or sleeve bearings, air or water cooled.

SPECIAL DESIGN FEATURES AND ACCESSORIES AVAILABLE

Inlet boxes, silencers, inlet screens, and shaft seals.
Variable inlet vanes, outlet dampers, and inlet box dampers.
Wheels shrink-fitted to shafts.

REFERENCES

Bulletins F-205, FD-500, and FD-906.

BUFFALO BACKWARD-CURVE MECHANICAL DRAFT FANS

Forced Draft Fan with Variable Inlet Vanes.

TYPICAL APPLICATIONS

Supply air for combustion (forced draft) and other high pressure industrial uses.
Exhaust products of combustion (induced draft) and other industrial gases.

DESCRIPTION AND PERFORMANCE

Backwardly-curved blades single thickness type for high efficiency.
Limit-load horsepower characteristic.
Sharply rising, stable pressure curve throughout entire range.
Best efficiency at from 20000 to 40000 specific speed SISW.

SIZES, CAPACITIES, AND PRESSURES

From 5000 to 600,000 cfm at up to 50″ SP.
Sizes and construction to meet operating requirements.

STANDARD ARRANGEMENTS

Single inlet. Arrangements 1, 3, 4, 7, and 8.
Double inlet. Arrangements 3 and 7.

STANDARD DESIGN FEATURES

Continuously welded steel housing. Flanged split joints for rotor removal.
Flanged inlet and outlet. Access doors. Drains.
Welded or riveted wheel construction of alloy steel where required.
Anti-friction or sleeve bearings, air or water-cooled.
Thermal stabilized shafts where required.

SPECIAL DESIGN FEATURES AND ACCESSORIES AVAILABLE

Inlet boxes, inlet screens, and shaft seals.
Variable inlet vanes, outlet dampers, and inlet box dampers.
Blade wear plates, scroll liners, and insulation clips.
Patented wheel support for high rates of temperature change.

REFERENCES

Bulletin FD-100 and FD-906.

BUFFALO AIRFOIL MECHANICAL DRAFT FANS

Forced Draft Fan with Inlet Boxes for Cyclone Fired Boiler.

TYPICAL APPLICATIONS

Supply air for combustion (forced draft including that for cyclone burner type furnaces) and for industrial uses.
Exhaust products of combustion (induced draft) and other industrial gases when non-erosive.

DESCRIPTION AND PERFORMANCE

Backwardly-curved blades of airfoil cross section for highest efficiency.
Limit-load horsepower characteristic.
Stable pressure curve throughout entire range.
Best efficiency at from 15000 to 40000 specific speed SISW.

SIZES, CAPACITIES, AND PRESSURES

From 5000 to 800,000 cfm at up to 100″ SP.
Sizes and construction to meet operating requirements.

STANDARD ARRANGEMENTS

Single inlet. Arrangements 1, 3, 4, 7, and 8.
Double inlet. Arrangements 3 and 7.

STANDARD DESIGN FEATURES

Continuously welded steel housing. Flanged split joints for rotor removal.
Flanged inlet and outlet. Access doors. Drains connections.
Airfoil blades continuously welded to flange and back or center plate.
Anti-friction or sleeve bearings, air or water cooled.

SPECIAL DESIGN FEATURES AND ACCESSORIES AVAILABLE

Inlet boxes, silencers, inlet screens, and shaft seals.
Variable inlet vanes, outlet dampers, and inlet box dampers.
Wheels shrink-fitted to shafts.

REFERENCES

Bulletins F-205, FD-500, and FD-906.

BUFFALO BACKWARD-CURVE MECHANICAL DRAFT FANS

Forced Draft Fan with Variable Inlet Vanes.

TYPICAL APPLICATIONS

Supply air for combustion (forced draft) and other high pressure industrial uses.
Exhaust products of combustion (induced draft) and other industrial gases.

DESCRIPTION AND PERFORMANCE

Backwardly-curved blades single thickness type for high efficiency.
Limit-load horsepower characteristic.
Sharply rising, stable pressure curve throughout entire range.
Best efficiency at from 20000 to 40000 specific speed SISW.

SIZES, CAPACITIES, AND PRESSURES

From 5000 to 600,000 cfm at up to 50″ SP.
Sizes and construction to meet operating requirements.

STANDARD ARRANGEMENTS

Single inlet. Arrangements 1, 3, 4, 7, and 8.
Double inlet. Arrangements 3 and 7.

STANDARD DESIGN FEATURES

Continuously welded steel housing. Flanged split joints for rotor removal.
Flanged inlet and outlet. Access doors. Drains.
Welded or riveted wheel construction of alloy steel where required.
Anti-friction or sleeve bearings, air or water-cooled.
Thermal stabilized shafts where required.

SPECIAL DESIGN FEATURES AND ACCESSORIES AVAILABLE

Inlet boxes, inlet screens, and shaft seals.
Variable inlet vanes, outlet dampers, and inlet box dampers.
Blade wear plates, scroll liners, and insulation clips.
Patented wheel support for high rates of temperature change.

REFERENCES

Bulletin FD-100 and FD-906.

BUFFALO RADIAL BLADE MECHANICAL DRAFT FANS

Battery of B.O.F. Exhaust Fans with Variable Speed Drives.

TYPICAL APPLICATIONS

Exhaust products of combustion (induced draft) or other industrial gases including those of an erosive character such as from cement or lime kilns, sintering machines, and basic oxygen furnaces.

Handling of high temperature gases such as gas-recirculation duty.

DESCRIPTION AND PERFORMANCE

Purely radial or radial tip, forward heel blade shapes for self-cleaning characteristics.

Stable, sharply rising pressure curve. Moderate efficiency.

Best efficiency at from 10000 to 40000 specific speed SISW.

SIZES, CAPACITIES, AND PRESSURES

From 5000 to 1000000 cfm at up to 90″ SP.

Sizes and construction to meet operating requirements.

STANDARD ARRANGEMENTS

Single inlet. Arrangements 1, 3, 7, and 8.

Double inlet. Arrangements 3 and 7.

STANDARD DESIGN FEATURES

Continuously welded steel housing. Flanged split joints for rotor removal.

Welded steel housing. Flanged inlet and outlet. Access doors. Drains.

Welded or riveted wheel construction of alloy steel where required.

Anti-friction or sleeve bearings air or water cooled.

Thermal stabilized shafts where required.

For varying temperature applications wheel is shrunk on shaft and factory balanced as a unit.

SPECIAL DESIGN FEATURES

Inlet boxes, inlet screens, and shaft seals.

Variable inlet vanes, outlet dampers, and inlet box dampers.

Blade wear plates, scroll liners, and insulation clips.

Patented wheel support for high rates of temperature change.

REFERENCES

Bulletins FD-300 and FD-906.

BUFFALO FORWARD-CURVE MECHANICAL DRAFT FANS

Induced Draft Fan Installation.

TYPICAL APPLICATIONS

Supply air for combustion (forced draft) and other industrial uses.
Exhaust products of combustion (induced draft) and other industrial gases.

DESCRIPTION AND PERFORMANCE

Forwardly-curved blades for moderate efficiency.
Rising horsepower characteristic.
Stable pressure curve from free delivery back to peak efficiency-unstable to left of that point.
Best efficiency at 20000-22000 specific speed SISW.

SIZES, CAPACITIES, AND PRESSURES

From 5000 cfm to 500,000 cfm at up to 40″ SP.
Sizes and construction to meet operating requirements.

STANDARD ARRANGEMENTS

Single inlet. Arrangements 1, 3, 4, 7, and 8.
Double inlet. Arrangements 3 and 7.

STANDARD DESIGN FEATURES

Continuously welded steel housing. Flanged joints for rotor removal.
Flanged inlet and outlet. Access doors. Drains.
Welded wheel construction of alloy steel where required.
Anti-friction or sleeve bearings, air or water-cooled.
Thermal stabilized shafts where required.

SPECIAL DESIGN FEATURES AND ACCESSORIES AVAILABLE

Inlet boxes, inlet screens, and shaft seals.
Inlet box dampers and outlet dampers.
Blade wear plates, scroll liners, and insulation clips.

REFERENCE

Bulletin FD-906.

BUFFALO CENTRIFUGAL VENTILATING FANS

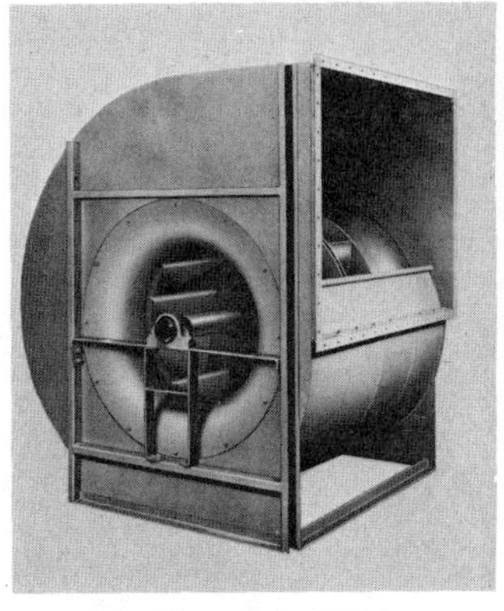

Type BL-Aerofoil—DIDW Arr. 3

Type BL-Aerofoil—SISW with VIV

TYPICAL APPLICATIONS

Supply air for ventilation (and complete air conditioning) of buildings, vehicular tunnels, motors, etc. and for combustion and other industrial systems.
Exhaust air from industrial processes and the above spaces and equipment.

DESCRIPTION AND PERFORMANCE

AMCA Class I, II, and III centrifugal fans. Type BL-Aerofoil® has double thickness airfoil-shaped blades. Type BL® has single thickness airfoil-shaped blades.
Limit-load horsepower characteristic.
Completely stable pressure characteristic.
Best efficiency at 40000 specific speed SISW.

STANDARD SIZES AND CAPACITIES

From 12¼ to 108¾″ wheel diameters.
From 700 to 600000 cfm at up to 12″ SP.

STANDARD ARRANGEMENTS

Single inlet. Arrangements 1, 2, 3, 4, 7, 8, and 9.
Double inlet. Arrangements 3 and 7.

STANDARD DESIGN FEATURES

Fabricated steel housing. Slip connections.
Either rotation—16 discharge positions.
Die-formed inlet bell, blades, and inlet shroud.
Anti-friction bearings mounted on housing or subbase.

SPECIAL DESIGN FEATURES

Heat-resistant, corrosion-resistant, and spark-resistant construction.
Special paints and coatings. Drains. Shaft seals.
Inlet screen. Inlet boxes. Access doors.
Variable inlet vanes. Outlet dampers. Flanged inlets and outlets.
Vibration isolators.

REFERENCE

Bulletin F-150.

BUFFALO AXIAL FLOW FANS

Type B Tubeaxial—Arr. 4

Type B Vaneaxial—Arr. 9

TYPICAL APPLICATIONS

Supply air for ventilation or air conditioning of ships, buildings, vehicular tunnels, motors, etc. and for combustion systems.
Exhaust air from spraybooths and the above spaces and equipment.

DESCRIPTION AND PERFORMANCE

Axial flow fans with discharge vanes (Vaneaxial) or without discharge vanes (Tubeaxial).
Best efficiency at from 75000 to 125000 specific speed.

STANDARD SIZES, CAPACITIES, AND PRESSURES

From 15 to 96″ diameters.
From 1500 to 300000 cfm at up to 4″ TP.

STANDARD ARRANGEMENTS

Arrangement 4 (Vaneaxial and Tubeaxial).
Arrangement 9 (Vaneaxial, Spraybooth™, and Clamshell®).

STANDARD DESIGN FEATURES

Welded steel housing. Flanged inlet and outlet.
Anti-friction bearings, belt-fairing, and adjustable motor base (Arr. 9).
Fabricated steel wheels with single thickness airfoil blades.

SPECIAL DESIGN FEATURES AND ACCESSORIES AVAILABLE

Cast aluminum wheels with full airfoil blades.
Special metal housing and wheel construction. FRP construction.
Special paints and coatings. Shaft seals. Patented bronze-tipped wheels.
Inlet and outlet cones. Inlet screens. Variable inlet vanes.
Access door (Spraybooth) or 180° full length doors (Clamshell).

REFERENCES

Bulletins F-300A and F-305A.

BUFFALO ADJUSTAX FANS

Adjustax—Arr. 4

Sound Attenuator

TYPICAL APPLICATIONS

Supply air for ventilation or air conditioning of ships, buildings, vehicular tunnels, motors, etc. and for combustion systems.
Exhaust air from the above spaces and equipment.

DESCRIPTION AND PERFORMANCE

Adjustable blade axial flow fan with discharge vanes.
Best efficiency at from 8000 to 175000 specific speed.

STANDARD SIZES, CAPACITIES, AND PRESSURES

From 22 to 84″ diameters.
From 3000 to 300000 cfm at up to 15″ TP.

STANDARD ARRANGEMENTS

Arrangements 4 and 9.

STANDARD DESIGN FEATURES

Welded steel housing. Flanged inlet and outlet.
Aluminum wheels with 5, 7, or 9 adjustable blades.
Anti-friction bearings, belt-fairing, and adjustable motor base (Arr. 9)

SPECIAL DESIGN FEATURES AND ACCESSORIES AVAILABLE

Special paints and coatings. Inlet screens.
Inlet and outlet cones. Inlet bells. Vortex breakers.
Variable inlet vanes. Inlet boxes.
Sound attenuators and attenuated housings.

REFERENCES

Bulletins F-300A and F-305A.

BUFFALO BELTED VENT SETS™

Belted Vent Set—Standard Construction.

TYPICAL APPLICATIONS

Ventilation of laboratories, toilet rooms, equipment rooms, etc.

DESCRIPTION AND PERFORMANCE

Double curved blade centrifugal fan complete with drive.
Limit load horsepower characteristic.
Completely stable pressure characteristic.
Best efficiency at 40000 specified speed.

STANDARD SIZES, CAPACITIES, AND PRESSURES

From 9⅛″ to 36½″ wheel diameters.
From 500 to 20,000 cfm at up to 2½″ SP.

STANDARD ARRANGEMENTS

Single inlet. Arrangement 10.

STANDARD DESIGN FEATURES

Fabricated steel housing. Slip connections.
Either rotation—16 discharge positions.
Die formed blades and wheel shrouds.
Stationary inlet guide vanes.
Anti-friction bearings mounted on subbase.
Adjustable motor base and adjustable pitch motor sheave.

SPECIAL DESIGN FEATURES AND ACCESSORIES AVAILABLE

Heat-resistant, corrosion-resistant, and spark-resistant construction.
Special paints and coatings. Drains.
All weather cover over motor, drive, and bearings.
Inlet screen. Access door. Vibration isolators.
Variable inlet vanes. Outlet dampers.

REFERENCE

Bulletin F-401.

BUFFALO BABY VENT SETS

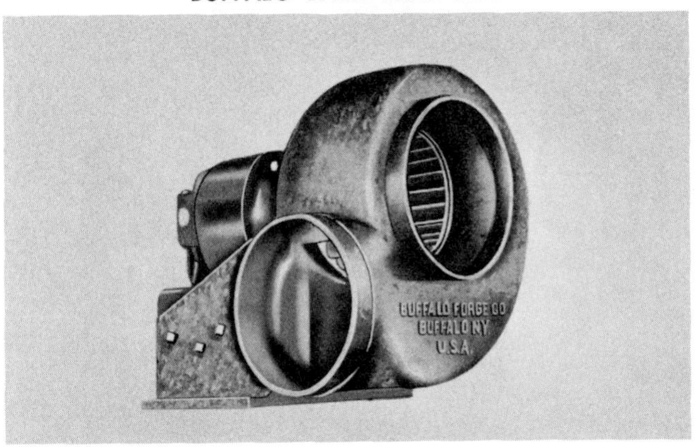

Baby Vent Set—Hot-dip Galvanized.

TYPICAL APPLICATIONS

Ventilation of small spaces and equipment.

DESCRIPTION AND PERFORMANCE

Forwardly curved blade centrifugal fan complete with drive.
Moderate efficiency for low pressure applications.

STANDARD SIZES, CAPACITIES, AND PRESSURES

From 3½ to 9″ wheel diameters.
From 40 to 1760 cfm at up to 1″ SP.

STANDARD ARRANGEMENTS

Single inlet. Arrangement 4.

STANDARD DESIGN FEATURES

Cast iron housing. Slip connections.
Either rotation—8 discharge positions.
Die formed blades and wheel shrouds.
Sheet steel motor base.
Wheel mounted directly on motor shaft.

SPECIAL DESIGN FEATURES AND ACCESSORIES AVAILABLE

Special metal housing and wheel construction.
Special paints and coatings. Drains.
All weather cover over motor. Inlet screens.

REFERENCE

Bulletin FMB-135.

BUFFALO STYLE V SKY-VENTS®

Type AF Unit—Arrangement 9.

So-Low Unit—Design 4.

TYPICAL APPLICATIONS

Exhaust ventilation of industrial spaces.
Spot ventilation.

DESCRIPTION AND PERFORMANCE

Clamshell dampers and windband with curb-mounted propeller (So-Low) or axial flow (AF) fan.

STANDARD SIZES, CAPACITIES, AND PRESSURES

From 15 to 72″ wheel diameters. Various designs.
From 2000 to 120,000 cfm at up to 1″ SP.

STANDARD ARRANGEMENTS

Belt-drive (Arr. 9) or direct-drive (Des 4)

STANDARD DESIGN FEATURES

Galvanized steel windband. Aluminum dampers.
Asphalt coating. Flanged curb sheets.
Propeller or axial flow wheels.

SPECIAL DESIGN FEATURES AND ACCESSORIES AVAILABLE

Tilt-up curbs for above roof access to motor and drives.
Modified curb sheets for pitched or peaked roofs.
Special metal or FRP wheel and unit construction.
Special paints and coatings. Special motors.
Fusible link fire release mechanism.

REFERENCE

Bulletin SV-200-B.

BUFFALO STYLE H SKY-VENT®

Style H Unit—Mushroom Head Open.

TYPICAL APPLICATIONS

Supply or exhaust ventilation of industrial spaces.
Make-up air units.

DESCRIPTION AND PERFORMANCE

Propeller or axial flow fan in a curb-mounted stack with a mushroom-type weather hood.

STANDARD SIZES, CAPACITIES, AND PRESSURES

From 12 to 108″ wheel diameters, 1000-200,000 cfm at up to 1″ SP for normal ventilation.
From 18 to 72″ wheel diameters, 2500-60,000 cfm at up to 1″ SP with filter hoods.
From 18 to 60″ wheel diameters, 2500-40,000 cfm with steam coils.

STANDARD DESIGN FEATURES

Galvanized steel casing, stack and hood. Bird Screen.
Flanged curb sheets. Asphalt coating.
Propeller or axial flow wheels.

SPECIAL DESIGN FEATURES AND ACCESSORIES AVAILABLE

Modified curb sheets for pitched or peaked roofs.
Filters mounted around peripheral head opening.
Face and by-pass dampers. Mixing boxes.
Steam or direct gas-fired heating elements and controls.
Spark-resistant construction. Reverse flow wheels.
Disconnect switch and interior wiring.

REFERENCE

Bulletin SV-100-2.

BUFFALO BELT-DRIVE PROPELLER FANS

Type MB Wheel

Design 53 Wheel

TYPICAL APPLICATIONS

Ventilation of commercial and industrial spaces.
Attic ventilation. Equipment ventilation.

DESCRIPTION AND PERFORMANCE

Propeller fans complete with motor and belt-drive.
Various wheel designs for operation at free delivery to 1″ SP.

STANDARD SIZES, CAPACITIES, AND PRESSURES

From 24 to 120″ wheel diameters. Various designs.
From 5000 to 250000 cfm at up to 1″ SP.

STANDARD MOUNTINGS

Panel mountings only.

STANDARD DESIGN FEATURES

Steel panels with streamlined orifice. Die-formed through 54″.
Anti-friction bearings. V-belt drive.
D-53 wheels—die-formed steel riveted to a fabricated spider.
D80, 65, and 50 NV wheels—die-formed steel riveted to a reinforced steel spider.
LB, MB, and HB wheel—all welded steel axial type with die-formed blades.

SPECIAL DESIGN FEATURES AND ACCESSORIES AVAILABLE

Special metal wheel and panel construction.
Special paints and coatings. Wire guards.
Penthouses. Gravity or motor operated shutters.
Special motors.

REFERENCES

Bulletins FP-200 and 3790-A.

BUFFALO DIRECT-DRIVE PROPELLER FANS

Breezo Unit—Small Package Fan. *NV Unit—Large Sizes.*

TYPICAL APPLICATIONS

Ventilation of commercial and industrial spaces.
Spot ventilation. Equipment ventilation.

DESCRIPTION AND PERFORMANCE

Direct-drive propeller fans complete with motor.
Various wheel designs for operation at free delivery to over 1″ SP.

STANDARD SIZES, CAPACITIES, AND PRESSURES

From 8 to 96″ wheel diameters. Various designs.
From 500 to 125,000 cfm at up to 1″ SP.

STANDARD MOUNTINGS

Panel, pedestal, and portable mountings.

STANDARD DESIGN FEATURES

Steel panels with streamlined orifices. Die-formed through 54″.
Steel channel arm, plate arm, or wire guard mount.
Breezo wheels—die-formed steel or aluminum blades on steel hub or spider.
D80, 65, and 50 NV wheels—die-formed steel blades on reinforced steel spider.
LB, MB, and HB wheels—all-welded steel axial type with die-formed blades.

SPECIAL DESIGN FEATURES AND ACCESSORIES AVAILABLE

Special metal wheel and panel construction. FRP construction.
Special paints and coatings. Wire guards. Special motors.
Penthouses. Gravity or motor operated shutters. Wall boxes.
Spot coolers. Man coolers. Filter-fan packages.

REFERENCES

Bulletins FP-100, FP-700, FP-800, and 3790-A.

AUTHOR INDEX

SUBJECT INDEX